U.S. Department
of Transportation

**United States
Coast Guard**

P9-DFE-222

**Merchant Marine Deck
Examination Reference Material**

REPRINTS FROM THE

LIGHT LISTS
AND
COAST PILOTS

THIS PUBLICATION CONTAINS INFORMATION TO BE USED IN
EXAMINATIONS FOR MERCHANT MARINE LICENSES AND DOCUMENTS

NOT TO BE USED FOR NAVIGATION

COMDTPUB P16721.38

U.S. Department of Transportation

United States Coast Guard

Commandant   (G-MVP)
United States Coast Guard

Mailing Address:
2100 SECOND STREET SW
WASHINGTON DC 20593-0001
(202) 267-2705

COMDTPUB   P16721.38

5 Aug 1993

COMMANDANT PUBLICATION P16721.38

Subj: MERCHANT MARINE DECK EXAMINATION REFERENCE MATERIAL,
       REPRINTS FROM THE LIGHT LISTS AND COAST PILOTS.

1. PURPOSE. This publication contains reference material for use
    during an examination for a merchant marine deck license. It
    contains excerpts from Light Lists, Volumes 1 and 2, and Coast
    Pilots 2 and 3. This manual is current with the training
    charts used in the examinations.

2. DISCUSSION. Applicants for merchant marine deck licenses are
    tested to ensure their professional qualification. Some
    practical navigation questions are based on material in this
    publication, and applicants must refer to this publication to
    develop the correct answer.

3. PROCEDURE. This publication is available to applicants taking
    a deck merchant marine examination. The covers available for
    sale from the the Government Printing Office (GPO) are printed
    with red ink. The covers used in the Regional Examination
    Centers are printed with green ink. Applicants who purchase
    copies of this publication from the GPO may not use their
    personal copies during examinations.

4. ORDERING INFORMATION.

    a. Regional Examination Centers will be provided with an
        intial supply of this publication. Replacement and
        additional copies are available through standard
        distribution sources.

DISTRIBUTION - SDL No. 131

	a	b	c	d	e	f	g	h	i	j	k	l	m	n	o	p	q	r	s	t	u	v	w	x	y	z
A																										
B		1	1		1		1	1					1					1								
C					*								*													
D																										
E																										
F																										
G																										
H																										

NON-STANDARD DISTRIBUTION (See page 2.)

INSTRUCTIONS

1. This reference contains extracts of the LIGHT LISTS and COAST PILOTS. Some practical navigation questions in the deck examination booklets require plotting on Training Charts to determine the answer. Navigational information necessary to aid in plotting these problems is contained in this manual.

2. Applicants may also refer to this manual when testing with any module except Rules of the Road. For example, if the question in a Navigation General module is, "You lose sight of Orient Point Light, on the eastern end of Long Island, at a distance of 9.0 miles. What is the approximate meteorological visibility?", then you must use the "Luminous Range Diagram" on page xxxiv of the LIGHT LIST found in PART 1, SECTION A.

3. This manual is in 2 parts to correspond with the Training Charts. Each part has a section A (Light List) and a section B (Coast Pilot). Each section has its own index and three sections are printed on colored paper. The other section is printed on white paper.
Part 1, Section A - Blue pages
Part 1, Section B - White pages
Part 2, Section A - Yellow pages
Part 2, Section B - Green pages

4. Applicants who wish to comment on any material in this publication should complete a Comment/Protest form for the question involved and give it to the examiner.

5. Individuals not taking an examination who wish to make a comment about this publication should send a written comment, citing this publication and the appropriate page and paragraph to:

> Commandant (G-MVP-5)
> U.S. Coast Guard
> REPRINTS from LIGHT LISTS & COAST PILOTS
> 2100 Second Street SW
> Washington, D.C. 20593-0001

All comments are welcomed and will be acknowledged. Valid comments will be incorporated into this publication.

b. The public and other Coast Guard units may order copies
    of this publication from the GPO at the following
    address:

>   Superintendent of Documents
>   U.S. Government Printing Office
>   Washington, D.C. 20402

This book may also be ordered by telephone and charged to
a national credit card by calling (202) 783-3238.

R. C. NORTH
Captain, U.S. Coast Guard
Acting Chief, Office of Marine Safety,
    Security and Environmental Protection

NON-STANDARD DISTRIBUTION:

C:e Toledo (350); Boston, Miami (225); New Orleans (150);
     Baltimore, San Francisco, Honolulu (125), Charleston, San
     Juan, Long Beach, Anchorage, Houston (75); Portland OR,
     Memphis, St. Louis, Puget Sound (50); Juneau, Norfolk, Guam,
     Ketchikan (25) (only)

C:m New York (250) (only).

For sale by the U.S. Government Printing Office
Superintendent of Documents, Mail Stop: SSOP, Washington, DC 20402-9328
ISBN 0-16-041958-1

MERCHANT MARINE DECK EXAMINATION
REFERENCE MATERIAL

Reprints from

LIGHT LISTS and COAST PILOTS

TABLE OF CONTENTS

NOTE: For general information, regulations, and appendix refer to appropriate section in PART 1. This general information has been deleted from PART 2.

PART 1 - SECTION A

LIGHT LIST

Volume I - Atlantic Coast

covering

BLOCK ISLAND SOUND and EASTERN LONG ISLAND SOUND

including

general information on pages i to xxxiv

contents found on page iv

DEPARTMENT OF TRANSPORTATION, U.S. COAST GUARD

LIGHT LIST

Volume I

ATLANTIC COAST

St. Croix River, Maine to
Toms River, New Jersey

IMPORTANT

**THIS PUBLICATION SHOULD BE CORRECTED
EACH WEEK FROM THE LOCAL NOTICES TO MARINERS
OR NOTICE TO MARINERS AS APPROPRIATE.**

COMDTPUB P16502.1

**U.S. GOVERNMENT PRINTING OFFICE
WASHINGTON, DC:**

For sale by Superintendent of Documents, U.S. Government Printing Office, Washington, DC 20402
Stock number: 050-012-00314-9

PREFACE

Lights and other marine aids to navigation, maintained by or under authority of the United States Coast Guard, on the Atlantic coast of the United States from St. Croix River, ME to Toms River, NJ are listed in this volume.

Included are all Coast Guard aids to navigation used for general navigation. Not included are Coast Guard mooring buoys and some buoys having no lateral significance such as special purpose, anchorage, fish net, and dredging.

PRIVATE AIDS TO NAVIGATION

Included–Class I: Aids to navigation on marine structures or other works which the owners are legally obligated to establish, maintain, and operate as prescribed by the Coast Guard.

Included–Class II: Aids to navigation exclusive of Class I, located in waters used by general navigation.

Not included–Class III: Aids to navigation exclusive of Class I and Class II, located in waters not ordinarily used by general navigation.

This list, published annually, is intended to furnish more complete information concerning aids to navigation then can be conveniently shown on charts. It is not intended to be used during navigation in place of charts or Coast Pilots and should not be so used. The charts should be consulted for the location of all aids to navigation. It may be dangerous to use aids to navigation without reference to charts.

This list is corrected to the date of the Notices to Mariners shown on the title page. Changes made to aids to navigation during the year are published in the Local Notice to Mariners and the Notice to Mariners. Important changes to aids to navigation are also broadcast by the U.S. Coast Guard through Coast Guard or Naval radio stations. Mariners should keep their Light List, as well as charts and other nautical publications, corrected from these notices and should consult all notices issued after the date of publication of the Light List.

IMPORTANT: A summary of corrections for this publication, which includes corrections from the dates shown on the title page to the date of availability, is published in the Local Notices to Mariners and the Notice to Mariners. These corrections must be applied, in order to bring the Light List up-to-date. Additionally, this publication should be corrected weekly from the Local Notice to Mariners or the Notice to Mariners as appropriate.

Mariners and others are requested to bring to the attention of the District Commander (see p. iii) or Commandant (G–NSR–3/14), U.S. Coast Guard, 2100 Second St., S.W., Washington, DC 20593-0001, any apparent errors or omissions in these lists.

RECORD OF CORRECTIONS PUBLISHED IN LOCAL/WEEKLY NOTICES TO MARINERS

YEAR 19___

1............	14............	27............	40............
2............	15............	28............	41............
3............	16............	29............	42............
4............	17............	30............	43............
5............	18............	31............	44............
6............	19............	32............	45............
7............	20............	33............	46............
8............	21............	34............	47............
9............	22............	35............	48............
10............	23............	36............	49............
11............	24............	37............	50............
12............	25............	38............	51............
13............	26............	39............	52............

YEAR 19___

1............	14............	27............	40............
2............	15............	28............	41............
3............	16............	29............	42............
4............	17............	30............	43............
5............	18............	31............	44............
6............	19............	32............	45............
7............	20............	33............	46............
8............	21............	34............	47............
9............	22............	35............	48............
10............	23............	36............	49............
11............	24............	37............	50............
12............	25............	38............	51............
13............	26............	39............	52............

North American Datum of 1983: Through the use of satellites and other modern surveying techniques, it is now possible to establish global reference systems which provide more accurate geographic positions. Currently, several datums such as the North American Datum of 1927, U.S. Standard Datum, Old Hawaiian Datum, Puerto Rican Datum, Local Astronomic Datum, and others are in use. The National Oceanic and Atmospheric Administration (NOAA) has identified the North American Datum of 1983 (NAD 83) to replace the various datums in use on charts.

NOTE: The geographic positions listed in the Light List are referenced to the horizontal datum of the current edition of the chart identified in the heading preceding an entry. Corrections to the geographic positions listed will appear in the Local Notices to Mariners and the Notice to Mariners as new charts referencing NAD 83 are issued.

COAST GUARD DISTRICTS AND ADDRESSES OF DISTRICT COMMANDERS

DISTRICT	ADDRESS	WATERS OF JURISDICTION
FIRST	408 Atlantic Avenue Boston, MA 02110-3350 PHONE: DAY 617-223-8338 PHONE: NIGHT 617-223-8558	Maine, New Hampshire, Massachusetts, Vermont (Lake Champlain), Rhode Island, Connecticut, New York, to Toms River, New Jersey.
SECOND	1222 Spruce Street St. Louis, MO 63103-2835 PHONE: DAY 314-539-3714 PHONE: NIGHT 314-539-3709	Mississippi River System, except that portion of the Mississippi River south of Baton Rouge, Louisiana and the Illinois River north of Joliet, Illinois and the Tennessee-Tombigbee Waterway below Mile 411.9.
FIFTH	Federal Building 431 Crawford Street Portsmouth, VA 23704-5004 PHONE: DAY 804-398-6486 PHONE: NIGHT 804-398-6231	Toms River, New Jersey to Delaware, Maryland, Virginia, District of Columbia and North Carolina.
SEVENTH	Brickell Plaza Building 909 SE 1st Avenue Miami, FL 33131-3050 PHONE: DAY 305-536-5621 PHONE: NIGHT 305-536-5611	South Carolina, Georgia, Florida to 83°50'W, and Puerto Rico and adjacent islands of the United States.
	Commander Greater Antilles Section U.S. Coast Guard P.O. Box S-2029 San Juan, PR 00903-2029 PHONE: 809-729-6870	Immediate jurisdiction of waters of Puerto Rico and adjacent islands of the United States.
EIGHTH	Hale Boggs Federal Building 501 Magazine Street New Orleans, LA 70130-3396 PHONE: DAY 504-589-6234 PHONE: NIGHT 504-589-6225	Florida from 83°50'W, thence westward, Alabama, Mississippi, Louisiana and Texas.
NINTH	1240 East 9th Street Cleveland, OH 44199-2060 PHONE: DAY 216-522-3991 PHONE: NIGHT 216-522-3984	Great Lakes and St. Lawrence River above St. Regis River.
ELEVENTH	Union Bank Building 400 Oceangate Blvd. Long Beach, CA 90822-5399 PHONE: DAY 310-499-5410 PHONE: NIGHT 310-499-5380	California.
THIRTEENTH	Federal Building 915 Second Avenue Seattle, WA 98174-1067 PHONE: DAY 206-553-5864 PHONE: NIGHT 206-553-5886	Oregon, Washington, Idaho, and Montana.
FOURTEENTH	Prince Kalanianaole Federal Bldg. 9th Floor, Room 9139 300 Ala Moana Blvd. Honolulu, HI 96850-4982 PHONE: DAY 808-541-2320 PHONE: NIGHT 808-541-2500	Hawaii, American Samoa, Marshall, Marianas, and Caroline Islands, and Subic Bay, Philippines.
SEVENTEENTH	P.O. Box 25517 Juneau, AK 99802-5517 PHONE: DAY 907-463-2245 PHONE: NIGHT 907-463-2000	Alaska.

CONTENTS

INTRODUCTION

Arrangement. Aids to navigation on the Atlantic coast from St. Croix River, ME to Toms River, NJ are listed in this volume.

Aids to navigation are arranged in geographic order from north to south along the Atlantic coast. Seacoast aids to navigation are listed first, followed by entrance and harbor aids to navigation listed from seaward to the head of navigation.

Names of aids to navigation are printed as follows to help distinguish at a glance the type of aid to navigation listed:

Seacoast Lights, Secondary Lights, and Large
  Navigational Buoys
Radiobeacons
Fog Signals
RIVER, HARBOR, AND OTHER LIGHTS
Lighted Buoys
Daybeacons and Unlighted Buoys

Light List numbers are assigned to all aids to navigation in order to facilitate reference in the Light List and to resolve ambiguity when referencing aids to navigation. Aids to navigation are numbered by fives in accordance with their order of appreance in each volume of the Light List. Other numbers and decimal fractions are assigned where newly established aids to navigation are listed between previously numbered aids to navigation. The Light Lists are renumbered periodically to assign whole numbers to all aids to navigation.

International numbers are assigned to certain aids to navigation in cooperation with the International Hydrographic Organization. They consist of an alphabetic character followed by three or four numeric characters. A cross reference listing appears after the index.

Description of Columns

Column (1)   Light List number.

Column (2)   Name of the aid to navigation.
A dash (–) is used to indicate the bold heading is part of the name of the aid. When reporting defects or making reference to such aids to navigation in correspondence, the full name of the aid to navigation, including the geographic heading, should be given.

Bearings are in degrees true, read clock wise from 000° through 359°. Bearings on rangelines are given in degrees and minutes.

Column (3)   Geographic position in latitude and longitude. *NOTE:* Latitude and longitude is approximate, to the nearest tenth of a minute, and is intended only to facilitate locating the aid to navigation on the chart.

Column (4)   Light characteristic for lighted aids to navigation. Morse characteristic for radiobeacons.

Column (5)   Height above water from the focal plane of the fixed light to mean high water, listed in feet. For metric conversion, see table inside rear cover.

Column (6)   The nominal range of lighted aids to navigation is listed in nautical miles, except for Lake Champlain which is listed in statute miles. Nominal range is further listed by color for alternating lights. The nominal range is not listed for ranges, directional lights or private aids to navigation. Effective range for radiobeacons is listed in nautical miles.

Column (7)   Structural characteristic of the aid to navigation, including: daymark (if any), description of fixed structure, color and type of buoy, height of structure above ground.

Column (8)   General remarks, including: fog signal characteristic, RACON characteristic, light sector's arc of visibility, radar reflector if installed on fixed structure, emergency lights, seasonal remarks, and private aid to navigation identification.

Abbreviations used in the Light Lists.

Al	– Alternating	lt	– Light
bl	– blast	LNB	– Large Navigational Buoy
C	– Canadian	MHz	– Megahertz
ec	– Eclipse	Mo	– Morse Code
ev	– Every	Oc	– Occulting
F	– Fixed	ODAS	– Anchored Oceangraphic
fl	– flash		Data Buoy
Fl	– Flashing	Q	– Quick (Flashing)
FS	– Fog Signal	Ra ref	– Radar reflector
Fl(2)	– Group flashing	R	– Red
G	– Green	RBN	– Radiobeacon
I	– Interrupted	s	– seconds
Iso	– Isophase (Equal	si	– Silent
	interval)	SPM	– Single Point Mooring Buoy
kHz	– Kilohertz	W	– White
LFl	– Long Flash	Y	– Yellow

RELATED PUBLICATIONS

Other Light Lists published by the Coast Guard

VOLUME II, ATLANTIC COAST, describes aids to navigation from Toms River, New Jersey to Little River, South Carolina.

VOLUME III, ATLANTIC AND GULF COASTS, describes aids to navigation from Little River, South Carolina to Econfina River, Florida.

VOLUME IV, GULF OF MEXICO, describes aids to navigation from Econfina River, Florida to the Rio Grande, Texas

VOLUME V, MISSISSIPPI RIVER SYSTEM, describes aids to navigation on the Mississippi River and its navigable tributaries.

VOLUME VI, PACIFIC COAST AND PACIFIC ISLANDS, describes aids to navigation on the Pacific coast and outlying Pacific islands.

VOLUME VII, GREAT LAKES, describes aids to navigation on the Great Lakes and the St. Lawrence River above the St. Regis River.

Coast Guard Light Lists are sold by the Superintendent of Documents, U.S. Government Printing Office (GPO), Washington, DC 20402, by GPO Bookstores, and by GPO Sales Agents.

Charts, Coast Pilots, Tide Tables, and Tidal Current Tables covering the United States and its territories are published by the National Ocean Service (NOS), Rockville, MD 20852, and are for sale by NOS and authorized NOS Sales Agents.

Maps for the Mississippi River System are published by the various District Engineers, U.S. Army Corps of Engineers.

Sailing Directions covering the waters outside of the U.S. and its territories are published by the Defense Mapping Agency Hydrographic/Topographic Center.

Radio Navigational Aids (RAPUB 117) is published by the Defense Mapping Agency Hydrographic/Topographic Center. This publication lists selected radio stations (worldwide) that provide services to mariners. Included are stations transmitting radio navigation warnings, radio time signals, medical advice; chapters on distress, emergency and safety traffic; AMVER, and miscellaneous navigational instructions and procedures. Also included are descriptions of long range aids to navigation such as Loran and Omega. Discussions and instructions for use of radio navigational aids are also provided.

Sailing Directions and Radio Navigational Aids can be purchased from Defense Mapping Agency (DMA) Combat Support Center, Washington, DC 20315-0010, or authorized DMA Sales Agents.

NOTICES TO MARINERS

Broadcast Notices to Mariners are made by the Coast Guard through Coast Guard and Navy radio stations. These broadcast notices, which are broadcast on VHF-FM, NAVTEX, and other frequencies, are navigational warnings containing information of importance to the safety of navigation. Included are reports of deficiencies and changes to aids to navigation, the positions of ice and derelicts, and other important hydrographic information.

Radio stations broadcasting Notices to Mariners are listed in the National Ocean Service Coast Pilots and in the Defense Mapping Agency publication Radio Navigational Aids (RAPUB 117).

Local Notices to Mariners (U.S. regional coverage) are another means by which the Coast Guard disseminates navigation information for the United States, its territories, and possessions. A Local Notice to Mariners is issued by each Coast Guard district. It reports changes to, and deficiencies in, aids to navigation maintained by and under the authority of the Coast Guard. It contains other marine information such as channel depths, naval operations, regattas, etc., which may affect vessels and waterways within the jurisdiction of each Coast Guard district. Reports of channel conditions, obstructions, menaces to navigation, danger areas, new chart editions, etc., are also included in the Local Notice to Mariners.

These notices are essential to all navigators for the purposes of keeping their charts, Lights Lists, Coast Pilots and other nautical publications up-to-date. These notices are published as often as required, but usually weekly. They may be obtained, free of charge, by making application to the appropriate Coast Guard district commander (see pg. iii). Vessels operating in ports and waterways in several districts will have to obtain the Local Notice to Mariners from each district in order to be fully informed.

Weekly Notices to Mariners (worldwide coverage) are prepared jointly by the Defense Mapping Agency Hydrographic/Topographic Center, the U.S. Coast Guard, and the National Ocean Service, and are published weekly by Defense Mapping Hydrographic/Topographic Center. The Weekly Notice to Mariners advises mariners of important matters affecting navigational safety including new hydrographic discoveries, changes in channels and aids to navigation. Also included are corrections to Light Lists, Coast Pilots, and Sailing Directions. Foreign marine information is also included. This notice is intended for mariners and others who have a need for information related to ocean-going operations. Because it is intended for use by ocean-going vessels, many corrections that affect small craft navigation and waters are not included. Information concerning small craft is contained in the Coast Guard Local Notices to Mariners only. The Weekly Notice to Mariners may be obtained, free of charge, upon request to: Director, Defense Mapping Agency, Combat Support Center, Code PMSA, Washington, DC 20315-0010.

Change of Address. Persons receiving the Local Notice to Mariners or the Weekly Notice to Mariners are requested to notify the appropriate agency of a change of address, or when the Notice to Mariners is no longer needed. Both the old and new address should be given in the case of an address change.

Notices to Mariners may be consulted at Coast Guard District Offices, National Ocean Service Field Offices, Defense Mapping Agency Hydrographic/Topographic Center offices and depots, local marine facilities, and chart sales agents.

REPORTING DEFECTS IN AIDS TO NAVIGATION

Mariners should realize the Coast Guard cannot keep the thousands of aids to navigation comprising the U.S. Aids to Navigation System under simultaneous and continuous observation and that it is impossible to maintain every aid to navigation operating properly and on its assigned position at all times. Therefore, for the safety of all mariners, any person who discovers an aid to navigation that is either off station or exhibiting characteristics other than those listed in the Light Lists should promptly notify the nearest Coast Guard unit. Radio messages should be prefixed "COAST GUARD" and transmitted directly to one of the U.S. Government radio stations listed in Chapter 4, Section 400B, Radio Navigational Aids (RAPUB 117).

Recommendations and requests pertaining to aids to navigation and to report aids to navigation that are no longer needed should be mailed to the Coast Guard district concerned (see pg. iii).

U.S. AIDS TO NAVIGATION SYSTEM

The waters of the United States and its territories are marked to assist navigation by the U.S. Aids to Navigation System. This system encompasses buoys and beacons, conforming to the

International Association of Lighthouse Authorities (IALA) buoyage guidelines, and other short range aids to navigation.

The U.S. Aids to Navigation System is intended for use with nautical charts. The exact meaning of a particular aid to navigation may not be clear to the mariner unless the appropriate nautical chart is consulted. Additional, important information supplementing that shown on charts is contained in the Light List, Coast Pilots, and Sailing Directions.

TYPES OF MARKS

Lateral marks are buoys or beacons that indicate the port and starboard sides of a route to be followed, and are used in conjunction with a "conventional direction of buoyage".

Generally, lateral aids to navigation indicate on which side of the aid to navigation a vessel should pass, when navigable channels are entered from seaward and a vessel proceeds in the conventional direction of buoyage. Since all channels do not lead from seaward, certain assumptions must be made so the system can be consistently applied. In the absence of a route leading from seaward, the conventional direction of buoyage generally follows a clockwise direction around land masses.

Virtually all U.S. lateral marks are located in IALA Region B and follow the traditional 3R rule of "red, right, returning". In U.S. waters, returning from seaward and proceeding toward the head of navigation is generally considered as moving southerly along the Atlantic coast, westerly along the Gulf coast and northerly along the Pacific coast. In the Great Lakes, the conventional direction of buoyage is generally considered westerly and northerly, except on Lake Michigan, where southerly movement is considered as returning from sea.

A summary of the port and starboard hand lateral mark characteristics is contained in the following table.

Characteristic	Port Hand Marks	Starboard Hand Marks
Color	Green	Red
Shape (buoys)	Cylindrical (can) or pillar	Conical (nun) or pillar
Dayboard or Topmark (when fitted)	Green square or cylinder	Red triangle or cone, point upward
Light Color (when fitted)	Green	Red
Reflector Color	Green	Red
Numbers	Odd	Even

Preferred channel marks are aids to navigation which mark channel **junctions** or **bifurcations** and often mark wrecks or obstructions. Preferred channel marks may normally be passed on either side by a vessel, but indicate to the mariner the preferred channel. Preferred channel marks are colored with red and green bands.

At a point where a channel divides, when proceeding in the "conventional direction of buoyage", a preferred channel in IALA Region B may be indicated by a modified port or starboard lateral mark as follows:

Characteristic	Preferred channel to starboard	Preferred channel to port
Color	Green with one broad red band	Red with one broad green band
Shape (buoys)	Cylindrical (can) or pillar	Conical (nun) or pillar
Dayboard	Green square, lower half red	Red triangle, lower half green
Topmark (when fitted)	Green square or cylinder	Red triangular cone, point upward
Light (when fitted)		
Color	Green	Red
Rhythm	Composite group flashing (2+1)	Composite group flashing (2+1)
Reflector color	Green	Red

NOTE: U.S. lateral aids to navigation at certain Pacific islands are located within Region A and thus exhibit opposite color significance. Port hand marks are red with square or cylindrical shapes while starboard hand marks are green with triangular or conical shapes.

CAUTION: It may not always be possible to pass on either side of preferred channel aids to navigation. The appropriate nautical chart should always be consulted.

Non-lateral marks have no lateral significance but may be used to supplement the lateral aids to navigation specified above. Occasionally, daybeacons or minor lights outside of the normal channel will not have lateral significance since they do not define limits to navigable waters. These aids to navigation will utilize diamond-shaped dayboards and are divided into four diamond-shaped sectors. The side sectors of these dayboards are colored white, and the top and bottom sectors are colored black, red, or green as the situation dictates.

Safe water marks are used to mark fairways, mid-channels, and offshore approach points, and have unobstructed water on all sides. They can also be used by the mariner transiting offshore waters to identify the proximity of intended landfall. Safe water marks are red and white striped and have a red spherical topmark to further aid in identification. If lighted, they display a white light with the characteristic Morse code "A".

Isolated danger marks are erected on, or moored above or near, an isolated danger, which has navigable water all around it. These marks should not be approached closely without special caution. These marks were introduced in 1991.

Isolated danger marks are colored with black and red bands, and if lighted, display a group flashing (2) white light. A topmark consisting of two black spheres, one above the other, is fitted for both lighted and unlighted marks.

Special marks are not intended to assist in navigation, but rather to alert the mariner to a special feature or area. The feature should be described in a nautical document such as a chart, Light List, Coast Pilot or Notice to Mariner. Some areas which may be marked by these aids to navigation are spoil areas, pipelines, traffic separation schemes, jetties, or military exercise areas. Special marks are yellow in color and, if lighted, display a yellow light.

Information and regulatory marks are used to alert the mariner to various warnings or regulatory matters. These marks have orange geometric shapes against a white background. The meanings associated with the orange shapes are as follows:

1) An open-faced diamond signifies danger.

2) A diamond shape having a cross centered within indicates that vessels are excluded from the marked area.

3) A circular shape indicates that certain operating restrictions are in effect within the marked area.

4) A square or rectangular shape will contain directions or instructions lettered within the shape.

BUOYS AND BEACONS

The IALA maritime buoyage guidelines apply to buoys and beacons that indicate the lateral limits of navigable channels, obstructions and other dangers such as wrecks, and other areas or features of importance to the mariner. This system provides five types of marks: lateral marks, safe water marks, special marks, isolated danger marks and cardinal marks. (Cardinal marks are not presently used in the United States.) Each type of mark is differentiated from other types by distinctive colors, shapes and light rhythms. Examples are provided on the enclosed color illustrations.

Buoys are floating aids to navigation used extensively throughout U.S. waters. They are moored to the seabed by concrete sinkers with chain or synthetic rope moorings of various lengths connected to the buoy body.

Buoy positions represented on nautical charts are approximate positions only, due to the practical limitations of positioning and maintaining buoys and their sinkers in precise geographical locations. Buoy positions are normally verified during periodic maintenance visits. Between visits, atmospheric and sea conditions, seabed slope and composition, and collisions or other accidents may cause buoys to shift from their charted locations, or cause buoys to be sunk or capsized.

Buoy moorings vary in length. The mooring lengths define a "watch circle", and buoys can be expected to move within this circle. Actual watch circles do not coincide with the symbols representing them on charts.

CAUTION: Mariners attempting to pass a buoy close aboard risk collision with a yawing buoy or with the obstruction which the buoy marks. Mariners must not rely on buoys alone for determining their positions due to factors limiting buoy reliability. Prudent mariners will use bearings or angles from fixed aids to navigation and shore objects, soundings and various methods of electronic navigation to positively fix their position.

Beacons are aids to navigation which are permanently fixed to the earth's surface. These structures range from lighthouses to small unlighted daybeacons, and exhibit a daymark to make these aids to navigation readily visible and easily identifiable against background conditions. The daymark conveys to the mariner, during daylight hours, the same significance as does the aid to navigation's light at night.

CAUTION: Vessels should not pass fixed aids to navigation close aboard due to the danger of collision with rip-rap or structure foundations, or with the obstruction or danger being marked.

LIGHTED AIDS TO NAVIGATION

Most lighted aids to navigation are equipped with controls which automatically cause the light to operate during darkness and to be extinguished during daylight. These devices are not of equal sensitivity, therefore all lights do not come on or go off at the same time. (Mariners should ensure correct identification of aids to navigation during twilight periods when some lighted aids to navigation are lit while others are not.)

The lighting apparatus is serviced at periodic intervals to assure reliable operation, but there is always the possibility of a light being extinguished or operating improperly.

The condition of the atmosphere has a considerable effect upon the distance at which lights can be seen. Sometimes lights are obscured by fog, haze, dust, smoke, or precipitation which may be present at the light, or between the light and the observer, and which is possibly unknown by the observer. Atmospheric refraction may cause a light to be seen farther than under ordinary circumstances. A light of low intensity will be easily obscured by unfavorable conditions of the atmosphere and little dependence can be placed on it being seen. For this reason, the intensity of a light should always be considered when expecting to sight it in thick weather. Haze and distance may reduce the apparent duration of the flash of a light. In some conditions of the atmosphere, white lights may have a reddish hue.

Lights placed at high elevations are more frequently obscured by clouds, mist, and fog than those lights located at or near sea level.

In regions where ice conditions prevail in the winter, the lantern panes of unattended lights may become covered with ice or snow, which will greatly reduce the visibility of the lights and may also cause colored lights to appear white.

The increasing use of brilliant shore lights for advertising, illuminating bridges, and other purposes, may cause marine navigational lights, particularly those in densely inhabited areas, to be outshone and difficult to distinguish from the background lighting. Mariners are requested to report such cases in order that steps may be taken to improve the conditions.

The "loom" (glow) of a powerful light is often seen beyond the limit of visibility of the actual rays of the light. The loom may sometimes appear sufficiently sharp enough to obtain a bearing.

At short distances, some flashing lights may show a faint continuous light between flashes.

The distance of an observer from a light cannot be estimated by its apparent intensity. Always check the characteristics of lights so powerful lights, visible in the distance, are not mistaken for nearby lights (such as those on lighted buoys) showing similar characteristics of low intensity.

If lights are not sighted within a reasonable time after prediction, a dangerous situation may exist requiring prompt resolution or action in order to ensure the safety of the vessel.

The apparent characteristic of a complex light may change with the distance of the observer. For example, a light which actually displays a characteristic of fixed white varied by flashes of alternating white and red (the rhythms having a decreasing range of visibility in the order: flashing white, flashing red, fixed white) may, when first sighted in clear weather, show as a simple flashing white light. As the vessel draws nearer, the red flash will become visible and the characteristics will apparently be alternating flashing white and red. Later, the fixed white light will be seen between the flashes and the true characteristic of the light will finally be recognized – fixed white, alternating flashing white and red (F W Al WR).

If a vessel has considerable vertical motion due to pitching in heavy seas, a light sighted on the horizon may alternately appear and disappear. This may lead the unwary to assign a false characteristic and hence, to err in its identification. The true characteristic will be evident after the distance has been sufficiently decreased or by increasing the height of eye of the observer.

Similarly, the effects of wave motion on lighted buoys may produce the appearance of incorrect light phase characteristics when certain flashes occur, but are not viewed by the mariner. In addition, buoy motion can reduce the distance at which buoy lights are detected.

Sectors of colored glass are placed in the lanterns of some lights in order to produce a system of light sectors of different colors. In general, red sectors are used to mark shoals or to warn the mariner of other obstructions to navigation or of nearby land. Such lights provide approximate bearing information since observers may note the change of color as they cross the boundary between sectors. These boundaries are indicated in the Light List (Col. 8) and by dotted lines on charts. These bearings, as all bearings referring to lights, are given in true

degrees from 000° to 359°, as observed from a vessel toward the light. Altering course on the changing sectors of a light or using the boundaries between light sectors to determine the bearing for any purpose is not recommended. Be guided instead by the correct compass bearing to the light and do not rely on being able to accurately observe the point at which the color changes. This is difficult to determine because the edges of a colored sector cannot be cut off sharply. On either side of the line of demarcation between white, red, or green sectors, there is always a small arc of uncertain color. Moreover, when haze or smoke are present in the intervening atmosphere, a white sector might have a reddish hue.

The area in which a light can be observed is normally an arc with the light as the center and the range of visibility as the radius. However, on some bearings the range may be reduced by obstructions. In such cases, the obstructed arc might differ with height of eye and distance. When a light is cut off by adjoining land and the arc of visibility is given, the bearing on which the light disappears may vary with the distance of the vessel from which observed and with the height of eye. When the light is cut off by a sloping hill or point of land, the light may be seen over a wider arc by a vessel farther away than by one closer to the light.

The arc drawn on charts around a light is not intended to give information as to the distance at which it can be seen, but solely to indicate, in the case of lights which do not show equally in all directions, the bearings between which the variation of visibility or obstruction of the light occurs.

OIL WELL STRUCTURES

Oil well structures in navigable waters are not listed in the Light List. The structures are shown on the appropriate nautical charts. Information concerning the location and characteristics of those structures which display lights and sound signals not located in obstruction areas are published in Local and/or Weekly Notices to Mariners.

In general, during the nighttime, a series of white lights are displayed extending from the platform to the top of the derrick when drilling operations are in progress. At other times, structures are usually marked with one or more fixed or quick flashing white or red lights, visible for at least one nautical mile during clear weather. Obstructions which are a part of the appurtenances to the main structure, such as mooring piles, anchor and mooring buoys, etc., normally are not lighted. In addition, some of the structures are equipped with sound signals (bell, siren, whistle, or horn). When operating, bells sound one stroke every 15 seconds, while sirens, whistles, or horns sound a single two-second blast every 20 seconds.

CHARACTERISTICS OF AIDS TO NAVIGATION

LIGHT COLORS

Only aids to navigation with green or red lights have lateral significance. When proceeding in the conventional direction of buoyage, the mariner in Region B, may see the following lighted aids to navigation:

Green lights on aids to navigation mark port sides of channels and locations of wrecks or obstructions which must be passed by keeping these lighted aids to navigation on the port hand of a vessel. Green lights are also used on preferred channel marks where the preferred channel is to starboard (i.e., aid to navigation left to port when proceeding in the conventional direction of buoyage).

Red lights on aids to navigation mark starboard sides of channels and locations of wrecks or obstructions which must be passed by keeping these lighted aids to navigation on the starboard hand of a vessel. Red lights are also used on preferred channel marks where the preferred channel is to port (i.e., aid to navigation left to starboard when proceeding in the conventional direction of buoyage).

White and yellow lights have no lateral significance. The purpose of aids to navigation exhibiting white or yellow lights may be determined by the shapes, colors, letters, and light rhythms.

Most aids to navigation are fitted with retroreflective material to increase their visibility in darkness. Red or green retroreflective material is used on lateral aids to navigation which, if lighted, will display lights of the same color.

LIGHT RHYTHMS

Light rhythms have no lateral significance. Aids to navigation with lateral significance exhibit flashing, quick, occulting or isophase light rhythms. Ordinarily, flashing lights (frequency not exceeding 30 flashes per minute) will be used.

Preferred channel marks exhibit a composite group-flashing light rhythm of two flashes followed by a single flash. Through 1989, some preferred channel marks may display the former interrupted quick flashing rhythm.

Safe water marks show a white Morse code "A" rhythm (a short flash followed by a long flash).

Isolated danger marks show a white flashing (2) rhythm (two flashes repeated regularly).

Special marks show yellow lights and exhibit a flashing or fixed rhythm; however, a flashing rhythm is preferred.

Information and regulatory marks, when lighted, display a white light with any light rhythm except quick flashing, flashing (2) and Morse code "A".

For situations where lights require a distinct cautionary significance, as at sharp turns, sudden channel constrictions, wrecks or obstructions, a quick flashing light rhythm will be used.

CHARACTERISTICS OF LIGHTS

1. FIXED.
A light showing continuously and steadily.

F

2. OCCULTING.
A light in which the total duration of light in a period is longer than the total duration of darkness and the intervals of darkness (eclipses) are usually of equal duration.

2.1 Single–occulting.
An occulting light in which an eclipse is regularly repeated.

Oc

period

2.2 Group–occulting.
An occulting light in which a group of eclipses, specified in numbers, is regularly repeated.

Oc(2)

period

2.3 Composite group–occulting.
A light, similar to a group–occulting light, except that successive groups in a period have different numbers of eclipses.

Oc(2+1)

period

3. ISOPHASE.
A light in which all durations of light and darkness are equal.

Iso

period

4. FLASHING.
A light in which the total duration of light in a period is shorter than the total duration of darkness and the appearances of light (flashes) are usually of equal duration.

4.1 Single–flashing.
A flashing light in which a flash is regularly repeated (frequency not exceeding 30 flashes per minute).

Fl

period

Illustration	Type Description	Abbreviation

4.2 Group–flashing.
A flashing light in which a group of flashes, specified in number, is regularly repeated.

Fl (2)

4.3 Composite group–flashing.
A light similar to a group flashing light except that successive groups in the period have different numbers of flashes.

Fl (2+1)

5. QUICK.
A light in which flashes are produced at a rate of 60 flashes per minute.

5.1 Continuous quick.
A quick light in which a flash is regularly repeated.

Q

5.2 Interrupted quick.
A quick light in which the sequence of flashes is interrupted by regularly repeated eclipses of constant and long duration.

IQ

6. MORSE CODE.
A light in which appearances of light of two clearly different durations (dots and dashes) are grouped to represent a character or characters in the Morse code.

Mo (A)

7. FIXED AND FLASHING.
A light in which a fixed light is combined with a flashing light of higher luminous intensity.

FFl

8. ALTERNATING.
A light showing different colors alternately.

Al RW

SHAPES

In order to provide easy identification, certain unlighted buoys and dayboards on beacons are differentiated by shape. These shapes are laterally significant only when associated with laterally significant colors.

Cylindrical buoys (referred to as "can buoys") and square dayboards mark the left side of a channel when proceeding from seaward. These aids to navigation are associated with solid green or green and red banded marks where the topmost band is green.

Conical buoys (referred to as "nun buoys") and triangular dayboards mark the right side of the channel when proceeding from seaward. These aids to navigation are associated with solid red or red and green banded marks where the topmost band is red.

Unless fitted with topmarks; lighted, sound, pillar, and spar buoys have no shape significance. Their meanings are conveyed by their numbers, colors, and light characteristics.

NUMBERS

All solid red and solid green aids to navigation are numbered, with red aids to navigation bearing even numbers and green aids to navigation bearing odd numbers. The numbers for each increase from seaward, proceeding in the conventional direction of buoyage. Numbers are kept in approximate sequence on both sides of the channel by omitting numbers where necessary.

Letters may be used to augment numbers when lateral aids to navigation are added to channels with previously completed numerical sequences. Letters will increase in alphabetical order from seaward, proceeding in the conventional direction of buoyage and are added to numbers as suffixes.

No other aids to navigation are numbered. Preferred channel, safe water, isolated danger, special marks, and information and regulatory aids to navigation may be lettered, but not numbered.

DAYBOARDS

In order to describe the appearance and purpose of each dayboard used in the U.S. System, standard designations have been formulated. A brief explanation of the designations and of the purpose of each type of dayboard in the system is given below, followed by a word description of the appearance of each dayboard type.

Designations:

1. First Letter – Shape or Purpose

S   Square used to mark the port (left) side of channels when proceeding from seaward.

T   Triangle used to mark the starboard (right) side of channels when proceeding from seaward.

J   Junction (square or triangle) used to mark (preferred channel) junctions or bifurcations in the channel, or wrecks or obstructions which may be passed on either side; color of top band has lateral significance for the preferred channel.

M   Safe water (octagonal) used to mark the fairway or

middle of the channel.

C   Crossing (western rivers only) diamond-shaped, used to indicate the points at which the channel crosses the river.

K   Range (rectangular) when both the front and rear range dayboards are aligned on the same bearing, the observer is on the azimuth of the range, usually used to mark the center of the channel.

N   No lateral significance (diamond or rectangular-shaped) used for special purpose, warning, distance, or location markers.

2. Second letter – Key color

    G – Green   R – Red

    B – Black   W – White

    Y – Yellow

3. Third letter (color of center stripe; range dayboards only)

4. Additional information after a (–)

    –I   Intracoastal Waterway; a yellow reflective horizontal strip on a dayboard; indicates the aid to navigation marks the Intracoastal Waterway.

    –SY   Intracoastal Waterway; a yellow reflective square on a dayboard; indicates the aid to navigation is a port hand mark for vessels traversing the Intracoastal Waterway. May appear on a triangular daymark where the Intracoastal Waterway coincides with a waterway having opposite conventional direction of buoyage.

    –TY   Intracoastal Waterway; a yellow reflective triangle on a dayboard; indicates the aid to navigation is a starboard hand mark for vessels traversing the Intracoastal Waterway. May appear on a square daymark where the Intracoastal Waterway coincides with a waterway having opposite conventional direction of buoyage.

Example: The designation KRW-I indicates a range dayboard (K); key color red (R); with a white stripe (W); in the Intracoastal Waterway (–I).

Descriptions:

SG	Square green dayboard with a green reflective border.
SG-I	Square green dayboard with a green reflective border and a yellow reflective horizontal strip.
SG-SY	Square green dayboard with a green reflective border and a yellow reflective square.
SG-TY	Square green dayboard with a green reflective border and a yellow reflective triangle.
SR	Square red dayboard with a red reflective border. (IALA Region "A")
TG	Triangular green dayboard with a green reflective

border. (IALA Region "A")

TR	Triangular red dayboard with a red reflective border.
TR-I	Triangular red dayboard with a red reflective border and a yellow reflective horizontal strip.
TR-SY	Triangular red dayboard with a red reflective border and a yellow reflective square.
TR-TY	Triangular red dayboard with a red reflective border and a yellow reflective triangle.
JG	Dayboard bearing horizontal bands of green and red, green band topmost, with a green reflective border.
JG-I	Square dayboard bearing horizontal bands of green and red, green band topmost, with a green reflective border and a yellow reflective horizontal strip.
JG-SY	Square dayboard bearing horizontal bands of green and red, green band topmost, with a green reflective border and a yellow reflective square.
JG-TY	Square dayboard bearing horizontal bands of green and red, green band topmost, with a green reflective border and a yellow reflective triangle.
JR	Dayboard bearing horizontal bands of red and green, red band topmost, with a red reflective border.
JR-I	Triangular dayboard bearing horizontal bands of red and green, red band topmost, with a red reflective border and a yellow horizontal strip.
JR-SY	Triangular dayboard bearing horizontal bands of red and green, red band topmost, with a red reflective border and a yellow reflective square.
JR-TY	Triangular dayboard bearing horizontal bands of red and green, red band topmost, with a red reflective border and a yellow reflective triangle.
MR	Octagonal dayboard bearing stripes of white and red, with a white reflective border.
MR-I	Octagonal dayboard bearing stripes of white and red, with a white reflective border and a yellow reflective horizontal strip.
CG	Diamond-shaped green dayboard bearing small green diamond shaped reflectors at each corner.
CR	Diamond-shaped red dayboard bearing small red diamond shaped reflectors at each corner.
KBG	Rectangular black dayboard bearing a central green stripe.
KBG-I	Rectangular black dayboard bearing a central green stripe and a yellow reflective horizontal strip.
KBR	Rectangular black dayboard bearing a central red stripe.
KBR-I	Rectangular black dayboard bearing a central red stripe and a yellow reflective horizontal strip.
KBW	Rectangular black dayboard bearing a central white stripe.
KBW-I	Rectangular black dayboard bearing a central white stripe and a yellow reflective horizontal strip.
KGB	Rectangular green dayboard bearing a central black stripe.
KGB-I	Rectangular green dayboard bearing a central black stripe and a yellow reflective horizontal strip.
KGR	Rectangular green dayboard bearing a central red stripe.
KGR-I	Rectangular green dayboard bearing a central red stripe and a yellow reflective horizontal strip.
KGW	Rectangular green dayboard bearing a central white stripe.
KGW-I	Rectangular green dayboard bearing a central white stripe and a yellow reflective horizontal strip.
KRB	Rectangular red dayboard bearing a central black stripe.
KRB-I	Rectangular red dayboard bearing a central black stripe and a yellow reflective horizontal strip.
KRG	Rectangular red dayboard bearing a central green stripe.
KRG-I	Rectangular red dayboard bearing a central green stripe and a yellow reflective horizontal strip.
KRW	Rectangular red dayboard bearing a central white stripe.
KRW-I	Rectangular red dayboard bearing a central white stripe and a yellow reflective horizontal strip.
KWB	Rectangular white dayboard bearing a central black stripe.
KWB-I	Rectangular white dayboard bearing a central black stripe and a yellow reflective horizontal strip.
KWG	Rectangular white dayboard bearing a central green stripe.
KWG-I	Rectangular white dayboard bearing a central green stripe and a yellow reflective horizontal strip.
KWR	Rectangular white dayboard bearing a central red stripe.
KWR-I	Rectangular white dayboard bearing a central red stripe and a yellow reflective horizontal strip.
NB	Diamond-shaped dayboard divided into four diamond-shaped colored sectors with the sectors at the side corners white and the sectors at the top and bottom corners black, with a white reflective border.

NG	Diamond-shaped dayboard divided into four diamond-shaped colored sectors with the sectors at the side corners white and the sectors at the top and bottom corners green, with a white reflective border.
NR	Diamond-shaped dayboard divided into four diamond-shaped colored sectors with the sectors at the side corners white and the sectors at the top and bottom corners red, with a white reflective border.
NW	Diamond-shaped white dayboard with an orange reflective border and black letters describing the information or regulatory nature of the mark.
ND	Rectangular white mileage marker with black numerals indicating the mile number (western rivers only).
NL	Rectangular white location marker with an orange reflective border and black letters indicating the location.
NY	Diamond-shaped yellow dayboard with a yellow reflective border.

These abbreviated descriptions are used in column (7) and may also be found on the illustration of U.S. Aids to Navigation System.

OTHER SHORT RANGE AIDS TO NAVIGATION

Lighthouses are placed on shore or on marine sites and most often do not show lateral markings. They assist the mariner in determining his position or safe course, or warn of obstructions or dangers to navigation. Lighthouses with no lateral significance usually exhibit a white light.

Occasionally, lighthouses use sectored lights to mark shoals or warn mariners of other dangers. Lights so equipped show one color from most directions and a different color or colors over definite arcs of the horizon as indicated on the appropriate nautical chart. These sectors provide approximate bearing information and the observer should note a change of color as the boundary between the sectors is crossed. Since sector bearings are not precise, they should be considered as a warning only, and used in conjunction with a nautical chart.

Large navigational buoys (LNBs) were developed to replace lightships and are placed at points where it is impractical to build lighthouses. The unmanned LNBs are 40 feet in diameter with light towers approximately 40 feet above the water. LNBs are equipped with lights, sound signals, radiobeacons, and racons. The traditional red color of LNBs has no lateral significance, but is intended to improve visibility.

Seasonal aids to navigation are placed into service or changed at specified times of the year. The dates shown in the Light List (Col. 8) are approximate and may vary due to adverse weather or other conditions.

Ranges are non-lateral aids to navigation systems employing dual beacons which when the structures appear to be in line, assist the mariner in maintaining a safe course. The appropriate nautical chart must be consulted when using ranges to determine whether the range marks the centerline of the navigable channel

and also what section of the range may be safely traversed. Ranges display rectangular dayboards of various colors and are generally, but not always lighted. When lighted, ranges may display lights of any color.

Sound signal is a generic term used to describe aids to navigation that produce an audible signal designed to assist the mariner in fog or other periods of reduced visibility. These aids to navigation can be activated by several means (i.e., manually, remotely, or fog detector). In cases where a fog detector is in use, there may be a delay in the automatic activation of the signal. Additionally, fog detectors may not be capable of detecting patchy fog conditions. Sound signals are distinguished by their tone and phase characteristics.

Tones are determined by the devices producing the sound, e.g., diaphones, diaphragm horns, sirens, whistles, bells, and gongs.

Phase characteristics are defined by the signal's sound pattern, i.e., the number of blasts and silent periods per minute and their durations. Sound signals sounded from fixed structures generally produce a specific number of blasts and silent periods each minute when operating. Buoy sound signals are generally activated by the motion of the sea and therefore do not emit a regular signal characteristic. It is common, in fact, for a buoy to produce no sound signal when seas are calm. Mariners are reminded that buoy positions are not always reliable.

The characteristic of a sound signal can be located in column (8) of the Light List. Unless it is specifically stated that a sound signal "Operates continuously", or the signal is a bell, gong, or whistle on a buoy, it can be assumed that the sound signal only operates during times of fog, reduced visibility, or adverse weather.

An emergency sound signal is sounded at some locations when the main and stand-by signals are inoperative. If the emergency signal is of a different type or characteristic than the main signal, its characteristic is listed in column (8) of this publication.

CAUTION: Mariners should not rely on sound signals to determine their position. Distance cannot be accurately determined by sound intensity. Occasionally, sound signals may not be heard in areas close to their location. Signals may not sound in cases where fog exists close to, but not at, the location of the sound signal.

VARIATIONS TO THE U.S. SYSTEM

Intracoastal Waterway aids to navigation: The Intracoastal Waterway runs parallel to the Atlantic and Gulf coasts from Manasquan Inlet, New Jersey to the Mexican border. Aids to navigation marking these waters have some portion of them marked with yellow. Otherwise, the coloring and numbering of the aids to navigation follow the same system as that in other U.S. waterways.

In order that vessels may readily follow the Intracoastal Waterway route, special markings are employed. These marks consist of a yellow square and yellow triangle and indicate which side the aid to navigation should be passed when following the conventional direction of buoyage. The yellow square indicates that the aid to navigation should be kept on the left side and the yellow triangle indicates that the aid to navigation should be kept on the right side.

NOTE: The conventional direction of buoyage in the Intracoastal Waterway is generally southerly along the Atlantic coast and generally westerly along the Gulf coast.

The **Western Rivers System**, a variation of the standard U.S. Aids to Navigation System described in the preceding sections, is employed on the Mississippi River and its tributaries above Baton Rouge, LA and on certain other rivers which flow toward the Gulf of Mexico.

The Western Rivers System varies from the standard U.S. system as follows:

1) Aids to navigation are not numbered.

2) Numbers on aids to navigation do not have lateral significance but, rather, indicate mileage from a fixed point (normally the river mouth).

3) Diamond shaped crossing dayboards, red or green as appropriate, are used to indicate where the river channel crosses from one bank to the other.

4) Lights on green aids to navigation show a single-flash characteristic which may be green or white.

5) Lights on red aids to navigation show a group-flash characteristic which may be red or white.

6) Isolated danger marks are not used.

Uniform State Waterway Marking System (USWMS): This system was developed in 1966 to provide an easily understood system for operators of small boats. While designed for use on lakes and other inland waterways that are not portrayed on nautical charts, the USWMS was authorized for use on other waters as well. It supplements the existing federal marking system and is generally compatible with it.

The conventional direction of buoyage is considered upstream or towards the head of navigation.

The USWMS varies from the standard U.S. system as follows:

1) The color black is used instead of green.

2) There are three aids to navigation which reflect cardinal significance:

   a. A white buoy with red top represents an obstruction and the buoy should be passed to the south or west.

   b. A white buoy with black top represents an obstruction and the buoy should be passed to the north or east.

   c. A red and white vertically striped buoy indicates that an obstruction exists between that buoy and the nearest shore.

3) Mooring buoys are white buoys with a horizontal blue band midway between the waterline and the top of the buoy. This buoy may be lighted and will generally show a slow flashing white light.

BRIDGE MARKINGS

Bridges across navigable waters are generally marked with red, green and/or white lights for nighttime navigation. Red lights mark piers and other parts of the bridge. Red lights are also used on drawbridges to show when they are in the closed position.

Green lights are used on drawbridges to show when they are in the open position. The location of these lights will vary according to the bridge structure. Green lights are also used to mark the centerline of navigable channels through fixed bridges. If there are two or more channels through the bridge, the preferred channel is also marked by three white lights in a vertical line above the green light.

Red and green retro-reflective panels may be used to mark bridge piers and may also be used on bridges not required to display lights.

Main channels through bridges may be marked by lateral red and green lights and dayboards. Adjacent piers should be marked with fixed yellow lights when the main channel is marked with lateral aids to navigation.

Centerlines of channels through fixed bridges may be marked with a safe water mark and an occulting white light when lateral marks are used to mark main channels. The centerline of the navigable channel through the draw span of floating bridges may be marked with a special mark. The mark will be a yellow diamond with yellow retro-reflective panels and may exhibit a yellow light that displays a Morse code "B"(—...).

Clearance gauges may be installed to enhance navigation safety. The gauges are located on the right channel pier or pier protective structure facing approaching vessels. They indicate the vertical clearance available under the span.

Drawbridges equipped with radiotelephones display a blue and white sign which indicates what VHF radiotelephone channels should be used to request bridge openings.

U.S. AIDS TO NAVIGATION SYSTEM
on navigable waters except Western Rivers

LATERAL SYSTEM AS SEEN ENTERING FROM SEAWARD

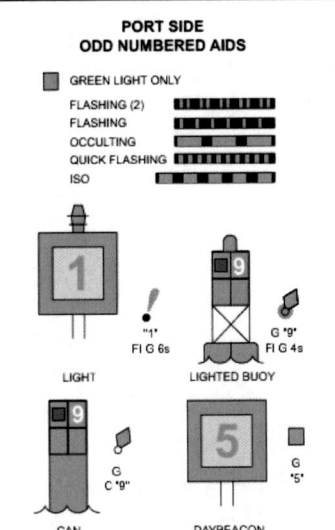

PORT SIDE
ODD NUMBERED AIDS

GREEN LIGHT ONLY

FLASHING (2)
FLASHING
OCCULTING
QUICK FLASHING
ISO

"1" FI G 6s — LIGHT
G "9" FI G 4s — LIGHTED BUOY
G C "9" — CAN
G "5" — DAYBEACON

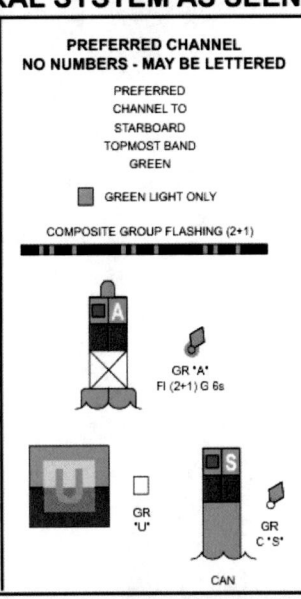

PREFERRED CHANNEL
NO NUMBERS - MAY BE LETTERED

PREFERRED
CHANNEL TO
STARBOARD
TOPMOST BAND
GREEN

GREEN LIGHT ONLY

COMPOSITE GROUP FLASHING (2+1)

GR "A" FI (2+1) G 6s
GR "U"
GR C "S" — CAN

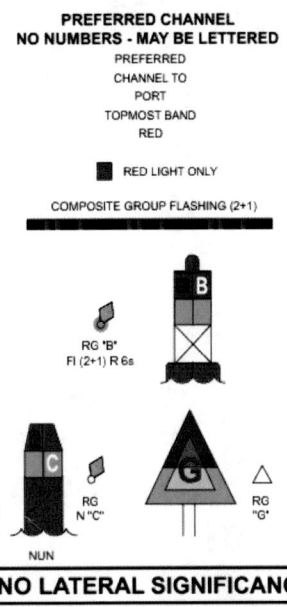

PREFERRED CHANNEL
NO NUMBERS - MAY BE LETTERED

PREFERRED
CHANNEL TO
PORT
TOPMOST BAND
RED

RED LIGHT ONLY

COMPOSITE GROUP FLASHING (2+1)

RG "B" FI (2+1) R 6s
RG N "C" — NUN
RG "G"

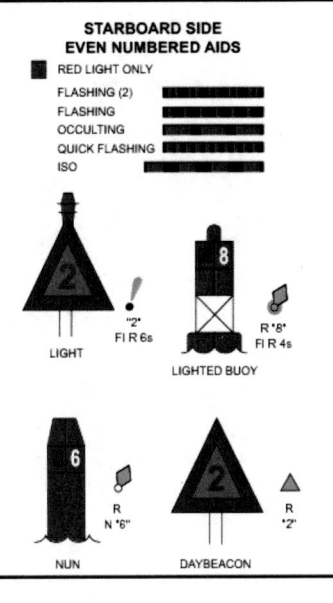

STARBOARD SIDE
EVEN NUMBERED AIDS

RED LIGHT ONLY

FLASHING (2)
FLASHING
OCCULTING
QUICK FLASHING
ISO

"2" FI R 6s — LIGHT
R "8" FI R 4s — LIGHTED BUOY
R N "6" — NUN
R "2" — DAYBEACON

AIDS TO NAVIGATION HAVING NO LATERAL SIGNIFICANCE

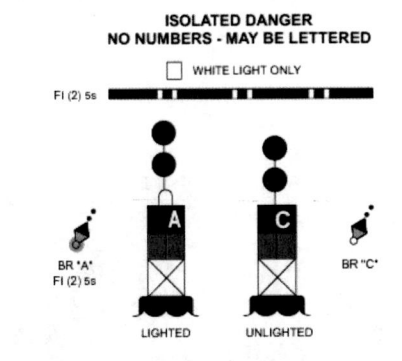

ISOLATED DANGER
NO NUMBERS - MAY BE LETTERED

WHITE LIGHT ONLY

FI (2) 5s

BR "A" FI (2) 5s — LIGHTED
BR "C" — UNLIGHTED

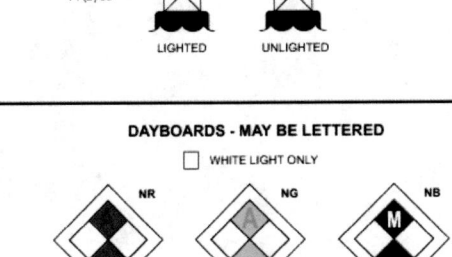

DAYBOARDS - MAY BE LETTERED

WHITE LIGHT ONLY

NR — RW Bn
NG — GW Bn
NB — BW Bn

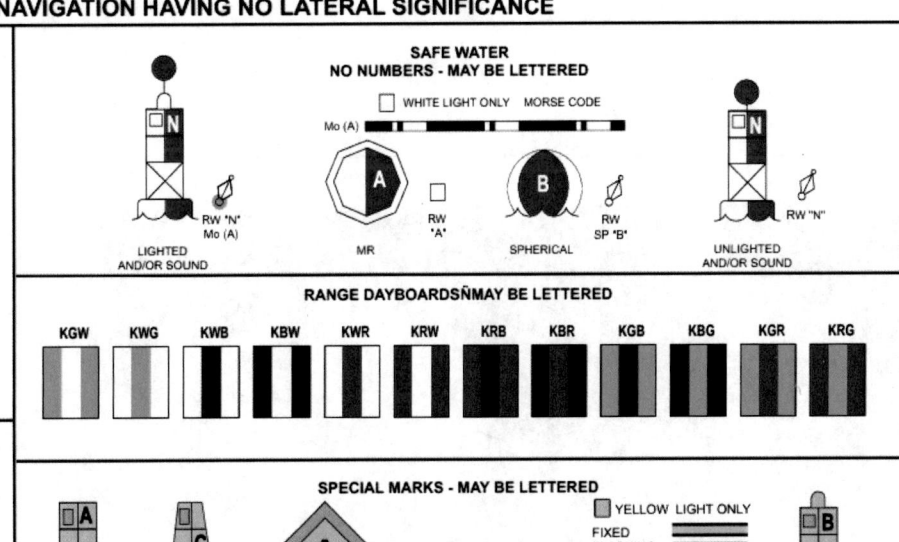

SAFE WATER
NO NUMBERS - MAY BE LETTERED

WHITE LIGHT ONLY   MORSE CODE

Mo (A)

RW "N" Mo (A) — LIGHTED AND/OR SOUND
RW "A" — MR
RW SP "B" — SPHERICAL
RW "N" — UNLIGHTED AND/OR SOUND

RANGE DAYBOARDS—MAY BE LETTERED

KGW KWG KWB KBW KWR KRW KRB KBR KGB KBG KGR KRG

SPECIAL MARKS - MAY BE LETTERED

YELLOW LIGHT ONLY
FIXED
FLASHING

C "A" — UNLIGHTED
N "C"
Y "A" Bn
Y "B" FI — LIGHTED

SHAPE OPTIONAL--BUT SELECTED TO BE APPROPRIATE
FOR THE POSITION OF THE MARK IN RELATION TO THE
NAVIGABLE WATERWAY AND THE DIRECTION
OF BUOYAGE.

Aids to Navigation marking the Intracoastal Waterway (ICW) display unique yellow symbols to distinguish them from aids marking other waters. Yellow triangles △ indicate aids should be passed by keeping them on the starboard (right) hand of the vessel. Yellow squares ▢ indicate aids should be passed by keeping them on the port (left) hand of the vessel. A yellow horizontal band ▭ provides no lateral information, but simply identifies aids as marking the ICW.

TYPICAL INFORMATION AND REGULATORY MARKS

INFORMATION AND REGULATORY MARKERS

WHEN LIGHTED, INFORMATION AND REGULATORY
MARKS MAY DISPLAY ANY WHITE LIGHT RHYTHM
EXCEPT QUICK FLASHING, Mo(A), AND FLASHING (2)

W Bn — DANGER NW

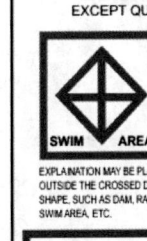

MOORING BUOY
WHITE WITH BLUE BAND
MAY SHOW WHITE REFLECTOR OR LIGHT

SWIM AREA — BOAT EXCLUSION AREA
EXPLANATION MAY BE PLACED OUTSIDE THE CROSSED DIAMOND SHAPE, SUCH AS DAM, RAPIDS, SWIM AREA, ETC.

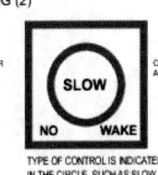

ROCK — DANGER
THE NATURE OF DANGER MAY BE INDICATED INSIDE THE DIAMOND SHAPE, SUCH AS ROCK, WRECK, SHOAL, DAM, ETC.

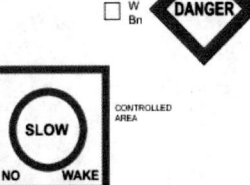

SLOW NO WAKE — CONTROLLED AREA
TYPE OF CONTROL IS INDICATED IN THE CIRCLE, SUCH AS SLOW, NO WAKE, ANCHORING, ETC.

MULLET LAKE
BLACK RIVER
FOR DISPLAYING INFORMATION SUCH AS DIRECTIONS, DISTANCES, LOCATIONS, ETC.

INFORMATION
BUOY USED TO DISPLAY REGULATORY MARKERS

5 MPH
MAY SHOW WHITE LIGHT
MAY BE LETTERED

PLATE 1

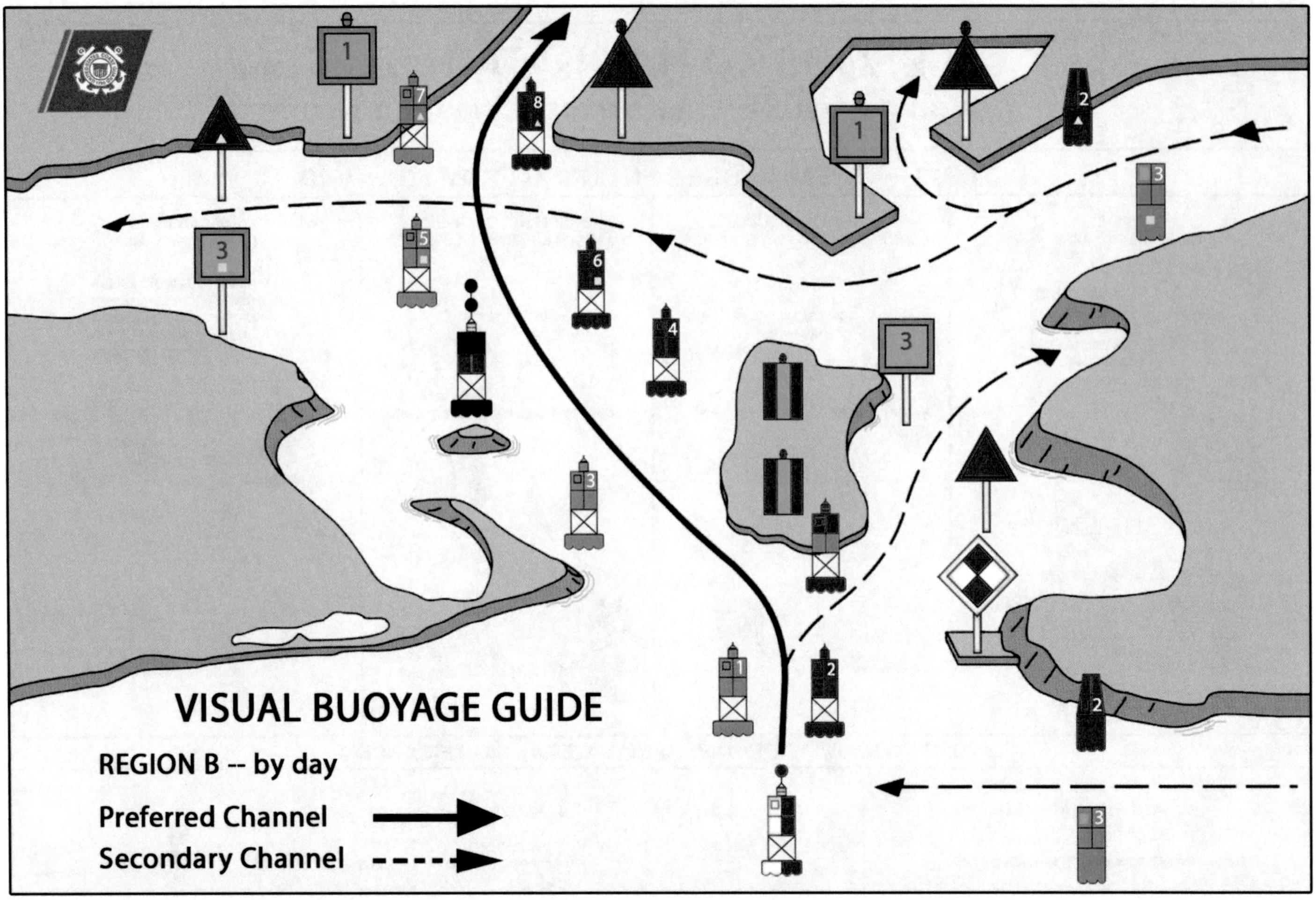

VISUAL BUOYAGE GUIDE

REGION B -- by day

Preferred Channel ⟶

Secondary Channel ⤍

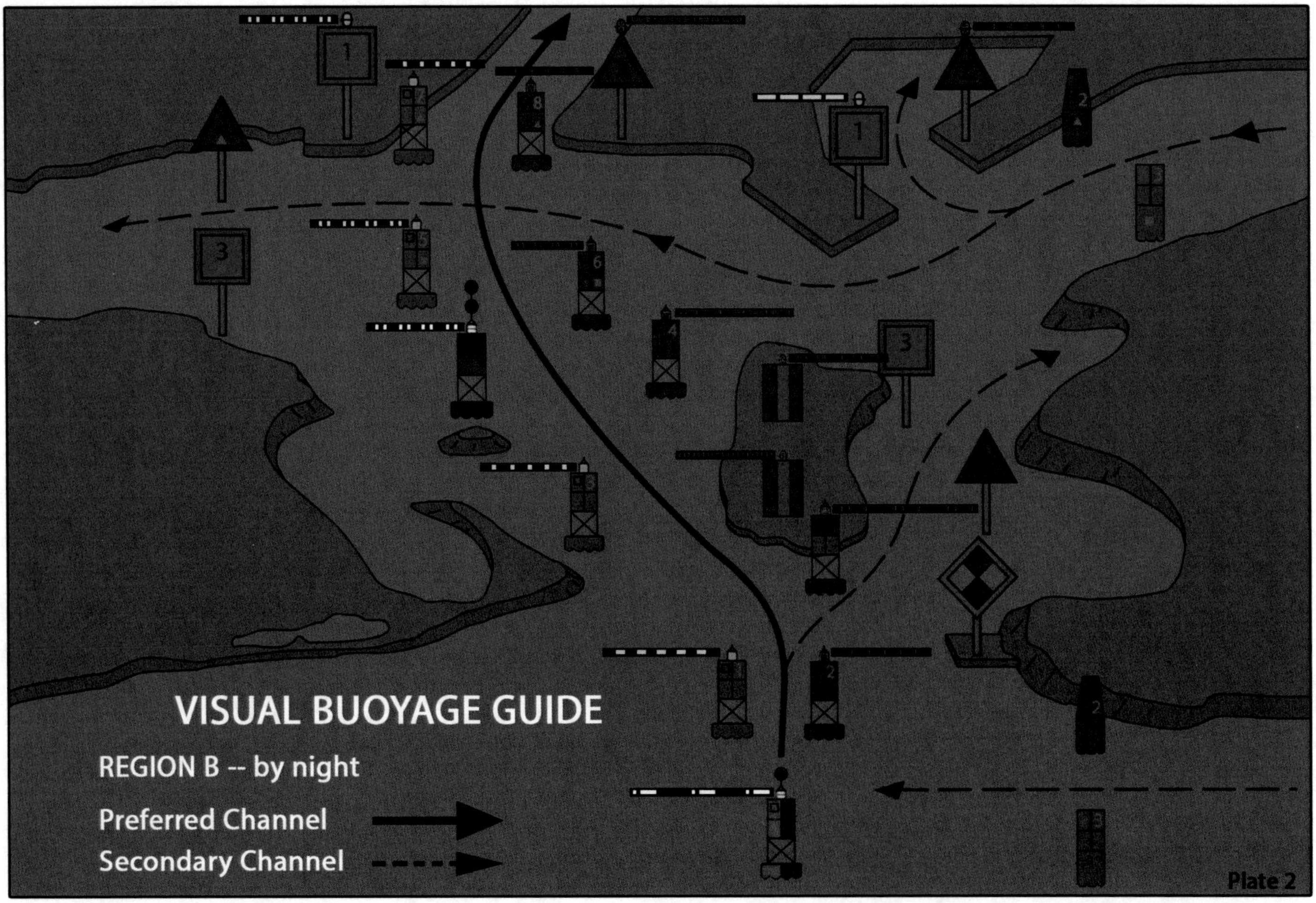

VISUAL BUOYAGE GUIDE

REGION B -- by night

Preferred Channel ⟶

Secondary Channel ⤍

Plate 2

FICTITIOUS NAUTICAL CHART

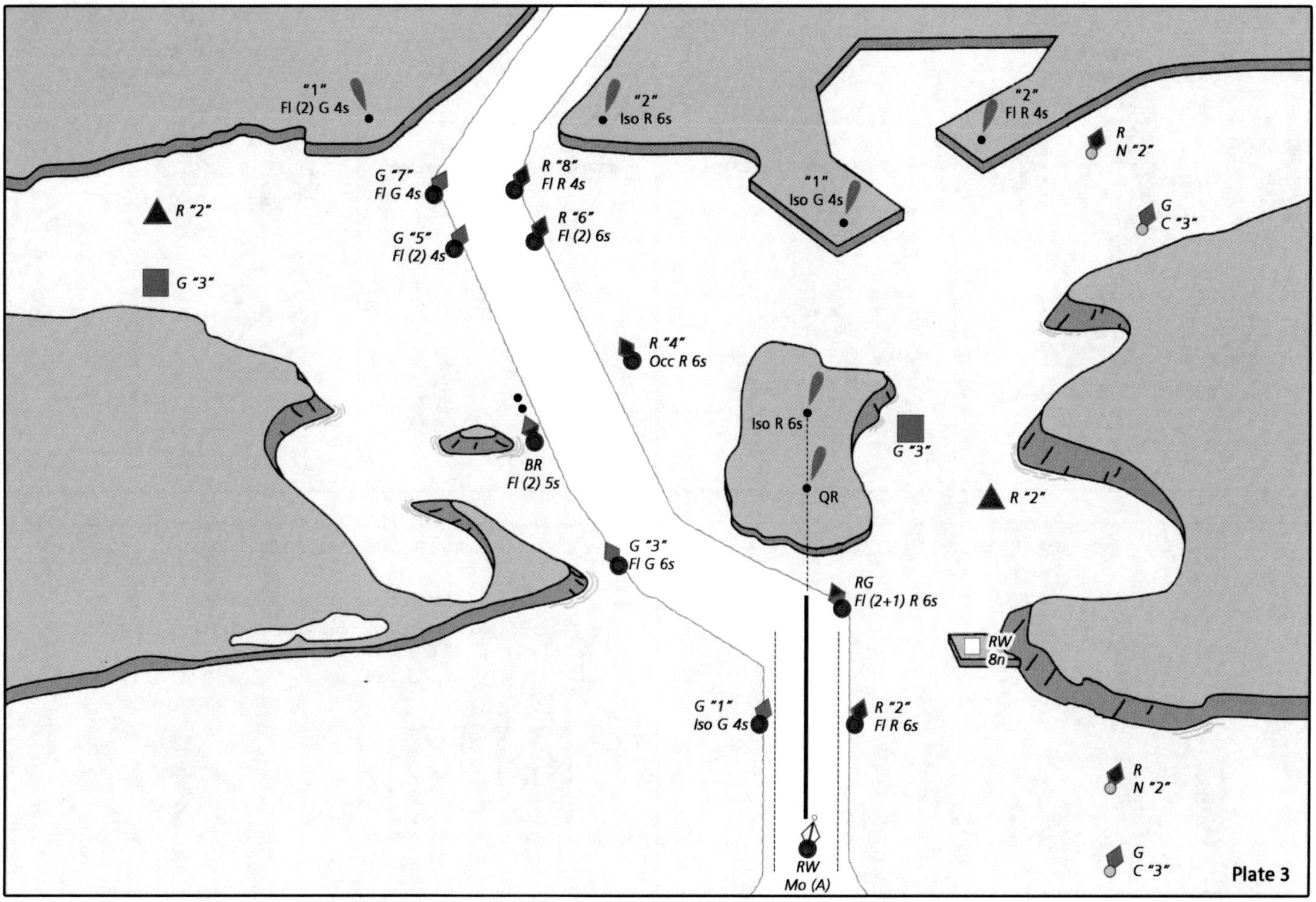

"1"
Fl (2) G 4s

"2"
Iso R 6s

"2"
Fl R 4s

R
N "2"

G "7"
Fl G 4s

R "8"
Fl R 4s

"1"
Iso G 4s

G
C "3"

R "2"

R "6"
Fl (2) 6s

G "5"
Fl (2) 4s

G "3"

R "4"
Occ R 6s

Iso R 6s

G "3"

BR
Fl (2) 5s

QR

R "2"

G "3"
Fl G 6s

RG
Fl (2+1) R 6s

RW
8n

G "1"
Iso G 4s

R "2"
Fl R 6s

R
N "2"

G
C "3"

RW
Mo (A)

Plate 3

U.S. AIDS TO NAVIGATION SYSTEM
on the Western River System

AS SEEN ENTERING FROM SEAWARD

PORT SIDE OR RIGHT DESCENDING BANK

GREEN OR ☐ WHITE LIGHTS (CROSSING)

FLASHING
ISO

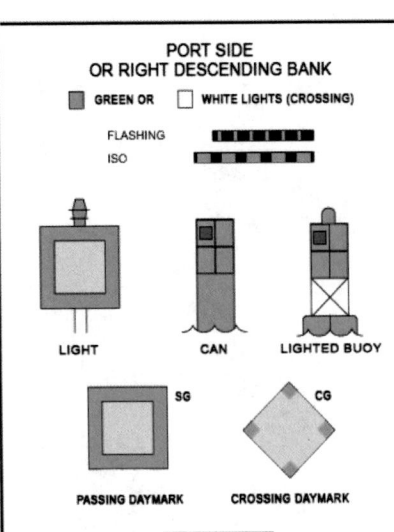

LIGHT CAN LIGHTED BUOY

SG CG

PASSING DAYMARK CROSSING DAYMARK

176.9
MILE BOARD

PREFERRED CHANNEL

MARK JUNCTIONS AND OBSTRUCTIONS
COMPOSITE GROUP FLASHING (2 + 1)

PREFERRED CHANNEL TO STARBOARD

TOPMOST BAND GREEN

Fl (2+ 1) G

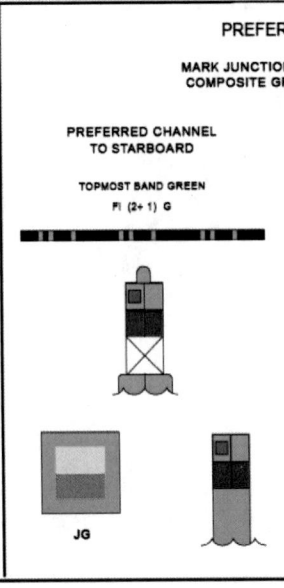

JG

PREFERRED CHANNEL TO PORT

TOPMOST BAND RED

Fl (2+ 1) R

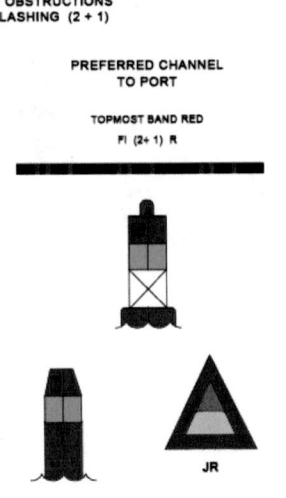

JR

STARBOARD SIDE OR LEFT DESCENDING BANK

RED OR ☐ WHITE LIGHTS (CROSSING)

FLASHING
ISO

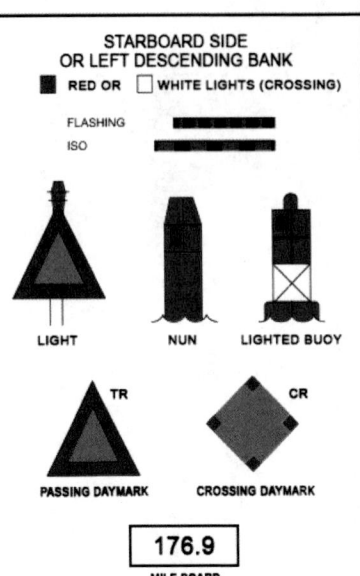

LIGHT NUN LIGHTED BUOY

TR CR

PASSING DAYMARK CROSSING DAYMARK

176.9
MILE BOARD

DAYMARKS HAVING NO LATERAL SIGNIFICANCE

MAY BE LETTERED

☐ WHITE LIGHT ONLY

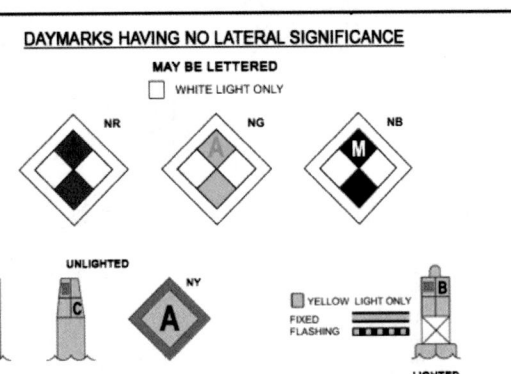

NR NG NB

UNLIGHTED

NY

A

 A  C

YELLOW LIGHT ONLY
FIXED
FLASHING

B

LIGHTED

RANGE DAYMARKS - MAY BE LETTERED

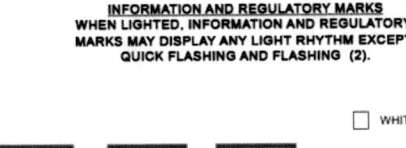

INFORMATION AND REGULATORY MARKS
WHEN LIGHTED, INFORMATION AND REGULATORY
MARKS MAY DISPLAY ANY LIGHT RHYTHM EXCEPT
QUICK FLASHING AND FLASHING (2).

☐ WHITE LIGHT ONLY

EXCLUSION AREA RESTRICTED OPERATIONS DANGER DANGER (NW)

UNIFORM STATE WATERWAY MARKING SYSTEM

STATE WATERS AND DESIGNATED STATE WATERS FOR PRIVATE AIDS TO NAVIGATION

REGULATORY MARKERS

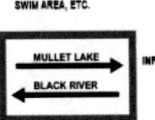

SWIM AREA — BOAT EXCLUSION AREA

ROCK — DANGER

SLOW NO WAKE — CONTROLLED AREA

EXPLANATION MAY BE PLACED OUTSIDE THE CROSSED DIAMOND SHAPE, SUCH AS DAM, RAPIDS, SWIM AREA, ETC.

THE NATURE OF DANGER MAY BE INDICATED INSIDE THE DIAMOND SHAPE, SUCH AS ROCK, WRECK, SHOAL, DAM, ETC.

TYPE OF CONTROL IS INDICATED IN THE CIRCLE, SUCH AS SLOW, NO WAKE, ANCHORING, ETC.

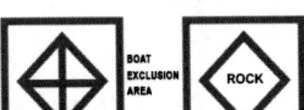

MULLET LAKE — INFORMATION
BLACK RIVER

FOR DISPLAYING INFORMATION SUCH AS DIRECTIONS, DISTANCES, LOCATIONS, ETC.

BUOY USED TO DISPLAY REGULATORY MARKERS

MAY SHOW WHITE LIGHT
MAY BE LETTERED

AIDS TO NAVIGATION

SOLID RED AND SOLID BLACK BUOYS
USUALLY FOUND IN PAIRS
PASS BETWEEN THESE BUOYS

MAY SHOW GREEN REFLECTOR OR LIGHT

MAY SHOW RED REFLECTOR OR LIGHT

3 4

PORT SIDE LOOKING UPSTREAM STARBOARD SIDE

LATERAL SYSTEM

MAY SHOW WHITE REFLECTOR OR LIGHT

RED-STRIPED WHITE BUOY

MAY BE LETTERED
DO NOT PASS BETWEEN BUOY AND NEAREST SHORE

BLACK-TOPPED WHITE BUOY

PASS TO NORTH OR EAST OF BUOY

MAY BE NUMBERED

RED-TOPPED WHITE BUOY

PASS TO SOUTH OR WEST OF BUOY

CARDINAL SYSTEM

WHITE WITH BLUE BAND
MAY SHOW WHITE REFLECTOR OR LIGHT

MOORING BUOY

Plate 4

ELECTRONIC AIDS TO NAVIGATION

Racons

Aids to navigation may be enhanced by the use of radar beacons (racons). Racons, when triggered by pulses from a vessel's radar, will transmit a coded reply to the vessel's radar. This reply serves to identify the racon station by exhibiting a series of dots and dashes which appear on the radar display emanating radially from the racon. This display will represent the approximate range and bearing to the racon. Although racons may be used on both laterally significant and non-laterally significant aids to navigation, the racon signal itself is for identification purposes only, and therefore carries no lateral significance. Racons are also used as bridge marks to mark the point of best passage.

All racons operate in the marine radar X-band from 9,300 to 9,500 MHz. Some frequency-agile racons also operate in the 2,900 to 3,000 MHz marine radar S-band.

Racons have a typical output of 100 to 300 milliwatts and are considered a short range aid to navigation. Reception varies from a nominal range of 6 to 8 nautical miles when mounted on a buoy to as much as 17 nautical miles for a racon with a directional antenna mounted at a height of 50 feet on a fixed structure. It must be understood that these are nominal ranges and are dependent upon many factors.

The beginning of the racon presentation occurs about 50 yards beyond the racon position and will persist for a number of revolutions of the radar antenna (depending on its rotation rate). Distance to the racon can be measured to the point at which the racon flash begins, but the figure obtained will be greater than the ship's distance from the racon. This is due to the slight response delay in the racon apparatus.

Radar operators may notice some broadening or spoking of the racon presentation when their vessel approaches closely to the source of the racon. This effect can be minimized by adjustment of the IF gain or sweep gain control of the radar. If desired, the racon presentation can be virtually eliminated by operation of the FTC (fast time constant) controls of the radar.

Radar Reflectors

Many aids to navigation incorporate special fixtures designed to enhance the reflection of radar energy. These fixtures, called radar reflectors, help radar equipped vessels to detect buoys and beacons which are so equipped. They do not however, positively identify a radar target as an aid to navigation.

Radiobeacons

As the first electronic system of navigation, radiobeacons provided offshore coverage and also became the first all-weather electronic aid to navigation. The Coast Guard operates about 200 radiobeacons located on the Atlantic, Gulf, and Pacific coasts, and on the Great Lakes. These radiobeacons are located at lighthouses, on large buoys and along the coasts. All positions are charted.

In order to use this system, the mariner needs a radio direction finder, which is a specifically designed radio receiver with a directional antenna. This antenna is used to determine the direction of the signal being emitted by the shore station, relative to the vessel.

The basic value of the radiobeacon system lies in its simplicity of operation and its relatively low user costs, even though the results obtained may be somewhat limited. The general problems and practices of navigation when using radiobeacons are very similar to those encountered when using visual bearings of lighthouses or other charted objects.

A radiobeacon is basically a short range navigational aid, with ranges from 10 to 175 nautical miles. Although bearings can be obtained at greater ranges, they will be of doubtful accuracy and should be used with caution. When the distance to a radiobeacon is greater than 50 miles, a correction is usually applied to the bearing before plotting on a Mercator chart. These corrections, as well as information on accuracy of bearings, plotting, and other matters are contained in the Defense Mapping Agency Hydrographic/Topographic Center publication, Radio Navigational Aids (RAPUB 117).

All radiobeacons operated and maintained by the U.S. Coast Guard are classified as either Sequenced or Continuous radiobeacons, and are usually organized into groups of six stations transmitting on a single frequency. Typically, one station in each group transmits for one minute out of six and is silent for the remaining five minutes. Continuous radiobeacons operate continuously through every minute of the hour. All Coast Guard-operated radiobeacons are assigned Morse code characteristics for ease in station identification.

The accuracy to be expected from radiobeacons depends to a large extent on the skill of the operator, the condition and type of equipment being used, the range from the stations, and the accuracy of the ship's calibration curve. The Coast Guard operates special calibration radiobeacons for use by the mariner. A comparison of visual bearings with radio bearings, will determine what, if any errors exist in the shipboard direction-finder installation. These calibration beacons transmit either continuously during scheduled hours or upon request.

The range at which a particular marine radiobeacon will be heard depends on atmospheric conditions and on the sensitivity of the receiver being used. The advertised service range of marine radiobeacons is expressed in miles; nautical miles for the Atlantic, Gulf, and Pacific coasts and statute miles for the Great Lakes.

In general, the better the sensitivity of a receiver (i.e., the lower the signal strength required to obtain satisfactory bearings) the better the receiver is for direction-finding purposes. Unless the receiver and antenna combination being used by the mariner is capable of obtaining a radio bearing on a signal as low as 50 microvolts per meter, full benefit will not be obtained from the system.

For example, a mariner using a direction-finder with a sensitivity of 50 microvolts per meter could obtain a bearing on a 50-mile radiobeacon located near New York at the advertised service range of 50 miles. However, using a direction-finder with a sensitivity of only 100 microvolts per meter, the mariner would not be able to obtain a bearing on the same 50-mile New York radiobeacon until approached to within approximately 25 miles of the radiobeacon station.

The selectivity of a receiver is important because it allows the direction finder to receive a desired signal on a particular frequency, while rejecting any undesired signals which may be present on adjacent frequencies.

Since the bandwidth of the transmitted radiobeacon signal is relatively narrow, being only 2.1 kilohertz, a narrow-band receiver, having good selectivity is well suited for direction-finding purposes. The narrow-band receiver should extract all of the useful information from the transmitted marine radiobeacon signal.

Although a wider-band receiver may also extract all of the useful information from the transmitted signal, it will also admit more noise and more undesired signals, if these signals are present on adjacent frequencies. The additional noise and undesired signal interference may reduce the usefulness of the desired signal and effectively reduce the service range of the radiobeacon below its advertised value. This is a receiver defect, not a system error.

Information regarding the location, and operation of marine radiobeacons is given on pages xxx – xxxii. Radiobeacons are individually listed in the Light List.

LORAN-C

LORAN, an acronym for LOng RAnge Navigation, is an electronic aid to navigation consisting of shore-based radio transmitters. The LORAN system enables users equipped with a LORAN receiver to determine their position quickly and accurately, day or night, in practically any weather.

A LORAN-C chain consists of three to five transmitting stations separated by several hundred miles. Within a chain, one station is designated as master while the other stations are designated as secondaries. Each secondary station is identified as either whiskey (W), x-ray (X), yankee (Y), or zulu (Z).

The master station is always the first station to transmit. It transmits a series of nine pulses. The secondary stations then follow in turn, transmitting eight pulses each, at precisely timed intervals. This cycle repeats itself endlessly. The length of the cycle is measured in microseconds and is called a Group Repetition Interval (GRI).

LORAN-C chains are designated by the four most significant digits of their GRI. For example, a chain with a GRI of 89,700 microseconds is referred to as 8970. A different GRI is used for each chain because all LORAN-C stations broadcast in the same 90 to 110 kilohertz frequency band and would otherwise interfere with one another.

The LORAN-C system can be used in either a hyperbolic or range mode. In the widely used hyperbolic mode, a LORAN-C line of position is determined by measuring the time difference between sychronized pulses received from two separate transmitting stations. In the range mode, a line of position is determined by measuring the time required for LORAN-C pulses to travel from a transmitting station to the user's receiver.

A user's position is determined by locating the crossing point of two lines of position on a LORAN-C chart. Many receivers have built-in coordinate converters which will automatically display the receiver's latitude and longitude. With a coordinate converter, a position can be determined using a chart that is not overprinted with LORAN-C lines of position.

CAUTION: The latitude/longitude computation on some models is based upon an all seawater propagation path. This may lead to error if the LORAN-C signals from the various stations involve appreciable overland propagation paths. These errors may put the mariner at risk in areas requiring precise positioning if the proper correctors (ASF) are not applied. *Therefore, it is recommended that mariners using Coordinate Converters check the manufacturer's operating manual to determine if and how corrections are to be applied to compensate for the discontinuity caused by the overland paths.*

There are two types of LORAN-C accuracy; absolute and repeatable. Absolute accuracy is a measure of the navigator's ability to determine latitude and longitude position from the LORAN-C time differences measured. Repeatable accuracy is a measure of the LORAN-C navigator's ability to return to a position where readings have been taken before.

The absolute accuracy of LORAN-C is 0.25 nautical miles, 95% confidence within the published coverage area using standard LORAN-C charts and tables. Repeatable accuracy depends on many factors, so measurements must be taken to determine the repeatable accuracy in any given area. Coast Guard surveys have found repeatable accuracies between 30 and 170 meters in most ground wave coverage areas. LORAN-C position determination on or near the baseline extensions are subject to significant errors and, therefore, should be avoided whenever possible. The use of skywaves is not recommended within 250 miles of a station being used, and corrections for these areas are not usually tabulated.

If the timing or pulse shape of a master-secondary pair deviates from specified tolerances, the first two pulses of the secondary station's pulse train will blink on and off. The LORAN-C receiver sees this blinking signal and indicates a warning to the user. This warning will continue until the signals are once again in tolerance. A blinking signal is not exhibited during off-air periods, so a separate receiver alarm indicates any loss of signal. Never use a blinking secondary signal for navigation.

In coastal waters, LORAN-C should not be relied upon as the only aid to navigation. A prudent navigator will use radar, radio direction finder, fathometer and any other aid to navigation, in addition to the LORAN-C receiver.

LORAN-C Interference

Interference to LORAN-C may result from radio transmissions by public or private sources operating near the LORAN-C band of 90-110 kHz. Anyone using the LORAN-C system, who observes interference to LORAN-C, should promptly report it to one of the Coast Guard commands listed below. Include in such reports information regarding the date, time, identifying characteristics, strength of the interfering signals and your own vessel's position. These interference reports are very important and cooperation from users of LORAN-C will assist the Coast Guard in improving LORAN-C service.

Atlantic Ocean and Gulf of Mexico
Commander (Atl)
Atlantic Area, U.S. Coast Guard
Governors Island
New York, NY 10004-5000

Pacific Ocean
Commander (Ptl)
Pacific Area, U.S. Coast Guard
Coast Guard Island
Alameda, CA 94501-5100

All areas
Commandant (G-NRN)
U.S. Coast Guard
Washington, DC 20593-0001

LORAN-C Charts and Publications

Navigational charts overprinted with LORAN-C lines of position are published by the National Ocean Service (NOS), Distribution Branch (N/CG33), 6501 Lafayette Avenue, Riverdale, MD 207371199 and the Defense Mapping Agency (DMA), Combat Support Center, Code: PMSR, Washington, DC 20315-0010, and may be purchased directly from NOS or DMA, or through local chart sales agents.

A general source of LORAN-C information is the LORAN-C User Handbook written by the U.S. Coast Guard. This publication can be purchased from the Superintendent of Documents, Order Section, U.S. Government Printing Office, Washington, DC 20402.

GLOBAL POSITIONING SYSTEM (GPS)

The Global Positioning System (GPS) is a satellite-based Radionavigation System providing continuous worldwide coverage. It provides navigation, position, and timing information to air, marine, and land users. Current plans call for GPS to be fully operational in late 1993. The GPS is being developed and will be operated and controlled by the Department of Defense (DOD) under U.S. Air Force management. Although originally intended for military use only, federal radionavigation policy has established that GPS will be available for civil use. Due to the orbiting nature of the incomplete satellite constellation, GPS coverage currently varies in quality throughout the day from place to place. Computer programs are available from commercial sources so that interested users can determine the quantity and quality of GPS coverage at their particular location.

The USCG is the government interface for civil users of GPS and has established a GPS Information Center (GPSIC) to meet the needs of the civil user. The GPSIC is a Coast Guard facility located in Alexandria, Virginia. It provides voice broadcasts, data broadcasts, and on-line computer-based information services, which are all available 24 hours a day. Personal telephone service is currently available Monday-Friday from 08:00 AM to 4:00 PM, excluding holidays. The information provided includes present or future satellite outages and constellation changes, user instructions and tutorials, lists of service and receiver provider/users, and other GPS-related information.

Users are cautioned that, per DOD policy:

The GPS system is not yet fully operational. Signal availability and accuracy are subject to change due to an incomplete satellite constellation and operational test activities.

However, whenever possible, advance notice of when the GPS satellites should not be used will be provided by the DOD and made available by the U.S Coast Guard.

Information concerning the GPS constellation is provided on a "test and evaluation" basis only. GPS advisory services are updated only during the time 8:00 AM and 4:00 PM, Monday through Friday (except Federal holidays). GPSIC services are described below.

The GPSIC 24 hour voice recording is a 3-line telephone answering machine. Up to 3 callers can listen to the 90 second recording at the same time.

The Department of Commerce transmits recorded time information on WWV/WWVH 5, 10, 15, and 20 MHz frequencies. During the 40 second interval between time ticks, atmospheric and navigation information is announced by voice. Listen at minute 14 & 15 on WWV and minute 43 & 44 on WWVH for GPS status information.

The computer bulletin board system (BBS) is capable of handling 16 simultaneous callers and provides GPS information such as GPS Status Messages, Satellite Almanacs, Notice Advisories to Navstar Users and post-mission ephemeris data. Also included is status information on the OMEGA navigation System and the Coast Guard's Differential GPS System.

The GPSIC disseminates safety GPS advisories broadcast messages through USCG broadcast stations utilizing VHF-FM voice, HF-SSB voice, and NAVTEX broadcasts. The broadcasts provide the GPS user in the marine environment with the current status of the GPS satellite constellation, as well as any planned/unplanned system outages that could affect GPS navigational accuracy.

To comment on any of these services or ask questions about GPS status, contact the GPSIC at:

Commanding Officer
U.S. Coast Guard ONSCEN
7323 Telegraph Road
Alexandria, VA 22310-3393

Phone: (703) 866-3806
FAX: (703) 866-3825

GLOSSARY OF AIDS TO NAVIGATION TERMS

Adrift: Afloat and unattached in any way to the shore or seabed.

Aid to navigation: Any device external to a vessel or aircraft specifically intended to assist navigators in determining their position or safe course, or to warn them of dangers or obstructions to navigation.

Alternating light: A rhythmic light showing light of alternating colors.

Arc of visibility: The portion of the horizon over which a lighted aid to navigation is visible from seaward.

Articulated beacon: A beacon-like buoyant structure, tethered directly to the seabed and having no watch circle. Called articulated light or articulated daybeacon, as appropriate.

Assigned position: The latitude and longitude position for an aid to navigation.

Beacon: A lighted or unlighted fixed aid to navigation attached directly to the earth's surface. (Lights and daybeacons both constitute "beacons".)

Bearing: The horizontal direction of a line of sight between two objects on the surface of the earth.

Bell: A sound signal producing bell tones by means of a hammer actuated by electricity or, on buoys, by sea motion.

Bifurcation: The point where a channel divides when proceeding from seaward. The place where two tributaries meet.

Broadcast Notice to Mariners: A radio broadcast designed to provide important marine information.

Buoy: A floating object of defined shape and color, which is anchored at a given position and serves as an aid to navigation.

Characteristic: The audible, visual, or electronic signal displayed by an aid to navigation to assist in the identification of an aid to navigation. Characteristic refers to lights, sound signals, racons, radiobeacons, and daybeacons.

Commissioned: The action of placing a previously discontinued aid to navigation back in operation.

Composite group-flashing light: A group-flashing light in which the flashes are combined in successive groups of different numbers of flashes.

Composite group-occulting light: A light similar to a group-occulting light except that the successive groups in a period have different numbers of eclipses.

Conventional direction of buoyage: The general direction taken by the mariner when approaching a harbor, river, estuary, or other waterway from seaward, or proceeding upstream or in the direction of the main stream of flood tide, or in the direction indicated in appropriate nautical documents (normally, following a clockwise direction around land masses).

Daybeacon: An unlighted fixed structure which is equipped with a dayboard for daytime identification.

Dayboard: The daytime identifier of an aid to navigation presenting one of several standard shapes (square, triangle, rectangle) and colors (red, green, white, orange, yellow, or black.)

Daymark: The daytime identifier of an aid to navigation. (See column 7 of the Light List.)

Diaphone: A sound signal which produces sound by means of a slotted piston moved back and forth by compressed air. A "two-tone" diaphone produces two sequential tones with the second tone of lower pitch.

Directional light: A light illuminating a sector or very narrow angle and intended to mark a direction to be followed.

Discontinued: To remove from operation (permanently or temporarily) a previously authorized aid to navigation.

Discrepancy: Failure of an aid to navigation to maintain its position or function as prescribed in the Light List.

Discrepancy buoy: An easily transportable buoy used to temporarily replace an aid to navigation not watching properly.

Dolphin: A minor aid to navigation structure consisting of a number of piles driven into the seabed or riverbed in a circular pattern and drawn together with wire rope.

Eclipse: An interval of darkness between appearances of a light.

Emergency light: A light of reduced intensity displayed by certain aids to navigation when the main light is extinguished.

Establish: To place an authorized aid to navigation in operation for the first time.

Extinguished: A lighted aid to navigation which fails to show a light characteristic.

Fixed light: A light showing continuously and steadily, as opposed to a rhythmic light. (Do not confuse with "fixed" as used to differentiate from "floating.")

Flash: A relatively brief appearance of a light, in comparison with the longest interval of darkness in the same character.

Flash tube: An electronically controlled high-intensity discharge lamp with a very brief flash duration.

Flashing light: A light in which the total duration of light in each period is clearly shorter than the total duration of darkness and in which the flashes of light are all of equal duration. (Commonly used for a single-flashing light which exhibits only single flashes which are repeated at regular intervals.)

Floating aid to navigation: A buoy, secured in its assigned position by a mooring.

Fog detector: An electronic device used to automatically determine conditions of visibility which warrant the turning on and off of a sound signal or additional light signals.

Fog signal: See sound signal.

Geographic range: The greatest distance the curvature of the earth permits an object of a given height to be seen from a particular height of eye without regard to luminous intensity or visibility conditions.

Gong: A wave actuated sound signal on buoys which uses a group of saucer-shaped bells to produce different tones.

Group-flashing light: A flashing light in which a group of flashes, specified in number, is regularly repeated.

Group-occulting light: An occulting light in which a group of eclipses, specified in number, is regularly repeated.

Horn: A sound signal which uses electricity or compressed air to vibrate a disc diaphragm.

Inoperative: Sound signal or electronic aid to navigation out of service due to a malfunction.

Interrupted quick light: A quick flashing light in which the rapid alternations are interrupted at regular intervals by eclipses of long duration.

Isolated danger mark: A mark erected on, or moored above or very near, an isolated danger which has navigable water all around it.

Isophase light: A rhythmic light in which all durations of light and darkness are equal. (Formerly called equal interval light.)

Junction: The point where a channel divides when proceeding seaward. The place where a distributary departs from the main stream.

Large navigation buoy (LNB): A 40-foot diameter, automated disc-shaped buoy used to replace lightships. Most LNB's are used in conjunction with major Traffic Separation Schemes. All LNB's are equipped with Emergency lights.

Lateral system: A system of aids to navigation in which characteristics of buoys and beacons indicate the sides of the channel or route relative to a conventional direction of buoyage (usually upstream).

Light: The signal emitted by a lighted aid to navigation. The illuminating apparatus used to emit the light signal. A lighted aid to navigation on a fixed structure.

Light sector: The arc over which a light is visible, described in degrees true, as observed from seaward towards the light. May be used to define distinctive color difference of two adjoining sectors, or an obscured sector.

Lighted ice buoy (LIB): A lighted buoy without sound signal, and designed to withstand the forces of shifting and flowing ice. Used to replace a conventional buoy when that aid to navigation is endangered by ice.

Lighthouse: A lighted beacon of major importance.

Local Notice to Mariners: A written document issued by each U.S. Coast Guard district to disseminate important information affecting aids to navigation, dredging, marine construction, special marine activities, and bridge construction on the waterways within that district.

Luminous range: The greatest distance a light can be expected to be seen given its nominal range and the prevailing meteorological visibility (see page xxviii).

Mark: A visual aid to navigation. Often called navigation mark, includes floating marks (buoys) and fixed marks (beacons).

Meteorological visibility: The greatest distance at which a black object of suitable dimension could be seen and recognized against the horizon sky by day, or, in the case of night observations, could be seen and recognized if the general illumination were raised to the normal daylight level.

Mileage number: A number assigned to aids to navigation which gives the distance in sailing miles along the river from a reference point to the aid to navigation. The number is used principally in the Mississippi River System.

Nominal range: The maximum distance a light can be seen in clear weather (meteorological visibility of 10 nautical miles). Listed for all lighted aids to navigation except range lights, directional lights, and private aids to navigation.

Occulting light: A light in which the total duration of light in each period is clearly longer than the total duration of darkness and in which the intervals of darkness (occultations) are all of equal duration. (Commonly used for single-occulting light which exhibits only single occultations which are repeated at regular intervals.)

Ocean Data Aquisition System (ODAS): Certain very large buoys in deep water for the collection of oceanographic and meteorlogical information. All ODAS buoys are yellow in color and display a yellow light.

Off shore tower: Monitored light stations built on exposed marine sites to replace lightships.

Off station: A floating aid to navigation not on its assigned position.

Passing light: A low intensity light which may be mounted on the structure of another light to enable the mariner to keep the latter light in sight when passing out of its beam during transit.

Period: The interval of time between the commencement of two identical successive cycles of the characteristic of the light or sound signal.

Pile: A long, heavy timber driven into the seabed or riverbed to serve as a support for an aid to navigation.

Port hand mark: A buoy or beacon which is left to the port hand when proceeding in the "conventional direction of buoyage".

Preferred channel mark: A lateral mark indicating a channel junction or bifurcation, or a wreck or other obstruction which, after consulting a chart, may be passed on either side.

Primary aid to navigation: An aid to navigation established for the purpose of making landfalls and coastwise passages from headland to headland.

Quick light: A light exhibiting very rapid regular alternations of light and darkness, normally 60 flashes per minute. (Formerly called quick flashing light.)

RACON: A radar beacon which produces a coded response, or radar paint, when triggered by a radar signal.

Radar: An electronic system designed to transmit radio signals and receive reflected images of those signals from a "target" in order to determine the bearing and distance to the "target".

Radar reflector: A special fixture fitted to or incorporated into the design of certain aids to navigation to enhance their ability to reflect radar energy. In general, these fixtures will materially improve the aid to navigation for use by vessels with radar.

Radiobeacon: Electronic apparatus which transmits a radio signal for use in providing a mariner a line of position.

Range: A line formed by the extension of a line connecting two charted points.

Range lights: Two lights associated to form a range which often, but not necessarily, indicates a channel centerline. The front range light is the lower of the two, and nearer to the mariner using the range. The rear range light is higher and further from the mariner.

Rebuilt: A fixed aid to navigation, previously destroyed, which has been restored as an aid to navigation.

Regulatory marks: A white and orange aid to navigation with no lateral significance. Used to indicate a special meaning to the mariner, such as danger, restricted operations, or exclusion area.

Relighted: An extinguished aid to navigation returned to its advertised light characteristics.

Replaced: An aid to navigation previously off station, adrift, or missing, restored by another aid to navigation of the same type and characteristics.

Replaced (temporarily): An aid to navigation previously off station, adrift, or missing, restored by another aid to navigation of different type and/or characteristic.

Reset: A floating aid to navigation previously off station, adrift, or missing, returned to its assigned position (station).

Rhythmic light: A light showing intermittently with a regular periodicity.

Setting a buoy: The act of placing a buoy on assigned position in the water.

Sector: See light sector.

Siren: A sound signal which uses electricity or compressed air to actuate either a disc or a cup-shaped rotor.

Skeleton tower: A tower, usually of steel, constructed of heavy corner members and various horizontal and diagonal bracing members.

Sound signal: A device which transmits sound, intended to provide information to mariners during periods of restricted visibility and foul weather.

Starboard hand mark: A buoy or beacon which is left to the starboard hand when proceeding in the "conventional direction of buoyage."

Station buoy: An unlighted buoy set near a Large Navigation Buoy or an important buoy as a reference point should the primary aid to navigation be moved from its assigned position.

Topmark: One or more relatively small objects of characteristic shape and color placed on an aid to identify its purpose.

Traffic Separation Scheme: Shipping corridors marked by buoys which separate incoming from outgoing vessels. Improperly called SEA LANES.

Watching properly: An aid to navigation on its assigned position exhibiting the advertised characteristics in all respects.

Whistle: A wave actuated sound signal on buoys which produces sound by emitting compressed air through a circumferential slot into a cylindrical bell chamber.

Winter marker: An unlighted buoy without sound signal, used to replace a conventional buoy when that aid to navigation is endangered by ice.

Winter light: A light which is maintained during those winter months when the regular light is extinguished. It is of lower candlepower than the regular light but usually of the same characteristic.

Withdrawn: The discontinuance of a floating aid to navigation during severe ice conditions or for the winter season.

ABBREVIATIONS USED IN COAST GUARD BROADCAST NOTICES TO MARINERS

Word/phrase	Abbrev
Light characteristics	
Fixed	F
Occulting	OC
Group–Occulting	OC(2)
Composite Group–Occulting	OC(2+1)
Isophase	ISO
Single–Flashing	FL
Group–Flashing	FL(3)
Composite Group–Flashing	FL(2+1)
Continuous Quick–Flashing	Q
Interrupted Quick–Flashing	IQ
Morse Code	MO(A)
Fixed and Flashing	FFL
Alternating	AL
Characteristic	CHAR
Colors	
Black	B
Blue	BU
Green	G
Orange	OR
Red	R
White	W
Yellow	Y
Aids to Navigation	
Aeronautical Radiobeacon	AERO RBN
Articulated Daybeacon	ART DBN
Articulated Light	ART LT
Destroyed	DESTR
Discontinued	DISCONTD
Established	ESTAB
Exposed Location Buoy	ELB
Fog signal station	FOG SIG
Large Navigation Buoy	LNB
Light	LT
Light List Number	LLNR
Lighted Bell Buoy	LBB
Lighted Buoy	LB
Lighted Gong Buoy	LGB
Lighted Horn Buoy	LHB
Lighted Whistle Buoy	LWB
Ocean Data Acquisition System	ODAS
Privately Maintained	PRIV MAINTD
Radar responder beacon	RACON
Radar Reflector	RA REF
Radiobeacon	RBN
Temporarily replaced by unlighted buoy	TRUB

Word/phrase	Abbrev
Temporarily replaced by lighted buoy	TRLB
Whistle	WHIS
Organizations	
Coast Guard	CG
Commander, Coast Guard District (#)	CCGD(#)
U.S. Army Corps of Engineers	COE
Defense Mapping Agency Hydro./Topo. Center	DMAHTC
National Ocean Service	NOS
National Weather Service	NWS
Vessels	
Aircraft	A/C
Fishing Vessel	F/V
Liquified Natural Gas Carrier	LNG
Motor Vessel	M/V[1]
Pleasure Craft	P/C
Research Vessel	R/V
Sailing Vessel	S/V
Compass Directions	
East	E
North	N
Northeast	NE
Northwest	NW
South	S
Southeast	SE
Southwest	SW
West	W
Months	
January	JAN
February	FEB
March	MAR
April	APR
May	MAY
June	JUN
July	JUL
August	AUG
September	SEP
October	OCT
November	NOV
December	DEC
Days of the Week	
Monday	MON
Tuesday	TUE
Wednesday	WED
Thursday	THU
Friday	FRI
Saturday	SAT
Sunday	SUN

---

[1] M/V includes: Steam Ship, Container Vessel, Cargo Vessel, etc.

ABBREVIATIONS USED IN COAST GUARD BROADCAST NOTICES TO MARINERS

Word/phrase	Abbrev	Word/phrase	Abbrev
Various		Prohibited	PROHIB
Anchorage	ANCH	Publication	PUB
Anchorage prohibited	ANCH PROHIB	Range	RGE
Approximate	APPROX	Reported	REP
Atlantic	ATLC	Restricted	RESTR
Authorized	AUTH	Rock	RK
Average	AVG	Saint	ST
Bearing	BRG	Second (time; geo pos)	SEC
Breakwater	BKW	Signal station	SIG STA
Broadcast Notice to Mariners	BNM	Station	STA
Channel	CHAN	Statute Mile(s)	SM
Code of Federal Regulations	CFR	Storm signal station	S SIG STA
Continue	CONT	Temporary	TEMP
Degrees (temperature; geo pos)	DEG	Through	THRU
Diameter	DIA	Thunderstorm	TSTM
Edition	ED	True	T
Effect/Effective	EFF	Uncovers; Dries	UNCOV
Entrance	ENTR	Universal Coordinate Time	UTC
Explosive Anchorage	EXPLOS ANCH	Urgent Marine	UMIB
Fathom(s)	FM(S)	Information Broadcast	
Foot/Feet	FT	Velocity	VLCTY
Harbor	HBR	Vertical clearance	VERT CL
Height	HT	Visibility	VSBY
Hertz	HZ	Warning	WRNG
Horizontal clearance	HOR CL	Weather	WEA
Hour	HR	Wreck	WK
International Regulations for Preventing Collisions at Sea, 1972	COLREGS	Yard(s)	YD
		Countries and States	
Kilohertz	KHZ	Alabama	AL
Kilometer	KM	Alaska	AK
Knot(s)	KT(S)	American Samoa	AS
Latitude	LAT	Arizona	AZ
Local Notice to Mariners	LNM	Arkansas	AR
Longitude	LONG	California	CA
Maintained	MAINTD	Canada	CN
Maximum	MAX	Colorado	CO
Megahertz	MHZ	Connecticut	CT
Millibar	MB	Delaware	DE
Millimeter	MM	District of Columbia	DC
Minute (time; geo pos)	MIN	Federated States of Micronesia	FSM
Moderate	MDT	Florida	FL
Mountain, Mount	MT	Georgia	GA
Nautical Mile(s)	NM	Guam	GU
Notice to Mariners	NTM	Hawaii	HI
Obstruction	OBSTR	Idaho	ID
Occasion/Occasionally	OCCASION	Illinois	IL
Operating Area	OPAREA	Indiana	IN
Pacific	PAC	Iowa	IA
Point(s)	PT(S)	Kansas	KS
Position	PSN	Kentucky	KY
Position Approximate	PA	Louisiana	LA
Pressure	PRES	Maine	ME
Private, Privately	PRIV	Maryland	MD
		Massachusetts	MA

ABBREVIATIONS USED IN COAST GUARD BROADCAST NOTICES TO MARINERS

Word/phrase	Abbrev	Word/phrase	Abbrev
Mexico	MX	Oregon	OR
Michigan	MI	Pennsylvania	PA
Minnesota	MN	Puerto Rico	PR
Mississippi	MS	Rhode Island	RI
Missouri	MO	South Carolina	SC
Montana	MT	South Dakota	SD
Nebraska	NE	Tennessee	TN
New Hampshire	NH	Texas	TX
Nevada	NV	United States	US
New Jersey	NJ	Utah	UT
New Mexico	NM	Vermont	VT
New York	NY	Virgin Islands	VI
North Carolina	NC	Virginia	VA
North Dakota	ND	Washington	WA
Northern Marianas	CM	West Virginia	WV
Ohio	OH	Wisconsin	WI
Oklahoma	OK	Wyoming	WY

RADIOBEACON SYSTEM – ATLANTIC COAST

SEQUENCED – By Frequency

Freq kHz	Sequence	Station	Characteristic	Range (n.m.)	Lat. (N) ° ' "	Long. (W) ° ' "
286	I	HIGHLAND	HI (.... ..)	100	42 02 24	70 03 40
	IV	AMBROSE	T (—)	125	40 27 32	73 49 52
	V	GREAT DUCK ISLAND	GD (——. —..)	50	44 08 32	68 14 47
	VI	MANANA ISLAND	MI (—— ..)	100	43 45 48	69 19 38
306	I, IV	CLINTON HARBOR	CL (—.—. .—..)	20	41 16 00	72 31 10
	II	LITTLE GULL	J (———)	20	41 12 22	72 06 29
	III, VI	HORTON POINT	HP (.... .——.)	20	41 05 06	72 26 48
	V	WATCH HILL	WH (.—— ....)	10	41 18 36	71 55 30
316	I, IV	EXECUTION ROCKS	XR (—..— .—.)	20	40 52 41	73 44 18
	II, V	OLDFIELD POINT	OP (——— .——.)	20	40 58 36	73 07 08
	III, VI	STRATFORD POINT	SP (... .——.)	20	41 09 06	73 06 13

CONTINUOUS – By Frequency

Freq kHz	Station	Characteristic	Range (n.m.)	Lat. (N) ° ' "	Long. (W) ° ' "
291	HALFWAY ROCK	HR (.... .—.)	10	43 39 21	70 02 15
291	NOBSKA POINT	NP (—. .——.)	20	41 30 58	70 39 20
291	FIRE ISLAND	RT (.—. —)	15	40 38 18	73 18 53
293	MONTAUK POINT	MP (—— .——.)	125	41 04 02	71 51 44
295	SCITUATE HARBOR	SH (... ....)	10	42 11 56	70 43 12
298	NANTUCKET LNB	NS (—. ...)	50	40 30 00	69 28 00
301	PORTLAND LIGHTED HORN BUOY P (LNB)	PH (.——. ....)	30	43 31 37	70 05 31
301	BLOCK ISLAND	BI (—... ..)	20	41 09 11	71 33 04
302	EAST ROCKAWAY INLET	ER (. .—.)	10	40 35 11	73 45 11
304	BOSTON LIGHTED HORN BUOY B (LNB)	BH (—... ....)	30	42 22 42	70 47 00
308	CLEVELAND LEDGE	CL (—.—. .—..)	10	41 37 51	70 41 42
308	MANASQUAN INLET	MI (—— ..)	20	40 06 03	74 02 03
310	BEAVERTAIL	N (—.)	20	41 26 58	71 23 58
311	CHATHAM	CH (—.—. ....)	20	41 40 17	69 57 02
311	SHINNECOCK INLET	SN (... —.)	20	40 50 32	72 28 44
314	MATINICUS ROCK	MR (.. .—.)	20	43 47 00	68 51 19

Freq kHz	Station	Characteristic	Range (n.m.)	Lat. (N) ° ′ ″	Long. (W) ° ′ ″
314	BUZZARDS BAY	BB (— ... — ...)	20	41 23 47	71 02 02
318	CAPE COD CANAL BREAKWATER	CC (— . — . — . — .)	20	41 46 19	70 30 04
319	JONES INLET	JI (. — — — . .)	10	40 34 50	73 34 24
320	THE CUCKOLDS	CU (— . — . .. —)	10	43 46 46	69 39 02
320	SAYBROOK BREAKWATER	SB (... — ...)	10	41 15 47	72 20 36
322	PORTSMOUTH HARBOR (NEW CASTLE) LIGHT	NCE (— . — . — . .)	10	43 04 15	70 42 36
322	NEW BEDFORD	NB (— . — ...)	10	41 37 28	70 54 22
325	EASTERN POINT	EP (. . — — .)	10	42 34 50	70 39 54
325	POINT JUDITH	PJ (. — — . . — — —)	10	41 21 39	71 28 55
325	BRANT POINT	BP (— ... . — — .)	10	41 17 23	70 05 27

United States Coast Guard
RADIOBEACON SYSTEM ATLANTIC COAST
VOLUME 1 1992 EDITION

Many radiobeacons must share a group frequency with other beacons. Therefore, radiobeacons in the same general geographic area are divided into groups of up to six beacons transmitting on a single frequency with the sequence being repeated continually. Each radiobeacon transmits for at least one minute out of each six-minute period in sequence with the other beacons of the group regardless of the weather conditions. If less than six radiobeacons are assigned to a sequence group, one or more of the beacons may transmit during two of the six one-minute periods.

The SEQUENCE within a group is indicated by a Roman numeral: If no numeral is shown, the identifying signal is transmitted continuously.

SERVICE RANGE is shown in nautical miles (M).

CHARACTERISTIC IDENTIFICATION consists of a combination of dots and dashes. The characteristic signal of all beacons is superimposed on a continuous carrier when they are transmitting. The last ten seconds of the minute are devoted to a long dash for maximum bearing accuracy using manual operation.

The FREQUENCY in kilohertz is indicated on the chart in Arabic numerals following the characteristic identification and preceding the sequence number.

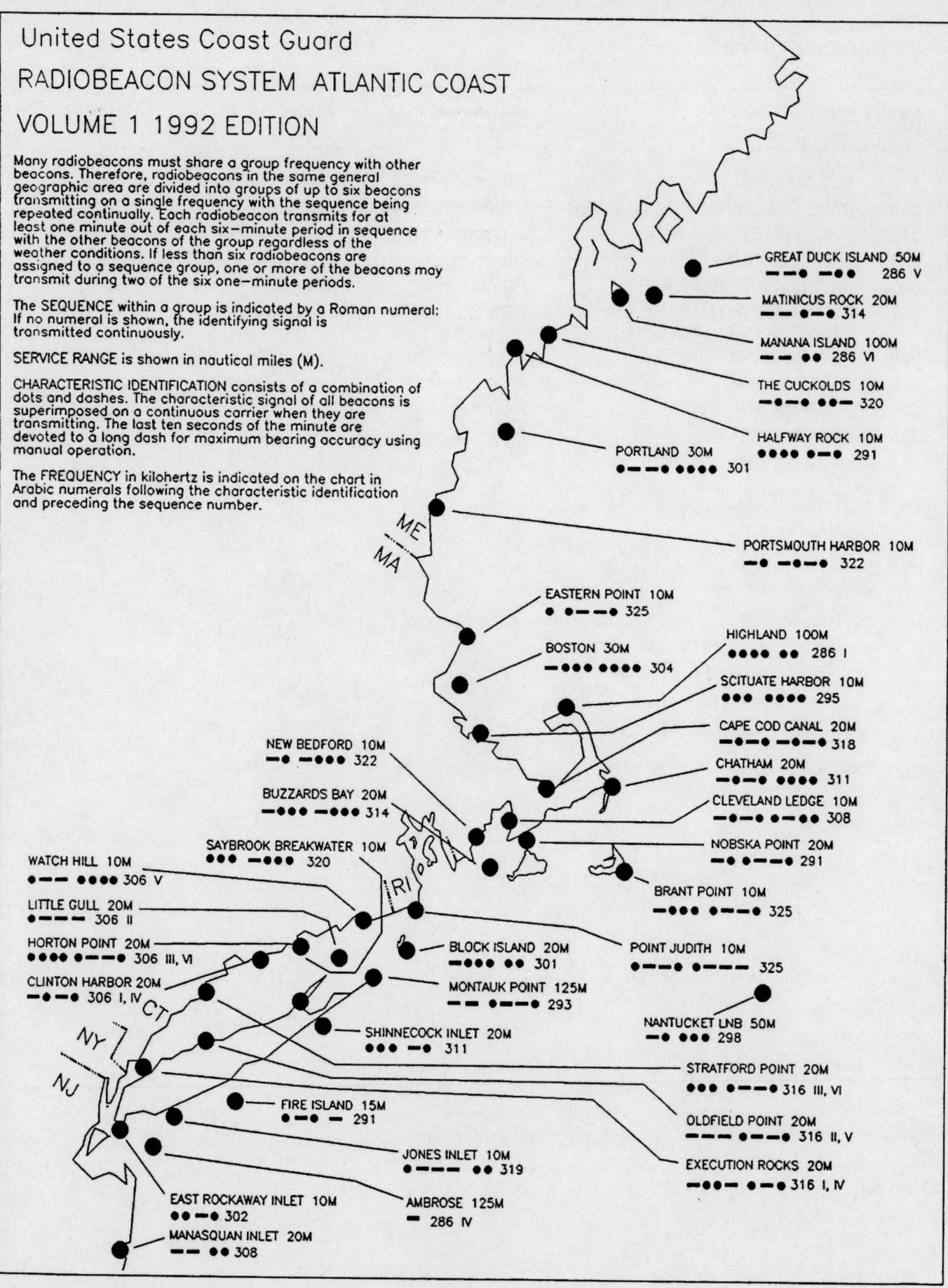

GREAT DUCK ISLAND 50M — — ● — ●● 286 V

MATINICUS ROCK 20M — — ●— ● 314

MANANA ISLAND 100M — — ●● 286 VI

THE CUCKOLDS 10M —●—●—● 320

HALFWAY ROCK 10M ●●●● ●● — 291

PORTLAND 30M ●— ——● ●●●● 301

PORTSMOUTH HARBOR 10M —● —●—● 322

EASTERN POINT 10M ● ●—●—● 325

BOSTON 30M — ●●●●●●● 304

HIGHLAND 100M ●●●● ●● 286 I

SCITUATE HARBOR 10M ●●● ●●●● 295

CAPE COD CANAL 20M —●— ● 318

CHATHAM 20M —●● —●●●● 311

CLEVELAND LEDGE 10M —●●●— ● 308

NOBSKA POINT 20M —●● ●— ● 291

BRANT POINT 10M —●●● ●—●— 325

POINT JUDITH 10M ●—●— ●—●— 325

NEW BEDFORD 10M —● —●●● 322

BUZZARDS BAY 20M —●●● —●●● 314

SAYBROOK BREAKWATER 10M ●●●● —●●● 320

WATCH HILL 10M ●—●— ●●●● 306 V

LITTLE GULL 20M ●—●— — 306 II

HORTON POINT 20M ●●●● —●— ● 306 III, VI

CLINTON HARBOR 20M —●—●— ● 306 I, IV

BLOCK ISLAND 20M —●●● ●● 301

MONTAUK POINT 125M — — ●—●— ● 293

SHINNECOCK INLET 20M ●●● —● 311

FIRE ISLAND 15M ●—● — 291

JONES INLET 10M ●—— — ●● 319

EAST ROCKAWAY INLET 10M ●●— ● 302

AMBROSE 125M — 286 IV

MANASQUAN INLET 20M —— ●● 308

NANTUCKET LNB 50M —● ●●● ● 298

STRATFORD POINT 20M ●●● ●—●— 316 III, VI

OLDFIELD POINT 20M — — —●—● ● 316 II, V

EXECUTION ROCKS 20M —●●— ●— ● 316 I, IV

GEOGRAPHIC RANGE TABLE

The following table gives the approximate geographic range of visibility for an object which may be seen by an observer at sea level. It is necessary to add to the distance for the height of any object the distance corresponding to the height of the observer's eye above sea level.

Distances of visibility for objects of various elevations above sea level.

Height Feet	Meters	Distance Nautical Miles (NM)	Distance Statute Miles (SM)	Height Feet	Meters	Distance Nautical Miles (NM)	Distance Statute Miles (SM)	Height Feet	Meters	Distance Nautical Miles (NM)	Distance Statute Miles (SM)
5	1.5	2.6	3.0	70	21.3	9.8	11.3	250	76.2	18.5	21.3
10	3.1	3.7	4.3	75	22.9	10.1	11.7	300	91.4	20.3	23.3
15	4.6	4.5	5.2	80	24.4	10.5	12.0	350	106.7	21.9	25.2
20	6.1	5.2	6.0	85	25.9	10.8	12.4	400	121.9	23.4	26.9
25	7.6	5.9	6.7	90	27.4	11.1	12.8	450	137.2	24.8	28.6
30	9.1	6.4	7.4	95	29.0	11.4	13.1	500	152.4	26.2	30.1
35	10.7	6.9	8.0	100	30.5	11.7	13.5	550	167.6	27.4	31.6
40	12.2	7.4	8.5	110	33.5	12.3	14.1	600	182.9	28.7	33.0
45	13.7	7.8	9.0	120	36.6	12.8	14.7	650	198.1	29.8	34.3
50	15.2	8.3	9.5	130	39.6	13.3	15.4	700	213.4	31.0	35.6
55	16.8	8.7	10.0	140	42.7	13.8	15.9	800	243.8	33.1	38.1
60	18.3	9.1	10.4	150	45.7	14.3	16.5	900	274.3	35.1	40.4
65	19.8	9.4	10.9	200	61.0	19.0	16.5	1000	304.8	37.0	42.6

Example: Determine the geographic visibility of an object, with a height above water of 65 feet, for an observer with a height of eye of 35 feet. Enter above table;

Height of object	65 feet	9.4 NM
Height of observer	35 feet	6.9 NM
Computed geographic visibility		16.3 NM

LUMINOUS RANGE DIAGRAM

The nominal range given in this Light List is the maximum distance a given light can be seen when the meteorological visibility is 10 nautical miles (or 11.5 statute miles on Lake Champlain). If the existing visibility is less than 10 NM (11.5 SM), the range at which the light can be seen will be reduced below its nominal range. And, if the visibility is greater than 10 NM (11.5 SM), the light can be seen at greater distances. The distance at which a light may be expected to be seen in the prevailing visibility is called its luminous range.

Nautical Miles

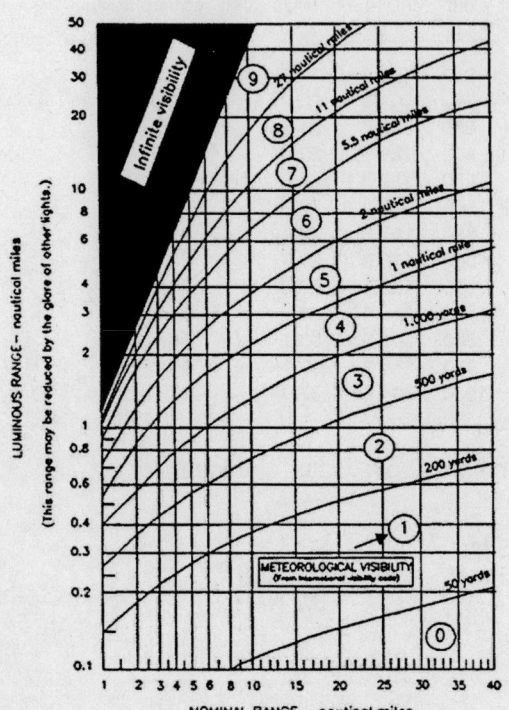

Statute Miles
(For Lake Champlain)

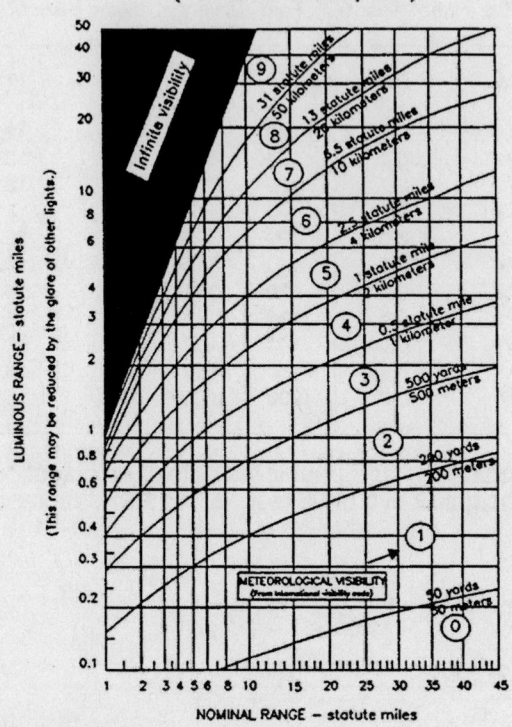

METEOROLOGICAL VISIBILITY
(From International Visibility code)

Code	Metric	Nautical (approximate)	Statute (approximate)
0	Less than 50 meters	Less than 50 yards	Less than 50 yards
1	50—200 meters	50—200 yards	50—200 yards
2	200—500 meters	200—500 yards	200—500 yards
3	500—1,000 meters	500—1,000 yards	500—1,000 yards
4	1—2 kilometers	1,000—2,000 yards	1,000—2,000 yards
5	2—4 kilometers	1—2 nautical miles	1—2.5 statute miles
6	4—10 kilometers	2—5.5 nautical miles	2.5—6.5 statute miles
7	10—20 kilometers	5.5—11 nautical miles	6.5—13 statute miles
8	20—50 kilometers	11—27 nautical miles	13—31 statute miles
9	Greater than 50 km	Greater than 27 nm	Greater than 31 miles

This diagram enables the mariner to determine the approximate luminous range of a light when the nominal range and the prevailing meteorological visibility are known. The diagram is entered from the bottom border using the nominal range listed in column 6 of this book. The intersection of the nominal range with the appropriate visibility curve (or, more often, a point between two curves) yields, by moving horizontally to the left border, the luminous range.

CAUTION: When using this diagram is must be remembered that:
1. The ranges obtained are approximate.
2. The transparency of the atmosphere may vary between the observer and the light.
3. Glare from background lighting will considerably reduce the range at which lights are sighted.
4. The rolling motion of the mariner and/or of a lighted aid to navigation may reduce the distance at which lights can be detected and identified.

(1) No.	(2) Name and location	(3) Position	(4) Characteristic	(5) Height	(6) Range	(7) Structure	(8) Remarks

SEACOAST (Rhode Island) – First District

N/W
APPROACHES TO NEW YORK - NANTUCKET SHOALS TO FIVE FATHOM BANK (Chart 12300)

(1) No.	(2) Name and location	(3) Position	(4) Characteristic	(5) Height	(6) Range	(7) Structure	(8) Remarks
655	**Block Island Southeast Light**	41 09.2 71 33.1	Fl G 5s	258	24	On steel tower. 67	Emergency light of reduced intensity when main light is extinguished. Lighted throughout 24 hours.
656	**Block Island Southeast Radiobeacon**	41 09.2 71 33.1	BI (—••• ••)		20		FREQ: 301 kHz. Antenna 70 feet east south east of tower.
660	*Southwest Ledge Lighted Bell Buoy 2 Marks southwest edge of shoals.*	41 06.7 71 40.3	Fl R 2.5s		4	Red.	

SEACOAST (New York) – First District

APPROACHES TO NEW YORK - NANTUCKET SHOALS TO FIVE FATHOM BANK (Chart 12300)

(1) No.	(2) Name and location	(3) Position	(4) Characteristic	(5) Height	(6) Range	(7) Structure	(8) Remarks
665	*Montauk Point Lighted Whistle Buoy MP*	41 01.8 71 45.7	Mo (A) W		6	Red and white stripes with red spherical topmark.	
670	**Montauk Point Light**	41 04.2 71 51.5	Fl W 5s	168	24	White octagonal, pyramidal tower with brown band midway of height, covered way to gray dwelling.	HORN: 1 blast ev 15s (2s bl). Emergency light (F W 5s) when main light is extinguished. Lighted throughout 24 hours.
671	**Montauk Point Radiobeacon**	41 04.2 71 51.5	MP (—— •—•)		125		FREQ: 286 kHz, III. Antenna 690 yards, 227° from light.
675 27180	*Shinnecock Inlet Approach Lighted Whistle Buoy SH*	40 49.0 72 28.6	Mo (A) W		6	Red and white stripes with red spherical topmark.	
680 27175	**Shinnecock Light**	40 50.5 72 28.7	Fl (2) R 15s 0.1s fl 3.6s ec. 0.1s fl 11.2s ec.	75	21	Red skeleton tower.	HORN: 1 blast ev 15s (2s bl).
681 27176	**Shinnecock Radiobeacon**	40 50.5 72 28.8	SN (••• —•)		20		FREQ: 311 kHz. Antenna at light tower.
685	*Moriches Inlet Approach Lighted Bell Buoy 2B*	40 44.1 72 45.2	Fl R 6s		4	Red.	
690	Cedar Island Beach Outfall Buoy A					Yellow can.	Private aid.
695	**Fire Island Light**	40 37.9 73 13.1	Fl W 7.5s	167	24	Black and white banded tower; black on top.	Lighted throughout 24 hours.
700	**Fire Island Radiobeacon**	40 38.3 73 18.9	RT (•—• —)		15		FREQ: 291 kHz.
705	*Fire Island Inlet Approach Lighted Whistle Buoy 4FI*	40 35.6 73 17.8	Fl R 2.5s		4	Red.	
720	*Nantucket Traffic Lane Lighted Horn Buoy NA*	40 25.7 73 11.5	Fl Y 6s		7	Yellow.	RACON: N (—•) HORN: 1 blast ev 15s (2s bl).
725	*Nantucket Traffic Lane Lighted Whistle Buoy NB*	40 26.5 73 40.8	Fl Y 4s		6	Yellow.	

(1) No.	(2) Name and location	(3) Position	(4) Characteristic	(5) Height	(6) Range	(7) Structure	(8) Remarks
			SEACOAST (New York) – First District				
	APPROACHES TO NEW YORK - NANTUCKET SHOALS TO FIVE FATHOM BANK (Chart 12300)	N/W					
730	**Ambrose Light**	40 27.6 73 49.9	Fl W 5ˢ	136	24	Red tower on white square superstructure on four piles. AMBROSE on sides	HORN: 1 blast ev 15ˢ (2ˢ bl). Emergency light of reduced intensity when main light is extinguished. Obstruction lights showing Fl W from all four corners. Piles floodlighted from sunset to sunrise. Lighted throughout 24 hours. RACON: N (—•).
731	**Ambrose Radiobeacon**	40 27.6 73 49.9	T (—)		125		286 kHz, IV.
			SEACOAST (New Jersey) – First District				
	APPROACHES TO NEW YORK - NANTUCKET SHOALS TO FIVE FATHOM BANK (Chart 12300)						
735	Hudson Canyon Traffic Lane Lighted Horn Buoy HA	40 07.6 73 21.4	Fl Y 4ˢ		6	Yellow.	RACON: C (—•—•). HORN: 1 blast ev 30ˢ (3ˢ bl).
740	Barnegat Traffic Lane Lighted Whistle Buoy BA	40 20.7 73 47.7	Fl Y 6ˢ		7	Yellow.	
745	Fishing Grounds Obstruction Lighted Bell Buoy FG	40 25.2 73 51.7	Fl (2+1) G 6ˢ		4	Green and red bands.	
750	New York Bight Dumping Ground Lighted Buoy NY	40 22.8 73 50.7	Fl Y 6ˢ		5	Yellow.	
755	New York Bight Dumping Ground Buoy KVK	40 22.2 73 51.2				Yellow nun.	
760	New York Bight Dumping Ground Buoy OM	40 22.7 73 50.4				Yellow can.	
765 32325	Shrewsbury Rocks Lighted Bell Buoy 1 Off east end of rocks.	40 20.5 73 55.6	Fl G 2.5ˢ		4	Green.	
770 37325	Shark River Inlet Lighted Whistle Buoy SI	40 11.2 74 00.1	Mo (A) W		6	Red and white stripes with red spherical topmark.	
775 37345	MANASQUAN INLET NORTH BREAKWATER LIGHT 4	40 06.1 74 01.9	Fl R 4s	30	6	TR on skeleton tower.	
780 37350	**Manasquan Inlet South Breakwater Light 3**	40 06.0 74 01.9	Fl G 6s	35	10	SG on spindle.	HORN: 1 blast ev 30ˢ (3ˢ bl).
	Sea Girt						
785	– Buoy A Marks firing range.					Yellow spar.	Private aid.
790	– Buoy B Marks firing range.					Yellow spar.	Private aid
795	– Buoy C Marks firing range.					Yellow spar.	Private aid.
800	– Buoy D Marks firing range.					Yellow spar.	Private aid.

(1) No.	(2) Name and location	(3) Position	(4) Characteristic	(5) Height	(6) Range	(7) Structure	(8) Remarks

(1) No.	(2) Name and location	(3) Position	(4) Characteristic	(5) Height	(6) Range	(7) Structure	(8) Remarks
	NARRAGANSETT BAY (Chart 13221)	N/W					
	Greenwich Bay						
	Warwick Cove						
17970	– Buoy 5	41 41.0 71 23.5				Green can.	
17975	– Buoy 7	41 41.0 71 23.5				Green can.	
17980	– Buoy 9					Green can.	
17985	– Buoy 10					Red nun.	
17990	– Buoy 12					Red nun.	
	Greenwich Bay						
17995	– Buoy 3					Green can.	
18000	– Buoy 5					Green can.	
18005	– Buoy 6					Red nun.	
18010	– Buoy 7 On edge of shoal.					Green can.	
18015	Cedar Tree Point Buoy 2					Red nun.	
18020	Apponaug Cove Approach Buoy 1					Green can.	
	Apponaug Cove Channel						
18025	– Buoy 3					Green can.	
18030	– Buoy 5					Green can.	
18035	– Buoy 6					Red nun.	
18040	– Buoy 7					Green can.	
18045	– Buoy 8					Red nun.	
	BLOCK ISLAND SOUND AND APPROACHES (Chart 13205)						
	West Passage						
18050	**Point Judith Light**	41 21.7 71 28.9	**Oc (3) W** 15^s 5^s fl 2^s ec. 2^s fl 2^s ec. 2^s fl 2^s ec.	65	16	Octagonal tower, lower half white, upper half brown. 51	HORN: I blast ev 15^s (2^s bl).
18051	**Point Judith Radiobeacon**	41 21.7 71 28.9	**PJ** (•—•• •———)		20		FREQ: 325 kHz. Antenna 36 feet, 195° from light tower.
18055	*Point Judith Lighted Whistle Buoy 2*	41 19.3 71 28.6	**Fl R** 4^s		4	Red.	
18060	Point Judith Bell Buoy 4					Red.	
18065	Nebraska Shoal Buoy 2NS	41 21.0 71 34.6				Red nun.	
18070	*Block Island North Reef Lighted Bell Buoy 1BI*	41 15.5 71 34.6	**Fl G** 4^s		4	Green.	

(1) No.	(2) Name and location	(3) Position	(4) Characteristic	(5) Height	(6) Range	(7) Structure	(8) Remarks

BLOCK ISLAND SOUND AND APPROACHES (Chart 13205) ^N/W^

West Passage

18075	**Block Island North Light**	41 13.7 71 34.6	Fl W 5s	58	13	Black tower on grey granite dwelling. 52	

Point Judith Harbor of Refuge

18080	- EAST ENTRANCE LIGHT 2	41 21.5 71 29.6	Fl R 4s	31	5	TR on white pile structure.	
18085	- EAST ENTRANCE LIGHT 3	41 21.6 71 29.9	Fl G 4s	39	5	SG on post on concrete base.	
18090	- MAIN BREAKWATER CENTER LIGHT	41 21.3 71 30.5	Fl W 2.5s	37	7	NR on post on concrete base.	
18095	- WEST ENTRANCE LIGHT 2	41 21.7 71 30.8	Fl R 4s	35	5	TR on post on concrete base.	
18100	- WEST ENTRANCE LIGHT 3	41 21.9 71 30.9	Fl G 6s	35	6	SG on post on concrete base.	HORN: 1 blast ev 30s (3s bl).
18105	South Lump Buoy					Red and green bands; nun.	
18110	Point Judith Harbor Buoy 2					Red nun.	
18115	Point Judith Harbor Buoy 4					Red nun.	
18120	Point Judith Harbor Buoy 6					Red nun.	
18125	Point Judith Inner Harbor Daybeacon 8	41 22.5 71 30.8				TR on spindle.	

Great Island Channel

18126	- Buoy 1					Green can.	
18127	- Buoy 3					Green can.	
18128	- Buoy 5					Green can.	

Point Judith Pond

18130	- Junction Buoy					Red and green bands; nun.	
18135	- Channel Buoy 2					Red nun.	
18140	- Channel Buoy 2A					Red nun.	
18145	- Channel Buoy 2B					Red nun.	
18150	- Channel Buoy 3					Green can.	
18155	- Channel Buoy 4					Red nun.	
18160	- Channel Buoy 5					Green can.	
18165	- Channel Buoy 6					Red nun.	
18170	- Channel Buoy 6A					Red nun.	
18175	- Channel Buoy 7					Green can.	
18180	- Channel Buoy 8					Red nun.	
18185	- Channel Buoy 8A					Red nun.	
18190	- Channel Buoy 9					Green can.	

RHODE ISLAND – First District

N/W

BLOCK ISLAND SOUND AND APPROACHES (Chart 13205)

Point Judith Pond

(1) No.	(2) Name and location	(3) Position	(4) Characteristic	(5) Height	(6) Range	(7) Structure	(8) Remarks
18195	– Channel Buoy 9A						Green can.
18200	– Channel Buoy 10						Red nun.
18205	– Channel Buoy 11						Green can.
18210	– Channel Buoy 12						Red nun.
18215	– Channel Buoy 14						Red nun.
18220	– Channel Buoy 15						Green can.
18225	– Channel Buoy 16						Red nun.
18230	– Channel Buoy 18						Red nun.
18235	– Channel Buoy 19						Green can.
18240	– Channel Buoy 20						Red nun.
18245	– Channel Buoy 21						Green can.
18250	– Channel Buoy 24	41 23.4 71 29.8					Red nun.
18255	– Channel Buoy 25						Green can.

BLOCK ISLAND (Chart 13217)

Block Island

(1) No.	(2) Name and location	(3) Position	(4) Characteristic	(5) Height	(6) Range	(7) Structure	(8) Remarks
18260	Clay Head Buoy 3 Marks rock.						Green can.
18265	– Northeast Whistle Buoy 5						Green.
18270	– Old Harbor Channel Bell Buoy 1						Green.
18275	– Old Harbor Channel Buoy 5 North end of shoal.						Green can.
18280	– Old Harbor Channel Buoy 6						Red nun.
18285	– Old Harbor Channel Buoy 7						Green can.
18290	– Old Harbor Point Buoy 7	41 09.3 71 32.5					Green can.
18295	Southeast Point Buoy 9	41 08.9 71 32.8					Green can.
18300	– BREAKWATER LIGHT 3	41 10.6 71 33.3	Fl G 2.5s	27	8	SG on white skeleton tower, white house, concrete base.	HORN: 2 blasts ev 30s (2s bl 2s si 2s bl 24s si).
18305	– **Breakwater Outer Basin Light 8**	41 10.5 71 33.4	F R	23	11	TR on skeleton tower.	Lighted throughout 24 hours.
18310	Black Rock Point Buoy 2 On south side of rock.	41 08.4 71 35.8					Red nun.
18315	*Southwest Point Lighted Whistle Buoy 4*	41 08.7 71 37.4	Fl R 6s		4		Red.

(1) No.	(2) Name and location	(3) Position	(4) Characteristic	(5) Height	(6) Range	(7) Structure	(8) Remarks

BLOCK ISLAND (Chart 13217)   N/W

Block Island

18320	Dickens Point Shoal Bell Buoy 6					Red.	

Great Salt Pond

18325	– Entrance Bell Buoy 2	41 12.1 71 35.7				Red.	
18330	– BREAKWATER LIGHT 4	41 12.0 71 35.6	F R	49	8	TR on white cylindrical tower; red top.	HORN: 1 blast ev 10s (1s bl).
18335	– Entrance Buoy 5	41 12.0 71 35.5				Green can.	
18340	– Entrance Buoy 7					Green can.	
18345	– Entrance Buoy 8					Red nun.	
18355	– Buoy 10					Red nun.	
18360	– Buoy 11					Green can.	
18365	– Buoy 12					Red nun.	
18370	– Buoy 13	41 11.2 71 34.7				Green can.	
18375	– Buoy 14					Red nun.	

BLOCK ISLAND SOUND AND APPROACHES (Chart 13205)

18380	**Watch Hill Light**	41 18.2 71 51.5	Al Oc W (2) R 15s 10.0s Wlt 1.1s ec 0.3s Rfl 2.2s ec 0.3s Rfl 1.1s ec	61	W 15 R 13	Square, gray granite tower attached to white building.	HORN: 1 blast ev 30s (3s bl). Emergency light of reduced intensity when main light is extinguished. Lighted throughout 24 hours.
18381	**Watch Hill Radiobeacon**	41 18.2 71 51.5	WH (•—— ••••)		10		FREQ: 306 kHz, V. Antenna 136 yards, 021° from light.
18385	*Watch Hill Lighted Whistle Buoy WH*	41 15.8 71 51.0	Mo (A) W		6	Red and white stripes.	

BLOCK ISLAND SOUND AND GARDINERS BAY (Chart 13209)

18390	*Cerberus Shoal Lighted Gong Buoy 9* Northeast of shoal.	41 10.4 71 57.2	Fl G 4s		4	Green.	
18395	**Race Rock Light**	41 14.6 72 02.8	Fl R 10s	67	19	Granite tower attached to dwelling, on granite pier. 45	Lighted throughout 24 hours. HORN: 2 blasts ev 30s (2s bl-2s si-2s bl-24s si). Horn points southeast. Emergency light of reduced intensity when main light is extinguished.
18400	Race Point Buoy 2 On west edge of shoal.					Red nun.	

NEW YORK – First District

(1) No.	(2) Name and location	(3) Position	(4) Characteristic	(5) Height	(6) Range	(7) Structure	(8) Remarks
	BLOCK ISLAND SOUND AND GARDINERS BAY (Chart 13209)	N/W					
18405	*Valiant Rock Lighted Bell* *Buoy 1A* Northerly of rock.	41 13.8 72 04.0	Q G		4	Green.	
18410	**Little Gull Island Light**	41 12.4 72 06.5	F W	91	18	Gray granite tower, attached to red dwelling on pier.	HORN: 1 blast ev 15ˢ (2ˢ bl). Operates continuously. Emergency light of reduced intensity when main light is extinguished. Lighted throughout 24 hours.
18411	**Little Gull Island** **Radiobeacon**	41 12.4 72 06.5	J (•– – –)		20		FREQ: 306 kHz, II. Antenna 60 yards, 200° from light tower.
18415	Little Gull Island Reef Buoy 1 On east side of shoal spot.					Green can.	
18420	*Block Island Sound* *South Entrance* *Obstruction Lighted* *Buoy BIS*	41 06.9 71 43.1	Fl (2+1) G 6ˢ		4	Green and red bands.	
18425	*Endeavor Shoals Lighted* *Gong Buoy 1*	41 06.1 71 46.3	Fl G 4ˢ		4	Green.	
18435	Blackfish Rock Buoy 3 On north side of rock.					Green can.	
18440	*Shagwong Rock Lighted* *Buoy SR* On northeast side of rock.		Fl (2+1) G 6ˢ		4	Green and red bands.	
18445	*Shagwong Reef Lighted* *Bell Buoy 7SR* On north side of reef.	41 07.0 71 54.8	Fl G 2.5ˢ		4	Green.	
18450	*Montauk Harbor Entrance* *Lighted Bell Buoy M*	41 05.1 71 56.4	Mo (A) W		6	Red and white stripes with red spherical topmark.	
18455	MONTAUK EAST JETTY LIGHT 1	41 04.8 71 56.3	Fl G 4ˢ	30	4	SG on skeleton tower.	
18460	**Montauk West Jetty** **Light 2**	41 04.7 71 56.4	Fl R 5ˢ	32	14	TR on skeleton tower.	HORN: 1 blast ev 30ˢ (3ˢ bl).
18465	Montauk Channel Shoal Buoy 1S					Green can.	Removed when endangered by ice.
18470	Montauk Harbor West Side Daybeacon Marks rocks near edge of channel.					NW on pile worded DANGER ROCK.	Sides of daymark form 45° angle to the centerline of channel with apex toward channel.
	Montauk Harbor						
18475	– Buoy 1					Green can.	Maintained from May 1 to Nov. 1. Private aid.
18480	– Buoy 3					Green can.	Maintained from May 1 to Nov. 1. Private aid.

(1) No.	(2) Name and location	(3) Position	(4) Characteristic	(5) Height	(6) Range	(7) Structure	(8) Remarks

N/W
BLOCK ISLAND SOUND AND GARDINERS BAY
(Chart 13209)

Montauk Harbor

18485	– Buoy 5					Green can.	Maintained from May 1 to Nov. 1. Private aid.
18490	– Buoy 7					Green can.	Maintained from May 1 to Nov. 1. Private aid.
18495	– Buoy 8					Red nun.	Maintained from May 1 to Nov. 1 Private aid.
18500	– Buoy 9					Green can.	Maintained from May 1 to Nov. 1. Private aid.
18505	– Buoy 10					Red nun.	Maintained from May 1 to Nov. 1. Private aid.
18510	– Buoy 11					Green can.	Maintained from May 1 to Nov. 1. Private aid.
18515	– Buoy 12					Red nun.	Maintained from May 1 to Nov. 1. Private aid.
18520	– Buoy 13					Green can.	Maintained from May 1 to Nov. 1. Private aid.
18525	– Buoy 15					Green can.	Maintained from May 1 to Nov. 1. Private aid.

Lake Montauk

18530	– Buoy 1					Green Spar.	Maintained from May 1 to Nov. 1. Private aid.
18535	– Buoy 3					Green can.	Maintained from May 1 to Nov. 1. Private aid.
18540	– Buoy 4					Red nun.	Maintained from May 1 to Nov. 1. Private aid.
18545	– Buoy 5					Green can.	Maintained from May 1 to Nov. 1. Private aid.
18550	– Buoy 6					Red nun.	Maintained from May 1 to Nov. 1. Private aid.
18555	– Buoy 7					Green can.	Maintained from May 1 to Nov. 1. Private aid.
18560	– Buoy 8					Red nun.	Maintained from May 1 to Nov. 1. Private aid.

(1) No.	(2) Name and location	(3) Position	(4) Characteristic	(5) Height	(6) Range	(7) Structure	(8) Remarks

NEW YORK – First District

BLOCK ISLAND SOUND AND GARDINERS BAY N/W
(Chart 13209)

Montauk Harbor

| 18565 | MONTAUK YACHT CLUB LIGHT | 41 04.2 71 56.0 | F W | 65 | | On lighthouse tower. | Private aid. |

CONNECTICUT – First District

FISHERS ISLAND SOUND (Chart 13214)

Southeast Entrance

18570	Catumb Passage Buoy 1C Off rock.	41 17.4 71 52.9				Green can.	
18575	Catumb Passage Buoy 3C Northeast side of Catumb Rocks.					Green can.	
18580	Catumb Rocks Buoy 2 Southwest of reef.					Red nun.	
18585	*Lords Passage Lighted Whistle Buoy L*	41 17.4 71 54.3	Mo (A) W		6	Red and white stripes with red spherical topmark.	
18590	Lords Passage Buoy 2L	41 17.5 71 54.0				Red nun.	
18595	Wicopesset Passage Bell Buoy W					Red and white stripes with red spherical topmark.	
18600	Wicopesset Passage Rock Buoy WP On north side of rock.					Green and red bands; can.	

Main Channel

18605	*Gangway Rock Lighted Bell Buoy 2*	41 18.0 71 51.5	Fl R 6s		4	Red.	Removed when endangered by ice.
18610	Watch Hill Reef Gong Buoy 1 On east side of reef.					Green.	
18615	Watch Hill Passage Buoy 3	41 17.9 71 51.7				Green can.	
18620	Sugar Reef Buoy 5					Green can.	
18625	*Napatree Point Ledge Lighted Bell Buoy 6*		Fl R 4s		4	Red.	
18630	Wicopesset Rock Buoy 7 Northeast of rock.					Green can.	
18635	Wicopesset Ledge Buoy 9					Green can.	
18640	Wicopesset Island Buoy 11					Green can.	
18645	Latimer Reef North Buoy N					Green and red bands; can.	
18650	Latimer Reef East Buoy E					Red and green bands; nun.	
18655	Seal Rocks Northeast Buoy S					Green and red bands; can.	
18660	Seal Rocks Buoy 13 On north side of rocks.					Green can.	

(1) No.	(2) Name and location	(3) Position	(4) Characteristic	(5) Height	(6) Range	(7) Structure	(8) Remarks
			CONNECTICUT – First District				
	FISHERS ISLAND SOUND (Chart 13214)	N/W					
	Main Channel						
18665	LATIMER REEF LIGHT	41 18.3 71 56.0	Fl W 6ˢ	55	9	White conical tower, brown midway of height; brown cylinder. 49	BELL: 2 strokes ev 15ˢ.
18670	Youngs Rock Buoy 15 At north end of rock.					Green can.	
18675	Eel Grass Ground Southeast Buoy 16					Red nun.	
18680	East Clump Buoy 17	41 17.8 71 57.6				Green can.	
18685	Eel Grass Ground Northwest Buoy 18					Red nun.	
18690	*Ram Island Reef Lighted Bell Buoy 20*	41 18.2 71 58.4	Fl R 4ˢ		4	Red.	
18695	Ram Island Reef Daybeacon RI On rocks.					NW on tower worded DANGER ROCKS.	
18700	Middle Clump Buoy 19					Green can.	
18705	Sweepers Ground Obstruction Buoy S					Red and green bands; nun.	
18710	Intrepid Rock Buoy IR On southeast side of rock					Red and green bands; nun.	
18715	Groton Long Point Buoy 22 On southwest end of reef.					Red nun.	
18720	Groton Long Point Buoy 24 On southwest side of 1/2 foot spot.					Red nun.	
18725	NORTH DUMPLING LIGHT	41 17.3 72 01.2	F W (R sector)	94 W R	9 7	Square house with light tower. 60	HORN: 1 blast ev 30ˢ (3ˢ bl). Operates automatically. Red from 257° to 023°.
18730	Horseshoe Reef Buoy 26 On southwest side of reef.					Red nun.	
18735	SEAFLOWER REEF LIGHT On southwest part of reef.	41 17.7 72 02.0	Fl W 4ˢ	28	7	NG on skeleton tower.	
	Stonington Harbor						
18740	– Approach Buoy 2	41 18.7 71 54.6				Red nun.	
18745	– Approach Gong Buoy 3 On southeast end of Noyes Shoal.					Green.	
18750	STONINGTON OUTER BREAKWATER LIGHT 4	41 19.0 71 54.5	Fl R 4ˢ	46	5	TR on skeleton tower, small house, concrete base.	HORN: 1 blast ev 10ˢ (1ˢ bl).
18755	STONINGTON BREAKWATER LIGHT 5	41 19.5 71 54.8	Fl G 4ˢ	31	5	SG on skeleton tower, concrete base.	
18760	Stonington Point Junction Buoy SP					Red and green bands; nun.	

(1) No.	(2) Name and location	(3) Position	(4) Characteristic	(5) Height	(6) Range	(7) Structure	(8) Remarks

FISHERS ISLAND SOUND (Chart 13214) N/W

Stonington Harbor

(1) No.	(2) Name and location	(3) Position	(4) Characteristic	(5) Height	(6) Range	(7) Structure	(8) Remarks
18765	STONINGTON INNER BREAKWATER LIGHT 8	41 19.8 71 54.6	Fl R 4s	27	5	TR on skeleton tower, concrete base.	
18770	– Buoy 7					Green can.	
18775	– Buoy 10 Marks end of outfall.					Red nun.	

Little Narragansett Bay

Channel buoys located 20-60 feet outside limit.

(1) No.	(2) Name and location	(3) Position	(4) Characteristic	(5) Height	(6) Range	(7) Structure	(8) Remarks
18780	*Academy Rock Lighted Buoy 2* Marks west side of rock.	41 19.6 71 54.3	Fl R 4s		3	Red.	Removed when endangered by ice.
18785	– Entrance Buoy 4 Marks northwesterly edge of shoal.					Red nun.	
18790	*– Entrance Lighted Buoy 3*		Fl G 4s		3	Green.	Removed when endangered by ice.
18795	– Buoy 5A On south side of rock.					Green can.	
18800	– Buoy 5					Green can.	
18805	– Buoy 6					Red nun.	
18810	– Channel Buoy 7	41 19.8 71 53.3				Green can.	
18815	*– Channel Lighted Buoy 9* 180 feet outside channel limit.		Fl G 4s		3	Green.	Removed when endangered by ice.
18820	– Channel Buoy 10					Red nun.	
18825	– Channel Buoy 11					Green can.	
18830	– Channel Buoy 12					Red nun.	
18835	*– Channel Lighted Buoy 13*		Fl G 2.5s		3	Green.	Removed when endangered by ice.
18840	– Channel Buoy 14					Red nun.	
18845	– Channel Buoy 16					Red nun.	
18850	– Channel Buoy 18					Red nun.	
18855	*– Channel Lighted Buoy 19* Marks south side of rock.		Fl G 4s		3	Green.	Removed when endangered by ice.
18860	Dennison Rock Buoy 2 Marks south side of rock.					Red nun.	

Pawcatuck River

Channel buoys located 20-30 feet outside channel limit.

(1) No.	(2) Name and location	(3) Position	(4) Characteristic	(5) Height	(6) Range	(7) Structure	(8) Remarks
18865	– Buoy 1 On south edge of shoal.	41 19.4 71 51.4				Green can.	

CONNECTICUT – First District

FISHERS ISLAND SOUND (Chart 13214) N/W

Pawcatuck River

Channel buoys located 20-30 feet outside channel limit.

(1) No.	(2) Name and location	(3) Position	(4) Characteristic	(5) Height	(6) Range	(7) Structure	(8) Remarks
18870	– Buoy 3 On south point of shoal.					Green can.	
18875	– Channel Buoy 4 On south point of shoal.					Red nun.	
18880	– Channel Buoy 6					Red nun.	
18885	– Channel Buoy 7					Green can.	
18890	– Channel Buoy 8					Red nun.	
18895	– Channel Buoy 10					Red nun.	
18900	– Channel Buoy 12 On west edge of rocky area.					Red nun.	
18905	– Channel Buoy 14					Red nun.	
18910	– Channel Buoy 16					Red nun.	
18915	– Channel Buoy 17					Green can.	
18920	– Channel Buoy 19					Black can.	Private aid.
18925	Thompson Cove Buoy 1					Black can.	Maintained from May 1 to Nov. 30. Private aid.
18930	Thompson Cove Buoy 3					Black can.	Maintained from May 1 to Nov. 30. Private aid.
18935	– Channel Buoy 20					Red nun.	Private aid.
18940	– Channel Buoy 22					Red nun.	Private aid.
18945	– Channel Buoy 24					Red nun.	Private aid.
18950	– Channel Buoy 24A					Red nun.	Private aid.
18955	– Channel Buoy 25					Green can.	Private aid.
18960	– Channel Buoy 26					Red nun.	Private aid.
18965	– Channel Buoy 26A					Red nun.	Private aid.
18970	– Channel Buoy 27					Green can.	Private aid.
18975	– Channel Buoy 27A					Green can.	Private aid.
18980	– Channel Buoy 28					Red nun.	Private aid.
18985	Gavitt Point Outfall Buoy	41 21.2 71 50.2				White with orange bands and diamond worded DANGER SUB PIPE.	Private aid.
	Watch Hill Cove						
18990	– *Channel Lighted Buoy 2*	41 18.9 71 51.7	Fl R 4ˢ	3		Red.	Removed when endangered by ice.
18995	– Channel Buoy 1					Green can.	

(1) No.	(2) Name and location	(3) Position	(4) Characteristic	(5) Height	(6) Range	(7) Structure	(8) Remarks

No.	Name and location	Position	Characteristic	Height	Range	Structure	Remarks
	FISHERS ISLAND SOUND (Chart 13214) N/W						
	Silver Eel Pond						
19825	– LIGHT 2	41 15.5 72 02.0	Fl R 4ˢ	14		Dolphin.	Private aid.
	LONG ISLAND SOUND (Connecticut and New York) – First District						
	LONG ISLAND SOUND (Eastern Part) (Chart 12354)						
19830	*Barlett Reef Lighted Bell Buoy 4*	41 15.6 72 08.4	Fl R 4ˢ		4	Red.	Removed when endangered by ice.
19835	**Bartlett Reef Light** On south end of reef.	41 16.5 72 08.2	Fl W 5ˢ	35	12	NR on skeleton tower.	HORN: 2 blasts ev 60ˢ (3ˢ bl-3ˢ si-3ˢ bl-51ˢ si).
19840	Bartlett Reef Buoy 1A					Green can.	
19845	*Plum Island Lighted Whistle Buoy Pl*	41 13.3 72 10.8	**Mo (A) W**		6	Red and white stripes with red spherical topmark.	
19850 26110	*Plum Gut Lighted Bell Buoy 2PG*		Fl R 4ˢ		4	Red.	
19855 26105	PLUM GUT LIGHT	41 10.4 72 12.7	Fl W 2.5ˢ	55	5	On brick shed.	
19860 26090	**Orient Point Light**	41 09.8 72 13.4	Fl W 5ˢ	64	17	Black conical tower with white band in center.	HORN: 2 blasts ev 30ˢ (2ˢ bl-2ˢ si-2ˢ bl-24ˢ si). Emergency light of reduced intensity when main light is extinguished. Lighted throughout 24 hours.
19865	Hatchett Reef Buoy 6 On south end of reef.					Red nun.	
19870	*Saybrook Bar Lighted Bell Buoy 8* On south point of shoal.	41 14.9 72 18.8	Fl R 4ˢ		4	Red.	
19875	Long Sand Shoal East End Buoy E	41 14.6 72 19.4				Red and green bands; nun.	
19880 21160	**Saybrook Breakwater Light**	41 15.8 72 20.6	Fl G 6ˢ	58	11	White conical tower on brown cylindrical pier. 49	HORN: 1 blast ev 30ˢ (3ˢ bl). Emergency light of reduced intensity when main light is extinguished. Lighted throughout 24 hours.
19881 21161	**Saybrook Breakwater Radiobeacon**	41 15.8 72 20.6	SB (••• —•••)		10		FREQ: 320 kHz. Antenna at light tower.
19885	Orient Shoal Buoy 3 On northeast side of shoal.	41 09.0 72 19.8				Green can.	
19895	*Long Sand Shoal Lighted Bell Buoy 8A*	41 13.5 72 23.1	Q R		4	Red.	
19900	*Cornfield Lighted Whistle Buoy CF*	41 11.3 72 22.3	**Mo (A) W**		6	Red and white stripes with red spherical topmark.	
19905	*Long Sand Shoal West End Lighted Horn Buoy W* At west point of shoal.	41 13.6 72 27.6	Fl (2+1) R 6ˢ		4	Red and green bands.	HORN: 1 blast ev 30 (3 bl).

(1) No.	(2) Name and location	(3) Position	(4) Characteristic	(5) Height	(6) Range	(7) Structure	(8) Remarks

LONG ISLAND SOUND (Eastern Part) (Chart 12354)

N/W

(1) No.	(2) Name and location	(3) Position	(4) Characteristic	(5) Height	(6) Range	(7) Structure	(8) Remarks
19910	**Horton Point Light**	41 05.1 72 26.8	Fl G 10s	103	14	White square tower, dwelling attached.	
19911	**Horton Point Radiobeacon**	41 05.1 72 26.8	HP (•••• •———•)		20		FREQ: 306 kHz, III, VI. Antenna 72 yards 162° from Light tower.
19915	Sixmile Reef Lighted Bell Buoy 8C At southerly edge of reef.		Fl R 4s		4	Red.	
19920	Twenty-Eight Foot Shoal Lighted Buoy TE	41 09.3 72 30.4	Fl (2+1) R 6s		4	Red and green bands.	
19925	Kimberly Reef Lighted Horn Buoy KR	41 12.8 72 37.4	Fl (2+1) R 6s		4	Red and green bands.	HORN: 1 blast ev 30s (3s bl).
19930	**Falkner Island Light**	41 12.7 72 39.2	Fl W 10s	94	13	White octagonal tower. 46	
19935	Goose Island Lighted Bell Buoy 10GI Off south end of shoal.	41 12.1 72 40.5	Fl R 4s		4	Red.	
19940	SACHEM HEAD BREAKWATER LIGHT On rock.	41 14.8 72 42.7	Fl R 3s			Pile.	Maintained from June 1 to Oct. 1. Private aid.
19945	BRANFORD REEF LIGHT	41 13.3 72 48.4	Fl W 6s	30	7	NR on skeleton tower.	
19950	Townsend Ledge Lighted Bell Buoy 10A Off south edge of ledge.		Fl R 4s		4	Red.	
19955	New Haven Dumping Ground Lighted Buoy SP	41 09.0 72 53.2	Fl Y 4s		5	Yellow.	
19960	CLIS Dumping Ground Lighted Buoy CDA	41 09.3 72 53.4	Fl Y 4s		5	Yellow.	Maintained from June 1 to Oct. 1. Private aid.
19965 22425	New Haven Harbor Lighted Whistle Buoy NH	41 12.1 72 53.8	Mo (A) W		6	Red and white stripes with red spherical topmark.	
19970 22470	**Southwest Ledge Light**	41 14.1 72 54.7	Fl R 5s	57	13	White octagonal house on brown cylindrical pier.	HORN: 1 blast ev 15s (2s bl). Emergency light of reduced intensity when main light is extinguished.
19975 22485	NEW HAVEN LIGHT	41 13.3 72 56.6	Fl W 4s	35	7	NG on pipe tower.	
19980	Pond Point Shoal Buoy 12 On south point of shoal.					Red nun.	
19985	Charles Island Lighted Bell Buoy 16 South point of shoal.	41 11.0 73 03.1	Fl R 4s		5	Red.	
19990	**Stratford Point Light**	41 09.1 73 06.2	Fl (2) W 20s	52	16	White conical tower, brown band midway of height.	HORN: 2 blasts ev 30s (2s bl-2s si-2s bl-24s si). Emergency light (Fl W 6s) of reduced intensity when main light is extinguished.

(1) No.	(2) Name and location	(3) Position	(4) Characteristic	(5) Height	(6) Range	(7) Structure	(8) Remarks

(1) No.	(2) Name and location	(3) Position	(4) Characteristic	(5) Height	(6) Range	(7) Structure	(8) Remarks
	LONG ISLAND SOUND (Eastern Part) (Chart 12354)	N/W					
19991	**Stratford Point Radiobeacon**	41 09.1 73 06.2	**SP** (••• •———•)		20		FREQ: 316 kHz, III, VI. Antenna 150 feet, 010° from light tower.
19995	Stratford Point Buoy 20 On south side of Point No Point Shoal.	41 07.8 73 07.5				Red nun.	
20000	*Stratford Point Lighted Bell Buoy 18*		Fl R 6s		4	Red.	Removed when endangered by ice.
	Stratford Shoal						
20005	– Buoy 1	41 04.2 73 05.2				Green can.	
20010	– Buoy 3 Off north point of shoal.					Green can.	
20015	– **(Middle Ground) Light**	41 03.6 73 06.1	Fl W 5s	60	13	Gray, granite octagonal tower projection from house on pier.	HORN: 1 blast ev 15s (2s bl).
20020	– *Middle Ground Lighted Bell Buoy 2* South of shoal.		Fl R 4s		4	Red.	
20025	Mount Misery Shoal Buoy 11 On northeast point of shoal.					Green can.	
	LONG ISLAND SOUND (Western Part) (Chart 12363)						
20030	**Old Field Point Light**	40 58.6 73 07.1	Al R G 24s R fl 12s ec G fl 12s ec	74	14	Black skeleton tower adjacent to old tower.	
20031	**Old Field Point Radiobeacon**	40 58.6 73 07.1	**OP** (——— •———•)		20		FREQ: 316 kHz, II, V.
20035	Old Field Point Gong Buoy 11A Off north point of shoal.					Green.	
20040	**Penfield Reef Light**		Fl R 6s	51	18	White tower on granite dwelling on pier.	HORN: 1 blast ev 15s (2s bl). Emergency light of reduced intensity when main light is extinguished. Lighted throughout 24 hours.
20045	*Pine Creek Point Lighted Bell Buoy 22* On south point of shoal.		Fl R 4s		4	Red.	
20050	*Cockenoe Island Shoal Lighted Bell Buoy 24* Southeast of shoal.	41 04.5 73 19.8	Fl R 2.5s		4	Red.	Removed when endangered by ice.
20055	*Norwalk Islands Lighted Bell Buoy 26* Off southeast end of shoal.	41 03.7 73 22.0	Fl R 4s		4	Red.	Removed when endangered by ice.
20060	*Eatons Neck Point Lighted Gong Buoy 11B* On north end of shoal.		Fl G 4s		5	Green.	Replaced by smaller LIB when endangered by ice.
20065	Eatons Neck Lump Buoy E On east side of shoal.					Green and red bands; can.	

LONG ISLAND SOUND (Connecticut and New York) – First District

No.	Name and location	Position	Characteristic	Height	Range	Structure	Remarks
	LONG ISLAND SOUND (Western Part) (Chart 12363)	N/W					
20250	**Stepping Stones Light** On outer end of reef.	40 49.5 73 46.5	F G	46	11	Red brick on granite pier; white band on southwest face of pier.	HORN: 1 blast ev 15s (2s bl). Emergency light of reduced intensity when main light is extinguished. Lighted throughout 24 hours.
20255	Locust Point Buoy 46A					Red nun.	
20260	*Throgs Neck Lighted Bell Buoy 48* Marks southern end of shoal.		Fl R 4s		4	Red.	
20265	**Throgs Neck Light**	40 48.3 73 47.5	F R	60	11	NB on tower.	
	WATCH HILL TO NEW HAVEN HARBOR (Chart 12372)						
	North Channel (Saybrook to New Haven)						
20275	Hatchett Reef Buoy 1 On northeast point of reef.	41 16.2 72 15.7				Green can.	
20280	*Cornfield Point Shoal Lighted Bell Buoy 2* South of shoal.	41 15.0 72 23.1	Fl R 4s		4	Red.	
20285	Hen and Chickens Buoy On southeast edge of shoal.					White can with orange bands and diamond worded ROCKS.	
	Old Saybrook Rock						
20290	– Regulatory Buoy A	41 15.7 72 24.1				White can with orange bands and diamond worded ROCKS.	Private aid.
20295	– Regulatory Buoy B					White can with orange bands and diamond worded ROCKS.	Private aid.
20300	– Regulatory Buoy C					White can with orange bands and diamond worded ROCKS.	Private aid.
20305	– Regulatory Buoy D					White can with orange bands and diamond worded ROCKS.	Private aid.
	North Channel (Saybrook to New Haven)						
20310	INDIAN TOWN EAST BREAKWATER LIGHT		Fl W 2s	28		On pile.	Maintained from Apr. 15 to Nov. 15. Private aid.
20315	Crane Reef Buoy 4 On south side of reef.					Red nun.	
20320	Duck Island Reef Buoy 6 On south end of reef.					Red nun.	
20325	Stone Island Reef Buoy 8 On south side of reef.					Red nun.	
20330	Hammonasset Point Reef Buoy 10 On southwest side of shoal.					Red nun.	

(1) No.	(2) Name and location	(3) Position	(4) Characteristic	(5) Height	(6) Range	(7) Structure	(8) Remarks

N/W

WATCH HILL TO NEW HAVEN HARBOR (Chart 12372)

North Channel (Saybrook to New Haven)

No.	Name and location	Position	Characteristic	Height	Range	Structure	Remarks
20335	Charles Reef Buoy 14 Off south end of reef.					Red nun.	
20340	*Falkner Island Reef Lighted Gong Buoy 15* North of shoal.		Fl G 4s		4	Green.	
20345	Indian Reef Southwest Buoy 16 On south side of shoal.					Red nun.	
20350	Chimney Corner Reef Buoy 20 South side of reef.					Red nun.	
20355	JOSHUA POINT LIGHT		Iso W 6s	10		Gray cement base.	Visible from 345.5° to 054° with higher intensity beam toward sound. Maintained from June 1 to to Oct. 15. Private aid.
20360	*Goose Rocks Shoal Lighted Bell Buoy 22* Marks southwest end of shoal.		Fl R 4s		4	Red.	
20365	*Browns Reef Lighted Bell Buoy 26* South of reefs.		Fl R 4s		5	Red.	
20370	*Negro Heads Lighted Buoy 28* On south end of reef.		Fl R 4s		4	Red.	Replaced by nun when endangered by ice.
20375	Five Foot Rock Buoy 32 On southwest side of rock.					Red nun.	
20380	*Cow and Calf Lighted Bell Buoy 34*	41 14.3 72 50.5	Fl R 2.5s		4	Red.	
20385	Round Rock Buoy 36 On south side of shoal.					Red nun.	

SHELTER ISLAND SOUND AND PECONIC BAYS (Chart 12358)

South Side

Mattituck Inlet

No.	Name and location	Position	Characteristic	Height	Range	Structure	Remarks
20390	– Buoy 1					Green can.	
20395	– Gong Buoy 3A					Green.	

LONG ISLAND SOUND (Eastern Part) (Chart 12354)

South Side

Mattituck Inlet

No.	Name and location	Position	Characteristic	Height	Range	Structure	Remarks
20400	– BREAKWATER LIGHT MI	41 00.9 72 33.7	Fl W 4s	25	6	NR on skeleton tower.	
20405	– Buoy 2					Red nun.	

LONG ISLAND SOUND (Connecticut and New York) – First District

N/W

LONG ISLAND SOUND (Eastern Part) (Chart 12354)

South Side

Mattituck Inlet

20410	– Buoy 3					Green can.	

Mattituck Creek

20415	– Buoy 1					Green can.	Maintained from May 1 to Oct. 31. Private aid.
20420	– Buoy 3					Green can.	Maintained from May 1 to Oct. 31. Private aid.
20425	– Buoy 5					Green can.	Maintained from May 1 to Oct. 31. Private aid.

Jacobs Point

20430	– PLATFORM LIGHTS (4)	41 00.0 72 38.8	Q W	25		On platform.	HORN: 1 blast ev 20s (2s bl). Lights flash in unison. Private aids.
20435	– Rock Buoy 3					Black can.	Private aid.
20440	– Shoal Buoy 5					Black can.	Private aid.
20442	– *Aquaculture Lighted Buoys (4)*		Fl W 2s			White with orange bands worded LONG LINE.	Private aid.
20445	Roanoke Point Shoal Buoy 5 On northwest side of shoal.	41 00.2 72 42.3				Green can.	

South Side (Mattituck to Mt. Sinai)

20450	Herod Point Shoal Buoy 7 On north point of shoal.					Green can.	
20455	Rocky Point Buoy 9 On north end of shoal.					Green can.	

LONG ISLAND SOUND (Connecticut) – First District

APPROACHES TO NEW LONDON HARBOR (Chart 13212)

Pine Island Channel

20460	Vixen Ledge Buoy VL Marks south side of ledge.	41 18.4 72 02.9				Red and green bands; nun.	
20465	*Pine Island Channel Lighted Bell Buoy 2* On southwest point of shoal.		Fl R 4s		4	Red.	
20470	Pine Island Channel Buoy 3 On north side of reef.					Green can.	
20475	*Pine Island Lighted Buoy 1* On southern tip of shoal.	41 18.9 72 03.7	Fl G 4s		3	Green.	Removed when endangered by ice.

(1) No.	(2) Name and location	(3) Position	(4) Characteristic	(5) Height	(6) Range	(7) Structure	(8) Remarks

N/W
APPROACHES TO NEW LONDON HARBOR (Chart 13212)

Pine Island Channel

(1) No.	(2) Name and location	(3) Position	(4) Characteristic	(5) Height	(6) Range	(7) Structure	(8) Remarks
20477	Pine Island Channel Avery Point Breakwater Light 1A Marks end of breakwater.	41 18.9 72 03.6	Q G			SG on spindle.	Private aid.
20480	Pine Island Buoy 2 On northern tip of shoal.					Red nun.	

West Approach

(1) No.	(2) Name and location	(3) Position	(4) Characteristic	(5) Height	(6) Range	(7) Structure	(8) Remarks
20485	Little Goshen Reef Buoy 3 On south point of shoal.	41 17.3 72 06.7				Green can.	
20490	Goshen Ledge Buoy 5 On south end of ledge.					Green can.	
20495	Rapid Rock Buoy R On southeast side of rock					Green and red bands; can.	
20500	Cormorant Rock Ledge Buoy 7 On point of ledge east of rock.					Green can.	
20505	Sarah Ledge Buoy SL					Green and red bands; can.	
20510	*Dumping Ground Lighted Buoy NL*	41 15.8 72 05.0	Fl Y 2.5s		5	Yellow.	

NEW LONDON HARBOR AND VICINITY (Chart 13213)

New London Harbor

(1) No.	(2) Name and location	(3) Position	(4) Characteristic	(5) Height	(6) Range	(7) Structure	(8) Remarks
20515	*– Channel Lighted Buoy 2*	41 17.6 72 04.7	Fl R 2.5s		4	Red.	
20520	*– Channel Lighted Buoy 1*	41 17.6 72 04.8	Fl G 2.5s		4	Green.	
20525	*– Channel Lighted Buoy 3*		Fl G 4s		4	Green.	
20530	*– Channel Buoy 4*	41 18.5 72 04.8				Red nun.	
20535	Black Ledge Buoy 2					Red nun.	
20540	Black Ledge Buoy 4					Red nun.	
20545	Black Ledge Buoy 6					Red nun.	
20550	**New London Ledge Light** On west side of Southwest Ledge.	41 18.3 72 04.7	Fl (3) W R 30s 0.3s W fl 4.7s ec 0.3s W fl 4.7s ec 0.3s W fl 9.7s ec 0.3s R fl 9.7s ec	58	W 17 R 14	Red brick dwelling on square pier.	HORN: 2 blast ev 20s (2s bl-2s si-2s bl-14s si). Emergency light of reduced intensity when main light is extinguished. Lighted throughout 24 hours.
20555	*New London Dumping Ground Lighted Buoy NDA*	41 16.4 72 04.3	Fl Y 4s			Yellow.	Maintained from Oct. 1 to June 1. Private aid.
20556	*New London Research Lighted Buoy (ODAS)*	41 15.8 72 04.0	Fl Y 4s			Yellow.	Private aid.
20560	Frank Ledge Buoy F On north side of ledge.					Green and red bands; can.	

LONG ISLAND SOUND (Connecticut) – First District

NEW LONDON HARBOR AND VICINITY (Chart 13213) N/W

New London Harbor

No.	Name and location	Position	Characteristic	Height	Range	Structure	Remarks
20565	– Light	41 19.0 72 05.4	Iso W 6s (R sector)	89	W 17 R 14	White octagonal pyramidal tower.	Red from 000° to 041°. Covers Sarah Ledge and shoals westward.
20570	– Channel Lighted Buoy 5		Fl G 2.5s		4	Green.	
20575	– Channel Lighted Buoy 6		Fl R 2.5s		4	Red.	
20580	– LOWER WHARF LIGHT	41 20.1 72 04.9	Fl R 15s	15		Pile.	Private aid.
20585	– UPPER WHARF LIGHT		Fl R 15s	15		Pile.	Private aid.
20587	Groton Outfall Lighted Buoy	41 20.2 72 04.9	Iso (2) W			White with orange bands.	Private aid.
20590	– Channel Lighted Buoy 7	41 20.3 72 05.1	Fl G 6s		5	Green.	
20595	– Channel Buoy 8					Red nun.	
20600	Powder Island Buoy 1 On north side of Melton Ledge.					Green can.	
20605	Fort Trumbull Outfall Buoy	41 20.5 72 05.2				White can with orange bands and diamond worded OUTFALL.	Private aid.
20610	GRAVING DOCK SOUTH LIGHT		Q R	22			Private aid.
20615	GRAVING DOCK CENTER LIGHT		Q R	22			Private aid.
20620	GRAVING DOCK NORTH LIGHT		Q R	22			Private aid.
20625	GRAVING DOCK 3 SOUTH LIGHT		Q R	18			Private aid.
20630	GRAVING DOCK 3 NORTH LIGHT		Q R	18			Private aid.
20635	– Buoy 9					Green can.	
20640	– Buoy 11					Green can.	
20645	– Channel Lighted Buoy 13	41 21.1 72 05.2	Fl G 4s		4	Green.	
20650	– Buoy 14					Red nun.	
20655	STATE PIER LIGHT		Iso G 6s	10		Mooring island.	Private aid.
20660	– Buoy 15					Green can.	
20665	– RANGE FRONT LIGHT	41 21.8 72 05.3	Iso R 6s	36		On southeast bridge abutment of railroad bridge.	Light obscured from 040° to 310° with higher intensity beam on channel line.
20670	– RANGE REAR LIGHT 3,814 yards, 354° from front light.		F G	80		Guyed tower.	Visible on rangeline only. Note: Does not mark center of channel at far end of range.

(1) No.	(2) Name and location	(3) Position	(4) Characteristic	(5) Height	(6) Range	(7) Structure	(8) Remarks

LONG ISLAND SOUND (Connecticut) – First District

NEW LONDON HARBOR AND VICINITY (Chart 13213) N/W

Upper Thames River

Channel buoys located 30 feet outside channel limit.

(1) No.	(2) Name and location	(3) Position	(4) Characteristic	(5) Height	(6) Range	(7) Structure	(8) Remarks
20860	INDIAN HILL LIGHT 29		Fl G 4s	9	4	SG on skeleton tower on concrete base.	
20865	PRIDE PIER LIGHT 30		Fl R 4s	20	4	TR on pile.	
20870	– Channel Buoy 31					Green can.	
20875	BURNT HOUSE PIER LIGHT 32	41 29.7 72 04.8	Fl R 2.5s	16	4	TR on pile.	
20880	PERCHE ROCK LIGHT 33 On rock.	41 29.8 72 05.0	Fl G 4s	16	4	SG on pile.	
20885	– Channel Buoy 34					Red nun.	
20890	– Channel Buoy 35					Green can.	
20895	SAND PIER LIGHT 37		Fl G 2.5s	16	4	SG on pile.	
20900	– Channel Buoy 38					Red nun.	
20905	LOWER COAL DOCK LIGHT 40		Fl R 4s	15	3	TR on skeleton tower on concrete base.	
20910	– Channel Buoy 41	41 30.7 72 04.8				Green can.	
20915	– Channel Buoy 43					Green can.	

NIANTIC BAY AND VICINITY (Chart 13211)

(1) No.	(2) Name and location	(3) Position	(4) Characteristic	(5) Height	(6) Range	(7) Structure	(8) Remarks
20920	Bartlett Reef North End Buoy 1	41 17.8 72 08.5				Green can.	
20925	Two Tree Island Shoal Buoy 3					Green can.	
20930	Flat Rock Buoy 2 On southwest side of rock					Red nun.	
20935	High Rock Buoy H					Green and red bands; can.	
20940	*White Rock Lighted Bell Buoy 4*		Fl R 4s		4	Red.	
20945	Threefoot Rock Buoy 5 On east side of rock.					Green can.	
20950	Black Rock Buoy 6 On west side of rock.					Red nun.	
20955	CRESCENT PARK BREAKWATER LIGHT		Fl W 6s	8		On pile.	Maintained from Apr. 15 to Nov. 15. Private aid.
20960	Crescent Beach Daybeacon					NW on pile.	Private aid.
20965	Wigwam Rock Danger Buoy					White with orange bands worded ROCKS.	Removed when endangered by ice.

Niantic River

The position of buoys frequently shifted with changing conditions.

(1) No.	(2) Name and location	(3) Position	(4) Characteristic	(5) Height	(6) Range	(7) Structure	(8) Remarks
20970	– Channel Daybeacon 1					SG on pile.	

(1) No.	(2) Name and location	(3) Position	(4) Characteristic	(5) Height	(6) Range	(7) Structure	(8) Remarks

N/W

NIANTIC BAY AND VICINITY (Chart 13211)

Niantic River

The position of buoys frequently shifted with changing conditions.

(1) No.	(2) Name and location	(4) Structure	(8) Remarks
20975	– Channel Buoy 3	Green can.	
20980	– Channel Buoy 4	Red nun.	
20985	– Channel Buoy 6	Red nun.	Removed when endangered by ice.
20990	– Channel Daybeacon 7	SG on pile.	
20995	– Channel Daybeacon 8	TR on pile.	
21005	– Channel Buoy 10	Red nun.	Removed when endangered by ice.
21010	– Channel Buoy 11	Green can.	Removed when endangered by ice.
21015	– Channel Buoy 12	Red nun.	
21020	– Channel Daybeacon 13	SG on pile.	
21025	– Channel Daybeacon 14	TR on pile.	
21030	– Channel Buoy 15	Green can.	Removed when endangered by ice.
21035	– Channel Buoy 16	Red nun.	Removed when endangered by ice.
21040	– Channel Daybeacon 17	SG on pile.	
21045	– Channel Buoy 18	Red nun.	Removed when endangered by ice.
21050	– Channel Buoy 19	Green can.	Removed when endangered by ice.
21055	– Channel Buoy 21	Green can.	Removed when endangered by ice.
21060	– Channel Buoy 21A	Green can.	Removed when endangered by ice.
21065	– Channel Buoy 22	Red nun.	Removed when endangered by ice.
21070	– Channel Buoy 22A	Red nun.	Removed when endangered by ice.
21075	– Channel Buoy 23	Green can.	Removed when endangered by ice.
21080	– Channel Daybeacon 24	TR on pile.	
21085	– Channel Buoy 25	Green can.	Removed when endangered by ice.
21090	– Channel Buoy 26	Red nun.	Removed when endangered by ice.
21095	– Channel Daybeacon 27	SG on pile.	
21100	– Channel Daybeacon 28	TR on pile.	
21105	– Channel Buoy 29	Green can.	Removed when endangered by ice.

(1) No.	(2) Name and location	(3) Position	(4) Characteristic	(5) Height	(6) Range	(7) Structure	(8) Remarks

NIANTIC BAY AND VICINITY (Chart 13211)   N/W

Niantic River

The position of buoys frequently shifted with changing conditions.

21110	– Channel Buoy 30					Red nun.	Removed when endangered by ice.

Smith Cove

21115	– Daybeacon 1	41 20.3 72 11.1				SB on pile.	Private aid.
21120	– Daybeacon 2					TR on pile.	Private aid.
21125	– Daybeacon 4					TR on pile.	Private aid.
21130	– Daybeacon 6					TR on pile.	Private aid.
21135	– Daybeacon 8					TR on pile.	Private aid.
21140	– Daybeacon 9					SB on pile.	Private aid.

Pattaganset River

21145	Blackboys Rocks Buoy 2 Marks southside of rock.					Red nun.	
21150	Long Rock Buoy 4 Marks southwest side of rocky shoal.					Red nun.	
21155	Seal Rock Buoy 5 Marks south end of rock.					Green can.	

CONNECTICUT RIVER - LONG ISLAND SOUND TO DEEP RIVER (Chart 12375)

Connecticut River

21160 19880	**Saybrook Breakwater Light**	41 15.8 72 20.6	Fl G 6s	58	11	White conical tower on brown cylindrical pier. 49	HORN: 1 blast ev 30s (3s bl). Emergency light of reduced intensity when main light is extinguished. Lighted throughout 24 hours.
21161 19881	**Saybrook Breakwater Radiobeacon**	41 15.8 72 20.6	SB (••• —•••)		10		FREQ: 320 kHz. Antenna at light tower.
21165	– Buoy 2	41 15.8 72 20.5				Red nun.	
21170	Saybrook Daybeacon	41 16.1 72 20.3				White globe on granite structure.	
21175	– Buoy 4					Red nun.	
21180	**Lynde Point Light**	41 16.3 72 20.6	F W	71	14	White stone tower.	
21185	– *Lighted Buoy 5*		Fl G 4s		3	Green.	Replaced by can when endangered by ice.
21190	– Buoy 6 Marks west edge of shoal					Red nun.	
21195	– Buoy 7 Marks east edge of shoal					Green can.	

	LONG ISLAND SOUND (Connecticut) – First District						
	BODKIN ROCK TO HARTFORD (Chart 12377)	N/W					
	Connecticut River						
22015	NORTH OIL DOCK LIGHT	41 44.3 72 38.5	F R	26		On pile.	Private aid.
22020	– LIGHT 142		Fl R 4s	34	4	TR on skeleton tower.	
22025	HARTFORD JETTY LIGHT 143		Fl G 4s	34	4	SG on skeleton tower.	
22029	Salt Island Rock Buoy	41 16.5 72 26.4				White with orange band; can.	Maintained from Apr. 1 to Nov. 30. Private aid.
22030	Westbrook Harbor Buoy Marks south side of Lobster Rock.	41 16.1 72 26.5				Red and green bands; nun.	
22031	West Beach Shoal Buoy	41 16.3 72 27.2				White with orange band; can.	Maintained from Apr. 1 to Nov. 30. Private aid.
22032	Menunketesuck Island Shoal Buoy	41 15.6 72 27.6				White with orange band; can.	Maintained from Apr. 1 to Nov. 30. Private aid.
22034	Menunketesuck Island Rock Buoy	41 15.7 72 28.0				White with orange band; can.	Maintained from Apr. 1 to Nov. 30. Private aid.
	DUCK ISLAND TO MADISON REEF (Chart 12374)						
	Duck Island Roads						
22035	DUCK ISLAND NORTH BREAKWATER LIGHT	41 15.6 72 28.5	Fl W 4s	22	7	NR on skeleton tower.	
22040	DUCK ISLAND WEST BREAKWATER LIGHT 2DI	41 15.4 72 29.1	Fl R 4s	25	5	TR on skeleton tower.	
	Patchogue River						
22045	– BREAKWATER LIGHT 3A	41 16.1 72 28.5	Fl G 4s	21	4	SG on skeleton tower.	
22050	– *Channel Lighted Buoy 2*	41 15.9 72 28.4	Fl R 4s		4	Red.	Removed when endangered by ice.
22055	– Channel Buoy 3	41 16.0 72 28.4				Green can.	
22060	– Channel Buoy 4	41 16.1 72 28.4				Red nun.	
22065	– Channel Buoy 5					Black can.	Private aid.
22066	Menunketesuck River Junction Buoy M					Green and red bands; can.	Maintained from Apr. 1 to Nov. 30. Private aid.
22070	– Channel Buoy 6					Red nun.	Private aid.
22075	– Channel Daybeacon 7					SG on pile.	Private aid.
22080	– Channel Daybeacon 8					TR on pile.	Private aid.
22085	– Channel Daybeacon 10					TR on pile.	Private aid.
22090	KELSEY POINT BREAKWATER LIGHT	41 14.6 72 30.5	Fl W 2.5s	33	7	NG on skeleton tower.	

LONG ISLAND SOUND (Connecticut) – First District

N/W
DUCK ISLAND TO MADISON REEF (Chart 12374)

Clinton Harbor

No.	Name and location	Position	Characteristic	Height	Range	Structure	Remarks
22095	– Rock Buoy C West of rock.						White nun with orange bands worded ROCKS.
22100	– *Lighted Buoy 3*		Fl G 4s		4	Green.	Removed when endangered by ice.
22105	– **Radiobeacon**	41 16.0 72 31.2	**CL** (— • — • • — • •)		20		FREQ: 306 kHz, I, IV.

Channel buoys located 20 feet outside channel limit.

No.	Name and location	Position	Characteristic	Height	Range	Structure	Remarks
22110	– Channel Buoy 6					Red nun.	
22115	– Channel Buoy 7					Green can.	
22120	– Channel Buoy 8	41 15.8 72 31.5				Red nun.	
22125	– Channel Buoy 9					Green can.	
22130	– Channel Buoy 11					Green can.	
22135	– Channel Buoy 11A					Green can.	
22140	– Channel Buoy 12					Red nun.	Maintained from May 1 to Dec. 1. Private aid.
22145	– Channel Buoy 13					Green can.	Maintained from May 1 to Dec. 1. Private aid.
22150	– Channel Buoy 14					Red nun.	Maintained from May 1 to Dec. 1. Private aid.
22155	– Channel Buoy 16					Red nun.	Maintained from May 1 to Dec. 1. Private aid.

Hammonasset River

No.	Name and location	Position	Characteristic	Height	Range	Structure	Remarks
22156	– Daybeacon 1H	41 16.0 72 32.1				SG on pile.	Private aid.
22156.1	– Daybeacon 2H					TR on pile.	Private aid.
22156.2	– Daybeacon 3H					SG on pile.	Private aid.
22156.3	– Daybeacon 4H					TR on pile	Private aid.
22156.4	– Daybeacon 5H					SG on pile.	Private aid.
22156.5	– Daybeacon 6H					TR on pile.	Private aid.
22156.6	– Daybeacon 8H					TR on pile.	Private aid.
22156.7	– Daybeacon 9H					SG on pile.	Private aid.
22156.8	– Daybeacon 10H					TR on pile.	Private aid.
22156.9	– Daybeacon 11H					SG on pile.	Private aid.
22157	– Daybeacon 12H					TR on pile.	Private aid.
22157.1	– Daybeacon 13H					SG on pile.	Private aid.

(1) No.	(2) Name and location	(3) Position	(4) Characteristic	(5) Height	(6) Range	(7) Structure	(8) Remarks

N/W
DUCK ISLAND TO MADISON REEF (Chart 12374)

Hammonasset River

(1) No.	(2) Name and location	(3) Position	(4) Characteristic	(5) Height	(6) Range	(7) Structure	(8) Remarks
22157.2	– Daybeacon 14H					TR on pile.	Private aid.
22157.3	– Daybeacon 15H					SG on pile.	Private aid.
22157.4	– Daybeacon 16H					TR on pile.	Private aid.
22157.5	– Daybeacon 17H					SG on pile.	Private aid.
22157.6	– Daybeacon 18H					TR on pile.	Private aid.
22157.7	– Daybeacon 19H					SG on pile.	Private aid.
22157.8	– Daybeacon 21H					SG on pile.	Private aid.
22157.9	– Daybeacon 22H					TR on pile.	Private aid.
22158	– Daybeacon 23H					SG on pile.	Private aid.
22158.1	– Daybeacon 24H					TR on pile.	Private aid.
22158.2	– Daybeacon 25H					SG on pile.	Private aid.
22158.3	– Daybeacon 26H					TR on pile.	Private aid.
22158.4	– Daybeacon 27H					SG on pile.	Private aid.
22158.5	– Daybeacon 28H					TR on pile.	Private aid.
22158.6	– Daybeacon 29H					SG on pile.	Private aid.
22158.7	– Daybeacon 30H					TR on pile.	Private aid.
22158.8	– Daybeacon 31H					SG on pile.	Private aid.
22158.9	– Daybeacon 32H					TR on pile.	Private aid.
22159	– Daybeacon 33H					SG on pile.	Private aid.
22159.1	– Daybeacon 34H					TR on pile.	Private aid.
22159.2	– Daybeacon 35H					SG on pile.	Private aid.
22159.3	– Daybeacon 36H					TR on pile.	Private aid.
22159.4	– Daybeacon 37H					SG on pile.	Private aid.
22159.5	– Daybeacon 38H					TR on pile.	Private aid.
22159.6	– Daybeacon 39H					SG on pile.	Private aid.
22159.7	– Daybeacon 40H					TR on pile.	Private aid.
22159.8	– Daybeacon HR	41 15.9 72 32.8				Square daymark, green and red bands.	Private aid.

GUILFORD HARBOR TO FARM RIVER (Chart 12373)

Guilford Harbor

(1) No.	(2) Name and location	(3) Position	(4) Characteristic	(5) Height	(6) Range	(7) Structure	(8) Remarks
22160	– Lighted Bell Buoy 4	41 15.0 72 39.2	Fl R 4s		4	Red.	Replaced by nun when endangered by ice.
22165	Indian Reef Buoy 1 South of reef.	41 14.6 72 40.5				Green can.	
22170	– Buoy 3 On southeast side of Netties Reef.					Green can.	

LONG ISLAND SOUND (Connecticut) – First District

GUILFORD HARBOR TO FARM RIVER (Chart 12373) N/W

Guilford Harbor

(1) No.	(2) Name and location	(3) Position	(4) Characteristic	(5) Height	(6) Range	(7) Structure	(8) Remarks
22175	– Buoy 5 On east end of reef.					Green can.	
22180	– *Channel Lighted Buoy 7*		Fl G 4s		3	Green.	Removed when endangered by ice.
22185	– Channel Buoy 9					Green can.	
22190	– Channel Buoy 10					Red nun.	
22195	– Channel Buoy 11					Green can.	
22200	– Channel Buoy 12					Red nun.	
22205	– Channel Buoy 13					Green can.	
22210	– Channel Buoy 14					Red nun.	

West River Entrance

(1) No.	(2) Name and location	(3) Position	(4) Characteristic	(5) Height	(6) Range	(7) Structure	(8) Remarks
22211	– Buoy 1W	41 15.4 72 39.9				Green can.	Private aid.
22211.5	– Buoy 2W	41 15.4 72 39.9				Red nun.	Private aid.
22212	– Buoy 3					Green can.	Private aid.
22212.5	– Buoy 4					Red nun.	Private aid.
22213	– Buoy 5					Green can.	Private aid.
22213.5	– Buoy 6					Red nun.	Private aid.
22214	– Buoy 7					Green can.	Private aid.
22214.5	– Buoy 8					Red nun.	Private aid.
22214.6	WEST RIVER RANGE FRONT LIGHT	41 16.1 72 40.7	Q W	16		KRW on pole.	Visible on rangeline only. Private aid.
22214.7	WEST RIVER RANGE REAR LIGHT 215 yards, 321.3° from front light.		Fl W 6s	30		KRW on pile.	Visible on rangeline only. Private aid.

The Thimbles

Thimble Shoals

(1) No.	(2) Name and location	(3) Position	(4) Characteristic	(5) Height	(6) Range	(7) Structure	(8) Remarks
22215	– Buoy 4 At southwest edge of rocky shoal.					Red nun.	
22220	– Buoy 6					Red nun.	
22225	– Buoy 8					Red nun.	
22230	– Buoy 10					Red nun.	
22235	– Buoy 11 On east side of shoal.					Green can.	

Stony Creek

(1) No.	(2) Name and location	(3) Position	(4) Characteristic	(5) Height	(6) Range	(7) Structure	(8) Remarks
22240	– Buoy 1	41 15.6 72 45.7				Green can.	

(1) No.	(2) Name and location	(3) Position	(4) Characteristic	(5) Height	(6) Range	(7) Structure	(8) Remarks

N/W

GUILFORD HARBOR TO FARM RIVER (Chart 12373)

The Thimbles

Stony Creek

22245	– Buoy 3					Green can.	
22250	– Buoy 4					Red nun.	
22260	– Buoy 5	41 15.9 72 45.2				Green can.	

The Thimbles

22270	Commander Rocks Buoy 2CR Marks southwest end of rocks.					Red nun.	
22275	High Island East Shoal Buoy 1 South of shoal.					Green can.	
22280	East Reef Buoy 1 Marks east side of reef.	41 13.9 72 45.8				Green can.	
22285	Wheaton Reef Buoy 3 On north side of reef.					Green can.	
22290	Inner Reef North Buoy 5 Marks northeast side of rock.	41 14.5 72 46.1				Green can.	
22295	Gangway Rock Buoy 1 Marks southeast side of rock.					Green can.	
22300	Northwest Reef Buoy 2NW Marks southwest side of reef.					Red nun.	
22305	Hookers Rock Buoy 3 Southeast side of rock.					Green can.	
22310	Inner Reef South Buoy 4 Marks southwest end of reef.					Red nun.	
22315	*Pine Orchard Approach Lighted Buoy 4A* Southeast of Hookers Rock.		Fl R 4s		4	Red.	Replaced by nun when endangered by ice.
22320	Pork Rocks Buoy 5 East of rocks.					Green can.	
22325	Dick Rocks Buoy 6 West of rocks.					Red nun.	
22330	*Pine Orchard Approach Lighted Buoy 8* Marks southwest edge of rocks.	41 15.3 72 46.2	Fl R 4s		4	Red.	Removed when endangered by ice.

Duck Island Roads

22342	JUNIPER POINT OBSTRUCTION LIGHTS (3)	41 15.8 72 46.0	Q Y	11		On dolphins.	Private aids.

LONG ISLAND SOUND (Connecticut) – First District

N/W
GUILFORD HARBOR TO FARM RIVER (Chart 12373)

Duck Island Roads

22345	QUARRY RANGE FRONT LIGHT	41 15.9 72 46.0	F R	20		Daymark consists of white arrows, vertically arranged.	Private aid.
22350	QUARRY RANGE MIDDLE LIGHT 40 yards, 028° from front light.		F R	27		Daymark consists of white arrows, vertically arranged.	Private aid.
22355	Quarry Range Rear Daybeacon					White diamond daymark with red center ball on skeleton structure.	Private aid.

Branford Harbor

22360	*Blyn Rock Lighted Buoy 2* On south side of rock.	41 14.8 72 49.9	Fl R 4s		3	Red.	Removed when endangered by ice.
22365	Bird Rock Buoy 4 On west side of reef.					Red nun.	
22370	Lovers Island Rock Buoy 5 East of rock.					Green can.	
22375	Little Mermaid Rock Buoy 6 West of rock.					Red nun.	
22380	BIG MERMAID LIGHT 7	41 15.4 72 49.7	Fl G 4s	28	5	SG on skeleton tower.	Higher intensity beam up and down channel.

Farm River

22385	– Approach Buoy 1					Green can.	
22390	– Approach Buoy 2					Red nun.	

NEW HAVEN HARBOR (Chart 12371)

New Haven Harbor

22395	– East Entrance Buoy 1 On northeast side of shoal.	41 14.2 72 53.7				Green can.	
22400	– East Entrance Buoy 2 On southwest side of shoal.					Red nun.	
22405	– East Entrance Buoy 4 On southwest side of shoal.					Red nun.	
22410	– East Entrance Buoy 5 On northeast end of Old Head Reef.					Green can.	
22415	Adams Fall Buoy A On southwest side of shoal.					Red and green bands; nun.	
22420	– East Entrance Channel Buoy 6 On southwest end of Lighthouse Point Shoal.					Red nun.	
22425 19965	– *Lighted Whistle Buoy NH*	41 12.1 72 53.8	**Mo (A) W**		6	Red and white stripes with red spherical topmark.	

(1) No.	(2) Name and location	(3) Position	(4) Characteristic	(5) Height	(6) Range	(7) Structure	(8) Remarks
	LONG ISLAND SOUND (Connecticut) – First District						
	NEW HAVEN HARBOR (Chart 12371)	N/W					
	New Haven Harbor						
22430	– OUTER CHANNEL RANGE FRONT LIGHT	41 15.7 72 56.1	F G	35		White skeleton tower with concrete base.	Higher intensity on rangeline.
22435	– OUTER CHANNEL RANGE REAR LIGHT 800 yards, 333.6° from front light.		F G	65		White skeleton tower with concrete base.	Higher intensity on rangeline.
22440	– *Channel Lighted Gong Buoy 1*		Fl G 2.5s		4	Green.	
22445	– Buoy 2					Red nun.	
22450	– Buoy 3					Green can.	
22455	– *Channel Lighted Buoy 4*	41 13.7 70 54.7	Fl R 4s		4	Red.	
22460	– *Channel Lighted Bell Buoy 6*		Fl R 2.5s		4	Red.	Replaced by LIB of reduced intensity when endangered by ice.
22465	– *Channel Lighted Buoy 7*		Fl G 2.5s		4	Green.	Replaced by smaller LIB of reduced intensity when endangered by ice.
22470 19970	**Southwest Ledge Light**	41 14.1 72 54.7	Fl R 5s	57	13	White octagonal house on cylindrical pier.	HORN: 1 blast ev 15s (2s bl). Emergency light of reduced intensity when main light is extinguished.
22475	NEW HAVEN MIDDLE BREAKWATER EAST END LIGHT		Fl G 4s	43	4	NG on skeleton tower.	
22480	NEW HAVEN MIDDLE BREAKWATER WEST END LIGHT		Fl R 4s	38	4	NR on skeleton tower.	
22485 19975	NEW HAVEN LIGHT	41 13.3 72 56.6	Fl W 4s	35	7	NG on skeleton tower.	
22490	NEW HAVEN WEST BREAKWATER WEST END LIGHT 2	41 13.5 72 57.4	Fl R 6s	29	4	TR on skeleton tower.	
22495	– *Channel Lighted Buoy 8*		Q R		4	Red.	Replaced by smaller LIB of reduced intensity when endangered by ice.
22500	– *Channel Lighted Buoy 9*		Fl G 4s		4	Green.	Replaced by can when endangered by ice.
22505	– Channel Buoy 9A					Green can.	
22510	– Channel Buoy 10					Red nun.	
22515	– *Channel Lighted Buoy 10A*		Fl R 2.5s		4	Red.	Replaced by smaller LIB of reduced intensity when endangered by ice.
22520	– Channel Buoy 12					Red nun.	
22525	– *Channel Lighted Buoy 11*		Fl G 4s		4	Green.	Replaced by can when endangered by ice.
22530	– Channel Buoy 13					Green can.	

(1) No.	(2) Name and location	(3) Position	(4) Characteristic	(5) Height	(6) Range	(7) Structure	(8) Remarks

N/W

HEMPSTEAD HARBOR TO TALLMAN ISLAND
(Chart 12366)

City Island

Hutchinson River

No.	Name and location	Position	Characteristic	Height	Range	Structure	Remarks
24440	– Buoy 6					Red nun.	
24445	– Buoy 7					Green can.	

PORT JEFFERSON AND MOUNT SINAI HARBORS
(Chart 12362)

Mount Sinai Harbor

No.	Name and location	Position	Characteristic	Height	Range	Structure	Remarks
24460	Mount Sinai Approach Buoy M					Red and white stripes; sphere.	
24465	MOUNT SINAI BREAKWATER LIGHT	40 57.9 73 02.6	Fl G 5ˢ	20		Concrete pedestal.	Private aid.
24470	– West Breakwater Daybeacon 2	40 57.9 73 02.7				TR on pile.	Private aid.
24475	– Buoy 1					Black can.	Private aid.
24480	– Buoy 2A					Red nun.	Private aid.
24485	– Buoy 3					Black can.	Private aid.
24490	– Buoy 4					Red nun.	Private aid.
24495	– Buoy 5					Black can.	Private aid.
24500	– Buoy 6					Red nun.	Private aid.
24505	– Buoy 8					Red nun.	Private aid.
24510	– Buoy 10					Red nun.	Private aid.
24515	– Buoy 12					Red nun.	Private aid.

Port Jefferson Harbor

No.	Name and location	Position	Characteristic	Height	Range	Structure	Remarks
24520	Port Jefferson Approach Lighted Whistle Buoy PJ	40 59.3 73 06.4	Mo (A) W		5	Red and white stripes with red spherical topmark.	
24525	– Entrance Lighted Buoy 1	40 58.4 73 05.6	Fl G 2.5ˢ		4	Green.	
24530	PORT JEFFERSON EAST BREAKWATER LIGHT	40 58.3 73 05.5	Fl W 4ˢ	35	7	NG on skeleton tower.	
24535	– Entrance Lighted Bell Buoy 2		Fl R 2.5ˢ		4	Red.	
24540	PORT JEFFERSON WEST BREAKWATER LIGHT 2A		Fl R 4ˢ	26	5	TR on skeleton tower.	
24545	LIGHTING COMPANY BOOM LIGHT		F R	71			Private aid.
24550	– RANGE FRONT LIGHT	40 56.9 73 04.3	Q R	20		KRW on pile.	
24555	– RANGE REAR LIGHT 225 yards, 146° from front light.		F R	32		KRW on pile.	
24560	– Buoy 4					Red nun.	

(1) No.	(2) Name and location	(3) Position	(4) Characteristic	(5) Height	(6) Range	(7) Structure	(8) Remarks

N/W

PORT JEFFERSON AND MOUNT SINAI HARBORS
(Chart 12362)

Port Jefferson Harbor

24565	– Lighted Bell Buoy 5		Fl G 4s		3	Green.	
24566	– Buoy 7					Green can.	
24567	– Buoy 8					Red nun.	
24568	– Buoy 9					Green can.	

Setauket Harbor

24570	– Anchorage Buoy A					Yellow nun.	Maintained from May 1 to Nov. 1. Private aid.
24575	– Anchorage Buoy B					Yellow nun.	Maintained from May 1 to Nov. 1. Private aid.
24580	– Anchorage Buoy C					Yellow nun.	Maintained from May 1 to Nov. 1. Private aid.
24585	– Buoy 1					Green can.	Maintained from May 1 to Nov. 1. Private aid.
24590	– Buoy 2					Red nun.	Maintained from May 1 to Nov. 1. Private aid.
24595	– Buoy 3					Green can.	Maintained from May 1 to Nov. 1. Private aid.
24600	– Buoy 4					Red nun.	Maintained from May 1 to Nov. 1. Private aid.
24605	– Buoy 5					Green can.	Maintained from May 1 to Nov. 1. Private aid.
24610	– Buoy 6					Red nun.	Maintained from May 1 to Nov. 1. Private aid.

LONG ISLAND SOUND (Western Part) (Chart 12363)

Smithtown Bay

24615	Stony Brook Harbor Entrance Lighted Buoy 1	40 56.3 73 09.8	Fl G 4s		4	Green.	Replaced by can from Dec. 15 to Mar. 15.
24620	Stony Brook Harbor Daybeacon	40 55.6 73 08.9				On pile.	Maintained from June 1 to Oct. 1. Private aid.

Porpoise Channel

24625	– Lighted Buoy 1		Fl G 4s			Green.	Maintained from Apr. 1 to Nov. 1. Private aid.
24630	– Lighted Buoy 2		Fl R 4s			Red.	Maintained from Apr. 1 to Nov. 1. Private aid.

(1) No.	(2) Name and location	(3) Position	(4) Characteristic	(5) Height	(6) Range	(7) Structure	(8) Remarks

NEW YORK – First District

TALLMAN ISLAND TO QUEENSBORO BRIDGE
(Chart 12339)

South Brother Island Channel

(1) No.	(2) Name and location	(3) Position	(4) Characteristic	(5) Height	(6) Range	(7) Structure	(8) Remarks
26015	– Lighted Buoy 3	40 47.8 73 53.6	Fl G 4ˢ		4	Green.	
26020	– Buoy 4	40 47.6 73 53.7				Red nun.	
26025	– Lighted Buoy 5	40 47.6 73 53.6	Fl G 6ˢ		4	Green.	
26030	– Lighted Buoy 7		Fl G 2.5ˢ		4	Green.	
26035	Rikers Island Basin Junction Lighted Buoy RI	40 47.3 73 53.7	Fl (2+1) R 6ˢ		4	Red and green bands.	
26040	– Buoy 9					Green can.	
26045	STEINWAY CREEK WHARF LIGHT	40 47.1 73 53.8	F R	20			Private aid.

Rikers Island Channel

(1) No.	(2) Name and location	(3) Position	(4) Characteristic	(5) Height	(6) Range	(7) Structure	(8) Remarks
26050	LAWRENCE POINT LEDGE LIGHT LP On ledge.		Fl W 4ˢ	25	5	NR on skeleton tower.	
26055	Lawrence Point Ledge Buoy 2					Red nun.	
26060	SOUTH BROTHER ISLAND LEDGE LIGHT 3 On ledge.		Fl G 4ˢ	17	5	SG on skeleton tower.	

BLOCK ISLAND SOUND AND GARDINERS BAY
(Chart 13209)

North Entrance

(1) No.	(2) Name and location	(3) Position	(4) Characteristic	(5) Height	(6) Range	(7) Structure	(8) Remarks
26065	Gardiners Island Shoal Buoy 1	41 07.3 72 06.7				Green can.	
26070	Constellation Rock Buoy 2 Marks 17-foot rock.	41 10.5 72 06.6				Red nun.	
26075	Gardiners Island Lighted Gong Buoy 1GI	41 09.0 72 08.9	Fl G 4ˢ		4	Green.	
26080	Plum Island Rock Buoy 4 On south side of rock.					Red nun.	

Plum Gut

(1) No.	(2) Name and location	(3) Position	(4) Characteristic	(5) Height	(6) Range	(7) Structure	(8) Remarks
26085	Midway Shoal Buoy MS On east side of shoal.	41 09.8 72 12.6				Green and red bands; can.	
26090 19860	**Orient Point Light**	41 09.8 72 13.4	Fl W 5ˢ	64	17	Black conical tower with white band in center.	HORN: 2 blasts ev 30ˢ (2ˢ bl-2ˢ si-2ˢ bl-24ˢ si). Emergency light of reduced intensity when main light is extinguished. Lighted throughout 24 hours.
26095	PLUM ISLAND HARBOR EAST DOLPHIN LIGHT		F R	10	6	On dolphin.	Maintained from sundown to 0130 daily. Maintained by the U.S. Dept. of Agriculture.

(1) No.	(2) Name and location	(3) Position	(4) Characteristic	(5) Height	(6) Range	(7) Structure	(8) Remarks
		N/W					
	BLOCK ISLAND SOUND AND GARDINERS BAY (Chart 13209)						
	North Entrance						
	Plum Gut						
26100	PLUM ISLAND HARBOR WEST DOLPHIN LIGHT	41 10.3 72 12.4	F G	12	6	On dolphin.	HORN: 1 blast ev 10ˢ (5ˢ bl). Sounded occasionally when USDA vessels are navigating in the area. Maintained from sundown to 0130 daily. Maintained by the U.S. Dept. Agriculture.
26105 19855	– LIGHT	41 10.4 72 12.7	Fl W 2.5ˢ	55	5	On brick shed.	
26110 19850	– Lighted Bell Buoy 2PG		Fl R 4ˢ		4	Red.	
	North Entrance						
26115	CAR FERRY LIGHT	41 09.3 72 14.4	F W	18		On dolphin.	Private aid.
	Research Basin						
	Aids are maintained by the U.S. Dept. of Agiculture.						
26120	– APPROACH LIGHT	41 08.9 72 14.5	Fl G 4ˢ	14		On pile.	Maintained from sundown to 0130 daily.
26125	– Bay Daybeacon 1					On piles.	
26130	– Bay Daybeacon 3					On piles.	
26135	– LIGHT	41 09.2 72 14.5	F R	10		On pile.	HORN: 1 blast ev 30ˢ (1ˢ bl). Maintained from sundown to 0130 daily.
	Gardiners Bay South Entrance						
26140	– Lighted Bell Buoy S	41 02.2 72 03.1	Mo (A) W		6	Red and white stripes with red spherical topmark. .	Replaced by red and white striped sphere from Nov. 15 to Apr. 15.
26145	– Buoy 2					Red nun.	
26147	NAPEAGUE HARBOR CLAM RAFT LIGHT		Fl W 2.5ˢ			NW on raft.	Maintained from May 1 to Nov. 30. Private aid.
26150	– Buoy 4					Red nun.	
26155	– Buoy 6					Red nun.	
26160	– Buoy 8					Red nun.	
26165	– Buoy 11					Green can.	
26170	Lionhead Rock Buoy 13					Green can.	
26175	Crow Shoal Buoy 14 Southwest of shoal.					Red nun.	
	Threemile Harbor						
26180	– Entrance Lighted Bell Buoy TM	41 02.7 72 11.3	Mo (A) W		6	Red and white stripes with red spherical topmark.	Replaced by red and white striped sphere from Nov. 15 to Apr. 15.

PART 1 - SECTION B

COAST PILOT 2

Atlantic Coast

covering

BLOCK ISLAND SOUND+EASTERN LONG ISLAND SOUND

including

general information and appendix

contents found on page vii

United States Coast Pilot

2

Atlantic Coast: Cape Cod to Sandy Hook

U.S. DEPARTMENT OF COMMERCE
Barbara Hackman Franklin, Secretary

National Oceanic and Atmospheric Administration (NOAA)
Dr. John A. Knauss, Under Secretary of Commerce for Oceans
and Atmosphere, and Administrator, NOAA

National Ocean Service
W. Stanley Wilson, Assistant Administrator for Ocean Services
and Coastal Zone Management

Washington, DC
For sale by the National Ocean Service and its sales agents.

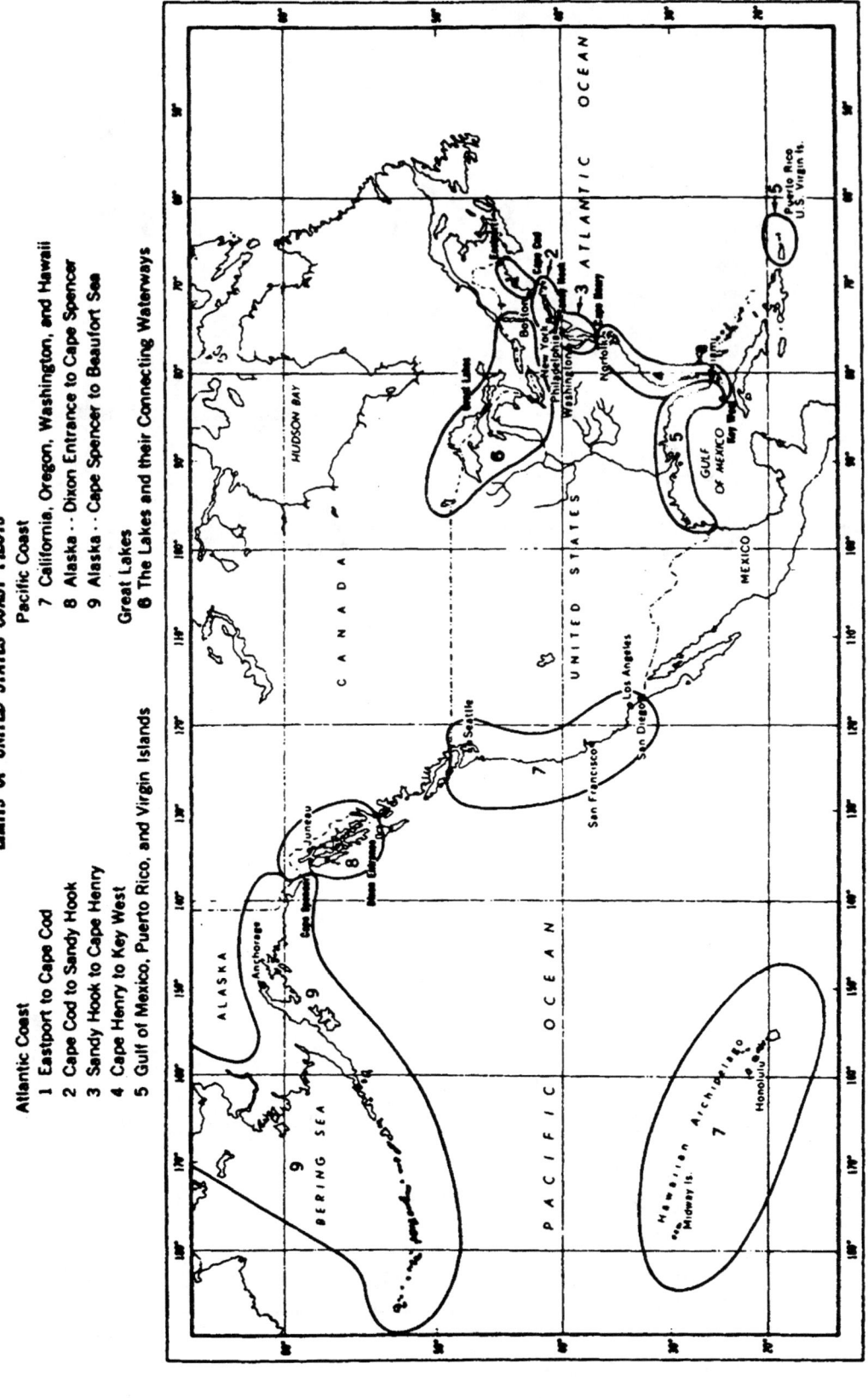

LIMITS OF UNITED STATES COAST PILOTS

Atlantic Coast
1 Eastport to Cape Cod
2 Cape Cod to Sandy Hook
3 Sandy Hook to Cape Henry
4 Cape Henry to Key West
5 Gulf of Mexico, Puerto Rico, and Virgin Islands

Pacific Coast
7 California, Oregon, Washington, and Hawaii
8 Alaska - - Dixon Entrance to Cape Spencer
9 Alaska - - Cape Spencer to Beaufort Sea

Great Lakes
6 The Lakes and their Connecting Waterways

Preface

The United States Coast Pilot is published by the National Ocean Service (NOS), Charting and Geodetic Services (C&GS), National Oceanic and Atmospheric Administration (NOAA), pursuant to the Act of 6 August 1947 (33 U.S.C. 883a and b) and the Act of 22 October 1968 (44 U.S.C. 1310).

The Coast Pilot supplements the navigational information shown on the nautical charts. The sources for updating the Coast Pilot include, but are not limited to, field inspections conducted by NOAA, information published in Notices to Mariners, reports from NOAA Hydrographic vessels and field parties, information from other Government agencies, State and local governments, maritime and pilotage associations, port authorities, and mariners.

This volume of Coast Pilot 2, Atlantic Coast, Cape Cod to Sandy Hook, cancels the 1991 (25th) Edition.

Notice.-Amendments are issued to this publication through U.S. Coast Guard Local Notices to Mariners. A subscription to the Local Notice to Mariners is available upon application to the appropriate Coast Guard District Commander (Aids to Navigation Branch). Consult appendix for address. All amendments are also issued in Defense Mapping Agency Notices to Mariners.

Mariners and others are urged to report promptly to the National Ocean Service errors, omissions, or any conditions found to differ from or to be additional to those published in the Coast Pilot or shown on the charts in order that they may be fully investigated and proper corrections made. A Coast Pilot Report form is included in the back of this book and a Marine Information Report form is published in the Defense Mapping Agency Hydrographic/Topographic Center Notice to Mariners for your convenience. These reports and/or suggestions for increasing the usefulness of the Coast Pilot should be sent to

Director,
Coast and Geodetic Survey (N/CG 2211),
National Ocean Service, NOAA,
Rockville, MD 20852-3806.

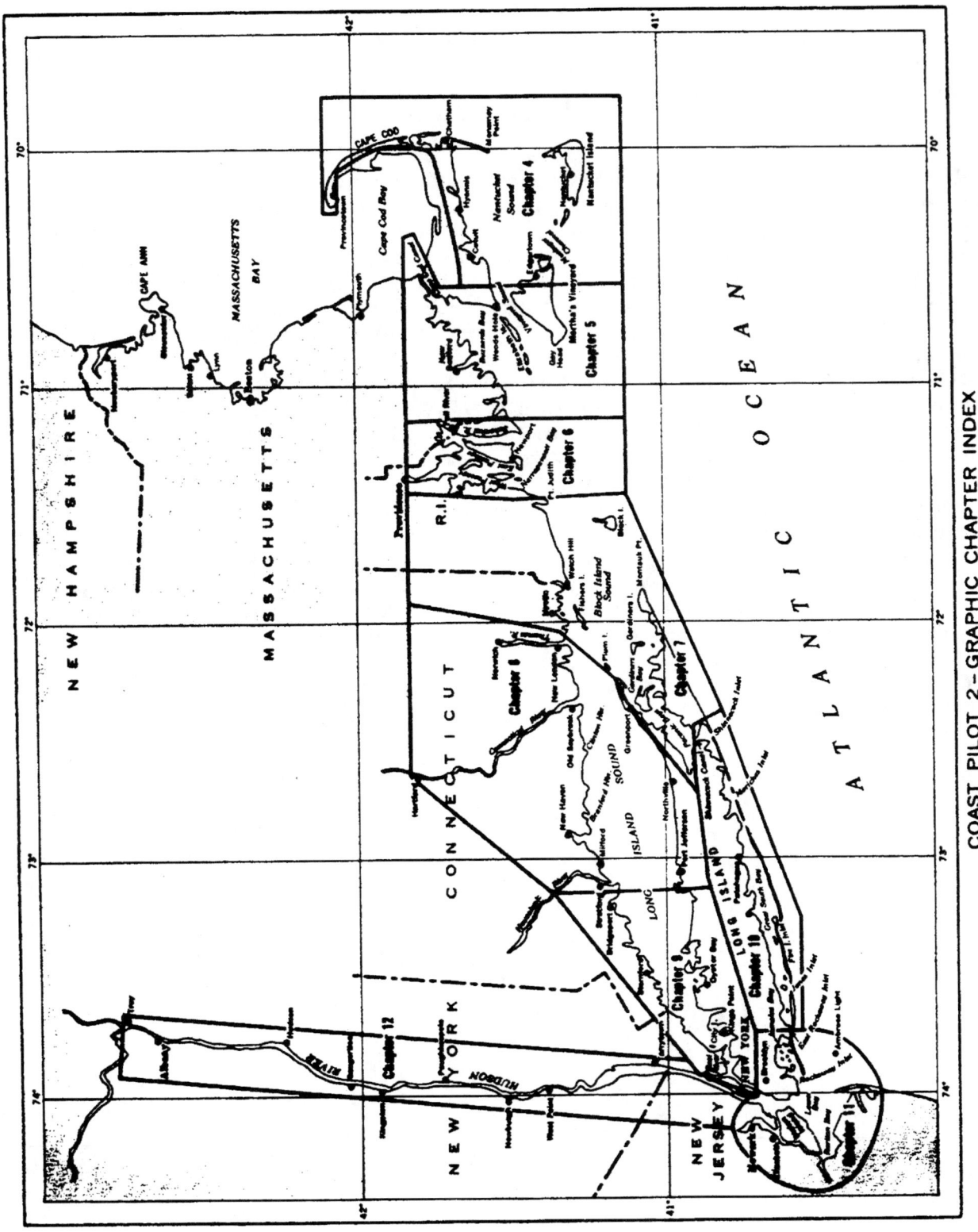

COAST PILOT 2 – GRAPHIC CHAPTER INDEX

IV

Contents

1. GENERAL INFORMATION

(1) **The UNITED STATES COAST PILOT.**–The National Ocean Service Coast Pilot is a series of nine nautical books that cover a wide variety of information important to navigators of U.S. coastal and intracoastal waters, and the waters of the Great Lakes. Most of this book information cannot be shown graphically on the standard nautical charts and is not readily available elsewhere. The subjects in the Coast Pilot include, but are not limited to, channel descriptions, anchorages, bridge and cable clearances, currents, tide and water levels, prominent features, pilotage, towage, weather, ice conditions, wharf descriptions, dangers, routes, traffic separation schemes, small-craft facilities, and Federal regulations applicable to navigation.

(2) **Notice-Amendments are issued to this publication through U.S. Coast Guard Local Notices to Mariners. A subscription to the Local Notice to Mariners is available upon application to the appropriate Coast Guard District Commander (Aids to Navigation Branch). Consult appendix for address. All amendments are also issued in Defense Mapping Agency Notices to Mariners.**

(3) **Bearings.**–These are true, and when given in degrees are clockwise from 000°(north) to 359°. Light-sector bearings are toward the light.

(4) **Bridges and cables.**–Vertical clearances of bridges and overhead cables are in feet above mean high water unless otherwise stated; clearances of drawbridges are for the closed position, although the open clearances are also given for vertical-lift bridges. Clearances given in the Coast Pilot are those approved for nautical charting, and are supplied by the U.S. Coast Guard (bridges) and U.S. Army Corps of Engineers (cables); they may be as-built (verified by actual inspection after completion of structures) or authorized (design values specified in permit issued prior to construction). No differentiation is made in the Coast Pilot between as-built and authorized clearances. (See charts for horizontal clearances of bridges, as these are given in the Coast Pilot only when they are less than 50 feet.) Submarine cables are rarely mentioned.

(5) **Cable ferries.**–Cable ferries are guided by cables fastened to shore and sometimes propelled by a cable rig attached to the shore. Generally, the cables are suspended during crossings and dropped to the bottom when the ferries dock. Where specific operating procedures are known they are mentioned in the text. Since operating procedures vary, mariners are advised to exercise extreme caution and seek local knowledge. **DO NOT ATTEMPT TO PASS A MOVING CABLE FERRY.**

(6) **Courses.**–These are true and are given in degrees clockwise from 000°(north) to 359°. The courses given are the courses to be made good.

(7) **Currents.**–Stated current velocities are the averages at strength. Velocities are in knots, which are nautical miles per hour. Directions are the true directions to which the currents set.

(8) **Depths.**–Depth is the vertical distance from the chart datum to the bottom and is expressed in the same units (feet, meters or fathoms) as soundings on the applicable chart. (See Chart Datum this chapter for further detail.) The **controlling depth** of a channel is the least depth within the limits of the channel; it restricts the safe use of the channel to drafts of less than that depth. The **centerline controlling depth** of a channel applies only to the channel centerline;

lesser depths may exist in the remainder of the channel. The **midchannel controlling depth** of a channel is the controlling depth of only the middle half of the channel. **Federal project depth** is the design dredging depth of a channel constructed by the Corps of Engineers, U.S. Army; the project depth may or may not be the goal of maintenance dredging after completion of the channel, and, for this reason, project depth must not be confused with controlling depth. **Depths alongside wharves** usually have been reported by owners and/or operators of the waterfront facilities, and have not been verified by Government surveys; since these depths may be subject to change, local authorities should be consulted for the latest controlling depths.

(9) In general, the Coast Pilot gives the project depths for deep-draft ship channels maintained by the Corps of Engineers. The latest controlling depths are usually shown on the charts and published in the Notices to Mariners. For other channels, the latest controlling depths available at the time of publication are given. **In all cases, however, mariners are advised to consult with pilots, port and local authorities, and Federal and State authorities for the latest channel controlling depths.**

(10) **Under-keel clearances.**–It is becoming increasingly evident that economic pressures are causing mariners to navigate through waters of barely adequate depth, with under-keel clearances being finely assessed from the charted depths, predicted tide levels, and depths recorded by echo sounders.

(11) It cannot be too strongly emphasized that even charts based on modern surveys may not show all sea-bed obstructions or the shoalest depths, and actual tide levels may be appreciably lower than those predicted.

(12) In many ships an appreciable correction must be applied to shoal soundings recorded by echo sounders due to the horizontal distance between the transducers. This separation corection, which is the amount by which recorded depths therefore exceed true depths, increases with decreasing depths to a maximum equal to half the distance apart of the transducers; at this maximum the transducers are aground. Ships whose transducers are more than 6 feet apart should construct a table of true and recorded depths using the Traverse Tables. (Refer to discussion of echo soundings elsewhere in chapter 1.)

(13) Other appreciable corrections, which must be applied to many ships, are for settlement and squat. These corrections depend on the depth of water below the keel, the hull form and speed of the ship.

(14) Settlement causes the water level around the ship to be lower than would otherwise be the case. It will always cause echo soundings to be less than they would otherwise be. Settlement is appreciable when the depth is less than seven times the draft of the ship, and increases as the depth decreases and the speed increases.

(15) Squat denotes a change in trim of a ship underway, relative to her trim when stopped. It usually causes the stern of a vessel to sit deeper in the water. However, it is reported that in the case of mammoth ships squat causes the bow to sit deeper. Depending on the location of the echo sounding transducers, this may cause the recorded depth to be greater or less than it ought to be. **Caution and common sense are continuing requirements for safe navigation.**

1

(16) **Distances.**–These are in nautical miles unless otherwise stated. A nautical mile is one minute of latitude, or approximately 2,000 yards, and is about 1.15 statute miles.

(17) **Heights.**–These are in feet above the tidal datum used for that purpose on the charts, usually mean high water. However, the heights of the decks of piers and wharves are given in feet above the chart datum for depths.

(18) **Light and fog signal characteristics.** These are not described, and light sectors and visible ranges are normally not defined. (See Coast Guard Light Lists.)

(19) **Obstructions.**–Wrecks and other obstructions are mentioned only if of a relatively permanent nature and in or near normal traffic routes.

(20) **Radio aids to navigation.**–These are seldom described. (See Coast Guard Light Lists and Defense Mapping Agency Radio Navigational Aids.)

(21) **Ranges.**–These are not fully described. "A 339° Range" means that the rear structure bears 339° from the front structure. (See Coast Guard Light Lists.)

(22) **Reported information.**–Information received by NOS from various sources concerning depths, dangers, currents, facilities, and other subjects, which has not been verified by Government surveys or inspections, is often included in the Coast Pilot; such **unverified information** is qualified as "reported," and should be regarded with caution.

(23) **Time.**–Unless otherwise stated, all times are given in local standard time in the 24-hour system. (Noon is 1200, 2:00 p.m. is 1400, and midnight is 0000.)

(24) **Winds.**–Directions are the true directions from which the winds blow. Unless otherwise indicated, speeds are given in knots, which are nautical miles per hour.

NOTICES TO MARINERS

(25) Notices to Mariners are published by Federal agencies to advise operators of vessels of marine information affecting the safety of navigation. The notices include changes in aids to navigation, depths in channels, bridge and overhead cable clearances, reported dangers, and other useful marine information. They should be used routinely for updating the latest editions of nautical charts and related publications.

(26) **Local Notice to Mariners** is issued by each Coast Guard District Commander for the waters under his jurisdiction. (See appendix for Coast Guard district(s) covered by this volume.) These notices are usually published weekly and may be obtained without cost by making application to the appropriate District Commander.

(27) **Notice to Mariners,** published weekly by the Defense Mapping Agency Hydrographic/Topographic Center, is prepared jointly with NOS and the Coast Guard. These notices contain selected items from the Local Notices to Mariners and other reported marine information required by oceangoing vessels operating in both **foreign** and **domestic** waters. Special items covering a variety of subjects and generally not discussed in the Coast Pilot or shown on nautical charts are published annually in Notice to Mariners No. 1. These items are important to the mariner and should be read for future reference. These notices may be obtained by operators or oceangoing vessels, without cost by making application to **Defense Mapping Agency** (see Defense Mapping Agency Procurement Information in appendix).

(28) Notices and reports of **improved channel depths** are also published by district offices of the Corps of Engineers,

U.S. Army (see appendix for districts covered by this volume). Although information from these notices/reports affecting NOS charts and related publications is usually published in the Notices to Mariners, the local district engineer office should be consulted where depth information is critical.

(29) **Marine Broadcast Notices to Mariners** are made by the Coast Guard through Coast Guard, Navy, and some commercial radio stations to report deficiencies and important changes in aids to navigation. (See Radio Navigation Warnings and Weather, this chapter.)

(30) Vessels operating within the limits of the Coast Guard districts can obtain information affecting NOS charts and related publications from the Local Notices to Mariners. Small craft using the Intracoastal Waterway and other waterways and small harbors within the United States that are not normally used by oceangoing vessels will require the Local Notices to Mariners to keep charts and related publications up-to-date. Information for oceangoing vessels can be obtained from the Notice to Mariners published by the Defense Mapping Agency Hydrographic/Topographic Center.

(31) Notices to Mariners may be consulted at Coast Guard district offices, NOS field offices, Defense Mapping Agency Hydrographic/Topographic Center offices and depots, most local marine facilities, and sales agents handling charts and related publications.

U.S. GOVERNMENT AGENCIES PROVIDING MARITIME SERVICES

(32) **Animal and Plant Health Inspection Service,** Department of Agriculture.–The Agricultural Quarantine Inspection Program and Animal Health Programs of this organization are responsible for protecting the Nation's animal population, food and fiber crops, and forests from invasion by foreign pests. They administer agricultural quarantine and restrictive orders issued under authority provided in various acts of Congress. The regulations prohibit or restrict the importation or interstate movement of live animals, meats, animal products, plants, plant products, soil, injurious insects, and associated items that may introduce or spread plant pests and animal diseases which may be new to or not widely distributed within the United States or its territories. Inspectors examine imports at ports of entry as well as the vessel, its stores, and crew or passenger baggage.

(33) The Service also provides an inspection and certification service for exporters to assist them in meeting the quarantine requirements of foreign countries. (See appendix for a list of ports where agricultural inspectors are located and inspections conducted.)

(34) **Customs Service,** Department of the Treasury.–The U.S. Customs Service administers certain laws relating to: entry and clearance of vessels and permits for certain vessel movements between points in the United States; prohibitions against coastwise transportation of passengers and merchandise; salvage, dredging and towing by foreign vessels; certain activities of vessels in the fishing trade; regular and special tonnage taxes on vessels; the landing and delivery of foreign merchandise (including unlading, appraisement, lighterage, drayage, warehousing, and shipment in bond); collection of customs duties, including duty on imported pleasure boats and yachts and 50% duty on foreign repairs to American vessels engaged in trade; customs treatment of sea and ship's stores while in port and the baggage of crewmen and passengers; illegally imported merchandise;

and remission of penalties or forfeiture if customs or navigation laws have been violated. The Customs Service also cooperates with many other Federal agencies in the enforcement of statutes they are responsible for. Customs districts and ports of entry, including customs stations, are listed in the appendix.

(35) The Customs Service may issue, without charge, a **cruising license,** valid for a period of up to 6 months and for designated U.S. waters, to a yacht of a foreign country which has a reciprocal agreement with the United States. A foreign yacht holding a cruising license may cruise in the designated U.S. waters and arrive at and depart from U.S. ports without entering or clearing at the customhouse, filing manifests, or obtaining or delivering permits to proceed, provided it does not engage in trade or violate the laws of the United States or visit a vessel not yet inspected by a Customs Agent and does, within 24 hours of arrival at each port or place in the United States, report the fact of arrival to the nearest customhouse. Countries which have reciprocal agreements granting these privileges to U.S. yachts are Argentina, Australia, Bahama Islands, Bermuda, Canada, Federal Republic of Germany, Great Britain, Greece, Honduras, Jamaica, Liberia, the Netherlands, and New Zealand. Further information concerning cruising licenses may be obtained from the headquarters port for the customs district in which the license is desired. U.S. yacht owners planning cruises to foreign ports may contact the nearest customs district headquarters as to customs requirements.

(36) **National Ocean Service** (NOS), National Oceanic and Atmospheric Administration (NOAA), Department of Commerce.–The National Ocean Service provides charts and related publications for the safe navigation of marine and air commerce, and provides basic data for engineering and scientific purposes and for other commercial and industrial needs. The principal facilities of NOS are located in Rockville, Md.; in Norfolk, Va. (Atlantic Marine Center); and in Seattle, Wash. (Pacific Marine Center). NOAA ships are based at the marine centers. These offices maintain files of charts and other publications which are available for the use of the mariners, who are invited to avail themselves of the facilities afforded. (See appendix for addresses.)

(37) **Sales agents** for Charts, the Coast Pilot, Tide Tables, Tidal and Current Tables, Tidal Current Diagrams, and Tidal Current Charts of the National Ocean Service are located in many U.S. ports and in some foreign ports. A list of authorized sales agents and chart catalogs may be had free upon request from National Ocean Service, Distribution Branch (N/CG33). (See appendix for address.)

(38) **Nautical charts** are published primarily for the use of the mariner, but serve the public interest in many other ways. They are compiled principally from NOS basic field surveys, supplemented by data from other Government organizations.

(39) **Tide Tables** are issued annually by NOS in advance of the year for which they are prepared. These tables include predicted times and heights of high and low waters for every day in the year for a number of reference stations and differences for obtaining similar predictions for numerous other places. They also include other useful information such as a method of obtaining heights of tide at any time, local mean time of sunrise and sunset for various latitudes, reduction of local mean time to standard time, and time of moonrise and moonset for various ports.

(40) **Caution.**–In using the Tide Tables, slack water should not be confused with high or low water. For ocean stations there is usually little difference between the time of

high or low water and the beginning of ebb or flood currents; but for places in narrow channels, landlocked harbors, or on tidal rivers, the time of slack current may differ by several hours from the time of high or low water. The relation of the times of high or low water to the turning of the current depends upon a number of factors, so that no simple general rule can be given. (To obtain the times of slack water, refer to the Tidal Current Tables.)

(41) **Tidal Current Tables** for the coasts of the United States are issued annually by NOS in advance of the year for which they are prepared. These tables include daily predictions of the times of slack water and the times and velocities of strength of flood and ebb currents for a number of waterways, together with differences for obtaining predictions for numerous other places. Also included is other useful information such as a method for obtaining the velocity of current at any time, duration of slack, coastal tidal currents, wind currents, combination of currents, and current diagrams. Some information on the Gulf Stream is included in the tables for the Atlantic coast.

(42) **Tidal Current Charts** are published by NOS for various localities. These charts depict the direction and velocity of the current for each hour of the tidal cycle. They present a comprehensive view of the tidal current movement in the respective waterways as a whole and when used with the proper current tables or tide tables supply a means for readily determining for any time the direction and velocity of the current at various localities throughout the areas covered.

(43) **Tidal Current Diagrams,** published annually by NOS, are a series of 12 monthly computer constructed diagrams used in conjunction with the Tidal Current Charts for a particular area. The diagrams present an alternate but more simplified method for calculating the speed and direction of the tidal currents in bays, estuaries, and harbors.

(44) **Coast Guard,** Department of Transportation.–The Coast Guard has among its duties the enforcement of the laws of the United States on the high seas and in coastal and inland waters of the U.S. and its possessions; enforcement of navigation and neutrality laws and regulations; establishment and enforcement of navigational regulations upon the Inland Waters of the United States, including the establishment of a demarcation line separating the high seas from waters upon which U.S. navigational rules apply; administration of the Oil Pollution Act of 1961, as amended; establishment and administration of vessel anchorages; approval of bridge locations and clearances over navigable waters; administration of the alteration of obstructive bridges; regulation of drawbridge operations; inspection of vessels of the Merchant Marine; admeasurement of vessels; documentation of vessels; preparation and publication of merchant vessel registers; registration of stack insignia; port security; issuance of Merchant Marine licenses and documents; search and rescue operations; investigation of marine casualties and accidents, and suspension and revocation proceedings; destruction of derelicts; operation of aids to navigation; publication of Light Lists and Local Notices to Mariners; and operation of ice-breaking facilities.

(45) The Coast Guard, with the cooperation of coast radio stations of many nations, operates the **Automated Mutual-assistance Vessel Rescue System (AMVER).** It is an international maritime mutual assistance program which provides important aid to the development and coordination of search and rescue (SAR) efforts in many offshore areas of the world. Merchant ships of all nations making offshore passages are encouraged to voluntarily send movement (sailing) reports and periodic position reports to the AMVER

Center at Coast Guard New York via selected radio stations. Information from these reports is entered into an electronic computer which generates and maintains dead reckoning positions for the vessels. Characteristics of vessels which are valuable for determining SAR capability are also entered into the computer from available sources of information.

(46) A worldwide communications network of radio stations supports the AMVER System. Propagation conditions, location of vessel, and traffic density will normally determine which station may best be contacted to establish communications. To ensure that no charge is applied, all AMVER reports should be passed through specified radio stations. Those stations which currently accept AMVER reports and apply no coastal station, ship station, or landline charge are listed in each issue of the "AMVER Bulletin" publication. Also listed are the respective International radio call signs, locations, frequency bands, and hours of operation. The "AMVER Bulletin" is available from Commander, Atlantic Area (As), U.S. Coast Guard, AMVER Center, Governors Island, New York, N.Y. 10004. Although AMVER reports may be sent through nonparticipating stations, the Coast Guard cannot reimburse the sender for any charges applied.

(47) Information concerning the predicted location and SAR characteristics of each vessel known to be within the area of interest is made available upon request to recognized SAR agencies of any nation or vessels needing assistance. Predicted locations are only disclosed for reasons related to marine safety.

(48) Benefits of AMVER participation to shipping include: (1) improved chances of aid in emergencies, (2) reduced number of calls for assistance to vessels not favorably located, and (3) reduced time lost for vessels responding to calls for assistance. An AMVER participant is under no greater obligation to render assistance during an emergency than a vessel who is not participating.

(49) All AMVER messages should be addressed to **Coast Guard New York** regardless of the station to which the message is delivered, except those sent to Canadian stations which should be addressed to **AMVER Halifax** or **AMVER Vancouver** to avoid incurring charges to the vessel for these messages.

(50) Instructions guiding participation in the AMVER System are available in the following languages: Chinese, Danish, Dutch, English, French, German, Greek, Italian, Japanese, Korean, Norwegian, Polish, Portuguese, Russian, Spanish, and Swedish. The AMVER Users Manual is available from: Commander, Atlantic Area, U.S. Coast Guard, Governors Island, N.Y. 10004-5000; Commander, Pacific Area, U.S. Coast Guard, Coast Guard Island, Alameda, CA. 94501-5100; and at U.S. Coast Guard District Offices, Marine Safety Offices, Marine Inspection Offices, and Captain of the Port Offices in major U.S. ports. Requests for instructions should state the language desired if other than English.

(51) For AMVER participants bound for U.S. ports there is an additional benefit. AMVER participation via messages which include the necessary information is considered to meet the requirements of 33 CFR 160. (See **160.201**, chapter 2, for rules and regulations.)

(52) **AMVER Reporting Required.**–U.S. Maritime Administration regulations effective August 1, 1983, state that certain U.S. flag vessels and foreign flag "War Risk" vessels must report and regularly update their voyages to the **AMVER** Center. This reporting is required of the following: (a) U.S. flag vessels of 1,000 gross tons or greater, operating in foreign commerce; (b) foreign flag vessels of 1,000 gross tons or greater, for which an Interim War Risk Insurance Binder has been issued under the provisions of Title XII, Merchant Marine Act, 1936.

(53) Details of the above procedures are contained in the AMVER Users Manual. The system is also published in DMAHTC Pub. 117.

(54) Search and Rescue Operation procedures are contained in the International Maritime Organization (IMO) SAR Manual (MERSAR). U.S. flag vessels may obtain a copy of MERSAR from local Coast Guard Marine Safety Offices and Marine Inspection Offices or by writing to U.S. Coast Guard (G-OSR), Washington, D.C. 20593-0001. Other flag vessels may purchase MERSAR directly from IMO.

(55) The Coast Guard conducts and/or coordinates **search and rescue** operations for surface vessels and aircraft that are in distress or overdue. (See Distress Signals and Communication Procedures this chapter.)

(56) **Light Lists,** published by the Coast Guard, describe aids to navigation, consisting of lights, fog signals, buoys, lightships, daybeacons, and electronic aids, in United States (including Puerto Rico and U.S. Virgin Islands) and contiguous Canadian waters. Light Lists are for sale by the Government Printing Office (see appendix for address) and by sales agents in the principal seaports. Mariners should refer to these publications for detailed information regarding the characteristics and visibility of lights, and the descriptions of light structures, lightships, buoys, fog signals, and electronic aids.

(57) **Documentation** (issuance of certificates of registry, enrollments, and licenses), admeasurements of vessels, and administration of the various navigation laws pertaining thereto are functions of the Coast Guard. Yacht commissions are also issued, and certain undocumented vessels required to be numbered by the Federal Boat Safety Act of 1971 are numbered either by the Coast Guard or by a State having an approved numbering system (the latter is most common). Owners of vessels may obtain the necessary information from any Coast Guard District Commander, Marine Safety Office, or Marine Inspection Office. Coast Guard District Offices, Coast Guard Stations, Marine Safety Offices, Captain of the Port Offices, Marine Inspection Offices, and Documentation Offices are listed in the appendix. (Note: A Marine Safety Office performs the same functions as those of a Captain of the Port and a Marine Inspection Office. When a function is at a different address than the Marine Safety Office, it will be listed separately in the appendix.)

(58) **Corps of Engineers,** Department of the Army.–The Corps of Engineers has charge of the improvement of the rivers and harbors of the United States and of miscellaneous other civil works which include the administration of certain Federal laws enacted for the protection and preservation of navigable waters of the United States; the establishment of regulations for the use, administration, and navigation of navigable waters; the establishment of harbor lines; the removal of sunken vessels obstructing or endangering navigation; and the granting of permits for structures or operations in navigable waters, and for discharges and deposits of dredged and fill materials in these waters.

(59) Information concerning the various ports, improvements, channel depths, navigable waters, and the condition of the Intracoastal Waterways in the areas under their jurisdiction may be obtained direct from the District Engineer Offices. (See appendix for addresses.)

(60) **Fishtraps.**–The Corps of Engineers has general supervision of location, construction, and manner of maintenance of all traps, weirs, pounds, or other fishing structures in the navigable waters of the United States. Where State and/or local controls are sufficient to regulate these structures, including that they do not interfere with navigation, the Corps of Engineers leaves such regulation to the State or local authority. (See **33 CFR 330** (not carried in this Pilot) for applicable Federal regulations.) Construction permits issued by the Engineers specify the lights and signals required for the safety of navigation.

(61) **Fish havens,** artificial reefs constructed to attract fish, can be established in U.S. coastal waters only as authorized by a Corps of Engineers permit; the permit specifies the location, extent, and depth over these "underwater junk piles."

(62) **Environmental Protection Agency (EPA).**–The U.S. Environmental Protection Agency provides coordinated governmental action to assure the protection of the environment by abating and controlling pollution on a systematic basis. The ocean dumping permit program of the Environmental Protection Agency provides that except when authorized by permit, the dumping of any material into the ocean is prohibited by the "Marine Protection, Research, and Sanctuaries Act of 1972, Public Law 92–532," as amended (33 USC 1401 et seq.).

(63) Permits for the **dumping of dredged material** into waters of the United States, including the territorial sea, and into ocean waters are issued by the Corps of Engineers. Permits for the dumping of fill material into waters of the United States, including the territorial sea, are also issued by the Corps of Engineers. Permits for the dumping of other material in the territorial sea and ocean waters are issued by the Environmental Protection Agency.

(64) Corps of Engineers regulations relating to the above are contained in **33 CFR 323-324**; Environmental Protection Agency regulations are in **40 CFR 220-229.** (See Disposal Sites, this chapter.)

(65) Persons or organizations who want to file for an application for an ocean dumping permit should write the Environmental Protection Agency Regional Office for the region in which the port of departure is located. (See appendix for addresses of regional offices and States in the EPA coastal regions.)

(66) The letter should contain the name and address of the applicant; name and address of person or firm; the name and usual location of the conveyance to be used in the transportation and dumping of the material involved; a physical description where appropriate; and the quantity to be dumped and proposed dumping site.

(67) Everyone who writes EPA will be sent information about a final application for a permit as soon as possible. This final application is expected to include questions about the description of the process or activity giving rise to the production of the dumping material; information on past activities of applicant or others with respect to the disposal of the type of material involved; and a description about available alternative means of disposal of the material with explanations about why an alternative is thought by the applicant to be inappropriate.

(68) **Federal Communications Commission.**–The Federal Communications Commission controls non-Government radio communications in the United States, Guam, Puerto Rico, and the Virgin Islands. Commission inspectors have authority to board ships to determine whether their radio stations comply with international treaties, Federal Laws, and Commission regulations. The commission has field offices in the principal U.S. ports. (See appendix for addresses.) Information concerning ship radio regulations and service documents may be obtained from the Federal Communications Commission, Washington, D.C. 20554, or from any of the field offices.

(69) **Immigration and Naturalization Service,** Department of Justice.–The Immigration and Naturalization Service administers the laws relating to admission, exclusion, and deportation of aliens, the registration and fingerprinting of aliens, and the naturalization of aliens lawfully resident in the United States.

(70) The designated ports of entry for aliens are divided into three classes. Class A is for all aliens. Class B is only for aliens who at the time of applying for admission are lawfully in possession of valid resident aliens' border-crossing identification cards or valid nonresident aliens' border-crossing identification cards or are admissible without documents under the documentary waivers contained in **8 CFR 212.1(a).** Class C is only for aliens who are arriving in the United States as crewmen as that term is defined in Section 101(a) (10) of the Immigration and Nationality Act. [The term "crewman" means a person serving in any capacity on board a vessel or aircraft. No person may enter the United States until he has been inspected by an immigration officer. A list of the offices covered by this Coast Pilot is given in the appendix.

(71) **Defense Mapping Agency Hydrographic/Topographic Center (DMAHTC),** Department of Defense.–The Defense Mapping Agency Hydrographic/Topographic Center provides hydrographic, navigational, topographic, and geodetic data, charts, maps, and related products and services to the Armed Forces, other Federal Agencies, the Merchant Marine and mariners in general. Publications include Sailing Directions, List of Lights, Distances Between Ports, Radio Navigational Aids, International Code of Signals, American Practical Navigator (Bowditch), and Notice to Mariners. (See Defense Mapping Agency Procurement Information in appendix.)

(72) **Public Health Service,** Department of Health and Human Services.–The Public Health Service administers foreign quarantine procedures at U.S. ports of entry.

(73) All vessels arriving in the United States are subject to public health inspection. Vessels subject routine boarding for quarantine inspection are only those which have had on board during the 15 days preceding the date of expected arrival or during the period since departure (whichever period of time is shorter) the occurrence of any death or ill person among passengers or crew (including those who have disembarked or have been removed). The master of a vessel must report such occurrences immediately by radio to the quarantine station at or nearest the port at which the vessel will arrive.

(74) In addition, the master of a vessel carrying 13 or more passengers must report by radio 24 hours before arrival the number of cases (including zero) of diarrhea in passengers and crew recorded in the ship's medical log during the current cruise. All cases that occur after the 24 hour report must also be reported not less than 4 hours before arrival.

(75) "Ill person" means person who:

(76) 1. Has a temperature of 100°F (or 38°C) or greater, accompanied by a rash, glandular swelling, or jaundice, or which has persisted for more than 48 hours; or

(77) 2. Has diarrhea, defined as the occurrence in a 24 hour period of three or more loose stools or of a greater than normal (for the person) amount of loose stools.

(78) Vessels arriving at ports under control of the United States are subject to sanitary inspection to determine whether measures should be applied to prevent the introduction, transmission, or spread of communicable disease.

(79) Specific public health laws, regulations, policies, and procedures may be obtained by contacting U.S. Quarantine Stations, U.S. Consulates or the Chief Program Operations, Division of Quarantine, Centers for Disease Control, Atlanta, Ga. 30333. (See appendix for addresses of U.S. Public Health Service Quarantine Stations.)

(80) **Food and Drug Administration (FDA)**, Public Health Service, Department of Health and Human Services.–Under the provisions of the Control of Communicable Diseases Regulations (**21 CFR 1240**) and Interstate Conveyance Sanitation Regulations (**21 CFR 1250**), vessel companies operating in interstate traffic shall obtain potable water for drinking and culinary purposes only at watering points found acceptable to the Food and Drug Administration. Water supplies used in watering point operations must also be inspected to determine compliance with applicable Interstate Quarantine Regulations (**42 CFR 72**). These regulations are based on authority contained in the Public Health Service Act (PL 78–410). Penalties for violation of any regulation prescribed under authority of the Act are provided for under Section 368 (42 USC 271) of the Act.

(81) **Vessel Watering Points.**–FDA annually publishes a list of Acceptable Vessel Watering Points. This list is available from most FDA offices or from Interstate Travel Sanitation Subprogram Center for Food Safety and Applied Nutrition, FDA (HFF-312), 200 C Street SW., Washington, D.C. 20204. Current status of watering points can be ascertained by contacting any FDA office. (See appendix for addresses.)

(82) **National Weather Service (NWS)**, National Oceanic and Atmospheric Administration (NOAA), Department of Commerce.–The National Weather Service provides marine weather forecasts and warnings for the U.S. coastal waters, the Great Lakes, offshore waters, and high seas areas. Scheduled marine forecasts are issued four times daily from more than 20 **National Weather Service Forecast Offices (WSFOs)** around the country, operating 24 hours a day. Marine services are also provided by over 50 **National Weather Service Offices** with local areas of responsibility. (See appendix for Weather Service Forecast Offices and Weather Service Offices for the area covered by this Coast Pilot.)

(83) Typically, the forecasts contain information on wind speed and direction, wave heights, visibility, weather, and a general synopsis of weather patterns affecting the region. The forecasts are supplemented with special marine warnings and statements, radar summaries, marine observations, small-craft advisories, gale warnings, storm warnings and various categories of tropical cyclone warnings e.g., tropical depression, tropical storm and hurricane warnings. Specialized products such as coastal flood, seiche, and tsunami warnings, heavy surf advisories, low water statements, ice forecasts and outlooks, and lake shore warnings and statements are issued as necessary.

(84) The principal means of disseminating marine weather services and products in coastal areas is **NOAA Weather Radio.** This network or more than 350 stations nationwide is operated by the NWS and provides continuous broadcasts of weather information for the general public. These broadcasts repeat taped messages every 4-6 minutes. Tapes are updated periodically, usually every 2-3 hours and amended as required to include the latest information. When severe weather threatens, routine transmissions are interrupted and the broadcast is devoted to emergency warnings. (See appendix for NOAA Weather Radio Stations covered by this Coast Pilot.)

(85) In coastal areas, the programming is tailored to the needs of the marine community. Each coastal marine forecast covers a specific area. For example, "Cape Henlopen to Virginia Beach, out 20 miles." The broadcast range is about 40 miles from the transmitting antenna site, depending on terrain and quality of the receiver used. When transmitting antennas are on high ground, the range is somewhat greater, reaching 60 miles or more. Some receivers are equipped with a warning alert device that can be turned on by means of a tone signal controlled by the NWS office concerned. This signal is transmitted for 13 seconds preceding an announcement of a severe weather warning.

(86) NWS marine weather products are also disseminated to marine users through the broadcast facilities of the Coast Guard, Navy, National Bureau of Standards, certain Sea Grant Universities, and commercial marine radio stations. Details on these broadcasts including times, frequencies, and broadcast content are listed in the joint NWS/Navy publication Selected Worldwide Marine Weather Broadcasts. For marine weather services in the coastal areas, the NWS publishes a series of Marine Weather Services Charts showing locations of NOAA Weather Radio stations, sites, telephone numbers of recorded weather messages and NWS offices, and other useful marine weather information.

(87) Ships of all nations share equally in the effort to report weather observations. These reports enable meteorologists to create a detailed picture of wind, wave, and weather patterns over the open waters that no other data source can provide and upon which marine forecasts are based. The effectiveness and reliability of these forecasts and warnings plus other services to the marine community are strongly linked to the observations received from mariners. There is an especially urgent need for ship observations in the coastal waters, and the NWS asks that these be made and transmitted whenever possible. Many storms originate and intensify in coastal areas. There may be a great difference in both wind direction and speed between the open sea, the offshore waters, and on the coast itself.

(88) Information on how ships, commercial fishermen, offshore industries, and others in the coastal zone may participate in the marine observation program is available from **National Weather Service Port Meteorological Officers (PMOs)**. Port Meteorological Officers are located in major U.S. port cities and the Republic of Panama, where they visit ships in port to assist masters and mates with the weather observation program, provide instruction on the interpretation of weather charts, calibrate barometers and other meteorological instruments, and discuss marine weather communications and marine weather requirements affecting the ships' operations. (See appendix for addresses of Port Meteorological Officers in or near the area covered by this Coast Pilot.)

(89) **National Environmental Satellite, Data, and Information Service (NESDIS)**, National Oceanic and Atmospheric Administration (NOAA), Department of Commerce.–Among its functions, NESDIS archives, processes,

and disseminates the non-realtime meteorological and oceanographic data collected by government agencies and private institutions. Marine weather observations are collected from ships at sea on a voluntary basis. About 1 million observations are received annually at NESDIS's National Climatic Center. They come from vessels representing every maritime nation. These observations, along with land data, are returned to the mariners in the form of climatological summaries and atlases for coastal and ocean areas. They are available in such NOAA publications as the **U.S. Coast Pilot, Mariners Weather Log,** and **Local Climatological Data, Annual Summary.** They also appear in the Defense Mapping Agency **Pilot Charts** and **Sailing Directions Planning Guides.**

DISTRESS SIGNALS AND COMMUNICATION PROCEDURES

(90) **Coast Guard search and rescue operations.**–The Coast Guard conducts and/or coordinates search and rescue operations for surface vessels or aircraft that are in distress or overdue. Search and Rescue vessels and aircraft have special markings, including a wide slash of red-orange and a small slash of blue on the forward portion of the hull or fuselage. Other parts of aircraft, normally painted white, may have other areas painted red to facilitate observation. The cooperation of vessel operators with Coast Guard helicopters, fixed-wing aircraft, and vessels may mean the difference between life and death for some seaman or aviator; such cooperation is greatly facilitated by the prior knowledge on the part of vessel operators of the operational requirements of Coast Guard equipment and personnel, of the international distress signals and procedures, and of good seamanship.

(91) **International distress signals.**–(1) A signal made by radiotelegraphy or by any other signalling method consisting of the group "SOS" in Morse Code.

(92) (2) A signal sent by radiotelephony consisting of the spoken word "MAYDAY."

(93) (3) The International Flag Code Signal of NC.

(94) (4) A signal consisting of a square flag having above or below it a ball or anything resembling a ball.

(95) (5) Flames on the craft (as from a burning oil barrel, etc.)

(96) (6) A rocket parachute flare or hand flare showing a red light.

(97) (7) Rockets or shells, throwing red stars fired one at a time at short intervals.

(98) (8) Orange smoke, as emitted from a distress flare.

(99) (9) Slowly and repeatedly raising and lowering arms outstretched to each side.

(100) (10) A gun or other explosive signal fired at intervals of about 1 minute.

(101) (11) A continuous sounding of any fog-signal apparatus.

(102) (12) The radiotelegraph alarm signal.

(103) (13) The radiotelephone alarm signal.

(104) (14) Signals transmitted by emergency position-indicating radiobeacons.

(105) (15) A piece of orange-colored canvas with either a black square and circle or other appropriate symbol (for identification from the air).

(106) (16) A dye marker.

(107) **Radio distress procedures.**–Distress calls are made on 500 kHz (SOS) for radiotelegraphy and on 2182 kHz or VHF-FM channel 16 (MAYDAY) for radiotelephony. For less serious situations than warrant the distress procedure, the urgency signal PAN-PAN (PAHN-PAHN, spoken three times), or the safety signal SECURITY (SAY-CURITAY, spoken three times), for radiotelephony, are used as appropriate. Since radiotelegraph transmissions are normally made by professional operators, and urgency and safety situations are less critical, only the distress procedures for voice radiotelephone are described. For complete information on emergency radio procedures, see **47 CFR 83** or DMAHTC Pub. 117. **(See appendix for a list of Coast Guard Stations which guard 2182 kHz and 156.80 MHz.)** Complete information on distress guards can be obtained from Coast Guard District Commanders.

(108) Distress calls indicate a vessel or aircraft is threatened by grave and imminent danger and requests immediate assistance. They have absolute priority over all other transmissions. All stations which hear a distress call must immediately cease any transmission capable of interfering with the distress traffic and shall continue to listen on the frequency used for the emission of the distress call. This call shall not be addressed to a particular station, and acknowledgement of receipt shall not be given before the distress message which follows it is sent.

(109) **Radiotelephone distress communications include the following actions:**

(110) (1) The **radiotelephone alarm signal** (if available): The signal consists of two audio tones, of different pitch, transmitted alternately; its purpose is to attract the attention of persons on radio watch or to actuate automatic alarm devices. It may only be used to announce that a distress call or message is about to follow.

(111) (2) The **distress call,** consisting of:–the distress signal MAYDAY (spoken three times);

(112) the words THIS IS (spoken once);

(113) the call sign or name of the vessel in distress (spoken three times).

(114) (3) The **distress message** follows immediately and consists of:

(115) the distress signal MAYDAY;

(116) the call sign and name of the vessel in distress;

(117) particulars of its position (latitude and longitude, or true bearing and distance from a known geographical position);

(118) the nature of the distress;

(119) the kind of assistance desired;

(120) the number of persons aboard and the condition of any injured;

(121) present seaworthiness of vessel;

(122) description of the vessel (length; type; cabin; masts; power; color of hull, superstructure, trim; etc.);

(123) any other information which might facilitate the rescue, such as display of a surface-to-air identification signal or a radar reflector;

(124) your listening frequency and schedule;

(125) THIS IS (call sign and name of vessel in distress). OVER.

(126) (4) **Acknowledgement of receipt of a distress message:** If a distress message is received from a vessel which is definitely in your vicinity, immediately acknowledge receipt. If it is not in your vicinity, allow a short interval of time to elapse before acknowledging, in order to permit vessels nearer to the vessel in distress to acknowledge receipt without interference. However, in areas where reliable communications with one or more shore stations are practicable, all vessels may defer this acknowledgement for a short interval so that a shore station may acknowledge receipt first. The acknowledgement of receipt of a distress is given as follows:

(127) the call sign or name of the vessel sending the distress (spoken three times);

(128)   the words THIS IS;

(129)   the call sign or name of acknowledging vessel (spoken three times);

(130)   The words RECEIVED MAYDAY.

(131)   After the above acknowledgement, allow a momentary interval of listening to insure that you will not interfere with another vessel better situated to render immediate assistance; if not, with the authority of the person in charge of the vessel, transmit:

(132)   the word MAYDAY;

(133)   the call sign and name of distressed vessel;

(134)   the words THIS IS;

(135)   the call sign and name of your vessel;

(136)   your position (latitude and longitude, or true bearing and distance from a known geographical position);

(137)   the speed you are proceeding towards, and the approximate time it will take to reach, the distressed vessel. OVER.

(138)   (5) **Further distress messages and other communications:** Distress communications consist of all messages relating to the immediate assistance required by the distressed vessel. Each distress communication shall be preceded by the signal MAYDAY. The vessel in distress or the station in control of distress communications may **impose silence** on any station which interferes. The procedure is:–the words SEELONCE MAYDAY (Seelonce is French for silence). Silence also may be imposed by nearby mobile stations other than the vessel in distress or the station in control of distress communications. The mobile station which believes that silence is essential may request silence by the following procedure:–the word SEELONCE, followed by the word DISTRESS, and its **own** call sign.

(139)   (6) **Transmission of the distress procedure by a vessel or shore station not itself in distress:** A vessel or a shore station which learns that a vessel is in distress shall transmit a distress message in any of the following cases:

(140)   (a) **When the vessel in distress is not itself able to transmit the distress message.**

(141)   (b) When a vessel or a shore station considers that further help is necessary.

(142)   (c) When, although not in a position to render assistance, it has heard a distress message that has not been acknowledged.

(143)   In these cases, the transmission shall consist of:

(144)   the radiotelephone alarm signal (if available);

(145)   the words MAYDAY RELAY (spoken three times);

(146)   the words THIS IS;

(147)   the call sign and name of vessel (or shore station), spoken three times.

(148)   When a vessel transmits a distress under these conditions, it shall take all necessary steps to contact the Coast Guard or a shore station which can notify the Coast Guard.

(149)   (7) **Termination of distress:** When distress traffic has ceased, or when silence is no longer necessary on the frequency used for the distress traffic, the station in control shall transmit on that frequency a message to all stations as follows:

(150)   the distress signal MAYDAY;

(151)   the call TO ALL STATIONS, spoken three times;

(152)   the words THIS IS;

(153)   the call sign and name of the station sending the message;

(154)   the time;

(155)   the name and call sign of the vessel in distress;

(156)   the words SEELONCE FEENEE (French for silence finished).

DISTRESS ASSISTANCE AND COORDINATION PROCEDURES

(157)   **Surface ship procedures for assisting distressed surface vessels.**

(158)   (1) The following immediate action should be taken by each ship on receipt of a distress message:

(159)   (a) Acknowledge receipt and, if appropriate, retransmit the distress message;

(160)   (b) Immediately try to take D/F bearings during the transmission of the distress message and maintain a D/F watch on 500 kHz and/or 2182 kHz;

(161)   (c) Communicate the following information to the ship in distress:

(162)   (i) identity;

(163)   (ii) position;

(164)   (iii) speed and estimated time of arrival (ETA);

(165)   (iv) when available, true bearing of the ship in distress.

(166)   (d) Maintain a continuous listening watch on the frequency used for the distress. This will normally be:

(167)   (i) 500 kHz (radiotelegraphy) and/or

(168)   (ii) 2182 kHz (radiotelephony).

(169)   (e) Additionally, maintain watch on VHF-FM channel 16 as necessary;

(170)   (f) Operate radar continuously;

(171)   (g) If in the vicinity of the distress, post extra lookouts.

(172)   (2) The following action should be taken when proceeding to the area of distress:

(173)   (a) Plot the position, course, speed, and ETA of other assisting ships.

(174)   (b) Know the communication equipment with which other ships are fitted. This information may be obtained from the International Telecommunication Union's List of Ship Stations.

(175)   (c) Attempt to construct an accurate "picture" of the circumstances attending the casualty. The important information needed is included under Distress Signals and Communication Procedures, this chapter. Should the ship in distress fail to transmit this information, a ship proceeding to assist should request what information is needed.

(176)   (3) The following on-board preparation while proceeding to the distress area should be considered:

(177)   (a) A rope (guest warp) running from bow to quarter at the waterline on each side and secured by lizards to the ship's side to assist boats and rafts to secure alongside;

(178)   (b) A derrick rigged ready for hoisting on each side of the ship with a platform cargo sling, or rope net, secured to the runner to assist the speedy recovery of exhausted or injured survivors in the water;

(179)   (c) Heaving lines, ladders, and scramble net placed ready for use along both sides of the ship on the lowest open deck and possibly crew members suitably equipped to enter the water and assist survivors;

(180)   (d) A ship's liferaft made ready for possible use as a boarding station;

(181)   (e) Preparations to receive survivors who require medical assistance including the provision of stretchers;

(182)   (f) When own lifeboat is to be launched, any means to provide communications between it and the parent ship will prove to be of very great help;

(183)   (g) A line throwing appliance with a light line and a heavy rope, ready to be used for making connection either with the ship in distress or with survival craft.

(184)   **Aircraft procedures for directing surface craft to scene of distress incident.**–The following procedures performed in sequence by an aircraft mean that the aircraft is

directing a surface craft toward the scene of a distress incident,

(185)   (a) Circling the surface craft at least once.

(186)   (b) Crossing the projected course of the surface craft close ahead at low altitude, rocking the wings, opening and closing the throttle, or changing the propeller pitch.

(187)   (c) Heading in the direction in which the surface craft is to be directed. The surface craft should acknowledge the signal by changing course and following the aircraft. If, for any reason, it is impossible to follow, the surface craft should hoist the international code flag NOVEMBER, or use any other signaling means available to indicate this.

(188)   The following procedures performed by an aircraft mean that the assistance of the surface craft is no longer required:

(189)   (a) Crossing the wake of the surface craft close astern at a low altitude, rocking the wings, opening and closing the throttle or changing the propeller pitch.

(190)   Since modern jet-engined aircraft cannot make the characteristic sound associated with opening and closing the throttle, or changing propeller pitch, ships should be alert to respond to the signals without the sounds, when jets or turboprop aircraft are involved.

(191)   **Surface ship procedures for assisting aircraft in distress.**

(192)   1. When an aircraft transmits a distress message by radio, the first transmission is generally made on the designated air/ground enroute frequency in use at the time between the aircraft and aeronautical station. The aircraft may change to another frequency, possibly another enroute frequency or the aeronautical emergency frequencies of 121.50 MHz or 243 MHz. In an emergency, it may use any other available frequency to establish contact with any land, mobile, or direction-finding station.

(193)   2. There is liaison between Coast Radio Stations aeronautical units, and land–based search and rescue organizations. Merchant ships will ordinarily be informed of aircraft casualties at sea by broadcast messages from Coast Radio Stations, made on the international distress frequencies of 500 kHz and 2182 kHz. Ships may, however, become aware of the casualty by receiving:

(194)   (a) An SOS message from an aircraft in distress which is able to transmit on 500 kHz or a distress signal from an aircraft using radiotelephone on 2182 kHz.

(195)   (b) A radiotelegraphy distress signal on 500 kHz from a hand-operated emergency transmitter carried by some aircraft.

(196)   (c) A message from a SAR aircraft.

(197)   3. For the purpose of emergency communications with aircraft, special attention is called to the possibility of conducting direct communications on 2182 kHz, if both ship and aircraft are so equipped.

(198)   4. An aircraft in distress will use any means at its disposal to attract attention, make known its position, and obtain help, including some of the signals prescribed by the applicable Navigation Rules.

(199)   5. Aircraft usually sink quickly (e.g. within a few minutes). Every endeavor will be made to give ships an accurate position of an aircraft which desires to ditch. When given such a position, a ship should at once consult any other ships in the vicinity on the best procedure to be adopted. The ship going to the rescue should answer the station sending the broadcast and give her identity, position, and intended action.

(200)   6. If a ship should receive a distress message direct from an aircraft, she should act as indicated in the immediately preceding paragraph and also relay the message to the nearest Coast Radio Station. Moreover, a ship which has received a distress message direct from an aircrft and is going to the rescue should take a bearing on the transmission and inform the Coast Radio Station and other ships in the vicinity of the call sign of the distressed aircraft and the time at which the distress message was received, followed by the bearing and time at which the signal ceased.

(201)   7. When an aircraft decides to ditch in the vicinity of a ship, the ship should:

(202)   (a) Transmit homing bearings to the aircraft, or (if so required) transmit signals enabling the aircraft to take its own bearings.

(203)   (b) By day, make black smoke.

(204)   (c) By night, direct a searchlight vertically and turn on all deck lights. Care must be taken not to direct a searchlight toward the aircraft, which might dazzle the pilot.

(205)   8. Ditching an aircraft is difficult and dangerous. A ship which knows that an aircraft intends to ditch should be prepared to give the pilot the following information:

(206)   (a) Wind direction and force.

(207)   (b) Direction, height, and length of primary and secondary swell systems.

(208)   (c) Other pertinent weather information.

(209)   The pilot of an aircraft will choose his own ditching heading. If this is known by the ship, she should set course parallel to the ditching heading. Otherwise the ship should set course parallel to the main swell system and into the wind component, if any.

(210)   9. A land plane may break up immediately on striking the water, and liferafts may be damaged. The ship should, therefore, have a lifeboat ready for launching, and if possible, boarding nets should be lowered from the ship and heaving lines made ready in the ship and the lifeboat. Survivors of the aircraft may have bright colored lifejackets and location aids.

(211)   10. The method of recovering survivors must be left to the judgment of the master of the ship carrying out the rescue operation.

(212)   11. It should be borne in mind that military aircraft are often fitted with ejection seat mechanisms. Normally, their aircrew will use their ejection seats, rather than ditch. Should such an aircraft ditch, rather than the aircrew bail out, and it becomes necessary to remove them from their ejection seats while still in the aircraft, care should be taken to avoid triggering off the seat mechanisms. The activating handles are invariably indicated by red and or black/yellow coloring.

(213)   12. A survivor from an aircraft casualty who is recovered may be able to give information which will assist in the rescue of other survivors. Masters are therefore asked to put the following questions to survivors and to communicate the answers to a Coast Radio Station. They should also give the position of the rescuing ship and the time when the survivors were recovered.

(214)   (a) What was the time and date of the casualty?

(215)   (b) Did you bail out or was the aircraft ditched?

(216)   (c) If you bailed out, at what altitude?

(217)   (d) How many others did you see leave the aircraft by parachute?

(218)   (e) How many ditched with the aircraft?

(219)   (f) How many did you see leave the aircraft after ditching?

(220)   (g) How many survivors did you see in the water?

(221)   (h) What flotation gear had they?

(222)   (i) What was the total number of persons aboard the aircraft prior to the accident?

(223)   (j) What caused the emergency?

(224) **Helicopter evacuation** of personnel.–Helicopter evacuation, usually performed by the Coast Guard, is a hazardous operation to the patient and to the flight crew, and should only be attempted in event of very serious illness or injury. Provide the doctor on shore with all the information you can concerning the patient, so that an intelligent evaluation can be made concerning the need for evacuation. Most rescue helicopters can proceed less than 150 miles offshore (a few new helicopters can travel 250 to 300 miles out to sea), dependent on weather conditions and other variables. If an evaluation is necessary, the vessel must be prepared to proceed within range of the helicopter, and should be familiar with the preparations which are necessary prior to and after its arrival.

(225) **When requesting helicopter assistance:**

(226) (1) Give the accurate position, time, speed, course, weather conditions, sea conditions, wind direction and velocity, type of vessel, and voice and CW frequency for your ship.

(227) (2) If not already provided, give complete medical information including whether or not the patient is ambulatory.

(228) (3) If you are beyond helicopter range, advise your diversion intentions so that a rendezvous point may be selected.

(229) (4) If there are changes to any items reported earlier, advise the rescue agency immediately. Should the patient die before the arrival of the helicopter, be sure to advise those assisting you.

(230) **Preparations prior to the arrival of the helicopter:**

(231) (1) Provide continuous radio guard on 2182 kHz or specified voice frequency, if possible. The helicopter normally cannot operate CW.

(232) (2) Select and clear the most suitable hoist area, preferably aft on the vessel with a minimum of 50 feet radius of clear deck. This must include the securing of loose gear, awnings, and antenna wires. Trice up running rigging and booms. If hoist is aft, lower the flag staff.

(233) (3) If the hoist is to take place at night, light the pickup areas as well as possible. Be sure you do not shine any lights on the helicopter, so that the pilot is not blinded. If there are any obstructions in the vicinity, put a light on them so the pilot will be aware of their positions.

(234) (4) Point searchlight vertically to aid the flight crew in locating the ship and turn them off when the helicopter is on the scene.

(235) (5) Be sure to advise the helicopter of the location of the pickup area on the ship before the helicopter arrives, so that the pilot may make his approach to aft, amidships, or forward, as required.

(236) (6) There will be a high noise level under the helicopter, so voice communications on deck are almost impossible. Arrange a set of hand signals among the crew who will assist.

(237) **Hoist operations:**

(238) (1) If possible, have the patient moved to a position as close to the hoist area as his condition will permit–**time is important.**

(239) (2) Normally, if a litter (stretcher) is required, it will be necessary to move the patient to the special litter which will be lowered by the helicopter. Be prepared to do this as quickly as possible. Be sure the patient is strapped in, face up, and with a life jacket on (if his condition will permit).

(240) (3) Be sure that the patient is tagged to indicate what medication, if any, was administered to him and when it was administered.

(241) (4) Have patient's medical record and necessary papers in an envelope or package ready for transfer with the patient.

(242) (5) Again, if the patient's condition permit, be sure he is wearing a life jacket.

(243) (6) Change the vessel's course to permit the ship to ride as easily as possible with the wind on the bow, preferably on the port bow. Try to choose a course to keep the stack gases clear of the hoist area. Once established, maintain course and speed.

(244) (7) Reduce speed to ease ship's motion, but maintain steerageway.

(245) (8) If you do not have radio contact with the helicopter, when you are in all respects ready for the hoist, signal the helicopter in with a "come on" with your hand, or at night by flashlight signals.

(246) (9) **Allow basket or stretcher to touch deck prior to handling to avoid static shock.**

(247) (10) If a trail line is dropped by the helicopter, guide the basket or stretcher to the deck with the line; keep the line free at all times. This line will not cause shock.

(248) (11) Place the patient in basket, sitting with his hands clear of the sides, or in the litter, as described above. Signal the helicopter hoist operator when ready for the hoist. Patient should signal by a nodding of the head if he is able. Deck personnel give thumbs up.

(249) (12) If it is necessary to take the litter away from the hoist point, unhook the hoist cable and keep it free for the helicopter to haul in. **Do not secure cable or trail line to the vessel or attempt to move stretcher without unhooking.**

(250) (13) When patient is strapped into the stretcher, signal the helicopter to lower the cable, attach cable to stretcher sling (bridle), then signal the hoist operator when the patient is ready to hoist. Steady the stretcher so it will not swing or turn.

(251) (14) If a trail line is attached to the basket or stretcher, use it to steady the patient as he is hoisted. Keep your feet clear of the line, and keep the line from becoming entangled.

(252) **Medical advice and/or evacuation.**–In the event a master of a vessel requires medical advice and/or there is a potential of evacuation the following should be volunteered by the master:

(253) Vessel's name and call sign.

(254) Vessel's position and time at position.

(255) Vessel's course, speed and next port and estimated time of arrival (ETA).

(256) Patient's name, nationality, age, race and sex.

(257) Patient's respiration, pulse and temperature.

(258) Patient's symptoms and nature of illness.

(259) Any known history of similar illness.

(260) Location and type of pain.

(261) Medical supplies carried on board vessel.

(262) Medication given to patient.

(263) Weather.

(264) Communication schedule and frequency.

(265) **Coast Guard droppable, floatable pumps.**–The Coast Guard often provides vessels in distress with emergency pumps by either making parachute drops, by lowering on helicopter hoist, or by delivering by vessel. The most commonly used type of pump comes complete in a sealed aluminum drum about half the size of a 50-gallon oil drum. One single lever on top opens it up. Don't be smoking as there may be gas fumes inside the can. The pump will draw about

90 gallons per minute. There should be a waterproof flashlight on top of the pump for night use. Operating instructions are provided inside the pump container.

(266) **Preparations for being towed by Coast Guard:**

(267) (1) Clear the forecastle area as well as you can.

(268) (2) If a line-throwing gun is used, keep everyone out of the way until line clears the boat. The Coast Guard vessel will blow a police whistle or otherwise warn you before firing.

(269) (3) Have material ready for chafing gear.

(270) **Radar reflectors on small craft.**—Operators of disabled wooden craft and persons adrift in rubber rafts or boats that are, or may consider themselves to be, the object of a search, should hoist on a halyard or otherwise place aloft as high as possible any metallic object that would assist their detection by radar. Coast Guard cutters and aircraft are radar equipped and thus are able to continue searching in darkness and during other periods of low visibility. It is advisable for coastal fishing boats, yachts, and other small craft to have efficient radar reflectors permanently installed aboard the vessel.

(271) **Filing Cruising schedules.**—Small-craft operators should prepare a cruising plan before starting on extended trips and leave it ashore with a yacht club, marina, friend, or relative. It is advisable to use a checking-in procedure by telephone for each point specified in the cruising plan. Such a trip schedule is vital for determining of a boat is overdue and will assist materially in locating a missing craft in the event search and rescue operations become necessary.

(272) **Medical advice.**—Free medical advice is furnished to seamen by radio through the cooperation of Governmental and commercial radio stations whose operators receive and relay messages prefixed DH MEDICO from ships at sea to the U.S. Coast Guard and/or directly to a hospital and then radio the medical advice back to the ships. (See appendix for list of radio stations that provide this service.)

RADIO NAVIGATION WARNINGS AND WEATHER

(273) Marine radio warnings and weather are disseminated by many sources and through several types of transmissions. Morse code radiotelegraph broadcasts of navigational warnings and other advisories are not described, since these transmissions are normally copied only by professional radio operators. U.S. Coast Guard NAVTEX, high-frequency (HF) narrow-band direct printing (radio telex), HF radiofacsimile, and radiotelephone broadcasts of maritime safety information are summarized here. (For complete information on radio warnings and weather see DMAHTC Pub. 117 and the joint National Weather Service/Navy publication Selected Worldwide Marine Weather Broadcasts.)

(274) **Frequency units.**—Hertz (Hz), a unit equal to one cycle per second, has been generally adopted for radio frequencies; accordingly, frequencies formerly given in the Coast Pilot in kilocycles (kc) and megacycles (mc) are now stated in **kilohertz (kHz)** and **Megahertz (MHz)**, respectively.

(275) **Coast Guard radio stations.**—Coast Guard radio stations provide urgent, safety, and scheduled marine information broadcasts with virtually complete coverage of the approaches and coastal waters of the United States, Puerto Rico, and the U.S. Virgin Islands.

(276) **Urgent and safety radiotelephone broadcasts** of important Notice to Mariners items, storm warnings, and other vital marine information are transmitted upon receipt,

and urgent broadcasts are repeated 15 minutes later; additional broadcasts are made at the discretion of the originator. **Urgent** broadcasts are preceded by the urgent signal PAN-PAN (PAHN-PAHN, spoken three times). **Both the urgent signal and message are transmitted on 2182 kHz and/or VHF-FM channel 16. Safety** broacasts are preceded by the safety signal SECURITY (SAY-CURITAY, spoken three times). **The Safety signal is given on 2182 kHz and/or VHF-FM channel 16, and the message is given on 2670 kHz and/or VHF-FM channel 22A.**

(277) Scheduled radiotelephone broadcasts include routine weather, small-craft advisories, storm warnings, navigational information, and other advisories. Short-range broadcasts are made on **2670 kHz and/or VHF-FM channel 22A,** following a preliminary call on **2182 kHz and/or VHF-FM channel 16.** (See appendix for a list of stations and their broadcast frequencies and times for the area covered by this Coast Pilot.)

(278) Weather information is not normally broadcast by the Coast Guard on VHF-FM channel 22A in areas where NOAA Weather Radio service is available. See note below regarding VHF-FM channel 22A.

(279) HF single-sideband broadcasts of high seas weather information is available on the (carrier) frequencies 4428.7, 6506.4, 8765.4, 13113.2, and 17307.3 kHz from Portsmouth, VA and San Francisco, CA.

(280) Narrow-band direct printing (radio telex or sitor) broadcasts of NAVAREA and other navigational warnings are transmitted on the following assigned frequencies:

(281) Atlantic ice reports: 5320, 8502, and 12750 kHz.

(282) Other Atlantic warnings: 8490, 16968.8 kHz.

(283) Pacific: 8710.5, 8714.5, 8718, 13077, 13084.5, 17203, 22567, and 22574.5 kHz.

(284) HF radiofacsimile broadcasts of weather and ice charts are made on the following frequencies:

(285) Atlantic: 3242, 7530, 8502 (ice only), 12750 (ice only) kHz.

(286) Pacific: 4298 (Kodiak), 4336, 8459 (Kodiak), 8682, 12730, 17151.2 kHz.

(287) **Warning Regarding Coast Guard VHF-FM Channel 22A Broadcasts.**—The Coast Guard broadcasts urgent and routine maritime safety information to ships on channel 22A (157.10 MHz), the ship station transmit frequency portion of channel 22, of Appendix 18 of the International Telecommunications Union (ITU) Radio Regulations. This simplex use of channel 22A is not compatible with the international duplex arrangement of the channel (coast transmit 161.70 MHz, ship transmit 157.10 MHz). As a result, many foreign flag vessels having radios tuned to the international channel 22 can not receive these maritime safety broadcasts. A 1987 Coast Guard survey of foreign vessels in U.S. waters indicated that half of foreign vessels in U.S. waters did not have equipment on board capable of receiving channel 22A broadcasts.

(288) Operators of vessels which transit U.S. waters and who do not have VHF-FM radios tunable to USA channel 22A are urged to either obtain the necessary equipment, to monitor the radiotelephone frequency 2182 kHz and tune to 2670 kHz when a broadcast is announced, or to carry a NAVTEX receiver.

(289) **NAVTEX Marine Information Broadcasts.**—NAVTEX is an international system used in the United States to broadcast printed copies of Coast Guard district notices to mariners, distress notices, weather forecasts and warnings, ice warnings, and Gulf Stream location (where applicable), and radionavigation information to all types of

ships. NAVTEX consists of a small, low-cost and self-contained "smart" printing radio receiver installed in the pilot house of a ship or boat. The receiver checks each incoming message to see if it has been received during an earlier transmission, or if it is of a category of no interest to the ship's master. If it is a new and wanted message, it is printed onadding-machine size paper; if not, the message is ignored. The adding-machine size paper; if not, the message is ignored. The ship's master can, at his convenience, read the latest notices he needs to know. A new ship coming into the area will receive many previously-broadcast messages for the first time; ships already in the area which had already received the message will not receive it again. NAVTEX can be received either by a dedicated receiver, or by any narrow-band direct printing (radio telex) receiver operating in the forward error correcting (FEC) mode, tuned to 518 kHz.

(290)　The accompanying chart shows NAVTEX predicted coverage area for the U.S. east coast. The propagation predictions were based upon a 90% probability of reception during an average season and time of atmospheric radio noise, with a received character error rate of 1 in 1,000. The Coast Guard operates NAVTEX from stations in Boston (NMF), Portsmouth, VA (NMN), Miami (NMA), New Orleans (NMG), San Juan, PR (NMR), Long Beach, CA, San Francisco (NMC), Astoria, OR, Kodiak, AK (NOJ), Honolulu (NMO) and Guam (NRV). The Canadian Coast Guard also broadcasts NAVTEX information from Sydney, Nova Scotia.

(291)　As of January 1988, 43 NAVTEX stations in 19 countries were in operation worldwide, and 7 other countries indicated they might soon begin operating NAVTEX.

(292)　Broadcasts are planned internationally. Mandatory carriage of NAVTEX receivers is required for Safety of Life at Sea (SOLAS) Convention regulated vessels (merchant vessels greater than 300 gross tons and passenger vessels on international voyages) after 1993.

(293)　Questions and comments concerning the NAVTEX service in the United States are solicited. Correspondence should be addressed to:

(294)　Commandant (G-TTS-3/63)

(295)　United States Coast Guard

(296)　Washington, DC 20593-0001

(297)　Telex: 89-2427 COMDT COGARD Washington, D.C.

(298)　**NOAA Weather Radio.**–The National Weather Service operates **VHF-FM radio stations,** usually on frequencies **162.40, 162.475, or 162.55 MHz,** to provide continuous recorded weather broadcasts. These broadcasts are available to those with suitable receivers within about 40 miles of the antenna site. (See the appendix for a list of these stations in the area covered by this Coast Pilot.)

(299)　**Commercial radiotelephone coast stations.**–Broadcasts of coastal weather and warnings are made by some commercial radiotelephone coast stations (marine operators) on the normal transmitting frequencies of the stations. Vessels with suitable receivers and desiring this service may determine the frequencies and schedules of these broadcasts from their local stations, from Selected Worldwide Marine Weather Broadcasts, or from the series of Marine Weather Services Charts published by NWS.

(300)　**Local broadcast-band radio stations.**–Many local radio stations in the standard AM and FM broadcast band give local marine weather forecasts from NWS on a regular schedule. These stations are listed on the series of Marine Weather Services Charts published by NWS.

(301)　**Reports from ships.**–The master of every U.S. ship equipped with radio transmitting apparatus, on meeting

with a tropical cyclone, dangerous ice, subfreezing air temperatures with gale force winds causing severe ice accretion on superstructures, derelict, or any other direct danger to navigation, is required to cause to be transmitted a report of these dangers to ships in the vicinity and to the appropriate Government agencies.

(302)　During the West Indies hurricane season, June 1 to November 30, ships in the Gulf of Mexico, Caribbean Sea area, southern North Atlantic Ocean, and the Pacific waters west of Central America and Mexico are urged to cooperate with NWS in furnishing these special reports in order that warnings to shipping and coastal areas may be issued.

(303)　**Time Signals.**–The **National Institute of Standards and Technology** broadcasts time signals continuously, day and night, from its radio stations WWV, near Fort Collins, Colorado, (40°49′49″N., 105°02′27″W.) on frequencies of 2.5, 5, 10, 15, and 20 MHz, and WWVH, Kekaha, Kauai, Hawaii (21°59′26″N., 159°46′00″W.) on frequencies 2.5, 5, 10, and 15 MHz. Services include time announcements, standard time intervals, standard audio frequencies, Omega Navigation System status reports, geophysical alerts, BCD (binary coded decimal) time code, UT1 time corrections, and high seas storm information.

(304)　Time announcements are made every minute, commencing at 15 seconds before the minute by a female voice and at 7½ seconds before the minute by a male voice, from WWVH and WWV, respectively. The time given is in Coordinated Universal Time (UTC) and referred to the time at Greenwich, England, i.e., Greenwich Mean Time.

(305)　**NIST Time and Frequency Dissemination Services, Special Publication 432,** gives a detailed description of the time and frequency dissemination services of the **National Institute of Standards and Technology.** Single copies may be obtained upon request from the National Institute of Standards and Technology, Time and Frequency Division, Boulder, CO 80303. Quantities may be obtained from the Government Printing Office (see appendix for address).

NAUTICAL CHARTS

(306)　**Reporting chart deficiencies.**–Users are requested to report all significant observed discrepancies in and desirable additions to NOS nautical charts, including depth information in privately maintained channels and basins; obstructions, wrecks, and other dangers; new landmarks or the nonexistence or relocation of charted ones; uncharted fixed private aids to navigation; and deletions or additions of small-craft facilities. All such reports should be sent to Director, Coast and Geodetic Survey (N/CG22), National Ocean Service, NOAA, Rockville, MD 20852-3806.

(307)　**Chart symbols and abbreviations.**–The standard symbols and abbreviations approved for use on all regular nautical charts published by the Defense Mapping Agency Hydrographic/Topographic Center and NOS are contained in **Chart No. 1,** United States of America **Nautical Chart Symbols and Abbreviations.** This publication is available from the Defense Mapping Agency Office of Distribution Services and NOS, and their sales agents.

(308)　On certain foreign charts reproduced by the United States, and on foreign charts generally, the symbols and abbreviations used may differ from U.S. approved standards. It is, therefore, recommended that navigators who acquire and use foreign charts and reproductions procure the symbol sheet or Chart No. 1 produced by the same foreign agency.

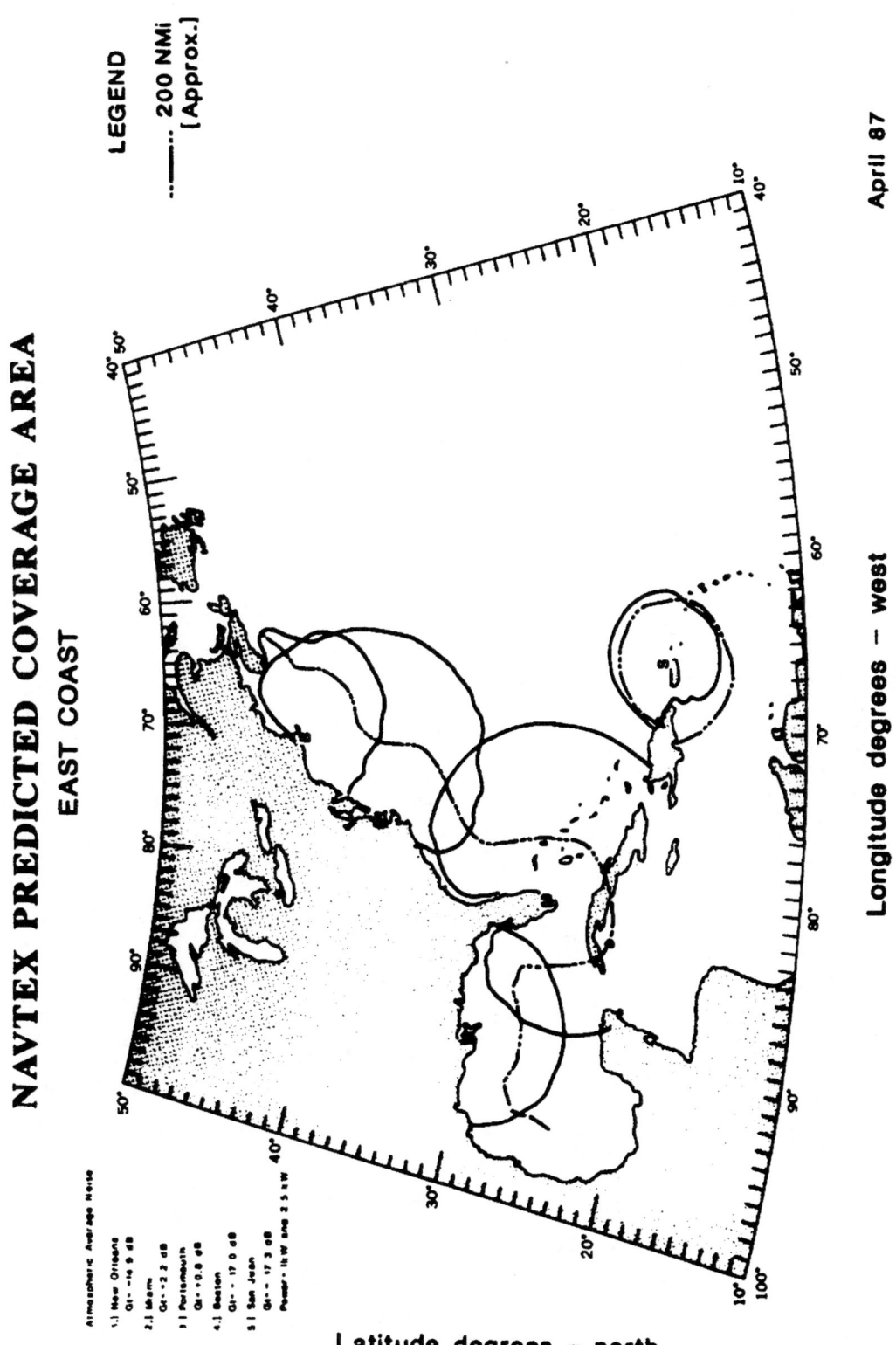

NAVTEX PREDICTED COVERAGE AREA
EAST COAST

LEGEND

------ 200 NMi
(Approx.)

April 87

Longitude degrees – west

Latitude degrees – north

(309)　The mariner is warned that the buoyage systems, shapes, and colors used by other countries often have a different significance than the U.S. system.

(310)　**Chart Datum.**–Chart Datum is the particular tidal datum to which soundings and depth curves on a nautical chart or bathymetric map are referred. The tidal datum of **Mean Low Water** has been used as Chart Datum along the east coast of the United States and in parts of the West Indies. It is presently being changed to Mean Lower Low Water, with no adjustments to soundings, shorelines, low water lines, clearances, heights, elevations, or in the application of tide predictions for navigational purposes. The tidal datum of **Mean Lower Low Water** is used as Chart Datum along the Gulf and west coasts; the coasts of Alaska, Hawaii, and other United States and United Nations islands of the Pacific; and in parts of the West Indies.

(311)　Mean Low Water is defined as the arithmetic mean of all the low water heights observed over the National Tidal Datum Epoch. Mean Lower Low Water is defined as the arithmetic mean of the lower low water height of each tidal day (24.84 hours) observed over the National Tidal Datum Epoch. The National Tidal Datum Epoch is the specific 19-year period adopted by the National Ocean Service, NOAA, as the official time segment over which tide observations are taken and reduced to obtain mean values for tidal datums. The present Epoch is 1960 through 1978.

(312)　**Accuracy of a nautical chart.**–The value of a nautical chart depends upon the accuracy of the surveys on which it is based. The chart reflects what was found by field surveys and what has been reported to NOS Headquarters. The chart represents general conditions at the time of surveys or reports and does not necessarily portray present conditions. Significant changes may have taken place since the date of the last survey or report.

(313)　Each sounding represents an actual measure of depth and location at the time the survey was made, and each bottom characteristic represents a sampling of the surface layer of the sea bottom at the time of the sampling. Areas where sand and mud prevail, especially the entrances and approaches to bays and rivers exposed to strong tidal current and heavy seas, are subject to continual change.

(314)　In coral regions and where rocks and boulders abound, it is always possible that surveys may have failed to find every obstruction. Thus, when navigating such waters, customary routes and channels should be followed and areas avoided where irregular and sudden changes in depth indicate conditions associated with pinnacle rocks, coral heads, or boulders.

(315)　Information charted as "reported" should be treated with caution in navigating the area, because the actual conditions have not been verified by government surveys.

(316)　**The date of a chart** is of vital importance to the navigator. When charted information becomes obsolete, further use of the chart for navigation may be dangerous. Announcements of new editions of nautical charts are usually published in notices to mariners. A quarterly list of the latest editions is distributed to sales agents; free copies may be obtained from the sales agents or by writing to Distribution Branch (N/CG33), National Ocean Service. (See appendix for address.)

(317)　**U.S. Nautical Chart Numbering System.**– This chart numbering system, adopted by the National Ocean Service and the Defense Mapping Agency Hydrographic/Topographic Center, provides for a uniform method of identifying charts published by both agencies. Nautical charts published by the Defense Mapping Agency Hydrographic/

Topographic Center are identified in the Coast Pilot by an asterisk preceding the chart number.

(318)　**Corrections to charts.**–It is essential for navigators to keep charts corrected through information published in the notices to mariners, especially since the NOS no longer hand-corrects charts prior to distribution.

(319)　**Caution in using small-scale charts.**–Dangers to navigation cannot be shown with the same amount of detail on small-scale charts as on those of larger scale. Therefore, the largest scale chart of an area should always be used.

(320)　The **scales of nautical charts** range from 1:2,500 to about 1:5,000,000. Graphic scales are generally shown on charts with scales of 1:80,000 or larger, and numerical scales are given on smaller scale charts. NOS charts are classified according to scale as follows:

(321)　**Sailing charts,** scales 1:600,000 and smaller, are for use in fixing the mariner's position as he approaches the coast from the open ocean, or for sailing between distant coastwise ports. On such charts the shoreline and topography are generalized and only offshore soundings, and the principal lights, outer buoys, and landmarks visible at considerable distances are shown.

(322)　**General charts,** scales 1:150,000 to 1:600,000, are for coastwise navigation outside of outlying reefs and shoals.

(323)　**Coast charts,** scales 1:50,000 to 1:150,000 are for inshore navigation leading to bays and harbors of considerable width and for navigating large inland waterways.

(324)　**Harbor charts,** scales larger than 1:50,000, are for harbors, anchorage areas, and the smaller waterways.

(325)　**Special charts,** various scales, cover the Intracoastal waterways and miscellaneous small-craft areas.

(326)　**Blue tint in water areas.**–A blue tint is shown in water areas on many charts to accentuate shoals and other areas considered dangerous for navigation when using that particular chart.Since the danger curve varies with the intended purpose of a chart a careful inspection should be made to determine the contour depth of the blue tint areas.

(327)　**Caution on bridge and cable clearances.**–For bascule bridges whose spans do not open to a full vertical position, unlimited overhead clearance is not available for the entire charted horizontal clearance when the bridge is open, due to the inclination of the drawspans over the channel.

(328)　The charted clearances of overhead cables are for the lowest wires at mean high water unless otherwise stated. **Vessels with masts, stacks, booms, or antennas should allow sufficient clearance under power cables to avoid arcing.**

(329)　**Submarine cables and pipelines** cross many waterways used by both large and small vessels, but all of them may not be charted. For inshore areas, they usually are buried beneath the seabed, but, for offshore areas, they may lie on the ocean floor. Warning signs are often posted to warn mariners of their existence.

(330)　The installation of submarine cables or pipelines in U.S. waters or the Continental Shelf of the United States is under the jurisdiction of one or more Federal agencies, depending on the nature of the installation. They are shown on the charts when the necessary information is reported to NOS and they have been recommended for charting by the cognizant agency. The chart symbols for submarine cable and pipeline areas are usually shown for inshore areas, whereas, chart symbols for submarine cable and pipeline routes may be shown for offshore areas. Submarine cables and pipelines are not described in the Coast Pilots.

(331)　In view of the serious consequences resulting from damage to submarine cables and pipelines, vessel operators should take special care when anchoring, fishing, or engaging in underwater operations near areas where these cables or pipelines may exist or have been reported to exist. Mariners are also warned that the areas where cables and pipelines were originally buried may have changed and they may be exposed; extreme caution should be used when operating vessels in depths of water comparable to the vessel's draft.

(332) Certain cables carry high voltage, while many pipelines carry natural gas under high pressure or petroleum products. Electrocution, fire, or explosion with injury, loss of life, or a serious pollution incident could occur if they are broached.

(333) Vessels fouling a submarine cable or pipeline should attempt to clear without undue strain. Anchors or gear that cannot be cleared should be slipped, but no attempt should be made to cut a cable or a pipeline.

(334) **Artificial obstructions to navigation.**—Disposal areas are designated by the Corps of Engineers for depositing dredged material where existing depths indicate that the intent is not to cause sufficient shoaling to create a danger to surface navigation. The areas are charted without blue tint, and soundings and depth curves are retained.

(335) **Disposal Sites** are areas established by Federal regulation (**40 CFR 220-229**) in which dumping of dredged and fill material and other nonbuoyant objects is allowed with the issuance of a permit. Dumping of dredged and fill material is supervised by the Corps of Engineers and all other dumping by the Environmental Protection Agency (EPA). (See Corps of Engineers and Environmental Protection Agency, this chapter, and appendix for office addresses.)

(336) **Dumping Grounds** are also areas that were established by Federal regulation (**33 CFR 205**). However, these regulations have been revoked and the use of the areas discontinued. These areas will continue to be shown on nautical charts until such time as they are no longer considered to be a danger to navigation.

(337) Disposal Sites and Dumping Grounds are rarely mentioned in the Coast Pilot, but are shown on nautical charts. **Mariners are advised to exercise caution in and in the vicinity of all dumping areas.**

(338) **Spoil areas** are for the purpose of depositing dredged material, usually near and parallel to dredged channels; they are usually a hazard to navigation. Spoil areas are usually charted from survey drawings from Corps of Engineers after-dredging surveys, though they may originate from private or other Government agency surveys. Spoil areas are tinted blue on the charts and labeled, and all soundings and depth curves are omitted. Navigators of even the smallest craft should avoid crossing spoil areas.

(339) **Fish havens** are established by private interests, usually sport fishermen, to simulate natural reefs and wrecks that attract fish. The reefs are constructed by dumping assorted junk ranging from old trolley cars and barges to scrap building material in areas which may be of very small extent or may stretch a considerable distance along a depth curve; oil automobile bodies are a commonly used material. The Corps of Engineers must issue a permit, specifying the location and depth over the reef, before such a reef may be built. However, the reefbuilders' adherence to permit specifications can be checked only with a wire drag. Fish havens are outlined and labeled on the charts and show the minimum authorized depth when known. Fish havens are tinted blue if they have a minimum authorized depth of 11 fathoms or less or if the minimum authorized depth is unknown and they are in depths greater than 11 fathoms but still considered a danger to navigation. Navigators should be cautious about passing over fish havens or anchoring in their vicinity.

(340) **Fishtrap areas** are areas established by the Corps of Engineers, or State or local authority, in which traps may be built and maintained according to established regulations. The fish stakes which may exist in these areas are obstructions to navigation and may be dangerous. The limits of fishtrap areas and a cautionary note are usually charted. Navigators should avoid these areas.

(341) **Local magnetic disturbances.**—If measured values of magnetic variation differ from the expected (charted) values by several degrees, a magnetic disturbance note will be printed on the chart. The note will indicate the location and magnitude of the disturbance, but the indicated magnitude should not be considered as the largest possible value that may be encountered. Large disturbances are more frequently detected in the shallow waters near land masses than on the deep sea. Generally, the effect of a local magnetic disturbance diminishes rapidly with distance, but in some locations there are multiple sources of disturbances and the effects may be distributed for many miles.

(342) **Compass roses on charts.**—Each compass rose shows the date, magnetic variation, and the annual change in variation. Prior to the new edition of a nautical chart, the compass roses are reviewed. Corrections for annual change and other revisions may be made as a result of newer and more accurate information. On some general and sailing charts, the magnetic variation is shown by isogonic lines in addition to the compass roses.

(343) The **Mercator projection** used on most nautical charts has straight-line meridians and parallels that intersect at right angles. On any particular chart the distances between meridians are equal throughout, but distances between parallels increase progressively from the Equator toward the poles, so that a straight line between any two points is a rhumb line. This unique property of the Mercator projection is one of the main reasons why it is preferred by the mariner.

(344) **Echo soundings.**—Ship's echo sounders may indicate small variations from charted soundings; this may be due to the fact that various corrections (instrument corrections, settlement and squat, draft, and velocity corrections) are made to echo soundings in surveying which are not normally made in ordinary navigation, or to observational errors in reading the echo sounder. Instrument errors vary between different equipment and must be determined by calibration aboard ship. Most types of echo sounders are factory calibrated for a velocity of sound in water of 800 fathoms per second, but the actual velocity may differ from the calibrated velocity by as much as 5 percent, depending upon the temperature and salinity of the waters in which the vessel is operating; the highest velocities are found in warm, highly saline water, and the lowest in icy freshwater. Velocity corrections for these variations are determined and applied to echo soundings during hydrographic surveys. All echo soundings must be corrected for the vessel's draft, unless the draft observation has been set on the echo sounder.

(345) Observational errors include misinterpreting false echos from schools of fish, seaweed, etc., but the most serious error which commonly occurs is where the depth is greater than the scale range of the instrument; a 400–fathom scale indicates 15 fathoms when the depth is 415 fathoms. Caution in navigation should be exercised when wide variations from charted depths are observed.

AIDS TO NAVIGATION

(346) **Reporting of defects in aids to navigation.**—Promptly notify the nearest Coast Guard District Commander if an aid to navigation is observed to be missing, sunk, capsized,

out of position, damaged, extinguished, or showing improper characteristics.

(347)   Radio messages should be prefixed "Coast Guard" and transmitted directly to any U.S. Government shore radio station for relay to the Coast Guard District Commander. If the radio call sign of the nearest U.S. Government radio shore station is not known, radiotelegraph communication may be established by the use of the general call "NCG" on the frequency of 500 kHz. Merchant ships may send messages relating to defects noted in aids to navigation through commercial facilities only when they are unable to contact a U.S. Government shore radio station. Charges for these messages will be accepted "collect" by the Coast Guard.

(348)   **Lights.**–The range of visibility of lights as given in the Light Lists and as shown on the charts is the **Nominal range,** which is the maximum distance at which a light may be seen in clear weather (meteorological visibility of 10 nautical miles) expressed in nautical miles. The Light Lists give the Nominal ranges for all Coast Guard lighted aids except range and directional lights. **Luminous range** is the maximum distance at which a light may be seen under the existing visibility conditions. By use of the diagram in the Light Lists, Luminous range may be determined from the known Nominal range, and the existing visibility conditions. Both the Nominal and Luminous ranges do not take into account elevation, observer's height of eye, or the curvature of the earth. **Geographic range** is a function of only the curvature of the earth and is determined solely from the heights above sea level of the light and the observer's eye; therefore, to determine the actual Geographic range for a height of eye, the Geographic range must be corrected by a distance corresponding to the height difference, the distance correction being determined from a table of "distances of visibility for various heights above sea level." (See Light List or Coast Pilot table following appendix.) The maximum distances at which lights can be seen may at times be increased by abnormal atmospheric refraction and may be greatly decreased by unfavorable weather conditions such as fog, rain, haze, or smoke. All except the most powerful lights are easily obscured by such conditions. In some conditions of the atmosphere white lights may have a reddish hue. During weather conditions which tend to reduce visibility, colored lights are more quickly lost to sight than are white lights. Navigational lights should be used with caution because of the following conditions that may exist;

(349)   A light may be extinguished and the fact not reported to the Coast Guard for correction, or a light may be located in an isolated area where it will take time to correct.

(350)   In regions where ice conditions prevail the lantern panes of unattended lights may become covered with ice or snow, which will greatly reduce the visibility and may also cause colored lights to appear white.

(351)   Brilliant shore lights used for advertising and other purposes, particularly those in densely populated areas, make it difficult to identify a navigational light.

(352)   At short distances flashing lights may show a faint continuous light between flashes.

(353)   The distance of an observer from a light cannot be estimated by its apparent intensity. The characteristics of lights in an area should always be checked in order that powerful lights visible in the distance will not be mistaken for nearby lights showing similar characteristics at low intensity such as those on lighted buoys.

(354)   The apparent characteristic of a complex light may change with the distance of the observer, due to color and intensity variations among the different lights of the group.

The characteristic as charted and shown in the Light List may not be recognized until nearer the light.

(355)   Motion of a vessel in a heavy sea may cause a light to alternately appear and disappear, and thus give a false characteristic.

(356)   Where lights have different colored sectors, be guided by the correct bearing of the light; do not rely on being able to accurately observe the point at which the color changes. On either side of the line of demarcation of colored sectors there is always a small arc of uncertain color.

(357)   On some bearings from the light, the range of visibility of the light may be reduced by obstructions. In such cases, the obstructed arc might differ with height of eye and distance. When a light is cut off by adjoining land and the arc of visibility is given, the bearing on which the light disappears may vary with the distance of the vessel from which observed and with the height of eye. When the light is cut ·off by a sloping hill or point of land, the light may be seen over a wider arc by a ship far off than by one close to.

(358)   Arcs of circles drawn on charts around a light are not intended to give information as to the distance at which it can be seen, but solely to indicate, in the case of lights which do not show equally in all directions, the bearings between which the variation of visibility or obscuration of the light occurs.

(359)   Lights of equal candlepower but of different colors may be seen at different distances. This fact should be considered not only in predicting the distance at which a light can be seen, but also in identifying it.

(360)   Lights should not be passed close aboard, because in many cases riprap mounds are maintained to protect the structure against ice damage and scouring action.

(361)   Many prominent towers, tanks, smokestacks, buildings, and other similar structures, charted as landmarks, display flashing and/or fixed red aircraft obstruction lights. Lights shown from landmarks are charted only when they have distinctive characteristics to enable the mariner to positively identify the location of the charted structure.

(362)   **Articulated lights.**–An articulated light is a vertical pipe structure supported by a submerged buoyancy chamber and attached by a universal coupling to a weighted sinker on the seafloor. The light, allowed to move about by the universal coupling, is not as precise as a fixed aid. However, it has a much smaller watch circle than a conventional buoy, because the buoyancy chamber tends to force the pipe back to a vertical position when it heels over under the effects of wind, wave, or current.

(363)   Articulated daybeacons.-Same description as for articulated lights (see above) except substitute daybeacon for light.

(364)   **Bridge lights and clearance gages.**–The Coast Guard regulates marine obstruction lights and clearance gages on bridges across navigable waters. Where installed, clearance gages are generally vertical numerical scales, reading from top to bottom, and show the actual vertical clearance between the existing water level and the lowest point of the bridge over the channel; the gages are normally on the right-hand pier or abutment of the bridge, on both the upstream and downstream sides.

(365)   Bridge lights are fixed red or green, and are privately maintained; they are generally not charted or described in the text of the Coast Pilot. All bridge piers (and their protective fenders) and abutments which are in or adjacent to a navigation channel are marked on all channel sides by red lights. On each channel span of a fixed bridge, there is a range of two green lights marking the center of the channel and a red light marking both edges of the channel, except

that when the margins of the channel are confined by bridge piers, the red lights on the span are omitted, since the pier lights then mark the channel edges; for multiplespan fixed bridges, the main-channel span may also be marked by three white lights in a vertical line above the green range lights.

(366)   On all types of drawbridges, one or more red lights are shown from the drawspan (higher than the pier lights) when the span is closed; when the span is open, the higher red lights are obscured and one or two green lights are shown from the drawspan, higher than the pier lights. The number and location of the red and green lights depend upon the type of drawbridge.

(367)   Bridges and their lighting, construction, maintenance, and operation are set forth in **33 CFR 114-118** (not carried in this Coast Pilot). Aircraft obstruction lights, prescribed by the Federal Aviation Administration, may operate at certain bridges. Drawbridge operation regulations are published in chapter 2 of the Coast Pilot.

(368)   **Fog signals.**–Caution should be exercised in the use of sound fog signals for navigation purposes. They should be considered solely as warning devices.

(369)   Sound travels through the air in a variable manner, even without the effects of wind; and, therefore, the hearing of fog signals cannot be implicitly relied upon.

(370)   Experience indicates that distances must not be judged only by the intensity of the sound; that occasionally there may be areas close to a fog signal in which it is not heard; and that fog may exist not far from a station, yet not be seen from it, so the signal may not be operating. It is not always possible to start a fog signal immediately when fog is observed.

(371)   **Avoidance of collision with offshore light stations and large navigational buoys (LNB).**–Courses should invariably be set to pass these aids with sufficient clearance to avoid the possibility of collision from any cause. Errors of observation, current and wind effects, other vessels in the vicinity, and defects in steering gear may be, and have been the cause of actual collisions, or imminent danger thereof, needlessly jeopardizing the safety of these facilities and their crews, and of all navigation dependent on these important aids to navigation.

(372)   Experience shows that offshore light stations cannot be safely used as leading marks to be passed close aboard, but should always be left broad off the course, whenever sea room permits. When approaching fixed offshore light structures and large navigational buoys (LNB) on radio bearings, the risk of collision will be avoided by ensuring that radio bearing does not remain constant.

(373)   It should be borne in mind that most large buoys are anchored to a very long scope of chain and, as a result, the radius of their swinging circle is considerable. The charted position is the location of the anchor. Furthermore under certain conditions of wind and current, they are subject to sudden and unexpected sheers which are certain to hazard a vessel attempting to pass close aboard.

(374)   **Buoys.**–The aids to navigation depicted on charts comprise a system consisting of fixed and floating aids with varying degrees of reliability. Therefore, prudent mariners will not rely solely on any single aid to navigation, particularly a floating aid.

(375)   The approximate position of a buoy is represented by the dot or circle associated with the buoy symbol. The approximate position is used because of practical limitations in positioning and maintaining buoys and their sinkers in precise geographical locations. These limitations include, but are not limited to, inherent imprecisions in position fixing methods, prevailing atmospheric and sea conditions, the

slope of and the material making up the seabed, the fact that buoys are moored to sinkers by varying lengths of chain, and the fact that buoy body and/or sinker positions are not under continuous surveillance, but are normally checked only during periodic maintenance visits which often occur more than a year apart. The position of the buoy body can be expected to shift inside and outside of the charting symbol due to the forces of nature. The mariner is also cautioned that buoys are liable to be carried away, shifted, capsized, sunk, etc. Lighted buoys may be extinguished or sound signals may not function as a result of ice, running ice or other natural causes, collisions, or other accidents.

(376)   For the foregoing reasons, a prudent mariner must not rely completely upon the charted position or operation of floating aids to navigation, but will also utilize bearings from fixed objects and aids to navigation on shore. Further, a vessel attempting to pass close aboard always risks collision with a yawing buoy or with the obstruction the buoy marks.

(377)   Buoys may not always properly mark shoals or other obstructions due to shifting of the shoals or of the buoys. Buoys marking wrecks or other obstructions are usually placed on the seaward or channelward side and not directly over a wreck. Since buoys may be located some distance from a wreck they are intended to mark, and since sunken wrecks are not always static, extreme caution should be exercised when operating in the vicinity of such buoys.

(378)   **Caution, channel markers.**–Lights, daybeacons, and buoys along dredged channels do not always mark the bottom edges. Due to local conditions, aids may be located inside or outside the channel limits shown by dashed lines on a chart. The Light List tabulates the offset distances for these aids in many instances.

(379)   Aids may be moved, discontinued, or replaced by other types to facilitate dredging operations. Mariners should exercise caution when navigating areas where dredges with auxiliary equipment are working.

(380)   Temporary changes in aids are not included on the charts.

(381)   **Radiobeacons.**–A map showing the locations and operating details of marine radiobeacons is given in each Light List. This publication describes the procedure to follow in using radiobeacons to calibrate radio direction finders as well as listing special radio direction finder calibration stations.

(382)   A vessel steering a course for a radiobeacon should observe the same precautions as when steering for a light or any other mark. If the radiobeacon is aboard a lightship, particular care should be exercised to avoid the possibility of collision, and sole reliance should never be placed on sighting the lightship or hearing its fog signal. If there are no dependable means by which the vessel's position may be fixed and the course changed well before reaching the lightship, a course should be selected that will ensure passing the lightship at a distance, rather than close aboard, and repeated bearings of the radiobeacon should show an increasing change in the same direction.

(383)   **Radio bearings.**–No exact data can be given as to the accuracy to be expected in radio bearings taken by a ship, since the accuracy depends to a large extent upon the skill of the ship's operator, the condition of the ship's equipment, and the accuracy of the ship's calibration curve. Mariners are urged to obtain this information for themselves by taking frequent radio bearings, when their ship's position is accurately known, and recording the results.

(384)   Radio bearings obtained at twilight or at night, and bearings which are almost parallel to the coast, should be

accepted with reservations, due to "night effect" and to the distortion of radio waves which travel overland. Bearings of aircraft ranges and standard broadcast stations should be used with particular caution due to coastal refraction and lack of calibration of their frequencies.

(385) **Conversion of radio bearings to Mercator bearings.**–Radio directional bearings are the bearings of the great circles passing through the radio stations and the ship, and, unless in the plane of the Equator or a meridian, would be represented on a Mercator chart as curved lines. Obviously it is impracticable for a navigator to plot such lines on a Mercator chart, so it is necessary to apply a correction to a radio bearing to convert it into a Mercator bearing, that is, the bearing of a straight line on a Mercator chart laid off from the sending station and passing through the receiving station.

(386) A table of corrections for the conversion of a radio bearing into a Mercator bearing follows the appendix. It is sufficiently accurate for practical purposes for distances up to 1,000 miles.

(387) The only data required are the latitudes and longitudes of the radiobeacons and of the ship by dead reckoning. The latter is scaled from the chart, and the former is either scaled from the chart or taken from the Light List.

(388) The table is entered with the differences of longitude in degrees between the ship and station (the nearest tabulated value being used), and opposite the middle latitude between the ship and station, the correction to be applied is read.

(389) The sign of the correction (bearings read clockwise from the north) will be as follows: In north latitude, the minus sign is used when the ship is east of the radiobeacon and the plus sign used when the ship is west of the radiobeacon. In south latitude, the plus sign is used when the ship is east of the radiobeacon, and the minus sign is used when the ship is west of the radiobeacon.

(390) To facilitate plotting, 180 degrees should be added to or subtracted from the corrected bearing, and the result plotted from the radiobeacon.

(391) Should the position by dead reckoning differ greatly from the true position of the ship as determined by plotting the corrected bearings, retrial should be made, using the new value as the position of the ship.

(392) **Radio bearings from other vessels.**–Any vessel with a radio direction-finder can take a bearing on a vessel equipped with a radio transmitter. These bearings, however, should be used only as a check, as comparatively large errors may be introduced by local conditions surrounding the radio direction-finder unless known and accounted for. Although any radio station, for which an accurate position is definitely known, may serve as a radiobeacon for vessels equipped with a radio direction-finder, extreme caution must be exercised in their use. Stations established especially for maritime services are more reliable.

(393) **SATELLITE POSITION INDICATING RADIO BEACON (EPIRB).**–Emergency position indicating radiobeacons (EPIRBs), devices which cost from $200 to over $2000, are designed to save your life if you get into trouble by alerting rescue authorities and indicating your location. EPIRB types are described in the accompanying table.

(394) **121.5/243 MHz EPIRBs.** These are the most common and least expensive type of EPIRB, designed to be detected by overflying commercial or military aircraft. Satellites were designed to detect these EPIRBs, but are limited for the following reasons:

(395) (i) Satellite detection range is limited for these EPIRBs (satellites must be within line of sight of both the

EPIRB Types		
Type	Frequency	Description
Class A	121.5/243 MHz	Float-free, automatically-activating, detectable by aircraft and satellite. Coverage limited (see Chart).
Class B	121.5/243 MHz	Manually activated version of Class A.
Class C	VHF ch 15/16	Manually activated, operates on maritime channels only. Not detectable by satellite.
Class S	121.5/243 MHz	Similar to Class B, except it floats, or is an integral part of a survival craft.
Cat I	406/121.5 MHz	Float-free, automatically activated EPIRB. Detectable by satellite anywhere in the world.
Cat II	406/121.5 MHz	Similar to Category I, except is manually activated.

EPIRB and a ground terminal for detection to occur) (see Chart),

(396) (ii) EPIRB design and frequency congestion cause these devices to be subject to a high false alert/false alarm rate (over 99%); consequently, confirmation is required before search and rescue forces can be deployed.

(397) (iii) EPIRBs manufactured before October 1989 may have design or construction problems (e.g. some models will leak and cease operating when immersed in water), or may not be detectable by satellite.

(398) **Class C EPIRBs.** These are manually activated devices intended for pleasure craft who do not venture far offshore and for vessels on the Great Lakes. They transmit a short burst on VHF-FM channel 16 and a longer homing signal on channel 15. Their usefulness depends upon a coast station or another vessel guarding channel 16 and recognizing the brief, recurring tone as an EPIRB. Class C EPIRBs are not recognized outside of the United States.

(399) **406 MHz EPIRBs.**–The 406 MHz EPIRB was designed to operate with satellites. Its signal allows a satellite local user terminal to accurately locate the EPIRB (much more accurately than 121.5/243 MHz devices), and identify the vessel (the signal is encoded with the vessel's identity) anywhere in the world (there is no range limitation). These devices also include a 121.5 MHz homing signal, allowing aircraft and rescue craft to quickly find the vessel in distress. These are the only type of EPIRB which must be certified by Coast Guard approved independent laboratories before they can be sold in the United States.

(400) An automatically activated, float-free version of this EPIRB will be required on Safety of Life at Sea Convention vessels (passenger ships and ships over 300 tons, on international voyages) of any nationality by 1 August 1993. The Coast Guard requires U.S. commercial fishing vessels carry this device (by May 1990, unless they carry a Class A EPIRB), and will require the same for other U.S. commercial uninspected vessels which travel more than 3 miles offshore.

(401) The **COSPAS-SARSAT system.**–COSPAS: Space System for Search of Distress Vessels (a Russian acronym); SARSAT: Search and Rescue Satellite-Aided Tracking. COSPAS-SARSAT is an international satellite-based search

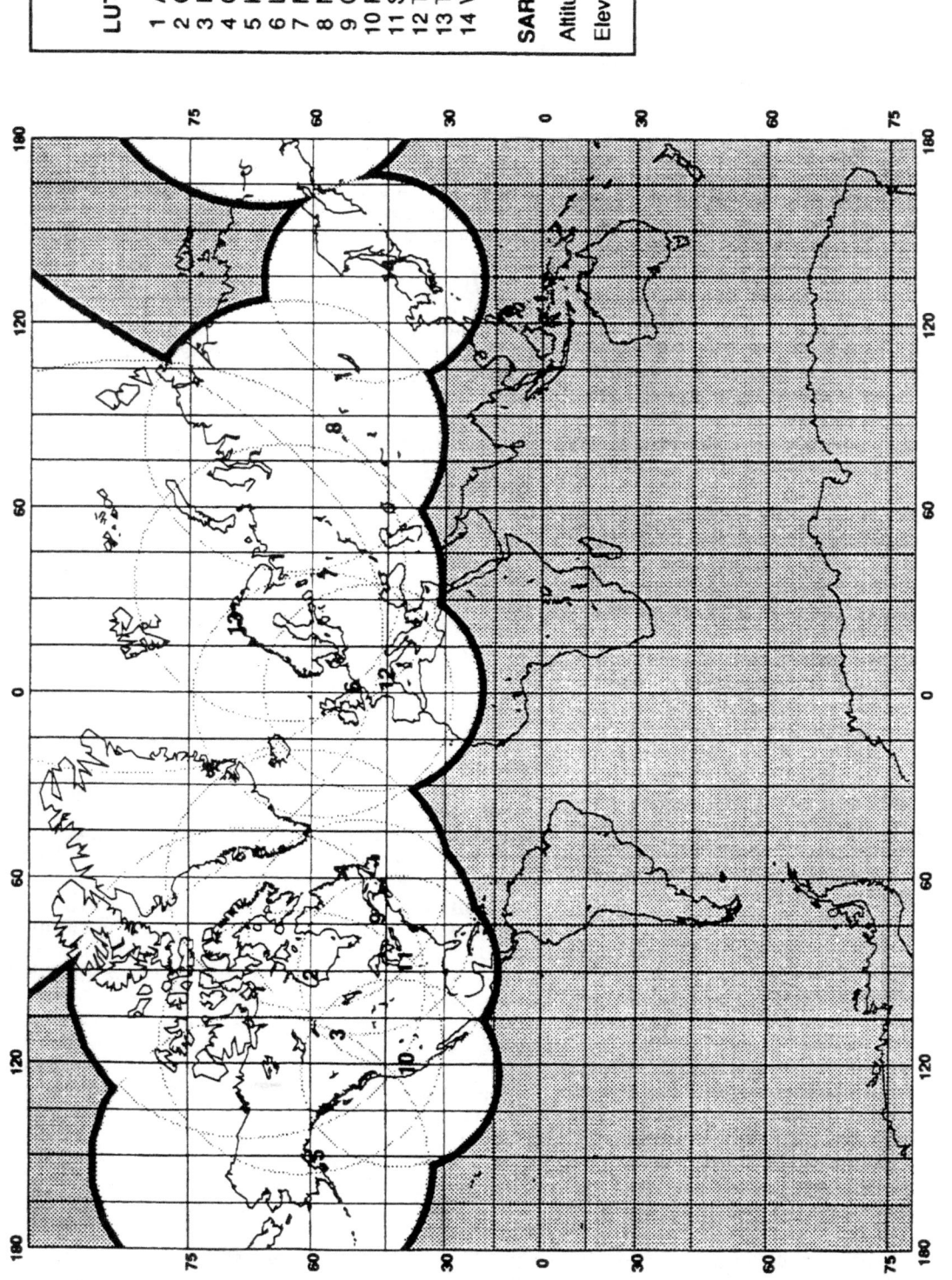

Notes

LUTs

1 Archangelsk
2 Churchill
3 Edmonton
4 Goose Bay
5 Kodiak
6 Lasham
7 Moscow
8 Novosibirsk
9 Ottawa
10 Pt. Reyes
11 Scott AFB
12 Toulouse
13 Tromsø
14 Vladivostok

SARSAT satellite

Altitude   850 km
Elevation Angle   5 deg

1988 Satellite Visibility Area of SARSAT LUTs
(represents approximate System coverage at 121.5 MHz;
at 406 MHz, the System covers the entire globe)

and rescue system established by the U.S., U.S.S.R., Canada and France to locate emergency radio beacons transmitting on the frequencies 121.5, 243 and 406 MHz. Since its inception only a few years ago, COSPAS-SARSAT has contributed to the saving of 1240 lives (as of June 6, 1989), 554 of these mariners. The Coast Guard operates two local user terminals, satellite earth stations designed to received EPIRB distress calls forwarded from COSPAS-SARSAT satellites, located in Kodiak, Alaska and Point Reyes, California. The Air Force operates a third terminal at Scott Air Force Base, Illinois.

(402)   **Testing EPIRBs.**–The Coast Guard urges those owning EPIRBs to periodically examine them for water tightness, battery expiration date and signal presence. FCC rules allow Class A, B, and S EPIRBs to be turned on briefly (for three audio sweeps, or one second only) during the first five minutes of each hour. Signal presence can be detected by an FM radio tuned to 99.5 MHz, or an AM radio tuned to any vacant frequency and located close to an EPIRB. FCC rules allow Class C EPIRBs to be tested within the first five minutes of every hour, for not more than five seconds. Class C EPIRBs can be detected by a marine radio tuned to channel 15 or 16. 406 MHz EPIRBs can be tested through its self-test function, which is an integral part of the device.

(403)   **Radar beacons (Racons)** are low-powered radio transceivers that operate in the marine radar X-band frequencies. When activated by a vessel's radar signal, **Racons** provide a distinctive visible display on the vessel's radarscope from which the range and bearing to the beacon may be determined. (See Light List and DMAHTC Pub. 117 for details.)

(404)   **LORAN-C.**–LORAN, an acronym for LOng RAnge Navigation, is an electronic aid to navigation consisting of shore-based radio transmitters. The LORAN system enables users equipped with a LORAN receiver to determine their position quickly and accurately, day or night, in practically any weather.

(405)   A LORAN-C chain consists of three to five transmitting stations separated by several hundred miles. Within a chain, one station is designated as master while the other stations are designated as secondaries. Each secondary station is identified as either whiskey, x-ray, yankee, or zulu.

(406)   The master station is always the first station to transmit. It transmits a series of nine pulses. The secondary stations then follow in turn, transmitting eight pulses each, at precisely timed intervals. This cycle repeats itself endlessly. The length of the cycle is measured in microseconds and is called a Group Repetition Interval (GRI).

(407)   LORAN-C chains are designated by the four most significant digits of their GRI. For example, a chain with a GRI of 89,700 microseconds is referred to as 8970. A different GRI is used for each chain because all LORAN-C stations broadcast in the same 90 to 110 kilohertz frequency band and would otherwise interfere with one another.

(408)   The LORAN-C system can be used in either a hyperbolic or range mode. In the widely used hyperbolic mode, a LORAN-C line of position is determined by measuring the time difference between sychronized pulses received from two separate transmitting stations. In the range mode, a line of position is determined by measuring the time required by LORAN-C pulses to travel from a transmitting station to the user's receiver.

(409)   A user's position is determined by locating the crossing point of two lines of position on a LORAN-C chart. Many receivers have built-in coordinate converters which will automatically display the receiver's latitude and longitude. With a coordinate converter, a position can be determined using a chart that is not overprinted with LORAN-C lines of position.

(410)   **CAUTION: The latitude/longitude computation on some models is based upon an all seawater propagation path. This may lead to error if the LORAN-C signals from the various stations involve appreciable overland propagation paths. These errors may put the mariner at risk in areas requiring precise positioning if the proper correctors (ASF) are not applied. Therefore, it is recommended that mariners using Coordinate Converters check the manufacturer's operating manual to determine if and how corrections are to be applied to compensate for the discontinuity caused by the overland paths.**

(411)   There are two types of LORAN-C accuracy: absolute and repeatable. Absolute accuracy is a measure of the navigator's ability to determine latitude and longitude position from the LORAN-C time differences measured. Repeatable accuracy is a measure of the LORAN-C navigator's ability to return to a position where readings have been taken before.

(412)   The absolute accuracy of LORAN-C is 0.25 nautical miles, 95% confidence within the published coverage area using standard LORAN-C charts and tables. Repeatable accuracy depends on many factors, so measurements must be taken to determine the repeatable accuracy in any given area. Coast Guard surveys have found repeatable accuracies between 30 and 170 meters in most ground wave coverage areas. LORAN-C position determination on or near the baseline extensions are subject to significant errors and, therefore, should be avoided whenever possible. The use of skywaves is not recommended within 250 miles of a station being used, and corrections for these areas are not usually tabulated.

(413)   If the timing or pulse shape of a master-secondary pair deviates from specified tolerances, the first two pulses of the secondary station's pulse train will blink on and off. The LORAN-C receiver sees this blinking signal and indicates a warning to the user. This warning will continue until the signals are once again in tolerance. A blinking signal is not exhibited during off-air periods, so a separate receiver alarm indicates any loss of signal. Never use a blinking secondary signal for navigation.

(414)   In coastal waters, LORAN-C should not be relied upon as the only aid to navigation. A prudent navigator will use radar, radio direction finder, fathometer and any other aid to navigation, in addition to the LORAN-C receiver.

(415)   **LORAN-C Interference**

(416)   Interference to LORAN-C may result from radio transmissions by public or private sources operating near the LORAN-C band of 90-110 kHz. Anyone using the LORAN-C system, who observes interference to LORAN-C, should promptly report it to one of the Coast Guard commands listed below. Include in such reports information regarding the date, time, identifying characteristics, strength of the interfering signals and your own vessel's position. These interference reports are very important and cooperation from users of LORAN-C will assist the Coast Guard in improving LORAN-C service.

(417)   **Atlantic Ocean and Gulf of Mexico**
(418)   Commander (Atl)
(419)   Atlantic Area, U.S. Coast Guard
(420)   Governors Island
(421)   New York, NY 10004-5000
(422)   **Pacific Ocean**
(423)   Commander (Ptl)

(424) Pacific Area, U.S. Coast Guard

(425) Coast Guard Island

(426) Alameda, CA 94501-5100

(427) **All areas**

(428) Commandant (G-NRN)

(429) U.S. Coast Guard

(430) Washington, DC 20593-0001

(431) **LORAN-C Charts and Publications**

(432) Navigational charts overprinted with LORAN-C lines of position are published by the National Ocean Service (NOS), Distribution Branch (N/CG33), 6501 Lafayette Avenue, Riverdale, MD 20737-1199 and the Defense Mapping Agency (DMA), Combat Support Center, Code: PMSR, Washington, DC 20315-0010, and may be purchased directly from NOS or DMA, or through local chart sales agents.

(433) A general source of LORAN-C information is the LORAN-C User Handbook written by the U.S. Coast Guard. This publication can be purchased from the Government Printing Office, Washington, DC (see appendix for address).

(434) **Omega.**–Omega is a continuous radionavigation system which provides hyperbolic lines of position through phase comparisons of very low frequency (10-14 kHz range) continuous wave signals transmitted on a common frequency on a time shared basis. With eight transmitting stations located throughout the world, Omega provides worldwide, all-weather navigation coverage. Six stations make Omega available in nearly all parts of the globe, with the two other stations providing redundancy and coverage during off-air time for maintenance.

(435) Users are cautioned that the Omega system is in an implementation stage. System changes and station off-air periods are promulgated by Notice to Mariners and radio navigational warning messages. Current information on the status of individual Omega transmitting stations is broadcast on station WWV, 16 minutes after the hour, and on station WWVH, 47 minutes after the hour. Current status reports are available by telephone (202-245-0298).

(436) At the present time the worldwide accuracy and reliability of this system cannot be precisely determined. Therefore positioning information derived from Omega should not be totally relied upon without reference to other positioning methods.

(437) **Uniform State Waterway Marking System.**–Many bodies of water used by boatmen are located entirely within the boundaries of a State. The Uniform State Waterway Marking System (USWMS) has been developed to indicate to the small-boat operator hazards, obstructions, restricted or controlled areas, and to provide directions. Although intended primarily for waters within the state boundaries, USWMS is suited for use in all water areas, since it supplements and is generally compatible with the Coast Guard lateral system of aids to navigation. The Coast Guard is gradually using more aids bearing the USWMS geometric shapes described below.

(438) Two categories of waterway markers are used. Regulatory markers, buoys, and signs use distinctive standard shape marks to show regulatory information. The signs are white with black letters and have a wide orange border. They signify speed zones, restricted areas, danger areas, and directions to various places. Aids to navigation on State waters use red and black buoys to mark channel limits. Red and black buoys are generally used in pairs. The boat should pass between the red buoy and its companion black buoy. If the buoys are not placed in pairs, the distinctive color of the buoy indicates the direction of dangerous water from the

buoy. White buoys with red tops should be passed to the south or west, indicating that danger lies to the north or east of the buoy. White buoys with black tops should be passed to the north or east. Danger lies to the south or west. Vertical red and white striped buoys indicate a boat should not pass between the buoy and the nearest shore. Danger lies inshore of the buoy.

(439) **DESTRUCTIVE WAVES.**–Unusual sudden changes in water level can be caused by tsunamis or violent storms. These two types of destructive waves have become commonly known as **tidal waves,** a name which is technically incorrect as they are not the result of tide-producing forces.

(440) **Tsunamis (seismic sea waves)** are set up by submarine earthquakes. Many such seismic disturbances do not produce sea waves and often those produced are small, but the occasional large waves can be very damaging to shore installations and dangerous to ships in harbors.

(441) These waves travel great distances and can cause tremendous damage on coasts far from their source. The wave of April 1, 1946, which originated in the Aleutian Trench, demolished nearby Scotch Cap Lighthouse and caused damages of $25 million in the Hawaiian Islands 2,000 miles away. The wave of May 22-23, 1960, which originated off Southern Chile, caused widespread death and destruction in islands and countries throughout the Pacific.

(442) The speed of tsunamis varies with the depth of the water, reaching 300 to 500 knots in the deep water of the open ocean. In the open sea they cannot be detected from a ship or from the air because their length is so great, sometimes a hundred miles, as compared to their height, which is usually only a few feet. Only on certain types of shelving coasts do they build up into waves of disastrous proportions.

(443) There is usually a series of waves with crests 10 to 40 minutes apart, and the highest may occur several hours after the first wave. Sometimes the first noticeable part of the wave is the trough which causes a recession of the water from shore, and people who have gone out to investigate this unusual exposure of the beach have been engulfed by the oncoming crest. Such an unexplained withdrawal of the sea should be considered as nature's warning of an approaching wave.

(444) Improvements have been made in the quick determination and reporting of earthquake epicenters, but no method has yet been perfected for determining whether a sea wave will result from a given earthquake. The Pacific Tsunami Warning Center, Oahu, Hawaii, of the National Oceanic and Atmospheric Administration is headquarters of a warning system which has field reporting stations (seismic and tidal) in most countries around the Pacific. When a warning is broadcast, waterfront areas should be vacated for higher ground, and ships in the vicinity of land should head for the deep water of the open sea.

(445) **Storm surge.**–A considerable rise or fall in the level of the sea along a particular coast may result from strong winds and sharp change in barometric pressure. In cases where the water level is raised, higher waves can form with greater depth and the combination can be destructive to low regions, particularly at high stages of tide. Extreme low levels can result in depths which are considerably less than those shown on nautical charts. This type of wave occurs especially in coastal regions bordering on shallow waters which are subject to tropical storms.

(446) **Seiche** is a stationary vertical wave oscillation with a period varying from a few minutes to an hour or more, but somewhat less than the tidal periods. It is usually attributed

to external forces such as strong winds, changes in barometric pressure, swells, or tsunamis disturbing the equilibrium of the watersurface. Seiche is found both in enclosed bodies of water and superimposed upon the tides of the open ocean. When the external forces cause a short-period horizontal oscillation on the water, it is called **surge**.

(447)　The combined effect of seiche and surge sometimes makes it difficult to maintain a ship in its position alongside a pier even though the water may appear to be completely undisturbed, and heavy mooring lines have been parted repeatedly under such conditions. Pilots advise taut lines to reduce the effect of the surge.

SPECIAL SIGNALS FOR CERTAIN VESSELS

(448)　**Special signals for surveying vessels.**–National Oceanic and Atmospheric Administration (NOAA) vessels engaged in survey operations and limited in their ability to maneuver because of the work being performed (handling equipment over-the-side such as water sampling or conductivity-temperature-density (CTD) casts, towed gear, bottom samplers, etc., and divers working on, below or in proximity of the vessel) are required by Navigation Rules, International-Inland, Rule 27, to exhibit:

(449)　(b)(i) three all-round lights in a vertical line where they can best be seen. The highest and lowest of these lights shall be red and the middle light shall be white;

(450)　(ii) three shapes in a vertical line where they can best be seen. The highest and lowest of these shapes shall be balls and the middle one a diamond;

(451)　(iii) when making way through the water, masthead lights, sidelights and a sternlight, in addition to the lights prescribed in subparagraph (b)(i); and

(452)　(iv) when at anchor, in addition to the lights or shapes prescribed in subparagraphs(b)(i) and (ii) the light, lights or shapes prescribed in Rule 30, Anchored Vessels and Vessels Aground.

(453)　The color of the above shapes is black.

(454)　A NOAA vessel engaged in hydrographic survey operations (making way on a specific trackline while sounding the bottom) is not restricted in its ability to maneuver and therefore exhibits at night only those lights required for a power-driven vessel of its length.

(455)　**Warning signals for Coast Guard vessels while handling or servicing aids to navigation** are the same as those prescribed for surveying vessels. (See Special signals for surveying vessels, this chapter.)

(456)　**Minesweeper signals.**–U.S. vessels engaged in minesweeping operations or exercises are hampered to a considerable extent in their maneuvering powers. With a view to indicating the nature of the work on which they are engaged, these vessels will show the signals hereinafter mentioned. For the public safety, all other vessels, whether steamers or sailing craft, must endeavor to keep out of the way of vessels displaying these signals and not approach them inside the distances mentioned herein, especially remembering that it is dangerous to pass between the vessels of a pair or group sweeping together.

(457)　All vessels towing sweeps are to show: **By day,** a black ball at or near the foremast head and a black ball at each end of the fore yard. **By night,** all around green lights instead of the black balls, and in a similar manner.

(458)　Vessels or formations showing these signals indicate that it is dangerous for another vessel to approach within 1,000 meters (3,280 feet) of the mineclearance vessel. Under no circumstances is a vessel to pass through a formation of minesweepers. Minesweepers should be prepared to warn merchant vessels which persist in approaching too close by means of any of the appropriate signals from the International Code of Signals. In fog, mist, falling snow, heavy rainstorms, or any other condition similarly restricting visibility, whether by day or night, minesweepers while towing sweeps when in the vicinity of other vessels will sound whistle signals for a vessel towing (one prolonged blast followed by two short blasts).

(459)　The United States is increasingly using helicopters to conduct minesweeping operations and exercises. When so engaged, helicopters, like vessels, are considerably hampered in their ability to maneuver. Helicopters may function at night as well as during the day and in varying types of weather. Accordingly, surface vessels approaching helicopters engaged in minesweeping operations should take precautions similar to those described above with regard to minesweeping vessels.

(460)　Helicopters towing minesweeping gear, and surface escorts, if any, will use all practical means to warn approaching ships of the operations being conducted. Where practical, measures will be taken to mark or light the gear being towed. While towing, the helicopter's altitude varies from 49.2 to 311.6 feet (15 to 95 meters) above the water, and speeds vary from 0 to 30 knots.

(461)　Minesweeping helicopters are equipped with a rotating beacon which has a selectable red and amber mode. The amber mode is used during towing operations to notify and warn other vessels that the helicopter is towing.

(462)　**Submarine emergency identification signals.**–U.S. submarines are equipped with signal ejectors which may be used to launch identification signals, including emergency signals. Two general types of signals may be used: smoke floats and flares or stars. The smoke floats, which burn on the surface, produce a dense colored smoke for a period of 15 to 45 seconds. The flares or stars are propelled to a height of 300 to 400 feet from which they descend by small parachute. The flares or stars burn for about 25 seconds. The color of the smoke or flare/star has the following meaning:

(463)　**Green or black** is used under training exercise conditions only to indicate that a torpedo has been fired or that the firing of a torpedo has been simulated.

(464)　**Yellow** indicates the submarine is about to rise to periscope depth. Surface craft terminate antisubmarine counterattack and clear vicinity of submarine. Do not stop propellers.

(465)　**Red** indicates an emergency inside the submarine; she will try to surface immediately, if possible. Surface ships clear the area and stand by to assist. In case of repeated red signals, or if the submarine fails to surface in a reasonable time, she may be presumed disabled. Buoy the location, look for submarine buoy, and attempt to establish sonar communications. Advise U.S. Navy authorities immediately.

(466)　Submarine marker buoys consist of two spheres 3 feet in diameter with connecting structure, painted international orange. The buoy has a wire cable to the submarine, to act as a downhaul line for a rescue chamber. The buoy may be accompanied by an oil slick release to attract attention. A submarine on the bottom in distress may release this buoy. If sighted, such a buoy should be investigated and reported immediately to U.S. Navy authorities.

(467)　The submarine may transmit the International Distress Signal (SOS) on its sonar gear independently or in conjunction with the red signal. Submarines also may use these other means of attracting attention: release of dye marker or air bubble; ejection of oil; pounding on hull.

(468)　**Vessels Constrained by their Draft.**–International Navigation Rules, Rule 28, states that a vessel constrained by her draft may, in addition to the lights prescribed for power-driven vessels in Rule 23, exhibit where they can best be seen three all-around red lights in a vertical line, or a cylinder.

NAVIGATION RESTRICTIONS AND REQUIREMENTS

(469) **Traffic Separation Schemes (Traffic Lanes).**–To increase the safety of navigation, particularly in converging areas of high traffic density, routes incorporating traffic separation have, with the approval of the International Maritime Organization (IMO), formerly the Inter-Governmental Maritime Consultative Organization (IMCO), been established in certain areas of the world. In the interest of safe navigation, it is recommended that through traffic use these schemes, as far as circumstances permit, by day and by night and in all weather conditions.

(470) General principles for navigation in Traffic Separation Schemes are as follows:

(471) 1. A ship navigating in or near a traffic separation scheme adopted by IMO shall in particular comply with Rule 10 of the 72 COLREGS to minimize the development of risk of collision with another ship. The other rules of the 72 COLREGS apply in all respects, and particularly the steering and sailing rules if risk of collision with another ship is deemed to exist.

(472) 2. Traffic separation schemes are intended for use by day and by night in all weather, in ice-free waters or under light ice conditions where no extraordinary maneuvers or assistance by icebreaker(s) are required.

(473) 3. Traffic separation schemes are recommended for use by all ships unless stated otherwise. Bearing in mind the need for adequate underkeel clearance, a decision to use a traffic separation scheme must take into account the charted depth, the possibility of changes in the seabed since the the time of last survey, and the effects of meteorological and tidal conditions on water depths.

(474) 4. A deepwater route is an allied routing measure primarily intended for use by ships which require the use of such a route because of their draft in relation to the available depth of water in the area concerned. Through traffic to which the above consideration does not apply should, if practicable, avoid following deepwater routes. When using a deepwater route mariners should be aware of possible changes in the indicated depth of water due to meteorological or other effects.

(475) 5. Users of traffic separation schemes adopted by IMO will be guided by Rule 10 of the 1972 International Regulations for Preventing Collisions at Sea (72 COLREGS) as follows:

(476) (a) This Rule applies to traffic separation schemes adopted by the Organization.

(477) (b) A vessel using a traffic separation scheme shall:

(478) (i) proceed in the appropriate traffic lane in the general direction of traffic flow for that lane;

(479) (ii) so far as practicable keep clear of a traffic separation line or separation zone;

(480) (iii) normally join or leave a traffic separation lane at the termination of the lane, but when joining or leaving from either side shall do so at as small an angle to the general direction of traffic flow as practicable.

(481) (c) A vessel shall so far as practicable avoid crossing traffic lanes, but if obliged to do so, shall cross as nearly as practicable at right angles to the general direction of traffic flow.

(482) (d) Inshore traffic zones shall not normally be used by through traffic which can safety use the appropriate traffic lane within the adjacent traffic separation scheme. However, vessels of less than 20 meters in length and sailing vessels may under all circumstances use inshore traffic zones.

(483) (e) A vessel, other than a crossing vessel, or a vessel joining or leaving a lane shall not normally enter a separation zone or cross a separation line except:

(484) (i) in cases of emergency to avoid immediate danger;

(485) (ii) to engage in fishing within a separate zone.

(486) (f) A vessel navigating in areas near the terminations of traffic separation schemes shall do so with particular caution.

(487) (g) A vessel shall so far as practicable avoid anchoring in a traffic separation scheme or in areas near its terminations.

(488) (h) A vessel not using a traffic separation scheme shall avoid it by as wide a margin as is practicable.

(489) (i) A vessel engaged in fishing shall not impede the passage of any vessel following a traffic lane.

(490) (j) A vessel of less than 20 meters in length or a sailing vessel shall not impede the safe passage of a power-driven vessel following a traffic lane.

(491) (k) A vessel restricted in her ability to maneuver when engaged in an operation for the maintenance of safety of navigation in a traffic separation scheme is exempted from complying with Rule 10 to the extent necessary to carry out the operation.

(492) (l) A vessel restricted in her ability to maneuver when engaged in an operation for laying, servicing or picking up of a submarine cable, within a traffic separation scheme, is exempted from complying with this Rule to the extent necessary to carry out the operation.

(493) 6. The arrows printed on charts merely indicate the general direction of traffic; ships need not set their courses strictly along the arrows.

(494) 7. The signal "YG" meaning "You appear not to be complying with the traffic separation scheme" is provided in the International Code of Signals for appropriate use.

(495) When approved or established, traffic separation scheme details are announced in Notice to Mariners, and later depicted on appropriate charts and included in the Coast Pilot and Sailing Directions.

(496) **Oil Pollution**–The Federal Water Pollution Control Act, as amended, prohibits the discharge of a harmful quantity of oil or a hazardous substance into or upon the United States navigable waters or adjoining shorelines, or into or upon the waters of the contiguous zone, or in connection with activities under the Outer Continental Shelf Lands Act or the Deepwater Port Act of 1974, or which may affect natural resources belonging to, appertaining to, or under the exclusive management authority of the United States including resources under the Fisher Conservation and Management Act of 1976. Discharges that do occur must be reported to the Coast Guard (National Response Center) by the most rapid available means. To assist in swift reporting of spills, a nationwide, 24-hour, toll-free telephone number has been established (1-800-424-8802).

(497) Hazardous quantities of oil have been defined by the Environmental Protection Agency as those which violate applicable water quality standards or cause a film or sheen upon or discoloration of the surface of the water or adjoining shorelines, or cause a sludge or emulsion to be deposited beneath the surface of the water or adjoining shorelines. (For regulations pertaining to this Act see **40 CFR 110.3**, not carried in this Pilot.)

(498) The Refuse Act of 1899 (33 U.S.C. 407) prohibits anyone from throwing, discharging or depositing any refuse matter of any kind in U.S. navigable waters or tributaries of navigable waters. The only exceptions to this prohibition are liquid sewage flowing from streets or sewers and discharges made from shore facilities under a permit granted by the U.S. Army Corps of Engineers.

(499) The Act to Prevent Pollution from Ships (33 U.S.C. 1901) is based on the International Convention for the Prevention of Pollution from Ships, as modified by the Protocol of 1978 (MARPOL 73/78). For tankers over 150 gross tons and all other ships over 400 gross tons, MARPOL 73/78 requires the installation of new equipment to control overboard discharges of oil and oily waste. This includes oily-water separating, monitoring and alarm systems for discharges from cargo areas, cargo pump rooms and machinery space bilges. New ships must have the equipment on board by October 2, 1983, while existing ships have until October 2, 1986 to comply.

(500) Ships are also required to have an International Oil Pollution Prevention Certificate verifying that the vessel is in compliance with MARPOL 73/78 and that any required equipment is on board and operational, and they must maintain a new Oil Record Book reporting all oil transfers and discharges. The Oil Record Book is available from the Government Printing Office (see appendix for address).

(501) **Other requirements for the protection of navigable waters.**–It is not lawful to tie up or anchor vessels or to float lografts in navigable channels in such manner as to obstruct normal navigation. When a vessel or raft is wrecked and sunk in a navigable channel it is the duty of the owner to immediately mark it with a buoy or beacon during the day and a light at night until the sunken craft is removed or abandoned.

(502) **Obligation of deck officers.**–Licensed deck officers are required to acquaint themselves with the latest information published in Notice to Mariners regarding aids to navigation.

(503) **Improper use of searchlights prohibited.**–No person shall flash or cause to be flashed the rays of a searchlight or other blinding light onto the bridge or into the pilothouse of any vessel underway. The International Code Signal "PG2" may be made by a vessel inconvenienced by the glare of a searchlight in order to apprise the offending vessel of the fact.

(504) **Use of Radar.**–Navigation Rules, International-Inland, Rule 7, states, in part, that every vessel shall use all available means appropriate to the prevailing circumstances and conditions to determine if risk of collision exists. If there is any doubt such risk shall be deemed to exist. Proper use shall be made of radar equipment if fitted and operational, including long-range scanning to obtain early warning of risk of collision and radar plotting or equivalent systematic observation of detected objects.

(505) This rule places an additional responsibility on vessels which are equipped and manned to use radar to do so while underway during periods of reduced visibility without in any way relieving commanding officers of the responsibility of carrying out normal precautionary measures.

(506) Navigation Rules, International-Inland, Rules 6, 7, 8, and 19 apply to the use of radar.

(507) **Danger signal.**–Navigation Rules, International-Inland, Rule 34(d), states that when vessels in sight of one another are approaching each other and from any cause either vessel fails to understand the intentions or actions of the other, or is in doubt whether sufficient action is being taken by the other to avoid collision, the vessel in doubt shall immediately indicate such doubt by giving at least five short and rapid blasts on the whistle. Such signal may be supplemented by a light signal of at least five short and rapid flashes.

(508) **Narrow channels.**–Navigation Rules, International-Inland, Rule 9(b) states: A vessel of less than 65.6 feet (20 meters) in length or a sailing vessel shall not impede the passage of a vessel that can safety navigate only within a narrow channel or fairway.

(509) **Control of shipping in time of emergency or war.**–In time of war or national emergency, merchant vessels of the United States and those foreign flag vessels, which are considered under effective U.S. control, will be subject to control by agencies of the U.S. Government. The allocation and employment of such vessels, and of domestic port facilities, equipment, and services will be performed by appropriate agencies of the War Transport Administration. The movement, routing, and diversion of merchant ships at sea will be controlled by appropriate naval commanders. The movement of merchant ships within domestic ports and dispersal anchorages will be coordinated by the U.S. Coast Guard. The commencement of naval control will be signaled by a general emergency message. (See DMAHTC Pub. 117 for emergency procedures and communication instructions.)

(510) **Exclusive Economic Zone of the United States.**–Established by a Presidential Proclamation on March 10, 1983, the Exclusive Economic Zone (EEZ) of the United States is a zone contiguous to the territorial sea, including zones contiguous to the territorial sea of the United States, the Commonwealth of Puerto Rico, the Commonwealth of the Northern Mariana Islands (to the extent consistent with the Covenant and the United Nations Trusteeship Agreement), and United States overseas territories and possessions. The EEZ extends to a distance of 200 nautical miles from the baseline from which the breadth of the territorial sea is measured. In cases where the maritime boundary with a neighboring state remains to be determined, the boundary of the EEZ shall be determined by the United States and the other state concerned in accordance with equitable principles.

(511) Within the EEZ, the United States has asserted, to the extent permitted by international law, (a) sovereign rights for the purpose of exploring, exploiting, conserving and managing natural resources, both living and nonliving, of the seabed and subsoil and the superjacent waters and with regard to other activities for the economic exploitation and exploration of the zone, such as the production of energy from the water, currents and winds; and (b) jurisdiction with regard to the establishment and use of artificial islands, and installations and structures having economic purposes, and the protection and preservation of the marine environment.

(512) Without prejudice to the sovereign rights and jurisdiction of the United States, the EEZ remains an area beyond the territory and territorial sea of the United States in which all states enjoy the high seas freedoms of navigation, overflight, the laying of submarine cables and pipelines, and other internationally lawful uses of the sea.

(513) This Proclamation does not change existing United States policies concerning the continental shelf, marine mammals and fisheries, including highly migratory species of tuna which are not subject to United States jurisdiction and require international agreements for effective management.

(514) The United States will exercise these sovereign rights and jurisdiction in accordance with the rules of international law.

(515) The seaward limit of the EEZ is shown on the nautical chart as a line interspersed periodically with EXCLUSIVE ECONOMIC ZONE. The EEZ boundary is coincidental with that of the Fishery Conservation Zone.

(516) **U.S. Fishery Conservation Zone.**– The United States exercises exclusive fishery management authority over all species of fish, except tuna, within the fishery conservation zone, whose seaward boundary is 200 miles from the baseline from which the U.S. territorial sea is measured; all anadromous species which spawn in the United States throughout their migratory range beyond the fishery conservation zone, except within a foreign country's equivalent fishery zone as recognized by the United States; all U.S. Continental Shelf fishery resources beyond the fishery conservation zone. Such resources include American lobster and species of coral, crab, abalone, conch, clam, and sponge, among others.

(517) No foreign vessel may fish, aid, or assist vessels at sea in the performance of any activity relating to fishing including, but not limited to preparation, supply, storage, refrigeration, transportation or processing, within the fishery conservation zone, or fish for anadromous species of the United States or Continental Shelf fishery resources without a permit issued in accordance with U.S. law. These permits may only be issued to vessels from countries recognizing the exclusive fishery management authority of the United States in an international agreement. The owners or operators of foreign vessels desiring to engage in fishing off U.S. coastal waters should ascertain their eligibility from their own flag state authorities. Failure to obtain a permit prior to fishing, or failure to comply with the conditions and restrictions established in the permit may subject both vessel and its owner or operators to administrative, civil, and criminal penalties. (Further details concerning foreign fishing are given in **50 CFR 611.**)

(518) Reports of foreign fishing activity within the fishery conservation zone should be made to the U.S. Coast Guard. Immediate reports are particularly desired, but later reports by any means also have value. Reports should include the activity observed, the position, and as much identifying information (name, number, homeport, type, flag, color, size, shape, etc.) about the foreign vessel as possible, and the reporting party's name and address or telephone number.

(519) **Bridge-to-bridge Radiotelephone Communication.**–Voice radio bridge-to-bridge communication between vessels is an effective aid in the prevention of collisions where there is restricted maneuvering room and/or visibility. VHF-FM radio is used for this purpose, due to its essentially line-of-sight characteristic and relative freedom from static. As VHF-FM has increasingly come into use for short-range communications in U.S. harbors and other high-traffic waters, so has the number of ships equipped with this gear increased.

(520) The Vessel Bridge-to-Bridge Radiotelephone Regulations, effective January 1, 1973, require vessels subject to the Act while navigating to be equipped with at least one single channel transceiver capable of transmitting and receiving on VHF-FM channel 13 (156.65 MHz), the Bridge-to-Bridge Radiotelephone frequency. Vessels with multichannel equipment are required to have an additional receiver so as to be able to guard VHF-FM channel 13 (156.65 MHz), the Bridge-to-Bridge Radiotelephone frequency, in addition to VHF-FM channel 16 (156.80 MHz), the National Distress, Safety and Calling frequency required by Federal Communications Commission regulations. (See **26.01 through 26.10**, chapter 2, for Vessel Bridge-to-Bridge Radiotelephone Regulations.)

(521) Mariners are reminded that the use of bridge-to-bridge voice communications in no way alters the obligation to comply with the provisions of the Navigation Rules, International-Inland.

(522) VHF-FM Radiotelephone.-The following table provides the frequency equivalents and general usage of selected VHF-FM channels which appear in the Coast Pilot. The letter "A" appended to a channel number indicates that U.S. operation of the particular channel is different than the international operation, i.e., U.S. stations transmit and receive on the same frequency and international stations use different frequencies.

(523) The information given here is extracted from the "Marine Radiotelephone Users Handbook" published by the Radio Technical Commission for Maritime Services. Ordering information for this valuable, comprehensive publication is included in the appendix.

(524) All channels given below are designated for both ship-to-ship and ship-to-coast communications except as noted.

Channel	Ship Frequency (MHz) Transmit	Receive	Channel Usage
1A	156.050	156.050	Port operations and commercial
5A	156.250	156.250	Port operations
6	156.300	156.300	Intership safety
7A	156.350	156.350	Commercial
8	156.400	156.400	Commercial (ship-to-ship only)
9	156.450	156.450	Commercial and non-commercial
10	156.500	156.500	Commercial
11	156.550	156.550	Commercial
12	156.600	156.600	Port operations (traffic advisories, including VTS in some ports)
13	156.650	156.650	Navigational (ship-to-ship), also used at locks and bridges
14	156.700	156.700	Port operations (traffic advisories, including VTS in some ports)
16	156.800	156.800	Distress, safety and calling
17	156.850	156.850	State or local government control
18A	156.900	156.900	Commercial

Channel	Ship Frequency (MHz) Transmit	Receive	Channel Usage
19A	156.950	156.950	Commercial
20	157.000	161.600	Port operations (traffic advisories)
22A	157.100	157.100	Coast Guard Liaison
24	157.200	161.800	Public correspondence (ship-to-coast)
25	157.250	161.850	Public correspondence (ship-to-coast)
26	157.300	161.900	Public correspondence (ship-to-coast)
27	157.350	161.950	Public correspondence (ship-to-coast)
28	157.400	162.000	Public correspondence (ship-to-coast)
63A	156.175	156.175	VTS New Orleans
65A	156.275	156.275	Port operations (traffic advisories)
66A	156.325	156.325	Port operations (traffic advisories)
67	156.375	156.375	Commercial (ship-to-ship only) (used in New Orleans VTS for ship-to-ship navigational purposes)
68	156.425	156.425	Non-commercial
69	156.475	156.475	Non-commercial
71	156.575	156.575	Non-commercial
72	156.625	156.625	Non-commercial (ship-to-ship only)
73	156.675	156.675	Port operations (traffic advisories)
74	156.725	156.725	Port operations (traffic advisories)
77	156.875	156.875	Port operations (ship-to-ship, to and from pilots docking ships)
78A	156.925	156.925	Non-commercial
79A	156.975	156.975	Commercial
80A	157.025	157.025	Commercial
84	157.225	161.825	Public correspondence (ship-to-coast)
85	157.275	161.875	Public correspondence (ship-to-coast)
86	157.325	161.925	Public correspondence (ship-to-coast)
87	157.375	161.975	Public correspondence (ship-to-coast)
88	157.425	162.025	Public correspondence in Puget Sound and parts of Great Lakes
88A	157.425	157.425	Commercial, fishing (ship-to-ship) (except in parts of Great Lakes)

2. NAVIGATION REGULATIONS

(1) This chapter contains the sections of **Code of Federal Regulations, Title 33, Navigation and Navigable Waters (33 CFR)**, that are of most importance in the areas covered by Coast Pilot 2. The sections are from:

(2) Part 26, Vessel Bridge-to-Bridge Radiotelephone Regulations,

(3) Part 80, COLREGS Demarcation Lines;

(4) Part 110, Anchorage Regulations;

(5) Part 117, Drawbridge Operation Regulations;

(6) Part 160, Ports and Waterways Safety-General;

(7) Part 162, Inland Waterways Navigation Regulations;

(8) Part 164, Navigation Safety Regulations (in part);

(9) Part 165, Regulated Navigation Areas and Limited Access Areas;

(10) Part 166, Shipping Safety Fairways;

(11) Part 167, Offshore Traffic Separation Schemes;

(12) Part 207, Navigation Regulations; and

(13) Part 334, Danger Zones and Restricted Area Regulations.

(14) **Note.**—These regulations can only be amended by the enforcing agency or other authority cited in the regulations. Accordingly, requests for changes to these regulations should be directed to the appropriate agency for action. In those regulations where the enforcing agency is not cited or is unclear, recommendations for changes should be directed to the following Federal agencies for action: U.S. Coast Guard (33 CFR 26, 80, 110, 117, 160, 164, and 165); U.S. Army Corps of Engineers (33 CFR 207 and 334).

Part 26–Vessel Bridge-to-Bridge Radiotelephone Regulations

(15) **§26.01 Purpose.**

(16) (a) The purpose of this part is to implement the provisions of the Vessel Bridge-to-Bridge Radiotelephone Act. This part–

(17) (1) Requires the use of the vessel bridge-to-bridge radiotelephone;

(18) (2) Provides the Coast Guard's interpretation of the meaning of important terms in the Act;

(19) (3) Prescribes the procedures for applying for an exemption from the Act and the regulations issued under the Act and a listing of exemptions.

(20) (b) Nothing in this part relieves any person from the obligation of complying with the rules of the road and the applicable pilot rules.

(21) **§26.02 Definitions.**

(22) For the purpose of this part and interpreting the Act–

(23) "Secretary" means the Secretary of the Department in which the Coast Guard is operating;

(24) "Act" means the "Vessel Bridge-to-Bridge Radiotelephone Act", 33 U.S.C. sections 1201–1208;

(25) "Length" is measured from end to end over the deck excluding sheer;

(26) "Power-driven vessel" means any vessel propelled by machinery; and

(27) "Towing vessel" means any commercial vessel engaged in towing another vessel astern, alongside, or by pushing ahead.

(28) **§26.03 Radiotelephone required.**

(29) (a) Unless an exemption is granted under §26.09 and except as provided in paragraph (a)(4) of this section, section 4 of the Act provides that–

(30) (1) Every power-driven vessel of 300 gross tons and upward while navigating;

(31) (2) Every vessel of 100 gross tons and upward carrying one or more passengers for hire while navigating;

(32) (3) Every towing vessel of 26 feet or over in length while navigating; and

(33) (4) Every dredge and floating plant engaged in or near a channel or fairway in operations likely to restrict or affect navigation of other vessels: Provided, That an unmanned or intermittently manned floating plant under the control of a dredge need not be required to have separate radiotelephone capability;

(34) Shall have a radiotelephone capable of operation from its navigational bridge, or in the case of a dredge, from its main control station, and capable of transmitting and receiving on the frequency or frequencies within the 156–162 Mega-Hertz band using the classes of emissions designated by the Federal Communications Commission, after consultation with other cognizant agencies, for the exchange of navigational information.

(35) (b) The radiotelephone required by paragraph (a) of this section shall be carried on board the described vessels, dredges, and floating plants upon the navigable waters of the United States inside the lines established pursuant to section 2 of the Act of February 19, 1895 (28 Stat. 672), as amended.

(36) **§26.04 Use of the designated frequency.**

(37) (a) No person may use the frequency designated by the Federal Communications Commission under section 8 of the Act, 33 U.S.C. 1207(a), to transmit any information other than information necessary for the safe navigation of vessels or necessary tests.

(38) (b) Each person who is required to maintain a listening watch under section 5 of the Act shall, when necessary, transmit and confirm, on the designated frequency, the intentions of his vessel and any other information necessary for the safe navigation of vessels.

(39) (c) Nothing in these regulations may be construed as prohibiting the use of the designated frequency to communicate with shore stations to obtain or furnish information necessary for the safe navigation of vessels.

(40) **Note.**—The Federal Communications Commission (FCC) has designated the frequency 156.65 MHz (Channel 13) for the use of bridge-to-bridge stations in most of the United States. However, FCC rules designate the frequency 156.375 MHz (Channel 67) to be used instead of Channel 13 in the following areas, except to facilitate transition from these areas: The Mississippi River from South Pass Lighted Bell Buoy "2" and Southwest Pass Entrance (midchannel) Lighted Whistle Buoy SW to mile 242.4 AHP (Above Head of Passes) near Baton Rouge; and, in addition, over the full length of the Mississippi River-Gulf Outlet Canal from entrance to its junction with the Inner Harbor Navigation Canal, and over the full length of the Inner Harbor Navigation Canal from its junction with the Mississippi River to its entry to Lake Pontchartrain at the New Seabrook vehicular bridge.

(41) **§26.05 Use of radiotelephone.**

(42) Section 5 of the Act states–

(43) (a) The radiotelephone required by this Act is for the exclusive use of the master or person in charge of the vessel, or the person designated by the master or person in charge

of the vessel, or the person designated by the master or person in charge to pilot or direct the movement of the vessel, who shall maintain a listening watch on the designated frequency. Nothing contained herein shall be interpreted as precluding the use of portable radiotelephone equipment to satisfy the requirements of this Act.

(44) **§26.06 Maintenance of radiotelephone; failure of radiotelephone.**

(45) Section 6 of the Act states—

(46) (a) Wherever radiotelephone capability is required by this Act, a vessel's radiotelephone equipment shall be maintained in effective operating condition. If the radiotelephone equipment carried aboard a vessel ceases to operate, the master shall exercise due diligence to restore it or cause it to be restored to effective operating condition at the earliest practicable time. The failure of a vessel's radiotelephone equipment shall not, in itself, constitute a violation of this Act, nor shall it obligate the master of any vessel to moor or anchor his vessel; however, the loss of radiotelephone capability shall be given consideration in the navigation of the vessel.

(47) **§26.07 English language.**

(48) No person may use the services of, and no person may serve as a person required to maintain a listening watch under section 5 of the Act, 33 U.S.C. 1204 unless he can speak the English language.

(49) **§26.08 Exemption procedures.**

(50) (a) Any person may petition for an exemption from any provision of the Act or this part;

(51) (b) Each petition must be submitted in writing to U.S. Coast Guard Office of Navigation Safety and Waterway Services, 2100 Second Street SW., Washington, DC 20593-0001, and must state—

(52) (1) The provisions of the Act or this part from which an exemption is requested; and

(53) (2) The reasons why marine navigation will not be adversely affected if the exemption is granted and if the exemption relates to a local communication system how that system would fully comply with the intent of the concept of the Act but would not conform in detail if the exemption is granted.

(54) **§26.09 List of exemptions.**

(55) (a) All vessels navigating on those waters governed by the navigation rules for Great Lakes and their connecting and tributary waters (33 U.S.C. 241 et seq.) are exempt from the requirements of the Vessel Bridge-to-Bridge Radiotelephone Act and this part until May 6, 1975.

(56) (b) Each vessel navigating on the Great Lakes as defined in the Inland Navigational Rules Act of 1980 (33 U.S.C. 2001 et seq.) and to which the Vessel Bridge-to-Bridge Radiotelephone Act (33 U.S.C. 1201–1208) applies is exempt from the requirements in 33 U.S.C. 1203, 1204, and 1205 and the regulations under §§26.03, 26.04, 26.05, 26.06, and 26.07. Each of these vessels and each person to whom 33 U.S.C. 1208(a) applies must comply with Articles VII, X, XI, XII, XIII, XV, and XVI and Technical Regulations 1–7 of "The Agreement Between the United States of America and Canada for Promotion of Safety on the Great Lakes by Means of Radio, 1973."

(57) **§26.10 Penalties**

(58) Section 9 of the Act states—

(59) (a) Whoever, being the master or person in charge of a vessel subject to the Act, fails to enforce or comply with the Act or the regulations hereunder; or whoever, being designated by the master or person in charge or a vessel subject to the Act to pilot or direct the movement of a vessel fails to

enforce or comply with the Act or the regulations hereunder–is liable to a civil penalty of not more than $500 to be assessed by the Secretary.

(60) (b) Every vessel navigated in violation of the Act or the regulations hereunder is liable to a civil penalty of not more than $500 to be assessed by the Secretary, for which the vessel may be proceeded against in any District Court of the United States having jurisdiction.

(61) (c) Any penalty assessed under this section may be remitted or mitigated by the Secretary, upon such terms as he may deem proper.

Part 80–COLREGS Demarcation Lines

(62) **§80.01 General basis and purpose of demarcation lines.**

(63) (a) The regulations in this part establish the lines of demarcation delineating those waters upon which mariners shall comply with the International Regulations for Preventing Collisions at Sea, 1972 (72 COLREGS) and those waters upon which mariners shall comply with the Inland Navigation Rules.

(64) (b) The waters inside of the lines are Inland Rules waters. The waters outside the lines are COLREGS waters.

(65) (c) Geographic coordinates expressed in terms of latitude or longitude, or both, are not intended for plotting on maps or charts whose referenced horizontal datum is the North American Datum of 1983 (NAD 83), unless such geographic coordinates are expressly labeled NAD 83. Geographic coordinates without the NAD 83 reference may be plotted on maps or charts referenced to NAD 83 only after application of the appropriate corrections that are published on the particular map or chart being used.

(66) **§80.135 Hull, Mass. to Race Point, Mass.** (a) Except inside lines described in this section, the 72 COLREGS apply on the harbors, bays, and inlets on the east coast of Massachusetts from the easternmost radio tower at Hull, charted in approximate position latitude 42°16.7′N., longitude 70°52.6′W., to Race Point on Cape Cod.

(67) (b) A line drawn from Canal Breakwater Light 4 south to the shoreline.

(68) **§80.145 Race Point, Mass., to Watch Hill, R.I.** (a) Except inside lines specifically described in this section, the 72 COLREGS shall apply on the sounds, bays, harbors, and inlets along the coast of Cape Cod and the southern coasts of Massachusetts and Rhode Island from Race Point to Watch Hill.

(69) (b) A line drawn from Nobska Point Light to Tarpaulin Cove Light on the southeastern side of Naushon Island; thence from the southernmost tangent of Naushon Island to the easternmost extremity of Nashawena Island; thence from the southwesternmost extremity of Nashawena Island to the easternmost extremity of Cuttyhunk Island; thence from the southwestern tangent of Cuttyhunk Island to the tower on Gooseberry Neck charted in approximate position latitude 41°29.1′N., longitude 71°02.3′W.

(70) (c) A line drawn from Sakonnet Breakwater Light 2 tangent to the southernmost part of Sachuest Point charted in approximate position latitude 41°28.5′N., longitude 71°14.8′W.

(71) (d) An east-west line drawn through Beavertail Light between Brenton Point and the Boston Neck shoreline.

(72) **§80.150 Block Island, R.I.**

(73) The 72 COLREGS shall apply on the harbors of Block Island.

(74) **§80.155 Watch Hill, R.I. to Montauk Point, N.Y.** (a) A line drawn from Watch Hill Light to East Point on Fishers Island.

(75) (b) A line drawn from Race Point to Race Rock Light; thence to Little Gull Island Light thence to East Point on Plum Island.

(76) (c) A line drawn from Plum Island Harbor East Dolphin Light to Plum Island Harbor West Dolphin Light.

(77) (d) A line drawn from Plum Island Light to Orient Point Light; thence to Orient Point.

(78) (e) A line drawn from the lighthouse ruins at the southwestern end of Long Beach Point to Cornelius Point.

(79) (f) A line drawn from Coecles Harbor Entrance Light to Sungic Point.

(80) (g) A line drawn from Nichols Point to Cedar Island Light.

(81) (h) A line drawn from Threemile Harbor West Breakwater Light to Threemile Harbor East Breakwater Light.

(82) (i) A line drawn from Montauk West Jetty Light 1 to Montauk East Jetty Light 2.

(83) **§80.160 Montauk Point, N.Y. to Atlantic Beach, N.Y.** (a) A line drawn from Shinnecock Inlet East Breakwater Light to Shinnecock Inlet West Breakwater Light 1.

(84) (b) A line drawn from Moriches Inlet East Breakwater Light to Moriches Inlet West Breakwater Light.

(85) (c) A line drawn from Fire Island Inlet Breakwater Light 348° true to the southernmost extremity of the spit of land at the western end of Oak Beach.

(86) (d) A line drawn from Jones Inlet Light 322° true across the southwest tangent of the island on the north side of Jones Inlet to the shoreline.

(87) **§80.165 New York Harbor.**

(88) A line drawn from East Rockaway Inlet Breakwater Light to Sandy Hook Light.

Part 110–Anchorage Regulations

(89) **§110.1 General.** (a) The areas described in Subpart A of this part are designated as special anchorage areas pursuant to the authority contained in an act amending laws for preventing collisions of vessels approved April 22, 1940 (54 Stat. 150); Article 11 of section 1 of the Act of June 7, 1897, as amended (30 Stat. 98; 33 U.S.C. 180), Rule 9 of section 1 of the act of February 8, 1895, as amended (28 Stat. 647; 33 U.S.C. 258), and Rule Numbered 13 of section 4233 of the Revised Statutes as amended (33 U.S.C. 322). Vessels not more than 65 feet in length, when at anchor in any special anchorage area shall not be required to carry or exhibit the white anchor lights required by the Navigation Rules.

(90) (b) The anchorage grounds for vessels described in Subpart B of this part are established, and the rules and regulations in relation thereto adopted, pursuant to the authority contained in section 7 of the act of March 4, 1915, as amended (38 Stat. 1053; 33 U.S.C. 471).

(91) (c) All bearings in the part are referred to true meridian.

(92) (d) Geographic coordinates expressed in terms of latitude or longitude, or both, are not intended for plotting on maps or charts whose referenced horizontal datum is the North American Datum of 1983 (NAD 83), unless such geographic coordinates are expressly labeled NAD 83. Geographic coordinates without the NAD 83 reference may be plotted on maps or charts referenced to NAD 83 only after application of the appropriate corrections that are published on the particular map or chart being used.

(93) **§110.1a Anchorages under Ports and Waterways Safety Act.** (a) The anchorages listed in this section are regulated under the Ports and Waterways Safety Act (33 U.S.C. 1221 et seq.):

(94) (1) Section 110.155 Port of New York.

(95) (b) Any person who violates any regulation issued under the Ports and Waterways Safety Act–

(96) (1) Is liable to a civil penalty, not to exceed $25,000 for each violation;

(97) (2) If the violation is willful, is fined not more than $50,000 for each violation or imprisoned for not more than five years, or both.

Subpart A–Special Anchorage Areas

(98) **§110.38 Edgartown Harbor, Mass.** An area in the inner harbor easterly of the project channel and south of Chappaquiddick Point bounded as follows: Beginning at

(99) 41°23′19″N., 70°30′32″W.; thence along the shore to

(100) 41°22′52″N., 70°30′12″W.; thence

(101) 287°30′, 1,600 feet; thence

(102) 327°30′, 700 feet; thence

(103) 359°, 800 feet; thence

(104) 024°15′, approximately 900 feet to the point of beginning.

(105) NOTE: The area is reserved for yachts and other small recreational craft. Fore and aft moorings and temporary floats or buoys for marking anchors in place will be allowed. All moorings shall be so placed that no vessel when anchored shall extend into waters beyond the limits of the area. Fixed mooring piles or stakes are prohibited.

(106) **§110.40 Silver Beach Harbor, North Falmouth, Mass.** All the waters of the harbor northward of the inner end of the entrance channel.

(107) **§110.45 Onset Bay, Mass.** Northerly of a line extending from the northernmost point of Onset Island to the easternmost point of Wickets Island; easterly of a line extending from the easternmost point of Wickets Island to the southwest extremity of Point Independence; southerly of the shore line; and westerly of the shore line and of a line bearing due north from the northernmost point of Onset Island.

(108) **§110.45a Mattapoisett Harbor, Mattapoisett, Mass.**

(109) (a) Area No. 1 beginning at a point on the shore at

(110) 41°39′23″N., 70°48′50″W.; thence 138.5°T. to

(111) 41°38′45″N., 70°48′02″W.; thence 031°T. to

(112) 41°39′02″N., 70°47′48″W.; thence along the shore to the point of beginning.

(113) (b) Area No. 2 beginning at a point on the shore at

(114) 41°39′24″N., 70°49′02″W.; thence 142.5°T to

(115) 41°38′10″N., 70°47′45″W.; thence 219°T. to

(116) 41°37′54″N., 70°48′02″W.; thence along the shore to the point of beginning.

(117) **Note.–**Administration of the Special Anchorage Area is exercised by the Harbormaster, Town of Mattapoisett pursuant to a local ordinance. The town of Mattapoisett will install and maintain suitable navigational aids to mark the perimeter of the anchorage area.

(118) **§110.46 Newport Harbor, Newport, R.I.** (a) Area No. 1. The waters of Brenton Cove south of a line extending from

(119) 41°28′50″N., 71°18′58″W.; to

(120) 41°28′45″N., longitude 71°20′08″W.; thence along the shoreline to the point of beginning.

(121) (b) Area No. 2. The waters east of Goat Island beginning at a point bearing 090°, 245 yards from Goat Island Shoal Light; thence

(122) 007°, 505 yards; thence

(123) 054°, 90 yards; thence

(124) 086°, 330 yards; thence

(125) 122°, 90 yards; thence

(126) 179°, 290 yards; thence

(127) 228°, 380 yards; thence

(128) 270°, 250 yards to the point of beginning.

(129) (c) Area No. 3. The waters north of Goat Island Causeway Bridge beginning at Newport Harbor Light; thence 023° to the southwest corner of Anchorage E; thence 081° following the southerly boundary of Anchorage E to the shoreline; thence south along the shoreline to the east foot of the Goat Island Causeway Bridge; thence west following Goat Island Causeway Bridge to the shoreline of Goat Island; thence north following the east shore of Goat Island to the point of beginning.

(130) **§110.47 Little Narragansett Bay, Watch Hill, R.I.** All of the navigable waters of Watch Hill Cove southeasterly of a line beginning at the shore end of the United States project groin on the southerly shore of the cove and running 41°30' true, to the northerly shore of the cove at a point about 200 feet west of the west side of the shore end of Meadow Lane, with the exception of a 100-foot wide channel running from the westerly end of the cove in a southeasterly direction to the Watch Hill Yacht Club pier, thence along in front of the piers on the easterly side of the cove northerly to the shore at the north end of the cove.

(131) **§110.48 Thompson Cove on east side of Pawcatuck River below Westerly, R.I.** Eastward of a line extending from the channelward end of Thompson Dock at the northern end of Thompson Cove 184° to the shore at the southern end of Thompson Cove.

(132) **§110.50 Stonington Harbor, Conn.** (a) Area No. 1. Beginning at the southeastern tip of Wamphassuc Point; thence to the northwesterly end of Stonington Inner Breakwater; thence along the breakwater to

(133) longitude 71°54'50.5"; thence to

(134) 41°20"25.3", 71°54'50.5"; thence to a point on the shoreline at

(135) 41°20'32", 71°54'54.8"; thence along the shoreline to the point of beginning.

(136) (b) Area No. 2. Beginning at a point on the shoreline at

(137) 41°19'55.8"N., 71°54'28.9"W.; thence to

(138) 41°19'55.8"N., 71°54'37.1"W.; thence to

(139) 41°20'01.6"N., 71°54'38.8"W.; thence to

(140) 41°20'02.0"N., 71°54'34.3"W.; thence along the shoreline to the point of beginning.

(141) (c) Area No. 3. Beginning at a point on the shoreline at

(142) 41°20'29.5"N., 71°54'43.0"W.; thence to

(143) 41°20'25.6"N., 71°54'48.5"W.; thence to

(144) 41°20'10.7"N., 71°54'48.5"W.; thence to the shoreline at

(145) 41°20'10.7"N.; thence along the shoreline to the point of beginning.

(146) NOTE: A fixed mooring stake or pile is prohibited. The General Statutes of the State of Connecticut authorizes the Harbor Master of Stonington to station and control a vessel in the harbor.

(147) **§110.50a Fishers Island Sound, Stonington, Conn.** An area on the east side of Mason Island bounded as follows:

(148) Beginning at the shore line on the easterly side of Mason Island at latitude 41°20'06"; thence due east about 600 feet to latitude 41°20'06", longitude 71°57'37"; thence due south about 2,400 feet to latitude 41°19'42", longitude 71°57'37"; thence due west about 1,000 feet to the shore line on the easterly side of Mason Island at latitude 41°19'42"; thence along the shore line to the point of beginning.

(149) NOTE: The area will be principally for use by yachts and other recreational craft. Temporary floats or buoys for marking anchors will be allowed. Fixed mooring piles or stakes will be prohibited. The anchoring of vessels and the placing of temporary moorings will be under the jurisdiction and the discretion of the local Harbor Master.

(150) **§110.50b Mystic Harbor, Groton and Stonington, Conn.** (a) Area No. 1. Beginning at Ram Point on the westerly side of Mason Island at

(151) 41°19'44"N., 71°58'42"W.; thence to

(152) 41°19'30"N., 71°58'43"W.; thence to

(153) 41°19'36"N., 71°58'58"W.; thence to

(154) 41°19'45"N., 71°58'56"W.; thence to the point of beginning.

(155) (b) Area No. 2. Beginning at a point about 250 feet southerly of Area 1 and on line with the easterly limit of Area 1 at

(156) 41°19'27"N., 71°58'44"W.; thence to

(157) 41°19'19"N., 71°58'45"W.; thence to

(158) 41°19'25"N., 71°58'59"W.; thence to

(159) 41°19'33"N., 71°58'48"W.; thence to the point of beginning.

(160) NOTE: The areas will be principally for use by yachts and other recreational craft. Temporary floats or buoys for marking anchors will be allowed. Fixed mooring piles or stakes are prohibited. All moorings shall be so placed that no vessel, when anchored, shall at any time extend beyond the limits of the areas. The anchoring of vessels and the placing of temporary moorings will be under the jurisdiction and at the discretion of the local Harbor Master.

(161) **§110.50c Mumford Cove, Groton, Conn.** (a) Area No. 1. Beginning at a point on the easterly shore of Mumford Cove at

(162) 41°19'36"N., 72°01'06"W.; to

(163) 41°19'30"N., 72°01'04"W.; thence to the shore at

(164) 41°19'31"N., 72°01'00"W.; and thence along the shoreline to the point of beginning.

(165) (b) Area No. 2. Beginning at a point on the easterly shore of Mumford Cove at

(166) 41°19'15.0"N., 72°00'54.0"W.; thence to

(167) 41°19'14.5"N., 72°00'59.0"W.; thence to

(168) 41°19'11.0"N., 72°00'58.0"W.; thence to

(169) 41°19'10.0"N., 72°00'54.0"W.; thence to

(170) 41°19'12.5"N., 72°00'52.0"W.; thence to

(171) 41°19'14.0"N., 72°00'55.0"W.; and thence to the point of beginning.

(172) NOTE. The areas are principally for use by yachts and other recreational craft. Temporary floats or buoys for marking anchors will be allowed. Fixed mooring piles or stakes will be prohibited. The anchoring of vessels and placing of temporary moorings will be under the jurisdiction, and at the discretion, of the local Harbor Master.

(173) **§110.50d Mystic Harbor, Noank, Conn.** (a) The area comprises that portion of the harbor off the easterly side of Morgan Point beginning at a point at

(174) 41°19'15.0"N., 71°59'13.5"W.; thence to

(175) 41°19'15.0"N., 71°59'00.0"W.; thence to

(176) 41°19'02.5"N., 71°59'00.0"W.; thence to

(177) 41°19'06.0"N., 71°59'13.5"W.; and thence to the point of beginning.

(178) (b) The following requirements shall govern this special anchorage area:

(179) (1) The area will be principally for use by yachts and other recreational craft.

(180) (2) Temporary floats or buoys for marking anchors will be allowed but fixed piles or stakes are prohibited. All moorings shall be so placed that no vessel, when anchored, shall extend beyond the limits of the area.

to such adjustments as may be necessary to accommodate all classes of vessels which may require anchorage room.

(476)   (ii) Temporary floats or buoys for marking anchors or moorings in place will be allowed in this area. Fixed mooring piles or stakes will not be allowed.

(477)   (5) **Anchorage E.** South of Coasters Harbor Island, east of a line bearing 341° from the outer end of Briggs Wharf to the southwestern shore of Coasters Harbor Island near the War College Building; and north of a line ranging 265° from the flagstaff at Fort Greene toward Rose Island Light.

(478)   (i) In this area the requirements of the naval service will predominate from May 1 to October 1, but will at all times be subject to such adjustment as may be necessary to accommodate all classes of vessels that may require anchorage room.

(479)   (ii) Temporary floats or buoys for marking anchors or moorings in place will be allowed in this area. Fixed mooring piles or stakes will not be allowed.

(480)   (b) **West Passage (1) Anchorage H.** North of a line 1,000 yards long bearing 88° from Bonnet Point; west of a line bearing 3° from the eastern end of the last-described line; and south of a line ranging 302° through a point 200 yards south of the Kearny wharf toward the church spire at South Ferry, Boston Neck.

(481)   (i) Temporary floats or buoys for marking anchors or moorings in place will be allowed in this area. Fixed mooring piles or stakes will not be allowed.

(482)   (2) **Anchorage I.** North of a line 1,000 yards long bearing 88° from Bonnet Point to the shore at Austin Hollow; east of a line bearing 183° from Dutch Island Light; and south of a line ranging 302° through a point 200 yards south of the Kearny wharf toward the church spire at South Ferry, Boston Neck.

(483)   (i) Temporary floats or buoys for marking anchors or moorings in place will be allowed in this area. Fixed mooring piles or stakes will not be allowed.

(484)   (3) **Anchorage J.** At Saunderstown, south of a line ranging 110° from the south side of the ferry wharf toward the cable crossing sign on Dutch Island; west of a line ranging 192° from Plum Beach Shoal Buoy 1 PB toward the east shore of The Bonnet; and north of a line from the shore ranging 108° toward Dutch Island Light and the north end of the wharf at Beaver Head.

(485)   (i) Temporary floats or buoys for marking anchors or moorings in place will be allowed in this area. Fixed mooring piles or stakes will not be allowed.

(486)   (4) **Anchorage K.** In the central and southern portion of Dutch Island Harbor, north of a line ranging 106° from Beaver Head Point Shoal Buoy 2 toward the Jamestown standpipe; east of a line ranging 14° from Beaver Head Point Shoal Buoy 2 toward the inshore end of the engineer wharf, Dutch Island; southeast of a line ranging 50° from Dutch Island Light toward the windmill north of Jamestown; and south of a line parallel to and 100 yards southwesterly from a line ranging 132° from the engineer wharf, Dutch Island, and the west ferry wharf, Jamestown.

(487)   (i) Temporary floats or buoys for marking anchors or moorings in place will be allowed in this area. Fixed mooring piles or stakes will not be allowed.

(488)   (5) **Anchorage L.** North of a line ranging 101° from a point on shore 300 yards northerly of the Saunderstown ferry wharf toward the entrance to Round Swamp, Conanicut Island; west of a line bearing 15° parallel to and 1,000 feet westerly from a line joining the western point of Dutch Island and Twenty-three Foot Rock Buoy 4, and a line ranging 6° from Dutch Island Light toward Warwick Light; and south of a line ranging 290° from Sand Point,

Conanicut Island, to Wickford Harbor Light, and a line bearing 226° from Wickford Harbor Light to Poplar Point tower.

(489)   (i) Temporary floats or buoys for marking anchors or moorings in place will be allowed in this area. Fixed mooring piles or stakes will not be allowed.

(490)   (6) **Anchorage M.** East and north of Dutch Island, northeast of a line ranging 316° from the inshore end of the west ferry wharf, Jamestown, toward the north end of Dutch Island to a point bearing 88°, 200 yards, from the engineer wharf, Dutch Island, thence ranging 3° toward the shore of Conanicut Island at Slocum Ledge; north of a line 200 yards off the Dutch Island shore ranging 281° from the entrance to Round Swamp toward a point on shore 300 yards northerly from the Saunderstown ferry wharf; east of a line ranging 15° from the western point of Dutch Island to Twenty-three Foot Rock Buoy 4; and south of a line bearing 77° from Twenty-three Foot Rock Buoy 4 to the shore.

(491)   (i) Temporary floats or buoys for marking anchors or moorings in place will be allowed in this area. Fixed mooring piles or stakes will not be allowed.

(492)   (7) **Anchorage N.** West of the north end of Conanicut Island, south of a line bearing 262° from Conanicut Island Light; east of a line bearing 8° from Twenty-three Foot Rock Buoy 4; and north of a line ranging 290° from Sand Point toward Wickford Harbor Light.

(493)   (i) Temporary floats or buoys for marking anchors or moorings in place will be allowed in this area. Fixed mooring piles or stakes will not be allowed.

(494)   (c) **Bristol Harbor–(1) Anchorage O.** South of the south line of Franklin Street extended westerly; west of a line bearing 164°30′ parallel to and 400 feet westerly from the State harbor line between Franklin and Constitution Streets, and of a line ranging 244° from a point on the north line of Constitution Street extended 400 feet beyond the State harbor line toward Usher Rock Buoy 3; and north of the north line of Union Street extended to the Popasquash Neck Shore.

(495)   (i) Temporary floats or buoys for marking anchors or moorings in place will be allowed in this area. Fixed mooring piles or stakes will not be allowed.

(496)   (d) **The regulations.** (1) Except in cases of great emergency, no vessels shall be anchored in the entrances to Narragansett Bay, in Newport Harbor, or in Bristol Harbor, outside of the anchorage areas defined in paragraphs (a), (b) and (c) of this section.

(497)   (2) Anchors must not be placed outside the anchorage areas, nor shall any vessel be so anchored that any portion of the hull or rigging shall at any time extend outside the boundaries of the anchorage area.

(498)   (3) Any vessel anchoring under the circumstances of great emergency outside the anchorage areas must be placed near the edge of the channel and in such position as not to interfere with the free navigation of the channel, nor obstruct the approach to any pier, nor impede the movement of any boat, and shall move away immediately after the emergency ceases, or upon notification by an officer of the Coast Guard.

(499)   (4) A vessel upon being notified to move into the anchorage limits or to shift its position on anchorage grounds must get under way at once or signal for a tug, and must change position as directed with reasonable promptness.

(500)   (5) Whenever the maritime or commercial interests of the United States so require, any officer of the Coast Guard is hereby empowered to shift the position of any vessel anchored within the anchorage areas, of any vessel anchored outside the anchorage areas, and of any vessel

which is so moored or anchored as to impede or obstruct vessel movements in any channel.

(501) (6) Nothing in this section shall be construed as relieving the owner or person in charge of any vessel from the penalties of the law for obstructing navigation or for obstructing or interfering with range lights, or for not complying with the navigation laws in regard to lights, fog signals, or for otherwise violating the law.

(502) **§110.147 New London Harbor, Conn. (a) The anchorage grounds–(1) Anchorage A.** In the Thames River east of Shaw Cove, bounded by lines connecting points which are the following bearings and distances from Monument, Groton (latitude 41°21′18″N., longitude 72°04′48″W.): 243°, 1,400 yards; 246°, 925 yards; 217°, 1,380 yards; and 235°, 1,450 yards.

(503) **(2) Anchorage B.** In the Thames River southward of New London, bounded by lines connecting points which are the following bearings and distances from New London Harbor Light (latitude 41°18′59″N., longitude 72°05′25″W.): 002°, 2,460 yards; 009°, 2,480 yards; 026°, 1,175 yards; and 008°, 1,075 yards.

(504) **(3) Anchorage C.** In the Thames River southward of New London Harbor, bounded by lines connecting a point bearing 100°, 450 yards from New London Harbor Light, a point bearing 270°, 575 yards from New London Ledge Light (latitude 41°18′21″N., longitude 72°04′41″W.), and a point bearing 270°, 1,450 yards from New London Ledge Light.

(505) **(4) Anchorage D.** In Long Island Sound approximately two miles west-southwest of New London Ledge Light, bounded by lines connecting points which are the following bearings and distances from New London Ledge Light; 246°, 2.6 miles; 247°, 2.1 miles; 233°, 2.1 miles; and 235°, 2.6 miles.

(506) **(5) Anchorage E.** The waters at the mouth of New London Harbor one mile southeast of New London Ledge Light beginning at latitude 41°17′26″N., longitude 72°04′21″W.;

(507) thence northeasterly to 41°17′38″N., 72°03′54″W.;

(508) thence southeasterly to 41°16′50″N., 72°03′16″W.;

(509) and thence southwesterly to 41°16′38″N., 72°03′43″W.;

(510) and thence northwesterly to the point of beginning.

(511) **(6) Anchorage F.** The waters off the mouth of New London Harbor two miles southeast of New London Ledge Light beginning at latitude 41°16′00″N., longitude 72°03′13″W.;

(512) thence westerly to 41°16′00″N., 72°03′38″W.;

(513) thence northerly to 41°16′35″N., 72°03′38″W.;

(514) thence easterly to 41°16′35″N., 72°03′13″W.;

(515) and thence southerly to the point of beginning.

(516) **(b) The regulations–(1)** Anchorage A is for barges and small vessels drawing less than 12 feet.

(517) **(2)** Anchorage F is reserved for the use of naval vessels and, except in cases of emergency, no other vessel may anchor in Anchorage F without permission from the Captain of the Port, New London, CT.

(518) **(3)** Except in emergencies, vessels shall not anchor in New London Harbor or the approaches thereto outside the anchorages defined in paragraph (a) of this section unless authorized to do so by the Captain of the Port.

(519) **§110.148 Johnsons River at Bridgeport, Conn. (a) The anchorage grounds.** In Johnsons River, beginning at

(520) point "A" 41°10′12.3″N., 73°09′50.2″W.; to

(521) point "B" 41°10′12.3″N., 73°09′52.1″W.; to

(522) point "C" 41°10′10.0″N., 73°09′54.9″W.; to

(523) point "D" 41°10′05.0″N., 73°09′56.1″W.; to

(524) point "E" 41°10′04.0″N., 73°09′55.9″W.; to

(525) point "F" 41°10′05.0″N., 73°00′54.5″W.,; to

(526) point "G" 41°10′05.8″N., 73°09′54.5″W.; thence to the point of beginning.

(527) **(b) The regulations.** The anchorage is for use by commercial and pleasure craft. Temporary floats or buoys for marking anchors or moorings will be allowed. The anchoring of vessels and placing of temporary anchors or mooring piles are under the jurisdiction of the local harbor master. Fixed mooring piles or stakes will not be allowed.

(528) **§110.150 Block Island Sound N.Y. (a) The anchorage ground.** A ¾- by 2-mile rectangular area approximately 3 miles east-northeast of Gardiners Island with the following coordinates:

(529) 41°06′12″N., 72°00′05″W.

(530) 41°07′40″N., 72°01′54″W.

(531) 41°08′12″N., 72°01′10″W.

(532) 41°06′46″N., 71°59′18″W.

(533) **(b) The regulations.** This anchorage ground is for use of U.S. Navy submarines. No vessel or person may approach or remain within 500 yards of a U.S. Navy submarine anchored in this anchorage ground.

(534) **§110.155 Port of New York. (a) Long Island Sound–(1) Anchorage No. 1.** Southwest of a line between Neptune Island and Glen Island ranging from Aunt Phebe Rock Light and tangent to the north edge of Glen Island; southwest of a line tangent to the northeast edge of Glen Island and Goose Island breakwater; southwest of a line bearing southeasterly from the southwest end of Goose Island breakwater and on range with the south gable of the Casino on the northeast end of Glen Island; west of a line ranging from the east edge of Goose Island breakwater to the west edge of the north end of Hart Island; west of Hart Island; and northwest of a line extending from Hart Island Light to Locust Point; excluding from this area, however, (i) the waters northeast of a line ranging 303° from the southwest end of Hart Island; northwest of a line ranging from the water tank at the north end of Davids Island 207°40′ to the northwest end of City Island; and south of latitude 40°52′12″; and (ii) the waters west of Hunter Island; and south of a line ranging from the most southerly end of Glen Island tangent to the most northerly end of Hunter Island.

(535) **(i)** Boats shall not anchor in this area in buoyed channels.

(536) **(ii)** Boats shall be so anchored as to leave at all times an open, usable channel, at least 50 feet wide, west and south of Glen Island.

(537) NOTE: Special anchorage areas in this anchorage are described in §110.60.

(538) **(2) Anchorage No. 1–A.** Southwest of a line ranging from Duck Point, Echo Bay, through Bailey Rock Lighted Buoy 3 BR; northwest of a line ranging from Hicks Ledge Buoy 2H to Old Tom Head Rocks Buoy 4; and north of a line ranging from Old Tom Head Rocks Buoy 4 to the southernmost point of Davenport Neck.

(539) NOTE: The special anchorage area in this anchorage is described in §110.60(b–1).

(540) **(3) Anchorage No. 1–B.** West of a line ranging from the point on the southwest side of the entrance of Horseshoe Harbor, Larchmont, to Hicks Ledge Buoy 2H; north of a line ranging from Hicks Ledge Buoy 2H to Duck Point; and in Echo Bay north and west of the channel.

(541) NOTE: The special anchorage area in this anchorage is described in §110.60(b–1).

(542) **(4) Anchorage No. 2.** West of a line from Locust Point tangent to the northeasterly sea wall at Throgs Neck.

(543) NOTE: Special anchorage areas in this anchorage are described in §110.60.

(829) Except as otherwise required by this subpart, drawbridges shall open promptly and fully for the passage of vessels when a request to open is given in accordance with this subpart.

(830) **§117.7 General duties of drawbridge owners and tenders.**

(831) (a) Drawbridge owners and tenders shall operate the draw in accordance with the requirement in this part.

(832) (b) Except for drawbridges not required to open for the passage of vessels, owners of drawbridges shall ensure that:

(833) (1) The necessary drawtenders are provided for the safe and prompt opening of the draw;

(834) (2) The operating machinery of the draw is maintained in a serviceable condition; and

(835) (3) The draws are operated at sufficient intervals to assure their satisfactory operation.

(836) **§117.9 Delaying opening of a draw.**

(837) No person shall unreasonably delay the opening of a draw after the signals required by §117.15 have been given.

(838) **Note.–**Trains are usually controlled by the block method. That is, the track is divided into blocks or segments of a mile or more in length. When a train is in a block with a drawbridge, the draw may not be able to open until the train has passed out of the block and the yardmaster or other manager has "unlocked" the drawbridge controls. The maximum time permitted for delay is defined in Subpart B for each affected bridge. Land and water traffic should pass over or through the draw as soon as possible in order to prevent unnecessary delays in the opening and closure of the draw.

(839) **§117.11 Appurtenances unessential to navigation.**

(840) No vessel owner or operator shall signal a drawbridge to open for any nonstructural vessel appurtenance which is not essential to navigation or which is easily lowered.

(841) **§117.15 Signals.**

(842) (a) General. (1) The operator of each vessel requesting a drawbridge to open shall signal the drawtender and the drawtender shall acknowledge that signal. The signal shall be repeated until acknowledged in some manner by the drawtender before proceeding.

(843) (2) The signals used to request the opening of the draw and to acknowledge that request shall be sound signals, visual signals, or radiotelephone communications described in this subpart.

(844) (3) Any of the means of signaling described in this subpart sufficient to alert the bridge being signaled may be used.

(845) (b) Sound signals. (1) Sound signals shall be made by whistle, horn, megaphone, hailer, or other device capable of producing the described signals loud enough to be heard by the drawtender.

(846) (2) As used in this section, "prolonged blast" means a blast of four to six seconds duration and "short blast" means a blast of approximately one second duration.

(847) (3) The sound signal to request the opening of a draw is one prolonged blast followed by one short blast sounded not more than three seconds after the prolonged blast. For vessels required to be passed through a draw during a scheduled closure period, the sound signal to request the opening of the draw during that period is five short blasts sounded in rapid succession.

(848) (4) When the draw can be opened immediately, the sound signal to acknowledge a request to open the draw is one prolonged blast followed by one short blast sounded not more than 30 seconds after the requesting signal.

(849) (5) When the draw cannot be opened immediately, or is open and shall be closed promptly, the sound signal to

acknowledge a request to open the draw is five short blasts sounded in rapid succession not more than 30 seconds after the vessel's opening signal. The signal shall be repeated until acknowledged in some manner by the requesting vessel.

(850) (c) Visual signals. (1) The visual signal to request the opening of a draw is–

(851) (i) A white flag raised and lowered vertically; or

(852) (ii) A white, amber, or green light raised and lowered vertically.

(853) (2) When the draw can be opened immediately, the visual signal to acknowledge a request to open the draw, given not more than 30 seconds after the vessel's opening signal, is–

(854) (i) A white flag raised and lowered vertically;

(855) (ii) A white, amber, or green light raised and lowered vertically, or

(856) (iii) A fixed or flashing white, amber, or green light or lights.

(857) (3) When the draw cannot be opened immediately, or is open and must be closed promptly, the visual signal to acknowledge a request to open the draw is–

(858) (i) A red flag or red light swung back and forth horizontally in full sight of the vessel given not more than 30 seconds after the vessel's opening signal; or

(859) (ii) A fixed or flashing red light or lights given not more than 30 seconds after the vessel's opening signal.

(860) (4) The acknowledging signal when the draw cannot open immediately or is open and must be closed promptly shall be repeated until acknowledged in some manner by the requesting vessel.

(861) (d) Radiotelephone communications. (1) Radiotelephones may be used to communicate the same information provided by sound and visual signals.

(862) **NOTE:** Call signs and radio channels for drawbridges equipped with radiotelephones are included with the bridge descriptions in chapters 4 through 12.

(863) (2) The vessel and the drawtender shall monitor the frequency used until the vessel has cleared the draw.

(864) (3) When radiotelephone contact cannot be initiated or maintained, sound or visual signals under this section shall be used.

(865) **§117.17 Signalling for contiguous drawbridges.**

(866) When a vessel must pass two or more drawbridges close together, the opening signal is given for the first bridge. After acknowledgment from the first bridge that it will promptly open, the opening signal is given for the second bridge, and so on until all bridges that the vessel must pass have been given the opening signal and have acknowledged that they will open promptly.

(867) **§117.19 Signalling when two or more vessels are approaching a drawbridge.**

(868) When two or more vessels are approaching the same drawbridge at the same time, or nearly the same time, whether from the same or opposite directions, each vessel shall signal independently for the opening of the draw and the drawtender shall reply in turn to the signal of each vessel. The drawtender need not reply to signals by vessels accumulated at the bridge for passage during a scheduled open period.

(869) **§117.21 Signalling for an opened drawbridge.**

(870) When a vessel approaches a drawbridge with the draw in the open position, the vessel shall give the opening signal. If no acknowledgment is received within 30 seconds, the vessel may proceed, with caution, through the open draw.

(871) **§117.23 Installation of radiotelephones.**

(872)   (a) When the District Commander deems it necessary for reasons of safety of navigation, the District Commander may require the installation and operation of a radiotelephone on or near a drawbridge.

(873)   (b) The District Commander gives written notice of the proposed requirement to the bridge owner.

(874)   (c) All comments the owner wishes to submit shall be submitted to the District Commander within 30 days of receipt of the notice under paragraph (b) of this section.

(875)   (d) If, upon consideration of the comments received, the District Commander determines that a radiotelephone is necessary, the District Commander notifies the bridge owner that a radiotelephone shall be installed and gives a reasonable time, not to exceed six months, to install the radiotelephone and commence operation.

(876)   §117.24 Radiotelephone installation identification.

(877)   (a) The Coast Guard authorizes, and the District Commander may require the installation of a sign on drawbridges, on the upstream and downstream sides, indicating that the bridge is equipped with and operates a VHF radiotelephone in accordance with §117.23.

(878)   (b) The sign shall give notice of the radiotelephone and its calling and working channels—

(879)   (1) In plain language; or

(880)   (2) By a sign consisting of the outline of a telephone handset with the long axis placed horizontally and a vertical three-legged lightning slash superimposed over the handset. The slash shall be as long vertically as the handset is wide horizontally and normally not less than 27 inches and no more than 36 inches long. The preferred calling channel should be shown in the lower left quadrant and the preferred working channel should be shown in the lower right quadrant.

(881)   §117.31 Closure of draw for emergency vehicles.

(882)   When a drawtender is informed by a reliable source that an emergency vehicle is due to cross the draw, the drawtender shall take all reasonable measures to have the draw closed at the time the emergency vehicle arrives at the bridge.

(883)   §117.33 Closure of draw for natural disasters or civil disorders.

(884)   Drawbridges need not open for the passage of vessels during periods of natural disasters or civil disorders declared by the appropriate authorities unless otherwise provided for in Subpart B or directed to do so by the District Commander.

(885)   §117.35 Operations during repair or maintenance.

(886)   (a) When operation of the draw must deviate from the regulations in this part for scheduled repair or maintenance work, the drawbridge owner shall request approval from the District Commander at least 30 days before the date of the intended change. The request shall include a brief description of the nature of the work to be performed and the times and dates of requested changes. The District Commander's decision is forwarded to the applicant within five working days of the receipt of the request. If the request is denied, the reasons for the denial are forwarded with the decision.

(887)   (b) When the draw is rendered inoperative because of damage to the structure or when vital, unscheduled repair or maintenance work shall be performed without delay, the drawbridge owner shall immediately notify the District Commander and give the reasons why the draw is or should be rendered inoperative and the expected date of completion of the repair or maintenance work.

(888)   (c) All repair or maintenance work under this section shall be performed with all due speed in order to return the draw to operation as soon as possible.

(889)   (d) If the operation of the draw will be affected for periods of less than 60 days, the regulations in this part will not be amended. Where practicable, the District Commander publishes notice of temporary deviations from the regulations in this part in the Federal Register and Local Notices to Mariners. If operation of the draw is expected to be affected for more than 60 days, the District Commander publishes temporary regulations covering the repair period.

(890)   §117.37 Opening or closure of draw for public interest concerns.

(891)   (a) For reasons of public health or safety or for public functions, such as street parades and marine regattas, the District Commander may authorize the opening or closure of a drawbridge for a specified period of time.

(892)   (b) Requests for opening or closure of a draw shall be submitted to the District Commander at least 30 days before the proposed opening or closure and include a brief description of the proposed event or other reason for the request, the reason why the opening or closure is required, and the times and dates of the period the draw is to remain open or closed.

(893)   (c) Approval by the District Commander depends on the necessity for the opening or closure, the reasonableness of the times and dates, and the overall effect on navigation and users of the bridge.

(894)   §117.39 Closure of draw due to infrequent use.

(895)   Upon written request by the owner or operator of a drawbridge, the District Commander may, after notice in the Federal Register and opportunity for public comment, permit the draw to be closed and untended due to infrequency of use of the draw by vessels. The District Commander may condition approval on the continued maintenance of the operating machinery.

(896)   §117.41 Maintenance of draw in fully open position.

(897)   The draw may be maintained in the fully open position to permit the passage of vessels and drawtender service discontinued if the District Commander is notified in advance. The draw shall remain in the fully open position until drawtender service is restored or authorization under §117.39 is given for the draw to remain closed and untended.

(898)   §117.43 Changes in draw operation requirements for regulatory purposes.

(899)   In order to evaluate suggested changes to the drawbridge operation requirements, the District Commander may authorize temporary deviations from the regulations in this part for periods not to exceed 60 days. Notice of these deviations is disseminated in the Local Notices to Mariners and published in the Federal Register.

(900)   §117.45 Operation during winter in the Great Lakes area.

(901)   (a) The Commander, Ninth Coast Guard District, may determine that drawbridges located in the Ninth Coast Guard District need not open during the winter season when general navigation is curtailed, unless a request to open the draw is given at least 12 hours before the time of the intended passage.

(902)   (b) Notice of these determinations is disseminated in Local Notices to Mariners and other appropriate media. Notices indicate—

(903)   (1) The name and location of the bridge affected;

(904)   (2) The period of time covered; and

(905)   (3) The telephone number and address of the party to whom requests for openings are given.

(906)   §117.47 Clearance gages.

(907)   (a) Clearance gages are required for drawbridges across navigable waters of the United States discharging into the Atlantic Ocean south of Delaware Bay (including

and maintained according to the provisions of §118.160 of these regulations.

(1230) (3) Trains and locomotives shall be controlled so that any delay in opening the draw shall not exceed five minutes. However, if a train moving toward the bridge has crossed the home signal for the bridge before the signal requesting opening of the bridge is given, that train may continue across the bridge and must clear the bridge and must clear the bridge interlocks before stopping.

(1231) (4) Except as provided in paragraphs (b) through (e) of this section, each draw shall open on signal.

(1232) (b) The draws of the Long Island Railroad bridges, mile 1.1 across Dutch Kills, both at New York City shall open on signal if at least six hours notice is given to the Long Island Railroad Movement Bureau except as provided in paragraphs (a)(1) and (a)(3) of this section.

(1233) (c) The draw of the Borden Avenue bridge, mile 1.2 across Dutch Kills at New York City (NYC), shall open on signal if at least one hour advance notice is given to the drawtender at the Grand Street/Avenue bridge, mile 3.1 across Newton Creek (East Branch), the New York City Department of Transportation (NYCDOT) Radio Hotline, or NYCDOT Bridge Operations Office. In the event the drawtender is at the Roosevelt Island bridge, mile 6.4 across East River of the Hunters Point Avenue bridge, mile 1.4 across Dutch Kills, New York, up to an additional half hour delay may be required.

(1234) (d) The draw of the Hunters Point Avenue bridge, mile 1.4 across Dutch Kill, New York City, shall open on signal if at least one hour advance notice is given to the drawtender at the Grand Street/Avenue bridge, mile 3.1 across Newtown Creek (East Branch), the New York City Department of Transportation (NYCDOT) Radio Hotline or NYCDOT Bridge Operations Office. In the event the drawtender is at the Roosevelt Island bridge, mile 6.4 across East River, or the Borden Avenue bridge, mile 1.2 across Dutch Kills, up to an additional half hour may be required.

(1235) (e) The draw of Grand Street/Avenue bridge, mile 3.1 across Newtown Creek (East Branch), at New York City, shall open on signal unless the drawtender is at the Borden Avenue or Hunters Point Avenue Bridges, mile 1.2 and 1.4, respectively, across Dutch Kills, New York or the Roosevelt Island bridge, mile 6.4 across East River. In this event, a notice to New York City Department of Transportation Radio Hotline, or NYCDOT Bridge Operations Office shall be given, to which a delay of up to one hour may be required.

(1236) **§117.805 Peekskill (Annsville) Creek.**

(1237) The draw of the Conrail bridge, mile 0.0 at Peekskill, need not be opened for the passage of vessels.

(1238) **§117.807 Richmond Creek.**

(1239) The draw of the Richmond Avenue bridge, mile 2.0 at New York City, need not open for the passage of vessels.

(1240) **§117.813 Wappinger Creek.**

(1241) The draw of the Metro-North Commuter railroad bridge, mile 0.0 at New Hamburg, need not be opened for the passage of vessels. However, the draw shall be returned to operable condition within six months after notification by the District Commander to do so.

(1242) **§117.815 Westchester Creek.**

(1243) The draw of the Bruckner Boulevard bridge, mile 1.7, shall open on signal; except that, from 7 a.m. to 9 a.m. and 4 p.m. to 6 p.m. Monday through Friday, the draw need not be opened for the passage of vessels. Public vessels of the United States, state or local vessels used for public safety, or vessels in distress shall be passed without delay. The owners of the bridge shall provide and keep in good legible condition two board gages painted white with black figures not

less than nine inches high to indicate the vertical clearance under the closed draw at all stages of the tide. The gages shall be so placed on the bridge that they are plainly visible to operators of vessels approaching the bridge either up or downstream.

(1244) **RHODE ISLAND**

(1245) **§117.907 Providence River.**

(1246) The draw of the US1 (Point Street) bridge, mile 7.5 at Providence, need not be opened for the passage of vessels from 7 a.m. to 9 a.m. and 4 p.m. to 6 p.m. At all other times, the draw shall open on signal if at least 24 hours notice is given to the Director of Public Works, City Hall, Providence. Public vessels of the United States, state and local vessels used for public safety, loaded, self-propelled cargo vessels, and assisting tugs shall be passed as soon as possible.

(1247) **Note.**—Call signs and radio channels for drawbridges equipped with radiotelephones are included with the bridge descriptions in chapters 4 through 12.

Part 160–Ports and Waterways Safety-General

Subpart A–General:

(1248) **§ 160.1 Purpose.**

(1249) Part 160 contains regulations implementing the Ports and Waterways Safety Act (33 U.S.C. 1221) and related statutes.

(1250) **§160.3 Definitions.**

(1251) (a) For the purposes of this part:

(1252) (1) "Commandant" means the Commandant of the United States Coast Guard.

(1253) (2) "District Commander" means the officer of the Coast Guard designated by the Commandant to command a Coast Guard District described in 33 CFR 3.

(1254) (3) "Captain of the Port" means the Coast Guard officer commanding a Captain of the Port zone described in 33 CFR 3.

(1255) (4) "Person" means an individual, firm, corporation, association, partnership, or governmental entity.

(1256) (5) "State" means each of the several States of the United States, the District of Columbia, the Commonwealth of Puerto Rico, Guam, American Samoa, the United States Virgin Islands, the Trust Territories of the Pacific Islands, the Commonwealth of the Northern Marianas Islands, and any other commonwealth, territory, or possession of the United States.

(1257) (6) "Vessel" means every description of watercraft or other artificial contrivance used, or capable of being used, as a means of transportation on water.

(1258) (7) "Vehicle" means every type of conveyance capable of being used as a means of transportation on land.

(1259) **§160.5 Delegations.**

(1260) (a) District Commanders and Captains of the Ports are delegated the authority to establish safety zones.

(1261) (b) Under the provisions of 33 CFR 6.04-1 and 6.04-6, District Commanders and Captains of the Ports have been delegated authority to establish security zones.

(1262) (c) Under the provisions of 33 CFR §1.05-1, District Commanders have been delegated authority to establish regulated navigation areas.

(1263) (d) Under the direction of the Captain of the Port Honolulu, the Commander, Marianas Section, may exercise the authority of a Captain of the Port within the waters surrounding Guam, and the Commonwealth of Marianas, all of which are in the Honolulu Captain of the Port Zone.

(1264) **§160.7 Appeals.**

(1265) (a) Any person directly affected by a safety zone or an order or direction issued under this subchapter (33 CFR

Subchapter P) may request reconsideration by the official who issued it or in whose name it was issued. This request may be made orally or in writing, and the decision of the official receiving the request may be rendered orally or in writing.

(1266)   (b) Any person directly affected by the establishment of a safety zone or by an order or direction issued by, or on behalf of, a Captain of the Port may appeal to the District Commander through the Captain of the Port. The appeal must be in writing, except as allowed under paragraph (d) of this section, and shall contain complete supporting documentation and evidence which the appellant wishes to have considered. Upon receipt of the appeal, the District Commander may direct a representative to gather and submit documentation or other evidence which would be necessary or helpful to a resolution of the appeal. A copy of this documentation and evidence is made available to the appellant. The appellant is afforded five working days from the date of receipt to submit rebuttal materials. Following submission of all materials, the District Commander issues a ruling, in writing, on the appeal. Prior to issuing the ruling, the District Commander may, as a matter of discretion, allow oral presentation on the issues.

(1267)   (c) Any person directly affected by the establishment of a safety zone or by an order or direction issued by a District Commander, or who receives an unfavorable ruling on an appeal taken under paragraph (b) of this section, may appeal through the District Commander to the Chief, Office of Marine Safety, Security and Environmental Protection, U.S. Coast Guard, Washington, D.C. 20593. The appeal must be in writing, except as allowed under paragraph (d) of this section. The District Commander forwards the appeal, all the documents and evidence which formed the record upon which the order or direction was issued or the ruling under paragraph (b) of this section was made, and any comments which might be relevant, to the Chief, Office of Marine Safety, Security and Environmental Protection. A copy of this documentation and evidence is made available to the appellant. The appellant is afforded five working days from the date of receipt to submit rebuttal materials to the Chief, Office of Marine Safety, Security and Environmental Protection. The decision of the Chief, Office of Marine Safety, Security and Environmental Protection is based upon the materials submitted, without oral argument or presentation. The decision of the Chief, Office of Marine Safety, Security and Environmental Protection is issued in writing and constitutes final agency action.

(1268)   (d) If the delay in presenting a written appeal would have significant adverse impact on the appellant, the appeal under paragraphs (b) and (c) of this section may initially be presented orally. If an initial presentation of the appeal is made orally, the appellant must submit the appeal in writing within five days of the oral presentation to the Coast Guard official to whom the presentation was made. The written appeal must contain, at a minimum, the basis for the appeal and a summary of the material presented orally. If requested, the official to whom the appeal is directed may stay the effect of the action while the ruling is being appealed.

Subpart B—Control of Vessel and Facility Operations
(1269)   **§160.101 Purpose.**
(1270)   This subpart describes the authority exercised by District Commanders and Captains of the Ports to insure the safety of vessels and waterfront facilities, and the protection of the navigable waters and the resources therein. The controls described in this subpart are directed to specific situations and hazards.
(1271)   **§160.103 Applicability.**

(1272)   (a) This subpart applies to any—
(1273)   (1) Vessel on the navigable waters of the United States, except as provided in paragraphs (b) and (c) of this section;
(1274)   (2) Bridge or other structure on or in the navigable waters of the United States; and
(1275)   (3) Land structure or shore area immediately adjacent to the navigable waters of the United States.
(1276)   (b) This subpart does not apply to any vessel on the Saint Lawrence Seaway.
(1277)   (c) Except pursuant to international treaty, convention, or agreement, to which the United States is a party, this subpart does not apply to any foreign vessel that is not destined for, or departing from, a port or place subject to the jurisdiction of the United States and that is in—
(1278)   (1) Innocent passage through the territorial sea of the United States;
(1279)   (2) Transit through the navigable waters of the United States which form a part of an international strait.
(1280)   **§160.105 Compliance with orders.**
(1281)   Each person who has notice of the terms of an order issued under this subpart must comply with that order.
(1282)   **§160.107 Denial of entry.**
(1283)   Each District Commander or Captain of the Port, subject to recognized principles of international law, may deny entry into the navigable waters of the United States or to any port or place under the jurisdiction of the United States, and within the district or zone of that District Commander or Captain of the Port, to any vessel not in compliance with the provisions of the Port and Tanker Safety Act (33 U.S.C. 1221-1232) or the regulations issued thereunder.
(1284)   **§160.109 Waterfront facility safety.**
(1285)   (a) To prevent damage to, or destruction of, any bridge or other structure on or in the navigable waters of the United States, or any land structure or shore area immediately adjacent to those waters, and to protect the navigable waters and the resources therein from harm resulting from vessel or structure damage, destruction, or loss, each District Commander or Captain of the Port may—
(1286)   (1) Direct the handling, loading, unloading, storage, stowage, and movement (including the emergency removal, control, and disposition) of explosives or other dangerous articles and substances, including oil or hazardous material as those terms are defined in Section 4417a of the Revised Statutes, as amended, (46 U.S.C. 391a) on any structure on or in the navigable waters of the United States, or any land structure or shore area immediately adjacent to those waters; and
(1287)   (2) Conduct examinations to assure compliance with the safety equipment requirements for structures.
(1288)   **§160.111 Special orders applying to vessel operations.**
(1289)   Each District Commander or Captain of the Port may order a vessel to operate or anchor in the manner directed when—
(1290)   (a) The District Commander or Captain of the Port has reasonable cause to believe that the vessel is not in compliance with any regulation, law or treaty;
(1291)   (b) The District Commander or Captain of the Port determines that the vessel does not satisfy the conditions for vessel operation and cargo transfers specified in §160.113; or
(1292)   (c) The District Commander or Captain of the Port has determined that such order is justified in the interest of safety by reason of weather, visibility, sea conditions, temporary port congestion, other temporary hazardous circumstances, or the condition of the vessel.
(1293)   **§160.113 Prohibition of vessel operation and cargo transfers.**

(1294)   (a) Each District Commander or Captain of the Port may prohibit any vessel subject to the provisions of section 4417a of the Revised Statutes (46 U.S.C. 391a) from operating in the navigable waters of the United States, or from transferring cargo or residue in any port or place under the jurisdiction of the United States, and within the district or zone of that District Commander or Captain of the Port, if the District Commander or the Captain of the Port determines that the vessel's history of accidents, pollution incidents, or serious repair problems creates reason to believe that the vessel may be unsafe or pose a threat to the marine environment.

(1295)   (b) The authority to issue orders prohibiting operation of the vessels or transfer of cargo or residue under paragraph (a) of this section also applies if the vessel:

(1296)   (1) Fails to comply with any applicable regulation;

(1297)   (2) Discharges oil or hazardous material in violation of any law or treaty of the United States;

(1298)   (3) Does not comply with applicable vessel traffic service requirements;

(1299)   (4) While underway, does not have at least one licensed deck officer on the navigation bridge who is capable of communicating in the English language.

(1300)   (c) When a vessel has been prohibited from operating in the navigable waters of the United States under paragraphs (a) or (b) of this section, the District Commander or Captain of the Port may allow provisional entry into the navigable waters of the United States, or into any port or place under the jurisdiction of the United States and within the district or zone of that District Commander or Captain of the Port, if the owner or operator of such vessel proves to the satisfaction of the District Commander or Captain of the Port, that the vessel is not unsafe or does not pose a threat to the marine environment, and that such entry is necessary for the safety of the vessel or the persons on board.

(1301)   (d) A vessel which has been prohibited from operating in the navigable waters of the United States, or from transferring cargo or residue in a port or place under the jurisdiction of the United States under the provisions of paragraph (a) or (b)(1), (2) or (3) of this section, may be allowed provisional entry if the owner or operator proves, to the satisfaction of the District Commander or Captain of the Port that has jurisdiction, that the vessel is no longer unsafe or a threat to the environment, and that the condition which gave rise to the prohibition no longer exists.

(1302)   **§160.115 Withholding of clearance.**

(1303)   (a) Each District Commander or Captain of the Port may request the Secretary of the Treasury, or the authorized representative thereof, to withold or revoke the clearance required by 46 U.S.C. 91 of any vessel, the owner or operator of which is subject to any penalties under 33 U.S.C. 1232.

Subpart C–Notifications of Arrivals, Departures, Hazardous Conditions, and Certain Dangerous Cargoes

(1304)   **§160.201 Applicability and exceptions to applicability.**

(1305)   (a) This subpart prescribes notification requirements for U.S. and foreign vessels bound for or departing from ports or places in the United States.

(1306)   (b) This subpart does not apply to boats under the Federal Boat Safety Act of 1971 (46 U.S.C. 1451, et seq.) and, except §161.215, does not apply to passenger and supply vessels when they are employed in the exploration for or in the exploitation of oil, gas, or mineral resources on the continental shelf.

(1307)   (c) Sections 160.207 and 160.209 do not apply to the following:

(1308)   (1) Each vessel of less than 1,600 gross tons.

(1309)   (2) Each vessel operating exclusively within a Captain of the Port zone.

(1310)   (3) Each vessel operating upon a route that is described in a schedule that is submitted to the Captain of the Port for each port or place of destination listed in the schedule at least 24 hours in advance of the first date and time of arrival listed on the schedule and contains—

(1311)   (i) Name, country of registry, and call sign or official number of the vessel;

(1312)   (ii) Each port or place of destination; and

(1313)   (iii) Dates and times of arrivals and departures at those ports or places.

(1314)   (4) Each vessel arriving at a port or place under force majeure.

(1315)   (5) Each vessel entering a port of call in the United States in compliance with the Automated Mutual Assistance Vessel Rescue System (AMVER).

(1316)   (6) Each vessel entering a port of call in the United States in compliance with the U.S. Flag Merchant Vessel Locator Filing System (USMER).

(1317)   (7) Each barge.

(1318)   (8) Each public vessel.

(1319)   (9) United States or Canadian flag vessels, except tank vessels or vessels carrying certain dangerous cargo, which operate solely on the Great Lakes.

(1320)   (d) Sections 160.207, 160.211, and 160.213 apply to each vessel upon the waters of the Mississippi River between its mouth and mile 235, Lower Mississippi River, above Head of Passes. Sections 160.207, 160.211, and 160.213 do not apply to each vessel upon the waters of the Mississippi River between its sources and mile 235, above Head of Passes, and all the tributaries emptying thereinto and their tributaries, and that part of the Atchafalaya River above its junction with the Plaquemine-Morgan City alternate waterway, and the Red River of the North.

(1321)   **§160.203 Definitions.**

(1322)   As used in this subpart:

(1323)   "Agent" means any person, partnership, firm, company or corporation engaged by the owner or charterer of a vessel to act in their behalf in matters concerning the vessel.

(1324)   "Carried in bulk" means a commodity that is loaded or carried on board a vessel without containers or labels and received and handled without mark or count.

(1325)   "Certain dangerous cargo" includes any of the following:

(1326)   (a) Class A explosives, as defined in 46 CFR 146.20–7 and 49 CFR 173.53.

(1327)   (b) Oxidizing materials or blasting agents for which a permit is required under 49 CFR 176.415.

(1328)   (c) Highway route controlled quantity radioactive material, as defined in 49 CFR 173.403(1), or Fissile Class III shipments of fissile radioactive material, as defined in 49 CFR 173.455(a)(3).

(1329)   (d) Each cargo under Table 1 of 46 CFR Part 153 when carried in bulk.

(1330)   (e) Any of the following when carried in bulk:

(1331)   Acetaldehyde

(1332)   Ammonia, anhydrous

(1333)   Butadiene

(1334)   Butane

(1335)   Butene

(1336)   Butylene Oxide

(1337)   Chlorine

(1338)   Ethane

(1339)   Ethylene

(1340)   Ethylene Oxide

(1341)   Methane

(1342) Methyl Acetylene, Propadiene Mixture, Stabilized
(1343) Methyl Bromide
(1344) Methyl Chloride
(1345) Phosphorous, elemental
(1346) Propane
(1347) Propylene
(1348) Sulfur Dioxide
(1349) Vinyl Chloride
(1350) "Great Lakes" means Lakes Superior, Michigan, Huron, Erie, and Ontario, their connecting and tributary waters, the Saint Lawrence River as far east as Saint Regis, and adjacent port areas.
(1351) "Hazardous condition" means any condition that could adversely affect the safety of any vessel, bridge, structure, or shore area or the environmental quality of any port, harbor, or navigable water of the United States. This condition could include but is not limited to, fire, explosion, grounding, leakage, damage, illness of a person on board, or a manning shortage.
(1352) "Port or place of departure" means any port or place in which a vessel is anchored or moored.
(1353) "Port or place of destination" means any port or place to which a vessel is bound to anchor or moor.
(1354) "Public vessel" means a vessel owned by and being used in the public service of the United States. This definition does not include a vessel owned by the United States and engaged in a trade or commercial service or a vessel under contract or charter to the United States.
(1355) **§160.205 Waivers.**
(1356) The Captain of the Port may waive, within that Captain of the Port's designated zone, any of the requirements of this subpart for any vessel or class of vessels upon finding that the vessel, route, area of operations, conditions of the voyage, or other circumstances are such that application of this subpart is unnecessary or impractical for purposes of safety, environmental protection, or national security.
(1357) **§160.207 Notice of arrival: vessels bound for ports or places in the United States.**
(1358) (a) The owner, master, agent or person in charge of a vessel on a voyage of 24 hours or more shall report under paragraph (c) of this section at least 24 hours before entering the port or place of destination.
(1359) (b) The owner, master, agent, or person in charge of a vessel on a voyage of less than 24 hours shall report under paragraph (c) of this section before departing the port or place of departure.
(1360) (c) The Captain of the Port of the port or place of destination in the United States must be notified of—
(1361) (1) The name and country of registry of the vessel;
(1362) (2) The name of the port or place of departure.
(1363) (3) The name of the port or place of destination; and
(1364) (4) The estimated time of arrival at the port or place.
(1365) If the estimated time of arrival changes by more than six hours from the latest reported time, the Captain of the Port must be notified of the correction as soon as the change is known.
(1366) **§160.209 Notice of arrival: vessels bound from the high seas for ports or places on the Great Lakes.**
(1367) In addition to complying with the requirement of §160.207, the owner, master, agent, or person in charge of a vessel bound from the high seas for any port or place of destination on the Great Lakes shall notify the Commander, Ninth Coast Guard District, at least 24 hours before arriving at the Snell Locks, Massena, New York of—
(1368) (a) The name and country of registry of the vessel; and
(1369) (b) The estimated time of arrival at the Snell Locks, Massena, New York.

(1370) **§160.211 Notice of arrival: vessels carrying certain dangerous cargo.**
(1371) (a) The owner, master, agent, or person in charge of a vessel, except a barge, bound for a port or place in the United States carrying certain dangerous cargo shall notify the Captain of the Port of the port or place of destination at least 24 hours before entering that port or place of—
(1372) (1) The name and country of registry of the vessel;
(1373) (2) The location of the vessel at the time of the report;
(1374) (3) The name of each certain dangerous cargo carried;
(1375) (4) The amount of each certain dangerous cargo carried;
(1376) (5) The stowage location of each certain dangerous cargo;
(1377) (6) The operational condition of the equipment under 33 CFR 164.35;
(1378) (7) The name of the port or place of destination; and
(1379) (8) The estimated time of arrival at that port or place. If the estimated time of arrival changes by more than six hours from the latest reported time, the Captain of the Port must be notified of the correction as soon as the change is known.
(1380) (b) The owner, master, agent or person in charge of a barge bound for a port or place in the United States carrying certain dangerous cargo shall report the information required in paragraph (a)(1) through (a)(8) of this section to the Captain of the Port of the port or place of destination at least 4 hours before entering that port or place.
(1381) **§160.213 Notice of departure; vessels carrying certain dangerous cargo.**
(1382) (a) The owner, master, agent, or person in charge of a vessel, except a barge, departing from a port or place in the United States for any other port or place and carrying certain dangerous cargo shall notify the Captain of the Port or place of departure at least 24 hours before departing, unless this notification was made within 2 hours after the vessel's arrival, of—
(1383) (1) The name and country of registry of the vessel;
(1384) (2) The name of each certain dangerous cargo carried;
(1385) (3) The amount of each certain dangerous cargo carried;
(1386) (4) The stowage location of each certain dangerous cargo carried;
(1387) (5) The operational condition of the equipment under 33 CFR 164.35;
(1388) (6) The name of the port or place of departure; and
(1389) (7) The estimated time of departure from the port or place.
(1390) If the estimated time of departure changes by more than six hours from the latest reported time, the Captain of the Port must be notified of the correction as soon as the change is known.
(1391) (b) The owner, master, agent, or person in change of a barge departing from a port or place in the United States for any other port or place and carrying certain dangerous cargo shall report the information required in paragraph (a)(1) through (a)(7) of this section to the Captain of the Port of the port or place of departure at least 4 hours before departing, unless this report was made within 2 hours after the barge's arrival.
(1392) **§160.215 Notice of hazardous conditions.**
(1393) Whenever there is a hazardous condition on board a vessel, the owner, master, agent or person in charge shall immediately notify the Captain of the Port of the port or place of destination and the Captain of the Port of the port

or place in which the vessel is located of the hazardous condition.

(1394) **Part 161 - Vessel Traffic Management**

(1395) **New York Vessel Traffic Service**

(1396) **General rules**

(1397) **§161.501 Purpose and applicability.**

(1398) (a) Sections 161.501 through 161.580 of this part prescribe rules for vessel operation in the Vessel Traffic Service New York Area (VTSNY Area) to prevent collisions and groundings and to protect the navigable waters of the VTSNY Area from environmental harm resulting from collisions and groundings.

(1399) (b) The General Rules in §§ 161.501 through 161.505 and 161.507 through 161.510, and the Use of Designated Frequency Rule in §161.523 of this part apply to the operation of all vessels.

(1400) (c) The Requirement to Carry Regulations Rule in §161.506, the Communications Rules in §§ 161.520 through 161.522 and 161.524 through 161.532, the Vessel Movement Reporting Rules in §§ 161.536 through 161.542, and the Special Rules of §161.575 of this part apply only to the operation of -

(1401) (1) Power driven vessels of 300 gross tons and upward while navigating;

(1402) (2) Vessels of 100 gross tons and upward carrying one or more passengers for hire while navigating;

(1403) (3) Commercial vessels of 26 feet or more in length engaged in towing another vessel astern, alongside, or by pushing ahead; and

(1404) (4) Every dredge and floating plant.

(1405) (d) Geographic coordinates expressed in terms of latitude and longitude are not intended for plotting on maps or charts whose referenced horizontal datum is the North American Datum of 1983 (NAD 83), unless such geographic coordinates are expressly labeled NAD 83. Geographic coordinates without the NAD 83 reference may be plotted on maps or charts referenced to NAD 83 only after application of the appropriate corrections that are published on the particular map or charts used.

(1406) **§161.503 Definitions.**

(1407) As used in any section of this part:

(1408) Commercial Vessel means any vessel operating in return for payment or other type of compensation.

(1409) ETA means estimated time of arrival.

(1410) Floating Plant means any vessel, other than a vessel underway and making way, engaged in any construction, manufacturing, or exploration operation, and which may restrict the navigation of other vessels. Master means a licensed master or operator or, on vessels not requiring a licensed operator, the person directing the movement of the vessel.

(1411) Person includes an individual, firm, corporation, association, partnership, and governmental entity.

(1412) Vessel Movement Reporting System (VMRS) is a method for monitoring vessel progress based on position reports from the vessel rather than on electronic surveillance.

(1413) Vessel Traffic Center (VTC) means the shore based facility that operates the New York Vessel Traffic Service.

(1414) Vessel Traffic Service New York Area (VTSNY Area) means the area described in §161.580 of this part.

(1415) **§161.504 Vessel operation in the VTSNY Area.**

(1416) No person may cause or authorize the operation of a vessel in the VTSNY Area contrary to the rules in this part.

(1417) **§161.505 VTC directions.**

(1418) (a) During conditions of vessel congestion, adverse weather, reduced visibility, other hazardous circumstances, the VTC may issue directions to control and supervise traffic by specifying times when vessels may enter, move within or

through, or depart from ports, harbors or other waters in the VTSNY Area.

(1419) (b) The master or pilot of a vessel in the VTSNY Area shall comply with each direction issued to the vessel under this section.

(1420) **§161.506 Requirement to carry regulations.**

(1421) The master of a vessel shall ensure that a copy of the current edition of the Vessel Traffic Service New York regulations, Title 33, Code of Federal Regulations, §§161.501 through 161.580, is available on board the vessels at all times when it is navigating in the VTSNY Area.

(1422) Note.-The New York VTS Operating Manual includes the VTS regulations described above. Additional information for efficient operation in the VTS system is also included. The manual may be obtained free-of-charge from U.S. Coast Guard Marine Inspection Office, Battery Park Building, New York, NY 16004, and from Commanding Officer, U.S. Coast Guard Vessel Traffic Service, Governors Island, New York, NY 10004.

(1423) **§161.507 Laws and regulations not affected.**

(1424) Nothing in this part is intended to relieve any person from complying with any other applicable laws or regulations.

(1425) **§161.508 Authorization to deviate from these rules.**

(1426) (a) The Commander, First Coast Guard District may, upon written request, issue an authorization to deviate from any rule in this part if he or she finds that the proposed operation can be done safely. An application for an authorization to deviate from a rule must state the need for the deviation and describe the proposed operation.

(1427) (b) The VTC may, upon verbal request, issue an authorization to deviate from any rule in this part for the voyage on which a vessel is embarked or about to embark.

(1428) **§161.510 Emergencies.**

(1429) In an emergency, any master or pilot may deviate from any rule in this part to the extent necessary to avoid endangering persons, property, or the environment but shall report the deviation to the VTC as soon as possible.

(1430) **Communications Rules**

(1431) **§161.520 Radiotelephone listening watch.**

(1432) The master or pilot shall continuously monitor the VTS radiotelephone frequency when operating in the VTS Area, except when transmitting on that frequency.

(1433) **§161.522 Radiotelephone equipment.**

(1434) The master or pilot shall ensure all reports and communications required by this part are made from the navigational bridge of the vessel, or in the case of a dredge, at its main control station. Such reports and communications must be made to the VTC on designated frequencies using a radiotelephone that is in effective operating condition.

(1435) **§161.523 Use of designated frequencies.**

(1436) (a) In accordance with Federal Communications Commission regulations, no person may use the frequencies designated in this section to transmit any information other than information necessary for the safety of vessel traffic.

(1437) (b) All transmissions on the VTS frequencies shall be initiated on low power, if available; high power may only be used if low power communications are unsuccessful or in an emergency.

(1438) (c) The following frequencies must be used when communicating with the VTC:

(1439) (1) Primary frequencies: 156.550 MHz (channel 11), 156.600 MHz (channel 12), and 156.700 MHz (channel 14).

(1440) (2) Secondary frequency (to be used if communication is not possible on a primary frequency): 156.650 MHz (channel 13).

(1441) **§161.524 English language.**

(1442)   Each report required by this part must be made in the English language.

(1443)   **§161.526 Time.**

(1444)   Each report required by this part must specify time using:

(1445)   (a) The time zone in effect in the VTSNY Area and

(1446)   (b) The 24-hour clock system.

(1447)   **§161.528 Radiotelephone failure.**

(1448)   Whenever a vessel's radiotelephone equipment fails -

(1449)   (a) While underway in the VTSNY Area or is inoperative when entering the VTSNY Area- (1) Compliance with §§ 161.520 and 161.538 of this part is not required; and

(1450)   (2) Compliance with §§ 161.536, 161.537, and 161.542 of this part is not required unless those reports can be made by other means.

(1451)   (b) Before getting underway in the VTSNY Area, permission to get underway must be obtained from the VTC; and

(1452)   (c) The master shall restore the radiotelephone to operating condition as soon as possible.

(1453)   **§161.530 Report of radiotelephone failure.**

(1454)   Whenever the master or pilot of a vessel deviates from any rule in this part because of radiotelephone failure, the deviation and radiotelephone failure shall be reported to the VTC by the most expedient means available.

(1455)   **§161.532 Report of impairment to the operation of the vessel.**

(1456)   The master of a vessel in the VTSNY Area shall report to the VTC as soon as possible -

(1457)   (a) Any condition on the vessel that may impair its navigation, such as fire, malfunctioning propulsion machinery, malfunctioning steering equipment, or malfunctioning radar;

(1458)   (b) Whenever the vessel has difficulty controlling its tow; and

(1459)   (c) Any grounding, collision or allision with a fixed or floating object.

(1460)   **Note.**–In the VTSNY Area, the reports required in 33 CFR part 164 are to be made to the VTC instead.

(1461)   **Vessel Movement Reporting Rules**

(1462)   **§161.536 Initial report.**

(1463)   Fifteen minutes before a vessel enters or gets underway in the VTSNY Area, the master of the vessel shall report the following information to the VTC:

(1464)   (a) The type and name of the vessel.

(1465)   (b) The estimated time and point of entry in the VTSNY Area.

(1466)   (c) Destination and route in the VTSNY Area.

(1467)   (d) Deepest draft of the vessel.

(1468)   (e) Speed of advance of the vessel.

(1469)   (f) Whether or not any dangerous cargo listed in part 160, subpart C, of this chapter, is onboard the vessel or its tow.

(1470)   (g) Any impairment to the operation of the vessel as described in §161.532 (a) and (b) of this part.

(1471)   (h) Any planned maneuvers that may impede traffic.

(1472)   **§161.537 Follow-up reports.**

(1473)   When entering or beginning to navigate in the VTSNY Area, or if the vessel deviates from its route plan as reported in the initial report, the master of the vessel shall report the following information by radiotelephone to the VTC:

(1474)   (a) Vessel name.

(1475)   (b) Location of the vessel.

(1476)   (c) Any revision to the initial report required by §161.536 of this part.

(1477)   **§161.538 Movement reports.**

(1478)   When the VMRS is in operation, or at other times when directed by the VTC, the master of a vessel passing a reporting point listed in §161.540 of this part shall report the following to the VTC by radiotelephone:

(1479)   (a) Vessel name.

(1480)   (b) Reporting point or location of the vessel.

(1481)   **§161.539 Invoking of the VMRS rules.**

(1482)   In the event of impairment of surveillance capability or when otherwise required for the safety of navigation, the Vessel Movement Reporting System (VMRS) may be invoked by the VTC.

(1483)   **§161.540 VMRS reporting points.**

No.	Position description	Geographic location
1.............	Verrazano-Narrows Bridge.	Upper New York Bay.
2.............	Brooklyn Bridge	East River.
3.............	Holland Tunnel Ventilator.	Hudson River.
4.............	Caven Point.................	Upper New York Bay.
5.............	Red Hook	Buttermilk Channel.
6.............	Constable Hook	Kill Van Kull.
7.............	Bayonne Bridge	Kill Van Kull.
8.............	AK Rail Bridge	Arthur Kill.
9.............	Lehigh Valley Draw Bridge.	Newark Bay.
10.............	Texaco Bayonne Facility.	Newark Bay.

(1484)   **§161.542 Final report.**

(1485)   When a vessel anchors in, moors in, or departs from the VTSNY Area, the master shall report the place of anchoring, mooring, or departing to the VTC.

(1486)   **Special Rules**

(1487)   **§161.575 Action during reduced visibility.**

(1488)   When visibility is less than 2 nautical miles in the VTSNY Area, any vessel that is operating without radar shall notify the VTC immediately.

(1489)   **Descriptions and Geographic Coordinates**

(1490)   **§161.580 VTSNY Area.**

(1491)   The VTSNY Area consists of the navigable waters of the United States bounded by the Verrazano-Narrows Bridge to the south, the Brooklyn Bridge to the east, and to the north, at a line drawn east-west from the Holland Tunnel ventilator shaft at latitude 40°43.7′N, longitude 74°01.6′W. The Kill Van Kull to the AK Rail Bridge and Newark Bay to the Lehigh Valley Draw Bridge are also included in the VTSNY Area.

Part 162–Inland Waterways Navigation Regulations

(1492)   **§162.1 General.**

(1493)   Geographic coordinates expressed in terms of latitude or longitude, or both, are not intended for plotting on maps or charts whose referenced horizontal datum is the North American Datum of 1983 (NAD 83), unless such geographic coordinates are expressly labeled NAD 83. Geographic coordinates without the NAD 83 reference may be plotted on maps or charts referenced to NAD 83 only after application of the appropriate corrections that are published on the particular map or chart being used.

(1494)   **§162.15 Manhasset Bay, N.Y.; seaplane restricted area. (a) The restricted area.** An area in Manhasset Bay between the shore at Manorhaven on the north and the southerly limit line of the special anchorage area in Manhasset Bay, west area at Manorhaven (described in 33 CFR 110.60), on the south; its axis being a line bearing 166°50′ true from latitude 40°50′17.337″, longitude 73°43′03.877″, which point is on the south side of Orchard Beach Boulevard at Manorhaven; and being 100 feet wide for a distance of 380 feet in a southerly direction from the south side of Orchard Beach Boulevard, and thence flaring to a width of 300 feet at the southerly limit line.

(1495)   (b) The regulations. (1) Vessels shall not anchor or moor within the restricted area.

(1496)   (2) All vessels traversing the area shall pass directly through without unnecessary delay, and shall give seaplanes the right-of-way at all times.

(1497)   **§162.20 Flushing Bay near La Guardia Airport, Flushing, N.Y.; restricted area.** (a) The area. An area in the main channel in Flushing Bay extending for a distance of 300 feet on either side of the extended center line of Runway No. 13–31 at La Guardia Airport.

(1498)   (b) The regulations. (1) All vessels traversing in the area shall pass directly through without unnecessary delay.

(1499)   (2) No vessels having a height of more than 35 feet with reference to the plane of mean high water shall enter or pass through the area whenever visibility is less than one mile.

(1500)   **§162.25 Ambrose Channel, New York Harbor, N.Y.; navigation.** (a) The use of Ambrose Channel (formerly and before improvement called "East Channel") is hereby restricted to navigation by vessels under efficient control with their own motive power and not having barges or other vessels or floats in tow. Sailing vessels and vessels carrying tows are not permitted to use this channel except under permit as provided in paragraph (b) of this section.

(1501)   (b) The Captain of the Port, New York may authorize vessels under tow to use Ambrose Channel in special cases when, in his judgement, the draft of such vessels or other conditions may render unsafe the use of other channels.

(1502)   (c) Vessels permitted to use Ambrose Channel under paragraphs (a) and (b) of this section must proceed through the channel at a reasonable speed such as not to endanger other vessels and not to interfere with any work which may become necessary in maintaining, surveying, or buoying the channel; and they must not anchor in the channel except in cases of emergency, such as fog or accident, which would render progress unsafe or impossible.

(1503)   (d) This section is not to be construed as prohibiting any necessary use of the channel by any Government boats while on Government duty, nor in emergencies by pilot boats whether steam or sail, nor by police boats.

(1504)   (e) This section shall remain in force until modified or rescinded, and shall supplant all prior regulations governing the use of Ambrose Channel, which are hereby revoked.

Part 164—Navigation Safety Regulations (in part). For a complete description of this part see 33 CFR 164.

(1505)   **§164.01 Applicability.**

(1506)   (a) This part (except as specifically limited herein) applies to each self-propelled vessel of 1600 or more gross tons (except foreign vessels described in §164.02) when it is operating in the navigable waters of the United States except the St. Lawrence Seaway.

(1507)   **§164.02 Applicability exception for foreign vessels.**

(1508)   (a) This part (including §§164.38 and 164.39) does not apply to vessels that:

(1509)   (1) Are not destined for, or departing from, a port or place subject to the jurisdiction of the United States; and

(1510)   (2) Are in:

(1511)   (i) Innocent passage through the territorial sea of the United States; or

(1512)   (ii) Transit through navigable waters of the United States which form a part of an international strait.

(1513)   **§164.03 Incorporation by reference.**

(1514)   (a) Certain materials are incorporated by reference into this part with the approval of the Director of the Federal Register. The Office of the Federal Register publishes a table, "Material Approved for Incorporation by Reference," which appears in the Finding Aids section of this volume. In that table is found the date of the edition approved, citations to the particular sections of this part where the material is incorporated, addresses where the material is available, and the date of the approval by the Director of the Federal Register. To enforce any edition other than the one listed in the table, notice of the change must be published in the FEDERAL REGISTER and the material made available. All approved material is on file at the Office of the Federal Register, Washington, DC 20408 and at Room 4402, U.S. Coast Guard Headquarters, 2100 Second St. SW, Washington, DC.

(1515)   (b) The materials approved for incorporation by reference in this part are: Radio Technical Commission For Marine Services (RTCM) Paper 12-78/DO-100 dated 12/20/77.

(1516)   **§164.11 Navigation underway: General.**

(1517)   The owner, master, or person in charge of each vessel underway shall ensure that:

(1518)   (a) The wheelhouse is constantly manned by persons who—

(1519)   (1) Direct and control the movement of the vessel; and

(1520)   (2) Fix the vessel's position;

(1521)   (b) Each person performing a duty described in paragraph (a) of this section is competent to perform that duty;

(1522)   (c) The position of the vessel at each fix is plotted on a chart of the area and the person directing the movement of the vessel is informed of the vessel's position;

(1523)   (d) Electronic and other navigational equipment, external fixed aids to navigation, geographic reference points, and hydrographic contours are used when fixing the vessel's position;

(1524)   (e) Buoys alone are not used to fix the vessel's position;

(1525)   **Note:** Buoys are aids to navigation placed in approximate positions to alert the mariner to hazards to navigation or to indicate the orientation of a channel. Buoys may not maintain an exact position because strong or varying currents, heavy seas, ice, and collisions with vessels can move or sink them or set them adrift. Although buoys may corroborate a position fixed by other means, buoys cannot be used to fix a position: however, if no other aids are available, buoys alone may be used to establish an estimated position.

(1526)   (f) The danger of each closing visual or each closing radar contact is evaluated and the person directing the movement of the vessel knows the evaluation;

(1527)   (g) Rudder orders are executed as given;

(1528)   (h) Engine speed and direction orders are executed as given;

(1529)   (i) Magnetic variation and deviation and gyrocompass errors are known and correctly applied by the person directing the movement of the vessel;

(1530)   (j) A person whom he has determined is competent to steer the vessel is in the wheelhouse at all times (See also 46 U.S.C. 672, which requires an able seaman at the wheel on U.S. vessels of 100 gross tons or more in narrow or crowded waters or during low visibility.);

(1531)   (k) If a pilot other than a member of the vessel's crew is employed, the pilot is informed of the draft, maneuvering characteristics, and peculiarities of the vessel and of any abnormal circumstances on the vessel that may affect its safe navigation.

(1532)   (1) Current velocity and direction for the area to be transited are known by the person directing the movement of the vessel;

(1533)   (m) Predicted set and drift are known by the person directing movement of the vessel;

(1534)   (n) Tidal state for the area to be transited is known by the person directing movement of the vessel;

(1535)   (o) The vessel's anchors are ready for letting go;

(1536)   (p) The person directing the movement of the vessel sets the vessel's speed with consideration for—

(1537)   (1) The prevailing visibility and weather conditions;

(1538)   (2) The proximity of the vessel to fixed shore and marine structures;

(1539)   (3) The tendency of the vessel underway to squat and suffer impairment of maneuverability when there is small underkeel clearance;

(1540)   (4) The comparative proportions of the vessel and the channel;

(1541)   (5) The density of marine traffic;

(1542)   (6) The damage that might be caused by the vessel's wake;

(1543)   (7) The strength and direction of the current; and

(1544)   (8) Any local vessel speed limit;

(1545)   (q) The tests required by §164.25 are made and recorded in the vessel's log; and

(1546)   (r) The equipment required by this part is maintained in operable condition.

(1547)   (s) Upon entering U.S. waters, the steering wheel or lever on the navigating bridge is operated to determine if the steering equipment is operating properly under manual control, unless the vessel has been steered under manual control from the navigating bridge within the preceding 2 hours, except when operating on the Great Lakes and their connecting and tributary waters.

(1548)   (t) At least two of the steering gear power units on the vessel are in operation when such units are capable of simultaneous operation, except when operating on the Great Lakes and their connecting and tributary waters.

(1549)   **§164.15 Navigation bridge visibility.**

(1550)   (a) The arrangement of cargo, cargo gear, and trim of all vessels entering or departing from U.S. ports must be such that the field of vision from the navigation bridge conforms as closely as possible to the following requirements:

(1551)   (1) From the conning position, the view of the sea surface must not be obscured by more than the lesser of two hip lengths or 500 meters (1640 feet) from dead ahead to 10 degrees on either side of the vessel. Within this arc of visibility any blind sector caused by cargo, cargo gear, or other permanent obstruction must not exceed 5 degrees.

(1552)   (2) From the conning position, the horizontal field of vision must extend over an arc from at least 22.5 degrees abaft the beam on one side of the vessel, through dead ahead, to at least 22.5 degrees abaft the beam on the other side of the vessel. Blind sectors forward of the beam caused by cargo, cargo gear, or other permanent obstruction must not exceed 10 degrees each, nor total more than 20 degrees, including any blind sector within the arc of visibility described in paragraph (a)(1) of this section.

(1553)   (3) From each bridge wing, the field of vision must extend over an arc from at least 45 degrees on the opposite bow, through dead ahead, to at least dead astern.

(1554)   (4) From the main steering position, the field of vision must extend over an arc from dead ahead to at least 60 degrees on either side of the vessel.

(1555)   (b) A clear view must be provided through at least two front windows at all times regardless of weather conditions.

(1556)   **§164.19 Requirements for vessels at anchor.**

(1557)   The master or person in charge of each vessel that is anchored shall ensure that—

(1558)   (a) A proper anchor watch is maintained;

(1559)   (b) Procedures are followed to detect a dragging anchor; and

(1560)   (c) Whenever weather, tide, or current conditions are likely to cause the vessel's anchor to drag, action is taken to ensure the safety of the vessel, structures, and other vessels, such a being ready to veer chain, let go a second anchor, or get underway using the vessel's own propulsion or tug assistance.

(1561)   **§164.25 Tests before entering or getting underway.**

(1562)   (a) Except as provided in paragraphs (b) and (c) of this section no person may cause a vessel to enter into or get underway on the navigable waters of the United States unless no more than 12 hours before entering or getting underway, the following equipment has been tested:

(1563)   (1) Primary and secondary steering gear. The test procedure includes a visual inspection of the steering gear and its connecting linkage, and where applicable, the operation of the following:

(1564)   (i) Each remote steering gear control system.

(1565)   (ii) Each steering position located on the navigating bridge.

(1566)   (iii) The main steering gear from the alternative power supply, if installed.

(1567)   (iv) Each rudder angle indicator in relation to the actual position of the rudder.

(1568)   (v) Each remote steering gear control system power failure alarm.

(1569)   (vi) Each remote steering gear power unit failure alarm.

(1570)   (vii) The full movement of the rudder to the required capabilities of the steering gear.

(1571)   (2) All internal vessel control communications and vessel control alarms.

(1572)   (3) Standby or emergency generator, for as long as necessary to show proper functioning, including steady state temperature and pressure readings.

(1573)   (4) Storage batteries for emergency lighting and power systems in vessel control and propulsion machinery spaces.

(1574)   (5) Main propulsion machinery, ahead and astern.

(1575)   (b) Vessels navigating on the Great Lakes and their connecting and tributary waters, having once completed the test requirements of this sub-part, are considered to remain in compliance until arriving at the next port of call on the Great Lakes.

(1576)   (c) Vessels entering the Great Lakes from the St. Lawrence Seaway are considered to be in compliance with this sub-part if the required tests are conducted preparatory to or during the passage of the St. Lawrence Seaway or within one hour of passing Wolfe Island.

(1577)   (d) No vessel may enter, or be operated on the navigable waters of the United States unless the emergency steering drill described below has been conducted within 48 hours prior to entry and logged in the vessel logbook, unless the drill is conducted and logged on a regular basis at least once every three months. This drill must include at a minimum the following:

(1578)   (1) Operation of the main steering gear from within the steering gear compartment.

(1579)   (2) Operation of the means of communications between the navigating bridge and the steering compartment.

(1580)   (3) Operation of the alternative power supply for the steering gear if the vessel is so equipped.

(1581)   **§164.30 Charts, publications, and equipment: General.**

(1582) No person may operate or cause the operation of a vessel unless the vessel has the marine charts, publications, and equipment as required by §§164.33 through 164.41 of this part.

(1583) **§164.33 Charts and publications.**

(1584) (a) Each vessel must have the following:

(1585) (1) Marine charts of the area to be transited, published by the National Ocean Service, U.S. Army Corps of Engineers, or a river authority that—

(1586) (i) Are of a large enough scale and have enough detail to make safe navigation of the area possible; and

(1587) (ii) Are currently corrected.

(1588) (2) For the area to be transited, a currently corrected copy of, or applicable currently corrected extract from, each of the following publications:

(1589) (i) U.S. Coast Pilot.

(1590) (ii) Coast Guard Light List.

(1591) (3) For the area to be transited, the current edition of, or applicable current extract from:

(1592) (i) Tide tables published by the National Ocean Service.

(1593) (ii) Tidal current tables published by the National Ocean Service, or river current publication issued by the U.S. Army Corps of Engineers, or a river authority.

(1594) (b) As an alternative to the requirements for paragraph (a) of this section, a marine chart or publication, or applicable extract, published by a foreign government may be substituted for a U.S. chart and publication required by this section. The chart must be of large enough scale and have enough detail to make safe navigation of the area possible, and must be currently corrected. The publication, or applicable extract, must singly or in combination contain similar information to the U.S. Government publication to make safe navigation of the area possible. The publication, or applicable extract must be currently corrected, with the exceptions of tide and tidal current tables, which must be the current editions.

(1595) (c) As used in this section, "currently corrected" means corrected with changes contained in all Notices to Mariners published by Defense Mapping Agency Hydrographic/Topographic Center, or an equivalent foreign government publication, reasonably available to the vessel, and that is applicable to the vessel's transit.

(1596) **§164.35 Equipment: All vessels.**

(1597) Each vessel must have the following:

(1598) (a) A marine radar system for surface navigation.

(1599) (b) An illuminated magnetic steering compass, mounted in a binnacle, that can be read at the vessel's main steering stand.

(1600) (c) A current magnetic compass deviation table or graph or compass comparison record for the steering compass, in the wheelhouse.

(1601) (d) A gyrocompass.

(1602) (e) An illuminated repeater for the gyrocompass required by paragraph (d) of this section that is at the main steering stand, unless that gyrocompass is illuminated and is at the main steering stand.

(1603) (f) An illuminated rudder angle indicator in the wheelhouse.

(1604) (g) The following maneuvering information prominently displayed on a fact sheet in the wheelhouse:

(1605) (1) A turning circle diagram to port and starboard that shows the time and distance and advance and transfer required to alter course 90 degrees with maximum rudder angle and constant power settings, for either full and half speeds, or for full and slow speeds. For vessels whose turning circles are essentially the same for both directions, a diagram showing a turning circle in one direction, with a note

on the diagram stating that turns to port and starboard are essentially the same, may be substituted.

(1606) (2) The time and distance to stop the vessel from either full and half speeds, or from full and slow speeds, while maintaining approximately the initial heading with minimum application of rudder.

(1607) (3) For each vessel with a fixed propeller, a table of shaft revolutions per minute for a representative range of speeds.

(1608) (4) For each vessel with a controllable pitch propeller, a table of control settings for a representative range of speeds.

(1609) (5) For each vessel that is fitted with an auxiliary device to assist in maneuvering, such as a bow thruster, a table of vessel speeds at which the auxiliary device is effective in maneuvering the vessel.

(1610) (6) The maneuvering information for the normal load and normal ballast condition for—

(1611) (i) Calm weather-wind 10 knots or less, calm sea;

(1612) (ii) No current;

(1613) (iii) Deep water conditions-water depth twice the vessel's draft or greater; and

(1614) (iv) Clean hull.

(1615) (7) At the bottom of the fact sheet, the following statement;

(1616) **Warning.**

(1617) The response of the (name of the vessel) may be different from that listed above if any of the following conditions, upon which the maneuvering information is based, are varied:

(1618) (1) Calm weather-wind 10 knots or less, calm sea;

(1619) (2) No current;

(1620) (3) Water depth twice the vessel's draft or greater;

(1621) (4) Clean hull; and

(1622) (5) Intermediate drafts or unusual trim.

(1623) (h) An echo depth sounding device.

(1624) (i) A device that can continuously record the depth readings of the vessel's echo depth sounding device, except when operating on the Great Lakes and their connecting and tributary waters.

(1625) (j) Equipment on the bridge for plotting relative motion.

(1626) (k) Simple operating instructions with a block diagram, showing the changeover procedures for remote steering gear control systems and steering gear power units, permanently displayed on the navigating bridge and in the steering gear compartment.

(1627) (1) An indicator readable from the centerline conning position showing the rate of revolution of each propeller, except when operating on the Great Lakes and their connecting and tributary waters.

(1628) (m) If fitted with controllable pitch propellers, an indicator readable from the centerline conning position showing the pitch and operational mode of such propellers, except when operating on the Great Lakes and their connecting and tributary waters.

(1629) (n) If fitted with lateral thrust propellers, an indicator readable from the centerline conning position showing the direction and amount of thrust of such propellers, except when operating on the Great Lakes and their connecting and tributary waters.

(1630) **§164.37 Equipment: Vessels of 10,000 gross tons or more.**

(1631) (a) Each vessel of 10,000 gross tons or more must have, in addition to the radar system under §164.35(a), a second marine radar system that operates independently of the first.

(1632) **Note:** Independent operation means two completely separate systems, from separate branch power supply circuits or distribution panels to antennas, so that failure of any component of one system will not render the other system inoperative.

(1633) (b) On each tanker of 10,000 gross tons or more that is subject to Section 5 of the Port and Tanker Safety Act of 1978 (46 U.S.C. 391a), the dual radar system required by this part must have a short range capability and a long range capability and each radar must have true north features consisting of a display that is stabilized in azimuth.

(1634) **§164.38 Automatic radar plotting aids (ARPA). (See 33 CFR 164.)**

(1635) **§164.39 Steering gear: Tankers. (See 33 CFR 164.)**

(1636) **§164.40 Devices to indicate speed and distance.**

(1637) (a) Each vessel required to be fitted with an Automatic Radar Plotting Aid (ARPA) under §164.38 must be fitted with a device to indicate speed and distance of the vessel either through the water, or over the ground. Vessels constructed prior to September 1, 1984, must have this equipment according to the following schedule:

(1638) (1) Each tank vessel constructed before September 1, 1984, operating on the navigable waters of the United States—

(1639) (i) If of 40,000 gross tons or more, by January 1, 1985;

(1640) (ii) If of 10,000 gross tons or more but less than 40,000 gross tons, by January 1, 1986.

(1641) (2) Each self-propelled vessel constructed before September 1, 1984, that is not a tank vessel, operating on the navigable waters of the United States—

(1642) (i) If of 40,000 gross tons or more, by September 1, 1986;

(1643) (ii) If of 20,000 gross tons or more, but less than 40,000 gross tons, by September 1, 1987;

(1644) (iii) If of 15,000 gross tons or more, but less than 20,000 gross tons, by September 1, 1988.

(1645) (b) The device must meet the following specifications:

(1646) (1) The display must be easily readable on the bridge by day or night.

(1647) (2) Errors in the indicated speed, when the vessel is operating free from shallow water effect, and from the effects of wind, current, and tide, should not exceed 5 percent of the speed of the vessel, or 0.5 knot, whichever is greater.

(1648) (3) Errors in the indicated distance run, when the vessel is operating free from shallow water effect, and from the effects of wind, current, and tide, should not exceed 5 percent of the distance run of the vessel in one hour or 0.5 nautical mile in each hour, whichever is greater.

(1649) **§164.41 Electronic position fixing devices.**

(1650) (a) Each vessel calling at a port in the continental United States, including Alaska south of Cape Prince of Wales, except each vessel owned or bareboat chartered and operated by the United States, or by a state or its political subdivision, or by a foreign nation, and not engaged in commerce, must have one of the following:

(1651) (1) A Type I or II LORAN C receiver as defined in Section 1.2(e), meeting Part 2 (Minimum Performance Standards) of the Radio Technical Commission for Marine Services (RTCM) Paper 12-78/D0-100 dated December 20, 1977, entitled "Minimum Performance Standards (MPS) Marine Loran-C Receiving Equipment". Each receiver installed on or after June 1, 1982, must have a label with the information required under paragraph (b) of this section. If the receiver is installed before June 1, 1982, the receiver must have the label with the information required under paragraph (b) by June 1, 1985.

(1652) (2) A satellite navigation receiver with:

(1653) (i) Automatic acquisition of satellite signals after initial operator settings have been entered; and

(1654) (ii) Position updates derived from satellite information during each usable satellite pass.

(1655) (3) A system that is found by the Commandant to meet the intent of the statements of availability, coverage, and accuracy for the U.S. Coastal Confluence Zone (CCZ) contained in the U.S. "Federal Radionavigation Plan" (Report No. DOD-NO 4650.4-P, I or No. DOT-TSC-RSPA-80-16, I). A person desiring a finding by the Commandant under this subparagraph must submit a written application describing the device to the Office of Navigation Safety and Waterway Services, 2100 Second Street, SW., Washington, DC 20593-0001. After reviewing the application, the Commandant may request additional information to establish whether or not the device meets the intent of the Federal Radionavigation Plan.

(1656) **Note.**–The Federal Radionavigation Plan is available from the National Technical Information Service, Springfield, Va. 22161, with the following Government Accession Numbers:

(1657) Vol 1, ADA 116468

(1658) Vol 2, ADA 116469

(1659) Vol 3, ADA 116470

(1660) Vol 4, ADA 116471

(1661) (b) Each label required under paragraph (a)(1) of this section must show the following:

(1662) (1) The name and address of the manufacturer.

(1663) (2) The following statement by the manufacturer:

(1664) This receiver was designed and manufactured to meet Part 2 (Minimum Performance Standards) of the RTCM MPS for Marine Loran-C Receiving Equipment.

(1665) **§164.42 Rate of turn indicator.**

(1666) Each vessel of 100,000 gross tons or more constructed on or after September 1, 1984, shall be fitted with a rate of turn indicator.

(1667) **§164.51 Deviations from rules: Emergency.**

(1668) Except for the requirements of §164.53(b), in an emergency, any person may deviate from any rule in this part to the extent necessary to avoid endangering persons, property, or the environment.

(1669) **§164.53 Deviations from rules and reporting: Non-operating equipment.**

(1670) (a) If during a voyage any equipment required by this part stops operating properly, the person directing the movement of the vessel may continue to the next port of call, subject to the directions of the District Commander or the Captain of the Port, as provided by 33 CFR 160.

(1671) (b) If the vessel's radar, radio navigation receivers, gyrocompass, echo depth sounding device, or primary steering gear stops operating properly, the person directing the movement of the vessel must report or cause to be reported that it is not operating properly to the nearest Captain of the Port, District Commander, or, if participating in a Vessel Traffic Service, to the Vessel Traffic Center, as soon as possible.

(1672) **§164.55 Deviations from rules: Continuing operation or period of time.**

(1673) The Captain of the Port, upon written application, may authorize a deviation from any rule in this part if he determines that the deviation does not impair the safe navigation of the vessel under anticipated conditions and will not result in a violation of the rules for preventing collisions at sea. The authorization may be issued for vessels operating in the waters under the jurisdiction of the Captain of the Port for any continuing operation or period of time the Captain of the Port specifies.

(1674) **§164.61 Marine casualty reporting and record retention.**

(1675) When a vessel is involved in a marine casualty as defined in 46 CFR 4.03-1, the master or person in charge of the vessel shall—

(1676) (a) Ensure compliance with 46 CFR 4.05, "Notice of Marine Casualty and Voyage Records," and

(1677) (b) Ensure that the voyage records required by 46 CFR 4.05-15 are retained for—

(1678) (1) 30 days after the casualty if the vessel remains in the navigable waters of the United States; or

(1679) (2) 30 days after the return of the vessel to a United States port if the vessel departs the navigable waters of the United States within 30 days after the marine casualty.

Part 165–Regulated Navigation Areas and Limited Access Areas

Subpart A–General

(1680) **§165.1 Purpose of part.**

(1681) The purpose of this part is to—

(1682) (a) Prescribe procedures for establishing different types of limited or controlled access areas and regulated navigation areas;

(1683) (b) Prescribe general regulations for different types of limited or controlled access areas and regulated navigation areas;

(1684) (c) Prescribe specific requirements for established areas; and

(1685) (d) List specific areas and their boundaries.

(1686) **§165.5 Establishment procedures.**

(1687) (a) A safety zone, security zone, or regulated navigation area may be established on the initiative of any authorized Coast Guard official.

(1688) (b) Any person may request that a safety zone, security zone, or regulated navigation area be established. Except as provided in paragraph (c) of this section, each request must be submitted in writing to either the Captain of the Port or District Commander having jurisdiction over the location as described in 33 CFR 3, and including the following:

(1689) (1) The name of the person submitting the request;

(1690) (2) The location and boundaries of the safety zone, security zone, or regulated navigation area;

(1691) (3) The date, time, and duration that the safety zone, security zone, or regulated navigation area should be established;

(1692) (4) A description of the activities planned for the safety zone, security zone, or regulated navigation area;

(1693) (5) The nature of the restrictions or conditions desired; and

(1694) (6) The reason why the safety zone, security zone, or regulated navigation area is necessary.

(1695) (Requests for safety zones, security zones, and regulated navigation areas are approved by the Office of Management and Budget under control numbers 2115-0076, 2115-0219, and 2115-0087.)

(1696) (c) Safety Zones and Security Zones. If, for good cause, the request for a safety zone or security zone is made less than 5 working days before the zone is to be established, the request may be made orally, but it must be followed by a written request within 24 hours.

(1697) **§165.7 Notification.**

(1698) (a) The establishment of these limited access areas and regulated navigation areas is considered rulemaking. The procedures used to notify persons of the establishment of these areas vary depending upon the circumstances and emergency conditions. Notification may be made by marine broadcasts, local notice to mariners, local news media, distribution in leaflet form, and on-scene oral notice, as well as publication in the Federal Register.

(1699) (b) Notification normally contains the physical boundaries of the area, the reasons for the rule, its estimated duration, and the method of obtaining authorization to enter the area, if applicable, and special navigational rules, if applicable.

(1700) (c) Notification of the termination of the rule is usually made in the same form as the notification of its establishment.

(1701) **§165.8 Geographic coordinates.**

(1702) Geographic coordinates expressed in terms of latitude or longitude, or both, are not intended for plotting on maps or charts whose referenced horizonal datum is the North American Datum of 1983 (NAD 83), unless such geographic coordinates are expressly labeled NAD 83. Geographic coordinates without the NAD 83 reference may be plotted on maps or charts referenced to NAD 83 only after application of the appropriate corrections that are published on the particular map or chart being used.

Subpart B–Regulated Navigation Areas

(1703) **§165.10 Regulated navigation area.**

(1704) A regulated navigation area is a water area within a defined boundary for which regulations for vessels navigating within the area have been established under this part.

(1705) **§165.11 Vessel operating requirements (regulations).**

(1706) Each District Commander may control vessel traffic in an area which is determined to have hazardous conditions, by issuing regulations—

(1707) (a) Specifying times of vessel entry, movement, or departure to, from, within, or through ports, harbors, or other waters;

(1708) (b) Establishing vessel size, speed, draft limitations, and operating conditions; and

(1709) (c) Restricting vessel operation, in a hazardous area or under hazardous conditions, to vessels which have particular operating characteristics or capabilities which are considered necessary for safe operation under the circumstances.

(1710) **§165.13 General regulations.**

(1711) (a) The master of a vessel in a regulated navigation area shall operate the vessel in accordance with the regulations contained in Subpart F.

(1712) (b) No person may cause or authorize the operation of a vessel in a regulated navigation area contrary to the regulations in this Part.

Subpart C–Safety Zones

(1713) **§165.20 Safety zones.**

(1714) A Safety Zone is a water area, shore area, or water and shore area to which, for safety or environmental purposes, access is limited to authorized persons, vehicles, or vessels. It may be stationary and described by fixed limits or it may be described as a zone around a vessel in motion.

(1715) **§165.23 General regulations.**

(1716) Unless otherwise provided in this part—

(1717) (a) No person may enter a safety zone unless authorized by the COTP or the District Commander;

(1718) (b) No person may bring or cause to be brought into a safety zone any vehicle, vessel, or object unless authorized by the COTP or the District Commander;

(1719) (c) No person may remain in a safety zone or allow any vehicle, vessel, or object to remain in a safety zone unless authorized by the COTP or the District Commander; and

(1720)   (d) Each person in a safety zone who has notice of a lawful order or direction shall obey the order or direction of the COTP or District Commander issued to carry out the purposes of this subpart.

Subpart D–Security Zones
(1721)   §165.30 Security zones.
(1722)   (a) A security zone is an area of land, water, or land and water which is so designated by the Captain of the Port or District Commander for such time as is necessary to prevent damage or injury to any vessel or waterfront facility, to safeguard ports, harbors, territories, or waters of the United States or to secure the observance of the rights and obligations of the United States.

(1723)   (b) The purpose of a security zone is to safeguard from destruction, loss, or injury from sabotage or other subversive acts, accidents, or other causes of a similar nature–

(1724)   (1) Vessels,
(1725)   (2) Harbors,
(1726)   (3) Ports and
(1727)   (4) Waterfront facilities– in the United States and all territory and water, continental or insular, that is subject to the jurisdiction of the United States.

(1728)   §165.33 General regulations.
(1729)   Unless otherwise provided in the special regulations in Subpart F of this part–

(1730)   (a) No person or vessel may enter or remain in a security zone without the permission of the Captain of the Port;

(1731)   (b) Each person and vessel in a security zone shall obey any direction or order of the Captain of the Port;

(1732)   (c) The Captain of the Port may take possession and control of any vessel in the security zone;

(1733)   (d) The Captain of the Port may remove any person, vessel, article, or thing from a security zone;

(1734)   (e) No person may board, or take or place any article or thing on board, any vessel in a security zone without the permission of the Captain of the Port; and

(1735)   (f) No person may take or place any article or thing upon any waterfront facility in a security zone without the permission of the Captain of the Port.

Subpart E–Restricted Waterfront Areas
(1736)   §165.40 Restricted Waterfront Areas.
(1737)   The Commandant, may direct the COTP to prevent access to waterfront facilities, and port and harbor areas, including vessels and harbor craft therein. This section may apply to persons who do not possess the credentials outlined in 33 CFR 125.09 when certain shipping activities are conducted that are outlined in 33 CFR 125.15.

Subpart F–Specific Regulated Navigation Areas and Limited Access Areas
(1738)   §165.121 Safety Zone Rhode Island Sound, Narragansett Bay, Providence River.
(1739)   (a) Location. The following areas are established as safety zones:

(1740)   (1) For Liquefied Petroleum Gas (LPG) vessels while at anchor in the waters of Rhode Island Sound; in position 41°25N., 71°23W., a Safety Zone with a radius of one-half mile around the LPG vessel.

(1741)   (2) For Liquefied Petroleum Gas (LPG) vessels while transitting Narragansett Bay and the Providence River; a moving Safety Zone from a distance of two (2) miles ahead to one (1) mile astern to the limits of the navigable channel around the LPG vessel.

(1742)   (3) For Liquefied Petroleum Gas (LPG) vessels while moored at the LPG facility, Port of Providence; a Safety Zone within 50 feet around the vessel. No vessel shall moor within 400 feet from the LPG vessel. All vessels transitting the area are to proceed with caution to minimize the effects of wake around the LPG vessel.

(1743)   (4) For Liquefied Petroleum Gas (LPG) vessels while moored with manifolds connected at the LPG Facility, Port of Providence; a Safety Zone within a 100 foot radius around the shoreside manifold while connected. This is in addition to the requirements for LPG vessels while moored at the LPG Facility, Port of Providence.

(1744)   (b) The Captain of the Port Providence will notify the maritime community of periods during which this safety zone will be in effect by providing advance notice of scheduled arrivals and departures of LPG vessels via Marine Safety Information Radio Broadcast on VHF Marine Band Radio, Channel 22 (157.1 MHz).

(1745)   (c) Regulations. The general regulations governing safety zones contained in §165.23 apply.

(1746)   §165.130 Sandy Hook Bay, New Jersey-security zone.
(1747)   (a) Naval Ammunition Depot Piers.–The waters within the following boundaries are a security zone-A line beginning on the shore at

(1748)   40°25'57"N., 74°04'32"W.; then to
(1749)   40°27'52.5"N., 74°03'14.5"W.; then to
(1750)   40°27'28.3"N., 74°02'12.4"W.; then to
(1751)   40°26'29.2"N., 74°02'53"W.; then to
(1752)   40°26'31.1"N., 74°02'57.2"W.; then to
(1753)   40°25'27.3"N., 74°03'41"W.; then along the shoreline to the beginning point.

(1754)   (b) Terminal Channel. The waters within the following boundaries are a security zone-A line beginning at

(1755)   40°27'41.2"N., 74°02'46"W.; then to
(1756)   40°28'27"N., 74°02'17.2"W.; then to
(1757)   40°28'21.1"N., 74°02'00"W.; then to
(1758)   40°28'07.8"N., 74°02'22"W.; then to
(1759)   40°27'39.8"N., 74°02'41.4"W.; then to the beginning.

(1760)   (c) The following rules apply to the security zone established in paragraph (b) of this section (Terminal Channel) instead of the rule in §165.33(a)

(1761)   (1) No vessel shall anchor, stop, remain or drift without power at any time in the security zone.

(1762)   (2) No vessel shall enter, cross, or otherwise navigate in the security zone when a public vessel, or any other vessel, that cannot safely navigate outside the Terminal Channel, is approaching or leaving the Naval Ammunition Depot Piers at Leonardo, New Jersey.

(1763)   (3) Vessels may enter or cross the security zone, except as provided in paragraph (c)(2) of this section.

(1764)   (4) No person may swim in the security zone.

(1765)   §165.140 New London Harbor, Connecticut-security zone.
(1766)   (a) Security zones–
(1767)   (1) Security Zone A. The waters of the Thames River off State Pier enclosed by a line beginning at the midpoint of the southeast face of State Pier; then to

(1768)   41°21'24"N., 72°05'21.2"W.; then to
(1769)   41°21'26.2"N., 72°05'19.3"W.; then to
(1770)   41°21'34"N., 72°05'18.1"W.; then extending northwest through buoy C15 to the shoreline at
(1771)   41°21'43.5"N., 72°05'23"W.; then along the shoreline and pier to the point of beginning.

(1772)   (2) Security Zone B. The waters of the Thames River west of the Electric Boat Division Shipyard enclosed by a line beginning at a point on the shoreline at
(1773)   41°20'22.1"N., 72°04'52.8"W.; then west to
(1774)   41°20'28.7"N., 72°05'03.5"W.; then to
(1775)   41°20'53.3"N., 72°05'06.6"W.; then to

(1776)   41°21'03"N., 72°05'06.7"W.; then due east to a point on the shoreline at

(1777)   41°21'03"N., 72°05'00"W.; then along the shoreline to the point of beginning.

(1778)   (3) Security Zone C. The waters of the Thames River, west of the Naval Submarine Base, New London, Conn., enclosed by a line beginning at a point on the shoreline at

(1779)   41°23'15.8"N., 72°05'17.9"W.; then to

(1780)   41°23'15.8"N., 72°05'22"W.; then to

(1781)   41°23'25.9"N., 72°05'29.9"W.; then to

(1782)   41°23'33.8"N., 72°05'34.7"W.; then to

(1783)   41°23'37.0"N., 72°05'38.0"W.; then to

(1784)   41°23'41.0"N., 72°05'40.3"W.; then to

(1785)   41°23'47.2"N., 72°05'42.3"W.; then to

(1786)   41°23'53.8"N., 72°05'43.7"W.; then to

(1787)   41°23'59.8"N., 72°05'43.0"W.; then to

(1788)   41°24'12.4"N., 72°05'43.2"W.; then to a point on the shoreline at

(1789)   41°24'14.4"N., 72°05'38"W.; then along the shoreline to the point of beginning.

(1790)   (4) Security Zone D. The waters of the Thames River east of the Naval Underwater Systems Center, New London, enclosed by a line beginning at

(1791)   41°20'36.0"N., 72°05'34.1"W.; then to

(1792)   41°20'36.0"N., 72°05'20"W.; then to

(1793)   41°20'41"N., 72°05'20"W.; then to

(1794)   41°20'43.7"N., 72°05'25.9"W.; then to

(1795)   41°20'41.6"N., 72°05'35.0"W.; then along the shoreline to the points of beginning.

(1796)   (b) Special regulation. Section 165.33 does not apply to public vessels when operating in Security Zones A or B, or to vessels owned by, under hire to, or performing work for the Electric Boat Division when operating in Security Zone B.

(1797)   **§165.150 New Haven Harbor, Quinnipiac River, Mill River.**

(1798)   (a) The following is a regulated navigation area: The waters surrounding the Tomlinson Bridge located within a line extending from a point A at the southeast corner of the Wyatt terminal dock at 41°17'50"N., 72°54'36"W.; thence along a line 126°T to point B at the southwest corner of the Gulf facility at 41°17'42"N., 72°54'21"W.; thence north along the shoreline to point C at the northwest corner of the Texaco terminal dock 41°17'57"N., 72°54'06"W.; thence along a line 303°T to point D at the west bank of the mouth of the Mill River 41°18'05"N., 72°54'23"W.; thence south along the shoreline to point A.

(1799)   (b) Regulations. (1) No person may operate a vessel or tow a barge in this Regulated Navigation Area in violation of these regulations.

(1800)   (2) Applicability. The regulations apply to barges with a freeboard greater than ten feet and to any vessel towing or pushing these barges on outbound transits of the Tomlinson Bridge.

(1801)   (3) Regulated barges may not transit the bridge—

(1802)   (i) During the period from one hour to five hours after high water slack,

(1803)   (ii) When the wind speed at the bridge is greater than twenty knots, and

(1804)   (iii) With the barge being towed on a hawser, stern first.

(1805)   (4) Regulated barges with a beam greater than fifty feet must be pushed ahead through the bridge.

(1806)   (5) If the tug operator does not have a clear view over the barge when pushing ahead, the operator shall post a lookout on the barge with a means of communication with the operator.

(1807)   (6) Regulated barges departing the Mill River may transit the bridge only between sunrise and sunset. Barges must be pushed ahead of the tug, bow first, with a second tug standing by to assist at the bow.

(1808)   (7) Nothing in this section is intended to relieve any person from complying with—

(1809)   (i) Applicable Navigation and Pilot Rules for Inland Waters;

(1810)   (ii) Any other laws or regulations;

(1811)   (iii) Any order or direction of the Captain of the Port.

(1812)   (8) The Captain of the Port, New Haven, may issue an authorization to deviate from any rule in this section if the COTP finds that an alternate operation can be done safely.

(1813)   **§165.155 Northville Industries Offshore Platform, Riverhead, Long Island, New York-safety zone.**

(1814)   (a) The following area is established as a safety zone during the specified condition:

(1815)   (1) The waters within a 500 yard radius of the Northville Industries Offshore Platform, Long Island, New York, 1 mile North of the Riverhead shoreline at 41°00'N., 072°38'W., while a liquefied Petroleum Gas (LPG) vessel is moored at the Offshore Platform. The safety zone remains in effect until the LPG vessel departs the Offshore Platform.

(1816)   (b) The general regulations governing safety zone contained in 33 CFR 165.23 apply.

(1817)   (c) The Captain of the Port will notify the maritime community of periods during which this safety zone will be in effect by providing notice of scheduled moorings at the Northville Industries Offshore Platform of LPG vessels via Marine Safety Information Radio Broadcast.

(1818)   **§165.160 New York, New Jersey, Sandy Hook Channel, Raritan Bay, Arthur Kill-Safety Zone.**

(1819)   (a) The following areas are established as Safety Zones during the specified conditions:

(1820)   (1) For incoming tank vessels loaded with Liquefied Petroleum Gas, the waters within a 100 yard radius of the LPG carrier while the vessel transits the Sandy Hook Channel, Raritan Bay East and West Reach, Ward Point Bend East and West Reach, and the Arthur Kill to the LPG receiving facility. The Safety Zone remains in effect until the LPG vessel is moored at the LPG receiving facility in the Arthur Kill.

(1821)   (2) For outgoing tank vessels loaded with LPG, the waters within a 100 yard radius of the LPG carrier while the vessel departs the LPG facility and transits the Arthur Kill, Ward Point Bend West and East Reach, Raritan Bay West and East Reach, and Sandy Hook Channel. The safety zone remains in effect until the LPG vessel passes the Scotland Lighted Horn Buoy "S" (LLNR 1619) at the entrance to the Sandy Hook Channel.

(1822)   (b) The general regulations governing safety zones contained in 33 CFR 165.23 apply.

(1823)   (c) The Captain of the Port will notify the maritime community of periods during which this safety zone will be in effect by providing advance notice of scheduled arrivals and departures of loaded LPG vessels via a Marine Safety Information Radio Broadcast.

Part 166-Shipping Safety Fairways

(1824)   **Subpart A-General**

(1825)   **§166.100 Purpose.**-The purpose of these regulations is to establish and designate shipping safety fairways and fairway anchorages to provide unobstructed approaches for vessels using U.S. ports.

(1826)   **§166.103 Geographic Coordinates.**

(1827)   Geographic coordinates expressed in terms of latitude or longitude, or both, are not intended for plotting on maps or charts whose referenced horizontal datum is the North American Datum of 1983 (NAD 83), unless such geographic coordinates are expressly labeled NAD 83. Geographic coordinates without the NAD 83 reference may be plotted on maps or charts referenced to NAD 83 only after application of the appropriate corrections that are published on the particular map or chart being used.

(1828)   **§166.105 Definitions.**

(1829)   (a) "Shipping safety fairway" or "fairway" means a lane or corridor in which no artificial island or fixed structure, whether temporary or permanent, will be permitted. Temporary underwater obstacles may be permitted under certain conditions described for specific areas in Subpart B. Aids to navigation approved by the U.S. Coast Guard may be established in a fairway.

(1830)   (b) "Fairway anchorage" means an anchorage area contiguous to and associated with a fairway, in which fixed structures may be permitted within certain spacing limitations, as described for specific areas in Subpart B.

(1831)   **§166.110 Modification of areas.**

(1832)   Fairways and fairway anchorages are subject to modification in accordance with 33 U.S.C. 1223(c); 92 Stat. 1473. Subpart B-Designation of Fairways and Fairway Anchorages (in part)

(1833)   **§166.500 Areas along the Atlantic Coast.**

(1834)   (a) Purpose. Fairways, as described in this section are established to control the erection of structures therein to provide safe vessel routes along the Atlantic Coast.

(1835)   (b) Designated areas.-(1) Off New York Shipping Safety Fairway.

(1836)   (i) Nantucket to Ambrose Safety Fairway. The area enclosed by rhumb lines, (North American Datum of 1927 (NAD-27)), joining points at:

(1837)   40°32′20″N., 73°04′57″W.
(1838)   40°30′58″N., 71°58′25″W.
(1839)   40°34′07″N., 70°19′23″W.
(1840)   40°35′37″N., 70°14′09″W.
(1841)   40°30′37″N., 70°14′00″W.
(1842)   40°32′07″N., 70°19′19″W.
(1843)   40°28′58″N., 72°58′25″W.
(1844)   40°27′20″N., 73°04′57″W.

(1845)   (ii) Ambrose to Nantucket Safety Fairway. The area enclosed by rhumb lines, NAD-27, joining points at:

(1846)   40°24′20″N., 73°04′58″W.
(1847)   40°22′58″N., 72°58′26″W.
(1848)   40°26′07″N., 70°19′09″W.
(1849)   40°27′37″N., 70°13′46″W.
(1850)   40°22′37″N., 70°13′36″W.
(1851)   40°24′07″N., 70°19′05″W.
(1852)   40°20′58″N., 72°58′26″W.
(1853)   40°19′20″N., 73°04′58″W.

Part 167-Offshore Traffic Separation Schemes

(1854)   **Subpart A-General**

(1855)   **§167.1 Purpose.** The purpose of the regulations in this part is to establish and designate traffic separation schemes and precautionary areas to provide access routes for vessels proceeding to and from U.S. ports.

(1856)   **§167.5 Definitions.**

(1857)   (a) "Traffic separation scheme" (TSS) means a designated routing measure which is aimed at the separation of opposing streams of traffic by appropriate means and by the establishment of traffic lanes.

(1858)   (b) "Traffic lane" means an area within defined limits in which one-way traffic is established. Natural obstacles, including those forming separation zones, may constitute a boundary.

(1859)   (c) "Separation zone or line" means a zone or line separating the traffic lanes in which ships are proceeding in opposite or nearly opposite directions; or separating a traffic lane from the adjacent sea area; or separating traffic lanes designated for particular classes of ships proceeding in the same direction.

(1860)   (d) "Precautionary area" means a routing measure comprising an area within defined limits where ships must navigate with particular caution and within which the direction of traffic flow may be recommended.

(1861)   **§166.10 Operating rules.**

(1862)   The operator of a vessel in a TSS shall comply with Rule 10 of the International Regulations for Preventing Collisions at Sea, 1972, as amended.

(1863)   **§167.15 Modification of schemes.**

(1864)   (a) A traffic separation scheme or precautionary area described in this Part may be permanently amended in accordance with 33 U.S.C. 1223 (92 Stat. 1473), and with international agreements.

(1865)   (b) A traffic separation scheme or precautionary area in this Part may be temporarily adjusted by the Commandant of the Coast Guard in an emergency, or to accommodate operations which would create an undue hazard for vessels using the scheme or which would contravene Rule 10 of the International Regulations for Preventing Collisions at Sea, 1972. Adjustment may be in the form of a temporary traffic lane shift, a temporary suspension of a section of the scheme, a temporary precautionary area overlaying a lane, or other appropriate measure. Adjustments will only be made where, in the judgment of the Coast Guard, there is no reasonable alternative means of conducting an operation and navigation safety will not be jeopardized by the adjustment. Notice of adjustments will be made in the appropriate Notice to Mariners and in the Federal Register. Requests by members of the public for temporary adjustments to traffic separation schemes must be submitted 150 days prior to the time the adjustment is desired. Such Requests, describing the interference that would otherwise occur to a TSS, should be submitted to the District Commander of the Coast Guard District in which the TSS is located. Atlantic East Coast

(1866)   **§167.150 Off New York Traffic Separation Scheme and Precautionary Areas.**

(1867)   The specific areas in the Off New York Traffic Separation Scheme and Precautionary Areas are described in §§167.151, 167.152, 167.153, 167.154, and 167.155 of this chapter.

(1868)   **§167.151 Precautionary areas.**

(1869)   (a) A circular precautionary area with a radius of seven miles is established centered upon Ambrose Light in geographic position

(1870)   40°27.50′N., 73°49.90′W.

(1871)   (b) A precautionary area is established between the traffic separation scheme "Eastern Approach, off Nantucket" and the traffic separation scheme "In the Approach to Boston, Massachusetts." (1) The precautionary area is bounded to the east by a circle of radius 15.5 miles, centered upon geographic position

(1872)   40°35.00′N., 69°00.00′W., and is intersected by the traffic separation scheme "In the Approach to Boston, Massachusetts" and "Off New York" at the following geographic positions:

(1873)   40°50.33′N., 68°57.00′W.
(1874)   40°23.75′N., 69°14.63′W.

(279) The cove has several boatyards. Berths, electricity, gasoline, water, diesel fuel, ice, marine supplies, wet and dry storage, launching ramps, lifts to 21 tons, and complete engine and hull repairs are available. The **harbormaster** in the cove controls anchoring and berthing; contact can be made through the Warwick City Hall.

(280) From **Sandy Point**, the eastern extremity of Potowomut Neck, shoals with depths of 2 to 9 feet extend northeasterly for about 0.6 mile. Extensive shoals extend off the eastern side of Warwick Neck to Ohio Ledge. **Rocky Point** is on the eastern side of the neck, 1.7 miles north-northeastward of Warwick Point.

(281) The natural channel between the shoals off Warwick Neck and the shoals northward of Patience and Prudence Islands has depths of 19 to 50 feet. A buoy marks the shoal off **Providence Point**, the northernmost point of Prudence Island.

(282) **Chart 13218.**–The shoreline of **Point Judith Neck** between West Passage and Point Judith should be given a berth of at least 0.6 mile. From Narragansett Pier to **Black Point**, a rocky promontory 1.9 miles southward, the shoreline is a rugged rocky ledge with deep water close inshore. The waters between Black Point and Point Judith are boulder-strewn and shoal up gradually.

(283) Three very prominent landmarks are Point Judith Light, the elevated water tank 1.7 miles north of Point Judith, and Hazard's Tower, a high, square stone tower 0.5 mile south of Narragansett Pier. Closer inshore the stone bathing pavilion at the State-operated **Scarborough Beach**, 0.5 mile south of Black Point, and an open stone tower on a house 0.4 mile north of Black Point are prominent.

7. BLOCK ISLAND SOUND

(1) This chapter describes Block Island Sound, Fishers Island Sound, Gardiners Bay, Little Peconic Bay, Great Peconic Bay, and the ports and harbors in the area, the more important of which are Point Judith Harbor, Great Salt Pond, Stonington, Mystic Harbor, and Greenport.

(2) **COLREGS Demarcation Lines.** –The lines established for this part of the coast are described in **80.150 and 80.155,** chapter 2.

(3) **Charts 13205, 13215.–Block Island North Reef** is a is a deep navigable waterway forming the eastern approach to Long Island Sound, Fishers Island Sound, and Gardiners Bay from the Atlantic Ocean. The sound is a link for waterborne commerce between Cape Cod and Long Island Sound. It has two entrances from the Atlantic; an eastern entrance from Rhode Island Sound between Block Island and Point Judith, and a southern entrance between Block Island and Montauk Point. The sound is connected with Long Island Sound by The Race and other passages to the southwestward, and with Fishers Island Sound by several passages between rocky reefs from Watch Hill Point to East Point, Fishers Island.

(4) The north shoreline of Block Island Sound and Fishers Island Sound from Point Judith to New London is generally rocky and broken with short stretches of sandy beach. Many inlets and harbors, especially in the vicinity of Fishers Island, afford harbors of refuge for vessels. Most of the rocks and shoals near the channels are marked with navigational aids.

(5) The southern part of Block Island Sound is bounded by Block Island on the east, the eastern extremity of Long Island, and Gardiners Island on the west. Plum Island and Fishers Island are at the western end of the sound.

(6) The deep water in the central part of Block Island Sound will accommodate vessels of the greatest draft.

(7) Westward of Gardiners Island, enclosed between the northeastern and eastern ends of Long Island, are Gardiners Bay, Shelter Island Sound, Little Peconic Bay, and Great Peconic Bay. This area is well protected but generally shallow, and is not suited for deep-draft vessels. The shoreline is marked by many indentations and shallow harbors. These waters are much used by commercial fishing vessels and small pleasure craft because of the protection afforded and the many anchorages.

(8) **Block Island North Reef** is a sand shoal with depths of 14 feet or less extending 1 mile northward from **Sandy Point** at the north end of Block Island. The shoal should be avoided by all vessels; its depths change frequently, and its position is also subject to a slow change. It is practically steep-to on all sides, so that soundings alone cannot be depended on to clear it. A lighted bell buoy is 1.5 miles northward of the point.

(9) **Southwest Ledge,** 5.5 miles west-southwestward of Block Island Southeast Light, has a least known depth of 23 feet and is marked on its southwest side by Southwest Ledge Lighted Bell Buoy 2. Rocky patches with least depths of 27 and 29 feet extend 1.5 miles northeastward from the ledge. The sea breaks on the shoaler places on the ledge in heavy weather.

(10) Several other dangers that must be guarded against are northward and westward of Southwest Ledge Lighted Bell Buoy 2. These dangers are: two obstructions, about 300 yards apart, covered 31 and 32 feet, marked by a lighted buoy, about 2.2 miles 280° from the lighted bell buoy; and two obstructions, cleared to a depth of 35 feet, about 0.75 mile north of the lighted bell buoy.

(11) The deepest passage in the southern entrance to Block Island Sound is just westward of Southwest Ledge and has a width of over 2 miles; this is the best passage for deep-draft vessels. In heavy weather vessels desiring to enter the sound westward of Block Island should pass westward of Southwest Ledge Lighted Bell Buoy 2, taking care to pass clear of the obstructions mentioned above.

(12) Between the inner patch of rocks and the shoals, which extend 0.9 mile from Block Island, is a channel 1.3 miles wide, with a depth of about 34 feet. Vessels using this channel round the southwest end of Block Island at a distance of 1.5 miles. It is not advisable to use this passage during heavy weather.

(13) The entrance between Point Judith and Block Island is used by vessels coming from the bays and sounds eastward to Long Island Sound. The route generally used is through The Race. Tows of light barges and vessels of 14 feet or less draft sometimes go through Fishers Island Sound, especially during daylight with a smooth sea. This entrance is clear with the exception of Block Island North Reef and the numerous large boulders extending about 4 miles south-southeastward of Point Judith. The coast from Point Judith nearly to Watch Hill should be given a berth of over 1 mile, avoiding the broken ground with depths less than 30 feet.

(14) (Full tidal information, including daily predictions is given in the Tide Tables.)

(15) The effect of strong winds, in combination with the regular tidal action, may at times cause the water to fall several feet below or rise the same amount above the plane of reference of the chart. The mean range of **tide** throughout Block Island Sound varies from about 3 feet at Point Judith to 2 feet at Montauk Point.

(16) **Tidal current** data for a number of locations in Block Island Sound are given in the Tidal Current Tables. Current directions and velocities throughout the sound for each hour of the tidal cycle are shown on Tidal Current Charts, Block Island Sound and Eastern Long Island Sound.

(17) The tidal currents throughout Block Island Sound have considerable velocity; the greatest velocities occur in the vicinity of The Race and in the entrances between Montauk Point, Block Island, and Point Judith. Soundings alone cannot be depended upon to locate the position; the shoaling is generally abrupt in approaching the shores or dangers.

(18) In the middle of the passage between Point Judith and Block Island, the velocity is 0.7 knot. The flood sets westward, and the ebb eastward.

(19) In the passage between Block Island and Montauk Point, the flood sets generally northwestward and the ebb southeastward. In the middle of the passage the velocity is 1.5 knots on the flood and 1.9 knots on the ebb. About 1.2 miles eastward of Montauk Point, the flood sets 346°, ebb 162°, with a velocity of 2.8 knots.

(20) In Block Island Sound and in the eastern part of Long Island Sound, **fogs** are generally heaviest with southeast winds. In these waters the usual duration of a fog is from 4 to 12 hours, but periods of from 4 to 6 days have been known with very short clear intervals. In the autumn, **land fogs,** as they are termed locally, sometimes occur with

northerly breezes, but are generally burned off before midday.

(21) The Race may be said to be the only locality where tidal currents have any decided influence on the movements of the ice. Large quantities of floe ice usually pass through The Race during the ebb, especially if the wind is westerly, and in severe winters this ice causes some obstruction in Block Island Sound and around Montauk Point. These obstructions are the most extensive around the middle of February.

(22) **Weather.**-Land influences the weather only at the northern edge of the Sound, with a northerly wind. Otherwise the waters are open, similar to the nearby ocean. Winds from all other directions have ample time to increase in strength and the Sound can be as turbulent as any water off the coast. Wind speeds can be double those found on the coast, especially in winter, when average speeds of 16 to 17 knots are common. Gales occur up to 5 percent of the time in winter and are most likely from the west and northwest. Seas built by winds from the southeast through southwest are usually highest since there is no land to interfere with the fetch. Seas of 10 feet or more are likely 5 to 7 percent of the time in winter.

(23) Because of relatively cold water, summer fog occurs two to three times more often in these waters than in either Narragansett or Buzzards Bays. For example, in June visibilities drop below 1/2 mile nearly 9 percent of the time.

(24) **Pilotage, Block Island Sound and Long Island Sound.**-Pilotage is compulsary for foreign vessels under register in Block Island Sound and Long Island Sound. A vessel traversing Block Island is enroute to or from Long Island Sound. See Pilotage, Long Island Sound (indexed as such), chapter 8. Vessels bound for Long Island Sound ports may board pilots in the vicinity of Point Judith Lighted Whistle Buoy 2, within a 1-mile radius circle centered in 41°17.2'N., 71°30.4'W.

(25) **Chart 13217.**-Block Island, 5 miles long, is hilly with elevations up to about 200 feet. The shore of the island is fringed in most places by boulders and should be given a berth of over 0.5 mile even by small craft; the shoaling is generally abrupt in approaching the island.

(26) **Weather.**-Block Island, formed by glaciers, consists of nearly 7,000 acres and lies in the Atlantic Ocean about 12 miles east-northeast of Long Island and about the same distance south of Charlestown, R.I. Hence, the climate is typically maritime, but under conditions of extreme cold or heat the effect is felt on the island as well as on the mainland. Temperatures of -10°F and 95°F have been recorded.

(27) Summers are usually dry. Recorded rainfall for any 1 month ranges from a trace to 12.93 inches. In July and August maximum temperatures average 74°F. The island is too small to build up cumulonimbus clouds, and local thunderstorms do not occur. Fog occurs on 1 out of 4 days in the early summer, when the ocean is relatively cold.

(28) Winters are distinguished for their comparative mildness, maximums average 4° to 10°F above freezing and minimums average 25°F in February. Since the surface winds are usually easterly when snow begins it soon changes to rain or melts rapidly after it piles up. The ocean temperatures are of course always somewhat above freezing and not far off shore are relatively high.

(29) The ocean has a dampening effect on hot winds in summer and an accelerating effect on cold winds from the mainland in the winter. Katabatic winds from Narrangansett Bay and Long Island reach as high as 35 knots when anticyclonic conditions prevail on the mainland in winter.

The wind velocity averages 15 knots for the year, but the mean is 17 knots in the winter, when gales are frequent. In the early fall most of the tropical storms moving up the coast affect the island to some extent.

(30) (See page T-3 for **Block Island climatological table.**)

(31) **Communications.**-A ferry operates daily from Galilee to Great Salt Pond or Old Harbor, carrying mail, passengers, freight, and vehicles. There is summer ferry service from Old Harbor to Providence, via Newport, and to New London. The island has telephone service to the mainland. Air service is also available.

(32) **Block Island Southeast Light** (41°09.2' N., 71°33.1'W.), 258 feet above the water, is shown from a steel tower on **Mohegan Bluffs** on the southeast point of the island. A radiobeacon is close east-southeast of the light.

(33) About 0.2 mile southeast of the light is the wreck of the large tanker SS LIGHTBURNE. The wreck is marked by a buoy. At **Clay Head,** on the northeast side of Block Island, is a lone white house on top of the bluff. Two nearby silos are conspicuous.

(34) **Block Island North Light** (41°13.7'N., 71°34.6'W.), 58 feet above the water, is shown from a black tower on a gray granite dwelling on Sandy Point at the north end of the island.

(35) **Old Harbor,** frequently used as a harbor of refuge, is an artificial harbor formed by two breakwaters on the east side of Block Island, 1.4 miles northward of Block Island Southeast Light. In March-November 1989, the controlling depth was 13 feet in the entrance, thence depths of 10 to 15 feet were available in the inner harbor anchorage with lesser depths along the north, northwest, and southwest sides, and thence 5½ feet was available in the basin in the southeast corner of the inner harbor. The harbor is occupied by pleasure craft during the summer. The eastern part of the inner harbor is left clear for the passage of the ferry to the wharf. The basin in the southeast corner of the inner harbor is usually occupied by fishing boats and local craft which tie up along the sides. Gasoline, diesel fuel, and berths are available. The **harbormaster** has an office at the Old Harbor town dock.

(36) The east breakwater extends about 300 yards northward of the entrance of the inner harbor, and is marked at its end by a light and fog signal. A bell buoy is 0.55 mile northward of the breakwater. A light marks the end of the breakwater on the west side at the entrance to the inner harbor.

(37) **Great Salt Pond (New Harbor),** on the west side of Block Island, is the best harbor in Block Island Sound for vessels of 15-foot draft or less. In easterly gales when the sea is too heavy to enter Old Harbor, a landing can be made at Great Salt Pond. The entrance, about 2 miles south-southwestward of Block Island North Light, is a dredged cut through the narrow beach. The southwestern side of the entrance is protected by a jetty, marked by a light and fog signal at its outer end and by a light at the inner end.

(38) In June 1987, the midchannel controlling depth in the entrance channel was 8½ feet. The channel is well marked, but subject to shoaling. Strangers should seek local knowledge before entering.

(39) The usual anchorage in Great Salt Pond is near the southeast end, off the ferry landing, in 15 to 48 feet, taking care to leave a fairway to the landing. A channel with a reported depth of about 8 feet in July 1981 leads to **Trim Pond,** where local fishing craft are moored.

(40) Small-craft facilities in Great Salt Pond can provide berths, electricity, gasoline, diesel fuel, water, ice, and marine supplies. The marina about 0.3 mile westward of the ferry landing had a reported depth of 16 feet at the face of

the dock in July 1981. Sail and engine repairs are available nearby.

(41)   The mean range of **tide** is about 2.6 feet.

(42)   **Tidal currents** in the entrance to Great Salt Pond have a velocity of 0.3 knot. (See Tidal Current Tables for predictions.)

(43)   **Chart 13219.**–Point Judith Light (41°21.7′N., 71°28.9′W.), 65 feet above the water, is shown from an octagonal tower, 51 feet high, with the lower half white, upper half brown. The station has a fog signal and a radiobeacon. About 100 yards north of the light is **Point Judith Coast Guard Station.** A lighted whistle buoy is about 2.4 miles southward of the light. (See chart 13218.) A prominent elevated water tank is about 1.8 miles northward of the light, and another globular water tank is about 3 miles northwestward of the light.

(44)   The area around Point Judith, including the approaches to Point Judith Harbor of Refuge, is irregular with rocky bottom and indications of boulders. Caution is advised to avoid the shoal spots, even with a smooth sea, and to exercise extra care where the depths are not more than 6 feet greater than the draft.

(45)   **Point Judith Harbor of Refuge,** on the west side of Point Judith, is formed by a main V-shaped breakwater and two shorearm breakwaters extending to the shore. The harbor is easy of access for most vessels except with a heavy southerly sea. It is little used by tows. The only soft bottom in the harbor is found in the southern part of the deeper water enclosed by the main breakwater. On the north side the shoaling is gradual; the 18-foot curve is about 0.3 to 0.5 mile offshore.

(46)   Near the central part of the harbor are two shoals; the northernmost one has depths of 14 to 18 feet, and the southernmost one has depths of 14 to 16 feet and is marked by a buoy.

(47)   The area within the V-shaped breakwater affords protected anchorage for small craft. The breakwater should be given a berth of 200 yards to avoid broken and hard bottom; a rocky shoal area about 100 yards wide, paralleling the west side of the main breakwater northward from the angle should be avoided. A good berth for a vessel is on a line between Point Judith Harbor of Refuge East Entrance Light 3 and Point Judith Harbor of Refuge West Entrance Light 2, midway between them in 22 to 30 feet. This position falls on the edge of the east-west thorofare used by pleasure craft and fishing boats.

(48)   In August 1984, a submerged obstruction was reported about 270 yards southeast of Point Judith Harbor of Refuge West Entrance Light 2 in about 41°21′37″N., 71°30′40″W. In July 1991, an obstruction, covered 5 feet, was reported in about 41°21′28″N., 71°30′20″W.

(49)   The southern entrance to the Harbor of Refuge, known locally as the East Gap, is 400 yards wide; in July 1981, it had a reported controlling depth of about 24 feet with deeper water in the western half of the channel.

(50)   The western entrance to the Harbor of Refuge, known locally as the West Gap, is 500 yards wide; in July 1981, it had a reported controlling depth of about 18 feet, with lesser depths on the north side of the entrance.

(51)   **Tides and Currents.**–The mean range of tide in the Harbor of Refuge is 3.1 feet. The tidal currents have a velocity of about 0.7 knot at the south entrance. The currents off the west entrance are rotary, with a velocity at strength of 0.5 knot. (See Tidal Current Tables for predictions.)

(52)   Considerably stronger currents have been reported to develop especially when the tide is ebbing.

(53)   **Point Judith Pond** is a saltwater tidal pond entered between two rock jetties at **The Breachway** in the northwestern part of Point Judith Harbor of Refuge. The east jetty is marked near its seaward end by a daybeacon. The pond extends 3.3 miles northerly to the town of **Wakefield.** It is used extensively by small fishing vessels and pleasure craft, and numerous fish wharves are inside the entrance. The north end of Point Judith Pond affords good anchorage for boats of 4 feet draft or less during a heavy blow.

(54)   The village of **Galilee** on the east side of the entrance and **Jerusalem** on the west side at **Succotach Point** have State piers and numerous small piers chiefly used by fishermen. A State fisheries laboratory is just above the State pier at Jerusalem. A State pier superintendent controls the State piers at Galilee and Jerusalem; his office is at the head of the Galilee State Pier.

(55)   A channel with three dredged sections marked by buoys and a daybeacon extends from Point Judith Harbor of Refuge along the west side of the pond to the State Pier at Jerusalem, and thence northerly to the turning basin at Wakefield. A branch channel, on the east side, extends northeasterly from the entrance to the pond to the State Pier at Galilee, and into anchorage areas westward of Galilee and southward of Little Comfort Island.

(56)   In February 1983, the controlling depths were 11 feet (13 feet at midchannel) to the junction with the Galilee branch channel, thence 11 feet to the State Pier at Jerusalem, thence in December 1985, 4½ feet to the turning basin at Wakefield with 6 feet in the basin except for shoaling to 5 feet along the west limit. In February 1983, the east branch channel had a controlling depth of 15 feet to the State Pier at Galilee, thence 11 feet (14 feet at midchannel) to the anchorage basin southward of Little Comfort Island, thence in October 1985, depths of 4½ to 7 feet were available in the anchorage except for shoaling to 1½ feet along the northeast limit. In February 1983, the anchorage westward of Galilee had depths of 10 feet.

(57)   **Tides and Currents.**–The mean range of tide in the pond is 2.8 feet and occurs later than in the Harbor of Refuge by about 10 minutes just inside the entrance and 30 minutes at the north end. The tidal currents in the entrance have a velocity of 1.8 knots on the flood and 1.5 knots on the ebb, and cause slight rips and overfalls at changes of tide. Higher current velocities are reported to occur. (See Tidal Current Tables for predictions.)

(58)   Several boatyards and marinas are at Galilee, Jerusalem, Wakefield, and at Snug Harbor, on the west side of the pond about 0.8 mile above the entrance. Berths, electricity, gasoline, diesel fuel, water, ice, marine supplies, storage, launching ramps, and hull and engine repairs are available. The largest marine railway in the area, at the southern end of the waterfront at Snug Harbor, can handle craft up to 150 feet long or 400 tons. In July 1981, a reported depth of 12 feet could be carried to the railway.

(59)   Daily ferry service is available to Block Island from Galilee. Daily bus service is operated to Providence.

(60)   **Potter Pond,** shallow and landlocked, is joined with Point Judith by a narrow channel near **Snug Harbor.** Local knowledge should be obtained before using this channel, which has depths of 2 to 4 feet and is crossed by overhead power and telephone cables with a clearance of 30 feet at the channel entrance and by a fixed highway bridge with a clearance of 5 feet about 0.4 mile above the entrance. A current of more than 3 knots develops through the channel on the ebb. The mean range of **tide** in the pond is about 1 foot, and it occurs about 2.5 hours later than in the Harbor of Refuge.

(61) **Chart 13215.**–From Point Judith to Watch Hill the shore is low and for the most part consists of sandy beaches which are broken by several projecting rocky points. Back from the immediate shore are areas of cultivation interspersed with rolling grass-covered or wooded hills. Except for Point Judith Pond, most pond outlets are used only by small local craft. The coast is fringed by broken ground and boulders in places, which should be avoided by deep-draft vessels where the depths are less than 36 to 42 feet.

(62) **Matunuck** is a summer resort about 3 miles west of Point Judith. Southwest of **Matunuck Point** is **Nebraska Shoal,** a patch of boulders covered 18 feet and marked by a buoy. The shoal is at the south end of broken ground, with depths less than 30 feet offshore; the water deepens abruptly around the patch.

(63) **Charlestown Breachway,** 4.5 miles westward of Matunuck Point, is a narrow inlet which leads to **Ninigret Pond,** also known as **Charlestown Pond,** to the westward, and the village of **Charlestown** to the northward. In July 1981, a reported depth of about 2 feet could be taken in the inlet, with depths of about 3 to 6 feet inside. The southern part of Ninigret Pond is mostly mud flats. Local knowledge is required in entering and moving about inside. A small-craft facility is at Charlestown, and one is at the western end of Ninigret Pond; berths, gasoline, electricity, marine supplies, and launching ramps are at both facilities.

(64) **Quonochontaug,** 10.8 miles westward of Point Judith, is a summer settlement at the outlet of **Quonochontaug Pond.** In July 1981, a reported depth of about 3 feet could be carried in **Quonochontaug Breachway,** with depths of 15 to 20 feet reported in the pond. Vessels favor the west side of the entrance to avoid rocks in the easterly half of the entrance.

(65) **Weekapaug Point,** 12.5 miles west of Point Judith, is bold, rocky, and prominent from the southwest and southeast. Two stone jetties, 1,500 feet long, protect the entrance to **Winnapaug Pond** just westward of the point. In July 1981, a reported depth of about 5 feet could be carried in **Weekapaug Breachway** to the pond; vessels favor the west side of the breachway above the bridge. Reported depths in Winnapaug Pond vary from bare to 10 feet. There are numerous shoals and sandbars. Southerly winds cause breakers at the ends of the jetties; extreme caution is advised. The fixed bridge over the entrance has a clearance of 6 feet.

(66) **Old Reef,** with a depth of 5 feet over it, is about 1.5 miles west of Weekapaug Point and about 0.5 mile offshore.

(67) **Chart 13214.**–**Watch Hill,** about 17.5 miles west of Point Judith, is a high bare bluff on its easterly side with several large hotels and summer houses.

(68) **Watch Hill Light** (41°18.2′N., 71°51.5′W.), 61 feet above the water, is shown from a square gray granite tower, 45 feet high, attached to a white building with a red roof, on **Watch Hill Point.** It is reported that the fog signal at the station is not easily heard eastward of the light, but from the southwest can be heard nearly to Montauk Point. A radiobeacon is 136 yards north-northeast of the light. A lighted whistle buoy, 2.5 miles southward of the light, marks a passage through Block Island Sound.

(69) **Gangway Rock,** awash at low water, is part of a boulder reef extending about 0.2 mile southward from Watch Hill Light. A lighted bell buoy marks the south end of the reef. A submerged rock is about 50 yards northward of the buoy.

(70) **Watch Hill Passage** is the principal entrance to Fishers Island Sound from eastward, and the only one used by strangers. It has a least depth of about 17 feet. A spot with 12 feet over it in the passage is marked by a buoy; the best channel is northward of this buoy, giving it a berth of about 150 yards.

(71) **Watch Hill Reef,** on the southwest side of Watch Hill Passage, has rocks that bare and is marked by a gong buoy.

(72) **Sugar Reef Passage,** between Watch Hill Reef and Sugar Reef, has a width of 0.3 mile; the least depths are about 22 feet.

(73) **Sugar Reef,** some 500 to 600 yards in extent, is covered 2 to 12 feet and should be avoided; it is marked by a buoy off its north side.

(74) **Catumb Passage,** between Sugar Reef and Catumb Rocks, has a width of 150 yards; its least depth is 13 feet.

(75) **Catumb Rocks,** the highest of which are awash, are marked by buoys on the north, southeast, and southwest sides. Rocks covered 1 to 18 feet extend 0.8 mile westward of Catumb Rocks to the buoy that marks the east side of **Lords Passage.** This passage, about 0.3 mile wide, has a least depth of 16 feet.

(76) **Wicopesset Rock,** on the northwesterly side of Lords Passage, is the easterly part of foul ground extending about 0.3 mile to **Wicopesset Island,** which is low and rocky.

(77) **Wicopesset Passage,** between Wicopesset Island and East Point, is narrow and is obstructed by a rock in the middle marked by a buoy; it is suitable only for small craft and should not be used by strangers. A bell buoy marks the southern entrance. Extreme caution is recommended when using the passage as the ebb current is apt to set boats on the foul ground.

(78) Information about the tides and tidal currents in the passages is given with the discussion of Fishers Island Sound.

(79) **Charts 13214, 13212.**–**Fishers Island,** 6 miles long, is hilly and sparsely wooded. **Chocomount,** 136 feet high, is the highest point on the island. **East Point,** at the east end of the island, is marked by several large houses. The former Coast Guard station at East Harbor, about 1 mile from East Point of Fishers Island, is prominent; numerous buildings on the western part of Fishers Island and a large yellow hotel building are conspicuous. The radar antenna on **Mount Prospect,** near the west end of the island, south shore, is the most prominent landmark on Fishers Island from seaward. The south side of the island is fringed with foul ground which rises abruptly from depths of 42 to 48 feet; but by giving the shore a berth of 0.5 mile, all dangers will be avoided.

(80) **Race Point Ledge,** partly bare at low water, extends about 0.2 mile southwestward from **Race Point,** the southwest extremity of Fishers Island, and is marked at its end by a buoy. Inside the buoy are boulders with 2 to 9 feet over them. The passage between the buoy and Race Rock Light has very irregular bottom; the least depth is about 24 feet. It is suitable only for small vessels with a comparatively smooth sea.

(81) **Race Rock,** on the northeast side of The Race, is nearly 200 yards in diameter, with a depth of 8 feet. A ridge with a least depth of 25 feet is reported extending about 370 yards south of Race Rock. Another ridge, oriented north-south and with a least depth of 40 feet, is about 380 yards east of Race Rock.

(82) **Race Rock Light** (41°14.6′N., 72°02.8′W.), 67 feet above the water, is shown from a granite tower attached to a dwelling on a granite pier on the rock. A fog signal is sounded at the station. The fog signal is reported at times to be inaudible when a vessel is approaching from eastward and is close southward of Fishers Island.

(83) **Charts 13209, 13212.**–The Race, the main entrance to Long Island Sound from eastward, extends between Fishers Island and Little Gull Island, between which is a width of about 3.5 miles. The only dangers are Valiant Rock, nearly in the middle, and Little Gull Island with its reefs.

(84) **Current.**–In the middle of The Race, the flood sets 295° and the ebb 100°, with average velocities of 2.9 knots and 3.5 knots, respectively. There are always strong rips and swirls in the wake of all broken ground in The Race, except for about one-half hour at slack water. The rips are exceptionally heavy during heavy weather, and especially when a strong wind opposes the current, or the current sets through against a heavy sea. (Predicted times of slack water and times and velocities of strength of current are given in the Tidal Current Tables.)

(85) **Little Gull Reef**, with little depth over it and foul ground, extends 0.3 mile east-northeastward from **Little Gull Island.** Deep-draft vessels should avoid this locality. **Little Gull Island Light** (41°12.4'N., 72°06.5'W.), 91 feet above the water, is shown from a gray granite tower, 81 feet high, attached to a red dwelling on a pier. A fog signal is at the light, and a radiobeacon is about 60 yards south-southwest of the light. The light and Race Rock Light are the guides, as soundings cannot be depended upon.

(86) In passing north of Valiant Rock, vessels should keep from 0.5 to 0.8 mile southwestward of Race Rock Light, and craft passing southward of Valiant Rock should hold to a course about 1 mile northeastward of Little Gull Island Light.

(87) **Cerberus Shoal**, 6 miles southeast of Race Rock Light, is about 0.4 mile in diameter, with a least depth of 19 feet on a small rocky patch near its north end. The seas break on this shoal during heavy swells. It is marked by a lighted gong buoy. Near the shoal, tide rips are unusually strong.

(88) **Great Gull Island**, 0.6 mile southwest of Little Gull Island, was formerly a military reservation, but is now privately owned. The pier on the north side is in ruins. A lookout tower on the island is conspicuous.

(89) **Valiant Rock**, with a least depth of 19 feet, is surrounded by shoal area, and the 10-fathom curve surrounding the rock marks the area which should be avoided by deep-draft vessels and preferably all vessels, on account of the heavy swirls and rips. A lighted bell buoy is northward of the rock.

(90) **The Sluiceway**, the passage between Great Gull Island and Plum Island, has several known dangers and very irregular bottom with boulders, and should be avoided. The velocity of the **tidal current** in the passage is 2.6 knots on the flood, and 3.2 knots on the ebb; flood sets 299°, and ebb 133°. Considerably higher velocities occur at times, and tide rips are very bad in heavy weather. Boulders covered 3 to 10 feet are between **Old Silas Rock** and Plum Island. Old Silas Rock is awash at high water. **Middle Shoal Rock**, 0.3 mile northeastward of Old Silas Rock, has a depth of 8 feet.

(91) **Bedford Reef** is broken ground, on which the least found depths are 14 to 16 feet, extending about 1.5 miles southward from broken ground lying between Great Gull and Plum Islands. It should be avoided. **Constellation Rock**, on the southeasterly extension on this broken ground, has 17 feet over it, is marked by a buoy, and lies 1.9 miles southward of Little Gull Island Light.

(92) **Chart 13209.**–Montauk Point, the easterly extremity of Long Island, is a high sandy bluff, on the summit of which is the light. The land is grass covered, with a height of 165 feet at **Prospect Hill**, 2 miles westward of the point. The south side of the point is bold, the 10-fathom curve is about

0.5 mile from shore; depths of 24 feet and less extend 0.8 mile off the northeast side of the point.

(93) **Montauk Point Light** (41°04.2'N., 71°51.5'W.), 168 feet above the water, is shown from a white octagonal, pyramidal tower, 108 feet high, with a brown band midway of its height and a covered way to a gray dwelling. A fog signal is at the light. A radiobeacon is 0.3 mile south-southwestward of the light.

(94) Surrounding Montauk Point for about 4 miles is a shoal area that has been closely surveyed (see also chart 13215); the bottom is very broken, and extra caution should be observed where the depths are less than 10 feet greater than the draft. In general, the shoals are a series of long narrow ridges, in places only a few yards wide, and their positions are indicated by the rips over them at the strength of the tidal currents.

(95) **Montauk Shoal**, about 2.5 miles south-southeastward of the light, has least depths of 28 feet. **Great Eastern Rock**, 1.5 miles east-northeast of the light, has a least depth of 24 feet. **Phelps Ledge**, just northerly of Great Eastern Rock, is covered by 24 feet. **Endeavor Shoals**, about 2.3 miles northeast of the light, are covered by 19 to 24 feet on a narrow ridge about 0.4 mile long. A lighted gong buoy is off the eastern end of the ridge. In 1981, a sunken wreck was reported about 1 mile north-northeast of Montauk Point Light in about 41°05.2'N., 71°50.8'W.

(96) Vessels drawing up to 20 feet can avoid the dangers eastward and northeastward of Montauk Point in smooth weather by giving the point a berth of over 1 mile and avoiding Great Eastern Rock.

(97) Broken ground with rocky bottom and boulders extends about 2 miles off the north coast west of Montauk Point. **Shagwong Reef**, with a least depth of 8 feet and marked by a lighted bell buoy, is the northern limit of this area. **Shagwong Rock**, with a least depth of 7½ feet and marked by a lighted buoy, and **Washington Shoal**, with a least depth of 15 feet, are between the shore and Shagwong Reef. The principal danger outside Shagwong Reef is a shoal with a depth of 30 feet, 5.3 miles northwestward of Montauk Point.

(98) **Pilotage Pickup Locations Off Montauk Point.**–Pilots generally, or by prearrangement, meet a ship "off Montauk Point". The following pilot associations meet vessels "off Montauk Point" at the locations indicated. For telephone number, FAX number, cable address, description of the boat, frequencies, etc., consult the name of the association under Pilotage, Narraganset Bay and Other Rhode Island Waters (indexed as such), chapter 6; Pilotage, Long Island Sound (indexed as such), chapter 8; and Pilotage, New York Harbor and Approaches (indexed as such), chapter 11.

(99) Sound Pilots, Inc. (division of Northeast Marine Pilots, Inc.), 2 miles east of Montauk Point Lighted Whistle Buoy MP;

(100) Connecticut State Pilots, 3 miles east-southeast of Montauk Point Lighted Whistle Buoy MP;

(101) Constitution State Pilots Association, 3 miles east of Montauk Point Lighted Whistle Buoy MP;

(102) Long Island Sound State Pilots Association, Inc., at Montauk Point Lighted Whistle Buoy MP.

(103) **Montauk Harbor**, in the northern part of **Lake Montauk**, is entered through a dredged channel on the northern shore about 3 miles west of Montauk Point. The entrance is protected by jetties, each of which is marked by a light, and the west jetty has a fog signal. A lighted bell buoy, about 0.3 mile north of the entrance, marks the approach to the harbor. In June 1988, the reported controlling depth in the channel was 12 feet to the boat basin northwestward of Star Island and to the yacht basin east of the island; in 1982, the

boat basin had depths of 9½ feet except for shoaling along the edges. The channel is marked by private seasonal buoys.

(104) **Star Island**, just inside Montauk Harbor, is connected to the mainland by a causeway. A private light is shown from the eastern side of the island. Depths of 8 to 16 feet are reported in the yacht basin off the eastern side of the island; caution is advised in selecting anchorage because lesser depths may be found. A privately marked channel with a reported controlling depth of about 3 feet in June 1981 leads from the yacht basin to the southern part of Lake Montauk where there are depths of 6 to 8 feet in the center.

(105) **COLREGS Demarcation Lines.**–The lines established for Montauk Harbor are described in **80.155**, chapter 2.

(106) The mean range of **tide** is 1.9 feet.

(107) Tidal **currents** at the entrance to Montauk Harbor have a velocity of 1.2 knots on the flood and about 0.5 knot on the ebb. They are reported to decrease rapidly after entering the harbor and are practically negligible near the yacht club landing on the east side of Star Island. (See Tidal Current Tables for predictions.) **Montauk Coast Guard Station** is at the northern end of Star Island.

(108) There are several small-craft facilities on both sides of the entrance to Montauk Harbor, and a yacht club and several marinas are on the east side of Star Island. Gasoline, diesel fuel, water, ice, marine supplies, and space for transients are available. Lifts to 80 tons can handle craft for complete engine and hull repairs. Groceries and other supplies may be obtained at the village of Montauk.

(109) **Fort Pond Bay** is a semicircular bight about 1 mile wide on the north side of Long Island, 5 miles westward of Montauk Point. The bay is free of dangers, but flats with 8 to 12 feet over them make out 0.2 mile from its eastern shore. The bay affords anchorage in 40 to 50 feet, soft bottom, but is exposed to northerly and northwesterly winds; the shoaling is abrupt on its east and south sides.

(110) **Montauk**, a summer resort at the southeast end of the bay, is the terminus of the Long Island Railroad. A depth of 10 feet was reported alongside the commercial pier on the east side of the bay. There are no public piers available.

(111) **Napeague Bay**, 8 miles westward of Montauk Point, is shallow in the western and southwestern part. **Promised Land Channel**, the buoyed passage southward of Gardiners and Cartwright Islands, has a least centerline depth of about 14 feet; however, the depth is continually changing due to the shifting shoals.

(112) The tidal currents have a velocity of about 1.5 knots through all the channels between the shoals. It is not advisable for vessels drawing more than 10 feet to attempt the passage without local knowledge, and then only when the buoys can be seen.

(113) **Napeague Harbor**, a small-craft refuge in the southwest part of Napeague Bay, can be entered through privately dredged channels northward and southward of **Hicks Island**. In June 1981, the reported controlling depths were 4 feet in the northerly and southerly entrances. Depths in the central part of the harbor range from 1½ to 7 feet; the chart is the best guide. The harbor is especially useful in northeasterly weather when the adjoining bays are unsafe. There are no landings in the harbor.

(114) **Promised Land** is a former fishing village on the southwest side of Napeague Bay. A depth of about 4 feet can be carried to the landing at the yacht club, 1.3 miles westward of Promised Land.

(115) **Gardiners Island**, 11 miles westward of Montauk Point, is partly wooded and has an elevation of 130 feet near its middle. **Cartwright Island** is narrow, low, and sandy, and

extends 1 mile in a southerly direction off the south tip of Gardiners Island. Its size and shape are subject to considerable change by storms.

(116) **Crow Head** is the high bluff at the western end of Gardiners Island. Shoal water with depths of 9 to 16 feet extends 1.8 miles southwestward from **Cherry Hill Point**, the westerly end of Gardiners Island, and terminates at **Crow Shoal**. The shoal has depths of 3 to 11 feet and is marked by a buoy. An obstruction covered 12 feet is 200 yards eastward of the buoy.

(117) The bight between the southern part of Gardiners Island and Crow Shoal is **Cherry Harbor**. It has depths of 24 to 27 feet with mud bottom and affords shelter from northeasterly winds. **Bostwick Bay** is the bight on the northwest side of Gardiners Island. It affords excellent anchorage in easterly winds in depths of about 25 feet, but is exposed to all westerly winds.

(118) **Gardiners Point**, a low spit, is at the northerly end of a very shoal bar which extends 1.5 miles north-northwestward from Gardiners Island. This shoal is steep-to on its north and west sides and is marked by a lighted gong buoy. A rock with a depth of 2 feet over it is about 0.8 mile eastward of the north point of Gardiners Island and is marked by a buoy.

(119) The **Ruins**, a concrete structure on Gardiners Point, is Government property and formerly a naval aircraft bombing target; it is prohibited to the public. The Ruins and the area within 300 yards radius of it is dangerous due to the possible existence of undetonated explosives.

(120) A **restricted anchorage** for U.S. Navy submarines is about 3 miles eastward of Gardiners Island. (See **110.1 and 110.150**, chapter 2, for limits and regulations.)

(121) **Gardiners Bay** is at the western end of Block Island Sound from which it is separated by Gardiners Island. The bay is an excellent anchorage easily entered day or night, and is the approach to Shelter Island Sound and the Peconic Bays. The principal entrance is northward of Gardiners Point. The entrance from Long Island Sound is through Plum Gut. The entrance southward of Gardiners Island is used by fishing vessels.

(122) The principal guides for the entrance to Gardiners Bay from Block Island Sound are the lighted gong buoy north of Gardiners Point, Little Gull Light, and Orient Point Light. The white church spires at Orient and Sag Harbor are prominent. When past the lighted gong buoy north of Gardiners Point, vessels can select the anchorage in Gardiners Bay which affords the best lee in the prevailing winds.

(123) The principal dangers in approaching Gardiners Bay from the northward are the broken ground between Constellation Rock and Plum Island, and the shoal making out to Gardiners Point. In the bay, Crow Shoal should be avoided. In general, the shoaling is rather abrupt in approaching these dangers and gradual in approaching the shoals on the western side of the bay.

(124) **Plum Island**, about 2 miles westward of Great Gull Island, is 2.5 miles long, hilly, and bare of trees except near the southwest end, and has several large buildings, and a prominent tank and flagpole. The island is a Government reservation and closed to the public.

(125) The bight in the southeast side of Plum Island is foul to **Plum Island Rock**, which is 0.5 mile from shore abreast of the middle of the island, has 1 foot over it and is marked by a buoy.

(126) **Plum Gut Harbor**, on the southwest side of Plum Island, has an entrance between jetties with private seasonal lights on dolphins off the outer ends. The lights are shown daily from sundown to 0130. A private fog signal at the west

jetty light is sounded occasionally when Department of Agriculture vessels are navigating in the area. A depth of about 14 feet is in the entrance. Small yachts seeking shelter in an emergency lie alongside the wharves. The harbor is under the supervision of the Department of Agriculture and the Coast Guard, and may be used only with permission.

(127)   **COLREGS Demarcation Lines.**–The lines established for Plum Gut Harbor are described in **80.155**, chapter 2.

(128)   **Plum Gut**, the entrance to Gardiners Bay from Long Island Sound, is nearly 0.6 mile wide and has sufficient water for vessels of the deepest draft; in the passage are several rocks with depths of 17 to 19 feet over them. Tidal currents set through the passage with great velocity. Steamers, or sailing vessels with a strong favorable wind, should have no difficulty in passing through.

(129)   Velocities of the current on flood and ebb are 3.5 and 4.3 knots, respectively. The flood sets northwestward and the ebb southeastward. Heavy tide rips occur. In November 1983, NOAA Ships RUDE and HECK reported that during the flood a countercurrent normally develops along the north shore of Plum Island. This countercurrent is most prevalent within 0.5 mile of the island. Caution is recommended when using this passage.

(130)   **Oyster Pond Reef**, extending about 0.5 mile east-northeastward from **Orient Point**, is marked by a light and fog signal. Caution is recommended regarding the fog signal, as it may be difficult to hear at times, particularly with an easterly wind. Numerous boulders and little depth are between the light and Orient Point. **Midway Shoal**, about 0.5 mile east of the light, has 17 feet over it and is marked by a buoy.

(131)   When using Plum Gut it is well to give Plum Island and Orient Point Light a berth of 0.2 mile. The best water in the passage will be found on a **295°** course, passing **Pine Point** and the buoy marking Midway Shoal at a distance of 350 yards and passing midway between Orient Point Light and the western end of Plum Island.

(132)   A wharf with a depth of 8 feet at its end is on the south side of Orient Point, 1 mile westward of Orient Point Light. A ferry operates between here and New London. A small-craft facility is about 0.1 mile westward of the wharf. Berths, electricity, gasoline, diesel fuel, water, ice, and a launching ramp are available. In June 1981, a reported depth of about 6 feet could be carried to the facility.

(133)   **Acabonack Harbor**, at the southeast end of Gardiners Bay, is entered through a privately maintained and marked channel with a reported controlling depth of 2½ feet in the entrance in June 1981. There is deeper water inside.

(134)   **Hog Creek Point**, on the southerly side of Gardiners Bay, is generally flat, with bluffs approximately 25 feet in height. **Lionhead Rock**, off the point and marked by a buoy, is awash at high water. Fishtraps are westward of the point.

(135)   **Threemile Harbor**, on the south side of Gardiners Bay 1.7 miles southwestward of Hog Creek Point, is entered through a channel with two privately dredged sections. In September 1980, a portion of the wooden bulkhead on the west side of the entrance collapsed into the channel. In June 1981, it was reported that by favoring the east side of the entrance channel a depth of 8 feet could be carried to a point opposite **Maidstone Park**, thence 7 feet to the basin at the head of the harbor. The approach to the harbor is marked by a seasonal lighted bell buoy, and the channel is marked by lighted and unlighted buoys. The jetties at the harbor entrance are marked on the outer ends by private lights. A public commercial landing with reported depths of 8 feet is on the east side of the channel about 0.6 mile above the entrance. A 5 mph **speed limit** is enforced in the harbor.

(136)   Anchorage is available in Threemile Harbor in depths of 9 to 14 feet with soft bottom and good holding ground; this is a good anchorage during strong winds. The range of **tide** in the entrance to the harbor is 2.4 feet. The **tidal current** has a velocity of about 3 knots through the entrance.

(137)   Small-craft facilities on the east and south sides of Threemile Harbor can provide berths, electricity, gasoline, diesel fuel, water, ice, launching ramps, storage, lifts to 40 tons, and hull and engine repair. Provisions can be obtained at the town of **East Hampton**, 3.5 miles south of Threemile Harbor.

(138)   In June 1989, the public pier maintained by the town of East Hampton at the head of the harbor had reported depths of 7 feet at its face and 4 feet on its west side.

(139)   **COLREGS Demarcation Lines.**–The lines established for Threemile Harbor are described in **80.155**, chapter 2.

(140)   **Chart 12358.**–**Shelter Island Sound** and Peconic Bays extend westward from Gardiners Bay about 22 miles to Riverhead, the head of navigation on Peconic River. They are much frequented by yachts and other small craft in the summer. Fishtraps and oyster stakes are on many of the shoals.

(141)   A depth of about 26 feet can be carried through the channel north of Shelter Island and through Little Peconic Bay as far as Robins Island, and about 13 feet through the channel south of Shelter Island. Across the bar between Little and Great Peconic Bays about 13 feet can be carried. With local knowledge greater depths can be carried in the channels and across the bar. A depth of about 6 feet can be taken to South Jamesport and Riverhead.

(142)   The mean range of **tide** is about 2.5 feet. The **tidal currents** have considerable velocity wherever the channel is narrowed. The velocity in the narrower places is about 1.8 knots.

(143)   **Ice** obstructs navigation in the coves and shallow harbors during January and February. In severe winters, drift ice is reported to interfere with navigation for short periods of time. In the south arm of Shelter Island Sound, the ice is heavy enough at times to destroy structures exposed to it.

(144)   Diesel fuel, gasoline, ice, water, marine supplies, and other provisions can best be obtained at Greenport and Sag Harbor. Several boatyards, shipyards, marine railways, and enclosed basins with excellent repair facilities are at Greenport.

(145)   **Ram Head** is a prominent sandy bluff on the western shore of Gardiners Bay. A lower bluff is nearly 1.5 miles westward of Ram Head with numerous houses along the top. A shoal with 7 to 17 feet over it extends about 2.4 miles southeastward from Ram Head.

(146)   A boulder with 1 foot over it is 230 yards from shore about 0.3 mile northeastward of the northern point of the entrance to Coecles Harbor. Other boulders with little depth are between this boulder and Ram Head.

(147)   The entrance to **Coecles Harbor** is at the south end of Ram Head; the channel is marked by private seasonal buoys and a private seasonal light. In June 1981, the reported controlling depth in the privately maintained entrance channel was 7 feet. The **speed limit** is 5 mph. A marina and boatyard are in the harbor. A mobile hoist at the boatyard can haul out craft up to 35 tons; gasoline, water, ice, diesel fuel, marine supplies, sewage pumpout, berths, guest moorings, storage facilities, and complete engine and hull repairs are available. In June 1981, a reported depth of 5½ feet could be carried to the marina and boatyard.

(148) A special anchorage is in Coecles Harbor. (See 110.1 and 110.60(y), chapter 2, for limits and regulations.)

(149) COLREGS Demarcation Lines.–The lines established for Coecles Harbor are described in 80.155, chapter 2.

(150) Extensive flats make off from Ram Head and the shore between it and Hay Beach Point, the northernmost point of Shelter Island, which is a low flat with a clump of scrub at its end and backed by wooded highland. Long Beach Point is a low spit eastward of Hay Beach Point. A bar with little depth extends southwesterly from Long Beach Point to the ruins of a former lighthouse of which only the 10-foot concrete foundation remains. A private light marks the ruins.

(151) Shoals with depths of 10 to 12 feet extend 0.5 mile eastward from Long Beach Point. The south and west sides of this shoal have depths of 12 to 15 feet, and rise abruptly from the channel. The limits of the shoal south of the point are marked by buoys. The bar has extended southward enough to be a real danger to small craft.

(152) COLREGS Demarcation Lines.–The lines established for the Long Island bays are described in 80.155, chapter 2.

(153) Orient Harbor, about 4 miles northwestward of Ram Head, is an excellent anchorage; the depths range from over 20 feet in its southern part to 16 feet at its northern end. Orient is a village at the northeast end of Orient Harbor. At the end of the main wharf the depth is 8½ feet. The eastern part of Orient Harbor has depths of 7 to 9 feet. Fish traps are on the shoals.

(154) About 0.4 mile northeastward of Cleaves Point, at the southwest end of Orient Harbor, the shore has been cut through to a small pond which is used as a private basin for small craft. The entrance, between two jetties, has a depth of about 3 feet over the bar, with about 6 feet in the basin. Permission is required before anchoring in the basin. Rocks are 0.2 mile south of the entrance.

(155) Hallock Bay makes eastward from Orient Harbor on the north side of Long Beach Point. A channel, marked by uncharted private daybeacons, leads into the bay. The bay is shallow and dangers and shoaling have been reported. Local knowledge is advised prior to entering.

(156) Gull Pond is 0.3 mile westward of Cleaves Point at the southwest end of Orient Harbor. In July 1981, a reported depth of 4 feet could be carried through the entrance, with depths of 10 to 15 feet reported in the pond. A State launching ramp is available in the pond.

(157) Greenport is an important town and the terminus of a branch of the Long Island Railroad. The white church spires, near the northern end of town, and a tank and TV radio tower in the center of town are prominent.

(158) Greenport Harbor is formed on the northeast by a 5-foot-high breakwater, which extends 0.2 mile southeastward from Youngs Point, nearly to the 18-foot curve, and is marked at its outer end by a light. The depths at the wharves range from 7 to 21 feet. The railroad wharf on the south side of the waterfront can accommodate a vessel up to 100 feet.

(159) Stirling Basin, on the northeast side of Greenport, is a part of Greenport Harbor. In July 1981, the reported controlling depth was 8 feet in the entrance channel with 10 to 12 feet in the mooring areas. The entrance channel is marked by private seasonal buoys. Two smaller privately dredged channels with depths of about 9 feet reported are in the northeastern part of the basin. The harbormaster for Greenport Harbor controls mooring and berthing in the basin. The speed limit is 5 mph.

(160) Small-craft facilities at Greenport can provide berths, electricity, gasoline, diesel fuel, water, ice, storage, marine supplies, and hull and engine repairs. The largest marine railway, at a shipbuilding company at the southeast end of the waterfront, can handle craft up to 400 tons and 15 feet in draft and has a 15-ton crane. Mobile hoists to 50 tons are available. A well-equipped machine shop is also in the town.

(161) A ferry operates between Greenport and Shelter Island. During the summer, bus service is available from Greenport to Orient Point where there is ferry service to New London.

(162) Dering Harbor, southward of Greenport and at the northwest end of Shelter Island, is a favorite anchorage for yachts and motorboats. The entrance to the harbor, marked by private buoys, is partially constricted by a disposal area in about midentrance and shoal area with a reported depth of 4 feet in June 1981 that extends from the southwestern entrance point to near the disposal area; caution is advised. In April 1989, it was reported that about 10 feet could be carried into the harbor with local knowledge. Depths of 10 to 14 feet are available in the central part of the harbor, with much lesser depths around the edges. Moorings and float landings for small craft are in the bight at the southwest end of the harbor. Vessels too large to enter can anchor outside the harbor in depths of 14 to 30 feet. The speed limit is 5 mph. Small-craft facilities, on the west side of the harbor, can provide berths, electricity, gasoline, diesel fuel, water, ice, marine supplies, sewage pumpout, and hull and outboard engine repairs. A launching ramp is also available. Shelter Island Heights is on the southwestern side of Dering Harbor.

(163) Fanning Point is on the north shore at the southwest end of Greenport. A shoal extends 300 yards off the point and is marked by a buoy. Four dolphins, part of a former oil facility, are northward of the point. Currents of 2 knots, running fair with the channel, have been reported in the vicinity of Fanning Point.

(164) Conkling Point, on the north shore 1 mile southwestward of Fanning Point, is low and sandy at the end and has deep water as close as 150 yards. A marina on the southwest side of the point had a reported depth of 5½ feet in the approach in July 1981. Berths, electricity, gasoline, marine supplies, storage, a launching ramp, and a 30-ton mobile hoist are available. Hull and engine repairs can be made.

(165) Mill Creek is the entrance to Hashamomuck Pond, about 1.1 miles westward of Conkling Point. In July 1981, the privately dredged entrance channel into the creek had a controlling depth of 4 feet, thence 3½ feet was reported in the channel along the northwest shore of Mill Creek. The entrance channel is marked by private seasonal buoys. About 400 yards eastward of the creek is a small bight entered through a channel with a depth of about 4 feet and marked by private seasonal lights and buoys.

(166) Jennings Point, the western end of Shelter Island, is high and wooded. Rocks are off the point close-to, and it should be given a berth of over 150 yards. A lighted buoy is off the point. A gazebo on the point is prominent.

(167) The town of Southold is at the head of Southold Bay, which is the bight at the western end of Shelter Island Sound westward of Jennings Point. For about a mile northeastward of the entrance jetty, shoals with 12 feet or less extend nearly 0.4 mile from shore and are generally steep-to. The southwest part of the bay is shoal for about 0.3 mile from shore. Anchorage can be selected east-southeast of the jetty at a distance of from 0.2 to 0.4 mile, in 12 to 18 feet.

(168) A small jettied basin is about 0.5 mile northeast of Southold entrance. The overhead power cable crossing the entrance has a clearance of 31 feet. There are no public landings in the basin.

(169) In April 1989, the reported controlling depth was about 3 feet in the privately maintained channels in **Town Creek**, **Jockey Creek**, and **Goose Creek**. The common entrance to Town Creek and Jockey Creek is marked by private seasonal buoys. The highway bridge at the mouth of Goose Creek has a clearance of 9 feet and the bridge that crosses Jockey Creek has a 45-foot fixed span with a vertical clearance of 6½ feet.

(170) On the shore south of Southold entrance jetty is a prominent white tower.

(171) There are several small-craft facilities on the creeks and along the west shore of Southold Bay from Paradise Point to Conkling Point. Berths, electricity, gasoline, water, ice, marine supplies, launching ramps, storage, lifts, and cranes are available. Provisions can be obtained at Southold.

(172) **Paradise Point**, on the west side of Shelter Island Sound, is low and wooded, and from the point a sloping sandspit extends about 0.3 mile eastward and is marked by a lighted buoy. Southward of Paradise Point, shoals with depths of 10 to 15 feet extend from the west shore to midsound; the southeast point of the shoals is marked by a buoy.

(173) The channel south of Shelter Island has numerous shoals, but is easily followed by vessels of 13 feet or less draft when the buoys can be seen. The channel is used by vessels going to Sag Harbor. Vessels operating between Greenport and Sag Harbor prefer the inside route around the western end of Shelter Island. The **tidal current** in the channel between Shelter Island and North Haven Peninsula has a velocity of about 2.4 knots. The approach from Gardiners Bay is across a shoal or bar which extends in a southeasterly direction from Ram Head to the south shore, the depths on which vary from 7 to 11 feet about 1.6 miles from Ram Head, and thence 13 to 17 feet to the buoys which mark the entrance.

(174) **Dangerous Rock**, awash at low water in surrounding depths of about 12 feet, is 0.2 mile south of the channel.

(175) A shoal extends 0.3 to 0.4 mile north of the shore of **Cedar Point** which is marked by a light. The shoal has boulders, and its edge is marked by buoys.

(176) Shoals with boulders and little water over them in places extend nearly 0.5 mile southeastward from **Nicoll Point**. Buoys mark the limit of the channel in this area.

(177) **Northwest Harbor**, between Cedar Island Light and **Barcelona Point**, is strewn with boulders covered by 4 to 6 feet.

(178) **Sand Spit**, an extensive shoal partly bare at half-tide, is between **Mashomack Point**, the southeastern extremity of Shelter Island, and Sag Harbor. The spit is marked by buoys and a light.

(179) A group of rocks locally known as **Gull Island**, showing bare at half-tide, is nearly 0.4 mile northeastward of the breakwater at Sag Harbor.

(180) **Sag Harbor**, about 2.5 miles southwestward of the light on Cedar Point, is protected on the northeast by a breakwater marked at the outer end by a light. A spherical tank, a radio tower, and several flagpoles are prominent landmarks.

(181) In entering Sag Harbor, do not round the breakwater too closely, as a depth of about 6 feet is found near its end. The deepest water is near the buoy. Anchor eastward or northeastward of the end of the former ferry wharf, locally known as Long Wharf. A 5 mph **speed limit** is enforced.

(182) In July 1974, the dredged channel into Sag Harbor had a controlling depth of 8 feet (10 feet at midchannel) through the entrance to the turning basin, 9 feet in the turning basin, 5 feet in the southerly anchorage area, and 7 feet in the main anchorage area. The channel to **Sag Harbor**

Cove is about 8 feet deep; this channel and the cove are marked by private seasonal lights and buoys. A 37-foot-wide fixed bridge at the entrance has a clearance of 20 feet. Berths, electricity, gasoline, diesel fuel, storage, marine supplies, water, ice, launching ramps, and complete engine, hull, rigging, and sail repairs are available at Sag Harbor; a 30-ton mobile hoist, near the inner end of the breakwater, can haul out craft up to about 60 feet.

(183) **Smith Cove**, a small bight on the south side of Shelter Island, is a good anchorage for small craft in northerly weather. Depths range from 11 to 30 feet. A marina on the west side of the cove can provide moorings, limited berths, gasoline, electricity, water, and some marine supplies. In June 1981, a depth of 6 feet was reported alongside the pier at the marina. A ferry operates between **South Ferry** on the southwest side of the cove to **North Haven Peninsula**.

(184) **West Neck Harbor** and **West Neck Bay** are shallow bodies of water on the southwest side of Shelter Island. In June 1989, it was reported that a depth of 2 feet could be carried over the bar and into the harbor from Shelter Island Sound. The entrance is close eastward of the seaward end of a peninsula, marked by a private lighted buoy, that separates the harbor from the sound, and the channel follows along the north side of this peninsula. The channel is marked by private buoys. The harbor has numerous private landings. A boatyard with a marine railway can handle craft up to 40 feet for hull and engine repairs. Berths, gasoline, water, ice, a launching ramp, and some marine supplies are available.

(185) A special anchorage is in West Neck Harbor. (See 110.1 and 110.60 y-1, chapter 2, for limits and regulations.)

(186) **Noyack (Noyac) Bay** is between North Haven Peninsula and Jessup Neck and southward of the western end of Shelter Island. No dangers will be encountered if the shores are given a berth of 0.4 mile.

(187) **Mill Creek**, in the southern part of Noyack Bay, is entered through a privately dredged channel that leads to a basin. The channel is marked by private seasonal lights and buoys. In June 1981, the reported controlling depths were 8 feet in the channel and 6 feet in the basin. A clubhouse on the west side of the entrance is prominent. Small-craft facilities in the creek can provide berths, electricity, gasoline, water, ice, storage, a launching ramp, marine supplies, and hull and engine repairs; a 25-ton mobile hoist is available.

(188) **Jessup Neck** is a long narrow strip, partly high and wooded, separating Noyack Bay from Little Peconic Bay. The north end of the neck is a sandspit from which a shoal with 4 to 12 feet over it extends nearly 0.4 mile north-northwestward. A lighted buoy marks the outer end of the shoal area.

(189) A shoal with depths of 5 to 7 feet extends 1.5 miles southwestward from **Great Hog Neck**, on the northwest side at the entrance to Little Peconic Bay; this shoal is marked by a buoy.

(190) Heavy tide rips occur southeast of Great Hog Neck during the flood with a southwesterly wind. At such times, small craft can avoid the worst of them by favoring the shore on the northwest side of the passage.

(191) **Richmond Creek** and **Corey Creek** are at the head of **Hog Neck Bay**. A depth of about 7 feet can be taken in the privately dredged channel leading to a basin in Richmond Creek; the channel is marked by private seasonal buoys. In 1964, the dredged channel leading into and connecting with small boat channels in Corey Creek had a controlling depth of 7 feet. Controlling depths in the small-boat channels inside Corey Creek were 5½ to 6 feet. The entrance channel is marked by private buoys.

(192) **Little Peconic Bay** is about 5 miles long. The southerly shore of the bay is clear if given a berth of 0.4 mile, but shoals extend 0.6 mile from the south end of the bay.

(193) An aquaculture site, marked by private seasonal buoys, is at the south end of Little Peconic Bay about 1 mile north-northwest of the entrance to North Sea Harbor.

(194) A prominent sandy bluff, known locally as **Holmes Hill**, is just west of the entrance to **North Sea Harbor.** In June 1981, the reported controlling depth through the dredged channel into the harbor was 4 feet. The channel is marked by private seasonal buoys and by a private seasonal light at the entrance. This is an excellent harbor of refuge for small craft with drafts not exceeding 3½ feet. The bottom is soft with good holding ground.

(195) A marina in the harbor has gasoline, ice, water, some marine supplies, and a lift that can handle craft to 10 tons; hull and engine repairs can be made.

(196) **Wooley Pond,** 1 mile northeastward of North Sea Harbor, is entered through a dredged channel which, in June 1981, had a reported controlling depth of 6 feet. The channel is marked by private seasonal buoys and by a private seasonal light on the north side of the entrance.

(197) A marina in the pond can provide berths, eletricity, gasoline, water, ice, storage, marine supplies, and hull and engine repairs; a 45-foot marine railway and a 12-ton forklift are available. In June 1981, depths of 5 to 6 feet were reported available at the marina.

(198) **Nassau Point,** the long neck on the northwest side of Little Peconic Bay, has high bluffs on the eastern side. A shoal with little depth over it extends 0.5 mile southward from Nassau Point and is marked by a lighted buoy.

(199) **Cutchogue Harbor,** between Nassau Point and New Suffolk, is used by local boats drawing 6 to 10 feet. On the east shore of the harbor, northwestward of Nassau Point, three channels leading into the ponds have been dredged by private interests. At the middle of the three channels, 0.9 mile northwest of the extremity of Nassau Point, are several private wharves. The channel leads between two jetties, and a depth of about 3 feet can be carried into the pond and 1 foot to some of the wharves.

(200) **Haywater Cove, Broadwater Cove, Mud Creek,** and **East Creek,** used by local interests and sharing a common entrance, are at the head of Cutchogue Harbor. The entrance channel and the channels through these waterways have been privately dredged. The controlling depths are: 6 feet reported in the entrance channel in July 1981, thence 7 feet in Haywater Cove, Broadwater Cove, and Mud Creek, and 6 feet in East Creek in 1966. Shoaling is reported to occur in these areas; caution is advised.

(201) A depth of 8 feet can be taken within 100 feet of the wharves at **New Suffolk** by passing eastward and about 200 yards northward of the buoy westward of Nassau Point and steering westward for the wharves. A small basin, with a depth of about 8 feet reported in 1981, is northward of the wharf. In July 1981, shoaling to 2 feet was reported in the southern part of Cutchogue Harbor, about 0.4 mile east of New Suffolk.

(202) A larger basin at the north end of New Suffolk, locally known as **School House Creek,** extends to the highway. The entrance channel is protected by a short rock jetty, covered at high water, on the south. The depth to the boatyard at the head of the basin was reported to be about 4 feet in June 1981. Berths, gasoline, storage, marine supplies, hull and engine repairs, and a 30-ton moblie hoist are available at the boatyard.

(203) **Wickham Creek,** locally known as Boatmens Harbor, 0.7 mile north of New Suffolk, is entered through a privately dredged entrance channel with a reported controlling depth

of 6 feet in July 1981. The channel is marked by private seasonal buoys and bush stakes. Gasoline, water, ice, storage, a launching ramp, and some marine supplies are available in the basin. A flatbed trailer can haul out craft to 32 feet.

(204) In southeast gales, local craft of less than 6-foot draft seek shelter in the small cove, locally known as **Horseshoe Cove,** in the northeast part of Cutchogue Harbor.

(205) The through channel in **North Race,** northward of **Robins Island,** is marked and used only by light-draft boats. **South Race,** the channel southward of Robins Island, has a controlling depth of about 13 feet and is marked by buoys.

(206) An aquaculture site, marked by private buoys, is 0.6 mile southwest of the south end of Robins Island.

(207) Tide rips occur between the mainland and the south end of Robins Island when the tidal current sets against the wind.

(208) **Great Peconic Bay,** about 5 miles in diameter, is used mostly by local motorboats from Shinnecock Canal and by yachts. The bay is generally clear, but extensive shoals make off from the shores, except on its south side. Shinnecock Canal, the entrance from the south, is described in chapter 10.

(209) **Rodgers Rock,** about 1.3 miles west-southwestward of **Cow Neck** and about 1.2 miles south-southwest of Robins Island, has a depth of 6 feet over it and is marked on the northeast side by a buoy. **Robins Island Rock,** 0.8 mile westward of the south end of Robins Island, is awash at low water. It is marked by a buoy. Caution is recommended in this vicinity.

(210) **Sebonac Creek,** on the southeast side of Great Peconic Bay, is used extensively by yachts, and serves as a yacht harbor for the town of Southampton. A privately dredged channel, marked by private seasonal lights and buoys, leads into the creek and had a reported controlling depth of 8 feet in June 1981. The landings are at **West Neck,** a small settlement northeastward of **Ram Island in Bullhead Bay.** An obstruction buoy is locally maintained during the summer to mark a rock, covered 1½ feet, about 100 feet westward of the town landing. In June 1981, a reported depth of 5 feet could be carried to the town landing. A 5 mph **speed limit** is enforced.

(211) **Cold Spring Pond,** about 1.6 miles southwestward of Sebonac Creek and 1.1 miles eastward of Shinnecock Canal entrance, is entered through a privately dredged channel which had a reported depth of 2 feet in June 1981. The entrance channel to the pond is marked by a private seasonal light and buoy. An overhead power cable at the entrance to the pond has a clearance of 34 feet.

(212) **James Creek,** on the north shore of Great Peconic Bay opposite the entrance to Shinnecock Canal, is entered through a privately dredged channel that had a reported controlling depth of 6 feet in 1981. The entrance is marked by private seasonal buoys. Small-craft facilities on the creek can provide berths, gasoline, storage, launching ramps, and hull and engine repairs. A flatbed trailer can haul out craft to 30 feet.

(213) **South Jamesport** is a village on **Miamogue Point,** 3.4 miles southwestward of James Creek. Local knowledge is necessary to avoid the shoals in this area, and strangers should take soundings frequently to keep in the best water. A small-craft facility at South Jamesport can provide berths, electricity, gasoline, water, ice, launching ramps, storage, marine supplies, and hull and engine repairs; a 25-ton mobile hoist is available. In June 1981, a reported depth of about 8 feet could be taken to the facility. The town has railroad passenger and bus service.

(214) **Peconic River** empties into the western end of Flanders Bay, about 1.5 miles westward of South Jamesport. The

river is entered through a dredged channel marked by private seasonal lights that leads from Flanders Bay to the head of navigation at **Riverhead**, about 2.4 miles above the channel entrance. The dredged channel is approached from deep water in Great Peconic Bay through a marked channel. In August-September 1981, the dredged channel had a centerline controlling depth of 4½ feet. A fixed highway bridge with a clearance of 25 feet crosses the river about 0.9 mile above the mouth.

(215) **Flanders Bay** is the scene of considerable small boat activity. A yacht club is at Riverhead; limited berths, electricity, and water are available.

(216) **Meetinghouse Creek, Terrys Creek,** and **Reeves Creek,** which empty into the northwestern part of Flanders Bay, are entered through privately dredged channels. In June 1981, the channels had reported controlling depths of 5 feet. The entrance channel leading to, and connecting with, Terrys Creek and Meetinghouse Creek is marked by private seasonal buoys and a private seasonal light. A marina is on Meetinghouse Creek. Berths, electricity, gasoline, water, ice, a 5-ton forklift, 30-ton mobile hoist, launching ramp, storage facilities, and hull and engine repairs are available. In June 1981, a reported depth of 7 feet was available at the marina.

(217) **Reeves Bay,** on the southwest side of Flanders Bay, is entered through a privately dredged channel that leads to the town of **Flanders** on the south side of the bay. In June 1981, the channel had a reported controlling depth of 4 feet. Other dredged channels lead from the entrance channel into several arms of the bay. A boatyard at Flanders has gasoline, storage facilities, marine supplies, and a 10-ton marine railway; hull and engine repairs can be made.

(218) **Chart 13214.–Fishers Island Sound** extends between the mainland of Connecticut and Fishers Island, and forms one of the entrances into Long Island Sound that is used to some extent by light tows and other vessels up to 14-foot draft. The sound has numerous shoals and lobster trap buoys, and the entire area is exceedingly treacherous, characterized by boulder patches that rise abruptly from deep water. Vessels should follow the deeper channels between the shoals and proceed with caution if obliged to cross shoal areas. In general, all shoal spots or abrupt changes of depth are indications of boulders and should be avoided as anchorages.

(219) **Tides and currents.**–In Watch Hill Passage the tidal currents are strong and necessitate caution in navigating. Buoys may be towed under. The flood current sets nearly in the direction of the channel, but has a tendency to northward and the ebb a tendency to southward. The northerly and southerly set is more marked between Napatree Point and Latimer Reef Light.

(220) In Sugar Reef and Catumb Passages the tidal currents set obliquely across the axis of the channel. The flood sets northwestward and the ebb southeastward. The tidal currents in Sugar Reef Passage are about the same velocity as in Watch Hill Passage, but are stronger in Catumb Passage.

(221) In Lords Passage the tidal currents set diagonally across the channel and have a velocity of nearly 2 knots, the ebb being greater than the flood.

(222) In the main channel of Fishers Island Sound, the flood sets westward and the ebb eastward. In the main channel between Napatree Point and Wicopesset Island, the velocity of flood is 1.7 knots and ebb 2.2 knots. The flood sets 284° and the ebb 113°.

(223) In the channel south of Ram Island Reef, the velocities of flood and ebb are 1.3 and 1.6 knots, respectively. The flood sets 255° and the ebb 088°. The direction and velocity of the current are affected by strong winds that may change the duration of flood or ebb.

(224) The strong tidal currents prevent the formation of heavy local **ice,** except in shoal tributaries. The only ice to give trouble is that set in from Long Island Sound by wind and current. The ice formations in Little Narragansett Bay are sufficiently heavy to be destructive to structures exposed to them.

(225) On the south side of Fishers Island Sound, off the north side of **East Point** on Fishers Island, are **Seal Rocks,** partly bare at low water and marked by a buoy. A rocky patch covered 11 feet and marked by a buoy is about 500 yards northeastward of Seal Rocks. **Youngs Rock,** about 0.4 mile westward of Seal Rocks, has about 1 foot over it and is marked by a buoy. A rocky patch extends about 400 yards to the east-northeastward.

(226) **East Harbor** and **Chocomount Cove,** in the north shore of Fishers Island, are sometimes used as anchorages by small craft. There is considerable foul ground in East Harbor and in the approach to Chocomount Cove. The harbor and cove are exposed to northerly winds. A former Coast Guard Station with a boathouse and dock is prominent near the south side of East Harbor. Several small private piers with about 6 feet at their ends are in East Harbor.

(227) The north shore of Fishers Island from East Harbor around into West Harbor has several private landings.

(228) **East Clump** is a cluster of rocks partly bare at high water and marked by a buoy about 0.8 mile north of Fishers Island. From East Clump for some 2.8 miles westward to North Dumpling, there are rocky islets and dangers which must be avoided. These are 0.5 to 0.8 mile off the Fishers Island shore, and most are buoyed. **North Dumpling,** an islet marked by a light and fog signal, is surrounded by rocks awash and foul ground. **Seaflower Reef,** marked by a light, is near the middle of the western entrance of Fishers Island Sound and 0.8 mile northwestward of North Dumpling Light.

(229) **West Harbor,** on the north side of Fishers Island southeastward of North Dumpling Light, affords shelter from southerly winds. In April 1986, the dredged channel leading into the harbor along the west shore had a controlling depth of 12 feet. Foul ground extends across the entrance of West Harbor to near the eastern edge of the dredged channel; the northern limits of the foul ground are buoyed.

(230) A yacht club wharf and another small-craft facility are on the southwest side of the harbor. Gasoline, diesel fuel, water, ice, and hull and engine repairs are available. A marine railway can handle craft up to 40 feet. The head of the harbor is used by boats drawing less than 5 feet which enter by the narrow unmarked channel southward of **Goose Island.**

(231) **Hay Harbor,** at the west end of Fishers Island, is used by small craft.

(232) **Silver Eel Cove (Silver Eel Pond)** is on the west side of Fishers Island, 0.6 mile northeastward of Race Point. The entrance, about 75 feet wide and jettied, is marked by a private light and has a depth of about 13 feet, with similar depths inside. Submerged fender pilings are reported on both sides of the entrance. Dolphins are on the northeast side of the cove, and the channel is clear between them and the wharves on the southwest side. Vessels must go to the wharves as there is no room for anchorage. There is very little dockage available. The entrance is difficult with northwesterly or westerly winds. A lighted bell buoy is about 450 yards off the entrance. A ferry which operates between Fishers Island and New London lands here. During the summer,

a Coast Guard unit is stationed inside the entrance to the cove.

(233)   On the north side of Fishers Island Sound are: Little Narragansett Bay, and Pawcatuck River leading to the towns of Westerly and Pawcatuck; Stonington Harbor and the town of Stonington; and Mystic Harbor leading to the towns of Noank and Mystic.

(234)   **Napatree Beach**, 1.3 miles long between Watch Hill Point and **Napatree Point**, is bare. **Sandy Point**, about 1.4 miles north-northwestward of Napatree Point, is at the northwestern end of a long and narrow sand island in Little Narragansett Bay. An extensive sandspit makes off from the northeasterly and southwesterly sides of the island; give these areas a good berth. The island is subject to continual change; caution is advised.

(235)   **Napatree Point Ledge**, a boulder reef with little depth, extends nearly 0.4 mile southward of the point. It is marked by a lighted bell buoy. A sunken wreck is about 0.3 mile eastward of the ledge in about 41°18′N., 71°53′W.

(236)   The west side of Napatree Point should not be approached closer than 175 yards to avoid a stone jetty which is covered at high water. Between Napatree Point and the Stonington outer breakwater is an extensive flat on which the depths are 3 to 10 feet, rocky bottom. **Middle Ground**, the western part of the flat, is marked by the outer breakwater, which has a light at its western end. A fog signal is at the light.

(237)   A depth of 17 feet can be taken to an anchorage inside this breakwater, giving the light on the breakwater a berth of more than 250 yards. In anchoring, give the inside of the breakwater a berth of over 300 yards to avoid shoals and fishweirs. This anchorage provides good shelter except in southwesterly and westerly winds, although it is seldom used.

(238)   **Little Narragansett Bay**, at the eastern end of Fishers Island Sound, is entered at its extreme western end southward of Stonington Point. The channel, with dredged sections, extends generally southeasterly across the bay into Pawcatuck River to Westerly. In December 1989, the controlling depth was 4½ feet from the entrance to Little Narragansett Bay to the entrance to Pawcatuck River, except for shoaling to bare in the middle of the dredged channel section near the turn opposite Little Narragansett Bay Entrance Lighted Buoy 3. Deep water is available, with local knowledge, north of the channel opposite the shoal. In March-April 1983, the controlling depth was 8 feet (10 feet at midchannel) to Certain Draw Point (41°20′33″N., 71°49′52″W.), thence 4 feet (7 feet at midchannel) for about 1.7 miles to a point in about 41°22.1′N., 71°50.1′W., thence 3½ feet at midchannel to Westerly. The channel is well marked.

(239)   Caution should be exercised in entering Little Narragansett Bay. Shoal water extends for about 200 yards off **Stonington Point**, and the shoal area north of **Sandy Point** is subject to continual change. Strangers are advised to obtain local information before entering because of rocks and shoal water near the edges of the channel.

(240)   In the dredged channel northward of Sandy Point, the currents have a velocity of 1.3 knots. The flood sets eastward and the ebb westward. (See the Tidal Current Tables for predictions and Tidal Current Charts, Block Island Sound and Eastern Long Island Sound, for hourly velocities and directions.)

(241)   **Watch Hill Cove**, in the southeastern part of Little Narragansett Bay, is used by small craft. In September-October 1978, the buoyed dredged channel leading to the cove had a controlling depth of 7½ feet (9 feet at midchannel). Depths of 5½ to 10 feet are inside the cove and at the wharves. A **special anchorage** is in the cove. (See **110.1** and **110.47**, chapter 2, for limits and regulations.)

(242)   A yacht club and town dock are in Watch Hill Cove; berths, guest moorings, electricity, diesel fuel, and water are available. In July 1981, a depth of 10 feet was reported at the face of the town dock.

(243)   **Pawcatuck River**, entered just south of **Pawcatuck Point**, extends about 4 miles to Westerly.

(244)   About 1 mile above the entrance to Pawcatuck River the **tidal current** has a velocity of 0.6 knot on flood, and 0.5 knot on the ebb. The river is generally closed by **ice** from January to March.

(245)   **Colonel Willie Cove**, 0.5 mile above Pawcatuck Point, has a boatyard with a marine railway that can handle craft up to 45 feet for hull and engine repairs. Berths, electricity, gasoline, water, ice, launching ramp, storage facilities, marine supplies, and a 20-ton crane are also available. In July 1981, a reported depth of 4 feet could be carried in the cove to the boatyard.

(246)   A **special anchorage** is in **Thompson Cove**, 2 miles above Pawcatuck Point. (See **110.1** and **110.48**, chapter 2, for limits and regulations.) A yacht club pier is in the cove. Private seasonal buoys mark the approach to the pier.

(247)   **Westerly**, 4 miles above Pawcatuck Point, is an important manufacturing town.

(248)   There are numerous small-craft facilities along both sides of the Pawcatuck River and at the head at Westerly and Pawcatuck, just across the river. The largest marine railway in the area is at Avondale and it can handle craft to 55 feet. Berths, electricity, gasoline, diesel fuel, water, ice, storage facilities, launching ramps, lifts, and marine supplies are available. Depths of 7 to 9 feet are reported at the town dock at Pawcatuck.

(249)   **Wequetequock Cove** is a shallow cove at the northern end of Little Narragansett Bay. A narrow unmarked channel leads eastward of **Elihu Island** into the cove. A depth of about 4 feet can be taken as far as **Goat Island**, about a mile above Sandy Point. A fixed railroad bridge with a clearance of 6 feet crosses the cove about 0.2 mile above Goat Island. A small-craft facility is on the west side of the cove near the head. Berths, gasoline, storage facilities, launching ramp, 4-ton forklift, marine supplies, and hull and engine repairs are available. In July 1981, a reported depth of 2 feet could be carried to the facility.

(250)   **Stonington Harbor**, 3 miles northwestward of Watch Hill Point, is protected by breakwaters on each side. Each of the breakwaters is marked at its seaward end by a light. The controlling depth to the inner harbor is about 11 feet. Anchorage can be selected inside the west breakwater in depths of 15 to 18 feet, taking care to keep the south end of Wamphassuc Point bearing northward of 270°. Vessels drawing up to 8 feet can find anchorage in the inner harbor. A rock that bares at low water is about 50 yards southward of the fishing wharf and is marked by a private buoy. **Special anchorages** are in Stonington Harbor. (See **110.1** and **110.50**, chapter 2, for limits and regulations.)

(251)   Stonington Harbor is approached from southeastward and westward. Vessels with local knowledge sometimes cross Noyes Shoal from southwestward. The southeastern approach is best, with fewer dangers, and the navigational aids serve as excellent guides to avoid them. In daytime with clear weather, no difficulty should be experienced in entering any of the approaches.

(252)   From southeastward, the course from south of Napatree Point Ledge should be west-northwestward until off the buoy at the southwest end of Middle Ground, from which a northerly course can be shaped past the breakwater lights and into the harbor.

(253)   From southwestward, a northeasterly course can be shaped from the lighted bell buoy south of Ram Island Reef to south of White Rock, and thence eastward past the north side of Noyes Rock to the harbor.

(254)   The inner breakwater, about 400 yards northward of Stonington Point on the east side of the entrance, extends westward about 250 yards and is marked by a light.

(255)   **Stonington** is on the east side of the harbor. Traffic is mostly fishing and recreational craft. The wharves have depths of 7 to 12 feet alongside. Following southerly weather, a surge is felt by vessels tied to the southern side of the seaward pier.

(256)   A boatyard is in the northeast part of the harbor. Berths, electricity, gasoline, diesel fuel, water, ice, storage, 40-ton lift, marine supplies, and hull, engine, and electronic repairs are available. In July 1981, a reported depth of 7 feet could be carried to the yard. A **harbormaster** is at Stonington.

(257)   A railroad causeway, with two fixed spans each having a clearance of 4 feet, crosses Stonington Harbor 0.4 mile above Stonington. Overhead power cables at the openings have clearances of 41 feet.

(258)   **Noyes Rock**, 0.4 mile southward of **Wamphassuc Point**, has a least depth of 8 feet. **Noyes Shoal**, with 8 to 17 feet over it, is nearly 1.5 miles long in a west-northwesterly direction; it is marked by a bell buoy near its eastern end.

(259)   **Latimer Reef**, about 0.6 mile south of Noyes Shoal, is a very broken and rocky area 0.4 mile long. It is marked by a light at its west end and a buoy at its east end. The eastern end of the reef has a least found depth of 6 feet.

(260)   **Latimer Reef Light** (41°18.3′N., 71°56.0′W.), 55 feet above the water, is shown from a white conical tower, brown midway of its height, on a brown cylindrical foundation. A fog signal is at the light.

(261)   A detached 11-foot spot, marked by a buoy, is about 0.4 mile northeast of Latimer Reef Light.

(262)   **Eel Grass Ground**, about 0.8 mile northwestward of Latimer Reef Light, is a shoal with a least depth of 4 feet, marked by buoys. **White Rock**, about 0.8 mile northeastward of Eel Grass Ground, is bare and prominent. **Red Reef**, covered 1 foot, is 0.2 mile north of White Rock and marked by a buoy. **Ellis Reef**, 0.4 mile northwestward of Eel Grass Ground, is marked on its east side by a daybeacon.

(263)   **Mason Island**, 2.5 miles west of Stonington Harbor, is joined to the mainland by a fixed bridge with an 18-foot span and a clearance of 3 feet; the sound end of the island is strewn with boulders. A **special anchorage** is on the east side of Mason Island. (See 110.1 and 110.50a, chapter 2, for limits and regulations.) An anchorage for small craft is on the west side of the south end of Mason Island where depths range from 8 to 11 feet; caution and local knowledge are required to use this anchorage because of the boulders in the area. A dangerous rock is off the east side of **Mason Point**, the southern extremity of Mason Island, in 41°19′21.6″ N., 71°58′05.0″W.

(264)   **Enders Island**, 0.3 mile eastward of the southern end of Mason Island, is connected to it by a fixed bridge with a 15-foot span and a clearance of 6 feet.

(265)   **Ram Island Reef**, 1.8 miles westward of Latimer Reef Light, has two detached parts: the southerly section is covered 6½ feet and marked by a lighted bell buoy, and the northerly section, covered by 1 foot, is marked by a daybeacon. Passage between the reef and island is unsafe because of shoals.

(266)   **Ram Island**, about 0.4 mile southwest of Mason Island, is wooded and grass-fringed. A shoal, on which are two rocky islets, extends about 0.2 mile northeastward from

Ram Island. **Ram Island Shoal**, extending nearly 0.5 mile westward from Ram Island, has little water over it and many rocks bare at low water. **Whaleback Rock** and the islet 300 yards northwestward of it are bare.

(267)   The narrow but deep channel along the north side of Ram Island Shoal is the easterly entrance to Mystic Harbor. Between the shoal and Groton Long Point is an area of foul ground and several dangerous rocks, including **Whale Rock**, which bares at low water, at the northwesterly end of Ram Island Shoal. This rock is marked by a seasonal lighted buoy. Leading across the shoal is the buoyed channel, good for about 11 feet, which is used by vessels entering Mystic Harbor from westward.

(268)   A rock covered 12 feet is 400 yards eastward of Groton Long Point; about 0.5 mile southerly of that rock is **Intrepid Rock**, with 13 feet over it and marked by a buoy, which should be avoided. **Mouse Island**, marked by several dwellings, is 150 yards southwestward of Morgan Point.

(269)   In November 1983, a rock, covered about 2 feet, was reported 0.2 mile west of Mouse Island in about 41°18′52″N., 71°59′50″W.

(270)   **Morgan Point**, on the west side at the entrance of Mystic Harbor, is marked by an abandoned light tower. A privately maintained and marked channel leading to the piers in **West Cove** at Noank westward of the point had a least depth of 4 feet reported in July 1981.

(271)   **Groton Long Point**, on which is a summer settlement, is about 0.9 mile southwestward of Morgan Point. A reef extends nearly 300 yards southwestward from the point and is marked by a buoy. About 0.3 mile to the west a rock awash at low water is 175 yards off the southwest end of Groton Long Point. It is marked by a buoy.

(272)   **Mystic Harbor**, about 6 miles westward of Watch Hill Point, is the approach to the towns of Noank and Mystic. A channel with two dredged sections leads from Fishers Island Sound through Mystic Harbor to the Mystic Seaport Museum Wharf, 0.6 mile northward of the highway bridge at Mystic on the Mystic River. In August-October 1987, the midchannel controlling depths were 10 feet to the highway bridge, thence 8 1/2 feet to the head of the Federal project. The channel is marked by buoys and a light. In November 1984, shoaling and timber debris were reported in the channel in the vicinity of the railroad swing bridge below Mystic.

(273)   **Special anchorages** are in Mystic Harbor. (See 110.1, 110.50b, and 110.50d, chapter 2, for limits and regulations.)

(274)   **Routes.**—To enter from eastward, lay a west-northwesterly course from south of the lighted bell buoy marking Napatree Point Ledge for a little over 3 miles to about 400 yards south of the buoy marking the south end of **Cormorant Reef**. From here steer **261°** for the abandoned light tower on Morgan Point in range with the north end of the northern rocky islet off the north end of Ram Island until Mason Point is abeam. Then follow the buoyed channel.

(275)   From westward, proceed cautiously from about 100 yards or more southward of the buoy southward of Groton Long Point on an easterly course for about 0.5 mile to Mystic Harbor Channel Buoy 1, then steer a northerly course through the buoyed channel into Mystic Harbor, rounding Noank Light 5 at a distance of about 75 yards.

(276)   **Noank** is a town on the west side of the channel through Mystic Harbor. The mean range of the tide is about 2.3 feet. There are several small-craft facilities at Noank and in **West Cove**. Berths, electricity, gasoline, diesel fuel, water, ice, storage facilities, launching ramps, 30-ton mobile lift, and marine supplies are available; hull, engine, sail, and electronic repairs can be made. A **harbormaster** is at Noank.

(277)   **Mystic River** flows into Mystic Harbor from northward just below Mystic. The river is used by recreational

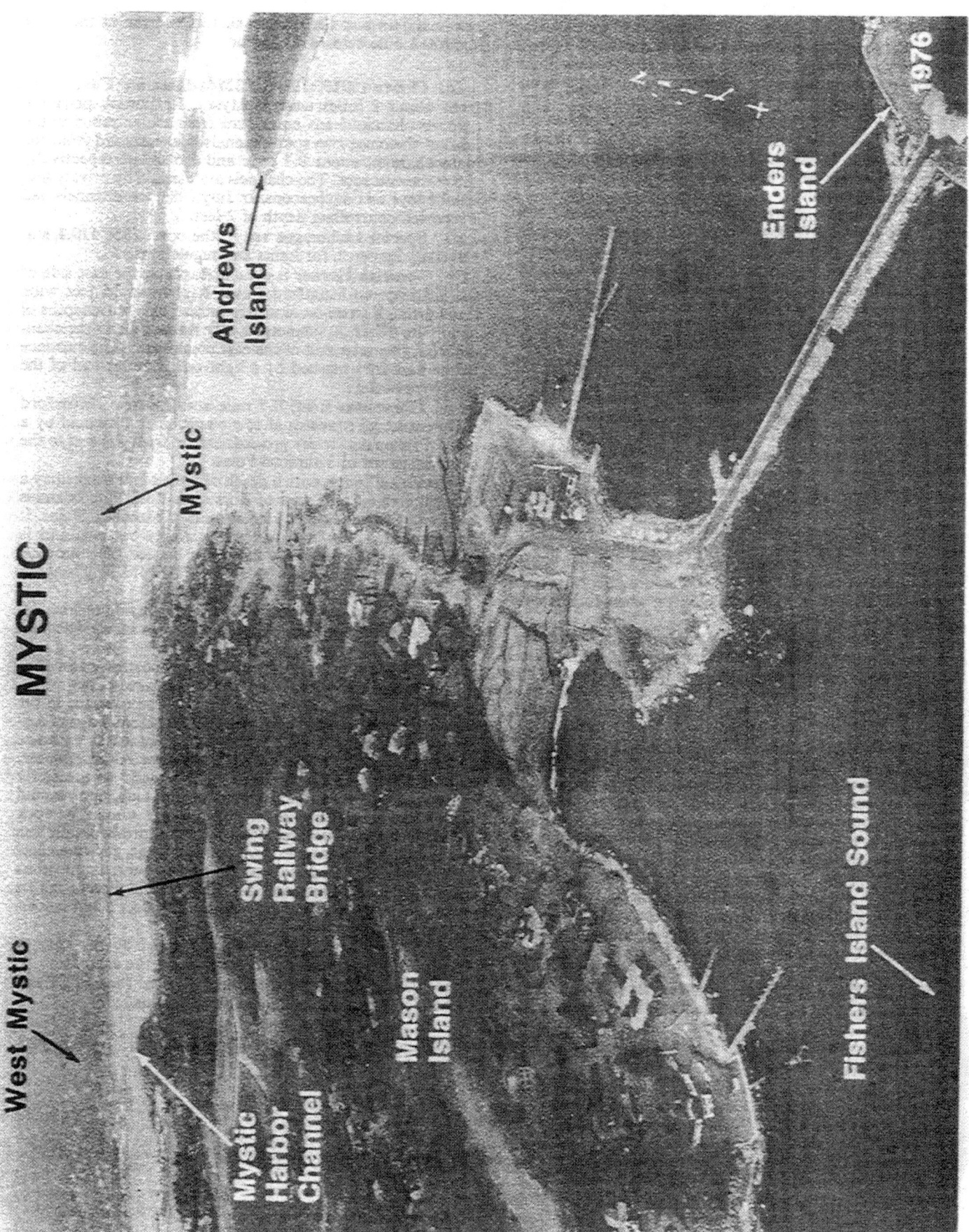

craft, the local fishing fleet, and by transient craft visiting Mystic Seaport. An **anchorage area** with depths of 3½ to 7 feet is in the lower part of the river between Willow Point and Murphy Point. Ice usually closes the river during January and February.

(278) **Willow Point,** 0.6 mile below Mystic, has several small-craft facilities that can provide berths, electricity, water, ice, some engine parts, and marine supplies. A 12-ton crane and 30-ton mobile hoist are available; hull and engine repairs can be made.

(279) A channel, privately marked by daybeacons, leads from the vicinity of Willow Point for 0.3 mile in an easterly direction, thence about 0.4 mile northeastward to a marina on the west side of the mouth of **Pequotsepos Brook,** just below the Amtrak railroad bridge. Berths, electricity, water, ice, storage, marine supplies, a 12-ton mobile hoist, and hull and engine repairs are available. In July 1981, a reported depth of 4 feet could be carried in the channel to the marina.

(280) Several small-craft facilities are on the northern end of Mason Island. Berths, electricity, water, ice, storage facilities, marine supplies, 25-ton mobile hoist, and hull and engine repairs are available. In July 1981, a reported depth of 4 feet could be carried to the facilities.

(281) The Amtrak railroad bridge over Mystic River below Mystic has a swing span with a clearance of 8 feet. The U.S. Route 1 highway bridge at Mystic has a bascule span with a clearance of 4 feet. (See **117.1 through 117.59 and 117.211,** chapter 2, for drawbridge regulations.) The bridgetenders monitor VHF-FM channel 13; call signs KJA–842 and KXR–912, respectively. In 1983, a railroad swing bridge with a design clearance of 8½ feet was under construction immediately south of the railroad bridge; when completed it will replace the existing bridge.

(282) **Mystic,** a town about 2 miles above Noank, has several small-craft facilities. Berths, electricity, gasoline, diesel fuel, water, ice, marine supplies, storage facilities, mobile hoists, and marine railways up to 110 feet are available; hull and engine repairs can be made. **A harbormaster** is at Mystic.

(283) The **Mystic Seaport Museum** is about 0.6 mile above the highway bridge at Mystic. The whaler CHARLES W. MORGAN, full-rigged training ship JOSEPH CONRAD, and Grand Banks fishing schooner L. A. DUNTON are permanently moored at the museum and open to the public. Along the waterfront of the museum property, a mid-19th Century coastal village has been recreated with shops and lofts of that period. Collections of maritime relics are on exhibit in several formal museum buildings.

(284) Above the Mystic Seaport Museum, the channel is very narrow and is marked by privately maintained seasonal daybeacons; boats of about 5-foot draft can be taken to the **Narrows,** and thence depths are 1 and 2 feet to **Old Mystic.** Twin fixed highway bridges crossing the Narrows have clearances of 25 feet. The stream follows the east bank to the next narrows and the west bank to a marina in the bight about 0.3 mile below Old Mystic.

(285) **Charts 13213, 13212, 13214.–Mumford Cove** is entered about 2 miles west of Mystic Harbor. A privately dredged channel leads northward from the entrance to the head of the cove; two spur channels lead eastward from the main channel, about 0.3 mile and 0.6 mile, respectively, above the entrance. The channels are marked by private seasonal buoys and daybeacons. In July 1981, the channels had a reported controlling depth of 2 feet.

(286) **Special anchorages** are in the cove. (See **110.1 and 110.50c,** chapter 2, for limits and regulations.)

(287) **Venetian Harbor** is a yacht basin on the east side of the entrance to Mumford Cove. A channel 75 feet wide leads through stone breakwaters into a basin with depths of about 3 to 7 feet. A submerged jetty extends along the channel from the outer end of the east breakwater. The entrance to the harbor is marked by a light on the outer end of the west breakwater.

(288) **Horseshoe Reef,** 0.5 mile southward of Mumford Cove entrance, is awash at low water, and is marked by a buoy. Broken and rocky grounds extend from the reef to the shore eastward of Mumford Point.

(289) **Vixen Ledge,** with a depth of 10 feet and marked by a buoy, is about 1 mile west of Horseshoe Reef. **Pine Island** is bluff and grassy, about 1.3 miles west of Mumford Point. It is surrounded by shoal water and rocky bottom, and is marked off the southwest side by a lighted bell buoy. A rock, covered 7 feet, in 41°18′35″ N., 72°03′17″W., is about 0.3 mile northwestward of Vixen Ledge.

(290) A **special anchorage** is on the north side of Pine Island. (See **110.1** and **110.51,** chapter 2, for limits and regulations.)

(291) The cove indenting the mainland northward of Pine Island and eastward of **Avery Point,** is entered between Avery Point and westward of Pine Island. The entrance to the cove is marked by two buoys just inside and eastward of Avery Point. Depths shoal from about 10 feet in the entrance to about 1 foot at the head of the cove. A breakwater, marked at its end by a private light, extends southeasterly from the east end of Avery Point. A yacht club, marina, and State launching ramp are in the cove. An unmarked rock awash is about 500 yards 060° from the former lighthouse tower at Avery Point. Berths, guest moorings, gasoline, electricity, water, ice, marine supplies, and a 14-ton mobile hoist are available at the marina; hull and engine repairs can be made. In July 1981, a reported depth of 5 feet could be carried to the marina.

(292) Special purpose buoys maintained by the City of Groton show a **speed limit** of 5 m.p.h. in the area.

(293) A **special anchorage** is in the cove. (See **110.1** and **110.51,** chapter 2, for limits and regulations.)

8. EASTERN LONG ISLAND SOUND

(1)   This chapter describes the eastern portion of Long Island Sound following the north shore from Thames River to and including the Housatonic River, and then the south shore from Orient Point to and including Port Jefferson. Also described are the Connecticut River; the ports of New London, New Haven, and Northville; and the more important fishing and yachting centers on Niantic River and Bay, and in Westbrook Harbor, Guilford Harbor, Branford Harbor, and Mattituck Inlet.

(2)   **COLREGS Demarcation Lines.**–The lines established for Long Island Sound are described in **80.155** chapter 2.

(3)   **Chart 12354.**–Long Island Sound is a deep navigable waterway lying between the shores of Connecticut and New York and the northern coast of Long Island.

(4)   In this region are boulders and broken ground, but little or no natural change in the shoals. The waters are well marked by navigational aids so that strangers should experience no difficulty in navigating them. As all broken ground is liable to be strewn with boulders, vessels should proceed with caution in the broken areas where the charted depths are not more than 6 to 8 feet greater than the draft. All of the more important places are entered by dredged channels; during fog, vessels are advised to anchor until the weather clears before attempting to enter. The numerous oyster grounds in this region are usually marked by stakes and flags. These stakes may become broken off and form obstructions dangerous to small craft. Mariners should proceed with caution especially at night.

(5)   **Caution.**–Submarine operating areas are in the approaches to New London Harbor, Connecticut River, and off the northern shore of Long Island. As submarines may be operating submerged in these areas, vessels should proceed with caution.

(6)   **Anchorages.**–New London Harbor is the most important of the anchorages sought for shelter in the eastern part of Long Island Sound. Niantic Bay and the approach between Bartlett Reef and Hatchett Reef are used to some extent by small vessels when meeting unfavorable weather or reaching the eastern part of the sound. Small vessels can select anchorage eastward or westward of Kelsey Point Breakwater, also in Duck Island Roads. Off Madison there is anchorage sheltered from northerly winds. New Haven Harbor is an important harbor of refuge.

(7)   **Tides.**–The time of tide is nearly simultaneous throughout Long Island Sound, but the range of tide increases from about 2.5 feet at the east end to about 7.3 feet at the west end. Daily predictions of the times and heights of high and low waters for New London, Bridgeport, and Willets Point are given in the Tide Tables.

(8)   The effect of strong winds, in combination with the regular tidal action, may at times cause the water to fall several feet below the plane of reference of the charts.

(9)   **Currents.**–In the eastern portion of Long Island Sound the current turns from ½ to 1½ hours earlier along the north shore than in the middle of the sound.

(10)   Proceeding westward from The Race in the middle of the sound, the velocity of current is 1.8 knots off Cornfield Point, about 1 knot off New Haven, 1 knot off Eatons Neck, 0.4 knot between Peningo Neck and Matinecock Point, and 0.5 knot eastward of Hart Island.

(11)   About 1.5 miles east-southeastward of Barlett Reef, the velocity of flood is 1.2 knots and ebb 1.6 knots. The flood current sets 285° and the ebb 062°.

(12)   At a point about 3 miles southward of Cornfield Point, the flood current sets 256° with a velocity of 2 knots and the ebb sets 094° with a velocity of 1.7 knots.

(13)   About 1 mile north of Stratford Shoal (Middle Ground) Light, the velocity is 1 knot, the flood setting westward and the ebb eastward. (See Tidal Current Tables for predictions.) Current directions and velocities at various places throughout the eastern portion of Long Island Sound for each hour of the tidal cycle are shown on the Tidal Current Charts, Block Island Sound and Eastern Long Island Sound.

(14)   **Weather.**–Weather is most favorable from mid-May to mid-October, when the most common hazards are thunderstorms and fog. There is also a rare threat of a tropical cyclone. During June, July and August on the average, there are 20 to 25 days per month with conditions generally considered ideal even for small boaters. Fog is most likely in spring and early summer. Fog, or the lack of it, at inland locations is not a guide to conditions in the Sound or its approaches. Areas along the coast, at the heads of bays and within rivers may be relatively clear, while offshore the fog is thick. For example, on exposed Block Island heavy fog is encountered about 10 to 12 percent of the time from April though August compared to 1 to 3 percent at Westhampton. Thunderstorms on the other hand are more likely over land, but can be viscous in the Sound, especially in a squall line preceding a cold front in spring and early summer. Winter winds are mostly out of the west through north, but gales blow less than 5 percent of the time in these somewhat sheltered waters. Waves are restricted by limited fetch except to the east. However, choppy conditions can create problems.

(15)   **Ice.**–In ordinary winters the floating and pack ice in Long Island Sound, while impeding navigation, does not render it absolutely unsafe; but in exceptionally severe winters the reverse is true, none but powerful steamers can make their way.

(16)   Drift ice, which is formed principally along the northern shore of the sound under the influence of the prevailing northerly winds, drifts across to the southern side and accumulates there, massing into large fields, and remains until removed by southerly winds, which drive it back to the northerly shore.

(17)   In ordinary winters ice generally forms in the western end of the sound as far as Eatons Neck; in exceptionally severe winters ice may extend to Falkner Island and farther eastward.

(18)   **Effects of winds on ice.**–In Long Island Sound northerly winds drive the ice to the southern shore of the sound and southerly winds carry it back to the northern shore. Northeasterly winds force the ice westward and cause formations heavy enough to prevent the passage of vessels of every description until the ice is removed by westerly winds. These winds carry the ice eastward and, if of long duration, drive it through The Race into Block Island Sound, thence it goes to sea and disappears.

(19)   In New Haven Harbor, the influence of the northerly winds clear the harbor and its approaches unless the local formation is too heavy to be moved. Southerly winds force

the drift ice in from the sound and prevent the local formations from leaving the harbor. Tides have little effect upon the ice. Additional information concerning ice conditions in the waters adjoining Long Island Sound is given under the local descriptions.

(20) **Vessel Traffic Service (New York)**, operated by the U.S. Coast Guard, serves New York Harbor (see **161.501 through 161.580**, chapter 2, for regulations).

(21) **Pilotage, Long Island Sound.**–Pilotage is compulsary in Long Island Sound for foreign vessels and U.S. vessels under register.

(22) The pilot boat sets radio guard at least 1 hour before a vessel's ETA.

(23) Vessels to be boarded should provide a ladder 3 feet above the water on the lee side.

(24) Pilot services are generally arranged at least 24 hours in advance through ships' agents or directly by shipping companies.

(25) Pilotage, in the waters of Long Island Sound, is available from, but not limited to:

(26) Sound Pilots, Inc. (a division of Northeast Marine Pilots, Inc.), 243 Spring Street, Newport RI 02840, telephone 401-847-9050 (24 hours), 800-274-1216, FAX 401-847-9052, Cable RISPILOT, Newport. Pilot boats are RHODE ISLAND PILOT, 35-foot, black hull, white superstructure, word PILOT on sides; NORTHEAST I, 49-foot, black hull, white superstructure, word PILOT on sides; and NORTHEAST II, 49-foot, gray hull, gray superstructure, word PILOT on sides. The boat monitor channels 16, 10, 13, 14; work on 10.

(27) Connecticut State Pilots (a division of Interport Pilots Agency, Inc.), State Pier, New London, CT 06320, telephone 800-346-4877 or 908-787-5554, FAX 908-787-5538, cable PORTPILOTS. Pilot boats are CONNECTICUT PILOT, 65-foot, with blue hull, white superstructure; CONNECTICUT PILOT II, 47-foot, with blue hull, and white superstructure. The boat monitors channels 16 and 13, works on 11.

(28) Constitution State Pilots Association, 500 Waterfront Street, New Haven, CT 06512, telephone 800-229-7456 or 203-783-5991, FAX 516-582-6327. The pilot boat CONSTITUTION, is 65-foot, with black hull, white superstructure, and the word PILOT on sides. The boat monitors 16, 13, and 9A; works on 13 or 9A.

(29) Long Island Sound State Pilots Association, Inc., 1440 Whalley Avenue, Suite 123, New Haven, CT 06515, telephone 203-772-0101, FAX 302-629-9392, Cable LISPILOT, New Haven. The pilot boat LONG ISLAND SOUND PILOT, is 46-foot, with black hull, white superstructure, and the word PILOT in black letters. The boat monitors channel 16; works on 11.

(30) See Pilotage, New London-Groton (indexed as such), this chapter; Pilotage, New Haven (indexed as such), this chapter; Pilotage, Bridgeport (indexed as such), chapter 9; Pilotage, Offshore Terminal, Northville-Riverhead (indexed as such), this chapter; see Pilotage, Offshore Terminal, Northport (indexed as such), chapter 9.

(31) **Charts 13213, 13212, 12372.**–**New London Harbor**, near the east end of Long Island Sound at the mouth of the **Thames River**, is an important harbor of refuge. Vessels of deep draft can find anchorage here in any weather and at all seasons.

(32) Waterborne commerce in New London Harbor and on the Thames River is chiefly in petroleum products, chemicals, lumber, pulpwood, and general cargo.

(33) **Security Zones** have been established in New London Harbor. (See **165.1 through 165.7, 165.30, 165.33, and 165.140**, chapter 2, for limits and regulations.)

(34) **New London** is a city on the west bank of Thames River about 2.5 miles above the mouth. The town of **Groton** on the east bank is connected to New London by a highway bridge and a railroad bridge. The main harbor comprises the lower 3 miles of Thames River from Long Island Sound to the bridges, and includes Shaw Cove, Greens Harbor, and Winthrop Cove. It is approached through the main entrance channel extending from deep water in Long Island Sound to deep water in the upper harbor. The harbor is generally used by vessels drawing 9 to 30 feet; the deepest draft entering is about 36 feet. Petroleum products, molasses, sulfuric acid, woodpulp, hemp fiber, coconut products, and lumber are the principal waterborne products handled at the port.

(35) **Greens Harbor**, a small-craft shelter just north of the entrance, has general depths of 6 to 17 feet. **Special anchorages** are in the harbor. (See **110.1** and **110.52**, chapter 2, for limits and regulations.)

(36) **New London Coast Guard Station** is at **Fort Trumbull**, on the west side of main channel northward of Greens Harbor.

(37) **Shaw Cove** is a dredged basin about 0.8 mile northward of Greens Harbor. In February 1986, the controlling depth was 15 feet in the entrance channel through the south draw of the bridge, thence depths of 11 to 15 feet were available in the basin. The railroad bridge over the entrance has a swing span with clearances of 6½ feet. (See **117.1 through 117.59 and 117.223**, chapter 2, for drawbridge regulations.)

(38) **Winthrop Cove**, northward of Shaw Cove, is part of the main waterfront channel. The fixed railroad bridge near the head of this cove has a clearance of 4 feet.

(39) **Prominent features.**–**New London Ledge Light** (41°18.3'N., 72°04.7' W.), 58 feet above the water, is shown from a red brick building on a square white pier on the west side of New London Ledge; a fog signal is sounded at the station.

(40) Other prominent features in approaching New London Harbor are: New London Harbor Light, on the west side of the entrance channel; the training tank at the submarine base; the globular tank at Fort Trumbull; the monument at Fort Griswold; the microwave tower atop a building in downtown New London; the large sheds at the shipyard on the east side of the river opposite Fort Trumbull; and the highway bridge at New London.

(41) **Channels.**–A U.S. Navy project for New London Harbor provides for a channel 40 feet deep to Fort Trumbull, thence 38 feet to State Pier No. 1, thence 36 feet to the U.S. Navy Submarine Base. A Federal project provides for a channel 23 feet deep in the waterfront channels north of Fort Trumbull and in Winthrop Cove. (See Notice to Mariners and latest editions of the charts for controlling depths.) Lighted and unlighted buoys and a **354°** lighted range mark the channel. The range does not mark the center of the lower end of the channel.

(42) **Pine Island Channel**, northeastward of New London Ledge Light, between Pine Island and Black Ledge, has a rocky and very broken bottom on which the least found depth is 10 feet. It is used some by local vessels between New London Harbor and Fishers Island Sound, but should be avoided by any vessel drawing more than 10 feet.

(43) **Anchorages.**–General and naval anchorages are in the approaches to, and in, New London Harbor. (See **110.1 and 110.147**, chapter 2, for limits and regulations.) Special anchorages are in Greens Harbor and in the vicinity of the U.S. Coast Guard Academy. (See **110.1 and 110.52**, chapter 2, for limits and regulations.)

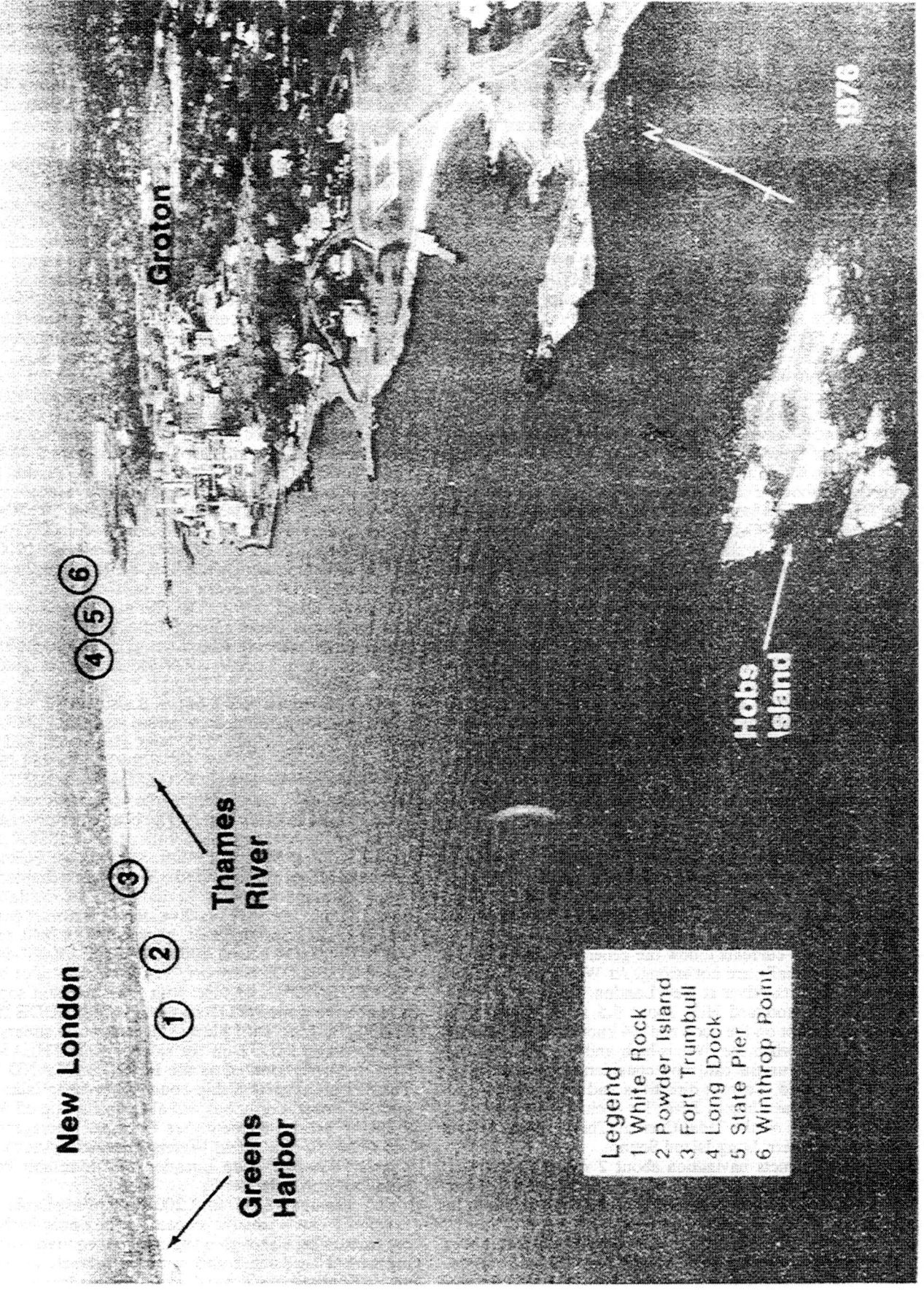

NEW LONDON HARBOR

New London

Greens Harbor

Thames River

Groton

Hobs Island

1976

Legend
1 White Rock
2 Powder Island
3 Fort Trumbull
4 Long Dock
5 State Pier
6 Winthrop Point

(44)   **Dangers.**–On the west side of the approach to New London Harbor, foul ground extends about 1 mile from shore in the vicinity of **Goshen Point** (chart 13211). The southerly and southeasterly limits of this area are marked by buoys. The area has numerous rocky patches and boulders, some showing above water, and should be avoided by small craft. **Rapid Rock,** marked by a buoy on its southeast side, is about 1.6 miles southwestward of New London Ledge Light. It has a least depth of 11 feet. An unmarked ledge covered 38 feet is about 750 yards southeast of Rapid Rock and is the outermost shoal to the southward. **Sarah Ledge,** 0.7 mile northeastward of Rapid Rock and marked by a buoy, has a least depth of 16 feet and is the easternmost shoal on the west side of the main channel approach.

(45)   On the east side of the main channel foul ground extends about 1 mile offshore. **New London Ledge,** marked by New London Ledge Light, has a least depth of 7 feet. **Black Ledge,** just to the northeastward of New London Ledge, has a rocky islet, 2 feet high, on it. Depths are 2 to 16 feet on the ledge. Buoys mark the shoal area.

(46)   Broken ground fringes the shore southwestward of New London Harbor Light. Rocks with 2 to 11 feet over them extend about 0.2 mile from shore in the bight just southward of the light.

(47)   **White Rock,** an islet in Greens Harbor, is 200 yards from the 18-foot curve on the western edge of the channel. **Hog Back,** a small ledge awash at low water, is 150 yards southwestward of White Rock and about 0.3 mile from the western shore, and is marked by two buoys. Rocks, covered 3 to 6 feet, are in the middle of the northern part of Greens Harbor. **Melton Ledge,** northward of White Rock, with one-half foot over it, is 125 yards eastward of **Powder Island** and is marked by a buoy; a rock awash is close westward of Melton Ledge.

(48)   **Bridges.**–Four bridges cross the Thames River below Norwich: three near Winthrop Point and one about 0.2 miles southward of Fort Point. The first is the railroad bridge, which has a bascule span with a clearance of 30 feet. (See **117.1 through 117.59 and 117.224,** chapter 2, for drawbridge regulations.) The bridgetender of the railroad bridge monitors VHF-FM channel 13; call sign KT-5473. Just above it are two high-level fixed bridges with clearances of 135 feet, and 7.9 miles farther up the Thames is a fixed highway bridge with a clearance of 75 feet.

(49)   Overhead power cables with a clearance of 160 feet cross the river about 5.5 miles below Norwich.

(50)   **Tides and currents.**–The mean range of tide at New London is 2.6 feet. Daily predictions are given in the Tide Tables.

(51)   The tidal currents follow the general direction of the channel and usually are not strong. At Winthrop Point, on the west side of the river at New London, the velocity is 0.4 knot, and at Stoddard Hill, about 6.5 miles above New London, 0.7 knot on the flood and 0.4 knot on the ebb. During freshets or when the river is high and the wind is from the north, the current can have considerable southerly set even on the flood. Current directions and velocities at various places on the Thames River for each hour of the tidal cycle are shown on the Tidal Current Charts, Block Island Sound and Eastern Long Island Sound.

(52)   **Ice** obstructs navigation about 2 months each year above the naval station, which is some 5 miles above New London Ledge Light, but seldom forms below the station. In extremely severe winters, however, heavy ice from the sound, driven in by winds, has been known to extend about 1.8 miles above the entrance. Between New London and the mouth of the river small vessels may navigate with comparative safety in ordinary winters; and even in severe weather it is rare that navigation for small vessels stops for more than a week. Steamers can nearly always enter and leave with safety. Drift ice sometimes forms a decidedly dangerous obstruction in the approaches through Long Island Sound during severe winters, especially during February and March; and small vessels are much hindered in their movements during January, February, and March.

(53)   **Freshets** usually occur in the river in the spring. It is reported that they seldom exceed 2 feet above high water at Norwich.

(54)   New London Harbor and Thames River are easy of access by day or night, but local knowledge is required to take drafts greater than 20 feet above the submarine base.

(55)   **Pilotage, New London-Groton.**–Pilotage is compulsary in Long Island Sound for foreign vessels and U.S. vessels under register. See Pilotage, Long Island Sound (indexed as such),chapter 8. Pilotage for New London is available from: New London Connecticut Pilots Association (NLCPA), 239 Ocean Avenue, New London, CT 06320, telephone 203-443-4431 or 203-443-2401. Pilot boat JM5, 35-foot, red hull, white superstructure, word PILOT on sides. The boat monitors channel 13; works 18 and 79. A NLCPA pilot boards a ship about 2 miles south of New London Ledge Light. The NLCPA requests a 48-hour advance notice of arrival with updates at 24, 12, and 6 hours.

(56)   Pilotage for New London is also available from Constitution State Pilots Association (CSPA), 500 Waterfront Street, New Haven, CT 06512, telephone 800-229-7456 or 203-783-5991, FAX 516-582-6327. Pilot boat CONSTITUTION is 65-foot, with black hull, white superstructure, and the word PILOT on sides. The boat monitors 16, 13, and 9A, works on 13 or 9A. The CSPA pilot will meet a New London bound vessel about 2 miles south of New London Ledge Light; also will meet a vessel off Montauk Point. See Pilotage Pickup Locations Off Montauk Point (indexed as such), chapter 7.

(57)   Pilotage for New London is also available from Long Island Sound State Pilots Association, Inc. (LISSPA), 1440 Whalley Avenue, Suite 123, New Haven, CT 06515, telephone 203-772-0101, FAX 302-629-9392, Cable LISPILOT, New Haven. Pilot boat LONG ISLAND SOUND PILOT is 46-foot, with black hull, white superstructure, and the word PILOT in black letters. The boat monitors channel 16; works on 11. Among other locations, the LISSPA pilot will meet a ship off Montauk Point. See Pilotage Pickup Locations Off Montauk Point (indexed as such), chapter 7.

(58)   Pilotage for New London is also available from Sound Pilots, Inc. (SPI) (a division of Northeast Marine Pilots, Inc.), 243 Spring Street, Newport, RI 02840, telephone 401-847-9050 (24 hours), 800-274-1216, FAX 401-847-9052, Cable RISPILOT, Newport, RI 02840. The pilot boats are NORTHEAST II, 49-foot, with grey hull and superstructure and the word PILOT on the side; or RHODE ISLAND PILOT, 35-foot, with black hull and white superstructure and the word PILOT on the side; or NORTHEAST I, 49-foot, similiarily marked as the RHODE ISLAND PILOT. The SPI pilots meet a ship bound for a Long Island Sound port, off Point Judith, but will also meet a ship off Montauk Point by prearrangement. See Pilotage, Narragansett Bay and Other Rhode Island Waters (indexed as such), chapter 6, and Pilotage Pickup Locations Off Montauk Point (indexed as such), chapter 7.

(59)   **Towage.**–Tugs to 3,200 hp are available at New London. Vessels usually proceed to the upper harbor without assistance, although a tug may be required when entering with a head wind and contrary current. Large vessels normally require tugs for docking and undocking.

(60)   New London is a **customs port of entry.**

(61) **Quarantine, customs, immigration, and agricultural quarantine.**–(See chapter 3, Vessel Arrival Inspections, and appendix for addresses.)

(62) **Quarantine** is enforced in accordance with regulations of the U.S. Public Health Service. (See Public Health Service, chapter 1.) New London has several hospitals.

(63) **Coast Guard.**–The **Captain of the Port** maintains an office at the New London Coast Guard Station. (See appendix for address.)

(64) **Harbor regulations** are in force for New London Harbor. The harbormaster has authority to berth vessels, shifting them if necessary, but occasion for doing so seldom arises.

(65) **Wharves.**–New London Harbor has more than 30 wharves and piers. Most of these facilities are used as repair berths, and for mooring recreational craft, fishing vessels, barges, ferries, and government vessels. Depths alongside these facilities range from 10 to 40 feet. Only the deep-draft facilities are described. For a complete description of the port facilities refer to Port Series No. 4, published and sold by the U.S. Army Corps of Engineers. (See appendix for address.) The alongside depths are reported; for information on the latest depths contact the private operator.

(66) **Amerada Hess Corp. Wharf** (41°20′09″N., 72°04′58″W.): on the east side of the river opposite Greens Harbor; T-head pier with 55-foot face, 960 feet of berthing space with dolphins; 40 feet alongside; deck height, 8 feet; pipelines to storage tanks; fresh water connection; railroad and highway connections; receipt and shipment of petroleum products and receipt of molasses; bunkering vessels; owned and operated by Hess Oil and Chemical Division, Amerada Hess Corp.

(67) **State Pier No. 1:** the more easterly of the two long piers southwestward of the Thames River bridges, about 1.3 miles northward of Amerada Hess Corp. Wharf; 200-foot face, 28 to 32 feet alongside; west side 1,000 feet, 28 to 36 feet alongside; east side 1,020 feet, 36 to 38 feet alongside; deck height, 10 feet; 20-ton crane; 153,000 square feet of covered storage, 5 acres open storage; electricity and potable and feed water connections on pier; railroad and highway connections; receipt and shipment of general cargo, woodpulp, copper, hemp, and paper products and mooring naval vessels; owned by State of Connecticut, west side operated by New London Terminal Co., east side and face by U.S. Navy.

(68) **Supplies** of all kinds are available. Gasoline and diesel oil can be obtained from oil companies on 48 hours' notice by tank truck. Water is available at most of the piers, wharves, and marinas.

(69) **Repairs.**–A shipbuilding company at New London can perform all kinds of repairs on steel-hulled vessels. The company has a floating drydock in Winthrop Cove. The drydock has a length of 180 feet, width of 84 feet, and a lifting capacity of 2,000 tons.

(70) Cranes to 70 tons and floating derricks to 25 tons are available at New London.

(71) Several companies in New London are in the business of wrecking, salvage, and marine contracting work. They are equipped with pumps, divers' outfits, floating equipment, and other gear.

(72) **Small-craft facilities.**–There are numerous small-craft facilities in Greens Harbor and Shaw Cove. (See the small-craft facilities tabulation on chart 12372 for services and supplies available.

(73) **Communications.**–New London has good railroad and bus communications. Automobile-passenger ferry service is available to Block Island, Fishers Island, and to Orient Point, Long Island.

(74) Thames River above New London has a dredged channel to Norwich, the head of navigation. In January-June 1978, the controlling depth was 35 feet from above the bridges at New London to the north end of the turning basin opposite Smith Cove, thence in August-September 1974, depths of 16 feet (23 feet at midchannel) to Stoddard Hill, and thence 18 feet to the turning basin at Norwich, and 11 feet in the turning basin. The channel is well marked by navigational aids.

(75) **Caution.**–The dikes along the Thames River from Easter Point (41°28.2′N., 72°04.5′W.) to Norwich are submerged at half tide.

(76) **Pilots** for the river are available at New London.

(77) The **U.S. Coast Guard Academy** is on the west side of Thames River about 1 mile north of the center of New London. The administration building, with its white tower and clock, and the lighted chapel spire are very prominent, but are not visible until almost abeam of the academy. Depths alongside the 410-foot-long academy pier are reported to be 17 feet at the face, 19 feet along the south side, and 15 to 17 feet on the north side.

(78) The **U.S. Naval Submarine Base** is on the east side of the Thames River about 2 miles above New London. The submarine escape training tank at the base, 143 feet high with a flashing white light atop, is prominent.

(79) A **restricted area** is off the U.S. Naval Submarine Base. (See **334.75**, chapter 2, for limits and regulations.)

(80) Just below **Gales Ferry**, on the east side about 4 miles above the bridges, are the crew training quarters and boathouses of Harvard and Yale Universities. Opposite Gales Ferry is the town of **Bartlett**, site of a prominent power plant with two tall and conspicuous stacks. A privately dredged channel with depths of about 19 feet leads to the dock and coal tipple.

(81) At **Montville Station**, just above Bartlett, is a dock with a depth of 23 feet at the face. The northeast end of the dock is in ruins. Overhead power cables with a clearance of 160 feet cross the river 0.5 mile above the station near **Kitemaug.**

(82) **Allyn Point**, on the east side about 5 miles above New London, is the site of a large private pier for receiving liquid chemicals, with a reported depth of about 30 feet alongside. It is marked by an elevated water sphere and several small tanks on the pier.

(83) **Fort Point**, on the east side 8 miles above New London, has a long fuel pier marked by privately maintained red lights, and on shore is a building with several stacks. Numerous piles are in the water southward of the pier. The fixed highway bridge crossing the river about 0.2 miles south of Fort Point has a clearance of 75 feet.

(84) The red brick buildings of the Norwich State Hospital are on a bluff just north of Fort Point and are a conspicuous landmark.

(85) At **Thamesville**, on the west side of the river about 1 mile below Norwich, are two finger piers each with breasting dolphins used to receive petroleum products from barges. Depths of 20 to 25 feet are reported alongside the face of the piers.

(86) **Norwich**, a city at the head of navigation on Thames River at its junction with **Shetucket River** and **Yantic River**, is about 11 miles above New London. In 1981, waterborne commerce to Norwich consisted of petroleum products. Small boats generally anchor in Shetucket River just above the fixed bridges at Norwich, which have a minimum clearance of 13 feet.

(87) **Charts 13211, 13212, 12372.**–Bartlett Reef Light (41°16.5′N., 72°08.2′W.), 35 feet above the water and shown

from a skeleton tower with a red and white diamond-shaped daymark, is about 3.3 miles southwestward of New London Ledge Light and marks the south end of **Bartlett Reef.** A fog signal is at the light. The reef, about 1.3 miles long in a general north-south direction and about 0.3 mile wide, is covered 2 to 12 feet and has rocks awash near its northern end. The north end of the reef is marked by a buoy. A lighted bell buoy and an unlighted buoy are about 0.9 mile southward and about 0.3 mile eastward of the light, respectively.

(88)　　A **general anchorage** is about 0.8 mile northeastward of Bartlett Reef Light. (See **110.1 and 110.147 (a) (4),** and **(b)**, chapter 2, for limits and regulations.)

(89)　　**Twotree Island,** small and bare, about 1.4 miles northwestward of Bartlett Reef Light, is surrounded by shoals. A buoy marks rocks awash that extend off the northern end of the island.

(90)　　**Twotree Island Channel** leads northward of Bartlett Reef and Twotree Island. With an adverse current in the sound, this channel is used to some extent by light tows and sailboats with a leading wind in the daytime, as the tidal currents turn about 1 hour earlier along the north shore than in the middle of the sound. About 0.3 mile southwestward of **Seaside,** the tidal currents have a velocity of 1.2 knots, and ebb 1.6 knots. Flood sets westerly and the ebb easterly. The channel is buoyed, but strangers are advised to use it with caution and should never attempt to beat through.

(91)　　From **Goshen Point** (41°18.0′ N., 72°06.8′W.) westward, there are scattered boulders which extend offshore as much as 0.2 mile in places. **Jordan Cove,** 1.5 miles west of Goshen Point, is foul in its northerly half, and the southerly part is obstructed by **Flat Rock,** bare at low water and marked by a buoy, and **High Rock,** which shows at high water and is marked by a buoy.

(92)　　**Millstone Point,** on the east side at the entrance of Niantic Bay, is occupied by the buildings of the Millstone Nuclear Power Station. A 389-foot red and white stack at the station and a radio tower on the point are the most conspicuous landmarks in the area. A cove with depths of 9 to 15 feet is on the west side of the point. A rock with 1 foot over it lies 60 feet off the mouth of the cove. The station maintains channel markers and a range for occasional barge traffic. A dredged area for the power station's water intakes is 0.2 mile northwest of the cove.

(93)　　**Charts 13211, 12372.**–White Rock is an islet on the east side of the entrance to Niantic Bay 0.5 mile westward of Millstone Point. **Little Rock,** two rocks partly bare at low water, is 150 yards east of White Rock. A rock over which the least depth is 8 feet is about midway between Little Rock and the cove at Millstone Point. A shoal spot, covered 12 feet, is 200 yards eastward of the rock. A rock, covered 14 feet, is about 300 yards south-southeast of White Rock and is marked by a lighted bell buoy.

(94)　　**Niantic Bay,** 4.5 miles westward of New London Harbor, is a good anchorage sheltered from easterly, northerly, and westerly winds. It is a harbor of refuge in northerly gales and can be used by small vessels and tows. The general depth of the bay is about 19 feet; the water shoals gradually northward. The entrance is 1.5 miles wide, and the dangers are marked by buoys or show above water.

(95)　　**Niantic** and **Crescent Beach** are summer resorts with railroad communication at the north end and northwest side of the bay.

(96)　　The Niantic Bay Yacht Club basin at Crescent Beach is protected on the south, east, and partially on the north side by a U-shaped breakwater; a private seasonal light is near the outer end of the breakwater.

(97)　　A **special anchorage** is on the west side of Niantic Bay off Crescent Beach. (See **110.1** and **110.53,** chapter 2, for limits and regulations.)

(98)　　**Niantic River** empties into the northeast end of Niantic Bay and is entered through a dredged channel that leads from the bay, thence through a narrow passage at the entrance, and thence to a point about 300 yards northward of the entrance to Smith Cove. In August-October 1988, the controlling depth was 6 feet at midchannel to the highway swing bridge about 0.4 mile above the channel entrance, thence 4½ feet to the head of the channel. The channel is marked by daybeacons and seasonal buoys. Two bridges cross the narrow passage at the entrance. The more southerly is the Amtrak bridge, with a 45-foot bascule span and a clearance of 11 feet; the State Route 156 highway bridge, about 0.1 mile northward, has a swing span with a clearance of 9 feet. (See **117.1 through 117.59 and 117.215,** chapter 2, for drawbridge regulations.) The bridgetender at each bridge monitors VHF-FM channel 13; call signs KGA-511 and KXR–911, respectively. In May 1989, a replacement bascule highway bridge with a design clearance of 30 feet was under construction just south of the existing bascule bridge.

(99)　　Strangers attempting to enter Niantic River are cautioned to pass through the bridges either at slack water or against the current.

(100)　　Above the head of the dredged channel, small craft can navigate for about another 1.5 miles to **Golden Spur (East Lyme)** with local knowledge. The river from westward of Sandy Point to the stone bulkhead at Golden Spur is deep and clear; vessels generally follow the west bank. **Pine Grove, Sandy Point,** and **Saunders Point** are summer resorts on Niantic River.

(101)　　The mean range of **tide** is about 2.7 feet in Niantic Bay.

(102)　　The **tidal currents** through the bridges set fair with the channel; the flood velocity is 1.6 knots and the ebb velocity, 0.8 knot. It has been reported that much greater velocities may be expected under storm and freshet conditions. (See Tidal Current Tables for predictions.) Current directions and velocities for the entrance to the Niantic River for each hour of the tidal cycle are shown on the Tidal Current Charts, Block Island Sound and Eastern Long Island Sound.

(103)　　Ice generally closes the river to navigation for about 3 months during the winter.

(104)　　**Smith Cove** is on the west side of Niantic River about 1.5 miles above the channel entrance. A channel, marked by private daybeacons, leads westward from the river channel into the cove. In July 1981, the channel had a reported depth of 5 feet.

(105)　　There are several small-craft facilities just above the entrance at Niantic and **Waterford,** on the west side and east side of Niantic River, respectively, and in Smith Cove. (See the small-craft facilities tabulation on chart 12372 for services and supplies available.) **Harbormasters** are at Niantic and Waterford. A 6 mph **speed limit** is enforced on the river.

(106)　　**Black Point,** on the west side at the entrance to Niantic Bay, is flat with bluffs at the water and is occupied by many summer cottages. Broken ground with a least found depth of 20 feet extends 0.6 mile south of the southwest side of the point.

(107)　　The bight between Black Point and Hatchet Point, about 2.3 miles to the westward, has many rocks showing above high water. **Griswold Island,** on the northeast side of the bight, is high and prominent. Rocks extend 0.35 mile

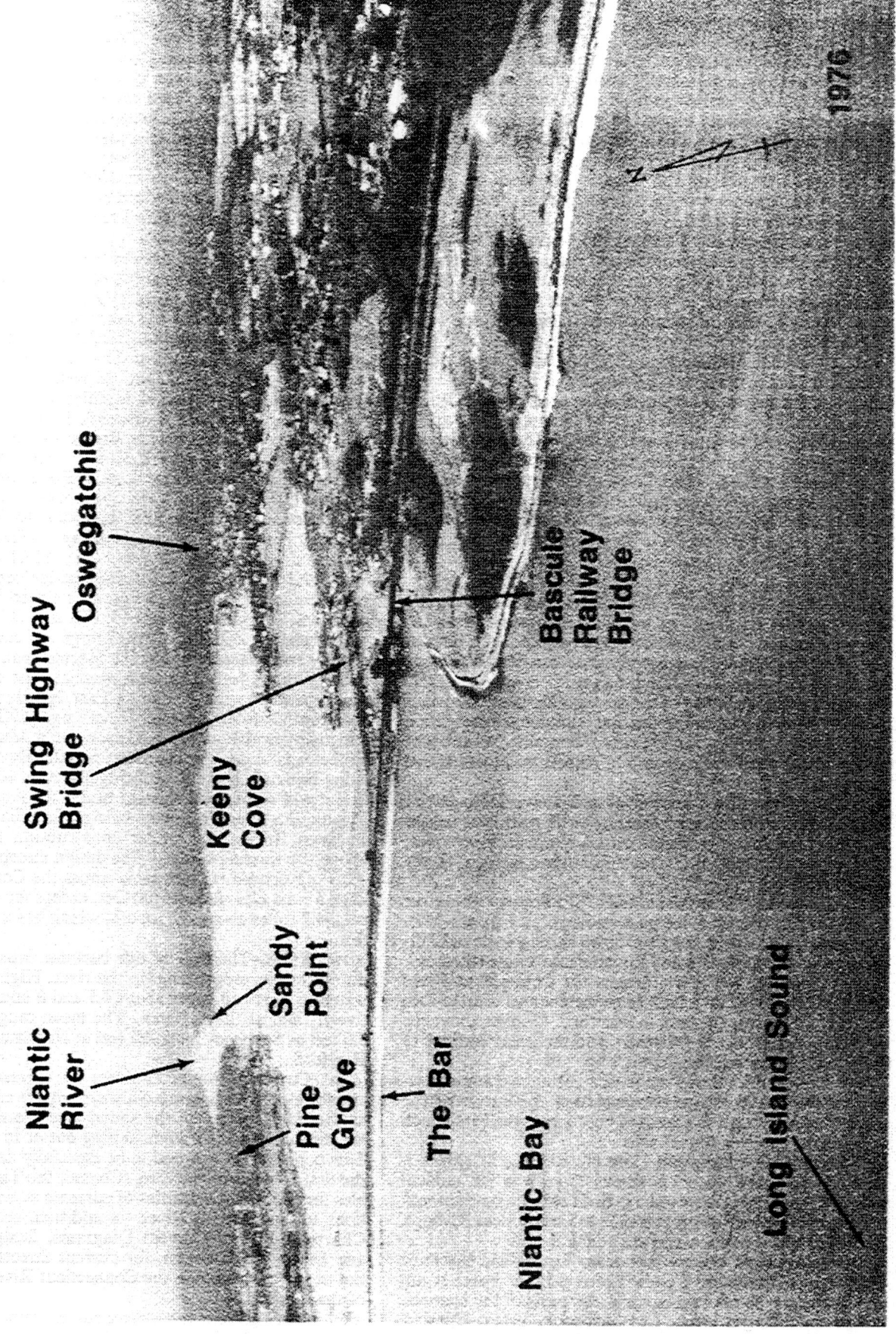

NIANTIC BAY

Oswegatchie

Swing Highway Bridge

Keeny Cove

Sandy Point

Niantic River

Pine Grove

The Bar

Niantic Bay

Bascule Railway Bridge

Long Island Sound

1976

southward and 0.2 mile southwestward of the island. The southwest rocks are marked by a buoy. **South Brother**, in the center, and **North Brother**, in the northwestern part of the bight, are prominent bare rocks. A rock, covered 6 feet, is 250 yards off the west side of Black Point. **Blackboys**, two rocks awash are 0.4 mile southward of Griswold Island. A rock, covered 3 feet and marked by a buoy, is about 0.2 mile southward of Blackboys. **Johns Rock**, covered 5 feet, is 0.3 mile off the northwest side of the bight, about 0.5 mile west-southwestward of South Brother; the range of South Brother well open northward of Griswold Island leads southward of Johns Rock.

(108)   Strangers entering the bight should proceed with caution, as the bottom is broken; the best route is to pass southward and westward of the buoy southward of Blackboys, and pass on either side of South Brother. **Seal Rock**, 160 yards south of the end of **Giants Neck**, is marked by a buoy on the south side.

(109)   A **special anchorage** is east of Giants Neck. (See **110.1** and **110.54**, chapter 2, for limits and regulations.) An unmarked rock is within the anchorage area, about 0.1 mile south of Giants Neck; depth over the rock is not known.

(110)   **Hatchett Point** has several large dwellings. A reef extends about 0.2 mile off the southwest side of the point.

(111)   **Hatchett Reef**, 0.6 to 1 mile south-southwestward of Hatchett Point, has a least depth of 5 feet and is marked by buoys. Close to the southeast side of the reef the depths are 30 to 48 feet. A bar with 10 to 16 feet over it extends westward from Hatchett Reef to Saybrook Bar.

(112)   **Charts 12375, 12377, 12372.**–**Connecticut River** rises in the extreme northern part of New Hampshire, near the Canadian border, and flows southerly between the States of Vermont and New Hampshire and across Massachusetts and Connecticut to Long Island Sound. It is approximately 375 miles long and is one of the largest and most important rivers in New England. The head of commercial navigation is at Hartford, about 45 miles from the mouth. Waterborne commerce on the river is mostly in petroleum products and chemicals.

(113)   The river water is fresh at and above Deep River. Each year after the spring freshets, shoals with least depths of 10 feet are found in places on bars in the upper river; dredging to remove such shoals is begun as soon as the water subsides.

(114)   Between the entrance and Middletown the river banks are hard and in some places rocky, but between Middletown and Hartford the river flows through alluvial bottom land, where freshets and ice jams may cause shoaling.

(115)   **Channels.**–A Federal project for Connecticut River provides for a 15-foot jettied entrance channel and 15-foot dredged cuts across the bars to Hartford, 45 miles above the entrance. (See Notice to Mariners and the latest editions of the charts for controlling depths.)

(116)   The channel above the jettied entrance channel usually follows the banks on the outside of the curves of the river, except through the dredged cuts across the bars which are marked by navigational aids.

(117)   **Saybrook Breakwater Light** (41°15.8′N., 72°20.6′W.), 58 feet above the water, is shown from a white conical tower, 49 feet high, on a brown cylindrical pier on the south end of the west jetty at the entrance to Connecticut River. A fog signal and a radiobeacon are at the light.

(118)   **Anchorages.**–Secure anchorage can be had eastward or northeastward of Lynde Point Light. Farther up anchorage can be selected in the wider parts of the channel. Special anchorages are at Old Saybrook, Essex, Chester, Lord Island, Eddy Rock Shoal in the vicinity of Connecticut

River Light 45, and Mouse Island Bar vicinity. (See **110.1** and **110.55**, chapter 2, for limits and regulations.)

(119)   **Dangers.**–**Saybrook Outer Bar**, which obstructs the mouth of the Connecticut River, is shifting, with depths of 4 to 12 feet extending nearly 2 miles off the mouth; it is marked off its southeastern end by a lighted bell buoy.

(120)   In March 1976, obstructions were reported in the channel at the railroad bascule bridge 3 miles above the mouth of the Connecticut River; a least depth of 13 feet is reported in the channel in area 40 to 50 feet from the east abutment of the bridge. Mariners requiring greater depths are advised to avoid this area of the channel during passages.

(121)   **Bridges.**–Several drawbridges and fixed bridges cross Connecticut River between the entrance and Hartford. The distance above the mouth, type, and clearance of each bridge follows: 3 miles, Amtrak railroad with bascule span, 19 feet; 3.5 miles, Raymond E. Baldwin (IS 95) Bridge, fixed highway, 81 feet; 14.6 miles, State Route 82 highway with swing span at East Haddam, 22 feet; 27.8 miles, ConRail railroad with swing span at Middletown, 25 feet; 28 miles, Arrigoni Bridge (State Route 66), fixed highway, 92 feet; 41.2 miles, Wm. H. Putnam Bridge (State Route 3), fixed highway near Wethersfield, 80 feet over main channel; 44 miles, **Charter Oak Bridge** (U.S. 5/State Route 15), a fixed highway at Hartford, 81 feet for a width of 214 feet; 44.9 miles, Founders Bridge, fixed highway, 46 feet; 45.2 miles, Bulkeley Bridge (I-84), fixed highway, 39 feet; and 46 miles, Conrail fixed railroad, 28 feet. (See **117.1 through 117.59 and 117.205**, chapter 2, for drawbridge regulations.) The bridgetender of the Amtrak bascule railroad bridge at mile 3 monitors VHF-FM channel 13; call sign KT-5414. Vessels requesting the opening of this bridge are cautioned to confirm by radiotelephone that the bascule span is safely raised and stabilized before making passage. The bridgetender of the highway swing bridge at East Haddam at mile 14.6 monitors VHF-FM channel 13; call sign KXR-913. In 1988, a highway bridge with a fixed span and a design clearance of 65 feet was under construction immediately south of the existing bridge (Charter Oak Bridge) at mile 44; upon completion it will replace the existing bridge. In August 1990, a replacement fixed highway bridge for the Raymond E. Baldwin Bridge was under construction about 0.5 mile above the existing bridge. The design clearance is 81 feet.

(122)   Overhead power cables across the Connecticut River have a least clearance of 100 feet, except for the one at **Laurel**, 24.2 miles above the mouth, which has a clearance of 65 feet.

(123)   **Tides.**–The time of tide becomes later and the range diminishes in progressing up the river. High water and low water at Hartford occur about 4.5 and 6 hours later, respectively, than at the entrance. The mean range of the tide is 3.5 feet at Saybrook jetty, 2.5 feet at Haddam, and 1.9 feet at Hartford.

(124)   **Currents.**–At the entrance the currents have considerable velocity at times and always require careful attention, as the tidal current of the sound often sets directly across the direction of the current setting out or in between jetties. This condition is reported to be especially dangerous during the first 3 hours of ebb tide. (Consult the Tidal Current Tables for times and velocities of currents at a number of locations in Connecticut River. In addition, see Tidal Current Charts and Tidal Current Diagrams, Long Island Sound and Block Island Sound, for current directions and velocities at various places in the Connecticut River for each hour of the tidal cycle.)

(125)   During the ebb, a strong current runs from the Lyme Landing toward the center of the railroad bridge. Towboats

with vessels in tow should steer for the east pier of the draw and should not swing out for the draw until almost in it, to avoid being set to the west side of the channel. Because of river discharge, the ebb current usually will be considerably stronger than the flood. Ebb current velocities of 1 knot or more have been observed under normal conditions on the bars in Connecticut River between Higganum and Hartford; the velocities of the flood currents are much less.

(126)   **Freshets** occur principally in the spring, when the snow is melting, although occasional floods have occurred in every month of the year except July and September. At Hartford the usual rise due to spring freshets is between 16 and 24 feet. The highest freshets are generally of short duration, but the period during which the river at Hartford is at the level of 8 feet or more above mean low water averages nearly 2 months of each year. Below Middletown the height of the crest of a freshet decreases rapidly. At the mouth the variation in water level is due to the tides.

(127)   **Ice** closes the river to navigation a part of every winter for wooden hull boats. The duration of closing is about 2 months.

(128)   **Weather.**–Hartford is well inside the northern temperate climatic zone in a prevailing west to east movement of air carrying the majority of weather systems into Connecticut from the west. The average wintertime position of the "Polar Front" boundary between cold dry polar air and warm moist tropical air is just south of New England, which helps to explain the extensive winter storm activity and the day-to-day variability of local weather. In the summer, the "Polar Front" has an average position along the New England-Canada border and Hartford has a warm and pleasant climate.

(129)   The location of Hartford, relative to the continent and ocean, is also significant. Rapid weather changes result when storms move northward along the Mid-Atlantic Coast, frequently producing strong and persistent northeast winds associated with storms known locally as coastals or northeasters. Seasonally, weather characteristics vary from the cold and dry continental-polar air of winter to the warm, maritimes air of summer, the one from Canada, the other from the Gulf of Mexico, Caribbean Sea, or Atlantic Ocean.

(130)   Summer thunderstorms develop in the Berkshire Mountains to the west and northwest, and move over the Connecticut Valley and, when accompanied by wind and hail, sometimes cause considerable damage to crops. During the winter, rain often falls through cold air trapped in the valley and creates extremely hazardous ice conditions. On clear nights in the late summer or early autumn, cool air drainage into the valley and the moisture from the Connecticut River produce steam and/or ground fog which becomes quite dense throughout the valley and temporarily hampers transportation.

(131)   Fog is reported to develop locally in the vicinity of the nuclear power plant's efflux at Haddam Neck and around Gildersleeve Island.

(132)   The National Weather Service office is at Bradley International Airport, northwest of Hartford. (See page T-4 for **Hartford climatological table.**)

(133)   **Routes.**–To enter Connecticut River from eastward, pass southward of Hatchett Reef and Saybrook Bar, until Saybrook Breakwater Light bears 315°. Steer for Saybrook Breakwater Light on this course through the buoyed opening between the south end of Saybrook Bar and the east end of Long Sand Shoal to the entrance channel between the jetties.

(134)   To enter from westward, pass 1 mile southward of Falkner Island Light on course **076°.** This will lead about 0.4 mile northward of the lighted bell buoy on the western end of Long Sand Shoal and about 0.2 mile southward of the lighted bell buoy southward of Cornfield Point. Then steer about **067°,** with Saybrook Breakwater Light a little on the port bow to the entrance channel between the jetties.

(135)   **Pilotage, Connecticut River.**–Pilotage is compulsary in Long Island Sound for foreign vessels and U.S. vessels under register. See Pilotage, Long Island Sound (indexed as such), chapter 8. Pilotage for the Connecticut River is available from Connecticut River Pilots Association (CRPA), 104 Nehantic Trail, Old Saybrook, CT 06475, telephone (203) 388-4167. Pilot boat TRUDEE II is 36-foot, with black hull, white superstructure, and with the word PILOT on the house, forward. The boat monitors channel 16 and 13; works on 13. The CRPA pilot boards vessels abeam of the marina at the south end of Saybrook Point.

(136)   Pilot services are arranged in advance through ships' agents or directly by shipping companies. A 24-hour advance notice is requested.

(137)   Hartford is a **customs port of entry.**

(138)   **Wharves.**–The Connecticut River has more than 20 commercial piers and wharves, most of which handle petroleum products from barges or coastal tankers. Most of the facilities below Rocky Hill, about 34 miles above Saybrook Point, are marginal-type wharves, while those above Rocky Hill are finger-type piers with breasting dolphins. Depths of 11 to 15 feet are reported alongside these facilities.

(139)   **Supplies and repairs.**–Gasoline, diesel fuel, water, ice, and marine supplies are available at the principal towns and landings along the Connecticut River. Boatyards along the river can make engine, hull, and electronic repairs.

(140)   **Charts 12375, 12372.**–Old Saybrook is a village on the west side of Connecticut River, about 1.4 miles northward of Saybrook Breakwater Light. There are several small-craft facilities along the west side of the river from Saybrook Point to **Ferry Point,** about 2 miles to the northward. (See the small-craft facilities tabulation on chart 12372 for services and supplies available.)

(141)   A 5 mph **speed limit** is enforced at Old Saybrook between the railroad bridge and the Connecticut Turnpike bridge.

(142)   **North Cove,** a dredged small-boat basin that affords excellent anchorage, is entered through a dredged channel that leads westward from the main channel about 0.4 mile northward of Saybrook Point. In April 1989, the midchannel controlling depth was 4½ feet in the channel with depths of 4 feet in the basin except for lesser depths along the edges. The entrance channel is marked by private buoys.

(143)   From Saybrook Point to Hartford local knowledge is required to carry the best water. Small craft should have no difficulty in following the channel.

(144)   **Lieutenant River,** leading to **Old Lyme,** enters the east side of Connecticut River about 1.4 miles northward of Saybrook Point. Pipe stakes mark the south side of the channel across the bar at the entrance A midchannel depth of about 3 feet can be carried over the bar to about 0.2 mile above the second bridge. A railroad bridge with a 33-foot fixed span and a clearance of 11 feet crosses the river 0.4 mile above the entrance. An overhead power cable with a reported clearance of about 10 feet is on the north side of the bridge. About 0.3 mile above that bridge is a highway bridge with a 24-foot fixed span and a clearance of 6 feet. A **harbormaster** is at Old Lyme.

(145)   The passage to the east and north of **Calves Island,** about 1 mile above the railroad bridge crossing Connecticut River, is used extensively for mooring small craft in the summer. This passage is subject to shoaling, particularly on the north side of Calves Island; caution is advised. A sunken

barge, covered 2 feet and marked by a private seasonal buoy, is close off the east side of Calves Island in 41°19'31" N., 72°20'37"W. A small-craft facility is on the east side of the passage just above the entrance. Berths, electricity, gasoline, diesel fuel, water, ice, marine supplies, a 25-ton mobile hoist, and a 20-ton crane are available; hull, engine, and electronic reparis can be made. In July 1981, depths of 25 feet were reported at the facility.

(146)   **Lord Cove** has its entrance about 300 yards northward of Calves Island. In July 1981, a depth of 3½ feet was available through the unmarked entrance. The marshlands surrounding Lord Cove and the other coves between Essex and the river mouth at Saybrook are frequented by duck hunters in October and November. Because of danger of gunfire, mariners are cautioned not to stray too close to the numerous duck blinds that exist in this area.

(147)   The dredged section of the main channel in Connecticut River westward of Calves Island has numerous obstructions and sunken rocks close to its edges; mariners are advised to exercise caution and to avoid the edges of the channel.

(148)   **Haydens Point**, about 4.6 miles above Saybrook Point, is marked by a light. Foul ground is between the light and the shore.

(149)   **Essex**, a town on the west bank about 5 miles above Saybrook Point, is the scene of considerable small-boat activity. Depths alongside the town landing are about 6 feet. **Essex Cove** is the area off the main river channel skirting the waterfront at Essex. A dredged channel, marked by private buoys, leads from the main channel through the cove, and thence rejoins the main channel to the northward. In 1973–1974, a controlling depth of 6½ feet was available in the buoyed channel.

(150)   A 5 mph **speed limit** is enforced.

(151)   A privately marked small-boat channel leads westward from near the southerly end of Essex Cove and northward of **Thatchbed Island** to **Middle Cove**. In July 1981, the channel had a reported depth of 6 feet.

(152)   Essex has excellent small-craft facilities. (See the small-craft facilities tabulation on chart 12372 for services and supplies available.)

(153)   **Special anchorages** are at Essex. (See **110.1** and **110.55 (a), (a-1), (b),** and **(c),** chapter 2, for limits and regulations.)

(154)   **Hamburg Cove** and **Eightmile River**, which empties into the north end of the cove, indent the east side of Connecticut River, 6 miles above Saybrook Point. A dredged channel leads from Connecticut River to a turning basin at **Hamburg**, a village at the head of navigation. In 1977, the controlling depth was 3 feet in the channel with 4 feet in the basin except for shoaling at the north end and along the east edge. There are boulders in places outside the dredged channel, and the entrance channel is outlined by grassy flats on each side. Buoys mark the entrance, and private seasonal buoys and daybeacons mark the remainder of the channel to Hamburg. The center of the turning basin has piles used for moorings. A small-craft facility, on the east side of the basin, has berths, electricity, gasoline, water, ice, and some marine supplies.

(155)   **Chart 12377.–Eustasia Island**, 8.5 miles above Saybrook Point, divides the Connecticut River into two channels. A light off the southeast end of the island marks the junction of the two channels. The eastern channel crossing **Potash Bar** through a dredged cut is better marked and easier to follow. The western channel leads to **Pratt Creek**, westward of the southerly end of Eustasia Island, and to the landing at **Deep River** and thence crosses **Chester Creek**

Bar through a swash channel to **Chester Creek**. A sand shoal and a rocky reef, both bare at low water, are north of Eustasia Island, between the main channel east of the island and Chester Creek.

(156)   In July 1981, it was reported that depths of 15 feet could be carried to the facilities on Pratt Creek and in March 1990, depths to 5 feet were reported to the facilities in Chester Creek. A rock, covered 3 feet, is on the south side of the entrance to Chester Creek in about 41°24'24.1"N., 72°25'46.6"W.

(157)   There are several small-craft facilities on Pratt Creek and Chester Creek. Lifts to 25 tons, berths, electricity, gasoline, water, ice, storage, marine supplies, launching ramp, and complete hull and engine repairs are available in the area.

(158)   **Special anchorages** are off Chester Creek. (See **110.1 and 110.55 (e–1) and (e–2),** chapter 2, for limits and regulations.)

(159)   The Chester-Hadlyme vehicular ferry crosses the river near **Fort Hill**, 2 miles above Eustasia Island. The ferry operates from April through November.

(160)   **Special anchorages** are northeastward of Connecticut River Light 45 (41°26.2' N., 72°27.6'W.), about 12.8 miles above Saybrook Point. (See **110.1** and **110.55 (d)** and **(e),** chapter 2, for limits and regulations.)

(161)   On the east side of the river, the turret of the opera house at **East Haddam**, 13.3 miles above Saybrook Point, is prominent. A marina is on the west side of the river just above the swing bridge between East Haddam and **Tylerville**. Limited guest berths, limited marine supplies, electricity, water, and ice are available. In March 1990, a reported depth of 5 feet was available in the marina basin.

(162)   The shoal off the west side of the river, just north of East Haddam, is reported to be increasing.

(163)   **Salmon Cove**, on the east side of the river, 1 mile above East Haddam, is reported to be navigable only by small craft at high tide. The entrance to the cove is subject to shoaling. Considerable grass in the channel and cove makes boat operation difficult.

(164)   Overhead power cables with a least clearance of 86 feet cross the cove about 1.2 miles above the mouth.

(165)   A small-craft facility is on the west side of the river about 1.1 miles above East Haddam. Berths, electricity, water, ice, a 10-ton mobile hoist, and a launching ramp are available; hull and engine repairs can be made. In March 1990, a depth of 6 feet was reported at the facility.

(166)   **Haddam Island** divides the Connecticut River about 3.2 miles above East Haddam. The main river channel leads eastward of the island through a dredged cut known as Haddam Island Bar Channel. A pinnacle rock, covered 13 feet, is in the approach to Haddam Island Bar Channel in 41°29'31"N., 72°30'49" W.

(167)   The passage westward of Haddam Island is closed by a bare sand shoal lying between the island's southerly tip and the westerly shore of the river.

(168)   The shoal off the east side of the river opposite **Higganum Creek**, 5.5 miles above East Haddam, is extending westward.

(169)   A rock breakwater extends southward from the east side of the river, 1 mile above Higganum Creek. In 1969, the shoal, about 200 yards southward of the breakwater, was found to be extending southward.

(170)   A boatyard is on the north side of the river at **Cobalt**, about 3.5 miles above Higganum Creek. Storage facilities and a 15-ton hoist are available. In October 1990, a reported depth of 7 feet could be carried to the facility.

(171)   After passing through the channel in **Paper Rock Shoal**, 9.7 miles above East Haddam, favor the south side of

the river to about 300 yards southeastward of **Bodkin Rock**, then cross to the north side and pass it close-to.

(172)   About 0.5 mile westward of Bodkin Rock, a dredged section of the channel leads along the southerly shore of Connecticut River and southward of Mouse Island Bar.

(173)   **Special anchorages** are along the north and east sides of the river, between Bodkin Rock and Portland. (See **110.1** and **110.55 (f)** and **(g)**, chapter 2, for limits and regulations.)

(174)   Caution is recommended when rounding the point on the south side of the river, about 1.5 miles above Bodkin Rock, to avoid a submerged crib that extends northward from the point.

(175)   **Portland**, 26.3 miles above Saybrook Point, has several boatyards with marine railways; the largest railway can handle craft to 60 feet for engine and hull repairs. Gasoline, water, berths, ice, storage, marine supplies, sewage pump-out, launching ramps, and lifts to 50 tons are available at Portland. In March 1990, depths of 7 to 9 feet were reported available.

(176)   Berthing and water are available at Harbor Park in **Middletown**, across the river from Portland. Depths of 18 feet are reported to be available along the wharves.

(177)   Two small-craft facilities are on the east side of the river at **Gildersleeve**, about 2.5 miles above Portland. Gasoline, diesel fuel, water, marine supplies, a launching ramp, and 15- and 20-ton mobile hoists are available, and hull and engine repairs can be made.

(178)   From **Belamose**, 6.5 miles above Portland, northward to Hartford, the land is much lower, and the Connecticut River narrows, its curves become more pronounced, and both of its shores have numerous wood-stake-and-rock groins.

(179)   A marina on the east side of the river opposite Belamose has gasoline, berths, electricity, water, ice, marine supplies, and a 15-ton lift; engine and hull repairs can be made. In July 1983, the privately marked channel into the marina basin had a reported controlling depth of 7 feet.

(180)   At **Rocky Hill**, 1 mile above Belamose, a seasonal vehicular ferry crosses the river to South Glastonbury. A small-craft launching ramp is just above the ferry landing.

(181)   The cove at **Crow Point**, on the west side of the river about 5.7 miles above Belamose, is used to obtain land fill. Dredging in the cove is uneven, but the bottom is soft ooze. In July 1981, it was reported that the entrance had shoaled to bare and could be used only by small outboards.

(182)   A rock, covered 5 feet, is on the south side of the dredged channel about 0.8 mile above Crow Point in about 41°42'43.0"N., 72°37'46.5"W.; and a shoal that bares is in 41°43'11"N., 72°38'52"W., on the west side of Connecticut River, about 1.9 miles above Crow Point.

(183)   **Wethersfield Cove**, on the west side of the river 14 miles above Portland, is entered through a narrow dredged channel that leads to a dredged anchorage basin about 0.3 mile above the entrance. In June 1977, the midchannel controlling depth was 3 feet, and depths of 6 feet were available in the basin. The channel is marked by daybeacons and buoys. The Interstate 91 highway bridge over the entrance has a fixed span with a clearance of 38 feet. The **speed limit** in the channel and cove is 5 knots. Gasoline, water, ice, transient berthing, and some supplies can be obtained at the yacht club on the south side of the cove. A town marina is on the east side of the cove; a launching ramp is available at the facility. The Wethersfield **harbormaster** can be contacted through the local police department or town hall.

(184)   The only remaining commercial docks at **Hartford** are the bulk fuel handling facility of the Hartford Electric Light Company's powerplant on the west side of the river,

about 0.2 mile below the Charter Oak Bridge, and the Hartford Gas Company's barge unloading facilities on the west side of the river, about 0.5 mile above the Charter Oak Bridge. A flood control dike is along the west side of the river from just north of the Charter Oak Bridge to the Bulkeley Bridge.

(185)   Connecticut River above Hartford is practically unimproved, but is navigable about 30 miles to **Holyoke** for boats not exceeding 3-foot draft, when the river is not low. The channel is constantly shifting.

(186)   **Chart 12354.–Long Sand Shoal** extends 6 miles westward from off the entrance of Connecticut River and has a greatest width of nearly 0.3 mile. The general depths on the shoal are 4 to 15 feet; bottom is hard and lumpy. Shoaling is abrupt on both sides, but especially on the south side, where the 5-fathom curve is only 100 yards from it in places. The shoal is marked at its eastern end by a buoy, and on the south side and west end by lighted sound buoys.

(187)   A fairway lighted whistle buoy is 4.5 miles south of Cornfield Point.

(188)   At the western end of Long Sand Shoal and 1 mile southward is an area about 0.6 mile long with rocky and broken bottom, and with a least found depth of 22 feet.

(189)   **Sixmile Reef**, about 3 miles southwestward of Long Sand Shoal, is an area of broken ground about 2.5 miles long in a west-northwesterly direction with depths of 19 to 30 feet. The bottom is rocky and shoaling is abrupt in places. A lighted bell buoy is off the southerly edge of this reef. With extreme low tides, due to northerly and westerly winds, this shoal may be dangerous to vessels with 15-foot draft. Tide rips occur on the reef whenever the direction of the tidal currents is opposed to that of the wind. This is especially true during spring tides and a southwest wind.

(190)   A ridge with depths of 24 to 36 feet is near the middle of Long Island Sound southward of Sixmile Reef and 5 miles north-northwestward of Horton Point Light. It is marked by a lighted buoy.

(191)   **Charts 12375, 12372.–Cornfield Point**, 2 miles westward of Saybrook Breakwater Light, is marked by a large red-roofed stone building. Rocky shoals and foul ground extend about 0.5 mile southerly from this point and for about 1.9 miles westerly. **Cornfield Point Shoal**, a small rocky patch covered 3 feet, is about 0.4 mile south of the point. Westward of this shoal are **Hen and Chickens**, bare in spots at low water, and **Crane Reef**, an area of broken ground with a least depth of 3 feet. These dangers are buoyed. About 0.5 mile westward of the point is **Halftide Rock**, surrounded by foul ground and marked by a private daybeacon.

(192)   **Charts 12374, 12372.–Westbrook Harbor** is the western part of the open bight between Cornfield Point and Menunketesuck Island. It has many unmarked submerged rocks and is seldom used as an anchorage; the anchorage in Duck Island Roads is better. The bight is characterized by boulders.

(193)   **Westbrook**, a town on the north side of Westbrook Harbor, is marked on its east side by an elevated tank. A **harbormaster** is at Westbrook and can be contacted through the town hall.

(194)   **Menunketesuck Island** is the outermost of several low narrow islands connected to the mainland at low water on the west side of Westbrook Harbor. It has boulders at the south end. A boulder reef extends nearly 0.5 mile south-southeastward from the point to the 18-foot curve. Tide rips frequently occur on this reef. A private seasonal buoy is about 0.3 mile southeastward of Menunketesuck Island.

(195)   Between Menunketesuck Island and Hammonasset Point, about 4 miles westward, broken ground extends about 1.5 miles offshore. A boulder reef extends 0.5 mile southward from Duck Island to the 18-foot curve and is marked by a buoy. A rock with 1 foot over it is on this reef about 300 yards south of Duck Island. Tide rips have been reported to extend from the vicinity of these rocks to the buoy. During strong flood currents and a southwest wind, tide rips extend from the shoal water southwest of Duck Island to the vicinity of **Southwest Reef** over 1 mile southwestward. Caution is advised when navigating small boats in this vicinity during these conditions.

(196)   **Duck Island Roads**, between Menunketesuck Island and **Kelsey Point**, is a harbor of refuge protected by breakwaters 1,100 feet northward and nearly 0.5 mile westward from **Duck Island**, with the added protection of Kelsey Point Breakwater on Stone Island Reef. A prominent landmark on Duck Island is a stone chimney. Both breakwaters extending from Duck Island are marked by lights.

(197)   The dredged anchorage enclosed by the breakwaters extending northward and westward from Duck Island is subject to shoaling. General depths of 4 to 7 feet are in the protected area, and 8 to 15 feet in the western end. In addition to the area inside the breakwaters, a small area northward and northeastward of Duck Island North Breakwater Light can be used as an anchorage in southwesterly weather.

(198)   The western entrance of Duck Island Roads is easy of access and should be used by vessels with greater draft than 8 feet.

(199)   **Routes.**–Pass southward of Duck Island and keep the light on the end of Kelsey Point Breakwater bearing northward of 264° until Duck Island West Breakwater Light 2DI bears 010°, then steer northward. Approaching from westward, the only dangers are the two 16-foot spots southsouthwestward of Kelsey Point Breakwater Light, the southerly of which is marked by a buoy.

(200)   The eastern entrance of Duck Island Roads is obstructed by a sand shoal with a least depth of 8 feet about 0.3 mile eastward of Duck Island, and by boulder reefs which extend about 0.2 mile off the western side of Menunketesuck Island. This entrance is easy of access for vessels drawing up to 8 feet.

(201)   Anchorage in 18 to 24 feet, bottom generally sticky, can be had between the Duck Island West Breakwater Light 2DI and the 17-foot rocky patches southeastward of Kelsey Point. This anchorage is exposed to winds southward of east and west.

(202)   **Patchogue River**, used chiefly by fishing and recreational craft, empties into Duck Island Roads just west of Menunketesuck Island. A channel leads from deep water in Duck Island Roads to the first fixed highway bridge, about 0.6 mile above the mouth. The approach channel is marked by buoys, and the river channel is marked by private aids. A light is on the outer end of the breakwater on the west side of the river mouth. In January 1990, the midchannel controlling depth was 7 feet from the entrance to the first turn near Menunketesuck River, thence 5½ feet in the western half of the channel to a point just above Buoy 6, thence a midchannel controlling depth of 6½ feet to the head of the project. The anchorage basin had depths of 4½ to 8 feet, except for shoaling to about 1 foot near the southeast corner.

(203)   In May 1991, shoaling to bare was reported near the channel edge between Buoy 3 and Light 3A.

(204)   Several **small-craft facilities** are on the river. (See the small-craft facilities tabulation on chart 12372 for services and supplies available.)

(205)   **Menunketesuck River**, sharing the same entrance channel as Patchogue River, is a shallow stream westward of Patchogue River. In July 1981, a depth of about 8 feet was reported to the first fixed highway bridge crossing the river above which depths of less than 1 foot are reported. A shoal was reported extending south from shore at the junction of Patchogue and Menunketesuck Rivers; caution is advised. The junction is marked by a private seasonal buoy. Small-craft facilities on the river can provide berths, electricity, gasoline, diesel fuel, water, ice, storage, marine supplies, and engine and hull repairs; a 12-ton mobile hoist is available. The privately maintained channel in the river is reported to be marked by seasonal private aids; local knowledge is advised.

(206)   A 6 mph **speed limit** is enforced on both rivers.

(207)   **Kelsey Point Breakwater** extends on **Stone Island Reef** over 0.6 mile south-southeastward from Stone Island and is marked by a light. The least depth on the rocky broken ground southwestward of the light is 16 feet. The outer spot is marked by a buoy. **Stone Island**, at the north end of the breakwater, is mostly covered at high water. Some rocks bare at low water are between the island and the shore. Tide rips frequently occur in the area southwestward from the end of the breakwater to the bell buoy. Depths of 18 feet or less near Kelsey Point Breakwater indicate areas of broken rocky bottom which should be avoided in anchoring. The broken ground east of the breakwater includes depths of 12 feet close to it; the 18-foot patch 0.2 mile east-northeast of the end of the breakwater; **East Ledge** with depths of 2 to 17 feet, which extends 0.4 mile southward from Kelsey Point; and the broken ground with depths of 8 to 17 feet which extends over 0.4 mile southeastward from Kelsey Point.

(208)   The bight at the entrance of Clinton Harbor and westward of Kelsey Point Breakwater affords anchorage, but is exposed to southeasterly and southwesterly winds.

(209)   **Clinton Harbor**, the bight westward of Kelsey Point Breakwater, is the entrance to **Hammonasset River**, a stream used chiefly by fishing and recreational craft. **Wheeler Rock**, with 1 foot over it, just outside the bar, is marked by a lighted buoy. The channel is marked by buoys to Cedar Island and thence by seasonal private buoys to the anchorage basin at **Clinton**. A radiobeacon is on the east side of the harbor about 0.55 mile north of **Hammock Point**. In July-August 1989, the midchannel controlling depth was 5½ feet to Buoy 11A, thence 7 feet in the north half of the channel to the head of the project, thence depths of 4½ to 8 feet were available in the anchorage basin on the northeast side of the channel east of the wharves at Clinton. From opposite the basin to the upstream limit of the Federal project, the southwest and south side of the channel is obstructed by a series of pilings. Boats may be moored between the pilings, caution is advised. Above the dredged channel, the midchannel controlling depth is about 2 feet in the Hammonasset River to the overhead pipeline and bridge crossing about 2 miles above Clinton. Private daybeacons mark this section of the channel.

(210)   Several boatyards and marinas are in the harbor. (See the small-craft facilities tabulation on chart 12372 for services and supplies available.) Mooring facilities are available by arrangement with the town **dockmaster** who can be contacted through the town hall or police department. A 6 mph **speed limit** is enforced in the harbor. The town maintains a fireboat at Clinton Harbor. The vessel can be contacted through the Clinton Police Department or the Coast Guard.

(211)   Northeastward of **Cedar Island** in Clinton Harbor are two narrow crooked channels close together, with depths of about 1 foot. The eastern one is usually marked by bush stakes; it leads to a marina and boatyard just inside the mouth of **Hammock River**. The western channel, marked by a private range, leads to a boatyard on **Indian River**.

(212) **Hammonasset Point**, on the southwest side of Clinton Harbor, is a low marshy area with many wooded knolls. The end of the point is a rocky knoll. **Hammonasset State Park** is marked by a conspicuous flagstaff and the buildings at the recreational center. In the summer it is an active resort. Broken ground with rocky irregular bottom and least depths of 10 to 11 feet extends 0.5 mile southward of Hammonasset Point.

(213) **West Rock** is the outermost of the bare rocks which extend a short distance off the east end of Hammonasset Point. A reef, with two bare rocks and a groin on its inner part, extends 0.3 mile southwestward from the point and is marked by a buoy, northeastward of which tide rips frequently occur. When rounding the point, vessels should not pass between the buoy and Hammonasset Point.

(214) **Madison Reef**, over 2 miles westward of Hammonasset Point, extends over a mile east and west. This reef consists of several rocky patches with depths of 4 to 17 feet, with deeper water between them. **Charles Reef**, with a least depth of 7 feet, is about 0.5 mile southwest of Madison Reef and marked by a buoy.

(215) **Kimberly Reef**, about 1.9 miles southward of Charles Reef, is an area of broken ground with a least depth of 12 feet. An isolated 27-foot spot, marked by a lighted horn buoy, is about 0.2 mile south of the shoal. A bank with depths of 14 to 28 feet extends about 1.5 miles west of Kimberly Reef to Falkner Island.

(216) Vessels of 10-foot draft can anchor northward of Madison Reef, but should proceed with caution to avoid the rocky patches at lesser depths.

(217) **Tuxis Island**, northward of Madison Reef and 0.2 mile south of **Middle Beach**, is high and rocky. Between the island and the shore the water is shallow and the ground foul. Rocks awash are 200 to 600 yards eastward of the island, and an islet is 100 yards westward of the island. A steel bulkhead in ruins, the top of which is awash at high water, extends from shore to **Gull Rock**, a high bare ledge about 300 yards east-northeastward of Tuxis Island.

(218) **Madison**, a town on the railroad, has one landing which bares alongside at low water and is in disrepair. A few small craft moor in the cove on its north side. Rocks, bare at low water, are 100 yards eastward of the landing. A beach club building, with a small stone landing, is northward of Tuxis Island. A church with a prominent tower and gilded dome is 0.8 mile northward of Tuxis Island.

(219) **Charts 12373, 12372.–Guilford Harbor**, a bight 5.5 miles westward of Hammonasset Point, is used only by small craft. **East River** and **Sluice Creek** empty into Guilford Harbor from the northward. The approach to the harbor is obstructed by rocks and foul ground. The outermost dangers are: **Half Acre Rock**, about 0.8 mile southeastward of the entrance channel, which shows at high water; scattered rocks, some bare at low water and others with 7 to 16 feet over them, extending about a mile eastward from Half Acre Rock; **Outer White Top**, about 0.6 mile southwestward of Half Acre Rock, and several rocks northward of it bare at low water; and **Indian Reef**, extending about 1 mile southwestward of Outer White Top, the highest part of which is covered at high water. Indian Reef is marked on its south and southwestern sides by buoys. Stakes and fish traps may exist northward of **Riding Rock**, 0.6 mile northwestward of Half Acre Rock.

(220) The approach channel to Guilford Harbor, marked by buoys, leads along the southeasterly side of Indian Reef, thence westward of Half Acre Rock to a dredged channel about 0.5 mile northwestward of Half Acre Rock. The dredged channel leads northward through the harbor and

eastward of **Guilford Point** to a junction with Sluice Creek and East River, about 0.6 mile above the channel entrance. At the junction, the dredged channel leads northwesterly into Sluice Creek for about 0.1 mile and northeasterly into East River for about 0.4 mile to an anchorage basin. Buoys and a private range mark the dredged channel to the junction. In 1985, the reported midchannel controlling depth in the dredged channel was 4 feet to the junction of East River and Sluice Creek, thence in 1981-1982, the midchannel controlling depths were 4 feet in Sluice Creek, thence 5½ feet in East River to the anchorage basin, with 5 to 6 feet in the basin except for shoaling to bare toward the north limit.

(221) In May 1988, a submerged obstruction was reported about 0.3 mile southwest of Half Acre Rock in about 41°51.1'N., 72°39.6'W.

(222) At high water and with local knowledge, small boats can go above the anchorage basin in East River to the fixed railway bridge, about 1.3 miles above the basin. The bridge has a clearance of 4 feet. An overhead power cable with a clearance of 45 feet is about 0.3 miles below the bridge. A town marina, just above the entrance to Sluice Creek, has berths, electricity, water, and a launching ramp. In July 1981, depths of 1 to 2 feet were reported alongside the marina.

(223) A 5 mph **speed limit** is enforced in the harbor.

(224) **West River** empties into the western side of Guilford Harbor 0.2 mile westward of Guilford Point. A railroad bridge about 0.7 mile above the mouth has a clearance of 6 feet. **Guilford** is the town above the railroad bridge. In September 1988-July 1989, a depth of 4½ feet was reported in West River entrance channel; the channel is marked by buoys and a 321° lighted range.

(225) There are two boatyards with several marinas and marine railways on West River. The largest marine railway can handle craft up to 40 feet; limited supplies, a 12-ton mobile crane, and complete engine and hull repairs are available.

(226) **Falkner Island** and **Goose Islands**, with **Stony Island** to the southward, are about 3 miles south of Guilford Harbor. Each is surrounded by reefs and rocks that bare at low water. A depth of about 16 feet can be carried between Goose Islands and Falkner Island by staying in the middle of the passage and avoiding the 8-foot and 11-foot spots, about 0.35 mile 244° and 0.4 mile 300° from the light on Falkner Island, respectively, and the shoals and reefs extending from the islands. **Falkner Island Light** (41°12.7'N., 72°39.2' W.), 94 feet above the water, is shown from a 46-foot white octagonal tower near the center of Falkner Island. A lighted gong buoy marks the shoal off the northern end of Falkner Island, and a lighted bell buoy is off the southern end of Stony Island.

(227) From Indian Reef westward are rocky shoals and islets extending from 0.2 to 0.7 mile off **Vineyard Point** and **Sachem Head**. **Chimney Corner Reef**, about 0.3 mile south of Sachem Head and marked by a buoy, is a rocky broken area on which the least depth is 9 feet. Westward of it are **Goose Rocks Shoals**, on which are **Goose Rocks**, the northerly of which is bare and the southerly one covered at high water. The outer limit of Goose Rocks Shoals is marked by a lighted bell buoy. To ensure clearing the westerly end of Goose Rocks Shoals, care must be taken not to round the buoy too closely.

(228) **Sachem Head Harbor**, an anchorage for small craft on the southwest side of Sachem Head, is 0.3 mile long and 0.1 mile wide, and has depths of 3 to 8 feet at the floats and in the moorings; it is sheltered except from westerly winds. The island forming the south point at the entrance is connected with the shore by a bridge. A yacht clubhouse is on

the island. From the north point of the island a breakwater extends 100 yards in a northwesterly direction; a rock awash, marked by a private seasonal light, is off the end of the breakwater. A rock covered at half tide is 50 yards off the southeast side of the harbor, about 350 yards eastward of the end of the breakwater.

(229)   The approach to Sachem Head Harbor for small craft from eastward is along the south side of the rocks making off from the south side of Sachem Head. Approaching eastward of Goose Rocks, give the rocks a berth of over 300 yards. The approach from westward is clear between Goose Rocks and Leetes Rocks.

(230)   **Joshua Point,** the western extremity of Sachem Head, is marked by a rocky islet on its west side and a privately maintained seasonal light. Just northward of the islet a stone jetty with a bulkhead on its north side extends about 100 yards in a northwesterly direction from the shore. Vessels can anchor in the angle near the shore where the depth is about 4½ feet.

(231)   **Joshua Cove,** northwestward of Sachem Head, is little used, but affords good anchorage in its entrance for small vessels in northerly or easterly winds in 6 to 10 feet, soft bottom. The approach from southwestward is clear between Goose Rocks and Leetes Rocks.

(232)   **Leetes Rocks,** midway between Sachem Head and the north end of The Thimbles, are two rocks bare at low water, with an area of broken ground around them. A 9-foot spot is about 200 yards southward of the southerly rock, and a 3-foot spot is 0.3 mile northeast of the southerly rock.

(233)   **Leetes Island Quarry** is a prominent feature on the south side of **Hoadley Point;** on the north side of the cove eastward of the point are the ruins of an old dock.

(234)   **The Thimbles,** about 1.6 miles west of Sachem Head, comprise many islands, islets, and rocks that bare. All of the area, extending over 2 miles from Hoadley Point southwestward to **East Reef,** is foul with rocky bottom and many shoals. To lesser extent, the area from East Reef for 2 miles westward and northwestward to Branford Harbor entrance is dotted with islets and rocks. The whole area is suitable only for small pleasure craft, which are very active here in summer. Many oyster stakes are encountered; these do not mark channels and caution should be used to avoid fouling them. Caution also is advised to avoid fouling the pipelines and cables in the area.

(235)   The outermost of The Thimbles proper is **Outer Island,** marked by a house chimney. A boat landing protected by a stone jetty is on the northeast side of this island, and an unmarked rock, bare at lowest tides, is 200 yards eastward. The reefs southwestward of Outer Island, to and including East Reef and **Browns Reef,** are buoyed.

(236)   From eastward a buoyed channel leads through The Thimbles. The channel passes between **Wayland Island** and a buoy marking the foul area southward of **Cat Island.** The channel extends between **Davis Island** and **Dogfish Island,** thence north of **East Crib** and **West Crib** into the more open water westward of The Thimbles; it is good for about 13 feet.

(237)   **Stony Creek,** a village on the railroad, extends southward to **Flying Point** (41°15.5'N., 72°45.1'W.). A dredged channel west of Flying Point leads north to a turning basin at Stony Creek. The channel is marked by private buoys. In December 1988, the midchannel controlling depths were 3 feet in the channel with 1 to 4 feet in the basin. Rocks were reported in the northwest corner of the basin. Gasoline, marine supplies, inside storage, and a small-craft launching ramp are available at marinas eastward of the turning basin; small craft can be hauled out on a flatbed trailer for hull and engine repairs. The village dock is on the southeast side of the turning basin.

(238)   Between the rocks westward of **Rogers Island** and **Blackstone Rocks,** a privately dredged channel, 0.9 mile westward of Flying Point, leads northeastward to a quarry wharf on the west side of a dredged basin. In 1980, the channel and basin had a reported controlling depth of 13 feet. The entrance channel is marked by a private **028°** range consisting of a front and middle light and a rear daybeacon.

(239)   **Thimble Island Harbor,** in the western part of The Thimbles, affords good shelter for small craft between **Pot Island** and **Money Island** on the east and **High Island** and **West Crib** on the west. Although open southwestward, the sea from that direction loses much of its force before reaching the inner harbor. A rock with 3 feet over it and marked by a buoy is 80 yards off the east side of High Island, just above its south end. Vessels sometimes anchor near midchannel, between this rock and the north end of Pot Island in depths of 13 to 18 feet, soft bottom, but care should be taken to avoid the cables in the area. The harbor is easy of access between Outer Island and Inner Reef.

(240)   **Pine Orchard,** about 3 miles westward of Sachem Head, is a summer resort extending northward and westward of **Brown Point.** A breakwater extending about 300 yards southeastward from Brown Point protects a yacht basin entered through a privately dredged channel that leads from southward of **St. Helena Island** north-northwestward to the basin. In 1978, the entrance channel and basin had reported depths of 7 feet. The basin approach northward of St. Helena Island has depths of 3 to 5 feet. Gasoline, diesel fuel, ice, and water may be obtained at the yacht club landing.

(241)   From Brown Point to Branford Harbor, 2.5 miles westward, bare rocks and shoals extend up to about 2 miles offshore. A seawall extends westward from Brown Point, and the shore is thickly settled. A rock bare at half tide is 600 yards westward of Brown Point and 300 yards from shore.

(242)   Rocks bare at low water are eastward of **Haycock Point,** and rocks that bare at half tide are off the southeast side and southwest end of **Green Island.** The foul ground extends about 0.6 mile south-southwestward from Haycock Point, including **Foot Rocks** which are partly above water.

(243)   **Branford Reef,** about 1.8 miles southward of Indian Neck and 5 miles eastward of New Haven entrance, is marked by a light. This reef is surrounded by shoal water for a distance of 150 to 450 yards from the light.

(244)   Deep water is between Branford Reef and **Negro Heads,** a reef bare in one place at low water about 0.9 mile northward. Shoreward of Negro Heads are **Spectacle Island, Sumac Island,** and **Clam Island,** together with numerous rocks bare and covered.

(245)   A private boat landing is on the northwest side of Clam Island. Small craft can enter **Maltby Cove** between the bare rocks off the southwest end of Clam Island and **Jeffrey Rock,** favoring the northwest side of Clam Island. Private markers are sometimes at the entrance. The northwest side of the cove is foul, the principal danger being a rock bare at low water near the middle, northwestward of Clam Island; the rock is sometimes marked by a seasonal private spindle.

(246)   **Jeffrey Point,** the eastern point at the entrance of Branford Harbor, has a bare rock close to its western end.

(247)   **Branford Harbor** is a shallow cove between Jeffrey Point and Johnson Point. Vessels up to 10-foot draft can select anchorage in the harbor southward of the Mermaids in 10 to 14 feet, protected against all but southerly and southwesterly winds. Boats up to 5-foot draft can select a well-

sheltered anchorage in the upper part of the harbor above the Mermaids. The harbor is used chiefly for recreational boating and by the small local lobster fishing fleet.

(248) The dangers in the approach and entrance to Branford Harbor either show above water or are marked by buoys. **Cow and Calf**, 1.3 miles southwestward of Jeffrey Point, are two boulders close together bare at low water. Boulders, reported covered 10 feet, are about 0.2 mile northward of Cow and Calf. **Five Foot Rock**, 0.5 mile northeastward of Cow and Calf, has 5 feet over it. **Taunton Rock**, 0.9 mile northeastward of Cow and Calf near the middle of the entrance to Branford Harbor, is large but low and bare. **Blyn Rock**, midway between Johnson Point and Taunton Rock, is covered at extreme high tide. **Bird Rock**, 0.2 mile northward of Blyn Rock, has 5 feet over it.

(249) **Little Mermaid**, showing a little above high water, and **Big Mermaid**, a high rock marked by a light, are near the middle of Branford Harbor. Two bare rocks are near the head of the harbor. A rock, bare at low water and usually marked by stakes, is about 100 feet north-northeastward of the north end of **Lovers Island**.

(250) **Routes.**–To enter Branford Harbor from eastward, pass southward of the lighted buoy marking Negro Heads, steer about **306°** heading for Taunton Rock, and enter between Taunton and Jeffrey Rocks; or a **333°** course with Branford Reef Light astern will lead into the harbor between Jeffrey and Taunton Rocks. From westward, pass southward and over 100 yards eastward of the lighted bell buoy marking Cow and Calf, thence westward of the buoys marking Blyn Rock and Bird Rock to the buoyed channel in the harbor.

(251) Local craft pass northwestward of Cow and Calf Shoal and midway between Johnson Point and Blyn Rock.

(252) **Branford River**, narrow and crooked, extends northeasterly from Branford Harbor. In February-March 1990, the controlling depths in the dredged channel were 8 feet from Branford Harbor to a point about 0.2 mile above **Branford Point**, thence 6½ feet at midchannel to the upstream limit of the dredged channel. In 1981, the wharves at Branford were in disrepair.

(253) At low water the channel above Branford Point is defined by bare shoals on each side. During the summer numerous stakes used as moorings mark both sides of the channel. A privately dredged channel and basin at a marina 0.5 mile east of Branford Point had reported depths of 7 feet in July 1981.

(254) The principal waterborne commerce at Branford is in petroleum products. There are several marinas and boatyards on the river. (See the small-craft facilities tabulation on chart 12372 for services and supplies available.)

(255) A 5 mph **speed limit** is enforced on the river.

(256) The **harbormaster** at Branford controls all moorings and anchoring; he can be contacted through the small-craft facilities.

(257) **Johnson Point** is the western entrance point to Branford Harbor; a rock covered 2 feet is about 100 yards off its south side. A small privately dredged basin on the southwest side of the point is well protected in all but southerly winds. In 1971, it was reported that 4 feet could be carried to and in the basin.

(258) **Gull Rocks**, about 0.3 mile westward of Johnson Point, consist of small islets and submerged rocks that extend about 0.5 mile southwestward from shore on the easterly side of the entrance to a large cove. A rock, bare at half tide, is in the northwestern part of the cove about 350 yards southward of **Short Beach**. The northwest end of the cove has a yacht club landing with a reported depth of 2 feet alongside.

(259) **Farm River Gut**, a small bight on the west side of the cove, is a good anchorage for small craft. Depths range from 4 to 5 feet in the eastern part of the gut with shoaling to bare in the northern and western parts. Two rocks awash are on the north side of the gut about 125 yards inside the entrance. The gut offers good protection from all but easterly winds, mud bottom. A marine railway at a boatyard on the north side of the gut can handle boats to 40 feet for engine and hull repairs. The yard can be reached only at high tide. **Old Clump** is a bare rock about 400 yards south of the bight.

(260) **Farm River**, locally known as East Haven River, about 1.5 miles westward of Branford Harbor, is used by local craft. In July 1981, it was reported that depths of 3 feet could be carried in the river to the fixed bridge with a clearance of 4 feet about 1 mile above the mouth. Several boatyards on the river provide gasoline, berths, electricity, water, storage, and limited marine supplies; diesel fuel can be delivered by truck. A 10-ton mobile hoist and a 12-ton crane can handle vessels for complete engine and hull repairs.

(261) **East Indies Rocks**, about 0.4 mile south of the entrance to Farm River, cover at half tide and are marked by a buoy to the eastward; a rocky shoal with a least depth of 5 feet is 0.2 mile to the eastward. A small ledge, bare at low water, is midway between East Indies Rocks and the south side of Mansfield Point, the western entrance point to Farm River. **Darrow Rocks**, a group of bare rocks, are on the east side of the entrance to the river. The westernmost rocky knoll is marked by a flagstaff. A ledge, bare at low water, with a buoy off its southern end, is 200 yards south of the flagstaff.

(262) **Mansfield Point** and the shore westward of the entrance to Farm River are thickly settled. Bus communication is available to New Haven.

(263) **Charts 12371, 12372.**–**New Haven Harbor**, an important harbor of refuge, is about 68 miles from New York, 179 miles from Boston via Cape Cod Canal, and 171 miles from Nantucket Shoals Lighted Horn Buoy N (LNB). It comprises all the tidewater northward of the breakwaters constructed across the mouth of the bay, including the navigable portions of the West, Mill, and Quinnipiac Rivers. It is about 2 miles wide. The inner harbor, northward of Sandy Point and Fort Hale, is shallow for the most part, except where the depths have been increased by dredging. The main entrance channel, between Middle Breakwater and the East Breakwater, leads northward to Tomlinson Bridge at New Haven. Anchorage basins for medium draft vessels are on the west side of the channel north of Sandy Point. Waterborne commerce in the harbor consists of petroleum products, scrap metal, lumber, automobiles, gypsum, paper and pulp products, steel products, chemicals, rock salt, and general cargo.

(264) **New Haven**, at the head of the harbor, is an important manufacturing city.

(265) **Prominent features.**–On the approach from well offshore in clear weather, the prominent landmarks are: on East Rock (41°19.7'N., 72°54.4'W.), the Soldiers and Sailors Monument; in New Haven, the Knights of Columbus Building, a tall rectangular structure with circular pillars at its corners; the lighted stack of the powerplant on the east side of the harbor opposite City Point; and on the west side of Mill River, a large gas tank with a red and white checkerboard band around the top and the words "New Haven Gas". The lights on the ends of the breakwaters, the aerolight at Tweed-New Haven Airport, and the abandoned tower on Lighthouse Point are also prominent.

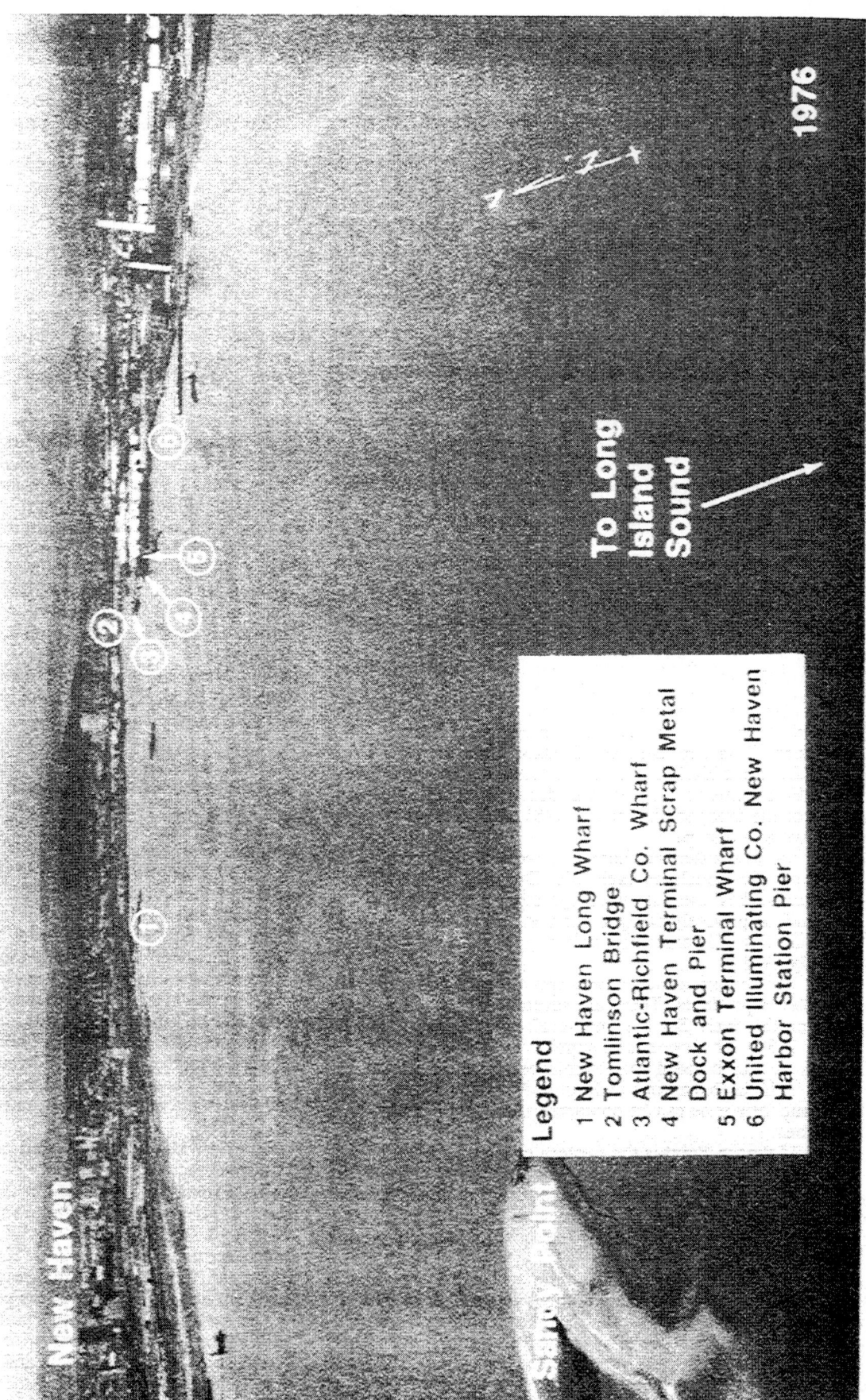

NEW HAVEN HARBOR

New Haven

Sandy Point

To Long Island Sound

1976

Legend

1 New Haven Long Wharf
2 Tomlinson Bridge
3 Atlantic-Richfield Co. Wharf
4 New Haven Terminal Scrap Metal
  Dock and Pier
5 Exxon Terminal Wharf
6 United Illuminating Co. New Haven
  Harbor Station Pier

(266) **Southwest Ledge Light** (41°14.1′N., 72°54.7′W.), 57 feet above the water, is shown from a white octagonal house on a brown cylindrical pier at the westerly end of East Breakwater. A fog signal is sounded at the light.

(267) **Channels.**–A Federal project for New Haven Harbor provides for an entrance channel 35 feet deep to a point just below the junction of Mill River and Quinnipiac River. The channel is well marked. (See Notice to Mariners and latest editions of the charts for controlling depths.)

(268) **West River**, on the west side of the main channel about 3 miles above Southwest Ledge Light, has a dredged channel marked by buoys to just below the first highway bridge (Kimberly Avenue Bridge), 1.2 miles above the channel entrance. In November 1988-March 1989, the midchannel controlling depth was 9½ feet from the channel entrance to Buoy 18, thence 5½ feet (8 feet at midchannel) to the Connecticut Turnpike Bridge, the head of navigation. An anchorage area is on the south side of the channel about 0.9 mile above the entrance; in 1988-March 1989, the controlling depth was 4½ feet. Principal waterfront facilities are at **City Point**.

(269) **Mill River**, on the west side of **Fair Haven** about 4 miles above Southwest Ledge Light, is entered from the main channel through a dredged entrance channel that branches into an east and west fork to the Grand Avenue Bridge, 0.6 mile above the mouth. In June 1982, the controlling depths were 6½ feet (11 feet at midchannel) to the Chapel Street Bridge about 0.25 mile above the entrance, thence 9 feet through the east bridge opening and 3½ feet through the west opening, thence 6½ feet to the junction with the east and west forks, thence 9½ feet at midchannel for about 250 yards in the east fork, thence in 1980, 1 foot at midchannel to the head of the channel, and in 1980-June 1982, 5½ feet at midchannel for about 225 yards in the west fork, thence in 1980, 1½ feet at midchannel to the head of the channel.

(270) **Quinnipiac River**, on the east side of Fair Haven about 4 miles above Southwest Ledge Light, has a dredged channel to Grand Avenue Bridge, about 1 mile above the mouth. In October 1982, the controlling depth was 15 feet at midchannel to the Ferry Street Bridge about 0.5 mile above the mouth, thence in 1977, 8 feet through the bridge, thence in 1980-October 1982, 10 feet to the Grand Avenue Bridge except for shoaling along the edges.

(271) **Anchorages.**–Inside West Breakwater and the southwest half of Middle Breakwater, anchorage is available for vessels up to 20-foot draft. Caution should be exercised to avoid the fish stakes in this area.

(272) Vessels may anchor northward of Southwest Ledge Light in depths of 18 to 20 feet, soft bottom in places. Care should be taken to avoid the ledges northward of the East Breakwater. Deep-draft vessels awaiting berthing assignments can anchor about 1 mile southward of the sea buoy; holding ground is excellent.

(273) **Morris Cove**, on the east side of the main channel just above Lighthouse Point, affords good anchorage and is used by yachts, but is rough in westerly and southerly winds. In July 1981, isolated, uncharted 40-foot spots were reported in the cove. Caution is advised when anchoring. **New Haven Coast Guard Station** is on the north side of the jutting point, about 1.5 miles northward of Lighthouse Point.

(274) An anchorage basin on the west side of the main channel southward of New Haven Long Wharf is sometimes used, but considerable shoaling is gradually extending into the anchorage from westward. A sunken barge with 5 feet over it is in this anchorage about 550 yards southward of

New Haven Long Wharf. In February-March 1985, depths of 10 to 5 feet were available in the anchorage basin with lesser depths along the edges.

(275) An anchorage area, sometimes used by small craft and scows, is northward of the New Haven Long Wharf (Naval Reserve Pier) in the northwest side of the main channel where depths range from about 5 to 6 feet.

(276) No special regulations prescribe the limits within which vessels must anchor, except that the dredged channels must be kept clear.

(277) **Dangers.**–**Townshend Ledge**, 2.7 miles southeastward of Southwest Ledge Light, has a least depth of 18 feet and is marked by a lighted bell buoy.

(278) **Stony Islet**, 2.2 miles eastward of Southwest Ledge Light, is low, bare, and surrounded by ledges bare at low water to a distance of about 100 yards. A partly bare ledge is about 0.2 mile north-northwestward of Stony Islet. From this ledge and Stony Islet westward to the entrance of New Haven Harbor, an area of foul ground with many rocks bare at low water extends about 0.5 mile offshore. This area should be avoided.

(279) Shoals with 16 to 18 feet over them extend over 0.5 mile southeastward from the breakwaters on both sides of the dredged entrance channel. A spoil area with reported depths of 15 feet is on the eastern side of the entrance channel. An 18-foot spot is on the east side of the main channel, at the first turn westward of Southwest Ledge Light.

(280) The bights on the west shore of New Haven Harbor from Pond Point northward are shoal with bare rocks and foul ground in most of them. The shore is rocky at **Woodmont**, about 2 miles northeastward of Pond Point.

(281) **Black Rock**, bare at low water and marked by a seasonal buoy, is 0.2 mile off the north end of Morris Cove. Opposite, on the west side, is a breakwater, partly covered, extending from **Sandy Point** and marked by a light. **Shag Bank**, a flat extending about 0.5 mile northward from Sandy Point, has a sand tip about 0.1 mile long.

(282) **Bridges.**–Tomlinson Bridge, at the head of the main harbor at the confluence of Mill and Quinnipiac Rivers, has a double bascule span with a clearance of 60 feet. Just above this bridge is a fixed highway bridge with a clearance of 60 feet. The bridgetender of the Tomlinson Bridge monitors VHF-FM channel 13; call sign KXJ-688. An overhead power cable with a clearance of 91 feet crosses the channel just above the fixed highway bridge.

(283) A **regulated navigation area** is at Tomlinson Bridge. (**See 165.1 through 165.13, and 165.304,** chapter 2, for limits and regulations.)

(284) Over Mill River, about 0.3 mile above the entrance, is the Chapel Street Bridge with a swing span having clearance of 7 feet. In April 1990, a replacement bridge with a design clearance of 7½ feet was under construction. The fixed highway bridge at Grand Avenue has a clearance of 6 feet over the east fork and a clearance of 2 feet over the west fork. Bridges above this point have minimum clearance of 2 feet. Small unmasted boats go as far as the bridge at State Street, 0.5 mile above Grand Avenue. Overhead power cables crossing the west fork have a minimum clearance of 80 feet.

(285) The Ferry Street Bridge over Quinnipiac River, 0.6 mile above the Tomlinson Bridge, has a bascule span with a clearance of 25 feet. The Grand Avenue Bridge, 0.5 mile farther upstream, has a center-pier swing span with a clearance of 9 feet. Above this are several fixed bridges and trestles.

(286) Kimberly Avenue Bridge over West River has a fixed span with a clearance of 23 feet.

(287) (**See 117.1 through 117.59 and 117.213,** chapter 2, for drawbridge regulations.)

(288) **Tides.**–The mean range of tide is 6.2 feet. Extreme tides have been recorded as reaching more than 2.5 feet below the plane of mean low water and more than 8 feet above the same datum.

(289) **Currents.**–In the entrance between the breakwaters, the tidal current has a velocity on flood of 1.4 knots, and ebb 0.9 knot. The flood sets 319° and the ebb 152°. In the draw of Tomlinson Bridge, the velocity is 0.4 knot. The flood sets 015° and the ebb 215°. Ebb velocities are increased by freshets. (Consult the Tidal Current Tables for predicted times and velocities of currents.)

(290) **Ice** generally obstructs navigation to some extent for low-powered vessels from December to March and sometimes extends to the mouth of the harbor. During severe winters the accumulation of ice is local. Except in severe weather, powered vessels can always enter and leave the harbor without much difficulty. In New Haven Harbor northerly winds tend to clear the harbor of ice if the formation is light; southerly winds are apt to force in drift ice from the sound.

(291) **Weather.**–New Haven's climate is typical of coastal areas of southern New England. It is vigorous without being overly severe. New Haven is located at the widest part of Long Island Sound, and the tempering effect of the water is most pronounced in this vicinity. During the summer season, the sea breeze holds temperatures 5° to 15° lower in the afternoon; during the winter season, minimum temperatures in the southern section of the city are usually 5° to 10° higher than those reported from northern sections. The highest summertime temperatures occur with a moderate northerly wind. The lowest winter readings also occur with a northerly wind.

(292) **Precipitation** is quite evenly distributed throughout the year. The elevation of the land increases northward from the station and results in somewhat higher amounts of precipitation in the northern suburbs as well as a few more thunderstorms each year. During the winter, a variety of precipitation is found in most storms. It is common to have rain along the shore, freezing rain and sleet a short distance inland, and snow in the northern parts of the city. Heavy snow is rather uncommon in the immediate coastal area and usually melts in a few days. Farther inland, the snow becomes progressively heavier and a layer of snow coversthe ground most of the winter.

(293) **Prevailing wind** direction varies with the seasons. From late spring until fall, winds are predominantly south to southwest due to the effect of the sea breeze. During the winter, the prevailing winds are northerly. Strong southeast winds cause unusually high tides and some local flooding in low-lying coastal areas two or three times a year.

(294) The National Weather Service maintains an office at the Tweed-New Haven Airport, about 3 miles southeast of the city. (See page T-6 for **New Haven climatological table.**)

(295) **Routes.**–To enter New Haven Harbor from eastward, it is safer for large vessels to pass southward of Branford Reef and Townshend Ledge to the entrance channel. To enter from westward, pass northward of Stratford Shoal Light at a distance of 1.8 miles and head for the entrance channel.

(296) The passage eastward of East Breakwater has boulder patches and is very broken, but can be used by small craft drawing less than 6 feet, taking care to avoid the foul ground along the northeast side of the passage. This passage is buoyed, and local vessels of 10- to 12-foot draft use it at high water. Avoid **Quixes Ledge**, which extends about 200 yards southeastward from the eastern end of the breakwater, and pass about 100 yards eastward of the breakwater. The principal danger inside the breakwater is the reef, marked by a buoy, that extends 300 yards southwestward from **Lighthouse Point. Adams Fall**, a rock with 5 feet over it and marked by a buoy, is 0.4 mile southwestward of Lighthouse Point.

(297) **Pilotage, New Haven.**–Pilotage is compulsary in Long Island Sound for foreign vessels and U.S. vessels under register. See Pilotage, Long Island Sound (indexed as such), chapter 8.

(298) Pilotage for New Haven is available from New Haven Bridgeport Pilots Association (NHBPA), 60 Appletree Lane, Hamden, CT 06518, telephone 203-878-8667.

(299) Pilot boats (rented) utilized by NHBPA pilots are SUSY II, 42-foot, blue hull, white superstructure, word PILOT on side; and GALE, 42-foot, white hull, white superstructure, word PILOT on side. The boat monitors channel 16, 13 and 77; works on 77 and 09. Pilots board about 1 mile south of New Haven Harbor Lighted Whistle Buoy NH.

(300) Pilotage for New Haven is also available from Constitution State Pilots Association (CSPA), 500 Waterfront Street, New Haven, CT 06512, telephone 800-229-7456 or 203-783-5991, FAX 516-582-6327. Pilots of CSPA board vessels from a launch or the tug, at New Haven Harbor Lighted Whistle Buoy NH.

(301) Pilotage for New Haven is also available from Long Island Sound State Pilots Association, Inc. (LISSPA), 1440 Whalley Avenue, Suite 123, New Haven, CT 06515, telephone 203-772-0101, FAX 302-629-9392, Cable LISPILOT, New Haven. Pilot boat LONG ISLAND SOUND PILOT is 46-foot, with black hull, white superstructure, and the word PILOT in black letters. The boat monitors channel 16; works on 11. Among other locations, the LISSPA pilot will meet a ship off Montauk Point. See Pilotage Pickup Locations Off Montauk Point (indexed as such), chapter 7.

(302) Pilotage for New Haven is also available from Sound Pilots, Inc. (SPI) (a division of Northeast Marine Pilots, Inc.), 243 Spring Street, Newport, RI 02840, telephone 401-847-9050 (24 hours), 800-274-1216, FAX 401-847-9052, Cable RISPILOT, Newport, RI 02840. The pilot boats are NORTHEAST II, 49-foot, with grey hull and superstructure and the word PILOT on the side; or RHODE ISLAND PILOT, 35-foot, with black hull and white superstructure and the word PILOT on the side; or NORTHEAST I, 49-foot, similiarly marked as the RHODE ISLAND PILOT. The SPI pilots meet a ship bound for a Long Island Sound port, off Point Judith, but will also meet a ship off Montauk Point, by prearrangement. See Pilotage, Narragansett Bay and Other Rhode Island Waters (indexed as such), chapter 6, and Pilotage Pickup Locations Off Montauk Point (indexed as such), chapter 7.

(303) Pilot services are arranged in advance through ships' agents or directly by shipping companies.

(304) **Towage.**–Tugs up to 1,800 hp are available at New Haven, and tugs to 4,000 hp can be obtained by prior arrangement. Vessels usually proceed to the harbor without assistance. Large vessels normally require tugs for docking and undocking. Arrangements for tug service should be made 24 hours in advance, usually through ships' agents or directly by shipping companies. The tugs monitor VHF-FM channels 13 and 16 and use channel 19A as a working frequency; call sign KEE-234.

(305) Launch service to ships at anchor is available. Launches monitor VHF-FM channel 16 (156.80 MHz) and use channel 19A (156.95 MHz) as a working frequency.

(306) New Haven is a **customs port of entry.**

(307) **Quarantine, customs, immigration, and agricultural quarantine.**–(See chapter 3, Vessel Arrival Inspections, and appendix for addresses.)

(308)   **Quarantine** is enforced in accordance with regulations of the U.S. Public Health Service. (See Public Health Service, chapter 1.)

(309)   New Haven has many public and private hospitals.

(310)   **Coast Guard.**–The **Captain of the Port** maintains an office in New Haven. The nearest **vessel documentation** office is in Bridgeport, Conn. (See appendix for addresses.)

(311)   The **harbormaster** at New Haven has charge of the anchoring of vessels; he can be contacted through the local police department.

(312)   The city police maintain a harbor patrol during the summer.

(313)   **Wharves.**–The deep-draft facilities at the Port of New Haven are along the north and east sides of the inner portion of New Haven Harbor. Facilities for smaller vessels and barges are along the sides of the harbor and in Mill, Quinnipiac, and West Rivers. Depths alongside the facilities in Quinnipiac River range from about 5 to 15 feet; Mill River, 12 to 13 feet; and West River about 12 to 18 feet. Only the deep-draft facilities are described. For a complete description of the port facilities refer to Port Series No. 4, published and sold by the U.S. Army Corps of Engineers. (See appendix for address.) The alongside depths for the facilities described are reported; for information on the latest depths contact the private operator. All the facilities have direct highway connections, and most have railroad connections. Water and electrical shore power connections are available at most piers and wharves.

(314)   General cargo at the port is usually handled by ship's tackle; special handling equipment, if available, is mentioned in the description of the particular facility. Cranes up to 250 tons and warehouses and cold storage facilities adjacent to the waterfront are available.

(315)   Wyatt Light Oil Pier: north end of harbor 0.35 mile northeastward of New Haven Long Wharf; 150-foot face, 715 feet of berthing space with dolphins, 38 feet alongside; deck height, 11 feet; receipt and shipment of petroleum products; owned and operated by Wyatt, Inc.

(316)   Wyatt Heavy Oil Wharf: 50 yards east of Wyatt Light Oil Pier; west side 210 feet, 480 feet of berthing space with dolphins; 30 feet alongside; deck height, 11 feet; receipt and shipment of petroleum products, receipt of asphalt; owned and operated by Wyatt, Inc.

(317)   Gulf Refining and Marketing Co. Wharf: on each side of harbor, 200 yards south of Tomlinson Bridge; 60-foot face, 735 feet of berthing space with dolphins; 35 feet alongside; deck height, 13 feet; vessels normally moor starboardside-to; receipt and shipment of petroleum products; owned and operated by Gulf Oil Refining and Marketing Co.

(318)   Gulf Refining and Marketing Co. Pier: 100 yards southward of Gulf Refining and Marketing Co. Wharf; north side 400 feet, 25 feet alongside; south side 380 feet, 25 feet alongside; deck height, 10 feet; receipt and shipment of petroleum products; owned and operated by Gulf Refining and Marketing Co.

(319)   ARCO Petroleum Products Co. Wharf: 300 yards southwestward of Gulf Refining and Marketing Co. Pier; 110-foot face, 760 feet with dolphins; 35 feet alongside; deck height, 15 feet; vessels normally moor starboardside-to; receipt and shipment of petroleum products; owned and operated by ARCO Petroleum Products Co.

(320)   New Haven Terminal, Scrap Metal Dock: 275 yards southward of ARCO Petroleum Products Co. Wharf; 640-foot face; 35 feet alongside; deck height, 14 feet; two 30-ton traveling gantry cranes, crawler cranes to 250 tons; receipt and shipment of general and containerized cargo and steel products, shipment of scrap metal, receipt of copper, zinc,

and lumber; owned and operated by New Haven Terminal, Inc.

(321)   New Haven Terminal Pier: 50 yards southward of Scrap Metal Dock; north and south sides, 650 feet usable, can accommodate tankers up to 700 feet; 35 and 39 feet alongside, north and south sides, respectively; deck height, 13 feet; cranes up to 50 tons; 36,000 square feet covered storage; receipt and shipment of general cargo, receipt of petroleum products, petrochemicals, chemicals, copper, zinc, lumber, and steel products; owned and operated by New Haven Terminal, Inc.

(322)   Exxon Co. Terminal Wharf: 175 yards southward of New Haven Terminal Pier; 80-foot face, 700 feet with dolphins; 35 feet alongside; deck height, 13 feet; vessels normally moor starboardside-to; receipt and shipment of petroleum products; owned and operated by Exxon Co., U.S.A.

(323)   **Supplies.**–Oil bunkering terminals at New Haven are maintained by the major oil companies. Fuel oil and diesel oil in the usual commercial grades are obtainable. Barges are available for bunkering in the anchorages outside the breakwaters or at the piers; 24-hour advance notice is required, and arrangements should be made through ships' agents. Water, provisions, and marine supplies can be procured.

(324)   **Repairs.**–New Haven has no facilities for making major repairs or for drydocking deep-draft vessels; the nearest such facilities are at Boston, Mass., and New York. Machine shops in the area can make limited repairs to machinery and boilers, and fabricate shafts and other pieces of equipment.

(325)   **Small-craft facilities.**–There are excellent facilities on the east and west sides of the harbor and on West and Quinnipiac Rivers. (See the small-craft facilities tabulation on chart 12372 for services and supplies available.)

(326)   **Charts 12370, 12364.**–**Pond Point,** about 5 miles southwestward of the New Haven Harbor entrance, has a rocky shoal with little depth over the greater part of it that extends about 0.3 mile southward. It is marked by a buoy. A prominent white mast is on the point.

(327)   **Welches Point,** 0.8 mile westward of Pond Point, forms the east side of the entrance of The Gulf. A reef extends 0.3 mile southward from the point and is marked by a buoy.

(328)   **The Gulf,** a bight between Welches Point and Charles Island, about 6.5 miles westward of New Haven Harbor entrance, affords anchorage in 6 to 15 feet and is sheltered in all but southerly and southeasterly winds. The entrance is clear. The shoaling is gradual, and soundings are the best guide on the northwest side of the bight; the western side of Welches Point and the reefs around Charles Island extending to the mainland should be approached with caution, as the shoaling is abrupt. The mean range of **tide** is about 6.6 feet.

(329)   **Milford Harbor,** comprising the lower portion of the **Wepawaug River,** is entered at the mouth of the river between two jetties at the head of The Gulf. The westerly jetty extends southward from **Burns Point,** and the easterly jetty is marked by Milford Harbor Light 10. The harbor is used chiefly for recreational boating, and occasionally for the receipt of shellfish and fish. The National Marine Fisheries Service, U.S. Department of Commerce, maintains a laboratory and research vessel base on the west side of the harbor, about 0.2 mile northward of Burns Point.

(330)   A dredged channel leads from The Gulf through the jettied entrance to a point about 400 feet above the town wharf, 0.6 mile above Burns Point. In June 1988, the reported controlling depth was 9½ feet to Burns Point, thence

8 feet to the head of the channel. In March 1986, depths of 3½ to 6 feet were available in the anchorage basin along the southwest side of the channel except for shoaling to 1 foot near the north end. The channel is marked by a lighted buoy and an unlighted buoy to the jettied entrance. An obstruction, a pile, is in the anchorage basin, about 0.2 mile northwestward of Burns Point.

(331)   Milford Harbor has several small-craft facilities. (See the small-craft facilities tabulation on chart 12364 for services and supplies available.)

(332)   A 5 mph **speed limit** is enforced in the harbor.

(333)   **Charles Island**, on the southwest side at the entrance to The Gulf, is low and partly covered with trees. A white flagpole, barely visible over the trees, is on the island. The island is connected to the mainland by **The Bar,** a narrow neck about 0.5 mile long and surrounded by rocks awash and shoals. A buoy marks the end of a shoal that extends 250 yards east-northeastward from the island, and a lighted bell buoy marks the end of a rocky area that extends 0.4 mile southward from the island. Northward of Charles Island is a good anchorage in 10 to 16 feet, sheltered from southerly to southwesterly winds.

(334)   Between Charles Island and **Stratford Point**, about 3 miles southwestward, several summer resorts are along the shore and the Housatonic River empties into Long Island Sound just above the point. The shoals which extend southward from Stratford Point toward Stratford Shoal Light (see chart 12354) consist of narrow ridges of hard sand with deeper water between, and have oyster beds marked with stakes. Depths of 12 feet or less extend 1 mile offshore.

(335)   **Stratford Point Light** (41°09.1'N., 73°06.2'W.), 52 feet above the water, is shown from a white conical tower, with brown band midway of its height, from the southerly part of the point; a radiobeacon and a fog signal are at the light.

(336)   **Chart 12370.–Housatonic River** rises in the Berkshire Hills of western Massachusetts and Connecticut, and empties into Long Island Sound about 10 miles southwestward of the New Haven Harbor entrance. The river is joined by the nonnavigable **Naugatuck River** in the vicinity of Derby, conn. Housatonic River is navigable to a point about 1 mile above Shelton, Conn., where it is closed by a power dam. The head of navigation for all practical purposes is at the towns of Derby and Shelton, 11.5 miles above the entrance. Small vessels can anchor in the river abreast of Stratford, where the channel has an available width of about 500 feet. The waterborne commerce on the river is principally in barge shipments of aggregate, fuel oil to the power plant at Devon, and seasonal commercial shellfishing. Navigation above Devon is limited to recreational boating.

(337)   On the east side of the entrance to Housatonic River, a breakwater extends out from **Milford Point** across the bar and is marked at its south end by Housatonic River Breakwater Light 2A. The inner section of the breakwater is awash at high water.

(338)   **Channels.**–A Federal project provides for an 18-foot dredged channel from Long Island Sound between the breakwater on the east and Stratford Point on the west upriver for about 4.3 miles to the lower end of Culver Bar. (See Notice to Mariners and the latest editions of the charts for controlling depths.) Above the lower end of Culver Bar, the river channel extends through several dredged sections across river bars to the towns of Derby and Shelton about 11.5 miles above the river entrance. In 1976-1978, the controlling depth was 5 feet (5½ feet at midchannel) to Camp Meeting Bar, 7.1 miles above the channel entrance, thence 2 feet to Twomile Island Bar, thence 1 foot (5½ feet at midchannel) across the bar, and thence 3 feet (5½ feet at midchannel) to Derby and Shelton. In September 1978, shoaling to 3 feet was reported in the channel across Mill Bar. The channel is marked to a point about 2.5 miles below Derby and Shelton.

(339)   **Stratford** is a town on the west side of the river 2.3 miles above the entrance. The principal wharf has a depth of about 9 feet at its end. The **harbormaster** at Stratford controls anchorages and moorings, and has jurisdiction from the entrance of the river to the Shelton town line. Harbor regulations may be obtained from the harbormaster who may be contacted through the Stratford police or at the Town Hall.

(340)   Stratford has several small-craft facilities. (See the small-craft facilities tabulation on chart 12364 for services and supplies available.)

(341)   **Devon** is on the east side about 1 mile above Stratford. Local small craft anchor near the east bank of the river, just north of the highway bridge, in depths up to 10 feet. A 40-foot marine railway at a small–craft facility at Devon can haul out craft for engine and hull repairs; gasoline, water, ice, marine supplies, and storage are available. In July 1981, depths of 4 feet were reported alongside the facility.

(342)   **Shelton**, a town on the west side of the river about 11.5 miles above the entrance is connected to **Derby** by two bridges; the town has several important factories. In 1971, the wharves at Derby and Shelton were in ruins and unsuitable for craft of any size.

(343)   **Bridges.**–About 1 mile above Stratford is U.S. Route 1 highway bridge with a bascule span having a clearance of 32 feet. Two bridges cross the river about 0.3 mile farther up: the first, Interstate Route 95 fixed highway bridge, has a clearance of 65 feet, and the second, a railroad bridge with a bascule span, has a clearance of 19 feet. The bridgetenders of the U.S. Route 1 bridge and the railroad bridge monitor VHF-FM channel 13; call signs KXJ-695 and KU-6035, respectively. An overhead power cable with a clearance of 135 feet crosses at the railroad bridge. Other cables, near **Pecks Mill**, 1.5 miles above, have minimum clearance of 79 feet.

(344)   The fixed highway bridge about 3.7 miles above Stratford has a clearance of 85 feet. At Shelton, two fixed highway bridges and a fixed railroad bridge have a least clearance of 17 feet. In April 1983, the railroad bridge suffered severe structural damage. The area should be avoided, but if transit is necessary, extreme caution should be exercised.

(345)   (See 117.1 through 117.59 and 117.207, chapter 2, for drawbridge regulations.)

(346)   **Tides.**–The mean range of tide is 5.5 feet at Stratford and 5 feet at Shelton. The time of the tide becomes later and the range diminishes in progressing up the river. At Stratford the tide is about 0.8 hour later than at the entrance whereas at Shelton high water is about 1.8 hours later and low water about 2.8 hours later than at the entrance. The river water is fresh about 6 miles above the entrance.

(347)   **Currents.**–At the entrance near the end of the breakwater the flood has a strong westerly set. Between Milford Point and **Crimbo Point**, flood and ebb have a velocity of about 1.2 knots. The flood sets about 330° and the ebb 135°. Just north of the draw of the railroad bridge above Stratford, the velocity of flood is 1.1 knots and of ebb, 1.3 knots. In the openings of the bridge the flood current has some easterly set, but the ebb sets fair with the openings. Between that bridge and Shelton the tidal current has a velocity of about 1 knot. Because of the drainage flow of the river, the

ebb is usually greater and the flood less than 1 knot. (Consult the Tidal Current Tables for current predictions and further details.)

(348) Spring **freshets** at Shelton rise 10 feet or more above mean high tide.

(349) **Ice** closes the river above Stratford during the winter and sometimes extends to the entrance.

(350) **Routes.**–The channel in Housatonic River is narrow and crooked, with little depth on either side, and across the bars in the channel are dredged cuts 100 feet wide. The tidal currents are strong, especially in the lower part of the river, and strangers are advised to take a pilot. Small craft, without a pilot, should proceed with caution and preferably on a rising tide.

(351) When entering the river during a flood current, care must be taken to avoid being set on the shoals on the west side by strong westerly currents. In the vicinity of Milford Point care should be exercised to avoid a shoal that reportedly extends from Milford Point to the eastern edge of the channel. Care should also be exercised off the extreme northern end of Nells Island as a shoal is reported to have encroached into the channel. By steering a midchannel course no difficulty should be encountered.

(352) **Pilots** and **tugs** can be obtained at New Haven.

(353) A 5 mph **speed limit** is enforced on the river near anchorage and mooring areas and near boat slips.

(354) **Chart 12354.**–Stratford Shoal Middle Ground, 5.4 miles south of Stratford Point and covered 4½ to 18 feet, is marked by **Stratford Shoal (Middle Ground) Light** (41°03.6′ N., 73°06.1′W.), 60 feet above the water and shown from a gray granite octagonal tower projecting from a house on a pier, and by buoys that mark the outer ends of shoal areas extending 1 mile north, 0.9 mile northeast, and 0.5 mile south of the light. A fog signal is at the light.

(355) **North Shore of Long Island.**–From Orient Point (41°09.6′N., 72°14.0′W.), for about 11 miles to Horton Point, the south shore of Long Island Sound is generally bluff and rocky. The 10-fathom curve is from 0.3 to 0.8 mile from shore, and the shoaling is generally abrupt. The outlying dangers are Orient Shoal and the rocky patch northward of Horton Point.

(356) The prominent features are Browns Hills, a tower at Rocky Point, a tank and television tower at Greenport, and Horton Point Light.

(357) Several rocky shoals, including **Orient Shoal** with a least depth of 7 feet, are offshore in the vicinity of **Rocky Point**, about 5 miles westward of Orient Point. The north end of Orient Shoal is marked by a buoy.

(358) **Horton Point Light** (41°05.1′ N., 72°26.8′W.), 103 feet above the water, is shown from a white square tower attached to a dwelling on the northwest part of the point. A radiobeacon is 72 yards south-southeastward of the light. The former lighthouse tower is close by, southwestward of the present light.

(359) A rocky shoal with a least found depth of 26 feet is 1.6 miles northward of Horton Point. The shoal is a ridge having a northeast-southwest direction, with abrupt shoaling on its northwest and southeast sides.

(360) From Horton Point for about 32 miles to Old Field Point, the shore is fringed with shoals that extend off a greatest distance of 1.5 miles and rise abruptly from the deep water of Long Island Sound. Boulders are found near the shore on the shoals which extend off 0.5 mile in places. A sand shoal, about 0.5 mile in extent with a least depth of 26 feet, is about 1.1 miles northwestward of Duck Pond Point.

(361) The bluffs begin about 1 mile westward of Goldsmith Inlet and reach their greatest elevation just eastward of **Duck Pond Point.** A valley, formed by a break in the bluffs, is just westward of the point; a bathing pavilion is on the beach. Boulders that bare at low water are on the shoals that fringe the shore between Duck Pond Point and Mattituck Inlet.

(362) **Chart 12358.**–Mattituck Inlet, 6.7 miles southwestward of Horton Point Light, is entered between two short jetties. The inlet is marked by a long break in the bluffs, and numerous storage tanks inside the inlet are prominent. The outer end of the west jetty is marked by a light. A gong buoy about 1 mile north of the jetty light marks the entrance of the inlet. The sides of the channel are sandy, and, although shoaling is liable to occur at the entrance, strangers can enter the inlet without great danger. In September 1987, the controlling depth was 4 feet (6 feet at midchannel) from the entrance for about 1.8 miles to the turning basin at Mattituck with 7 feet available in the basin. The channel is marked by buoys and private markers. The overhead power cable about 1 mile above the entrance has a clearance of 78 feet.

(363) The **tidal currents** have an estimated velocity of about 3 knots in the narrow parts of the entrance of Mattituck Inlet. Slack waters occur possibly 1 hour after the time of high and low water. With northerly and westerly winds, the sea is rough in the entrance. The mean range of **tide** is 5.2 feet at the entrance. The inlet is sometimes closed by **ice** during portions of cold winters.

(364) Several marinas and a boatyard are inside the inlet. A 50-ton mobile hoist at the boatyard can haul out craft for engine, hull, and radio repairs. Marine supplies, gasoline, diesel fuel, water, and covered and wet storage can be obtained. A transient dock, operated by the Mattituck Park Commission, is at the head of the inlet; depths of about 6 feet are at the dock. A **dockmaster** is at the dock; water is available.

(365) **Mattituck** is a village on the railroad at the head of the inlet. Provisions can be obtained.

(366) **Jacobs Point** is about 11 miles southwestward of Horton Point Light. An aquaculture site, marked by private buoys, is about 1.4 miles west-northwest of Jacobs Point.

(367) **Offshore Terminal, Northville-Riverhead.**–An offshore platform for the delivery and receipt of petroleum products is in open roadstead, off Northville, NY (and Riverhead, NY), about 1.2 miles northward of Jacobs Point. It is owned and operated by Northville Industries Corporation, Riverhead, NY.

(368) A safety zone surrounds the offshore facility. (See **166.155**, chapter 2, for limits and regulations.

(369) The facility consists of a 45- by 100-foot steel platform structure with breasting dolphins and mooring dolphins providing two berths; one on the north side and one on the south side. The deck height is 24.5 feet. The north berth has depths alongside of 64 feet, and can accomodate tankers up to 225,000 DWT and up to 1,150-foot length, of 62-foot maximum draft.

(370) The south berth has depths alongside of 50 feet, and can accomodate tankers of up to 42,000 DWT and up to 6,00-foot length, of 42-foot maximum draft. Barges mooring in this berth must be at least 220 feet long.

(371) A private fog signal is on the platform and private lights mark the four corners.

(372) **Wharf.**–An 800-foot barge pier is just east of Jacobs Point and southward of the platform. In May 1991, only the

west side of the pier was used for the transhipment of petroleum products. Barges to 30,000 barrel capacity are received. Depth alongside is 16 feet. However, depths of 13 feet surround the area and a 11-foot shoal marked by a private buoy, must be cleared on the recommended southwest approach to, and northwest departure from the west pier berth. Vessels with draft greater than 12 feet should exercise caution when approaching the pier and should endeavor to arrive or depart at high water.

(373)   **Prominent feature.**–The numerous light green oil storage tanks on Jacobs Point are prominent.

(374)   **Communications.**–Vessels transitting Long Island Sound or approaching the facility may do so through a VHF-FM marine operator. Available marine operator stations' name and channel are:

(375)   Riverhead   28
(376)   New Bedford   26
(377)   New London   26
(378)   Bridgeport   24.

(379)   Upon the approach of an incoming vessel, the platform, voice call "Northville Industries Offshore Platform", or "Northville-Riverhead Platform", or "Northville-Riverhead Terminal", or "Northville-Riverhead Dock", monitors VHF-FM channels 16, 13 and 19A; works channel 19A.

(380)   Vessels calling at the platform are moored at any time, weather conditions permitting. The tidal current periods are substantially the same as at The Race. Strong winds from the north and northwest are experienced during the winter and spring. Tidal currents during maximum ebb and flood may reach 3 knots. The mean range of tide is 5.4 feet.

(381)   Vessels awaiting berth at the platform will normally anchor north of the platform. A vessel drawing more than 50 feet of water may wish to anchor in deeper water northwest of the platform. Pilots are familiar with the best anchorages. Holding ground is good and a scope of 8 shots (120 feet) is considered adequate.

(382)   **Pilotage, Offshore Terminal, Northville-Riverhead.**–Pilotage is compulsary in Long Island Sound for foreign vessels and U.S. vessels under register. For these vessels, pilotage to this terminal is available from:

(383)   Sound Pilots, Inc. (a division of Northeast Marine Pilots, Inc.).

(384)   For U.S. enrolled vessels in the coastwise trade, pilotage to this terminal is available from

(385)   Connecticut State Pilots (a division of Interport Pilots Agency, Inc.),

(386)   Constitution State Pilots Association,

(387)   Long Island Sound State Pilots Association, Inc., and

(388)   Sound Pilots, Inc. (a division of Northeast Marine Pilots, Inc.).

(389)   See Pilotage, Long Island Sound (indexed as such), early this chapter, and Pilotage, New York Harbor and Approaches, (indexed as such), chapter 11.

(390)   The pilot serves as docking master and remains on board on standby while the vessel is moored at the platform. Pilot services are arranged in advance through ships' agents or directly by shipping companies.

(391)   **Tugs.**–Tug service is available from New Haven, Providence, Brooklyn, or Staten Island on advance notice. Normally two or three tugs are used for docking and one or two tugs for undocking.

(392)   **Launch service.**–J & H Launch Service, Port Jefferson (516-331-5336), provides transfer service for vessels at anchor or alongside the platform.

(393)   **Supplies.**–Fueling of a ship alongside the platform is not permitted. A ship may fuel while at anchor from a barge. Water is not available from this facility. Stores may be brought on board via launch while alongside or at anchor.

(394)   New York City is the **quarantine, customs, immigration,** and **agricultural quarantine** port of entry for Northville. Officials are stationed in New York City. (See appendix for addresses.) Arrangements for such inspections must be made by ships' agents in advance, usually not less than 24 hours Monday through Friday and 48 hours on Saturday and Sunday. Officials will board vessels in the anchorage prior to arrival within the vicinity of the offshore mooring facility.

(395)   **Chart 12354.**–Between Mattituck Inlet and Port Jefferson the shore is fringed with rock shoals extending in places 1.5 miles offshore. The outer ends of the shoals are marked by buoys.

(396)   **Horse in Bank**, 7.3 miles westward of Mattituck Inlet, is an area of white patches in the brush-covered bluff at **Friars Head.** The feature is at the western end of **Roanoke Point Shoal** and 14 miles westward of Horton Point Light.

(397)   The valley of **Wading River**, about 20 miles westward of Horton Point Light, forms a broad break in the high bluffs. The entrance to Wading River is protected by a short jetty on the west side. In July 1981, a reported depth of about 3 feet could be carried in the river to a town launching ramp 0.1 mile above the entrance. A small canal, about 350 yards westward of the entrance to Wading River, leads southward to the site of a nuclear power station. The canal, closed to general navigation, had a reported depth of about 12 feet in June 1989.

(398)   **Tuttles White Bank** is a high white bluff 0.6 mile westward of Wading River.

(399)   **Charts 12362, 12364.**–Mount Sinai Harbor, 22.5 miles westward of Mattituck Inlet, is marked by a low break in the beach nearly 1 mile long. The approach to the harbor is marked by a buoy. The entrance is protected by two jetties, the outer parts of which are awash at high water. Caution should be exercised when rounding them. A private light and a private daybeacon mark the outer ends of the east and west jetties, respectively. In June 1981, a depth of about 8 feet was reported available through the entrance. The northern part of the harbor has general depths of 10 to 20 feet. A channel marked by private buoys leads eastward from the entrance to small-craft facilities on the north shore of the harbor. The southern part of the harbor is shoal; the chart is the guide. Several **small-craft facilities** are in the harbor. (See the small-craft facilities tabulation on chart 12364 for services and supplies available.) A **speed limit** of 6 mph is enforced in the harbor by the Suffolk County Police.

(400)   **Mount Misery**, 180 feet high, between Mount Sinai Harbor and Port Jefferson, slopes off gradually toward the sound where the bluffs are about 60 feet high and very prominent. Sand banks dug out by sand and gravel companies are very conspicuous.

(401)   **Port Jefferson Harbor**, on the south shore of Long Island Sound eastward of Old Field Point, is entered through a dredged channel that leads between two jetties to a docking area near the southwestern end of the harbor; the jetties are each marked by a light. The approach is marked by a lighted whistle buoy, about 1.1 miles northwest of the entrance. Three stacks on the west side near the head of the harbor are conspicuous landmarks. A 12 mph **speed limit** is enforced in the main entrance channel, and a 5 mph **speed limit** is enforced at the head of the harbor in the vicinity of the mooring areas and wharves.

(402)   A **121°-301° measured nautical mile** is westward of the entrance to Port Jefferson Harbor on Old Field Beach.

The front markers are orange posts about 8 feet high; the rear markers are rectangles mounted on legs about 12 feet high, painted red with a 6-inch black vertical stripe in the middle.

(403)   The approach to Port Jefferson Harbor is clear, taking care to avoid **Mount Misery Shoal** with depths of 7 to 12 feet, about 0.8 mile north-northeast of the east jetty light.

(404)   In November 1990, the controlling depth was 23 feet (26 feet at midchannel) in the dredged channel through Port Jefferson Harbor to the docking area off an oil wharf at the southern end. Shoaling to 10 feet is near the southwest corner of the southern limit of the project. The channel is marked by lighted and unlighted buoys and a **146°** lighted range. In September 1982, it was reported that due to the closeness of the range lights it may be difficult to determine when they are in line. It was further reported that the range may be obscured by vessels tied up at the oil wharf on the west side of the harbor.

(405)   Shoals with little depth are on both sides of the channel from the entrance to Port Jefferson to Lighted Bell Buoy 5 inside the entrance. The ground from the east jetty to the lighted bell buoy is broken, with shoals covered 4 to 11 feet. The lighted bell buoy cannot be seen over the breakwater at low tide by small vessels approaching the harbor.

(406)   The mean range of **tide** is 6.6 feet.

(407)   **Currents.**–In the channel between the jetties the velocity of the tidal currents is 2.6 knots on flood and 1.9 on ebb; flood sets 151° and the ebb 323°. It is reported that on the ebb there is a current with a velocity of 1 to 2 knots across the entrance to the harbor.

(408)   **Ice** forms over the entire harbor and interrupts navigation in very cold weather, but does not endanger shipping in the harbor.

(409)   **Pilotage, Port Jefferson.**–Pilotage is compulsary in Long Island Sound for foreign vessels and U.S. vessels under register. For these vessels, pilotage is available from:

(410)   Sound Pilots, Inc. (a division of Northeast Marine Pilots, Inc.).

(411)   For U.S. enrolled vessels in the coastwise trade, pilotage is available from:

(412)   Connecticut State Pilots (a division of Interport Pilots Agency, Inc.),

(413)   Constitution State Pilots Association,

(414)   Long Island Sound State Pilots Association, Inc., and

(415)   Sound Pilots, Inc. (a division of Northeast Marine Pilots, Inc.).

(416)   See Pilotage, Long Island Sound (indexed as such), early this chapter, and Pilotage, New York Harbor and Approaches, (indexed as such), chapter 11.

(417)   Pilot services are arranged in advance through ships' agents or directly by shipping companies.

(418)   **Tugs.**–Tug service is available from New Haven, Providence, Brooklyn, or Staten Island on advance notice. Normally, two tugs are used for docking and one for undocking.

(419)   **Port Jefferson** is a town at the southern end of the harbor. The principal industries of the port are the shipping of sand and gravel and the distribution of petroleum products. There are small-craft facilities at the head of the harbor. (See the small-craft facilities tabulation on chart 12364 for services and supplies available.) A launching ramp is at the head of the harbor.

(420)   **Wharves.**–Depths ranging from 16 feet to bare are reported alongside the small commercial wharves and piers at the head of the harbor. In June 1983, the depths were 31 feet alongside the oil wharf on the west side of the harbor about 400 yards from the head. The powerplant wharf about 150 yards to the northwestward had depths of 25 to 28 feet alongside in June 1983.

(421)   **Communications.**–Port Jefferson is served by railroad and bus. A ferry operates to Bridgeport, Conn.

(422)   **Conscience Bay** is entered through a long, narrow channel at the northwest end of Port Jefferson Harbor. The bay and entrance have depths of 1 to 2 feet. Strangers should not attempt to enter as there are many rocks at the entrance.

(423)   **Setauket Harbor**, on the western side of Port Jefferson Harbor, has a narrow crooked channel. In June 1981, a reported depth of about 2½ feet was available in the channel to the boatyard at Setauket. The entrance from Port Jefferson is marked by private seasonal buoys. Gasoline, moorings, and limited marine supplies are available at the boatyard; a flatbed trailer can haul out craft to 32 feet long.

(424)   **Setauket** is a village on the south shore of Setauket Harbor about 1 mile above the entrance.

9. WESTERN LONG ISLAND SOUND

(1) This chapter describes the western part of Long Island Sound along the north shore from Bridgeport to Throgs Neck, the south shore from Old Field Point to Willets Point, and the East and Harlem Rivers. Also described are the many bays and their tributaries that make into this part of the sound including Bridgeport Harbor, Stamford Harbor, Captain Harbor, Mamaroneck Harbor, Norwalk Harbor, Eastchester Bay, Huntington Bay, Oyster Bay, Hempstead Harbor, Manhasset Bay, Flushing Bay, and New Rochelle Harbor, and the commercial and small-craft facilities found in these waters.

(2) **COLREGS Demarcation Lines.**–The lines established for Long Island Sound are described in **80.155**, chapter 2.

(3) **Chart 12363.**–**Western Long Island Sound** is that portion of the deep navigable waterway between the shores of Connecticut and New York and the northern coast of Long Island westward of the line between Bridgeport and Old Field Point.

(4) This region has boulders and broken ground, with little or no natural change in the shoals. the waters are well marked by navigational aids so that strangers should experience no difficulty in navigating them. As all broken ground is liable to be strewn with boulders, vessels should proceed with caution when in the vicinity of broken areas where the charted depths are less than 6 to 8 feet greater than the draft. All of the more important places are entered through dredged channels. During fog, vessels are advised to anchor until the weather clears before attempting to enter. The numerous oyster grounds in this region are usually marked by stakes and flags. These stakes may become broken off and form obstructions dangerous to small craft which, especially at night, should proceed with caution when crossing oyster areas.

(5) **Anchorages.**–There is anchorage for large vessels in the bight outside Bridgeport Harbor Light. Cockenoe Harbor is sometimes used by small vessels, but Sheffield Island Harbor is preferred and is sometimes used by tows. Westward of Norwalk Islands, seagoing vessels can anchor toward the north shore and, with good ground tackle, hold on in northerly winds. Captain Harbor affords good shelter, but is rarely used except by local vessels. On the south shore, Huntington Bay and Hempstead Harbor are available for large vessels; Oyster Bay is also used, and Manhasset Bay is available for light-draft vessels. City Island Harbor is a fine resort for coasters.

(6) **Tides.**–The time of tide is nearly simultaneous throughout Long Island Sound, but the range of tide increases from about 2.5 feet at the east end to about 7.3 feet at the west end. Daily predictions of the times and heights of high and low waters for New London, Bridgeport, and Willets Point are given in the Tide Tables.

(7) The effect of strong winds, in combination with the regular tidal action, may at times cause the water to fall several feet below the plane of reference of the charts.

(8) **Currents.**–About 1.3 miles northward of Eatons Neck Light the ebb runs about 5 hours longer than the flood. The current has a velocity of 1.4 knots; the flood sets 283° and the ebb sets 075°.

(9) The direction and velocity of the currents are affected by strong winds which may increase or diminish the periods of flood or ebb. Directions and velocities from Point Judith to Throgs Neck for each hour of the tidal cycle will be found in Tidal Current Charts, Long Island Sound and Block Island Sound. Currents in East River are described in the latter part of this chapter.

(10) **Weather.**–These waters are more protected than the eastern Sound resulting in fewer gales. However, winters are colder and summers warmer due to this sheltering effect. Fog is not so frequent either and tends to burn off quicker than farther east. Winter winds of 16 knots or more are likely about 12 to 15 percent of the time and are predominantly from the west through northwest. Harbors such as Cold Spring, Oyster Bay, Hempstead and Manhasset offer additional shelter. In summer thunderstorms may develop on 4 to 5 days per month. These are most likely during the afternoon or evening.

(11) In Long Island Sound the north and south shores are equally subject to fog, except that on spring and summer mornings, when there is little or no wind, fog will often hang along the Connecticut shore while it is clear offshore and southward.

(12) In the western end of Long Island Sound, although fogs are liable to occur at any time, they are not encountered so often nor do they generally last so long as farther eastward.

(13) **Ice.**–In ordinary winters the floating and pack ice in Long Island Sound, while impeding navigation, does not render it absolutely unsafe, but in exceptionally severe winters the reverse is true; then only the powerful steamers can make their way.

(14) Drift ice, which is formed principally along the northern shore of the sound under the influence of the prevailing northerly winds, drifts across to the southern side and accumulates there, massing into large fields, and remains until removed by southerly winds which drive it back to the northerly shore.

(15) In ordinary winters ice generally forms in the western end of the sound as far as Eatons Neck; in exceptionally severe winters ice may extend to Falkner Island and farther eastward.

(16) **Effects of winds on ice.**–In Long Island Sound northerly winds drive the ice to the southern shore of the sound and southerly winds carry it back to the northern shore. Northeasterly winds force the ice westward and cause formations heavy enough to prevent the passage of vessels of every description until the ice is removed by westerly winds. These winds carry the ice eastward and, if of long enough duration, drive it through The Race into Block Island Sound, from where it goes to sea and disappears.

(17) In Bridgeport Harbor winds from north to northwest clear the harbor of drift ice, and those from southeast through south to southwest force the ice into the harbor from the sound. The outer buoys may be carried out of position by heavy ice during severe winters.

(18) Additional information concerning ice conditions in the waters adjoining Long Island Sound is given under the local descriptions.

(19) **Vessel Traffic Service (New York),** operated by the U.S. Coast Guard, serves New York Harbor (see **161.501 through 161.580,** chapter 2, for regulations).

(20) **Pilotage, Western Long Island Sound.**–Pilotage is compulsary in Long Island Sound for foreign vessels and U.S. vessels under register. For vessels entering Long Island

APPENDIX

(1) **Sales Information.**–National Ocean Service publications and nautical charts are sold by NOS and its authorized sales agents in many U.S. ports and in some foreign ports. Mail orders should be addressed to:

(2) National Ocean Service,

(3) Distribution Branch (N/CG33),

(4) 6501 Lafayette Avenue,

(5) Riverdale, MD 20737-1199.

(6) Orders should be accompanied by a check or money order payable to NOS, Department of Commerce. Remittance from outside the United States should be made either by an International Money Order or by a check payable on a U.S. bank. Chart catalogs, which include a listing of authorized sales agents, are free upon request. The National Ocean Service maintains over-the-counter cash sales offices at Distribution Branch, Riverdale (see address above), and at 701 C Street, Box 38, Anchorage, AK 99513.

(7) **National Ocean Service Offices**

(8) **Washington, DC** (Headquarters): Assistant Administrator, National Ocean Service, NOAA, Herbert C. Hoover Bldg., 14th Street and Constitution Avenue, NW., Room 5805, Washington, DC 20230-0001.

(9) **Rockville:** Director, Coast and Geodetic Survey, National Ocean Service, NOAA, 6001 Executive Boulevard, Rockville, MD 20852-3806.

(10) **Norfolk:** Director, Atlantic Marine Center, National Ocean Service, NOAA, 439 West York Street, Norfolk, VA 23510-1114.

(11) **Seattle:** Director, Pacific Marine Center, National Ocean Service, NOAA, 1801 Fairview Avenue East, Seattle, WA 98102-3767.

(12) **Charts and Publications-National Ocean Service**

(13) **Nautical Charts** (See Chart Catalogs)

(14) United States Coastal and Intracoastal Waters, and possessions.

(15) Great Lakes, Lake Champlain, New York State Canals, and the St. Lawrence River-St. Regis to Cornwall, Canada.

(16) **Publications** (See Chart Catalogs for latest editions and prices)

(17) **Coast Pilots**

(18) U. S. Coast Pilot 1, Atlantic Coast, Eastport to Cape Cod.

(19) U. S. Coast Pilot 2, Atlantic Coast, Cape Cod to Sandy Hook.

(20) U. S. Coast Pilot 3, Atlantic Coast, Sandy Hook to Cape Henry.

(21) U. S. Coast Pilot 4, Atlantic Coast, Cape Henry to Key West.

(22) U. S. Coast Pilot 5, Atlantic Coast–Gulf of Mexico, Puerto Rico, and Virgin Islands.

(23) U.S. Coast Pilot 6, Great Lakes, Lakes Ontario, Erie, Huron, Michigan, and Superior and St. Lawrence River.

(24) U.S. Coast Pilot 7, Pacific Coast, California, Oregon, Washington, and Hawaii.

(25) U.S. Coast Pilot 8, Pacific Coast Alaska, Dixon Entrance to Cape Spencer.

(26) U.S. Coast Pilot 9, Pacific and Arctic Coasts, Alaska–Cape Spencer to Beaufort Sea.

(27) **Distance Tables**

(28) Distances Between United States Ports.

(29) **Tide Tables**

(30) Europe and West Coast of Africa.

(31) East Coast, North and South America.

(32) West Coast, North and South America.

(33) Central and Western Pacific Ocean and Indian Ocean.

(34) Supplemental Tidal Predictions-Anchorage, Nikiski, Seldovia, and Valdez, Alaska.

(35) **Tidal Current Tables**

(36) Atlantic Coast, North America.

(37) Pacific Coast, North America and Asia.

(38) **Tidal Current Charts/Atlas**

(39) Boston Harbor.

(40) Narragansett Bay to Nantucket Sound.

(41) Narragansett Bay.

(42) Long Island Sound and Block Island Sound.

(43) Delaware Bay and River Atlas.

(44) Upper Chesapeake Bay.

(45) Charleston Harbor, S.C.

(46) Tampa Bay.

(47) Puget Sound, Northern Part.

(48) Puget Sound, Southern Part.

(49) **Tidal Current Diagrams**

(50) Boston Harbor.

(51) Long Island Sound and Block Island Sound.

(52) New York Harbor.

(53) **Regional Tide and Tidal Current Table.**

(54) New York to Chesapeake Bay.

(55) **Charts and Publications-Other U.S. Government Agencies**

(56) A partial list of publications and charts considered of navigational value is included for the ready reference of the mariner. In addition to the agents located in the principal seaports handling publication sales, certain libraries have been designated by the Congress of the United States to receive the publications as issued for public review.

(57) **Government Printing Office.**–Publications of the U.S. Government Printing Office may be ordered from Superintendent of Documents, U.S. Government Printing Office, Washington, DC 20402-9325. Orders may be charged to Visa, Mastercard, or Choice by calling (202) 783-3238 during normal business hours.

(58) **Defense Mapping Agency Procurement Information.**–Publications and charts of the Defense Mapping Agency Hydrographic/Topographic Center are available from Defense Mapping Agency Combat Support Center (Code DDCP), Washington, DC 20315-0020 and its sales agents.

(59) **Nautical Charts**

(60) U.S. Waters:

(61) Apalachicola, Chattahoochee and Flint Rivers Navigation Charts, Alabama River Charts, and Black Warrior-Tombigbee Rivers River Charts: Published and for sale by U.S. Army Engineer District Mobile, P.O. Box 2288, 109 St. Joseph Street, Mobile, Ala. 36628-0001.

(62) Flood Control and Navigation Maps of the Mississippi River, Cairo, Ill. to the Gulf of Mexico: Published by Mississippi River Commission and for sale by U.S. Army Engineer District Vicksburg, P.O. Box 60, U.S. Post Office and Courthouse, Vicksburg, Miss. 39180-0060.

(63) Upper Mississippi River Navigation Charts (Mississippi River, Cairo, Ill. to Minneapolis, Minn.): Published by U.S. Army Engineer North Central Division and for sale by

U.S. Army Engineer District St. Louis, 210 N. Tucker Boulevard, St. Louis, Mo. 63101-1986.

(64) Charts of the Illinois Waterway, from Mississippi River at Grafton, Ill. to Lake Michigan at Chicago and Calumet Harbors: Published and for sale by U.S. Army Engineer District Rock Island, Clock Tower Bldg., Rock Island, Ill. 61201-2004.

(65) Foreign Waters: Published by Defense Mapping Agency Hydrographic/Topographic Center (see Defense Mapping Agency Procurement Information above).

(66) **Marine Weather Service Charts**: Published by the National Weather Service; for sale by NOS Distribution Branch (see Sales Information above).

(67) **Publications**

(68) **Notices to Mariners**:

(69) The Local Notice to Mariners is available without charge upon application to the appropriate Coast Guard District Commander (see address further on). The Defense Mapping Agency Notice to Mariners is available without charge by operators of ocean-going vessels (see Defense Mapping Agency Procurement Information above).

(70) **Special Notice to Mariners** are published annually in Defense Mapping Agency Notice to Mariners 1. These notices contain important information of considerable interest to all mariners. Interested parties are advised to read these notices.

(71) **Light Lists (United States and Possessions)**: Published by U.S. Coast Guard; for sale by the Government Printing Office. (See Government Printing Office, early this appendix.)

(72) **List of Lights (Foreign Countries)**: Published by Defense Mapping Agency Hydrographic/Topographic Center (see Defense Mapping Agency Procurement Information above).

(73) **Sailing Directions (Foreign Countries)**: Published by Defense Mapping Agency Hydrographic/Topographic Center (see Defense Mapping Agency Procurement Information above).

(74) **Radio Navigational Aids**, Pub. 117: Published by Defense Mapping Agency Hydrographic/Topographic Center (see Defense Mapping Agency Procurement Information above).

(75) The **Nautical Almanac**, the **Air Almanac**, and **Astronomical Almanac**: Published by U.S. Naval Observatory; for sale by Government Printing Office. (see Government Printing Office, early this appendix.)

(76) **American Practical Navigator (Bowditch) (Pub. 9)**: Published by Defense Mapping Agency Hydrographic/Topographic Center (see Defense Mapping Agency Procurement Information above).

(77) **International Code of Signals (Pub. 102)**: Published by Defense Mapping Hydrographic/Topographic Center (see Defense Mapping Agency Procurement Information above).

(78) **Selected Worldwide Marine Weather Broadcasts**: Published by National Weather Service; for sale by the Government Printing Office. (See Government Printing Office, early this appendix.)

(79) **Navigation Rules**: Navigation Rules, International-Inland (COMDTINST M16672.2 series): Published by the U.S. Coast Guard; for sale by Government Printing Office. (see Government Printing Office, early this appendix.)

(80) **Federal Requirements for Recreational Boats**: Published by U.S. Coast Guard; available without charge by contacting the toll free Boating Safety Hotline (telephone, 800-368-5647).

(81) **Port Series of the United States**: Published and sold by Corps of Engineers, U.S. Army, Water Resources Support Center, Port Facilities Branch, Casey Building, Fort Belvoir, VA 22060-5586.

(82) **Maritime Radio User Handbook**: Published and sold by Radio Technical Commission for Maritime Services, 655 Fifteenth Street, N.W., Suite 300, Washington, DC 20005-5701.

(83) **Corps of Engineers Offices**

(84) **New England Division Office**: 424 Trapelo Road, Waltham, MA 02254-9149.

(85) The New England Division, an operating division with both district and division functions, covers all of New England except western Vermont and small portions of Massachusetts and Connecticut along their western boundaries, and includes small portions of southeastern New York, all embraced in the drainage basins tributary to Long Island Sound and the Atlantic Ocean east of the New York-Connecticut State line. It also includes Fishers Island, N.Y.

(86) **New York District Office**: 26 Federal Plaza, New York, NY 10278-0090.

(87) The New York District includes western Vermont, small portions of western Massachusetts and Connecticut, eastern and south-central New York, including Long Island, and northeastern New Jersey embraced in the drainage basins tributary to Lake Champlain and the St. Lawrence River system east thereof and to the Atlantic Ocean from New York-Connecticut State line to, but not including, Manasquan Inlet, N.J.

(88) It exercises jurisdiction, however, over all matters pertaining to the improvement of the Great Lakes to Hudson River waterway. Under the direction of the Secretary of the Army, the district engineer, as Supervisor of New York Harbor, also exercises jurisdiction under the laws enacted for the preservation of the tidal waters of New York Harbor, its adjacent or tributary waters, and the waters of Long Island Sound.

(89) **Environmental Protection Agency (EPA) Offices.**–Regional offices and States in the EPA coastal regions:

(90) **Region I** (New Hampshire, Vermont, Maine, Massachusetts, Connecticut, Rhode Island): J. F. Kennedy Federal Bldg., Boston, Mass. 02203.

(91) **Region II** (New Jersey, New York, Puerto Rico, Virgin Islands): 26 Federal Plaza, New York, N.Y. 10278.

(92) **Region III** (Delaware, Maryland, Virginia, District of Columbia, Pennsylvania): 841 Chestnut Street, Philadelphia, PA 19107.

(93) **Region IV** (Alabama, Florida, Georgia, Mississippi, South Carolina, North Carolina): 345 Courtland Street, N.E., Atlanta, Ga. 30365.

(94) **Region V** (Illinois, Indiana, Michigan, Minnesota, Ohio, Wisconsin): 230 South Dearborn Street, Chicago, Ill. 60604.

(95) **Region VI** (Louisiana, Texas): First International Bldg., 1201 Elm Street, Dallas, Tex. 75270.

(96) **Region IX** (California, Hawaii, Guam): 215 Fremont Street, San Francisco, Calif. 94105.

(97) **Region X** (Alaska, Oregon, Washington): 1200 Sixth Avenue, Seattle, Wash. 98101.

(98) **Coast Guard District Offices**

(99) Commander, First Coast Guard District, 408 Atlantic Avenue, Boston, MA 02210-3350. Maine; New Hampshire; Vermont; Massachusetts; Rhode Island; Connecticut; New York except that part north of latitude 42°N. and west

of longitude 74°39'W; that part of New Jersey north of 39°57'N. (about the mouth of Toms River), east of 74°27'W. and northeast of a line from 39°57'N. 74°27'W. north west to the New York, New Jersey, and Pennsylvania boundaries at Tristate.

(100) **Note:** A Marine Safety Office combines the functions of the Captain of the Port and Marine Inspection Office.

(101) The symbol (D) preceding an office indicates that a Documentation Office is at the same address.

(102) **Coast Guard Marine Safety Offices**

(103) (D) Boston, MA: 447 Commercial Street 02109-1045.

(104) Portland ME: 312 Fore Street 04112-0108.

(105) Providence, RI: John O. Pastore Federal Building 02903-1790.

(106) **Coast Guard Captains of the Port**

(107) Long Island Sound Captain of the Port, 120 Woodward Avenue, New Haven, CT 06512-3698.

(108) New York Captain of the Port, Governors Island, New York, NY 10004-5098.

(109) **Coast Guard Marine Inspection Offices**

(110) (D) New York, N.Y.: Battery Park Bldg. 10004-1466.

(111) **Coast Guard Stations.**—The stations listed are in the area covered by this Coast Pilot. They have search and rescue capabilities and may provide lookout, communication, and/or patrol functions to assist vessels in distress. The National VHF-FM Distress System provides continuous coastal radio coverage outwards to 20 miles on channel 16. After contact on channel 16, communications with the Coast Guard should be on channel 22. If channel 22 is not available to the mariner, communications may be made on channel 12. Selected stations guard the International Radiotelephone Distress, Safety and Calling Frequencies.

(112) **Massachusetts:**

(113) Cape Cod Canal (41°46.4'N., 70°30.0'W.). East entrance to the canal, near Sandwich, Mass.

(114) Cape Cod Coast Guard Air Station (41°37.5'N., 70°31.5'W.). On Cape Cod at Otis Air Force Base.

(115) Provincetown (42°02.7'N., 70°11.6'W.). On southwest side of harbor, about 0.4 mile southwest of town pier.

(116) Chatham (41°40.3'N., 69°57.0'W.). Southeastern Cape Cod, near Chatham Light.

(117) Woods Hole (41°31.2'N., 70°40.0'W.). On west side of Little Harbor, about 450 yards northward of Juniper Point.

(118) Brant Point (41°17.4'N., 70°05.5'W.). On west side of entrance to Nantucket Harbor, near Brant Point Light.

(119) Menemsha (41°21.0'N., 70°45.9'W.). West end of Martha's Vineyard, near Menemsha Light.

(120) **Rhode Island:**

(121) Castle Hill (41°27.7'N., 71°21.5'W.). On west shore of Newport Neck, near Castle Hill Light.

(122) Point Judith (41°21.7'N., 71°28.9'W.). On Point Judith, near Point Judith Light, 0.5 mile east of Point Judith Harbor of Refuge.

(123) **Connecticut:**

(124) New London (41°20.7'N., 72°05.7'W.). At Fort Trumbull, on west side of main channel northward of Greens Harbor.

(125) New Haven (41°16.4'N., 72°54.2'W.). On the north side of the jutting point, about 1.5 miles northward of Lighthouse Point.

(126) **New York:**

(127) Fishers Island (41°15.4'N., 72°01.9'W.). In Silver Eel Pond, on west end of island (manned during summer months only).

(128) Eatons Neck (40°57.3'N., 73°23.9'W.). Near Eatons Neck Light, north shore of Long Island, east side of entrance to Huntington Bay.

(129) Montauk Point (41°04.3'N., 71°56.1'W.). In Montauk Harbor, Long Island.

(130) Shinnecock (40°51.0'N., 72°30.3'W.). East side of Ponquogue Point, 1.3 miles northwest of Shinnecock Inlet.

(131) Fire Island (40°37.5'N., 73°15.6'W.). Near west end of island, 0.2 mile northeast of Fire Island Light.

(132) Rockaway (40°34.1'N., 73°53.1'W.). On Rockaway Beach, 2.5 miles east of Rockaway Point.

(133) Coast Guard Air Station Brooklyn, Floyd Bennett Field (40°35.3'N., 73°53.5'W.). On Barren Island.

(134) Fort Totten (40°47.6'N., 73°46.9'W.). On the east side of Little Bay.

(135) New York (40°41.5'N., 74°01.0'W.). On Governors Island.

(136) **New Jersey:**

(137) Sandy Hook (40°28.2'N., 74°00.8'W.). On the Bay side, 0.5 mile south of the northern extremity of Sandy Hook.

(138) **Coast Guard Radio Broadcasts.**—Urgent, safety, and scheduled marine information broadcasts are made by Coast Guard radio stations. In general, these broadcasts provide information vital to vessels operating in the approaches and coastal waters of the United States including Puerto Rico and U.S. Virgin Islands. Transmissions are as follows:

(139) **Urgent and safety broadcasts:**

(140) (1) **By radiotelegraph:** (a) Upon receipt, except within 10 minutes of the next silent period, for urgent messages only; (b) during the last 15 seconds of the first silent period after receipt: (c) repeated at the end of the first silent period which occurs during the working hours of one-operator ships unless the original warning has been cancelled or superseded by a later warning message.

(141) (2) **By radiotelephone:** (a) upon receipt; (b) repeated 15 minutes later (for urgent messages only); (c) text only on the first scheduled broadcast unless cancelled; (d) additional broadcasts at the discretion of the originator.

(142) (3) Urgent broadcasts are preceded by the urgent signal; XXX for radiotelegraph; PAN for radiotelephone. Both the urgent signal and message are transmitted on 500 kHz, 2182 kHz, and channel 16. Safety broadcasts are preceded by the safety signal: TTT for radiotelegraph; SECURITY for radiotelephone. After the preliminary signal on 500 kHz and 2182 kHz, the station shifts to its assigned working medium frequency for the radiotelegraph broadcast and 2670 kHz for the radiotelephone transmission. Those stations broadcasting on VHF will announce on channel 16, shifting to channel 22.

(143) **Scheduled broadcasts.**—The following Coast Guard radio stations make scheduled broadcasts, preceded by a preliminary call on 500 kHz, 2182 kHz, and VHF-FM channel 16, at the times and frequencies indicated:

(144) **Radiotelegraph**

(145) NMF, Boston, Mass., 472 kHz, 0950 and 1900 e.s.t.

(146) **Radiotelephone**

(147) NMF, Boston, 2670 kHz, 1140 and 2340 e.s.t.

(148) **NMF-7**, Boston, channel 22a 0535 and 1735 e.s.t., antennas: Boston Bank Building, Boston (42°21.5'N., 71°03.5'W.), Eastern Point, Gloucester (42°34.8'N., 70°39.9'W.).

(149) **NMF-2**, Woods Hold, MA, channel 22A, 0505 and 1705 e.s.t., antennas: Pilgrim Monument, Provincetown (42°03'N., 70°11'W.), Nobska Point, Woods Hole (41°31'N., 70°39.5'W.), Brant Point, Nantucket Harbor (41°17.5'N., 70°06'W.).

(150) **NMY-41**, East Moriches, Long Island, 2670 kHz, 0710 and 1910 e.s.t., antenna: 1.5 miles north of Moriches Inlet (40°47.3'N., 72°44.9'W.).

(151) Channel 22A, 0710 and 1910 e.s.t., antennas: atop Montauk Point Light, 1.2 miles northwest of Shinnecock Inlet (40°50.9'N., 72°30.2'W.), and Fire Island CG Station (40°37.3'N., 73°15.7'W.).

(152) **NMK**, Cape May, 2670 kHz, 0603 and 1803 e.s.t., antenna: Cape May.

(153) Channel 22A, 0603 and 1803 e.s.t., antennas: Atlantic City, Cape May, Fortescue, and Indian River.

(154) **Customs Ports of Entry and Stations**
(155) Vessels may be entered and cleared at any port of entry or customs station, but at the latter only with advance authorization from the Customs Service district director.
(156) **Northeast Region**
(157) Boston District:
(158) Ports of Entry: New Bedford and Fall River, Mass.; New London, Hartford, New Haven, and Bridgeport, Conn.
(159) Customs Station: Provincetown, Mass. (supervised by Plymouth port of entry).
(160) Providence District:
(161) Ports of Entry: Newport and Providence, R.I.
(162) **New York Region**
(163) New York District:
(164) Ports of Entry: Albany and New York, N.Y.; Perth Amboy, N. J.

(165) **National Weather Service Offices.**-The following offices will provide forecasts and climatological data or arrange to obtain these services from other offices. They will also check barometers in their offices or by telephone; refer to the local telephone directory for numbers:
(166) Bridgeport, CT: Sikorsky Memorial Airport, Stratford, CT 06497;
(167) Hartford, CT: Bradley International Airport, Windsor Locks, CT 06096.
(168) Newark, NJ: Newark International Airport, Building 51, Room 421, 07114.
(169) New York, NY: 30 Rockefeller Plaza, Mezzanine Floor, Room 9, 10112.
(170) Providence, RI: T.F. Green Airport, 562 Airport Road, Warwick, RI 02886.
(171) **Radio Weather Broadcasts.**-Taped or direct broadcasts of marine weather forecasts and storm warnings are made by commercial and Coast Guard radio stations in the area covered by this Coast Pilot. The Coast Guard broadcast coastal and offshore marine weather forecasts of the times and frequencies indicated:
(172) **NMN**, Portsmouth, Va.:
(173) 4426.0 kHz, 0030, 0500, and 2300 e.s.t.
(174) 6501.0 kHz, 0030, 0500, 0630, 1100, 1700, 1830, and 2300 e.s.t.
(175) 8764.0 kHz, 0030, 0500, 0630, 1100, 1230, 1700, 1830, and 2300 e.s.t.
(176) 13089.0 kHz, 0630, 1100, 1230, 1700, and 1830 e.s.t.
(177) 17314.0 kHz, 1230 e.s.t.
(178) Marine Weather Services Charts are available for the following areas covered by this Coast Pilot:
(179) Eastport, ME to Montauk Point, NY.
(180) Montauk Point, NY to Manasquan, NJ.
(181) VHF-FM weather broadcast schedules of Coast Guard radio stations are also listed in the description of Coast Guard Radio Broadcasts found elsewhere in this appendix.
(182) **NOAA Weather Radio.**-National Weather Service VHF-FM radio stations provide mariners with continuous FM broadcasts of weather warnings, forecasts, radar reports, and surface weather observations. These stations usually transmit on 162.55, 162.475, or 162.40 MHz. Reception

range is up to 40 miles from the antenna site, depending on the terrain, type of receiver, and antenna used. The following VHF-FM radio stations with location of antenna are in or near the area covered by this Coast Pilot:
(183) KHB-35, Boston, Mass. (42°12'N., 71°06'W.), 162.475 MHz.
(184) KEC-73, Hyannis, Mass. (41°41'N., 70°20'W.), 162.55 MHz.
(185) WXJ-39, Providence, R.I. (41°48'N., 71°28'W.), 162.40 MHz.
(186) WXJ-42, Meriden, Conn. (41°33'N., 72°50'W.), 162.40 MHz.
(187) KHB-47, New London, Conn. (41°26'N., 72°08'W.), 162.55 MHz.
(188) WXM-80, Riverhead, NY (40°53'N., 72°43'W.), 162.475 MHz.
(189) KWO-35, New York, N. Y. (40°45'N., 73°58'W.), 162.55 MHz.
(190) **National Weather Service Forecast Offices (WSFOs).**-Scheduled coastal marine forecasts are issued four times daily by Weather Service Forecast Offices. (See National Weather Service, chapter 1, for further details.) Individual WSFO's and their specific areas of broadcast coverage are as follows:
(191) Boston, MA: From New Hampshire-Massachusetts border to Watch Hill, RI, out 25 miles.
(192) New York, N.Y.: (1) From Watch Hill to Montauk Point, to and including Manasquan, N.J., out 20 miles; (2) Long Island Sound; (3) New York Harbor.
(193) **National Weather Service Port Meteorological Officers (PMOs).**-Port Meteorological Officers provide assistance on matters of weather chart interpretation, instruments, marine weather communication, and requirements affecting ship operations. (See National Weather Service, chapter 1, for further details.) PMO offices in the area covered by this Coast Pilot are as follows:
(194) New York, N.Y.: 30 Rockefeller Plaza 10112.
(195) Newark, N.J.: Newark International Airport, Bldg. 51, 07114.

(196) **Public Health Service Quarantine Stations.**-Stations where quarantine examinations are performed:
(197) Boston: U.S. Quarantine Station. Logan International Airport, East Boston, Mass. 02128.
(198) New York: U.S. Quarantine Station, International Arrivals Bldg., J.F. Kennedy International Airport, Jamaica, NY 11430-1081.
(199) At other ports, quarantine and/or medical examinations are usually performed by Public Health Service contract personnel or by quarantine inspectors from the nearest quarantine station. Inquiries concerning quarantine matters should be directed to the nearest quarantine station.

(200) **Food and Drug Administration (FDA) Regional Offices**
(201) **Northeast Region** (New York, Maine, Connecticut, New Hampshire, Vermont, Rhode Island): 830 Third Avenue, Brooklyn, NY 11232.
(202) **Mid-atlantic Region** (Delaware, Pennsylvania, Virginia, Maryland, Ohio, New Jersey): U.S. Customhouse, 2nd and Chestnut Streets, Philadelphia, PA 19106.
(203) **Southeast Region** (South Carolina, North Carolina, Georgia, Alabama, Louisiana, Mississippi, Florida, Puerto Rico): 60 Eighth Street, N.E., Atlanta, GA 30309.
(204) **Midwest Region** (Illinois, Indiana, Michigan, Wisconsin): 20 N. Michigan Avenue, Chicago, IL 60602.
(205) **Southwest Region** (Texas): 3032 Bryan Street, Dallas, TX 75204.

(206) **Pacific Region** (California, Hawaii, Alaska, Washington, Oregon): 50 U.N. Plaza, San Francisco, CA 94102

(207) **Department of Agriculture, Animal and Plant Health Inspection Service (APHIS) Offices.** Department of, Animal and Plant Health Inspection Service (APHIS) Offices' > (APHIS)' > –Listed below are ports covered by this volume where APHIS inspectors are available to inspect plants, and plant and animal products, and locations of Animal Import Centers where livestock and birds are inspected.

(208) Information on importation of plants, animals, and plant and animal products is available from APHIS, Department of Agriculture, Federal Building, 6505 Belcrest Road, Hyattsville, Md. 20782. The specific offices to contact are as follows: for plants, including fruits and vegetables, and plant products, Plant Protection and Quarantine, Room 635, telephone 301-436-6799; for animal products, Import-Export Animals and Products Staff, Room 756A, telephone 301-436-7885; and for live ruminants, swine, equines, and poultry and other birds, Veterinary Services, Import-Export Animals and Products Staff, Room 764, telephone 301-436-8590.

(209) **Connecticut:**
(210) Wallingford: Federal Bldg., P.O. Box 631, 06492.
(211) **Massachusetts:**
(212) Boston: U.S. Custom House 02109; Logan International Airport, East Boston 02128.
(213) **New Jersey:**
(214) Hoboken: 209 River Street 07030.
(215) **New York:**
(216) Albany: 80 Wolf Road, Suite 503, 12205.
(217) New York: 26 Federal Plaza 10007.
(218) New York: John F. Kennedy International Airport, International Arrivals Bldg., Jamaica 11430.
(219) **Rhode Island:**
(220) Warwick: 48 Quaker Lane, West Warwick 02893.
(221) **Animal Import Centers:**
(222) Honolulu, Hawaii: P.O. Box 50001, 96850.
(223) Miami, Fla.: 8120 NW 53rd Street 33166.
(224) Rock Tavern, N.Y.: New York Animal Import Center, Stewart Airport Rural Route 1, Box 74, 12575.

(225) **Immigration and Naturalization Service Offices**
(226) **Connecticut:**
(227) Hartford: Ribicoff Federal Bldg., 450 Main Street 06103-3060.
(228) **Massachusetts:**
(229) Boston: John F. Kennedy Federal Bldg., Government Center 02203.
(230) **New Jersey:**
(231) Newark: Federal Bldg., 970 Broad Street 07102.

(232) **New York:**
(233) Albany: U.S. Post Office and Courthouse, 445 Broadway 12207.
(234) Flushing: Flushing Federal Savings Bldg., 136–21 Roosevelt Avenue 11354.
(235) New York: 26 Federal Plaza 10278.
(236) **Rhode Island:**
(237) Providence: John O. Pastore Federal Bldg.-U.S. Post Office, Exchange Terrace 02903.

(238) **Federal Communications Commission Offices**
(239) **District field offices:**
(240) Boston, Massachusetts: U.S. Customhouse, 165 State Street 02109.
(241) New York, N.Y., 201 Varick Street 10014.

(242) **Canadian Government Agencies.** –Hydrographic Chart Distribution Office, Department of Fisheries and Oceans, P.O. Box 8080, 1675 Russell Road, Ottawa, Ontario, KIG 3H6 Canada.
(243) Superintendent, Quebec Canals, Parks, Canada, 200 Churchill Boulevard, Greenfield Park, Quebec, J4V 2M4, Canada.

(244) **Radio shore stations providing medical advice.** –Messages to shore stations may be transmitted in code groups or plain language; messages should be signed by the master and be prefixed: "DH MEDICO". The following stations maintain a continuous guard on 500 kHz. (See Medical advice, chapter 1.)
(245) NMF, Sandwich, Cape Cod, Mass., U.S. Coast Guard.
(246) WCC, Chatham, Cape Cod, Mass., RCA Global Communications, Inc.

(247) **Measured Courses.** –The positions of measured courses are shown on the chart and their description is included in the Coast Pilots when information is reported to the National Ocean Service. Courses are located in the following places covered by this Coast Pilot.
(248) Beach Channel, along south shore of Jamaica Bay 12350.
(249) Captain Harbor, on south side of Great Captain Island 12367.
(250) Eatons Neck, on west side of Eatons Neck 12365.
(251) Port Jefferson, off Port Jefferson Harbor 12362.
(252) West Gilgo Beach, along State Boat Channel 12352.
(253) Sandy Hook Bay, on south side of Sandy Hook Bay off Municipal Yacht Basin 12327.
(254) The pages in the text describing the courses can be obtained by referring to the index for the geographic places; chart numbers follow the names.

COASTAL WARNING DISPLAYS

DAYTIME SIGNALS

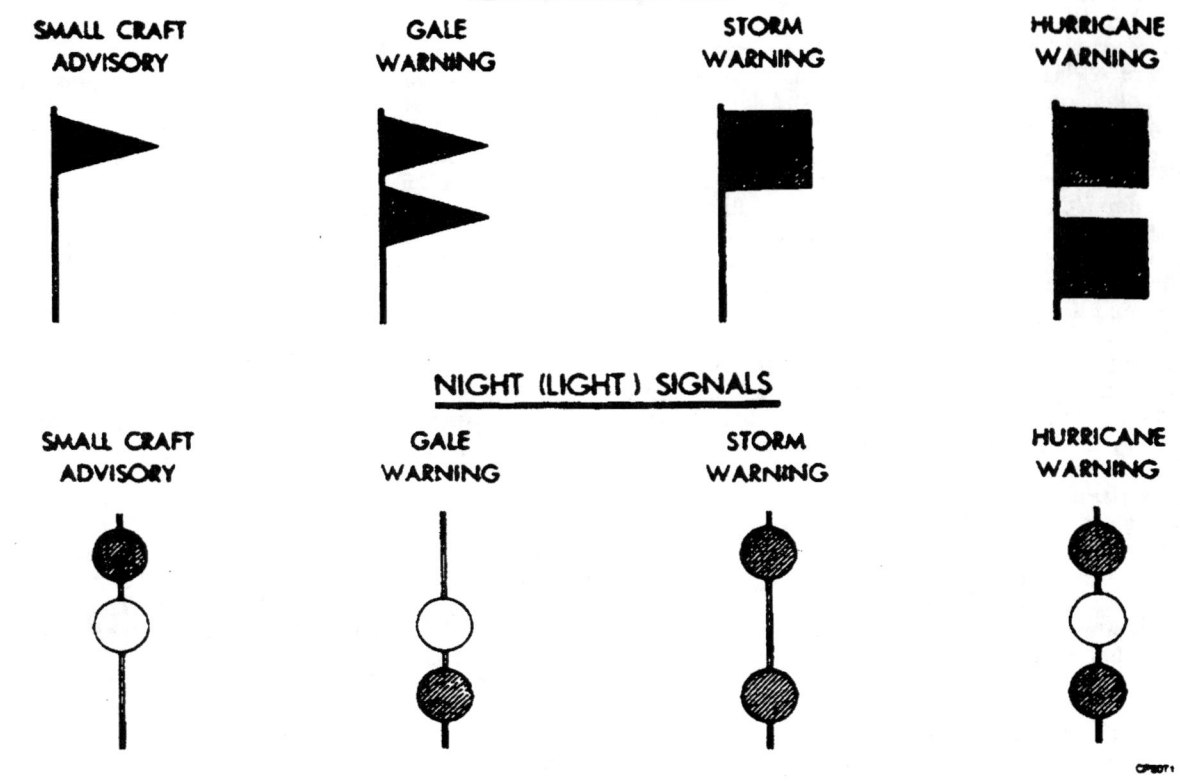

SMALL CRAFT ADVISORY	GALE WARNING	STORM WARNING	HURRICANE WARNING

NIGHT (LIGHT) SIGNALS

SMALL CRAFT ADVISORY	GALE WARNING	STORM WARNING	HURRICANE WARNING

EXPLANATION OF DISPLAYS

Small Craft Advisory: One RED pennant displayed by day and a RED light ABOVE a WHITE light at night, to alert mariners to sustained (more than two hours) weather or sea conditions, either present or forecast, that might be hazardous to small boats. Mariners learning of a Small Craft Advisory are urged to determine immediately the reason by tuning their radios to the latest marine broadcasts. Decision as to the degree of hazard will be left up to the boatman, based on his experience and size and type of boat. The threshold conditions for the Small Craft Advisory are usually 18 knots of wind (less than 18 knots in some dangerous waters) or hazardous wave conditions.

Gale Warning: Two RED pennants displayed by day and a WHITE light ABOVE a RED light at night to indicate that winds within the range 34 to 47 knots are forecast for the area.

Storm Warning: A single square RED flag with a BLACK center displayed during daytime and two RED lights at night to indicate that winds 48 knots and above, no matter how high the speed, are forecast for the area. However, if the winds are associated with a tropical cyclone (hurricane) the STORM WARNING display indicates that winds within the range 48 to 63 knots are forecast.

Hurricane Warning: Displayed only in connection with a tropical cyclone (hurricane). Two square RED flags with BLACK centers displayed by day and a WHITE light between two RED lights at night to indicate that winds 64 knots and above are forecast for the area.

Note: A "HURRICANE WATCH" is an announcement issued by the National Weather Service via press and radio and television broadcasts whenever a tropical storm or hurricane becomes a threat to a coastal area. The "Hurricane Watch" announcement is not a warning, rather it indicates that the hurricane is near enough that everyone in the area covered by the "Watch" should listen to their radios for subsequent advisories and be ready to take precautionary action in case hurricane warnings are issued.

Note: As of 1 February 1989 the National Weather Service discontinued its operation of the above visual system. Some local organizations, however, continued this program using information from a NOAA Weather Radio or some similar source for activating or ending their display. A SPECIAL MARINE WARNING BULLETIN is issued whenever a severe local storm or strong wind of brief duration is imminent and is not covered by existing warnings or advisories. Boaters will be able to receive these special warnings by keeping tuned to a NOAA VHF-FM radio station or to Coast Guard and commercial radio stations that transmit marine weather information.

ATLANTIC OCEAN DISTANCES
MONTREAL, CANADA, TO PANAMA CANAL ZONE
(Nautical Miles)

Figure at intersection of columns opposite ports in question is the nautical mileage between the two. Example: New York, N. Y., is 1399 nautical miles from San Juan, P. R.

*Quebec, Canada - SUBTRACT 139 miles.

All tabular distances are by outside routes which can be used by the deepest-draft vessel that the listed ports can accommodate. Lighter-draft vessels can save considerable mileage by transiting Canso Lock (Canada), the Cape Cod Canal (Massachusetts), and the Chesapeake and Delaware Canal (Delaware-Maryland); see the detailed tables. Gulf of Mexico distances are through the Shipping Safety Fairways.

Ports listed (with coordinates), in table order:

#	Port	Coordinates
1	MONTREAL, CANADA* (St. Lambert Lock)	—
2	Cabot Strait	47°07.0'N, 60°17.0'W
3	Gut of Canso (Lock)	45°39.0'N, 61°25.0'W
4	Portland, Maine	43°39.4'N, 70°14.1'W
5	Boston, Mass.	42°22.0'N, 71°03.0'W
6	NANTUCKET SHOALS	40°30.0'N, 69°25.0'W
7	NEW YORK, N.Y.	40°30.0'N, 74°01.0'W
8	Philadelphia, Pa	39°56.8'N, 75°08.0'W
9	Baltimore, Md.	39°16.0'N, 76°34.5'W
10	CHESAPEAKE BAY ENT.	36°56.3'N, 75°56.6'W
11	Norfolk, Va.	36°50.9'N, 76°17.9'W
12	DIAMOND SHOALS	35°08.0'N, 75°15.0'W
13	Wilmington, N.C.	34°14.0'N, 77°57.0'W
14	Charleston, S.C.	32°47.2'N, 79°55.2'W
15	Savannah, Ga.	32°05.0'N, 81°05.7'W
16	Jacksonville, Fla	30°19.2'N, 81°39.0'W
17	Key West, Fla	24°33.1'N, 81°48.5'W
18	STRAITS OF FLORIDA	24°25.0'N, 83°00.0'W
19	Tampa, Fla	27°56.5'N, 82°26.7'W
20	Pensacola, Fla	30°24.0'N, 87°13.0'W
21	Mobile, Ala	30°42.5'N, 88°02.5'W
22	NEW ORLEANS, La (via SW Pass)	29°57.0'N, 90°03.7'W
23	Port Arthur, Tex	29°49.5'N, 93°57.6'W
24	Galveston, Tex	29°19.0'N, 94°47.0'W
25	Corpus Christi, Tex	27°48.8'N, 97°24.0'W
26	San Juan, P. R.	18°27.8'N, 66°06.7'W
27	YUCATAN CHANNEL	21°50.0'N, 85°03.0'W
28	Panama Canal (Atlantic Ent.)	9°23.5'N, 79°55.3'W
29	PANAMA CANAL (Pacific Ent.)	8°53.0'N, 79°31.0'W

Distance matrix (nautical miles) — clearly legible origin rows. Each value is the distance from the origin port (row) to the destination port (column).

From \ To	Can	Por	Bos	Nan	NY	Phi	Bal	Che	Nor	Dia	Wil	Cha	Sav	Jac	KW	StrFla	Tam	Pen	Mob	NewOrl	PtArt	Galv	Corp	SanJ	Yuc	PanAtl	PanPac
Montreal (Cabot=681)	717	1276	1316	1311	1534	1682	1838	1669	1716	1729	1948	2014	2068	2172	2470	2540	2772	2277	3011	3080	3240	3242	3347	2445	2730	3203	3249
Cabot Strait	120	595	637	630	853	1001	1157	1008	1035	1048	1267	1333	1407	1491	1706	1859	2091	2296	2330	2399	2559	2561	2666	1764	2049	2522	2568
Gut of Canso		494	526	519	742	890	1046	896	923	936	1155	1221	1295	1379	1690	1751	1963	2188	2222	2291	2451	2453	2558	1660	1937	2419	2465

(The remainder of the triangular distance table — origin rows Portland, Boston, Nantucket Shoals, New York, Philadelphia, Baltimore, Chesapeake Bay Ent., Norfolk, Diamond Shoals, Wilmington, Charleston, Savannah, Jacksonville, Key West, Straits of Florida, Tampa, Pensacola, Mobile, New Orleans, Port Arthur, Galveston, Corpus Christi, San Juan, Yucatan Channel, Panama Canal Atlantic Ent. — is printed in the same triangular format on this page.)

COASTWISE DISTANCES
CAPE COD, MASS., TO NEW YORK, N.Y.
(Nautical Miles)

Figure at intersection of columns opposite ports in question is the nautical mileage between the two. Example: New Bedford, Mass., is 74 nautical miles from New London, Conn.

Ports (read along the diagonal):

- 40°41. 8'N. 74°09. 0'W.
- Port Newark, N.J. 40°38. 8'N. 74°11. 2'W.
- Elizabethport, N.J. 40°30. 3'N. 74°15. 7'W.
- Perth Amboy, N.J. 40°42. 0'N. 74°01. 0'W.
- NEW YORK, N.Y. 41°01. 7'N. 71°47. 3'W.
- MONTAUK POINT, N.Y. 40°57. 0'N. 73°04. 5'W.
- Port Jefferson, N.Y. 41°06. 0'N. 72°21. 5'W.
- Greenport, N.Y. 41°00. 2'N. 72°17. 7'W.
- Sag Harbor, N.Y. 41°02. 8'N. 71°57. 5'W.
- Montauk, N.Y. 41°01. 8'N. 73°32. 3'W.
- Stamford, Conn. 41°05. 7'N. 73°24. 7'W.
- South Norwalk, Conn. 41°10. 3'N. 73°10. 8'W.
- Bridgeport, Conn. 41°11. 3'N. 73°07. 3'W.
- Stratford, Conn. 41°17. 4'N. 72°54. 5'W.
- New Haven, Conn. 41°45. 0'N. 72°39. 0'W.
- Hartford, Conn. 41°21. 4'N. 72°05. 4'W.
- New London, Conn. 41°19. 9'N. 71°54. 6'W.
- Stonington, Conn. 41°11. 1'N. 71°34. 9'W.
- Great Salt Pond, R.I. 41°48. 5'N. 71°24. 0'W.
- Providence, R.I. 41°42. 4'N. 71°09. 8'W.
- Fall River, Mass. 41°29. 8'N. 71°19. 8'W.
- Newport, R.I. 41°38. 1'N. 70°55. 1'W.
- New Bedford, Mass. 41°31. 4'N. 70°40. 4'W.
- Woods Hole, Mass. 41°27. 3'N. 70°35. 8'W.
- Vineyard Haven, Mass. 41°17. 2'N. 70°05. 7'W.
- Nantucket, Mass. 41°17. 2'N. 70°05. 0'W.
- NANTUCKET SHOALS 40°30. 0'N. 69°25. 0'W.
- CAPE COD CANAL E ENT. 41°46. 8'N. 70°29. 0'W.

Ambrose Light (40°27. 5'N., 73°49. 9'W.) to New York (The Battery), 20.7 miles.

INSIDE-ROUTE DISTANCES

SOUTH SIDE OF LONG ISLAND
GREENPORT, N.Y., TO EAST ROCKAWAY INLET, N.Y.
(Nautical Miles)

Figure at intersection of columns opposite ports in question is the nautical mileage between the two. Example: Freeport is 61 nautical miles from Shinnecock Canal North End.

Ports (with positions):

- Greenport — 41°06.0'N., 72°21.5'W.
- Sag Harbor — 41°00.2'N., 72°17.7'W.
- Riverside — 40°55.0'N., 72°39.4'W.
- Shinnecock Canal, N. End — 40°53.9'N., 72°30.3'W.
- Shinnecock Inlet — 40°50.3'N., 72°28.6'W.
- Westhampton Beach — 40°48.2'N., 72°38.4'W.
- Moriches Inlet — 40°45.8'N., 72°45.3'W.
- Bellport — 40°45.1'N., 72°56.0'W.
- Patchogue — 40°45.5'N., 73°01.2'W.
- Bay Shore — 40°42.6'N., 73°14.2'W.
- Fire Island Inlet — 40°37.8'N., 73°18.6'W.
- Babylon — 40°41.2'N., 73°18.9'W.
- Amityville — 40°39.6'N., 73°24.8'W.
- Jones Beach — 40°36.2'N., 73°30.8'W.
- Jones Inlet — 40°34.4'N., 73°34.9'W.
- Freeport — 40°37.6'N., 73°34.9'W.
- Long Beach — 40°35.7'N., 73°39.4'W.
- East Rockaway Inlet — 40°34.9'N., 73°45.4'W.
- Rockaway Point • — 40°32.4'N., 73°56.5'W.
- NEW YORK (The Battery) • — 40°42.0'N., 74°01.0'W.
- Manasquan Inlet, N. J. • — 40°06.1'N., 74°01.9'W.

Distance table (nautical miles) — distance from the port at left to each following port:

From	to next ports →
Greenport	11, 21, 16, 21, 28, 34, 42, 48, 57, 62, 61, 66, 72, 76, 77, 80, 85, 94, 107, 116
Sag Harbor	22, 17, 22, 29, 35, 43, 49, 58, 63, 62, 67, 73, 77, 78, 81, 86, 95, 108, 117
Riverside	8, 13, 20, 26, 34, 40, 49, 54, 53, 58, 64, 68, 69, 72, 77, 86, 99, 108
Shinnecock Canal, N. End	5, 12, 18, 26, 32, 41, 46, 45, 50, 56, 60, 61, 64, 69, 78, 91, 100
Shinnecock Inlet	9, 15, 23, 29, 39, 44, 42, 47, 54, 58, 58, 61, 66, 75, 88, 97
Westhampton Beach	7, 15, 21, 30, 35, 34, 39, 45, 49, 49, 53, 58, 67, 80, 89
Moriches Inlet	11, 17, 27, 32, 30, 35, 42, 45, 46, 49, 54, 63, 76, 85
Bellport	6, 16, 21, 19, 24, 31, 35, 35, 38, 44, 53, 66, 75
Patchogue	13, 18, 17, 22, 28, 32, 32, 41, 50, 63, 72
Bay Shore	9, 5, 10, 17, 21, 21, 24, 29, 38, 51, 60
Fire Island Inlet	8, 12, 16, 20, 21, 24, 29, 38, 51, 60
Babylon	6, 13, 17, 18, 21, 26, 35, 48, 57
Amityville	7, 11, 12, 15, 20, 29, 42, 51
Jones Beach	4, 4, 8, 13, 22, 35, 44
Jones Inlet	4, 5, 10, 19, 32, 41
Freeport	6, 11, 20, 33, 42
Long Beach	5, 14, 27, 36
East Rockaway Inlet	9, 22, 31
Rockaway Point	13, 27
NEW YORK (The Battery)	40

• Outside distances westward of East Rockaway Inlet.

DISTANCES ON HUDSON RIVER
NEW YORK, N.Y., TO TROY LOCK, N.Y.
(Nautical Miles)

Figure at intersection of columns opposite ports in question is the nautical mileage between the two. Example: Poughkeepsie, N.Y., is 60 nautical miles from Albany, N.Y.

Port coordinates

Port	Latitude / Longitude
Troy Lock	41°45.1'N. 73°41.1'W.
Watervliet	42°43.7'N. 73°41.9'W.
Troy	42°43.7'N. 73°41.8'W.
Rensselaer	42°37.9'N. 73°45.1'W.
Albany	42°37.9'N. 73°45.3'W.
Coeymans	42°28.5'N. 73°47.4'W.
Coxsackie	42°21.0'N. 73°47.6'W.
Athens	42°15.6'N. 73°48.5'W.
Hudson	42°15.3'N. 73°48.1'W.
Catskill	42°13.0'N. 73°52.1'W.
Saugerties	42°04.4'N. 73°56.7'W.
Kingston	41°55.1'N. 73°59.0'W.
Hyde Park	41°47.3'N. 73°56.9'W.
Poughkeepsie	41°42.3'N. 73°56.5'W.
Newburgh	41°30.1'N. 74°00.3'W.
West Point	41°23.1'N. 73°57.3'W.
Peekskill	41°17.3'N. 73°56.0'W.
Haverstraw	41°11.8'N. 73°57.5'W.
Ossining	41°09.6'N. 73°52.3'W.
Nyack	41°05.4'N. 73°54.9'W.
Tarrytown	41°04.7'N. 73°52.2'W.
Yonkers	40°56.1'N. 73°54.3'W.
New York (The Battery)	40°42.0'N. 74°01.0'W.

Mileage chart (nautical miles) — distance read at intersection of the two ports.

From \ To	TroyLk	Watvlt	Troy	Rens	Alb	Coey	Coxs	Ath	Hud	Cat	Saug	King	HydeP	Pok	Newb	WPt	Peek	Havr	Oss	Nyack	Tarry	Yonk
Watervliet	2																					
Troy	2	0																				
Rensselaer	8	6	6																			
Albany	8	6	6	0																		
Coeymans	18	16	16	10	10																	
Coxsackie		26	24	24	18	7																
Athens		32	30	24	24	14	6															
Hudson		32	30	24	24	14	7	1														
Catskill		37	35	35	29	19	11	5	5													
Saugerties	46	44	44	38	38	28	21	14	14	11												
Kingston	56	54	54	48	48	38	30	24	24	21	12											
Hyde Park		63	61	61	55	44	37	31	31	28	19	9										
Poughkeepsie		68	66	66	60	49	42	36	36	33	24	14	5									
Newburgh	81	79	79	73	73	62	55	49	49	46	37	27	18	13								
West Point	89	87	87	81	81	70	63	57	57	54	45	35	26	21	8							
Peekskill	96	94	94	88	88	78	71	64	64	61	52	43	34	29	15	8						
Haverstraw	102	100	100	94	94	84	76	70	70	67	58	48	39	34	21	13	6					
Ossining	106	104	104	98	98	88	80	74	74	71	62	52	43	38	25	17	11	5				
Nyack	110	108	108	102	102	92	85	78	78	75	66	57		43	29	22	15	10	6			
Tarrytown	110	108	108	102	102	92	85	78	78	75	66	56	47	42	29	21	15	9	6	2		
Yonkers	118	116	116	110	110	100	93	86	86	83	74	64	55	50	37	29	23	18	14	10	9	
New York (The Battery)	134	132	132	126	126	115	108	102	102	98	89	80	71	66	53	45	38	33	29	25	24	16

INDEX

The numbers of the largest scale charts on which the names appear follow the indexed items. Some geographic names are indexed more than once when more than one place has the same geographic name. Charts published by the Defense Mapping Agency Hydrographic/Topographic Service are indicated by an asterisk.

I-2

PART 2 - SECTION A

LIGHT LIST

Volume II - Atlantic Coast

covering

CHESAPEAKE BAY ENTRANCE and approaches

for

general information refer to PART 1, SECTION A

DEPARTMENT OF TRANSPORTATION, U.S. COAST GUARD

LIGHT LIST

Volume II

ATLANTIC COAST

TOMS RIVER, NEW JERSEY TO
LITTLE RIVER, SOUTH CAROLINA

IMPORTANT

THIS PUBLICATION SHOULD BE CORRECTED
EACH WEEK FROM THE LOCAL NOTICE TO MARINERS
OR NOTICE TO MARINERS AS APPROPRIATE.

COMDTPUB P16502.2

U.S. GOVERNMENT PRINTING OFFICE
WASHINGTON, DC:

For sale by Superintende   Documer   S. Government Printing Office, Washington, DC 20402
Stock number: 050-012-00321-1

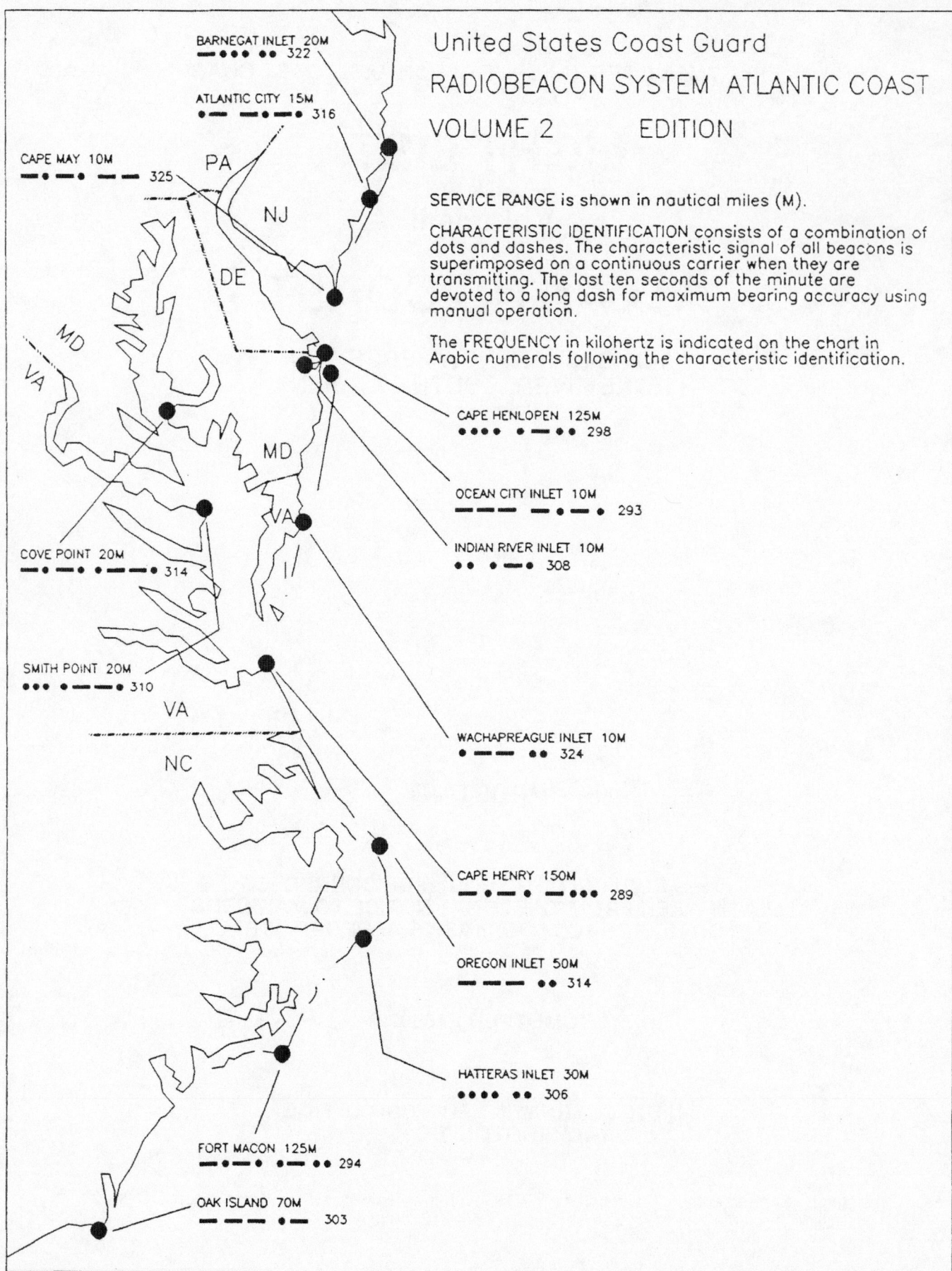

United States Coast Guard
RADIOBEACON SYSTEM ATLANTIC COAST
VOLUME 2   EDITION

SERVICE RANGE is shown in nautical miles (M).

CHARACTERISTIC IDENTIFICATION consists of a combination of dots and dashes. The characteristic signal of all beacons is superimposed on a continuous carrier when they are transmitting. The last ten seconds of the minute are devoted to a long dash for maximum bearing accuracy using manual operation.

The FREQUENCY in kilohertz is indicated on the chart in Arabic numerals following the characteristic identification.

BARNEGAT INLET 20M
322

ATLANTIC CITY 15M
316

CAPE MAY 10M
325

PA

NJ

DE

MD

VA

MD

VA

CAPE HENLOPEN 125M
298

OCEAN CITY INLET 10M
293

INDIAN RIVER INLET 10M
308

COVE POINT 20M
314

SMITH POINT 20M
310

VA

WACHAPREAGUE INLET 10M
324

NC

CAPE HENRY 150M
289

OREGON INLET 50M
314

HATTERAS INLET 30M
306

FORT MACON 125M
294

OAK ISLAND 70M
303

RADIOBEACON SYSTEM – ATLANTIC COAST

CONTINUOUS – By Frequency

Freq kHz	Station	Characteristic	Range (n.m.)	Lat. (N) ° ' "	Long. (W) ° ' "
289	CAPE HENRY	CB (−.−. −...)	150	36 55 35	76 00 27
293	OCEAN CITY INLET	OC (−−− −.−.)	10	38 19 30	75 05 18
294	FORT MACON	CL (−.−. .−..)	150	34 41 53	76 41 00
298	CAPE HENLOPEN	HL (.... .−..)	125	38 47 39	75 05 26
303	OAK ISLAND	OA (−−− .−)	70	33 53 33	78 02 06
308	INDIAN RIVER INLET	IR (.. .−.)	10	38 36 35	75 04 06
309	HATTERAS INLET STATION	HI (.... ..)	30	35 12 27	75 42 21
310	SMITH POINT	SP (... .−−.)	20	37 52 47	76 11 03
314	COVE POINT	CP (−.−. .−−.)	20	38 23 10	76 22 55
314	OREGON INLET	OI (−−− ..)	50	35 47 48	75 33 01
316	ATLANTIC CITY	AC (.− −.−.)	15	39 21 57	74 24 37
322	BARNEGAT INLET	BI (−... ..)	20	39 45 28	74 06 21
324	WATCHAPREAGUE INLET	WI (.−− ..)	10	37 34 24	75 37 30
325	CAPE MAY	CM (−.−. −−)	10	38 56 38	74 52 20

GEOGRAPHIC RANGE TABLE

The following table gives the approximate geographic range of visibility for an object which may be seen by an observer at sea level. It is necessary to add to the distance for the height of any object the distance corresponding to the height of the observer's eye above sea level.

Distances of visibility for objects of various elevations above sea level.

Height Feet	Height Meters	Distance Nautical Miles (NM)	Height Feet	Height Meters	Distance Nautical Miles (NM)	Height Feet	Height Meters	Distance Nautical Miles (NM)
5	1.5	2.6	70	21.3	9.8	250	76.2	18.5
10	3.1	3.7	75	22.9	10.1	300	91.4	20.3
15	4.6	4.5	80	24.4	10.5	350	106.7	21.9
20	6.1	5.2	85	25.9	10.8	400	121.9	23.4
25	7.6	5.9	90	27.4	11.1	450	137.2	24.8
30	9.1	6.4	95	29.0	11.4	500	152.4	26.2
35	10.7	6.9	100	30.5	11.7	550	167.6	27.4
40	12.2	7.4	110	33.5	12.3	600	182.9	28.7
45	13.7	7.8	120	36.6	12.8	650	198.1	29.8
50	15.2	8.3	130	39.6	13.3	700	213.4	31.0
55	16.8	8.7	140	42.7	13.8	800	243.8	33.1
60	18.3	9.1	150	45.7	14.3	900	274.3	35.1
65	19.8	9.4	200	61.0	19.0	1000	304.8	37.0

Example: Determine the geographic visibility of an object, with a height above water of 65 feet, for an observer with a height of eye of 35 feet. Enter above table;

Height of object	65 feet	9.4 NM
Height of observer	35 feet	6.9 NM
Computed geographic visibility		16.3 NM

LUMINOUS RANGE DIAGRAM

The nominal range given in this Light List is the maximum distance a given light can be seen when the meteorological visibility is 10 nautical miles. If the existing visibility is less than 10 miles, the range at which the light can be seen will be reduced below its nominal range. And, if the visibility is greater than 10 miles, the light can be seen at greater distances. The distance at which a light may be expected to be seen in the prevailing visibility is called its luminous range.

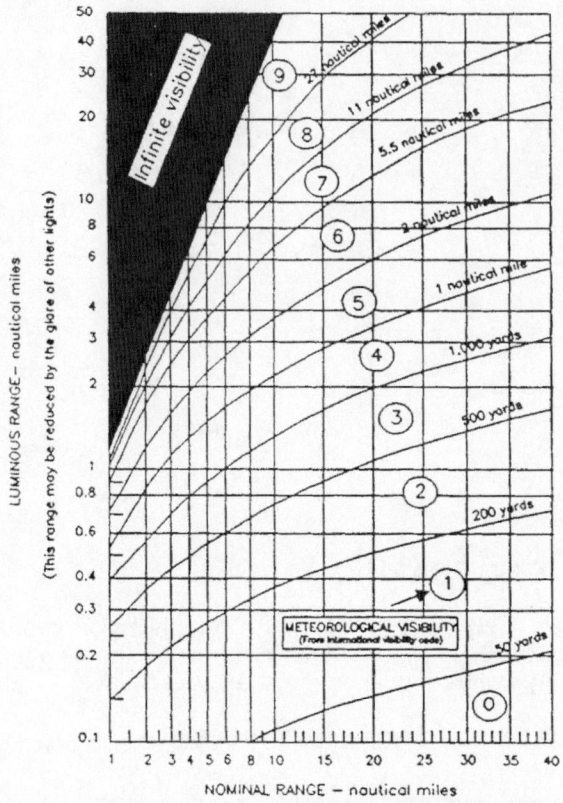

NOMINAL RANGE — nautical miles

METEORLOGICAL VISIBILITY		
(From International Visibility code)		
Code	Metric	Nautical (approximate)
0	Less than 50 meters	Less than 50 yards
1	50–200 meters	50–200 yards
2	200–500 meters	200–500 yards
3	500–1,000 meters	500–1,000 yards
4	1–2 kilometers	1,000–2,000 yards
5	2–4 kilometers	1–2 nautical miles
6	4–10 kilometers	2–5.5 nautical miles
7	10–20 kilometers	5.5–11 nautical miles
8	20–50 kilometers	11–27 nautical miles
9	Greater than 50 km	Greater than 27 nm

This diagram enables the mariner to determine the approximate luminous range of a light when the nominal range and the prevailing meteorological visibility are known. The diagram is entered from the bottom border using the nominal range listed in column 6 of this book. The intersection of the nominal range with the appropriate visibility curve (or, more often, a point between two curves) yields, by moving horizontally to the left border, the luminous range.

CAUTION: When using this diagram is must be remembered that:
1. The ranges obtained are approximate.
2. The transparency of the atmosphere may vary between the observer and the light.
3. Glare from background lighting will considerably reduce the range at which lights are sighted.
4. The rolling motion of the mariner and/or of a lighted aid to navigation may reduce the distance at which lights can be detected and identified.

(1) No.	(2) Name and location	(3) Position	(4) Characteristic	(5) Height	(6) Range	(7) Structure	(8) Remarks

(1) No.	(2) Name and location	(3) Position N/W	(4) Characteristic	(5) Height	(6) Range	(7) Structure	(8) Remarks
	CAPE MAY TO FENWICK ISLAND (Chart 12214)						
190 1275	*Hen and Chickens Shoal Lighted Gong Buoy 1 HC* Off southeast end of shoal.	38 42.4 75 00.0	Fl **G** 2.5ˢ		4	Green.	
195 4125	*Indian River Inlet Lighted Gong Buoy 1*	38 36.6 75 02.8	Fl **G** 2.5ˢ		5	Green.	
200 4135	**Indian River Inlet Radiobeacon**	38 36.6 75 04.1	IR (•• •—•)	80	10	Whip antenna.	FREQ: 308 kHz.
	FENWICK ISLAND TO CHINCOTEAGUE ISLAND (Chart 12211)						
205	FENWICK ISLAND LIGHT	38 27.1 75 03.3	Oc **W** 13ˢ 7.5ˢ fl 5.5ˢ ec	83	8	White tower. 87	Private aid.
210	*Fenwick Shoal Lighted Gong Buoy 1 FIS* On west side of shoal.	38 26.8 74 57.4	Fl **G** 4ˢ		5	Green.	
215	Isle of Wight Shoal Buoy IWS	38 23.5 74 56.0				Green and red bands; can.	
220	*Great Gull Bank Lighted Whistle Buoy 4*	38 16.4 75 00.4	Fl **R** 4ˢ		5	Red.	

SEACOAST (Atlantic Ocean)

(1) No.	(2) Name and location	(3) Position	(4) Characteristic	(5) Height	(6) Range	(7) Structure	(8) Remarks
	CAPE SABLE TO CAPE HATTERAS (Chart 13003)						
225	*NOAA Data Lighted Buoy 44004 (ODAS)*	38 32.2 70 43.3	Fl (4) **Y** 20ˢ			Yellow boat-shaped buoy.	

SEACOAST (Maryland) – Fifth District

(1) No.	(2) Name and location	(3) Position	(4) Characteristic	(5) Height	(6) Range	(7) Structure	(8) Remarks
	OCEAN CITY INLET TO CAPE HATTERAS (Chart 12200)						
230 4485	OCEAN CITY INLET JETTY LIGHT	38 19.5 75 05.1	Iso **W** 6ˢ	28	9	NB on skeleton tower.	HORN: 1 blast ev 15ˢ (2ˢ bl).
235 4490	**Ocean City Inlet Radiobeacon**	38 19.5 75 05.3	OC (——— —•—•)		10		FREQ: 293 kHz. Antenna located on Ocean City Inlet Jetty Light.
240	*Ocean City Lighted Research Buoy*	38 20.1 75 01.0	Fl **Y** 20ˢ			Yellow.	Maintained by US Army Corps of Engineers.
245 4495	*Ocean City Inlet Lighted Bell Buoy 2*	38 19.5 75 04.1	Fl **R** 4ˢ		3	Red.	
250	Ocean City Warning Buoy	38 18.9 75 05.1				White with orange bands worded, DANGER SUBMERGED OBJECT; can.	
255	Little Gull Bank Buoy LG	38 16.9 75 04.3				Green and red bands; can.	
260	Sugar Point Buoy 4A	38 04.8 75 00.4				Red nun.	
265	Jack Spot Buoy 2JS	38 05.3 74 45.1				Red nun.	

3

(1) No.	(2) Name and location	(3) Position	(4) Characteristic	(5) Height	(6) Range	(7) Structure	(8) Remarks
		N/W					

SEACOAST (Virginia) – Fifth District

OCEAN CITY INLET TO CAPE HATTERAS (Chart 12200)

(1) No.	(2) Name and location	(3) Position	(4) Characteristic	(5) Height	(6) Range	(7) Structure	(8) Remarks
270	Winter Quarter Shoal Buoy 5	37 58.3 75 09.2				Green can.	
275	Winter Quarter Shoal Lighted Buoy 6	37 59.7 75 01.4	Fl R 6s		4	Red.	
280	**Assateague Light**	37 54.7 75 21.4	Fl (2) W 5s 0.1sfl 1.0s ec. 0.1sfl 3.8s ec.	154	22	Conical tower with red and white bands. 142	
285	Ship Shoal Buoy SS	37 50.9 75 19.9				Red and white stripes; nun.	
290	Blackfish Bank Buoy 8A	37 50.4 75 15.9				Red.	
295	Blackfish Bank Lighted Whistle Buoy 8 East of 24 foot spot.	37 50.6 75 12.1	Fl R 2.5s		4	Red.	
300	Turners Lump Buoy 2	37 48.9 75 19.5				Red nun.	
305	Turners Lump Lighted Bell Buoy 2TL	37 48.9 75 22.5	Fl R 4s		5	Red.	
310 6210	Wachapreague Inlet Lighted Whistle Buoy A	37 35.0 75 33.7	Mo (A) W		6	Red and white stripes with red spherical topmark.	
315 6250	**Wachapreague Inlet Radiobeacon**	37 34.4 75 37.1	WI (•—— ••)		10	Lookout tower.	FREQ: 324 kHz.
320	Parramore Bank Lighted Gong Buoy 10	37 32.0 75 25.9	Fl R 4s		5	Red.	
325 6305	Quinby Inlet Lighted Buoy Q	37 28.1 75 36.1	Mo (A) W		6	Red and white stripes.	
330 6335	QUINBY INLET ENTRANCE LIGHT	37 27.8 75 40.2	Fl W 4s	28	8	NB on skeleton tower on structure.	
332 6400	Great Machipongo Inlet Lighted Whistle Buoy GM		Mo (A) W		5	Red and white stripes with red spherical topmark.	
335	Hog Island Lighted Bell Buoy 12	37 17.7 75 34.7	Fl R 2.5s		5	Red.	
340	Cape Charles Lighted Bell Buoy 14	37 07.4 75 41.0	Fl R 2.5s		5	Red.	
345	**Cape Charles Light**	37 07.4 75 54.4	Fl W 5s	180	24	Octagonal, pyramidal skeleton tower, upper part black, lower part white. 191	Operates 24 hours.
350	Surface Gunnery Area 7 Lighted Buoy GA	37 00.0 75 21.5	Fl Y 6s		6	Yellow.	
355	**Chesapeake Light**	36 54.3 75 42.8	Fl (2) W 15s 0.1sfl 2.9s ec. 0.1sfl 11.9s ec.	117	24	Blue tower on white square superstructure on four black piles. CHESAPEAKE on sides.	Emergency light of lower intensity will be displayed when main light is inoperative. RACON: N (—•). HORN: 1 blast ev 30s (3s bl). Operates continuously.
360	Navy SESEF Lighted Buoy A	36 55.0 75 38.3	Fl Y 2.5s		5	Yellow.	

(1) No.	(2) Name and location	(3) Position	(4) Characteristic	(5) Height	(6) Range	(7) Structure	(8) Remarks

OCEAN CITY INLET TO CAPE HATTERAS
(Chart 12200)

N/W

(1) No.	(2) Name and location	(3) Position	(4) Characteristic	(5) Height	(6) Range	(7) Structure	(8) Remarks
365	**Cape Henry Light**	36 55.6 76 00.4	Mo (U) W 20^s (R sector) 1^s fl 2^s ec. 1^s fl 2^s ec. 7^s fl 7^s ec.	164	W 17 R 15	Octagonal pyramidal tower. upper and lower half of each face alternately black and white. 163	Red from 154° to 233°, covers shoals outside Cape Charles and Middle Ground inside bay. Emergency light of lower intensity will be displayed when main light is extinguished.
366	**Cape Henry Radiobeacon**		CB (—•—• —•••)		150		FREQ: 289 kHz. Antenna 80 yards, 326° from Cape Henry Light.
370	Middle Ground South End Lighted Bell Buoy 4A	37 00.3 75 55.8	Fl R 4^s		4	Red.	
375	North Chesapeake Entrance Lighted Whistle Buoy NCA	36 58.7 75 48.6	Fl Y 2.5^s		6	Yellow.	
380	North Chesapeake Entrance Lighted Gong Buoy NCB	36 58.0 75 50.8	Fl Y 6^s		7	Yellow.	
385	North Chesapeake Entrance Lighted Bell Buoy NCC	36 57.4 75 53.0	Fl Y 4^s		6	Yellow.	
390	North Chesapeake Entrance Lighted Gong Buoy NCD	36 56.8 75 55.1	Fl Y 2.5^s		6	Yellow.	
395	Chesapeake Bay Entrance Junction Lighted Gong Buoy CBJ	36 56.1 75 57.5	Fl (2+1) G 6^s		5	Green and red bands.	

Chesapeake Bay Southern Approach

(1) No.	(2) Name and location	(3) Position	(4) Characteristic	(5) Height	(6) Range	(7) Structure	(8) Remarks
400	– Lighted Whistle Buoy CB	36 49.0 75 45.6	Mo (A) W		6	Red and white stripes with red spherical topmark.	RACON: K(—•—).
401	– Lighted Buoy 1	36 49.5 75 46.9	Fl G 2.5^s		4	Green.	
402	– Lighted Buoy 2	36 49.7 75 46.7	Fl R 2.5^s		4	Red.	
403	– Lighted Buoy 3	36 50.2 75 48.3	Fl G 4^s		4	Green.	
404	– Lighted Buoy 4	36 50.3 75 48.1	Fl R 4^s		4	Red.	
405	– Lighted Buoy 5	36 50.9 75 49.6	Fl G 4^s		4	Green.	
406	– Lighted Buoy 6	36 51.0 75 49.5	Fl R 4^s		4	Red.	
407	– Lighted Buoy 7	36 51.5 75 50.9	Fl G 2.5^s		4	Green.	
408	– Lighted Buoy 8	36 51.7 75 50.8	Fl R 2.5^s		4	Red.	
409	– Lighted Buoy 9	36 52.2 75 52.3	Q G		4	Green.	

(1) No.	(2) Name and location	(3) Position	(4) Characteristic	(5) Height	(6) Range	(7) Structure	(8) Remarks
			SEACOAST (Virginia) – Fifth District				
	OCEAN CITY INLET TO CAPE HATTERAS (Chart 12200)	N/W					
	Chesapeake Bay Southern Approach						
410	– Lighted Buoy 10	36 52.4 75 52.1	Q R		4	Red.	
411	– Lighted Buoy 11	36 53.1 75 53.3	Fl G 2.5ˢ		4	Green.	
412	– Lighted Buoy 12	36 53.3 75 53.1	Fl R 2.5ˢ		4	Red.	
413	– Lighted Buoy 13	36 54.0 75 54.3	Fl G 4ˢ		4	Green.	
414	– Lighted Buoy 14	36 54.2 75 54.2	Fl R 4ˢ		4	Red.	
415	– Lighted Buoy 15	36 55.0 75 55.4	Q G		4	Green.	
416	– Lighted Buoy 16	36 55.1 75 55.2	Q R		4	Red.	
420	Navy SESEF Lighted Buoy B	36 55.0 75 45.5	Fl Y 4ˢ		5	Yellow.	
425	Rudee Inlet Lighted Whistle Buoy RI	36 50.0 75 56.8	Mo (A) W		5	Red and white stripes.	
430	RUDEE INLET JETTY LIGHT 2	36 49.8 75 58.0	Fl R 2.5ˢ	22	3	TR on pile.	
435	RUDEE INLET JETTY LIGHT 1	36 49.8 75 58.0	Fl G 4ˢ	21	4	SG on pile.	
440	Dam Neck Disposal Area Lighted Buoy A		Fl Y 2.5ˢ		4	Yellow.	Position changed frequently for dredging.
442	Dam Neck Disposal Area Lighted Buoy B		Fl Y 4ˢ		4	Yellow.	Position changed frequently for dredging.
444	Dam Neck Disposal Area Lighted Buoy C		Fl Y 6ˢ		4	Yellow.	Position changed frequently for dredging.
452	Dam Neck Firing Zone Lighted Buoy A	36 49.5 75 51.1	Fl Y 2.5ˢ		5	Yellow.	
455	Virginia Beach Wreck Lighted Bell Buoy WR2V Marks wreck of TIGER.	36 46.1 75 46.1	Q R		4	Red.	
457	Dam Neck Firing Zone Lighted Buoy B	36 43.8 75 54.4	Fl Y 4ˢ		5	Yellow.	
460	False Cape Lighted Buoy 4A	36 35.6 75 44.0	Fl R 2.5ˢ		5	Red.	
462	NOAA Data Lighted Buoy 44014 (ODAS)	36 35.0 74 50.0	Fl (4) Y 20ˢ			Yellow disc-shaped hull.	
			SEACOAST (North Carolina) – Fifth District				
	OCEAN CITY INLET TO CAPE HATTERAS (Chart 12200)						
465	**Currituck Beach Light**	36 22.6 75 49.8	Fl W 20ˢ	158	18	Red conical tower. 163	

(1) No.	(2) Name and location	(3) Position	(4) Characteristic	(5) Height	(6) Range	(7) Structure	(8) Remarks
			VIRGINIA – Fifth District				

N/W

CHINCOTEAGUE INLET TO GREAT MACHIPONGO INLET
(Chart 12210)

Virginia Inside Passage

(1) No.	(2) Name and location	(3) Position	(4) Characteristic	(5) Height	(6) Range	(7) Structure	(8) Remarks
6465 5900	– Daybeacon 187					SG on pile.	
6470 5895	– LIGHT 186		Fl R 4s	16	3	TR on dolphin.	

Great Machipongo Channel

6474	– Buoy 1					Green can.	
6475	– LIGHT 1A	37 27.8 75 47.1	Fl G 4s	15	4	SG on dolphin.	Light equipment removed when endangered by ice.
6480	– Daybeacon 3					SG on pile.	
6481	– Daybeacon 3A					SG on pile.	
6482	– Daybeacon 3B					SG on pile.	
6485	– LIGHT 4		Q R	15	4	TR on pile.	Light equipment remove when endangered by ice.
6490	– LIGHT 6	37 27.8 75 48.4	Fl R 4s	15	4	TR on pile.	Light equipment removed when endangered by ice.
6500	– LIGHT 8	37 28.4 75 48.4	Fl R 4s	15	3	TR on pile.	Light equipment removed when endangered by ice.
6505	– Daybeacon 10	37 29.0 75 48.0				TR on pile.	
6510	– LIGHT 11	37 29.4 75 47.7	Fl G 4s	15	4	SG on pile.	Light equipment removed when endangered by ice.
6515	– LIGHT 12	37 29.9 75 47.7	Fl R 4s	15	3	TR on pile.	Light equipment removed when endangered by ice.
6520	– LIGHT 13	37 30.2 75 47.6	Fl G 4s	15	4	SG on dolphin.	
6525	– Daybeacon 15	37 30.3 75 48.2				SG on pile.	
6530	– Daybeacon 17					SG on pile.	
6535	– Daybeacon 18					TR on pile.	

CHESAPEAKE BAY ENTRANCE (Chart 12221)

6540	RAMSHORN CHANNEL LIGHT 2	37 23.4 75 51.2	Fl R 4s	18	4	TR on pile.	Light equipment removed from Dec 1. to Mar. 15.

Sand Shoal Inlet

Positions of buoys frequently shifted with changing conditions.

6545	– Lighted Bell Buoy A	37 17.8 75 42.9	Mo (A) W		6	Red and white stripes with red spherical topmark.	
6550	– Lighted Buoy 1		Fl G 4s		4	Green.	
6555	– Lighted Buoy 3		Fl G 4s		4	Green.	
6560	– Buoy 5					Green can.	
6565	– Lighted Buoy 6		Fl R 4s		4	Red.	

(1) No.	(2) Name and location	(3) Position	(4) Characteristic	(5) Height	(6) Range	(7) Structure	(8) Remarks

VIRGINIA – Fifth District

N/W
CHESAPEAKE BAY ENTRANCE (Chart 12221)

Sand Shoal Inlet

Positions of buoys frequently shifted with changing conditions.

6570	– SOUTH LIGHT	37 17.9 75 48.2	Fl W 4s	15	5	NB on dolphin.	
6575 6065	OYSTER CHANNEL JUNCTION LIGHT OC	37 17.4 75 53.7	Fl (2+1) R 6s	15	6	JR on slatted pile structure.	
6580	– Daybeacon 2					TR on pile.	
6585	– LIGHT 3		Fl G 2.5s	16	5	SG on dolphin.	
6590	– Daybeacon 5 Marks encroaching shoal.					SG on pile.	
6595	– LIGHT 6		Fl R 4s	16	3	TR on dolphin.	
6600	– LIGHT 8		Fl R 4s	16	3	TR on dolphin.	
6605	– LIGHT 10		Fl R 4s	16	3	TR on dolphin.	

CHESAPEAKE BAY (Virginia) – Fifth District

CHESAPEAKE BAY ENTRANCE (Chart 12221)

Chesapeake Channel

6610	Cape Henry Buoy 1	36 55.0 75 58.0					Green can.
6615	– Lighted Bell Buoy 2C	36 57.3 75 58.4	Fl R 2.5s		4		Red.
6620	Cape Henry Wreck Lighted Buoy 2CH 250 yards, 225° from last reported position of wreck. Marks wreck of CHILORE.	36 57.6 76 00.8	Q R		4		Red.
6625	– Lighted Buoy 3 75 feet outside channel limit.		Fl G 4s		4		Green.
6630	– Lighted Buoy 4 75 feet outside channel limit.		Fl R 4s		4		Red.
6635	– Lighted Bell Buoy 5 75 feet outside channel limit.		Fl G 2.5s		4		Green.
6640	– Lighted Buoy 6 75 feet outside channel limit.		Q R		4		Red.
6645	Tail Of The Horseshoe Shoal Lighted Bell Buoy 2T		Fl R 4s		4		Red.

Fish net buoys in Chesapeake Bay and tributary waters are not listed; however, they are shown on the nautical charts. Fish net buoys are painted yellow and are maintained for the Corps of Engineers to mark boundaries of fishing areas where fish nets and traps are permitted as prescribed by the Corps of Engineers.

(1) No.	(2) Name and location	(3) Position	(4) Characteristic	(5) Height	(6) Range	(7) Structure	(8) Remarks

N/W

CHESAPEAKE BAY ENTRANCE (Chart 12221)

Chesapeake Channel

(1) No.	(2) Name and location	(3) Position	(4) Characteristic	(5) Height	(6) Range	(7) Structure	(8) Remarks
6650	– Lighted Buoy 7 75 feet outside channel limit.		Q G		4	Green.	
6660	– Lighted Buoy 9		Fl G 4s		4	Green.	
6665	– Lighted Buoy 10		Fl R 4s		4	Red.	
6667	– Lighted Buoy 11		Q G		4	Green.	
6669	– Lighted Bell Buoy 12		Q R		4	Red.	
6670	– TUNNEL SOUTH LIGHT		F G	22	6	Mounted atop wall on centerline.	BELL: 1 stroke ev 10s Operates during periods of low visibility only. Ra ref. Private aid.
6675	– TUNNEL NORTH LIGHT		F R	22	6	Mounted atop wall on centerline.	HORN: 1 blast ev 20s (2s bl). Operates during periods of low visibility only. Private aid.
6677	– Lighted Buoy 13		Fl G 4s		4	Green.	
6679	– Lighted Buoy 14		Fl R 4s		4	Red.	
6680	– Lighted Bell Buoy 15 75 feet outside channel limit.		Q G		4	Green.	
6685	– Lighted Buoy 16 75 feet outside channel limit.		Q R		4	Red.	
6688	–Lighted Buoy 18		Fl R 2.5s		5	Red.	
6690	– Junction Lighted Gong Buoy CY 75 feet outside channel limit.		Fl (2+1) G 6s		5	Green and red bands.	
6695	– Lighted Buoy 19 75 feet outside channel limit.		Fl G 4s		4	Green.	
6700	– Lighted Buoy 20 75 feet outside channel limit.		Fl R 4s		4	Red.	
6705	– Lighted Bell Buoy 22 75 feet outside channel limit.		Q R		4	Red.	
6710	– Lighted Buoy 23 75 feet outside channel limit.		Q G		4	Green.	
6715	– Lighted Buoy 24 75 feet outside channel limit.		Fl R 2.5s		4	Red.	

Fish net buoys in Chesapeake Bay and tributary waters are not listed; however, they are shown on the nautical charts. Fish net buoys are painted yellow and are maintained for the Corps of Engineers to mark boundaries of fishing areas where fish nets and traps are permitted as prescribed by the Corps of Engineers.

(1) No.	(2) Name and location	(3) Position	(4) Characteristic	(5) Height	(6) Range	(7) Structure	(8) Remarks

CHESAPEAKE BAY ENTRANCE (Chart 12221) N/W

Chesapeake Channel

(1) No.	(2) Name and location	(3) Position	(4) Characteristic	(5) Height	(6) Range	(7) Structure	(8) Remarks
6720	– *Lighted Buoy 25* 75 feet outside channel limit.		Fl G 4s		4	Green.	
6725	– *Lighted Buoy 26* 75 feet outside channel limit.		Fl R 4s		4	Red.	
6730	– *Lighted Buoy 28* 75 feet outside channel limit.		Q R		4	Red.	
6735	– *Lighted Buoy 29* 75 feet outside channel limit.		Q G		4	Green.	
6740	– *Lighted Buoy 30* 75 feet outside channel limit.		Fl R 2.5s		4	Red.	
6745	– *Lighted Buoy 31* 75 feet outside channel limit.		Fl G 4s		4	Green.	
6750	– *Lighted Buoy 32* 75 feet outside channel limit.		Fl R 4s		4	Red.	
6755	– Calibration Buoy	37 12.3 76 08.5				White with green band.	Maintained by U.S. Army Corps of Engineers.
6770	– *Lighted Buoy 33* 75 feet outside channel limit.		Fl G 6s		4	Green.	
6775	– *Lighted Buoy 34* 75 feet outside channel limit.		Fl R 6s		4	Red.	
6780	– *Lighted Buoy 35* 75 feet outside channel limit.		Fl G 4s		4	Green.	
6785	– *Lighted Buoy 36* 75 feet outside channel limit.		Fl R 4s		4	Red.	
6787	– *Lighted Buoy 37* 75 feet outside channel limit.		Fl G 2.5s		5	Green.	
6788	– *Lighted Buoy 38* 75 feet outside channel limit.		Fl R 2.5s		5	Red.	
6789	– *Lighted Buoy 40*		Fl R 4s		5	Red.	Replaced by nun when endangered by ice.
6790 19585	OLD PLANTATION FLATS LIGHT	37 13.8 76 02.8	Fl W 4s	39	7	NB on pile.	Higher intensity beam toward 200°.

Fish net buoys in Chesapeake Bay and tributary waters are not listed; however, they are shown on the nautical charts. Fish net buoys are painted yellow and are maintained for the Corps of Engineers to mark boundaries of fishing areas where fish nets and traps are permitted as prescribed by the Corps of Engineers.

CHESAPEAKE BAY (Virginia) – Fifth District

N/W

WOLF TRAP TO SMITH POINT (Chart 12225)

Chesapeake Channel

(1) No.	(2) Name and location	(3) Position	(4) Characteristic	(5) Height	(6) Range	(7) Structure	(8) Remarks
6800	**Wolf Trap Light**	37 23.4 76 11.4	Fl W 15s	52	11	Octagonal red brick dwelling, square tower on brown cylinder.	
6805	*Wolf Trap Degaussing Lighted Bell Buoy WT2 150 yards west of obstruction.*	37 24.2 76 03.7	Q R		3	Red.	
6808	*– Lighted Buoy 41*		Fl G 4s		4	Green.	
6810	*– Lighted Gong Buoy 42*	37 25.6 76 05.1	Fl R 4s		5	Red.	
6820	*– Mid Channel Lighted Whistle Buoy CB*	37 30.0 76 02.6	Mo (A) W		6	Red and white stripes.	Replaced by nun when endangered by ice.
6821	RAPPAHANNOCK SHOAL CHANNEL SOUTH RANGE FRONT LIGHT	37 32.3 76 00.9	F W	31		Red monopod with white equipment hut on top.	
6821.1	RAPPAHANNOCK SHOAL CHANNEL SOUTH RANGE REAR LIGHT 7,300 yards, 140° from front light.		F W	220		Skeleton tower on caisson.	
6822	*– Lighted Buoy 43*		Fl G 2.5s		5	Green.	Replaced by can when endangered by ice.
6823	*– Lighted Buoy 44*		Fl R 2.6s		5	Red.	Replaced by nun when endangered by ice.
6823.5	*– Lighted Buoy 45*		Fl G 2.5s		4	Green.	Replaced by can when endangered by ice.
6824	*– Lighted Bell Buoy 46*		Q R		4	Red.	Replaced by nun when endangered by ice.
6824.5	*– Lighted Buoy 47*		Q G		4	Green.	Replaced by can when endangered by ice.
6825	STINGRAY POINT LIGHT	37 33.7 76 16.2	Fl W 4s	34	8	NG on pile.	
6830	WINDMILL POINT LIGHT	37 35.8 76 14.2	Fl W 6s (2 R sectors)	31	W 8 R 6	NR on pile.	Red from 293° to 082° and from 091.5° to 113°.
6835 13475	*Rappahannock River Junction Lighted Bell Buoy R*	37 33.6 76 10.3	Fl (2+1) G 6s		4	Green and red bands.	
6836	*Rappahannock Dumping Ground Lighted Buoy A*		Fl Y 4s			Yellow.	
6837	*Rappahannock Dumping Ground Lighted Buoy B*		Fl Y 2.5s			Yellow.	
6838	*Rappahannock Dumping Ground Lighted Buoy C*		Fl Y 6s			Yellow.	

Fish net buoys in Chesapeake Bay and tributary waters are not listed; however, they are shown on the nautical charts. Fish net buoys are painted yellow and are maintained for the Corps of Engineers to mark boundaries of fishing areas where fish nets and traps are permitted as prescribed by the Corps of Engineers.

(1) No.	(2) Name and location	(3) Position	(4) Characteristic	(5) Height	(6) Range	(7) Structure	(8) Remarks

CHESAPEAKE BAY (Maryland) – Fifth District

N/W
SANDY POINT TO SUSQUEHANNA RIVER (Chart 12273)

Harbor North Channel

Aberdeen Restricted Area

8295	– Buoy 5					Green can.	Maintained from Apr. 1 to Nov. 15. Private aid.
8300	– Buoy 6					Red nun.	Maintained from Apr. 1 to Nov. 15. Private aid.
8305	– Buoy 7					Green can.	Maintained from Apr. 1 to Nov. 15. Private aid.
8310	– Buoy 8					Red nun.	Maintained from Apr. 1 to Nov. 15. Private aid.

Elk River Channel

8313	– Lighted Buoy 21		Fl G 4s		4	Green.	Replaced by LIB of lower intensity from Dec. 1 to Mar. 15.
8315	– Lighted Buoy 22 75 feet outside channel limit.		Fl R 4s		4	Red.	Replaced by LIB of lower intensity from Dec. 1 to Mar. 15.
8317	BOHEMIA RIVER LIGHT 2	39 28.5 75 53.2	Fl R 4s	15	4	TR on pile.	
8318	Bohemia River Daybeacon 4					TR on pile.	
8319	Bohemia River Daybeacon 6					TR on pile.	

Back Creek Channel

8325	– Lighted Buoy 24		Fl R 2.5s		4	Red.	Replaced by LIB of lower intensity from Dec. 1 to Mar. 15.
8330	– LIGHT 25		Fl G 2.5s	25	4	SG on pile.	
8335	– LIGHT 26		Fl R 4s	25	4	TR on pile.	
8337	– Lighted Buoy 27 30 feet outside channel limit.		Fl G 4s		5	Green.	Replaced by LIB of lower intensity from Dec. 1 to Mar. 15.
8339	– Lighted Buoy 28		Fl R 2.5s		5	Red.	Replaced by LIB of lower intensity from Dec. 1 to Mar. 15.

CHESAPEAKE BAY (Virginia) – Fifth District

CAPE HENRY TO THIMBLE SHOAL LIGHT
(Chart 12254)

Thimble Shoal Channel

Vessels drawing less than 25 feet are not permitted to use this channel.

8340	– Lighted Bell Buoy 1TS	36 56.9 76 01.4	Fl G 2.5s		4	Green.	

Fish net buoys in Chesapeake Bay and tributary waters are not listed; however, they are shown on the nautical charts. Fish net buoys are painted yellow and are maintained for the Corps of Engineers to mark boundaries of fishing areas where fish nets and traps are permitted as prescribed by the Corps of Engineers.

(1) No.	(2) Name and location	(3) Position	(4) Characteristic	(5) Height	(6) Range	(7) Structure	(8) Remarks

CHESAPEAKE BAY (Virginia) – Fifth District

N/W
CAPE HENRY TO THIMBLE SHOAL LIGHT
(Chart 12254)

Thimble Shoal Channel

Vessels drawing less than 25 feet are not permitted to use this channel.

8345	– Lighted Buoy 2		Fl R 2.5ˢ		4	Red.	
8350	– Lighted Buoy 3		Fl G 4ˢ		4	Green.	
8355	– Lighted Gong Buoy 4		Fl R 4		4	Red.	
8360	– Lighted Bell Buoy 5		Fl G 6ˢ		4	Green.	
8365	– Lighted Buoy 6		Fl R 6ˢ		4	Red.	
8370	– Lighted Buoy 7		Fl G 2.5ˢ		4	Green.	
8375	– Lighted Gong Buoy 8		Fl R 2.5ˢ		4	Red.	
8380	THIMBLE SHOAL TUNNEL SOUTH LIGHT		F G	32		On wall.	BELL: 1 stroke ev 10ˢ. Operates during periods of low visibility only. Private aid.
8385	THIMBLE SHOAL TUNNEL NORTH LIGHT		F R	32		On wall.	HORN: 1 blast ev 20ˢ (2ˢ bl). Operates during periods of low visibility only. Private aid.
8390	– Lighted Bell Buoy 9		Fl G 4ˢ		4	Green.	
8395	– Lighted Buoy 10		Fl R 4ˢ		4	Red.	
8400	– Lighted Buoy 11		Fl G 6ˢ		4	Green.	
8405	– Lighted Gong Buoy 12		Fl R 6ˢ		4	Red.	
8410	– Lighted Bell Buoy 13		Fl G 2.5ˢ		4	Green.	
8415	– Lighted Buoy 14		Fl R 2.5ˢ		4	Red.	
8420	– Lighted Buoy 15		Fl G 4ˢ		4	Green.	
8425	– Lighted Gong Buoy 16		Fl R 4ˢ		4	Red.	

CHESAPEAKE BAY - THIMBLE SHOAL CHANNEL
(Chart 12245)

Thimble Shoal Channel

Vessels drawing less than 25 feet are not permitted to use this channel.

8430	– Lighted Gong Buoy 17		Fl G 2.5ˢ		4	Green.	
8435	– Lighted Buoy 18		Q R		4	Red.	
8440	– Lighted Buoy 19		Q G		4	Green.	

Fish net buoys in Chesapeake Bay and tributary waters are not listed; however, they are shown on the nautical charts.
Fish net buoys are painted yellow and are maintained for the Corps of Engineers to mark boundaries of fishing areas
where fish nets and traps are permitted as prescribed by the Corps of Engineers.

(1) No.	(2) Name and location	(3) Position	(4) Characteristic	(5) Height	(6) Range	(7) Structure	(8) Remarks

N/W

CHESAPEAKE BAY - THIMBLE SHOAL CHANNEL
(Chart 12245)

Thimble Shoal Channel

Vessels drawing less than 25 feet are not permitted to use this channel.

No.	Name and location	Position	Characteristic	Height	Range	Structure	Remarks
8450	**Thimble Shoal Light**	37 00.9 76 14.4	**Iso W** 6s	55	13	Red conical tower on brown cylindrical pier.	HORN: 1 blast ev 30s (3s bl). Operates continuously.
8455	– *Lighted Bell Buoy 21*		**Q G**		4	Green.	
8460	– *Lighted Buoy 22*	37 00.1 76 17.9	**Q R**		4	Red.	

Naval Ordnance

No.	Name and location	Position	Characteristic	Height	Range	Structure	Remarks
8475	– *Buoy F*					Orange and white bands; sphere.	Maintained by U.S. Navy.
8480	– *Buoy G*					Orange and white bands; sphere.	Maintained by US. Navy.
8485	– *Buoy H*					Orange and white bands; sphere.	Maintained by U.S Navy
8490	– *Buoy K*					Orange and white bands; sphere.	Maintained by U.S. Navy.
8495	– *Buoy L*					Orange and white bands; sphere.	Maintained by U.S. Navy.
8500	– *Buoy M*					Orange and white bands; sphere.	Maintained by U.S. Navy.
8505	– *Lighted Buoy P*	37 00.3 76 17.0	**Fl Y** 4s		6	Yellow.	
8510	– *Lighted Buoy R*		**Fl Y** 4s		6	Yellow.	
8515	– *Lighted Buoy T*		**Fl Y** 4s		6	Yellow.	
8517	NORFOLK ENTRANCE REACH RANGE FRONT LIGHT	37 00.7 76 17.1	**Occ W** 4s	20		On platform on four pile structure.	Lighted throughout 24 hours.
8518	NORFOLK ENTRANCE REACH RANGE REAR LIGHT 960 yards, 045° from front light.		**F W**	58		On platform on four pile structure.	Lighted throughout 24 hours.

HAMPTON ROADS (Chart 12245)

Hampton Bar

No.	Name and location	Position	Characteristic	Height	Range	Structure	Remarks
8520	**Old Point Comfort Light**	37 00.1 76 18.4	**Fl (2) R** 12s (W sector) 2s fl 2s ec 2s fl 6s ec	54	W 16 R 14	White tower.	White from 265° to 038°. Emergency light of reduced intensity will be displayed when main light is inoperative.
8525	FORT WOOL LIGHT	36 59.2 76 18.2	**Fl W** 4s	25	8	On small gray house.	
8530	– *Buoy 14*					Red nun.	

Fish net buoys in Chesapeake Bay and tributary waters are not listed; however, they are shown on the nautical charts. Fish net buoys are painted yellow and are maintained for the Corps of Engineers to mark boundaries of fishing areas where fish nets and traps are permitted as prescribed by the Corps of Engineers.

(1) No.	(2) Name and location	(3) Position	(4) Characteristic	(5) Height	(6) Range	(7) Structure	(8) Remarks

N/W

JAMESTOWN ISLAND TO JORDAN POINT (Chart 12251)

James River

(1) No.	(2) Name and location	(3) Position	(4) Characteristic	(5) Height	(6) Range	(7) Structure	(8) Remarks
11400	– CHANNEL LIGHT 124 190 feet outside channel limit.	37 20.0 77 16.4	Fl R 4ˢ	18	4	TR on dolphin.	
11405	– *Channel Lighted Buoy 126*	37 20.4 77 16.2	Fl R 4ˢ		4	Red.	
11410	– LIGHT 127		Fl G 2.5ˢ	15	3	SG on pile.	
11415	– *Lighted Buoy 128* 300 feet outside channel limit.	37 20.7 77 16.1	Fl R 4ˢ		4	Red.	
11420	– LIGHT 132	37 21.2 77 16.5	Fl R 4ˢ	24	3	TR on pile.	
11425	– LIGHT 133		Fl G 4ˢ	20	4	SG on pile.	
11430	– OBSTRUCTION LIGHT A	37 21.1 77 17.1	F W	15		On dolphin.	Private aid.
11435	– LIGHT 135		Fl G 2.5ˢ	16	3	SG on pile.	
11440	– LIGHT 137		Fl G 4ˢ	18	4	SG on pile.	
11445	– *Channel Lighted Buoy 138*	37 21.8 77 18.4	Fl R 4ˢ		3	Red.	
11450	– LIGHT 139		Fl G 6ˢ	18	4	SG on pile.	
11455	– *Channel Lighted Buoy 140*	37 22.1 77 18.5	Fl R 4ˢ		3	Red.	
11460	– LIGHT 143		Fl G 4ˢ	16	4	SG on pile.	
11465	– LIGHT 144		Fl R 4ˢ	16	3	TR on dolphin.	
11470	– LIGHT 146		Fl R 4ˢ	15	3	TR on pile.	
11475	– LIGHT 147		Fl G 4ˢ	16	4	SG on pile.	
11480	– LIGHT 150		Fl R 4ˢ	18	3	TR on pile.	
11485	DUTCH GAP LIGHT	37 22.5 77 21.5	Q W			On dolphin.	Private aid.
11490	– LIGHT 151		Q G	15	3	SG on pile.	
11495	– LIGHT 152	37 22.7 77 21.7	Fl R 4ˢ	19	3	TR on pile.	
11497	– LIGHT 152A		Fl R 2.5ˢ	18	3	TR on pile.	
11500	– LIGHT 154		Fl R 4ˢ	15	3	TR on dolphin.	
11505	VIRGINIA POWER WHARF LIGHT	37 22.9 77 22.7	Fl G 11ˢ	11		On wharf.	Private aid.
11510	Virginia Power Turning Basin Daybeacon					On black and white striped pile.	Private aid.
11515	– LIGHT 155		Q G	18	3	SG on pile.	

Fish net buoys in Chesapeake Bay and tributary waters are not listed; however, they are shown on the nautical charts. Fish net buoys are painted yellow and are maintained for the Corps of Engineers to mark boundaries of fishing areas where fish nets and traps are permitted as prescribed by the Corps of Engineers.

(1) No.	(2) Name and location	(3) Position	(4) Characteristic	(5) Height	(6) Range	(7) Structure	(8) Remarks
			CHESAPEAKE BAY (Virginia) – Fifth District				
	N/W **JAMESTOWN ISLAND TO JORDAN POINT** (Chart 12251)						
	James River						
11517	– LIGHT 155A		Fl G 2.5s	18	3	SG on pile.	
11520	– LIGHT 156		Q R	18	3	TR on pile.	
11525	– LIGHT 157		Fl G 4s	18	4	SG on pile.	
11530	– LIGHT 158		Fl R 4s	18	3	TR on pile.	
11535	– LIGHT 160		Q R	18	3	TR on pile.	
11540	– LIGHT 161		Fl G 4s	18	3	SG on pile.	
11545	– *Channel Lighted* *Buoy 162*	37 25.3 77 25.1	Fl R 2.5s		4	Red.	
11550	EXXON PIER LIGHTS	37 25.4 77 25.5	(3) F G	12		On pile.	Private aids.
11555	– LIGHT 163		Fl G 4s	18	4	SG on pile.	
11560	– LIGHT 165	37 26.2 77 25.7	Fl G 4s	20	4	SG on pile.	
11565	– LIGHT 166		Fl R 4s	18	3	TR on pile.	
11570	– LIGHT 168		Fl R 4s	18	3	TR on pile.	
11575	– Channel Buoy 169					Green can.	
11580	– Channel Buoy 171					Green can.	
11585	– Channel Buoy 172					Red nun.	
11590	– LIGHT 173		Fl G 4s	15	4	SG on pile.	
	CAPE CHARLES TO NORFOLK HARBOR (Chart 12222)						
	Chesapeake Bay						
11595	*Horseshoe Crossing* *Lighted Bell Buoy HC*	37 01.3 76 08.9	Mo (A) W		6	Red and white stripes with red spherical topmark.	
11600	BUCKROE BEACH FISHING PIER LIGHT	37 02.3 76 17.3	F W	16		White circular daymark on white structure.	Private aid.
	Salt Ponds						
11610	– Buoy 1					Green can.	Private aid.
11615	– Daybeacon 2					TR on pile.	Private aid.
11620	– Daybeacon 3					SG on pile.	Private aid.
11625	– Daybeacon 4					TR on pile.	Private aid.
11630	– Daybeacon 5					SG on pile.	Private aid.
11635	– LIGHT 6	37 03.7 76 16.7	Fl R 4s	19		TR on pile.	Private aid.
11640	– LIGHT 7	37 03.8 76 17.0	Fl G 2.5s			SG on pile.	Private aid.

Fish net buoys in Chesapeake Bay and tributary waters are not listed; however, they are shown on the nautical charts.
Fish net buoys are painted yellow and are maintained for the Corps of Engineers to mark boundaries of fishing areas
where fish nets and traps are permitted as prescribed by the Corps of Engineers.

(1) No.	(2) Name and location	(3) Position	(4) Characteristic	(5) Height	(6) Range	(7) Structure	(8) Remarks

N/W
CAPE CHARLES TO NORFOLK HARBOR (Chart 12222)

Salt Ponds

(1) No.	(2) Name and location	(3) Position	(4) Characteristic	(5) Height	(6) Range	(7) Structure	(8) Remarks
11645	– Daybeacon 8					TR on pile.	Private aid.
11650	– Daybeacon 10					TR on pile.	Private aid.
11655	– Daybeacon 12					TR on pile.	Private aid.
11660	– Daybeacon 14					TR on pile.	Private aid.
11665	– Daybeacon 16					TR on pile.	Private aid.
11670	GRAND VIEW FISHING PIER LIGHT	37 04.4 76 16.6	F W	22			Private aid.

MOBJACK BAY AND YORK RIVER ENTRANCE (Chart 12238)

Back River

(1) No.	(2) Name and location	(3) Position	(4) Characteristic	(5) Height	(6) Range	(7) Structure	(8) Remarks
11675	– *Entrance Lighted Bell Buoy 1*	37 05.6 76 15.0	Fl G 4s		4	Green.	
11680	– Channel Daybeacon 2					TR on pile.	
11685	– CHANNEL LIGHT 4		Fl R 4s	17	3	TR on pile.	
11690	– CHANNEL LIGHT 5		Fl G 4s	19	4	SG on pile.	
11695	– Channel Daybeacon 6					TR on pile.	
11700	– CHANNEL LIGHT 7		Fl G 4s	15	4	SG on pile.	
11705	– CHANNEL LIGHT 8		Fl R 4s	14	3	TR on pile.	Light equipment removed from Dec. 1 to Mar. 15.
11710	– CHANNEL LIGHT 9	37 06.6 76 17.6	Fl G 4s	19	4	SG on pile.	
11715	– South Channel Daybeacon 1					SG on pile.	
11720	– South Channel Daybeacon 3					SG on pile.	

Dandy Haven Marina Entrance

(1) No.	(2) Name and location	(3) Position	(4) Characteristic	(5) Height	(6) Range	(7) Structure	(8) Remarks
11725	– Daybeacon 1	37 06.0 76 18.1				SB on pile.	Private aid.
11730	– Daybeacon 2					TR on pile.	Private aid.
11735	– Daybeacon 3					SB on pile.	Private aid.
11740	– Daybeacon 4					TR on pile.	Private aid.
11745	– Daybeacon 5					SB on pile.	Private aid.
11750	– Daybeacon 6					TR on pile.	Private aid.
11755	– Daybeacon 7					SB on pile.	Private aid.
11760	– Daybeacon 8					TR on pile.	Private aid.
11765	– Daybeacon 9					SB on pile.	Private aid.

Fish net buoys in Chesapeake Bay and tributary waters are not listed; however, they are shown on the nautical charts. Fish net buoys are painted yellow and are maintained for the Corps of Engineers to mark boundaries of fishing areas where fish nets and traps are permitted as prescribed by the Corps of Engineers.

(1) No.	(2) Name and location	(3) Position	(4) Characteristic	(5) Height	(6) Range	(7) Structure	(8) Remarks

CHESAPEAKE BAY (Virginia) – Fifth District

N/W
MOBJACK BAY AND YORK RIVER ENTRANCE
(Chart 12238)

Back River

Dandy Haven Marina Entrance

11770	– Daybeacon 10					TR on pile.	Private aid.
11775	– Daybeacon 11					SB on pile.	Private aid.
11780	– Daybeacon 12					TR on pile.	Private aid.

Back River

11785	– Channel Daybeacon 10					TR on pile.	
11790	– Channel Daybeacon 12					TR on pile.	
11795	– CHANNEL LIGHT 13		Fl G 4s	15	4	SG on pile.	
11800	– Channel Daybeacon 14					TR on pile.	
11805	– Channel Daybeacon 16					TR on pile.	

Harris River Approach

11810	– Daybeacon 2	37 06.1 76 19.0				TR on pile.	Private aid.
11815	– Daybeacon 3					SB on pile.	Private aid.
11820	– Daybeacon 4					TR on pile.	Private aid.
11825	– Daybeacon 5					SB on pile.	Private aid.
11830	– Daybeacon 6					TR on pile.	Private aid.
11835	– Daybeacon 8					TR on pile.	Private aic.

Back River

11840	– CHANNEL LIGHT 17		Fl G 2.5s	14	3	SG on pile.	Light equipment removed from Dec. 1 to Mar. 15.
11845	– CHANNEL LIGHT 18		Q R	14	4	TR on pile.	
11850	– Channel Daybeacon 20					TR on pile.	
11855	– CHANNEL LIGHT 21		Fl G 4s	14	4	SG on pile.	
11860	– CHANNEL LIGHT 22		Fl R 4s	14	3	TR on pile.	Light equipment removed from Dec. 1 to Mar. 15.
11865	– CHANNEL LIGHT 25		Fl G 2.5s	15	4	SG on pile.	
11870	– CHANNEL LIGHT 27		Fl G 4s	12	4	SG on pile.	Light equipment removed from Dec. 1 to Mar. 15.
11875	Langley Yacht Club Buoy A	37 04.8 76 20.5				White can with orange bands and orange circle worded NO WAKE.	Private aid.
11880	Langley Yacht Club Buoy B					White can with orange bands and orange circle worded NO WAKE.	Private aid.

Fish net buoys in Chesapeake Bay and tributary waters are not listed; however, they are shown on the nautical charts.
Fish net buoys are painted yellow and are maintained for the Corps of Engineers to mark boundaries of fishing areas
where fish nets and traps are permitted as prescribed by the Corps of Engineers.

(1) No.	(2) Name and location	(3) Position	(4) Characteristic	(5) Height	(6) Range	(7) Structure	(8) Remarks
			CHESAPEAKE BAY (Virginia) – **Fifth District**				
	N/W						
	MOBJACK BAY AND YORK RIVER ENTRANCE (Chart 12238)						
	Back River						
11885	– NORTHWEST BRANCH LIGHT 1		Fl G 2.5s	14	3	SG on pile.	Light equipment removed when endangered by ice.
11890	– NORTHWEST BRANCH LIGHT 3		Fl G 4s	14	4	SG on pile.	Light equipment removed when endangered by ice.
11895	– Northwest Branch Daybeacon 4					TR on pile.	
11900	– Northwest Branch Daybeacon 5					SG on pile.	
11905	– Northwest Branch Daybeacon 6					TR on pile.	
	Poquoson River						
11910	– Entrance Lighted Buoy 2	37 13.5 76 19.5	Fl R 4s		3	Red.	
11915	– Entrance Buoy 4					Red nun.	
11920	– Entrance Lighted Buoy 6		Fl R 4s		4	Red.	
11925	– Entrance Buoy 8					Red nun.	
11930	– Entrance Lighted Buoy 10		Fl R 2.5s		3	Red.	
11935	– ENTRANCE LIGHT 11		Fl G 4s	15	4	SG on dolphin.	
11940	– Daybeacon 13					SG on pile.	
11945	– LIGHT 14		Fl R 4s	16	4	TR on pile.	Light equipment removed from Dec. 1 to Mar. 15.
11950	Chisman Creek Daybeacon 2					TR on pile.	
11955	Chisman Creek Daybeacon 4	37 10.8 76 24.5				TR on pile.	
11960	Chisman Creek Daybeacon 5					SG on pile.	
11965	GOOSE CREEK JUNCTION LIGHT GC	37 11.1 76 25.4	Fl (2+1) R 6s	15	4	JR on pile.	Light equipment removed from Dec. 1 to Mar. 15.
11970	Chisman Creek Daybeacon 6					TR on pile.	
11975	Goose Creek Daybeacon 2					TR on pile.	
11980	– LIGHT 15		Fl G 2.5s	15	4	SG on pile.	Light equipment removed from Dec. 1 to Mar. 15.
11985	– Daybeacon 16					TR on pile.	
11990	– Daybeacon 17					SG on pile.	
11995	Quarter March Creek Entrance Daybeacon 2					TR on pile.	

Fish net buoys in Chesapeake Bay and tributary waters are not listed; however, they are shown on the nautical charts.
Fish net buoys are painted yellow and are maintained for the Corps of Engineers to mark boundaries of fishing areas where fish nets and traps are permitted as prescribed by the Corps of Engineers.

(1) No.	(2) Name and location	(3) Position	(4) Characteristic	(5) Height	(6) Range	(7) Structure	(8) Remarks

MOBJACK BAY AND YORK RIVER ENTRANCE N/W
(Chart 12238)

Poquoson River

No.	Name and location	Position	Characteristic	Height	Range	Structure	Remarks
12000	Quarter March Creek Daybeacon 4					TR on pile.	
	Bennett Creek						
12005	– Daybeacon 1	37 09.7 76 22.8				SG on pile.	
12010	– LIGHT 2		Fl R 4s	15	4	TR on pile.	Light equipment removed from Dec. 1 to Mar. 15.
12015	– Daybeacon 4					TR on pile.	
12020	– Daybeacon 6					TR on pile.	
12025	– Daybeacon 8					TR on pile.	
12030	– LIGHT 10		Fl R 4s	19	4	TR on pile.	
12035	White House Cove Daybeacon 1	37 08.7 76 22.4				SG on pile.	
12040	White House Cove Daybeacon 1A	37 08.6 76 22.6		15		SG on pile.	
12045	White House Cove Daybeacon 2					TR on pile.	
12050	POQUOSON RIVER MARINA PIER LIGHTS	37 08.5 76 22.8	(3) F W	8			Private aids.
	Goodwin Thorofare						
12055	– LIGHT 2	37 12.3 76 22.9	Fl R 2.5s	18	4	TR on pile.	Light equipment removed when endangered by ice.
12060	– LIGHT 3	37 12.6 76 23.4	Fl G 4s	18	4	SG on dolphin.	
12065	– LIGHT 4		Fl R 4s	18	3	TR on dolphin.	
12070	– Daybeacon 5					SG on pile.	
12075	– Daybeacon 7					SG on pile.	
12080	– Daybeacon 8					TR on pile.	
12085	– CHANNEL LIGHT 10		Fl R 4s	19	4	TR on pile.	
12090	– CHANNEL LIGHT 12		Fl R 4s	15	3	TR on pile.	
12095	– CHANNEL LIGHT 13		Fl G 4s	15	4	SG on pile.	
12100	– Channel Daybeacon 14					TR on pile.	
12105	– Channel Daybeacon 15					SG on pile.	
12110	– CHANNEL LIGHT 16		Fl R 4s	14	4	TR on pile.	Light equipment removed when endangered by ice.

Fish net buoys in Chesapeake Bay and tributary waters are not listed; however, they are shown on the nautical charts.
Fish net buoys are painted yellow and are maintained for the Corps of Engineers to mark boundaries of fishing areas
where fish nets and traps are permitted as prescribed by the Corps of Engineers.

(1) No.	(2) Name and location	(3) Position	(4) Characteristic	(5) Height	(6) Range	(7) Structure	(8) Remarks

CHESAPEAKE BAY (Virginia) – Fifth District

N/W

MOBJACK BAY AND YORK RIVER ENTRANCE (Chart 12238)

Back Creek

12115	– Daybeacon 1	37 12.6 76 24.8				SG on pile.	
12120	– Daybeacon 2					TR on pile.	
12125	– Daybeacon 3					SG on pile.	

CHESAPEAKE BAY ENTRANCE (Chart 12221)

York River

Entrance channel buoys located 75 feet outside channel limit.

12130	– *Entrance Channel Lighted Gong Buoy 2*	37 07.4 76 09.2	Fl R 4s		4	Red.	
12135	– *Entrance Channel Lighted Buoy 1YR*		Fl G 4s		4	Green.	
12140	– Entrance Channel Buoy 3					Green can.	
12145	– Entrance Channel Buoy 4					Red nun.	
12150	– *Entrance Channel Lighted Buoy 5*		Fl G 4s		4	Green.	
12155	– *Entrance Channel Lighted Buoy 6*		Fl R 4s		4	Red.	
12160	– Entrance Channel Buoy 7					Green can.	
12165	– Entrance Channel Buoy 8					Red nun.	
12170	– *Entrance Channel Lighted Buoy 9*	37 10.3 76 13.9	Fl G 4s		4	Green.	
12175	– *Entrance Channel Lighted Buoy 10*		Fl R 4s		4	Red.	
12180	– Entrance Channel Buoy 11					Green can.	
12185	– Entrance Channel Buoy 12					Red nun.	
12190	YORK SPIT LIGHT	37 12.6 76 15.3	Fl W 6s	30	8	NR on pile.	
12195	– *Entrance Channel Lighted Buoy 13*		Fl G 4s		4	Green.	
12200	– *Entrance Channel Lighted Buoy 14*		Fl R 4s		4	Red.	
12205	– Entrance Channel Buoy 15					Green can.	

*Fish net buoys in Chesapeake Bay and tributary waters are not listed; however, they are shown on the nautical charts.
Fish net buoys are painted yellow and are maintained for the Corps of Engineers to mark boundaries of fishing areas
where fish nets and traps are permitted as prescribed by the Corps of Engineers.*

(1) No.	(2) Name and location	(3) Position	(4) Characteristic	(5) Height	(6) Range	(7) Structure	(8) Remarks

N/W
CHESAPEAKE BAY ENTRANCE (Chart 12221)

York River

Entrance channel buoys located 75 feet outside channel limit.

12210	– Entrance Channel Buoy 16					Red nun.	
12215	– *Entrance Channel Lighted Buoy 17*		Fl G 4s		4	Green.	
12220	– *Entrance Channel Lighted Gong Buoy 18*		Q R		4	Red.	
12225	York Spit Warning Daybeacon					NW on pile worded DANGER SHOAL.	

YORK RIVER - YORKTOWN AND VICINITY (Chart 12241)

York River

12230	– *Lighted Bell Buoy 21*		Fl G 4s		4	Green.	Replaced by can when endangered by ice.
12235	– *Lighted Bell Buoy 22*		Q R		4	Red.	
12240	TUE MARSHES LIGHT	37 14.1 76 23.2	Fl W 6s	41	8	NG on pile.	

Perrin River

12245	– *Junction Lighted Buoy PR*	37 14.8 76 23.5	Fl (2+1) R 6s		3	Red and green bands.	
12250	– Entrance Buoy 2					Red nun.	
12255	– ENTRANCE LIGHT 4		Fl R 4s	19	3	TR on pile.	
12260	– Entrance Daybeacon 6					TR on pile.	
12265	– ENTRANCE LIGHT 7		Fl G 4s	19	4	SG on pile.	
12270	– ENTRANCE LIGHT 8	37 15.6 76 25.2	Fl R 4s	19	3	TR on pile.	
12275	– Entrance Daybeacon 9					SG on pile.	
12280	– Daybeacon 11					SG on pile.	

York River

12285	– RANGE FRONT LIGHT	37 13.6 76 29.3	Q W	11		KRG on small white house on pile structure.	
12290	– RANGE REAR LIGHT 575 yards, 258° from front light.		Iso W 6s	65	13	KRG on skeleton tower.	
12295	– Buoy 24					Red nun.	
12300	– Buoy 23					Green can.	

Fish net buoys in Chesapeake Bay and tributary waters are not listed; however, they are shown on the nautical charts. Fish net buoys are painted yellow and are maintained for the Corps of Engineers to mark boundaries of fishing areas where fish nets and traps are permitted as prescribed by the Corps of Engineers.

CHESAPEAKE BAY (Virginia) – Fifth District

N/W

YORKTOWN TO WEST POINT (Chart 12243)

York River

Queen Creek

No.	Name and location	Position	Characteristic	Height	Range	Structure	Remarks
12520	– Daybeacon 7					SG on pile.	
12525	– Daybeacon 8					TR on pile.	
12530	– Daybeacon 10					TR on pile.	
12535	– Daybeacon 11					SG on pile.	
12538	– Daybeacon 12					TR on pile.	
12540	– Daybeacon 13					SG on pile.	
12543	– Daybeacon 14					TR on pile.	
12544	– Daybeacon 15					SG on pile.	
12545	– Daybeacon 15A					SG on pile.	
12550	– Daybeacon 16					TR on pile.	
12555	– Daybeacon 18					TR on pile.	
12560	– Daybeacon 20					TR on pile.	

York River

No.	Name and location	Position	Characteristic	Height	Range	Structure	Remarks
12565	Cedarbush Creek Daybeacon 2	37 18.6 76 33.9				TR on pile.	
12570	PAGES ROCK LIGHT Off rock.	37 18.7 76 35.2	Fl W 6s	43	8	NR on skeleton tower.	
12575	– Channel Buoy 35					Green can.	

Aberdeen Creek

No.	Name and location	Position	Characteristic	Height	Range	Structure	Remarks
12580	– ENTRANCE LIGHT 2	37 20.1 76 36.1	Fl R 4s	15	5	TR on pile.	
12585	– LIGHT 3		Fl G 4s	15	4	SG on pile.	
12590	– Daybeacon 5					SG on pile.	
12595	– Daybeacon 7					SG on pile.	
12600	– Daybeacon 9					SG on pile.	
12605	– Daybeacon 11					SG on pile.	

York River

No.	Name and location	Position	Characteristic	Height	Range	Structure	Remarks
12610	– Channel Buoy 37					Green can.	
12615	Carter Creek Entrance Daybeacon 2					TR on pile.	
12620	– LIGHT 39		Fl G 4s	14	5	SG on pile.	
12625	– Channel Buoy 41					Green can.	
12630	– LIGHT 42		Fl R 4s	15	5	TR on pile.	

Fish net buoys in Chesapeake Bay and tributary waters are not listed; however, they are shown on the nautical charts. Fish net buoys are painted yellow and are maintained for the Corps of Engineers to mark boundaries of fishing areas where fish nets and traps are permitted as prescribed by the Corps of Engineers.

(1) No.	(2) Name and location	(3) Position	(4) Characteristic	(5) Height	(6) Range	(7) Structure	(8) Remarks
			CHESAPEAKE BAY (Virginia) – **Fifth District**				
	N/W **YORKTOWN TO WEST POINT** (Chart 12243)						
	York River						
12635	– Channel Buoy 43					Green can.	
12640	– Channel Buoy 44					Red nun.	
	Croaker Landing						
12645	– Daybeacon 1	32 25.7 76 43.4				SG on pile.	Private aid.
12650	– Daybeacon 2					TR on pile.	Private aid.
12655	– Daybeacon 3					SG on pile.	Private aid.
12660	– Daybeacon 4					TR on pile.	Private aid.
	York River						
12665	– LIGHT 46		Fl R 4s	15	5	TR on pile.	
12670	– Channel Buoy 47					Green can.	
12675	BELLS ROCK LIGHT		Fl W 4s (R sector)	40	W 8 R 6	NR on white skeleton tower on piles.	Red from 120° to 329°.
12680	– Channel Buoy 49					Green can.	
12685	– Channel Buoy 50					Red nun.	
12690	– LIGHT 51		Fl G 4s	14	5	SG on pile.	
12695	– Channel Buoy 53					Green can.	
12700	– Channel Buoy 54					Red nun.	
12705	– Channel Buoy 55					Green can.	
12710	– Channel Buoy 57					Green can.	
12715	West Point Spit Junction Buoy					Red and green bands; nun.	
12720	– Channel Buoy 59					Green can.	
12725	– Channel Buoy 61					Green can.	
	MOBJACK BAY AND YORK RIVER ENTRANCE (Chart 12238)						
	Mobjack Bay						
12730	NEW POINT COMFORT SPIT LIGHT 2		Fl R 2.5s	18	4	TR on pile.	Light equipment removed when endangered by ice.
12735	NEW POINT COMFORT SPIT LIGHT 4		Fl R 4s	15	5	TR on dolphin.	
	York Spit Swash Channel						
12740	– Daybeacon 1					SG on pile.	
12745	– Daybeacon 2					TR on pile.	

*Fish net buoys in Chesapeake Bay and tributary waters are not listed; however, they are shown on the nautical charts.
Fish net buoys are painted yellow and are maintained for the Corps of Engineers to mark boundaries of fishing areas
where fish nets and traps are permitted as prescribed by the Corps of Engineers.*

(1) No.	(2) Name and location	(3) Position	(4) Characteristic	(5) Height	(6) Range	(7) Structure	(8) Remarks

		N/W					
MOBJACK BAY AND YORK RIVER ENTRANCE (Chart 12238)							
Mobjack Bay							
York Spit Swash Channel							
12750	– LIGHT 3	37 15.7 76 20.0	Fl G 4s	15	4	SG on pile.	
12755	– Daybeacon 5					SG on pile.	
12760	DUTCHMAN POINT LIGHT 6		Fl R 4s	15	5	TR on dolphin.	
Davis Creek							
12765	– CHANNEL LIGHT 1	37 19.2 76 18.0	Fl G 4s	15	4	SG on dolphin.	
12770	– CHANNEL LIGHT 2		Fl R 4s	14	3	TR on dolphin.	
12775	– Channel Daybeacon 4					TR on pile.	
12780	– CHANNEL LIGHT 6		Fl R 4s	15	3	TR on dolphin.	
12785	– CHANNEL LIGHT 8		Q R	15	3	TR on pile.	
12790	– CHANNEL LIGHT 10		Fl R 4s	14	4	TR on pile.	
12795	Pepper Creek Daybeacon 1	37 20.0 76 19.6				SG on pile.	
12800	Pepper Creek Daybeacon 2					TR on pile.	
East River							
12805	– ENTRANCE LIGHT 1 On south end of shoal.	37 21.3 76 21.1	Fl G 4s	15	4	SG on dolphin.	Light equipment removed when endangered by ice.
12810	– Daybeacon 2					TR on pile.	
12815	– LIGHT 3		Fl G 4s	16	3	SG on slatted pile structure.	
12820	Mobjack Marina Channel Daybeacon 1	37 22.7 76 20.6				SG on pile.	
12825	Mobjack Marina Channel Daybeacon 3	37 22.7 76 20.7				SG on pile.	
12830	– LIGHT 5		Q G	15	4	SG on pile.	
12835	– LIGHT 9		Fl G 4s	15	4	SG on pile.	Obscured from 120° to 180°.
12840	– Daybeacon 7					SG on pile.	
12845	– Daybeacon 11					SG on pile.	
12850	– Daybeacon 13					SG on pile.	
12855	– Daybeacon 15					SG on pile.	
12860	– Daybeacon 17					SG on pile.	
12865	– Daybeacon 18					TR on pile.	

Fish net buoys in Chesapeake Bay and tributary waters are not listed; however, they are shown on the nautical charts.
Fish net buoys are painted yellow and are maintained for the Corps of Engineers to mark boundaries of fishing areas
where fish nets and traps are permitted as prescribed by the Corps of Engineers.

(1) No.	(2) Name and location	(3) Position	(4) Characteristic	(5) Height	(6) Range	(7) Structure	(8) Remarks

CHESAPEAKE BAY (Virginia) – Fifth District

N/W

MOBJACK BAY AND YORK RIVER ENTRANCE
(Chart 12238)

Mobjack Bay

Browns Bay

12870	– LIGHT 1	37 18.1 76 22.9	Fl G 4ˢ	16	4	SG on slatted pile structure.	Light equipment removed when endangered by ice.
12875	– Entrance Daybeacon 2					TR on pile.	
12880	– LIGHT 3		Fl G 4ˢ	12	4	SG on pile.	Light equipment removed from Dec. 1 to Mar. 15.
12885	– LIGHT 4		Fl R 4ˢ	12	3	TR on pile.	

Severn River

12890	– JUNCTION LIGHT SR	37 20.2 76 23.7	Fl (2+1) R 6ˢ	16	4	JR on pile.	
12895	– LIGHT 1		Fl G 4ˢ	16	4	SG on pile.	Light equipment removed when endangered by ice.
12897	– Daybeacon 2					TR on pile.	
12900	– LIGHT 3		Fl G 4ˢ	16	4	SG on slatted pile structure.	
12905	– Daybeacon 5					SG on pile.	

Southwest Branch

12910	– Daybeacon 1					SG on pile.	
12915	– Daybeacon 2					TR on pile.	
12920	– Daybeacon 3					SG on pile.	
12925	– Daybeacon 4					TR on pile.	
12930	Rowes Creek Daybeacon 2					TR on pile.	Private aid.
12935	Rowes Creek Daybeacon 3					SG on pile.	Private aid.
12940	Rowes Creek Range Marker					KRW on pile.	Private aid.

Ware River

12945	– Daybeacon 2					TR on pile.	
12950	– LIGHT 3		Fl G 2.5ˢ	15	4	SG on pile.	
12955	– Daybeacon 5					SG on pile.	
12960	– LIGHT 6		Q R	16	4	TR on dolphin.	
12965	– Daybeacon 7					SG on pile.	
12970	– LIGHT 9		Fl G 6ˢ	15	4	SG on pile.	
12975	– Daybeacon 10					TR on pile.	
12980	– Daybeacon 11					SG on pile.	
12985	– Daybeacon 12					TR on pile.	

Fish net buoys in Chesapeake Bay and tributary waters are not listed; however, they are shown on the nautical charts. Fish net buoys are painted yellow and are maintained for the Corps of Engineers to mark boundaries of fishing areas where fish nets and traps are permitted as prescribed by the Corps of Engineers.

CHESAPEAKE BAY (Virginia) – Fifth District

No.	Name and location	Position	Characteristic	Height	Range	Structure	Remarks
		N/W					
	MOBJACK BAY AND YORK RIVER ENTRANCE **(Chart 12238)**						
	Mobjack Bay						
	North River						
12990	– ENTRANCE LIGHT 1	37 22.1 76 23.6	Fl G 4s	16	5	SG on dolphin.	
12995	BLACKWATER CREEK LIGHT 2		Fl R 2.5s		3	TR on pile.	
12996	Blackwater Creek Daybeacon 3					SG on pile.	
13000	– Daybeacon 3					SG on pile.	
13005	Green Mansion Cove Junction Daybeacon					JR on pile.	
13010	– LIGHT 5		Fl G 4s	16	3	SG on slatted pile structure.	
13015	– LIGHT 6		Fl R 4s	16	3	TR on slatted pile structure.	
13020	– Daybeacon 7					SG on pile.	
13025	Green Mansion Cove Daybeacon 2					TR on pile.	Private aid.
13030	Green Mansion Cove Daybeacon 3					SG on pile.	Private aid.
	Horn Harbor						
13035	– ENTRANCE LIGHT HH	37 20.2 76 15.1	Mo (A) W	19	5	MR on pile.	
13040	– LIGHT 2		Fl R 4s	15	3	TR on house on cylindrical base.	
13045	– LIGHT 3		Fl G 2.5s	15	3	SG on pile.	
13052	– Daybeacon 4					TR on pile.	
13053	– LIGHT 5		Q G	14	3	SG on pile.	
13054	– Daybeacon 6					TR on pile.	
13055	– LIGHT 7		Fl G 4s	14	3	SG on pile.	
13060	– Daybeacon 7A					SG on pile.	
13065	– LIGHT 8		Fl R 6s	16	4	TR on dolphin.	
13070	– LIGHT 10		Fl R 2.5s	15	3	TR on dolphin.	
13075	– LIGHT 12		Fl R 4s	15	3	TR on pile.	
13080	– Daybeacon 14					TR on pile.	
13085	– LIGHT 16		Fl R 6s	15	4	TR on pile.	
13090	– Daybeacon 17					SG on pile.	
13095	– Daybeacon 18					TR on pile.	

Fish net buoys in Chesapeake Bay and tributary waters are not listed; however, they are shown on the nautical charts.
Fish net buoys are painted yellow and are maintained for the Corps of Engineers to mark boundaries of fishing areas
where fish nets and traps are permitted as prescribed by the Corps of Engineers.

(1) No.	(2) Name and location	(3) Position	(4) Characteristic	(5) Height	(6) Range	(7) Structure	(8) Remarks
						CHESAPEAKE BAY (Virginia) – Fifth District	
	N/W **MOBJACK BAY AND YORK RIVER ENTRANCE** (Chart 12238)						
	Horn Harbor						
13100	– Daybeacon 19					SG on pile.	
	Winter Harbor						
13105	– CHANNEL LIGHT 1		Fl G 2.5s	15	3	SG on pile.	
13110	– Channel Daybeacon 1A					SG on pile.	
13115	– CHANNEL LIGHT 3		Fl G 4s	15	4	SG on pile.	
13120	– Channel Daybeacon 4					TR on pile.	
13125	– Channel Daybeacon 4A					TR on pile.	
13130	– Channel Daybeacon 6					TR on pile.	
13135	– Channel Daybeacon 8					TR on pile.	
13140	– Channel Daybeacon 10					TR on pile.	
13145	– Channel Daybeacon 12					TR on pile.	
13150	– Channel Daybeacon 14					TR on pile.	
13155	– Channel Daybeacon 16					TR on pile.	
	RAPPAHANNOCK RIVER ENTRANCE (Chart 12235)						
	Milford Haven						
13160	– East Lighted Buoy 1		Fl G 4s		4	Green.	Remove from station when endangered by ice.
13165	– EAST LIGHT 3	37 27.2 76 12.7	Fl G 2.5s	15	4	SG on pile.	Light equipment removed when endangered by ice.
13170	– EAST LIGHT 5		Fl G 4s	15	5	SG on pile.	Light equipment removed when endangered by ice.
13175	– EAST LIGHT 6		Fl R 4s	15	4	TR on pile.	
13180	– EAST LIGHT 8		Fl R 2.5s	15	4	TR on pile.	
13185	– EAST LIGHT 9		Fl G 4s	12	4	SG on pile.	Light equipment removed when endangered by ice.
13190	– EAST LIGHT 11		Fl G 2.5s	12	4	SG on pile.	
13195	– East Daybeacon 12					TR on pile.	
13200	– EAST LIGHT 14		Q R	15	4	TR on pile.	
13202	– East Daybeacon 16					TR on pile.	
	Stutts Creek						
13205	– Entrance Daybeacon 1					SG on pile.	
13210	– Entrance Daybeacon 2					TR on pile.	
13215	– Daybeacon 3					SG on pile.	

Fish net buoys in Chesapeake Bay and tributary waters are not listed; however, they are shown on the nautical charts. Fish net buoys are painted yellow and are maintained for the Corps of Engineers to mark boundaries of fishing areas where fish nets and traps are permitted as prescribed by the Corps of Engineers.

(1) No.	(2) Name and location	(3) Position	(4) Characteristic	(5) Height	(6) Range	(7) Structure	(8) Remarks

	CHESAPEAKE BAY (Maryland) – Fifth District						

APPROACHES TO BALTIMORE HARBOR (Chart 12278)

Patapsco River

Spring Garden Channel

No.	Name and location	Position	Characteristic	Height	Range	Structure	Remarks
19450	– Daybeacon 2	39 15.6 76 37.1				TR on pile.	
19455	– Daybeacon 4					TR on pile.	
19460	– Daybeacon 6					TR on pile.	

Port Covington Basin

No.	Name and location	Position	Characteristic	Height	Range	Structure	Remarks
19465	– Buoy 1					Green can.	
19470	PORT COVINGTON MOORING PLATFORM LIGHT	39 15.5 76 36.3	F R	12		On 20' X 30' mooring platform.	Private aid.
19475	– Buoy 3					Green can.	
19480	Elevator Channel Buoy 2					Red nun.	
19485	Elevator Channel Buoy 4					Red nun.	

Northwest Harbor

No.	Name and location	Position	Characteristic	Height	Range	Structure	Remarks
19489	– *Lighted Buoy 2NH* 75 feet outside channel limit.		Q R		4	Red.	Replaced by nun when endangered by ice.
19495	– *Lighted Buoy 3* 75 feet outside channel limit.		Q G		3	Green.	Replaced by can when endangered by ice.
19496	– *Lighted Buoy 5*		Fl G 4s		4	Green.	
19498	– *Lighted Buoy 7*		Q G		4	Green.	
19500	Navy Reserve Pier Buoy					Orange sphere.	Maintained by U.S. Navy.
19505	HUMBLE OIL COMPANY OBSTRUCTION LIGHT	39 16.5 76 34.5	F W	12		On dolphin.	Private aid.
19510	– *Junction Lighted Buoy NH*		Fl (2+1) R 6s		4	Red and green bands.	

	CHESAPEAKE BAY (Virginia) – Fifth District						

CHESAPEAKE BAY ENTRANCE (Chart 12221)

North Channel

No.	Name and location	Position	Characteristic	Height	Range	Structure	Remarks
19515	– Entrance Buoy 2	37 01.3 75 54.1				Red nun.	
19520	– Buoy 4					Red nun.	
19525	– Buoy 6					Red nun.	
19530	– Buoy 8					Red nun.	
19535	– Buoy 10					Red nun.	
19540	– Buoy 11					Green can.	

Fish net buoys in Chesapeake Bay and tributary waters are not listed; however, they are shown on the nautical charts.
Fish net buoys are painted yellow and are maintained for the Corps of Engineers to mark boundaries of fishing areas
where fish nets and traps are permitted as prescribed by the Corps of Engineers.

(1) No.	(2) Name and location	(3) Position	(4) Characteristic	(5) Height	(6) Range	(7) Structure	(8) Remarks

CHESAPEAKE BAY (Virginia) – **Fifth District**

N/W
CHESAPEAKE BAY ENTRANCE (Chart 12221)

North Channel

19545	**North Channel Bridge** **Fog Signals**	37 05.3 75 59.2					HORN: 1 blast ev 20ˢ (2ˢ bl). Continuous. Private aid.

CAPE CHARLES TO WOLF TRAP (Chart 12224)

Beach Channel

19550	– Buoy 13					Green can.	
19555	Latimer Shoal Junction Buoy					Red and black bands; nun.	
19560	– Buoy 16					Red nun.	
19565 6205	VIRGINIA INSIDE PASSAGE LIGHT 270		Fl R 2.5ˢ	18	4	TR on pile.	Light equipment removed from Dec. 1 to Mar. 15.

Kiptopeke Beach

19570	– BREAKWATER SOUTH OBSTRUCTION LIGHT		Fl W 5ˢ	14		Black skeleton tower.	Private aid.
19575	– BREAKWATER NORTH OBSTRUCTION LIGHT		Fl W 5ˢ	14		Black skeleton tower.	Private aid.
19580	CHERRYSTONE CHANNEL LIGHT 2	37 12.1 76 01.6	Fl R 2.5ˢ	18	4	TR on pile.	Higher intensity toward North Channel and up Cherrystone Channel. Light equipment removed from Dec. 1 to Mar. 15.
19585 6790	OLD PLANTATION FLATS LIGHT	37 13.8 76 02.8	Fl W 4ˢ	39	7	NB on pile.	Higher intensity beam toward 200°.
19595	CAPE CHARLES CITY RANGE A FRONT LIGHT	37 14.8 76 01.5	Q W	19		KRW on slatted pile structure.	Visible on rangeline only.
19600	CAPE CHARLES CITY RANGE A REAR LIGHT 400 yards, 054° from front light.		Iso W 6ˢ	33		KRW on skeleton tower.	Visible on rangeline only.

Cape Charles City

19605	– Lighted Buoy 1		Fl G 4ˢ		4	Green.	
19610	– Lighted Buoy 2		Q R		3	Red.	
19615	– RANGE B FRONT LIGHT 8	37 15.8 76 01.7	Q R	16		KRW and TR on upstream side of pile.	Visible all around; higher intensity on rangeline. Ra ref.
19620	– RANGE B REAR LIGHT 520 yards, 020.3° from front light.		Iso R 6ˢ	41		KRW on white skeleton tower.	
19625	– Lighted Buoy 4		Fl R 4ˢ		3	Red.	
19630	– APPROACH LIGHT C	37 15.4 76 01.9	Fl W 4ˢ	30	5	NB on skeleton tower on caisson.	
19635	– Buoy 5					Green can.	

*Fish net buoys in Chesapeake Bay and tributary waters are not listed; however, they are shown on the nautical charts.
Fish net buoys are painted yellow and are maintained for the Corps of Engineers to mark boundaries of fishing areas
where fish nets and traps are permitted as prescribed by the Corps of Engineers.*

(1) No.	(2) Name and location	(3) Position	(4) Characteristic	(5) Height	(6) Range	(7) Structure	(8) Remarks

		N/W					
	CAPE CHARLES TO WOLF TRAP (Chart 12224)						
	Cape Charles City						
19640	– Buoy 6					Red nun.	
19645	– LIGHT 7		Fl G 4s	14	4	SG on pile.	Light equipment removed from Dec. 1 to Mar. 15.
19650	– JETTY LIGHT		Q W	18	5	NR on red skeleton tower.	
19655	– LIGHT 11		Fl G 2.5s	15	3	SG on dolphin.	Light equipment removed from Dec. 1 to Mar. 15.
19660	**Cape Charles Railroad Terminal Fog Signal**	37 15.9 76 01.3				On pile.	SIREN: 1 blast ev 25s (5s bl). Operates continuously. Private aid.
19665	Mud Creek Channel Daybeacon 1 10 feet outside channel limit.					SG on pile.	
19670	Mud Creek Channel Daybeacon 2 10 feet outside channel limit.					TR on pile.	
	Kings Creek						
19675	– LIGHT 1		Fl G 4s	16	4	SG on dolphin.	Light equipment removed when endangered by ice.
19680	– LIGHT 3		Fl G 4s	15	3	SG on dolphin.	Light equipment removed from Dec. 1 to Mar. 15.
19685	– JUNTION LIGHT KC	37 16.9 76 01.4	Fl (2+1) G 6s	14	3	JG on pile.	
19690	– LIGHT 6		Fl R 2.5s	15	4	TR on pile.	Light equipment removed when endangered by ice.
19695	– Daybeacon 7					SG on pile.	
19700	– LIGHT 8		Fl R 4s	15	4	TR on pile.	Light equipment removed from Dec. 1 to Mar. 15.
19705	– LIGHT 9		Fl G 4s	15	3	SG on pile.	
19710	– Daybeacon 10					TR on pile.	
19715	– LIGHT 11		Fl G 4s	15	4	SG on pile.	
19720	– Daybeacon 12					TR on pile.	
19725	– LIGHT 15		Fl G 4s	15	4	SG on pile.	
19730	– Daybeacon 14					TR on pile.	
	WOLF TRAP TO PUNGOTEAGUE CREEK (Chart 12226)						
	Mattawoman Creek						
19735	– LIGHT 1	37 23.4 75 59.7	Fl W 4s	15	5	SG on pile.	Light equipment removed from Dec. 1 to Mar. 15.

Fish net buoys in Chesapeake Bay and tributary waters are not listed; however, they are shown on the nautical charts.
Fish net buoys are painted yellow and are maintained for the Corps of Engineers to mark boundaries of fishing areas where fish nets and traps are permitted as prescribed by the Corps of Engineers.

(1) No.	(2) Name and location	(3) Position	(4) Characteristic	(5) Height	(6) Range	(7) Structure	(8) Remarks

WOLF TRAP TO PUNGOTEAGUE CREEK (Chart 12226) N/W

Mattawoman Creek

(1) No.	(2) Name and location	(3) Position	(4) Characteristic	(5) Height	(6) Range	(7) Structure	(8) Remarks
19740	– LIGHT 2		Fl R 4s	15	3	TR on pile.	Light equipment removed from Dec. 1 to Mar. 15.
19745	– LIGHT 3		Fl G	10	4	SG on pile.	Light equipment removed from Dec. 1 to Mar. 15.
19750	– Daybeacon 5					SG on pile.	
19755	– LIGHT 6		Fl R 4s	10	3	TR on pile.	Light equipment removed from Dec. 1 to Mar. 15.

Hungar Creek

(1) No.	(2) Name and location	(3) Position	(4) Characteristic	(5) Height	(6) Range	(7) Structure	(8) Remarks
19760	– Daybeacon 2	37 24.4 75 58.5				TR on pile.	
19765	– Daybeacon 3					SG on pile.	
19770	– Daybeacon 5					SG on pile.	
19775	– Daybeacon 7					SG on pile.	
19780	– Daybeacon 9					SG on pile.	

Nassawadox Creek

(1) No.	(2) Name and location	(3) Position	(4) Characteristic	(5) Height	(6) Range	(7) Structure	(8) Remarks
19785	– LIGHT 2	37 27.9 75 58.4	Fl R 2.5s	15	4	TR on pile.	Light equipment removed from Dec. 1 to Mar. 15.
19790	– Daybeacon 3					SG on pile.	
19793	– Daybeacon 5	37 28.2 75 57.9				SG on pile.	
19795	– Daybeacon 6					TR on pile.	
19800	– Daybeacon 7					SG on pile.	
19805	– Buoy 8					Red nun.	Removed from station Dec. 1 to Mar. 15.
19810	– Daybeacon 10					TR on pile.	
19815	– Daybeacon 12					TR on pile.	
19820	– Daybeacon 14					TR on pile.	
19825	– Daybeacon 15					SG on pile.	
19830	– Daybeacon 16					TR on pile.	

Occohannock Creek

(1) No.	(2) Name and location	(3) Position	(4) Characteristic	(5) Height	(6) Range	(7) Structure	(8) Remarks
19835	– ENTRANCE LIGHT 1	37 32.5 75 57.8	Fl G 4s	15	4	SG on pile.	Light equipment removed from Dec. 1 to Mar. 15.
19840	– LIGHT 3		Fl G 4s	15	3	SG on pile.	Light equipment removed from Dec. 1 to Mar. 15.
19845	– Daybeacon 5					SG on pile.	
19850	– Daybeacon 6					TR on pile.	

Fish net buoys in Chesapeake Bay and tributary waters are not listed; however, they are shown on the nautical charts.
Fish net buoys are painted yellow and are maintained for the Corps of Engineers to mark boundaries of fishing areas
where fish nets and traps are permitted as prescribed by the Corps of Engineers.

PART 2 - SECTION B

COAST PILOT 3

Atlantic Coast

covering

CHESAPEAKE BAY ENTRANCE and approaches

for

general information refer to PART 1, SECTION B

contents found on page vii

United States Coast Pilot

3

Atlantic Coast:
Sandy Hook to
Cape Henry

This publication is a reproduction of a work originally published by the National Oceanic and Atmospheric Administration (NOAA), and is not a NOAA publication. NOAA is not responsible for any reproduction errors.

U.S. DEPARTMENT OF COMMERCE
Barbara Hackman Franklin, Secretary

National Oceanic and Atmospheric Administration (NOAA)
Dr. John A. Knauss, Under Secretary of Commerce for Oceans
and Atmosphere, and Administrator, NOAA

National Ocean Service
W. Stanley Wilson, Assistant Administrator for Ocean Services
and Coastal Zone Management

Washington, DC:
For sale by the National Ocean Service and its sales agents.

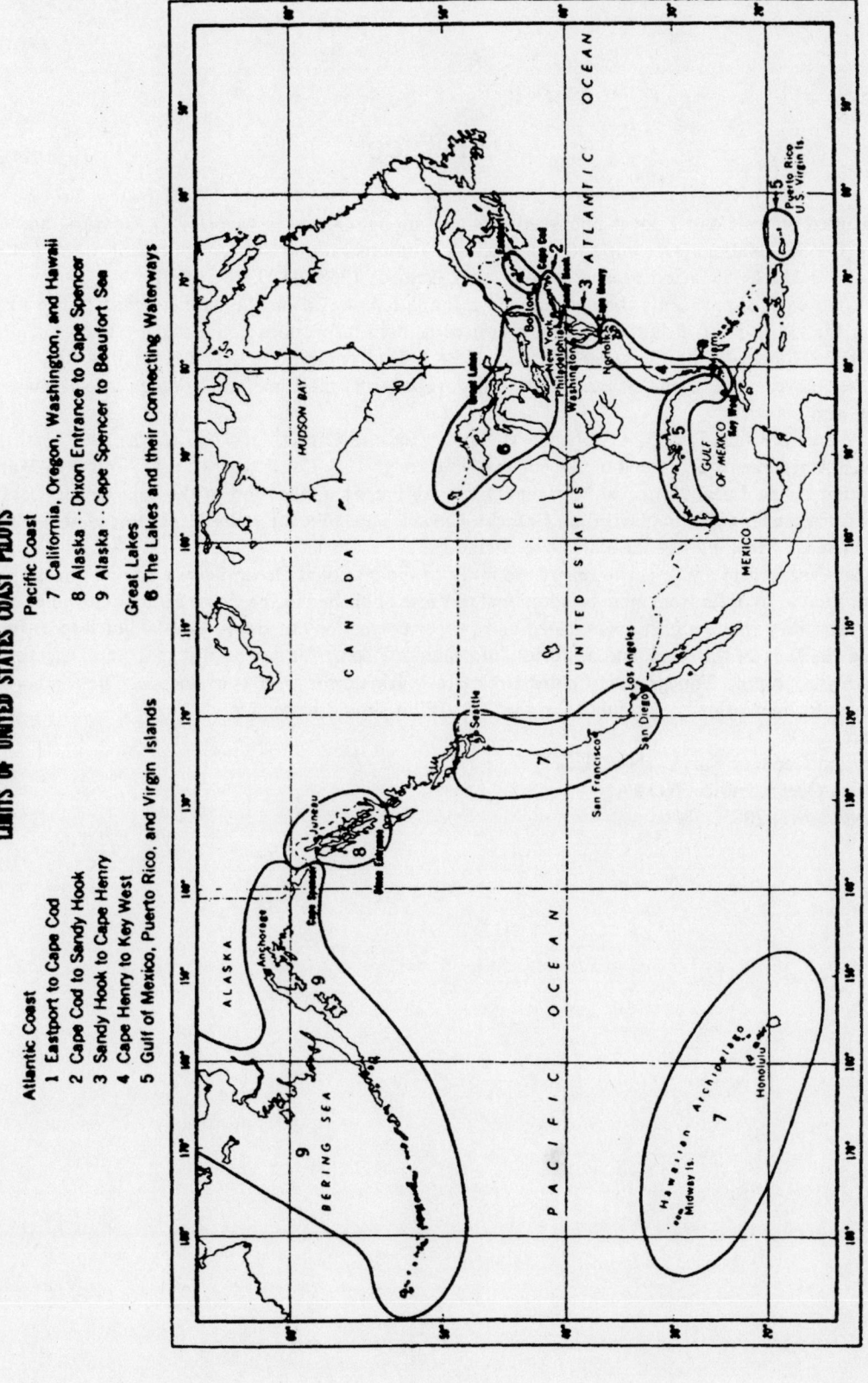

LIMITS OF UNITED STATES COAST PILOTS

Atlantic Coast

1 Eastport to Cape Cod
2 Cape Cod to Sandy Hook
3 Sandy Hook to Cape Henry
4 Cape Henry to Key West
5 Gulf of Mexico, Puerto Rico, and Virgin Islands

Pacific Coast

7 California, Oregon, Washington, and Hawaii
8 Alaska -- Dixon Entrance to Cape Spencer
9 Alaska -- Cape Spencer to Beaufort Sea

Great Lakes

6 The Lakes and their Connecting Waterways

II

Preface

The United States Coast Pilot is published by the National Ocean Service (NOS), Charting and Geodetic Services (C&GS), National Oceanic and Atmospheric Administration (NOAA), pursuant to the Act of 6 August 1947 (33 U.S.C. 883a and b), and the Act of 22 October 1968 (44 U.S.C. 1310).

The Coast Pilot supplements the navigational information shown on the nautical charts. The sources for updating the Coast Pilot include but are not limited to field inspections conducted by NOAA, information published in Notices to Mariners, reports from NOAA Hydrographic vessels and field parties, information from other Government agencies, State and local governments, maritime and pilotage associations, port authorities, and mariners.

This volume of Coast Pilot 3, Atlantic Coast, Sandy Hook to Cape Henry, cancels the 1991 (28th) Edition.

Notice.–Amendments are issued to this publication through U.S. Coast Guard Local Notices to Mariners. A subscription to the Local Notice to Mariners is available upon application to the appropriate Coast Guard District Commander (Aids to Navigation Branch). Consult appendix for address. All amendments are also issued in Defense Mapping Agency Notices to Mariners.

Mariners and others are urged to report promptly to the National Ocean Service errors, omissions, or any conditions found to differ from or to be additional to those published in the Coast Pilot or shown on the charts in order that they may be fully investigated and proper corrections made. A Coast Pilot Report form is included in the back of this book and a Marine Information Report form is published in the Defense Mapping Agency Hydrographic/Topographic Center Notice to Mariners for your convenience. These reports and/or suggestions for increasing the usefulness of the Coast Pilot should be sent to

Director,
Coast and Geodetic Survey (N/CG2211),
National Ocean Service, NOAA,
Rockville, MD 20852-3806.

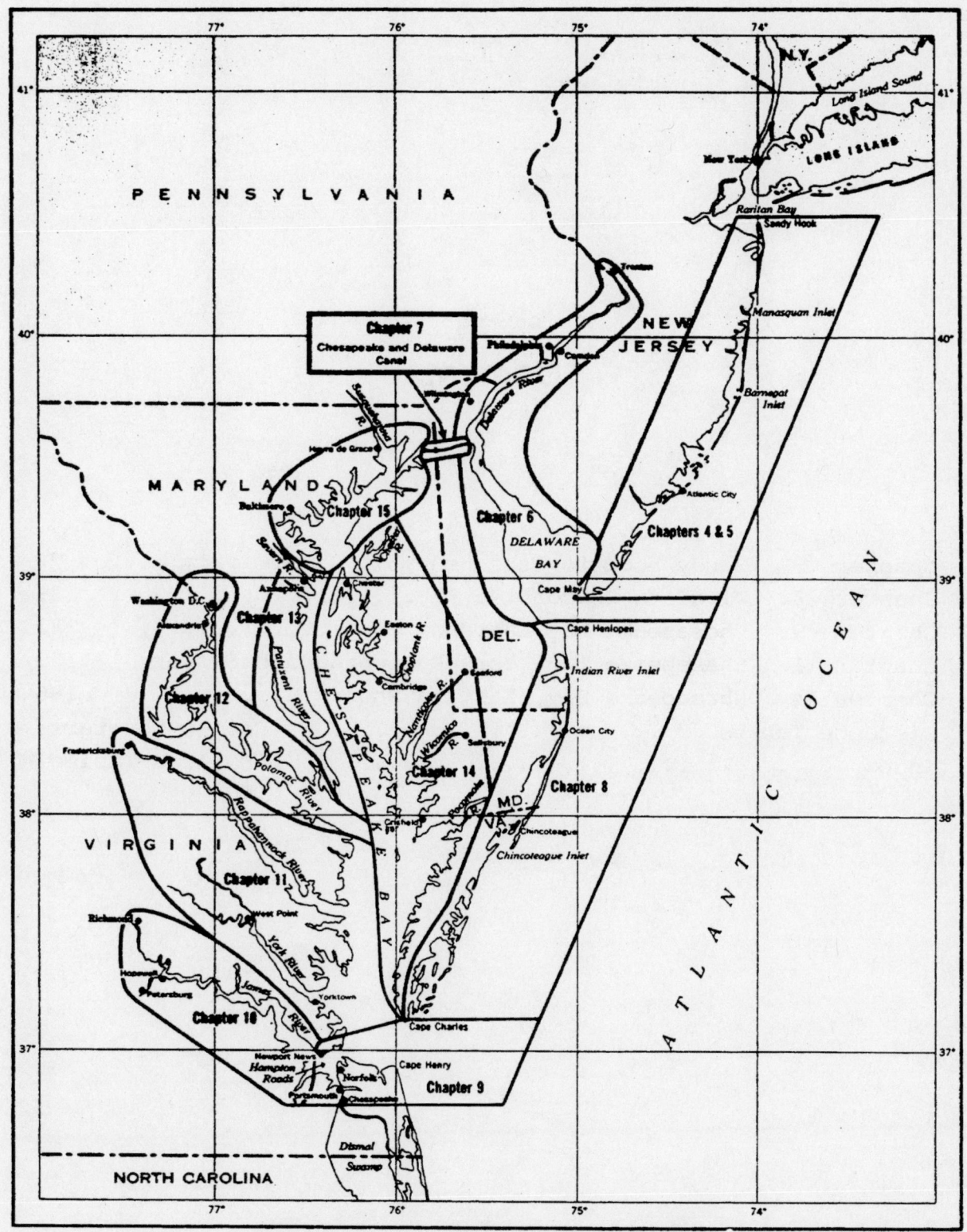

COAST PILOT 3 – GRAPHIC CHAPTER INDEX

IV

Contents

(184)   (b) The regulations. This anchorage is reserved for the exclusive use of naval vessels and except in cases of emergency, no other vessel shall anchor therein without permission from the local naval authorities, obtained through the Captain of the Port, Norfolk, Virginia. Movement of vessels through the anchorage will not be restricted.

(185)   §110.168 Hampton Roads, Virginia, and adjacent waters.

(186)   (a) Anchorage Grounds–(1) Cape Henry Anchorage. Anchorage A (Naval Anchorage). The waters bounded by the shoreline and a line connecting the following points:
(187)   36°55'33.0"N., 76°02'47.0"W.
(188)   36°57'02.8"N., 76°03'02.6"W.
(189)   36°56'45.0"N., 76°01'30.0"W.
(190)   36°55'54.0"N., 76°01'37.0"W.

(191)   (2) Chesapeake Bay, Thimble Shoals Channel Anchorages–(i) Anchorage B (Naval Anchorage). The waters bounded by a line connecting the following points:
(192)   36°57'58.0"N., 76°06'07.0"W.
(193)   36°57'11.0"N., 76°03'02.1"W.
(194)   36°55'48.8"N., 76°03'14.0"W.
(195)   36°56'31.8"N., 76°06'07.0"W.
(196)   36°57'04.0"N., 76°06'07.0"W.
(197)   36°57'08.5"N., 76°06'24.5"W.

(198)   (ii) Anchorage C (Naval Anchorage). The waters bounded by a line connecting the following points:
(199)   36°58'54.8"N., 76°09'41.5"W.
(200)   36°58'18.8"N., 76°07'18.0"W.
(201)   36°57'27.0"N., 76°07'37.5"W.
(202)   36°58'04.0"N., 76°10'00.0"W.

(203)   (iii) Anchorage D (Naval Anchorage). The waters bounded by the shoreline and a line connecting the following points:
(204)   36°55'49.0"N., 76°10'32.8"W.
(205)   36°58'04.0"N., 76°10'02.1"W.
(206)   36°57'31.2"N., 76°07'54.8"W.
(207)   36°55'24.1"N., 76°08'28.8"W.

(208)   (iv) Anchorage E (Commercial Explosive Anchorage). The waters bounded by a line connecting the following points:
(209)   36°59'58.7"N., 76°13'47.0"W.
(210)   36°59'08.2"N., 76°10'33.8"W.
(211)   36°58'13.0"N., 76°10'51.8"W.
(212)   36°59'02.0"N., 76°14'10.2"W.

(213)   (A) Explosive Handling Berth E-1: (Explosives Anchorage Berth): The waters bounded by the arc of a circle with a radius of 500 yards and with the center located at:
(214)   36°59'05.0"N., 76°11'23.0"W.

(215)   (3) Hampton Roads Anchorages–(i) Anchorage F, Hampton Bar. The waters bounded by a line connecting the following points:
(216)   36°59'51.6"N., 76°19'12.0"W.
(217)   36°59'25.2"N., 76°18'48.5"W.
(218)   36°58'49.1"N., 76°19'33.8"W.
(219)   36°59'25.0"N., 76°20'07.0"W.

(220)   (A) Anchorage Berth F-1. The waters bounded by the arc of a circle with a radius of 400 yards and with the center located at:
(221)   36°59'16.7"N., 76°19'39.0"W.

(222)   (B) Anchorage Berth F-2. The waters bounded by the arc of a circle with a radius of 400 yards and with the center located at:
(223)   36°59'31.8"N., 76°19'16.0"W.

(224)   (ii) Anchorage G, Hampton Flats (Naval Explosives Anchorage). The waters bounded by a line connecting the following points:
(225)   36°59'25.0"N., 76°20'07.0"W.
(226)   36°58'49.1"N., 76°19'33.8"W.

(227)   36°57'41.4"N., 76°21'07.7"W.
(228)   36°57'34.6"N., 76°21'26.7"W.
(229)   36°57'31.1"N., 76°22'01.9"W.
(230)   36°57'07.0"N., 76°22'03.0"W.
(231)   36°58'54.8"N., 76°21'42.6"W.

(232)   (A) Explosives Handling Berth G-1. The waters bounded by the arc of a circle with a radius of 500 yards and with the center located at:
(233)   36°57'50.0"N., 76°21'37.0"W.

(234)   (B) Explosives Handling Berth G-2. The waters bounded by the arc of a circle with a radius of 500 yards and with the center located at:
(235)   36°58'14.0"N., 76°21'01.5"W.

(236)   (C) Explosives Handling Berth G-3. The waters bounded by the arc of a circle with a radius of 500 yards and with the center located at:
(237)   36°58'34.5"N., 76°20'31.0"W.

(238)   (D) Explosives Handling Berth G-4. The waters bounded by the arc of a circle with a radius of 500 yards and with the center located at:
(239)   36°58'53.4"N., 76°20'05.0"W.

(240)   (iii) Anchorage H, Newport New Bar. The waters bounded by a line connecting the following points:
(241)   36°58'07.0"N., 76°22'03.0"W.
(242)   36°57'31.1"N., 76°22'01.9"W.
(243)   36°57'18.0"N., 76°24'11.2"W.
(244)   36°57'38.3"N., 76°24'20.0"W.
(245)   36°57'51.8"N., 76°22'31.0"W.

(246)   (4) James River Anchorage–(i) Anchorage I, Newport News. The waters bounded by a line connecting the following points:
(247)   36°57'06.7"N., 76°24'44.3"W.
(248)   36°56'22.6"N., 76°24'28.0"W.
(249)   36°56'03.0"N., 76°24'37.0"W.
(250)   36°57'53.7"N., 76°26'41.5"W.
(251)   36°58'23.0"N., 76°27'11.0"W.
(252)   36°58'48.5"N., 76°27'11.0"W.
(253)   36°58'35.4"N., 76°26'38.4"W.
(254)   36°57'51.7"N., 76°26'02.8"W.
(255)   36°57'30.6"N., 76°25'34.5"W.

(256)   (A) Anchorage Berth I-1. The waters bounded by the arc of a circle with a radius of 400 yards and with the center located at:
(257)   36°57'08.5"N., 76°25'21.6"W.

(258)   (B) Anchorage Berth I-2. The waters bounded by the arc of a circle with a radius of 400 yards and with the center located at:
(259)   36°57'22.4"N., 76°25'47.7"W.

(260)   (ii) Anchorage J, Newport News Middle Ground. The waters bounded by a line connecting the following points:
(261)   36°57'21.0"N., 76°22'22.1"W.
(262)   36°56'46.5"N., 76°22'39.3"W.
(263)   36°56'25.3"N., 76°23'48.0"W.
(264)   36°57'10.2"N., 76°24'09.9"W.

(265)   (iii) Anchorage K, Newport News Middle Ground. The waters bounded by a line connecting the following points:
(266)   36°57'55.8"N., 76°20'20.1"W.
(267)   36°57'07.9"N., 76°20'32.2"W.
(268)   36°56'48.8"N., 76°20'32.2"W.
(269)   36°55'59.9"N., 76°22'11.7"W.
(270)   36°55'59.9"N., 76°24'00.0"W.
(271)   36°56'25.3"N., 76°23'48.0"W.
(272)   36°56'46.5"N., 76°22'39.3"W.
(273)   36°57'21.0"N., 76°22'22.1"W.
(274)   36°57'28.1"N., 76°21'11.7"W.

Subpart B–Regulated Navigation Areas

(1113) §165.10 Regulated navigation area.

(1114) A regulated navigation area is a water area within a defined boundary for which regulations for vessels navigating within the area have been established under this part.

(1115) §165.11 Vessel operating requirements (regulations).

(1116) Each District Commander may control vessel traffic in an area which is determined to have hazardous conditions, by issuing regulations–

(1117) (a) Specifying times of vessel entry, movement, or departure to, from, within, or through ports, harbors, or other waters;

(1118) (b) Establishing vessel size, speed, draft limitations, and operating conditions; and

(1119) (c) Restricting vessel operation, in a hazardous area or under hazardous conditions, to vessels which have particular operating characteristics or capabilities which are considered necessary for safe operation under the circumstances.

(1120) §165.13 General regulations.

(1121) (a) The master of a vessel in a regulated navigation area shall operate the vessel in accordance with the regulations contained in Subpart F.

(1122) (b) No person may cause or authorize the operation of a vessel in a regulated navigation area contrary to the regulations in this Part.

Subpart C–Safety Zones

(1123) §165.20 Safety zones.

(1124) A Safety Zone is a water area, shore area, or water and shore area to which, for safety or environmental purposes, access is limited to authorized persons, vehicles, or vessels. It may be stationary and described by fixed limits or it may be described as a zone around a vessel in motion.

(1125) §165.23 General regulations.

(1126) Unless otherwise provided in this part–

(1127) (a) No person may enter a safety zone unless authorized by the COTP or the District Commander;

(1128) (b) No person may bring or cause to be brought into a safety zone any vehicle, vessel, or object unless authorized by the COTP or the District Commander;

(1129) (c) No person may remain in a safety zone or allow any vehicle, vessel, or object to remain in a safety zone unless authorized by the COTP or the District Commander; and

(1130) (d) Each person in a safety zone who has notice of a lawful order or direction shall obey the order or direction of the COTP or District Commander issued to carry out the purposes of this subpart.

Subpart D–Security Zones

(1131) §165.30 Security zones.

(1132) (a) A security zone is an area of land, water, or land and water which is so designated by the Captain of the Port or District Commander for such time as is necessary to prevent damage or injury to any vessel or waterfront facility, to safeguard ports, harbors, territories, or waters of the United States or to secure the observance of the rights and obligations of the United States.

(1133) (b) The purpose of a security zone is to safeguard from destruction, loss, or injury from sabotage or other subversive acts, accidents, or other causes of a similar nature–

(1134) (1) Vessels,

(1135) (2) Harbors,

(1136) (3) Ports and

(1137) (4) Waterfront facilities– in the United States and all territory and water, continental or insular, that is subject to the jurisdiction of the United States.

(1138) §165.33 General regulations.

(1139) Unless otherwise provided in the special regulations in Subpart F of this part–

(1140) (a) No person or vessel may enter or remain in a security zone without the permission of the Captain of the Port;

(1141) (b) Each person and vessel in a security zone shall obey any direction or order of the Captain of the Port;

(1142) (c) The Captain of the Port may take possession and control of any vessel in the security zone;

(1143) (d) The Captain of the Port may remove any person, vessel, article, or thing from a security zone;

(1144) (e) No person may board, or take or place any article or thing on board, any vessel in a security zone without the permission of the Captain of the Port; and

(1145) (f) No person may take or place any article or thing upon any waterfront facility in a security zone without the permission of the Captain of the Port.

Subpart E–Restricted Waterfront Areas

(1146) §165.40 Restricted Waterfront Areas.

(1147) The Commandant, may direct the COTP to prevent access to waterfront facilities, and port and harbor areas, including vessels and harbor craft therein. This section may apply to persons who do not possess the credentials outlined in 33 CFR 125.09 when certain shipping activities are conducted that are outlined in 33 CFR 125.15.

Subpart F–Specific Regulated Navigation Areas and Limited Access Areas

(1148) §165.501 Chesapeake Bay Entrance and Hampton Roads, Virginia and Adjacent Waters-Regulated Navigation Area.

(1149) (a) Regulated Navigation Area. The waters enclosed by the shoreline and the following lines are a Regulated Navigation Area:

(1150) (1) A line drawn across the entrance to Chesapeake Bay between Wise Point and Cape Charles Light, and then continuing to Cape Henry Light.

(1151) (2) A line drawn across the Chesapeake Bay between Old Point Comfort Light and Cape Charles City Range "A" Rear Light.

(1152) (3) A line drawn across the James River along the eastern side of the U.S. Route 17 highway bridge, between Newport News and Isle of Wight County, Virginia.

(1153) (4) A line drawn across Chuckatuck Creek along the northern side of the north span of the U.S. Route 17 highway bridge, between Isle of Wight County and Suffolk, Virginia.

(1154) (5) A line drawn across the Nansemond River along the northern side of the Mills Godwin (U.S. Route 17) Bridge, Suffolk, Virginia.

(1155) (6) A line drawn across the mouth of Bennetts Creek, Suffolk, Virginia.

(1156) (7) A line drawn across the Western Branch of the Elizabeth River along the eastern side of the West Norfolk Bridge, Portsmouth, Virginia.

(1157) (8) A line drawn across the Southern Branch of the Elizabeth River along the northern side of the I-64 highway bridge, Chesapeake, Virginia.

(1158) (9) A line drawn across the Eastern Branch of the Elizabeth River along the western side of the west span of the Campostella Bridge, Norfolk, Virginia.

(1159) (10) A line drawn across the Lafayette River along the western side of the Hampton Boulevard Bridge, Norfolk, Virginia.

(1160)   (11) A line drawn across Little Creek along the eastern side of the Ocean View Avenue (U.S. Route 60) Bridge, Norfolk, Virginia.

(1161)   (12) A line drawn across Lynnhaven Inlet along the northern side of the Shore Drive (U.S. Route 60) Bridge, Virginia Beach, Virginia.

(1162)   (b) Definitions. In this section:

(1163)   (1) "CBBT" means the Chesapeake Bay Bridge Tunnel.

(1164)   (2) "Thimble Shoal Channel" consists of the waters bounded by a line connecting Thimble Shoal Channel Lighted Bell Buoy 1TS, thence to Lighted Gong Buoy 17, thence to Lighted Buoy 19, thence to Lighted Buoy 21, thence to Lighted Buoy 22, thence to Lighted Buoy 18, thence to Lighted Buoy 2, thence to the beginning.

(1165)   (3) "Thimble Shoal North Auxiliary Channel" consists of the waters in a rectangular area 450 feet wide adjacent to the north side of Thimble Shoal Channel, the southern boundary of which extends from Thimble Shoal Channel Lighted Buoy 2 to Lighted Buoy 18.

(1166)   (4) "Thimble Shoal South Auxiliary Channel" consists of the waters in a rectangular area 450 feet wide adjacent to the south side of the Thimble Shoal Channel, the northern boundary of which extends from Thimble Shoal Channel Lighted Bell Buoy 1TS, thence to Lighted Gong Buoy 17 thence to Lighted Buoy 19, thence to Lighted Buoy 21.

(1167)   (c) Applicability. This section applies to all vessels operating within the Regulated Navigation Area, including naval and public vessels, except vessels that are engaged in the following operations:

(1168)   (1) Law Enforcement

(1169)   (2) Servicing aids to navigation

(1170)   (3) Surveying, maintenance, or improvement of waters in the Regulated Navigation Area.

(1171)   (d) Regulations.-(1) Anchoring restrictions.

(1172)   (i) No vessel over 65 feet long may anchor or moor in this Regulated Navigation Area outside an anchorage designated in §110.168 of this title, unless:

(1173)   (A) The vessel has the permission of the Captain of the Port.

(1174)   (B) The vessel is carrying explosives for use on river or harbor works or on other work under a permit issued by the District Engineer, Corps of Engineers, and the vessel is anchored in or near the vicinity of the work site. The District Engineer shall prescribe the quantities of explosives allowed on the vessel and the conditions under which the vessel may store or handle explosives. The vessel may not anchor unless a copy of the permit and instructions relating to the carriage and handling of explosives from the Corps of Engineers to the vessel or contractor are provided to the Captain of the Port before the vessel anchors.

(1175)   (ii) A vessel may anchor in a channel with the permission of the Captain of the Port, if the vessel is authorized by the District Engineer to engage in recovery of sunken property, to lay or repair a legally established pipeline or cable, or to engage in dredging operations.

(1176)   (iii) A vessel engaged in river and harbor improvement work under the supervision of the District Engineer may anchor in a channel, if the District Engineer notifies the Captain of the Port in advance of the start of the work.

(1177)   (iv) Except as provided in paragraphs (d)(1)(ii) and (iii) of this section, a vessel may not anchor in a channel unless it is unable to proceed without endangering the safety of persons, property, or the environment.

(1178)   (v) A vessel that is anchored in a channel because it is unable to proceed without endangering the safety of persons, property or the environment, shall:

(1179)   (A) Not anchor, if possible, within a cable or pipeline area.

(1180)   (B) Not obstruct or endanger the passage of any vessel.

(1181)   (C) Anchor near the edge of the channel, if possible.

(1182)   (D) Not interfere with the free navigation of any channel.

(1183)   (E) Not obstruct the approach to any pier.

(1184)   (F) Not obstruct aids to navigation or interfere with range lights.

(1185)   (G) Move to a designated anchorage or get underway as soon as possible or when directed by the Captain of the Port.

(1186)   (vi) A vessel may not anchor within the confines of Little Creek Harbor, Desert Cove, or Little Creek Cove without the permission of the Captain of the Port. The Captain of the Port shall consult with the Commander, Naval Amphibious Base Little Creek, before granting permission to anchor within this area.

(1187)   (2) Secondary Towing Rig Requirements. (i) A vessel over 100 gross tons may not be towed in this Regulated Navigation Area unless it is equipped with a secondary towing rig, in addition to its primary towing rig, that:

(1188)   (A) Is of sufficient strength for towing the vessel.

(1189)   (B) Has a connecting device that can receive a shackle pin of at least two inches in diameter.

(1190)   (C) Is fitted with a recovery pickup line led outboard of the vessel's hull.

(1191)   (ii) A tow consisting of two or more vessels, each of which is less than 100 gross tons, that has a total gross tonnage that is over 100 gross tons, shall be equipped with a secondary towing rig between each vessel in tow, in addition to its primary towing rigs, while the tow is operating within this Regulated Navigation Area. The secondary towing rig must:

(1192)   (A) Be of sufficient strength for towing the vessels.

(1193)   (B) Have connecting devices that can receive a shackle pin of at least two inches in diameter.

(1194)   (C) Be fitted with recovery pickup lines led outboard of the vessels' hulls.

(1195)   (3) Anchoring Detail Requirements. A self-propelled vessel over 100 gross tons, which is equipped with an anchor or anchors (other than a tugboat equipped with bow fenderwork of a type of construction that prevents an anchor being rigged for quick release), that is underway within two nautical miles of the CBBT or the I-664 Bridge Tunnel shall station its personnel at locations on the vessel without delay in an emergency.

(1196)   (4) Draft Limitations. A vessel drawing less than 25 feet may not enter the Thimble Shoal Channel, unless the vessel is crossing the channel. Channel crossings shall be made as perpendicular to the channel axis as possible.

(1197)   (5) Traffic Directions. (i) Except when crossing the channel, a vessel in the Thimble Shoal North Auxiliary Channel shall proceed in a westbound direction.

(1198)   (ii) Except when crossing the channel, a vessel in the Thimble Shoal South Auxiliary Channel shall proceed in an eastbound direction.

(1199)   (6) Restrictions of Vessels With Impaired Maneuverability.-(i) Before entry. A vessel over 100 gross tons whose ability to maneuver is impaired by hazardous weather, defective steering equipment, defective main propulsion machinery, or other damage, may not enter the Regulated Navigation Area without the permission of the Captain of the Port, unless the vessel is attended by one or more tugboats with sufficient total power to ensure the vessel's safe passage through the Regulated Navigation Area.

(1200) (ii) After entry. The master of a vessel over 100 gross tons, which is underway in the Regulated Navigation Area, shall, as soon as possible, do the following, if the vessel's ability to maneuver becomes impaired for any reason:

(1201) (A) Report the impairment to the Captain of the Port.

(1202) (B) Unless the Captain of the Port waives this requirement, have one or more tugboats with sufficient total power to ensure the vessel's safe passage through the Regulated Navigation Area, attend the vessel.

(1203) (7) Requirements for Navigation Charts, Radars, and Pilots. No vessel over 100 gross tons may enter the Regulated Navigation Area, unless it has on board:

(1204) (i) Corrected charts of the Regulated Navigation Area.

(1205) (ii) An operative radar during periods of reduced visibility; or

(1206) (iii) A pilot or other person on board with previous experience navigating vessel on the waters of the Regulated Navigation Area.

(1207) (8) Emergency Procedures. (i) Except as provided in paragraphs (d)(8)(ii) and (iii) of this section, in an emergency any vessel may deviate from the regulations in this section to the extent necessary to avoid endangering the safety of persons, property, or the environment.

(1208) (ii) A vessel over 100 gross tons with an emergency that is located within two nautical miles of the CBBT or I-664 Bridge Tunnel (other than a self-propelled vessel that is capable of getting underway in 30 minutes, has sufficient power to avoid any bridge, tunnel island, or vessel, and whose maneuverability is not impaired by a steering equipment or main propulsion defect):

(1209) (A) Shall notify the Captain of the Port of its location and the nature of the emergency, as soon as possible.

(1210) (B) May not anchor outside an anchorage designated in §110.168 of this title, unless the vessel is unable to proceed to an anchorage without endangering the safety of persons, property, or the environment.

(1211) (C) Shall make arrangements for one or more vessels to attend the vessel, with sufficient power to keep the vessel in position.

(1212) (iii) If a vessel over 100 gross tons must anchor outside an anchorage because the vessel is unable to proceed without endangering the safety of persons, property, or the environment, the vessel shall:

(1213) (A) Not anchor, if possible, within a cable or pipeline area.

(1214) (B) Not obstruct or endanger the passage of any vessel.

(1215) (C) Not interfere with the free navigation of any channel.

(1216) (D) Not obstruct the approach to any pier.

(1217) (E) Not obstruct aids to navigation or interfere with range lights.

(1218) (F) Move to a designated anchorage or get underway as soon as possible or when directed by the Captain of the Port.

(1219) (9) Vessel Speed Limits on Little Creek. A vessel may not proceed at a speed over five knots between the Route 60 bridge and the mouth of Fishermans Cove (Northwest Branch of Little Creek).

(1220) (10) Vessel Speed Limits on the Southern Branch of the Elizabeth River. A vessel may not proceed at a speed over six knots between the junction of the Southern and Eastern Branches of the Elizabeth River and the Norfolk and Portsmouth Belt Line Railroad Bridge between Chesapeake and Portsmouth, Virginia.

(1221) (11) Restrictions on Vessel Operations During Aircraft Carrier and Other Large Naval Vessel Transits of the Elizabeth River. (i) Except for a vessel that is moored at a marina, wharf, or pier or that is anchored, no vessel may, without the permission of the Captain of the Port, come within or remain within 500 yards from a naval aircraft carrier or other large naval vessel, which is restricted in its ability to maneuver in the confined waters, while the aircraft carrier or large naval vessel is transiting the Elizabeth River between the Norfolk Naval Base, Norfolk, Virginia, and the Norfolk Naval Shipyard, Portsmouth, Virginia.

(1222) (ii) The permission required by paragraph (d)(11)(i) of this section may be obtained from a designated representative of the Captain of the Port, including the duty officer at the Coast Guard Marine Safety Office, Hampton Roads, or from the Coast Guard patrol commander.

(1223) (iii) The Captain of the Port issues a Broadcast Notice to Mariners to inform the marine community of scheduled vessel movements that are covered by paragraph (d)(11) of this section.

(1224) (iv) Notwithstanding paragraph (d)(11)(i) of this section, a vessel may not remain moored at the Elizabeth River Ferry dock at the foot of High Street in Portsmouth, Virginia, when the dock is within a safety zone for a naval aircraft carrier or other large naval vessel.

(1225) (12) Restrictions on Vessel Operations During Liquefied Petroleum Gas Carrier Movements on the Chesapeake Bay and Elizabeth River. (i) Except for a vessel that is moored at a marina, wharf, or pier or that is anchored, and which remains moored or at anchor, no vessel may, without the permission of the Captain of the Port, come within or remain within 250 feet from the port and starboard sides and 300 feet from the bow and stern of a vessel that is carrying liquefied petroleum gas in bulk as cargo, while the gas carrier transits between Thimble Shoal Lighted Buoy 3 and the Atlantic Energy Terminal on the Southern Branch of the Elizabeth River.

(1226) (ii) The permission required by paragraph (d)(12)(i) of this section may be obtained from a designated representative of the Captain of the Port, including the duty officer at the Coast Guard Marine Safety Office, Hampton Roads, or from the Coast Guard patrol commander.

(1227) (iii) A vessel that has carried liquefied petroleum gas in a tank is carrying the liquefied petroleum gas as cargo for the purposes of paragraph (d)(12)(i) of this section, unless the tank has been gas freed since liquefied petroleum gas was last carried as cargo.

(1228) (iv) The Captain of the Port issues a Broadcast Notice to Mariners to inform the marine community of scheduled vessel movements that are covered by paragraph (d)(12) of this section.

(1229) (v) Notwithstanding paragraph (d)(12)(i) of this section, a vessel may not remain moored at the Elizabeth River Ferry dock at the foot of High Street in Portsmouth, Virginia, when the dock is within a safety zone for a liquefied petroleum gas carrier.

(1230) (13) Restrictions on the Use of the Elizabeth River Ferry Dock at the Foot of High Street, Portsmouth, Virginia.

(1231) (i) No vessels, other than those being operated as ferries for the Tidewater Transportation District Commission, may embark or disembark passengers or otherwise moor at the Elizabeth River Ferry dock at the foot of High Street, Portsmouth, Virginia.

(1232) (ii) Any vessel being operated for the Tidewater Transportation District Commission may not moor at the dock longer than necessary to embark passengers awaiting

area (prohibited). A rectangular area surrounding Piers 1 and 2, Naval Weapons Station, and extending upstream therefrom, beginning at a point on the shore line at latitude 37°15′25″ N., longitude 76°32′32″ W.; thence to latitude 37°15′42″ N., longitude 76°32′06″ W.; thence to latitude 37°15′27″ N., longitude 76°31′48″ W.; thence to latitude 37°15′05″ N., longitude 76°31′27″ W.; thence to a point on the shore line at latitude 37°14′51″ N., longitude 76°31′50″ W.; and thence along the shore line to the point of beginning.

(1623) (2) Naval mine service-testing area (restrict ed). A rectangular area adjacent to the northeast boundary of the prohibited area described in subparagraph (1) of this paragraph, beginning at latitude 37°16′00″ N., longitude 76°32′29″ W.; thence to latitude 37°16′23″ N., longitude 76°32′00″ W.; thence to latitude 37°15′27″ N., longitude 76°30′54″ W.; thence to latitude 37°15′05″ N., longitude 76°31′27″ W.; thence to latitude 37°15′27″ N., longitude 76°31′48″ W.; thence to latitude 37°15′42″ N., longitude 76°32′06″ W.; thence to latitude 37°15′40″ N., longitude 76°32′09″ W.; and thence to the point of beginning.

(1624) (3) Explosives-Handling Berth (Naval). A circular area of 600 yards radius with its center at latitude 37°13′56″ N., longitude 76°28′48″ W.

(1625) (b) The regulations. (1) All persons and all vessels other than naval craft are forbidden to enter the prohibited area described in paragraph (a)(1) of this section.

(1626) (2) Trawling, dragging, and net-fishing are prohibited, and no permanent obstructions may at any time be placed in the area described in paragraph (a) (2) of this section. Upon official notification, any vessel anchored in the area and any person in the area will be required to vacate the area during the actual mine-laying operation. Persons and vessels entering the area during mine-laying operations by aircraft must proceed directly through the area without delay, except in case of emergency. Naval authorities are required to publish advance notice of mine-laying and/or retrieving operations scheduled to be carried on in the area, and during such published periods of operation, fishing or other aquatic activities are forbidden in the area. No vessel will be denied passage through the area at any time during either mine-laying or retrieving operations.

(1627) (3) The Explosives-Handling Berth (Naval) described in paragraph (a)(3) of this section is reserved for the exclusive use of naval vessels and except in cases of emergency no other vessel shall anchor therein without the permission of local naval authorities, obtained through the Captain of the Port, U.S. Coast Guard, Norfolk, Va. There shall be no restriction on the movement of vessels through the Explosive-Handling Berth.

(1628) (4) Vessels shall not be anchored, nor shall persons in the water approach within 300 yards of the perimeter of the Explosives-Handling Berth when that berth is occupied by a vessel handling explosives.

(1629) (5) The regulations of this section shall be enforced by the Commander, Naval Base, Norfolk, Virginia, and such agencies as he may designate.

(1630) §334.270 York River adjacent to Cheatham Annex Depot, Naval Supply Center, Williamsburg, Virginia; restricted area. (a) The area. The waters of York River bounded as follows: Beginning at a point on shore at Cheatham Annex Depot at latitude 37°17′14″ N., longitude 76°35′38″ W.; thence to a point offshore at latitude 37°17′52″ N., longitude 76°35′20″ W.; thence approximately parallel to the shore to a point at latitude 37°17′23″ N., longitude 76°34′39″ W.; thence to the shore at latitude 37°16′58″ N., longitude 76°35′03″ W.; and thence along the shore at Cheatham Annex Depot to the point of beginning.

(1631) (b) The regulations. (1) No loitering will be permitted within the area. Oystermen may work their own leaseholds or public bottom within the area, provided they obtain special permission from the Officer in Charge, Cheatham Annex Depot, Naval Supply Center, Williamsburg, Virginia.

(1632) (2) The regulations in this section shall be enforced by the Officer in Charge, Cheatham Annex Depot, U.S. Naval Supply Center, Williamsburg, Virginia.

(1633) §334.280 James River between the entrance to Skiffes Creek and Mulberry Point, Va.; Army training and small craft testing area. (a) The restricted area. Beginning on the shore at latitude 37°09′54″N., longitude 76°36′25″W.; thence westerly to latitude 37°09′50″N., longitude 76°37′45.5″W.; thence southerly to latitude 37°09′00″N., longitude 76°38′05″W.; thence southerly to latitude 37°08′22″N., longitude 76°37′55″W.; thence due east to the shore at latitude 37°08′22″N., longitude 76°37′22″W.; thence northerly along the shore to the point of beginning.

(1634) (b) The regulations. (1) No vessels other than Department of the Army vessels, and no persons other than persons embarked in such vessels shall remain in or enter the restricted area except as provided in paragraph (b)(2) of this section.

(1635) (2) Nothing in the regulations of this section shall prevent the harvesting and cultivation of oyster beds or the setting of fish traps within the restricted area under regulations of the Department of the Army, nor will the passage of fishing vessels to or from authorized traps be unreasonably interfered with or restricted.

(1636) (3) Vessels anchored in the area shall be so anchored as not to obstruct the arc of visibility of Deepwater Shoals Light.

(1637) (4) The Commanding General, Fort Eustis, Va., will, to the extent possible give public notice from time to time through local news media and the Coast Guard's Local Notice to Mariners of the schedule of intended Army use of the restricted area.

(1638) (5) The continuation of the restricted area for more than 3 years after the date of its establishment shall be dependent upon the outcome of the consideration of a request for its continuance submitted to the District Engineer, U.S. Army Engineer District, Norfolk, Virginia, by the using agency at least 3 months prior to the expiration of the 3 years.

(1639) (6) The regulations in this section shall be enforced by the Commanding General, Fort Eustis, Va., and such agencies as he may designate.

(1640) §334.290 Elizabeth River, Southern Branch, Va., naval restricted areas. (a) The areas–(1) St. Helena Annex Area. Beginning at a point at St. Helena Annex of the Norfolk Naval Shipyard, on the eastern shore of Southern Branch of Elizabeth River, at latitude 36°49′43″, longitude 76°17′26.5″; thence in a southwesterly direction to a point on the eastern boundary of Norfolk Harbor 40-foot channel at latitude 36°49′42″, longitude 76°17′33″; thence in a southerly direction along the eastern boundary of Norfolk Harbor 40-foot channel to latitude 36°49′28″, longitude 76°17′27″; thence easterly to the shore at latitude 36°49′28″, longitude 76°17′22″; and thence, northerly along the shore to the point of beginning.

(1641) (2) Norfolk Naval Shipyard Area. Beginning at a point on the shore at the northeast corner of the Norfolk Naval Shipyard, at latitude 36°49′43.5″, longitude 76°17′41.5″; thence due east approximately 100 feet to the western boundary of Elizabeth River channel; thence in a southerly direction along the western boundary of the channel to the point where it passes through the draw of the

Norfolk and Portsmouth Belt Line Railroad bridge, thence in a southwesterly direction along the northerly side of the bridge to the western shore of Southern Branch of Elizabeth River; and thence along the shore in a northerly direction to the point of beginning.

(1642)   (3) Southgate Terminal Area. Beginning at a point at the northeast corner of Southgate Terminal Annex of Norfolk Naval Shipyard, at latitude 36°48′23″, longitude 76°17′39″; thence east to latitude 36°48′23″, longitude 76°17′29″; thence southerly along the western boundary of Norfolk Harbor 35-foot channel to latitude 36°48′04″, longitude 76°17′33″; thence west to latitude 36°48′04″, longitude 76°17′41″; and thence along the shore in a northerly direction to the point of beginning.

(1643)   (b) The regulations. (1) No vessels other than Naval vessels and other vessels authorized to move to and from piers at the Norfolk Naval Shipyard and its two annexes described in paragraph (a) (1) and (3) of this section, and no person other than persons embarked in such vessels, shall enter the restricted areas.

(1644)   (2) This section shall be enforced by the Commander, Norfolk Naval Shipyard, Portsmouth, Va., and such agencies as he may designate.

(1645)   §334.300 Hampton Roads and Willoughby Bay, off Norfolk Naval Base; naval restricted area. (a) The area. (1) Beginning at a point on shore at the Destroyer Submarine Piers at latitude 36°56′00″N., longitude 76°19′30″W.; thence westerly to 36°55′59″N., 76°20″08.5″W.; thence northerly along the eastern limit of Norfolk Harbor Channel to 36°57′52″N., 76°20′00″W.; thence easterly to 36°57′52″N., 76°19′35″W.; thence to 36°57′47.7″N., 76°18′57″W.; thence southeasterly to 36°57′26″N., 76°18′42″W.; thence easterly to 36°57′26.2″N., 76°17′55.2″W.; thence southerly to 36°57′05″N., 76°17′52″W.; thence southeasterly to 36°56′56.2″N., 76°17′27″W.; thence northeasterly to 36°57′10″N., 76°16′29″W.; and thence to the shoreline at 36°57′18.8″N., 76°16′22″W.; at the Naval Air Station.

(1646)   (2) Beginning at a point on the Naval Station shore at latitude 36°56′37.5″N., longitude 76°19′44″W.; thence westerly and northerly along the breakwater to its extremity at latitude 36°56′41.5″N., longitude 76°19′54″W.; thence westerly to a point on the eastern limit of Norfolk Harbor Channel at latitude 36°56′41.5″N., longitude 76°20′05.5″W.; thence northerly along the eastern limit of Norfolk Harbor Channel to latitude 36°57′52″N., longitude 76°20′00″W.; thence easterly to latitude 36°57′52″N., longitude 76°19′35″W.; thence to latitude 36°57′47.7″N., longitude 76°18′57″W.; thence southeasterly to latitude 36°57′26″N., longitude 76°18′42″W.; thence easterly to latitude 36°57′26.2″N., longitude 76°17′55.2″W.; thence southerly to latitude 36°57′05″N., longitude 76°17′52″W.; thence southeasterly to latitude 36°56′56.2″N., longitude 76°17′27″W.; thence northeasterly to latitude 36°57′10″N., longitude 76°16′29″W.; and thence to the shoreline at latitude 36°57′18.8″N., longitude 76°16′22″W.; at the Naval Air Station.

(1647)   (b) The regulations. (1) No vessels other than Naval vessels and other vessels authorized to move to and from piers at the Norfolk Naval Base, and no person other than persons embarked in such vessels, shall enter the restricted areas.

(1648)   (2) This section shall be enforced by the Commander, Naval Base, Norfolk, Virginia, and such agencies as he/she may designate.

(1649)   §334.310 Chesapeake Bay, Lynnhaven Roads; Navy amphibious training area. (a) The restricted area. Beginning at latitude 36°55′47″, longitude 76°11′04.5″; thence to latitude 36°59′04″, longitude 76°10′11″; thence to latitude 36°58′28.5″, longitude 76°07′54″; thence to latitude 36°55′27.5″, longitude 76°08′42″; thence westerly along the shore and across the mouth of Little Creek to the point of beginning.

(1650)   (b) The regulations. (1) No fishpound stakes or structures shall be allowed in the restricted area.

(1651)   (2) No vessel shall approach within 300 yards of any naval vessel or within 600 yards of any vessel displaying the red "baker" burgee.

(1652)   (3) This section shall be enforced by the Commandant, Fifth Naval District, and such agencies as he may designate.

(1653)   §334.320 Chesapeake Bay entrance; naval restricted area. (a) The area. Beginning at a point on the south shore of Chesapeake Bay at longitude 76°03′06″; thence to latitude 37°01′18″, longitude 76°02′06″; thence to latitude 37°00′18″, longitude 75°55′54″; thence to latitude 36°58′00″, longitude 75°48′24″; thence to latitude 36°51′48″, longitude 75°51′00″; thence to the shore at longitude 75°58′48″, and thence northwesterly and southwesterly along the shore at Cape Henry to the point of beginning.

(1654)   (b) The regulations. (1) Anchoring, trawling, crabbing, fishing, and dragging in the area are prohibited, and no object attached to a vessel or otherwise shall be placed on or near the bottom.

(1655)   (2) This section shall be enforced by the Commandant, Fifth Naval District, Norfolk, Va.

(1656)   §334.330 Atlantic Ocean and connecting waters in vicinity of Myrtle Island, Va.; Air Force practice bombing, rocket firing, and gunnery range. (a) The danger zone. The waters of the Atlantic Ocean and connecting waters within an area described as follows: Beginning at

(1657)   37°12′18″, 75°46′00″; thence southwesterly to

(1658)   37°08′21″, 75°50′00″; thence northwesterly along the arc of a circle having a radius of three nautical miles and centered at

(1659)   37°11′16″, 75°49′29″, to

(1660)   37°10′14″, 75°52′57″; thence northeasterly to

(1661)   37°14′30″, 75°48′32″; thence southeasterly to

(1662)   37°13′38″, 75°46′18″; and thence southeasterly to the point of beginning.

(1663)   (b) The regulations. (1) No vessel shall enter or remain in the danger zone except during intervals specified and publicized from time to time in local newspapers or by radio announcement.

(1664)   (2) This section shall be enforced by the Commanding General, Tactical Air Command, Langley Air Force Base, Virginia, and such agencies as he may designate.

(1665)   §334.340 Chesapeake Bay off Plumtree Island, Hampton, Va.; Air Force precision test area. (a) The danger zone. The waters of Chesapeake Bay and connecting waters within an area bounded as follows: Beginning at latitude 37°08′12″, longitude 76°19′30″, which is a point on the circumference of a circle of 10,000-foot radius with its center on Plumtree Point at latitude 37°07′30″, longitude 76°17′36″; thence clockwise along the circumference of the circle to latitude 37°09′06″, longitude 76°18′00″; thence southeasterly to latitude 37°08′12″, longitude 76°17′48″; thence clockwise along the circumference of a circle of 4,000-foot radius (with its center at latitude 37°07′30″, longitude 76°17′36″ to latitude 37°07′48″, longitude 76°18′24″; thence northwesterly to the point of beginning.

(1666)   (b) The regulations. (1) The danger zone will be in use not more than a total of 4 hours per month, which hours shall be during not more than any 2 days per month.

(1667)   (2) No vessel shall enter or remain in the danger zone during periods of firing or bombing or when the zone is otherwise in use.

(1668)   (3) The Commander, Tactical Air Command, Langley Air Force Base, Va., shall be responsible for publicizing in advance through the Coast Guard's "Local Notice to Mariners," in the local press, and by radio from time to time the schedule of use of the area, and shall station patrol boats to warn vessels during periods of use.

(1669)   (4) This section shall be enforced by the Commander, Tactical Air Command, Langley Air Force Base, Va., or such agency as he may designate.

(1670)   (c) Disestablishment of danger zone. The danger zone will be disestablished not later than December 31, 1967, unless written application for its continuance shall have been made to and approved by the Secretary of the Army prior to that date.

(1671)   §334.350 Chesapeake Bay off Fort Monroe, Va.; firing range danger zone. (a) The danger zone. All of the water area lying within a section extending seaward a distance of 4,600 yards between radial lines bearing 83° True and 115° True, respectively, from a point on shore at latitude 37°01'30" N., longitude 76°17'54" W.

(1672)   (b) The regulations. (1) No weapon having a greater range than the 30-calibre carbine is to be fired into the firing range danger zone.

(1673)   (2) During periods when firing is in progress, red flags will be displayed at conspicuous locations on the beach. Observers will be on duty and firing will be suspended as long as any vessel is within the danger zone.

(1674)   (3) Passage of vessels through the area will not be prohibited at any time, nor will commercial fishermen be prohibited from working fish nets within the area. No loitering or anchoring for other purposes will be permitted during announced firing periods.

(1675)   (4) No firing will be done during hours of darkness or low visibility.

(1676)   (5) The Commander, Fort Monroe, Va., is responsible for furnishing in advance the firing schedule to the Commander, 5th Coast Guard District, for publication in his "Local Notice to Mariners" and to the local press at Norfolk and Newport News, Va.

(1677)   (c) The regulations in this section shall be enforced by the Commanding Officer, Fort Monroe, Va., and such agencies as he may designate.

(1678)   §334.360 Chesapeake Bay off Fort Monroe, Virginia; restricted area, U.S. Naval Base and Naval Surface Weapon Center.

(1679)   (a) The area. Beginning at

(1680)   37°00'30" N., 76°18'05" W.; thence to

(1681)   37°00'38" N., 76°17'42" W.; thence to

(1682)   37°00'39" N., 76°16'11" W.; thence to

(1683)   36°59'18" N., 76°17'52" W.; thence to

(1684)   37°00'05" N., 76°18'17" W.; and thence north along the seawall to the point of beginning.

(1685)   (b) The regulations. (1) Anchoring, trawling, fishing, and dragging are prohibited in the danger zone, and no object, either attached to a vessel or otherwise, shall be placed on or near the bottom.

(1686)   (2) This section shall be enforced by the Commander, Naval Base, Norfolk, Virginia, and such agencies as he may designate.

(1687)   §334.370 Chesapeake Bay, Lynnhaven Roads; danger zones, U.S. Naval Amphibious Base. (a) Underwater demolitions area (prohibited)—(1) The area. A portion of the restricted area for Navy amphibious training operations described in §207.157, along the south shore of Chesapeake Bay, bounded as follows: Beginning at a point on the mean low-water line at longitude 76°08'59"; thence 200 yards to latitude 36°55'36", longitude 76°08'57"; thence 400 yards to latitude 36°55'34", longitude 76°08'43"; thence 200 yards to a point on the mean low-water line at longitude 76°08'45"; and thence approximately 400 yards along the mean low-water line to the point of beginning. The area will be marked by range poles set on shore on the prolongation of the lines forming its eastern and western boundaries.

(1688)   (2) The regulations. Vessels other than those owned and operated by the United States shall not enter the prohibited area at any time unless authorized to do so by the enforcing agency.

(1689)   (b) Small-arms firing range—(1) The Area. Beginning at a point on the shore line at

(1690)   36°55'27" N., 76°08'38" W.; thence to

(1691)   36°55'50" N., 76°08'37" W.; thence to

(1692)   36°57'11" N., 76°08'11" W.; thence to

(1693)   36°56'53" N., 76°07'18" W., thence to

(1694)   36°55'39" N., 76°07'46" W.; thence to

(1695)   36°55'22" N., 76°08'17" W.; thence along the shore line to the point of beginning.

(1696)   (2) The regulations. (i) Passage of vessels through the area will not be prohibited at any time, nor will commercial fishermen be prohibited from working fish nets within the area. No loitering or anchoring for other purposes will be permitted.

(1697)   (ii) A large red warning flag will be flown on shore during periods when firing is in progress. Observers will be on duty and firing will be suspended for the passage of vessels and for the placing and maintenance of fish nets within the area.

(1698)   (c) This section shall be enforced by the Commanding Officer, U.S. Naval Amphibious Base, Little Creek, Norfolk, Virginia.

3. SANDY HOOK TO CAPE HENRY

(1) Between New York Bay and Delaware Bay is the New Jersey coast with its many resorts, its inlets, and its Intracoastal Waterway. Delaware Bay is the approach to Wilmington, Chester, Philadelphia, Camden, and Trenton; below Wilmington is the Delaware River entrance to the Chesapeake and Delaware Canal, the deep inside link between Chesapeake and Delaware Bays. The Delaware-Maryland-Virginia coast has relatively few resorts; the numerous inlets are backed by a shallow inside passage that extends all the way from Delaware Bay to Chesapeake Bay. The last seven chapters, nearly half of this book, are required to describe Chesapeake Bay to Norfolk and Newport News, to Washington and Baltimore, and to Susquehanna River 170 miles north of the Virginia Capes.

(2) A vessel approaching this coast from seaward will be made aware of its nearness by the number of vessels passing up and down in the coastal trade. The coast of New Jersey is studded with large hotels, prominent standpipes, and elevated tanks. South of Delaware Bay, the principal landmarks are the lighthouses and Coast Guard stations.

(3) The general tendency along this mostly sandy coast is for the ocean beaches and the points on the north sides of the entrances to wash away and for the points on the south sides of the entrances to build out. Protective works have done much to stabilize the New Jersey coast, but several lighthouses have been abandoned between Delaware Bay and Chesapeake Bay because of erosion.

(4) The shores of Delaware Bay and Delaware River are mostly low and have few conspicuous marks, other than lights, below the industrial centers along the river. The shores of Chesapeake Bay are low as far north as Patuxent River, then rise to considerable heights at the head of the bay.

(5) **Disposal Sites** and **Dumping Grounds.**–These areas are rarely mentioned in the Coast Pilot, but are shown on the nautical charts. (See Disposal Sites and Dumping Grounds, chapter 1, and charts for limits.)

(6) **Aids to navigation.**–Lights are numerous along the section of the coast covered by this Coast Pilot. Radiobeacons and fog signals are at most of the principal light stations. Marker radiobeacons, low-powered and for local use only, are at the entrances to many of the inlets. Many coastal and harbor buoys are equipped with radar reflectors, which greatly increase the range at which the buoys may be detected on the radarscope. The critical dangers are marked.

(7) **Loran.**–Loran C stations provide the mariner with good navigation coverage along this section of the coast.

(8) **Radar,** though always a valuable navigational aid, is generally of less assistance in navigation along this coast due to the relatively low relief; the accuracy of radar ranges to the beach cannot be relied upon. Coastal buoys equipped with radar reflectors are of help in this regard. It is sometimes possible to obtain a usable radar return from the larger lighthouses, but positive target identification is usually difficult. Radar is of particular importance in detecting other traffic and in the prevention of collisions during periods of inclement weather, and in fog and low visibility.

(9) **COLREGS Demarcation Lines.**–Lines have been established to delineate those waters upon which mariners must comply with the International Regulations for Preventing Collisions at Sea, 1972 (72 COLREGS) and those waters upon which mariners must comply with the Inland Navigational Rules Act of 1980 (Inland Rules). The waters inside of the lines are **Inland Rules Waters,** and the waters outside of the lines are **COLREGS Waters.** (See **Part 80,** chapter 2, for specific lines of demarcation.)

(10) **Ports and Waterways Safety.**–(See **Part 160,** chapter 2, for regulations governing vessel operations and requirements for notification of arrivals, departures, hazardous conditions, and certain dangerous cargoes to the Captain of the Port.)

(11) **Harbor and Inlet Entrances.**–The channels into Delaware and Chesapeake Bays are broad and deep. The entrances to the inlets are comparatively shallow and are more or less obstructed by shifting sandbars. Some of the inlets have been improved by dredging and by the construction of jetties. On many of the bars the buoys are moved from time to time to mark the shifting channels. The best time to enter most of the inlets is on a rising tide with a smooth sea. Strangers should not attempt to enter the inlets without assistance when the seas are breaking on the bars. The tidal currents have considerable velocity in all of the entrances, and their direction is affected by the force and direction of the wind.

(12) **Traffic Separation Schemes (Traffic Lanes)** have been established at the entrances to New York Harbor, Delaware Bay and Chesapeake Bay, and in the main channel of Chesapeake Bay off Smith Point just south of the entrance to the Potomac River. (See chapters 4, 6, 9, and 12, respectively, for details.)

(13) **Anchorages.**–The only protected anchorage for deep-draft vessels between New York Bay and Chesapeake Bay is outside the channel limits in Delaware Bay according to draft. Absecon Inlet, Cape May Inlet, and some of the others can accommodate light-draft vessels such as trawlers and small yachts, but not medium or deep drafts. Small local craft often seek shelter inside the shallower inlets, but entrance is difficult in heavy weather, and the unimproved inlets are often difficult even in good weather, particularly for strangers.

(14) A number of anchorage areas have been established by Federal Regulations within the area of this Coast Pilot. (See **Part 110,** chapter 2, for limits and regulations.)

(15) **Dangers.**–The principal dangers along this coast are the outlying sand shoals, the fogs, and the doubtful direction and velocity of the currents after heavy gales. Depths of 7½ fathoms are found as far as 20 miles from shore. There are many wrecks along this coast, but most of them have been blasted off or cleared to safe navigational depths; the others are marked by obstruction buoys.

(16) Gales from northeast to southeast cause heavy breakers on the beaches and outlying shoals; the sea breaks in 4 to 5 fathoms of water, and shoals of that depth or less usually are marked during easterly gales. The bars across the inlets are then impassable and are defined by breakers even in comparatively smooth water with a light swell. The heaviest surf on the beach is on a rising tide near high-water springs; the least surf is encountered on a falling tide near low water. A very heavy surf makes on the beaches after a southeasterly gale followed by a sudden shift of wind to northwest.

(17) **Danger zones** have been established within the area of this Coast Pilot. (See **Part 334,** chapter 2, for limits and regulations.)

(18) **Fishweirs** are numerous along the outside coast and in Chesapeake Bay and tributaries. The stakes often become broken off and form a hazard to navigation, especially at

swing span with a clearance of 15 feet over the main channel. (See **117.1 through 117.49**, chapter 2, for drawbridge regulations.) The town is principally a shellfish and fishing center, but pleasure craft operate from here during the summer. The wharves and piers along the waterfront have depths of 3 to 10 feet alongside. There are small-craft facilities at Chincoteague that can provide gasoline, diesel fuel, water, berths, and limited marine supplies. Hull and engine repairs can be made; a 40-ton marine railway at Chincoteague can handle craft up to 80 feet.

(79)   A boat basin is at the extreme southwest end of Chincoteague Island. In May 1988, the dredged entrance channel, marked by a light, had a midchannel controlling depth of 7 feet with 7 to 8 feet in basin.

(80)   **Chincoteague Coast Guard Station** is on the east side of Chincoteague Channel, 0.3 mile south of the highway bridge.

(81)   **Chart 12210.**—The 35-mile stretch of coast between Chincoteague Inlet and Great Machipongo Inlet is formed by six islands of about equal length. The islands are separated from each other by narrow inlets and from the mainland by marsh and flats through which are numerous sloughs and channels.

(82)   **Wallops Island,** northernmost of the six, is on the southwest side of Chincoteague Inlet.

(83)   A **danger zone** extends for about 5 miles off the coast of Wallops Island and covers the entrance to Chincoteague Inlet. A strobe light is displayed at night from a tower in about 37°15'16"N., 75°29'06"W., about 30 minutes prior to the commencement of and during rocket launching operations. (See **334.130** chapter 2, for limits and regulations.)

(84)   **Assawoman Inlet,** the ocean entrance between **Wallops Island** and **Assawoman Island,** is very shallow and is not used. **Gargathy Inlet,** the ocean inlet separating Assawoman Island and **Metompkin Islands,** is not used.

(85)   **Metompkin Inlet,** the ocean entrance between Metompkin Islands and **Cedar Island,** is used by some small local fishing and oyster boats. The changeable entrance channel is unmarked and should not be entered without local knowledge.

(86)   **Porpoise Banks,** 10 miles offshore from Metompkin Inlet, have irregular bottom with depths of 34 to 40 feet.

(87)   **Wachapreague Inlet,** between Cedar Island and **Parramore Island,** is 20 miles south-southwestward of Chincoteague Inlet. The entrance is marked by a lighted bell buoy and unlighted buoys that are shifted in position with changing channel conditions. The controlling depth is about 5 feet through the inlet, which is used by many fishing boats and by some boats seeking shelter, but should be entered only with local knowledge. The best anchorage is in **Horseshoe Lead,** southwest of the entrance, where there are depths of 20 to 30 feet west of the middle ground. **Parramore Beach Coast Guard Station** is on the inner side of Parramore Island 0.5 mile south of the inlet. A radiobeacon is atop the lookout tower at the Coast Guard station.

(88)   **Parramore Banks** extend about 8 miles offshore from Wachapreague Inlet. The area is lumpy and has numerous depths of 18 to 30 feet. A lighted gong buoy is east of the banks.

(89)   Two fish havens are about 2.6 miles and 7.5 miles east-southeast, respectively, from Wachapreague Inlet. The fish haven nearer to shore is marked by buoys.

(90)   **Wachapreague,** a town on the mainland about 4 miles west-northwest of Wachapreague Inlet, is an oystering and fishing center, and is a base for some pleasure boats during the summer. A depth of about 4 feet can be carried from Wachapreague Inlet through **Hummock Channel** and **Wachapreague Channel,** marked by lights, to the wharves and marinas at the town. Gasoline, diesel fuel, berths, and some marine supplies can be obtained. Hull and engine repairs can be made; largest marine railway, 50 feet.

(91)   **Quinby Inlet,** the ocean entrance between Parramore Island and Hog Island, has a fan of breakers across the bar at the entrance. The buoys marking the inlet are frequently shifted and not charted. In 1982, a draft of 5 feet could be carried through the inlet. The inlet should not be used without local knowledge.

(92)   **Quinby** is a village on the mainland about 6 miles north-northwest of Quinby Inlet. A channel to the village, marked by lights, follows **Sandy Island Channel** to **Upshur Bay,** thence through a slough in the mudflats to a dredged channel leading to a basin that has a public landing; gasoline, diesel fuel, berths, some marine supplies, and a pumpout station are available. In May 1988, the midchannel controlling depth was 5 feet in the dredged channel with 5 to 6½ feet in the basin. A no-wake **speed limit** is enforced.

(93)   **Great Machipongo Inlet,** the ocean entrance between Hog Island and **Cobb Island,** has breakers that form on the shoals on either side of the entrance at all times, but on the bar only in heavy weather. The inlet is marked by buoys that are shifted in position with changing channel conditions. The controlling depth is about 12 feet over the bar.

(94)   **Great Machipongo Channel** extends northwestward through Hog Island Bay from the inlet to the mainland where it continues as **Machipongo River. Willis Wharf,** on the west bank of **Parting Creek** 1 mile above the junction with Machipongo River, is a base for shellfish and fishing boats. Gasoline and diesel fuel are available. A marine railway here can handle craft up to 60 feet for do-it-yourself repairs. In January 1989, the dredged channel in Parting Creek had a midchannel controlling depth of 7 feet from the junction with Machipongo River to Willis Wharf.

(95)   A state-owned boat harbor is just below Willis Wharf on the west side of Parting Creek between Daybeacons 17 and 18. An area with about 41 slips is available for commercial fishing boats. The harbor has electricity, water, and a launching ramp.

(96)   **Chart 12224.**—**Sand Shoal Inlet,** the ocean entrance between Cobb Island and **Wreck Island,** may be entered through three channels. **Northeast Channel,** protected by extensive shoaling to northward and marked by buoys shifted in position with changing channel conditions, leads along the south end of Cobb Island; the controlling depth is about 10 feet over the bar. **Southeast Channel** is straight, but the bar breaks in heavy weather; the controlling depth is about 10 feet over the bar. **South Channel,** east of Wreck Island, has a controlling depth of about 8 feet. The latter two channels are not marked and should not be used by strangers.

(97)   A good fair-weather anchorage is in the channel near the discontinued Coast Guard station east of **Little Cobb Island** for boats able to cross the entrance bar with 3 feet over it.

(98)   **Sand Shoal Channel,** marked by lights and daybeacons, extends westward from Sand Shoal Inlet for 6 miles where it joins a marked dredged channel leading to the wharves and public bulkhead at **Oyster** on the mainland. In June 1984, the controlling depth was 6 feet in the dredged channel and in the basin at Oyster. Public piers and a launching ramp are on the northern side of the basin. Numerous wrecks are reported near these facilities; caution is advised.

(99)   Oyster is the shipping point for large amounts of clams and oysters. Gasoline, diesel fuel, and some marine supplies are available.

(100)   **Ship Shoal Inlet,** the ocean entrance between Ship Shoal Island and **Myrtle Island,** is shallow and unmarked; it is used only by local oyster boats. There is deep water back of the inlet, but the channels to the inside passages are shallow and tortuous.

(101)   The **danger zone** of a bombing and gunnery range is centered on Myrtle Island, 6 miles northeastward of Cape Charles Light. (See **334.330,** chapter 2, for limits and regulations.)

(102)   **Little Inlet,** between Myrtle Island and Smith Island, is shallow and is little used. Small boats can connect with the inside passage at high water.

(103)   **Cape Charles** and the islands on the north side of the entrance to Chesapeake Bay are described in chapter 9.

(104)   **Smith Island Inlet,** between Smith Island and Fishermans Island, is fairly wide, but the narrow, changeable channel lies between sandbars and breakers. The inlet is used by many local boats with drafts of 3 to 4 feet, but it is unmarked and should not be used by strangers. The controlling depth over the bar is said to be 1½ feet.

(105)   **Charts 12211, 12210, 12221.–Virginia Inside Passage** is between the barrier beach along the Atlantic Ocean on the east and the Virginia portion of the mainland peninsula on the west. The passage extends 74 miles from the south end of Chincoteague Bay through creeks, thorofares, marshy cuts, and bays to enter Chesapeake Bay at Cape Charles. The route is marked with lights and daybeacons which have daymarks with white reflector borders to distinguish them from aids to navigation marking other waterways. Buoys are temporarily established from time to time to mark destroyed aids or critical places.

(106)   The Federal project depth is 6 feet for the waterway. Maintenance dredging is performed to provide a 6-foot controlling depth, but due to continuous shoaling 3 feet or less may be found in places, particularly inside the ocean inlets. The overhead clearance is limited only by the 40-foot fixed bridge across Cat Creek, 8 miles southward of Chincoteague, the 50-foot clearance of the power cable over Longboat Creek inshore from Metompkin Inlet, 22 miles southward of Chincoteague, and the 40-foot fixed bridge at Cape Charles.

(107)   The mean range of tide varies from 2.5 to 4.5 feet in the inlets along the Virginia coast; greater fluctuations in the water level in the inside waters are caused by high winds and storms.

(108)   Gasoline, diesel fuel, and some marine supplies are available at Wachapreague, 29 miles south of Chincoteague; at Quinby, 33 miles south of Chincoteague; at Willis Wharf, 37 miles south of Chincoteague; and at Oyster, 60 miles south of Chincoteague and 12 miles north of Cape Charles. Hull and engine repairs can be made at Wachapreague.

(109)   From Chincoteague, the Virginia Inside Passage follows Chincoteague Channel across Chincoteague Inlet to **Walker Point,** thence through **Balfast Narrows, Island Hole Narrows,** the dredged cut in **Bogues Bay,** and **Cat Creek** to

the sloughs marked by lights and daybeacons back of Assawoman Inlet, 10 miles southwestward of Chincoteague. The fixed highway bridge over Cat Creek has a clearance of 40 feet. The overhead power cable just north of the bridge has a clearance of 60 feet.

(110)   From 1 mile back of Assawoman Inlet, the inside passage continues through **Northam Narrows,** thence through dredged cuts in **Kegotank Bay** and back of Gargathy Inlet to **Wire Passage,** 15 miles southwestward of Chincoteague.

(111)   From Gargathy Inlet, the inside passage goes through Wire Passage into a dredged cut in **Metompkin Bay,** and enters Folly Creek westward of Metompkin Inlet. A dredged channel with a controlling depth of 5 feet in February 1991, extends about 0.8 mile up **Parker Creek** from Virginia Inside Passage Light 80. The channel is marked by daybeacons. **Folly Creek,** which leads westward from the south end of Metompkin Bay, has a depth of 1 foot to the landing at its head, 3 miles above the mouth. A launching ramp and a pier are on the south side of Folly Creek about 1 mile west of Light 87.

(112)   The passage continues through a dredged cut from Folly Creek into **Longboat Creek,** which has a power cable over its northern part with a clearance of 50 feet, thence through cuts in **Cedar Island Bay, Teagles Ditch,** and **Burtons Bay** into Wachapreague Channel which leads to Wachapreague, 29 miles southward of Chincoteague. Supplies and repair facilities are available at Wachapreague. (Refer to previous description in this chapter.)

(113)   From Wachapreague Channel, the passage continues through a cut in **Bradford Bay,** a part of **Millstone Creek,** a cut in **Swash Bay,** a part of **The Swash,** and Little Sloop Channel to Sandy Island Channel, 3 miles inside Quinby Inlet and 36 miles southward of Chincoteague.

(114)   The passage southward of Quinby Inlet follows **Sloop Channel** and a dredged cut into **Cunjer Channel,** thence westward in **North Channel** at the north end of **Hog Island Bay** to Great Machipongo Channel, 43 miles southward of Chincoteague.

(115)   After passing through Great Machipongo Channel to a point 2 miles inside Great Machipongo Inlet, the route goes westward through **Gull Marsh Channel,** thence southwestward through a natural channel and cut in **Outlet Bay** and **Spidercrab Bay** to Eckichy Channel, thence southeastward to Sand Shoal Channel, 1.5 miles inside Sand Shoal Inlet, 56 miles southward of Chincoteague.

(116)   From inside of Sand Shoal Inlet, the passage continues westward through Sand Shoal Channel and southward through **Mockhorn Channel** to Magothy Bay.

(117)   **Magothy Bay,** which extends southward from Mockhorn Channel to Smith Island Inlet, is shallow except in the well-marked inside passage which passes through the bay to Cape Charles. **Magotha** is a village on the west side of the bay 3.5 miles northwestward of Cape Charles Light.

(118)   From the southern part of Magothy Bay, the passage continues southwestward through a dredged cut across Cape Charles into the deep water in Chesapeake Bay. The fixed highway bridge over the passage from Cape Charles to Fishermans Island has a clearance of 40 feet.

9. CHESAPEAKE BAY ENTRANCE

(1)   This chapter describes the deep-draft southerly entrance to Chesapeake Bay from the Atlantic Ocean; the waters of Lynnhaven Roads, Lynnhaven Inlet, Little Creek, Hampton Roads, Willoughby Bay, Lafayette River, and Elizabeth River, including Western, Eastern, and Southern Branches; and the ports of Hampton, Newport News, Norfolk, Berkley, Portsmouth, and Chesapeake.

(2)   **COLREGS Demarcation Lines.**—The lines established for Chesapeake Bay are described in **80.510**, chapter 2.

(3)   **Weather.**—This summary provides climatological information applicable to the entire Chesapeake Bay. From November through April Chesapeake Bay, particularly the southern portion, is rough sailing. Storms moving up the Atlantic coast generate winds out of the northeast quadrant ahead of their centers; speeds often reach 30 to 50 knots. Several days of strong and gusty northwest winds may follow. Strong cold fronts from the west can generate 25 to 45 knot gusts over open water. Waves associated with strong winds can be rough and bad chop develops when these winds oppose strong tidal currents. Northerlies of 25 knots or more, over a long fetch of the bay, can easily build 8 to 10 foot seas in the central portion and 5 to 7 foot seas in the south. Seas of 8 feet or more occur about 2 to 4 percent of the time from fall through early spring, in the bay. Gales can occur from September through March.

(4)   Another problem during this period is poor visibilities. Fog forms most often when warm, moist air moves across the bay's cold waters from the southeast through south. Most of the 30 to 40 dense fog days each year develop from January through April. Dens. fog is more common offshore and should be expected on unusually warm, humid winter and spring days. Fog over particularly cold waters with winds less than 10 knots may drop visibilities to near zero. Precipitation, particularly snow, may also hamper visibilities.

(5)   When temperatures drop below about 28°F and winds are blowing at 13 knots or more, there exists a potential for moderate superstructure icing. This potential exists in the bay from November through March; January and February are the worst months when the potential exists about 3 percent of the time.

(6)   During March and April, cold fronts often trigger fast-moving narrow bands of thunderstorms. Preceding the cold front these bands move eastward at 10 to 30 knots generating lightning and gusty winds of gale force. Thunderstorms are also a bay-wide threat during spring and summer when they develop about 6 to 9 days each month. They may develop over land during the afternoon as warm, humid air is forced aloft by surface heating. The thunderstorm may precede a cold front. When a cold front passes during a period of maximum afternoon heating thunderstorms may be severe. In spring and early summer they usually develop to the west of the bay and move toward the northeast at speeds of 25 to 35 knots. Occasionally thunderstorms will approach from the northwest; these are often severe, tend to move very fast, and can pack winds reaching 70 to 90 knots. This type of storm struck Norfolk in June 1977 capsizing a charter fishing boat and tearing away the end of a fishing pier. Severe squall lines can also generate tornadoes which may move over the bay developing waterspouts; winds can exceed 200 knots in these systems. By midsummer, fronts become weaker and less frequent and thunderstorms are mainly the air mass type which move at 10 to 20 knots and usually do not organize into a squall line. Thunderstorms are likely to occur on 8 to 9 days in July compared to 6 to 7 days in August.

(7)   Good weather in late summer and fall is compromised mainly by the threat of a tropical cyclone, particularly from mid-August through the first week in October. A hurricane affects the Chesapeake Bay about once every 10 years on the average. Thunderstorms occur on 1 to 3 days per month in September and October and are usually associated with increasingly frequent and rigorous cold fronts. Fog becomes more of a problem, particularly north of Annapolis. This is a morning fog that forms on 1 to 4 days per month during September and October over the upper reaches of the bay; it usually lifts by noon. In late summer and autumn waterspouts may be sighted. These are short-lived and less severe than those associated with thunderstorms; maximum winds climb to about 50 knots. They are caused by cooler air overriding a body of warm moist air in association with a cloud build up over the bay; they usually occur in fair weather.

(8)   (See page T-11 for **Chesapeake Bay climatological table.**)

(9)   **Charts 12221, 12220, 12260.**—Chesapeake Bay, the largest inland body of water along the Atlantic coast of the United States, is 168 miles long with a greatest width of 23 miles. The bay is the approach to Norfolk, Newport News, Baltimore, and many lesser ports. Deep-draft vessels use the Atlantic entrance, which is about 10 miles wide between Fishermans Island on the north and Cape Henry on the south. Medium-draft vessels can enter from Delaware Bay on the north via Chesapeake and Delaware Canal, and light-draft vessels can enter from Albemarle Sound on the south via the Intracoastal Waterway.

(10)   The waters surrounding a vessel that is carrying liquefied petroleum gas are a **safety** zone while the vessel transits the Chesapeake Bay and Elizabeth River. (See 165.506, chapter 2, for limits and regulations.)

(11)   **Mileages.**—Many of the distances in this and later Chesapeake Bay chapters are given in nautical miles above the **Virginia Capes,** or "the **Capes,**" which is a short way of referring to a line from Cape Charles Light to Cape Henry Light.

(12)   **Chesapeake Light** (36°54.3'N., 75°42.8'W.), 117 feet above the water, is shown from a blue tower on a white superstructure on four piles, 14 miles eastward of Cape Henry. The name CHESAPEAKE is displayed on all sides. A fog signal and radiobeacon are operated at the station. A racon is at the light. A fish haven, consisting of sunken fishing-boat hulls and marked by private unlighted buoys, is about 0.4 mile southwestward of the light.

(13)   **Cape Charles,** on the north side of the entrance, is low and bare, but the land back of it is high and wooded. **Wise Point** is the most southerly mainland tip of the cape. **Low Fishermans Island,** a National Wildlife Refuge, is 1 mile south of Wise Point.

(14)   The southwest end of **Smith Island** is 2.4 miles eastward of Wise Point; the island is 6 miles long, low and sparsely wooded, and awash at half tide midway along its length.

(15)   **Cape Charles Light** (37°07.4'N., 75°54.4'W.), 180 feet above the water, is shown from an octagonal, pyramidal

skeleton tower, upper part black and lower part white, on the southwestern part of Smith Island. The ruins of the old lighthouse are in shallow water 0.7 mile eastward of the light.

(16)   **Smith Island Shoal,** which breaks in heavy weather, has depths of 21 feet 7.5 miles east-southeast of Cape Charles Light. Depths less than 40 feet extend another 5 miles northeastward. Outer limits of the shoal area are marked by a lighted buoy.

(17)   **Nautilus Shoal,** which extends 4 miles southeastward from Fishermans Island, has patches with depths of 6 to 11 feet. The buoyed channel along the southwest side of Nautilus Shoal, thence northward between Fishermans Island and **Inner Middle Ground,** had a controlling depth of about 16 feet in 1977-1980. The channel is used by local vessels drawing up to 12 feet. This channel is not recommended for strangers because of shifting shoals.

(18)   Breakers frequently occur along the axis of Inner Middle Ground, starting on the seaward side of the Chesapeake Bay Bridge-Tunnel and continuing the entire length of the shoal. This phenomenon appears to be associated with large swells rolling in from sea from the south-southeast to southeast.

(19)   Charts **12222, 12221, 12225.**—**Cape Henry,** on the south side of the entrance, has a range of sand hills about 80 feet high.

(20)   **Cape Henry Light** (36°55.6'N., 76°00.4'W.), 164 feet above the water, is shown from an octagonal, pyramidal tower, upper and lower half of each face alternately black and white, on the beach near the turn of the cape. A radiobeacon is close NW of the light.

(21)   The gray octagonal, pyramidal tower 110 yards southwest of Cape Henry Light is the abandoned 1791 lighthouse.

(22)   **Local magnetic disturbance.**—Differences of as much as 6° from the normal variation have been observed 3 to 17 miles offshore from Cape Henry to Currituck Beach Light.

(23)   A **naval restricted area** extends northward and eastward from Cape Henry. (See **334.320,** chapter 2, for limits and regulations.)

(24)   The summer resort of **Virginia Beach** is about 5 miles southward of Cape Henry Light. Many high-rise buildings, two water tanks, and an aerobeacon 2.8 miles inland are prominent. A hotel cupola, 3.4 miles south of Cape Henry Light, is distinctive.

(25)   The **Chesapeake Bay Bridge-Tunnel** extends from Cape Charles across the bay entrance to a point 6 miles westward of Cape Henry. The 15-mile crossing has vehicular tunnels under Chesapeake Channel and Thimble Shoal Channel with fixed bridges over Fishermans Inlet and secondary channels. In addition to the channel buoys and lights, daybeacons and fog signals mark the openings at Chesapeake and Thimble Shoal Channels. At night the floodlighted tunnel houses are more prominent than the privately maintained lights marking the channels.

(26)   **Caution.**—The Chesapeake Bay Bridge-Tunnel complex has on several occasions suffered damage from vessels. In every case, adverse weather prevailed with accompanying strong winds from the northwest quadrant generally related to a frontal system. Weather deterioration in the lower bay is quite often sudden and violent and constitutes an extreme hazard to vessels operating or anchoring in this area. The proximity of the bridge-tunnel complex to main shipping channels and anchorages adds to the danger. Currents in excess of 3.0 knots can be expected in the area.

(27)   Normal precautions dictated by prudent seamanship are expected of all vessels. Mariners transiting this area are,

however, urged to be particularly alert in regards to the weather. To assist in this respect, the National Weather Service provides 24-hour weather broadcasting on 162.55 MHz. The local Marine Operator also transmits weather information at 0000, 0600, 1200, and 1800 local time on 2450 kHz and 2538 kHz. Information of a pending weather frontal passage should be met with advance preparations. Engines readied for short notice maneuvering and anchor details alerted are considered minimum prudent precautions. Maneuvering in close proximity of the bridge-tunnel complex is also discouraged.

(28)   A **Regulated Navigation Area** has been established in the waters of the Atlantic Ocean and in Chesapeake Bay. (See **165.1 through 165.13, and 165.501,** chapter 2, for limits and regulations.)

(29)   **Traffic Separation Schemes (Chesapeake Bay Entrance and Smith Point)** have been established for the control of maritime traffic at the entrance of Chesapeake Bay and off Smith Point Light (37°52.8'N., 76°11.0'W.). They have been designed to aid in the prevention of collisions, but are not intended in any way to supersede or alter the applicable Navigation Rules. (See Traffic Separation Schemes, chapter 1, for additional information.)

(30)   **Traffic Separation Scheme (Chesapeake Bay Entrance).**—The scheme provides for inbound-outbound traffic lanes to enter or depart Chesapeake Bay from the northeastward and from the southeastward. (See chart 12221.)

(31)   A precautionary area with a radius of 2 miles is centered on Chesapeake Bay Entrance Junction Lighted Gong Buoy CBJ (36°56.1'N., 75°57.5'W.).

(32)   The northeasterly inbound-outbound traffic lanes are separated by a line of four fairway buoys on bearing 250°–070°. The outermost buoy in the line is 6.4 miles 313° from Chesapeake Light and the innermost buoy is 4.5 miles 074° from Cape Henry Light.

(33)   The southeasterly approach is marked by Chesapeake Bay Southern Approach Lighted Whistle Buoy CB (36°49.0'N., 75°45.6'W.). A racon is on the buoy. The inbound/outbound traffic lanes are separated by a **Deep-Water Route** marked by lighted buoys on bearings 302°-122° and 317°-137°. The Deep-Water Route is intended for deep draft vessels and naval aircraft carriers entering or departing Chesapeake Bay. A vessel using the Deep-Water Route is advised to announce its intentions on VHF-FM channel 16 as it approaches Lighted Whistle Buoy CB on the south end, and Lighted Gong Buoy CBJ on the north end of the route. All other vessels approaching the Chesapeake Bay Traffic Separation Scheme should use the appropriate inbound/outbound lanes of the northeasterly or southeasterly approaches.

(34)   The Coast Guard advises that upon entering the traffic lanes, all inbound vessels are encouraged to make a security broadcast on VHF-FM channel 13, announcing the vessel's name, location, and intentions.

(35)   **Exercise extreme caution where the two routes converge off Cape Henry.** Mariners are also warned that vessels may be maneuvering in the pilotage area which extends into the western part of the precautionary area.

(36)   **Traffic Separation Scheme (Smith Point).**—The turn in the main channel in Chesapeake Bay off Smith Point is marked by a fairway buoy 1.5 miles 090° from Smith Point Light. Northbound traffic will pass eastward of the buoy, and southbound traffic will pass westward of the buoy.

(37)   **Channels.**—The deepest route to and from Chesapeake Bay is south of Chesapeake Light through the buoyed Deep-Water Route in the southeasterly approach. In September-October 1990, the controlling depth in the Deep-Water Route was 50 feet, except for a 47-foot spot in about

36°51'47"N., 75°51'06"W. The southeasterly approach inbound traffic lane has a controlling depth of about 40 feet, and the outbound lane has a controlling depth of about 47 feet. The route north of Chesapeake Light through the buoyed northeasterly approach traffic lanes has a controlling depth of about 29 feet in the inbound lane and about 34 feet in the outbound lane. Federal project main channel depths are 50 feet from the Virginia Capes to Baltimore and 55 feet from the Capes to Hampton Roads. (See Notice to Mariners and latest editions of charts for controlling depths.)

(38)   The well-marked channel to Baltimore is discussed further in chapters 11 to 15.

(39)   **Tides.**–The mean range of tide is 2.8 feet at Cape Henry.

(40)   **Currents.**–The current velocity is 1.0 knot on the flood and 1.5 knots on the ebb in Chesapeake Bay Entrance. (See the Tidal Current Tables for daily predictions.)

(41)   **Pilotage** is compulsory for all foreign vessels and for U.S. vessels under register in the foreign trade. Pilotage is optional for U.S. vessels under enrollment in the coastwise trade if they have on board a pilot licensed by the Federal Government to operate in these waters.

(42)   The Association of Maryland Pilots has an office in Baltimore (301–342–6013, 301–276–1337; cable address MARPILOT) and provides service to any port in Maryland. The Virginia Pilots Association has an office in Norfolk (804–496–0995; cable address VAPILOT) and provides service to any port in Virginia. Vessels bound for Washington, D.C. may take a pilot from either association.

(43)   A pilot boat from the Association of Maryland Pilots is stationed in the pilot cruising area off Cape Henry. The pilot boat, a 180-foot converted tugboat, has a black hull, white superstructure, and a blue stack with the number "1" in the center. The pilot boat monitors VHF-FM channels 16, 11, and 13. The pilot boat displays the standard day and night signals. The pilots are carried to and from the ships in 35- and 47-foot-long launches with blue hulls, white houses, and the word "PILOT" across the wheelhouses. The pilots carry portable radiotelephones for bridge-to-bridge communications on channel 13. Vessels proceeding from the Virginia Capes to Washington, D.C. or the upper part of Chesapeake Bay and northward, when using Maryland pilots, sometimes transfer pilots at a designated transfer area off Piney Point on the Potomac River or in Chesapeake Bay off the entrance to Patuxent River, depending on the port of call.

(44)   The Virginia Pilots Association maintains a pilot station at Cape Henry, just north of Cape Henry Light. The pilots monitor VHF-FM channels 11, 16, and 74. Other channels are used on request. Four pilot boats are stationed in Lynnhaven Inlet; two are in use at any given time. The pilot boats are 50 feet long with orange hulls and gray houses with the word "PILOT" on each side.

(45)   The Chesapeake and Interstate Pilots Association offers pilot services to vessels engaged in the coastwise trade and public vessels between Cape Henry and any port or place on the Chesapeake Bay and its tributaries. Arrangements for pilots are made through ships' agents or the pilot office in Norfolk (telephone, 804-855-2733; cable, CINPILOT). Pilots meet vessels day or night aboard the pilot boat "CHESAPEAKE II" which is black with a white house and the word "PILOT" on the sides. At night, the standard pilot lights are displayed. A 12-hour estimated time of arrival (ETA) is requested with any change greater than 1 hour being advised to the pilots. The pilot boat "CHESAPEAKE II" monitors VHF-FM channels 16 and 13 about 1 hour and 30 minutes prior to the vessel's ETA or

Departure and switches to VHF-FM channel 6 for working traffic. The pilot boat call sign is WTR 3711.

(46)   Vessels are usually boarded at Chesapeake Bay Entrance Lighted Junction Buoy CBJ, but with prior arrangement and if scheduling permits, vessels can be boarded at other places in the lower Chesapeake Bay.

(47)   The Interport Pilots Agency, Inc. offers pilotage to public and U.S. vessels in the coastwise trade transiting to Baltimore, the Chesapeake and Delaware Canal, Philadelphia, New York, Long Island Sound, Cape Cod Canal, and ports in the northeast. Arrangements for any of the above services are made in advance through ships' agents or with their office in Atlantic Highlands, N.J. (telephone 201-291-1310; cable, PORTPILOTS). An updated 12-hour estimated time of arrival (ETA) is requested.

(48)   The pilot boat "CHESAPEAKE II" is also used by Interport Pilots Agency,

(49)   It has been noted that sometimes considerable differences occur between a vessel's ETA and her actual arrival due to conditions encountered between Cape Hatteras and Cape Henry. Revisions to the ETA of 1 hour or greater should be passed to the pilots especially if the vessel's arrival will be sooner than previously advised.

(50)   **Charts 12254, 12222, 12256.**–**Thimble Shoal Channel,** the improved approach to Hampton Roads, begins 2.3 miles northwest of Cape Henry Light and extends 9.5 miles west-northwestward; a Federal project provides for a 55-foot-deep channel with a 32-foot-deep auxiliary channel on each side of the main channel. (See Notice to Mariners and latest editions of the charts for controlling depths.)

(51)   **Naval** and **general anchorages** are south of Thimble Shoal Channel. (See **110.1 and 110.168**, chapter 2, for limits and regulations.)

(52)   Thimble Shoal Channel is a **Regulated Navigation Area** and draft limitations apply. A vessel drawing less than 25 feet may not enter the channel, unless the vessel is crossing the channel. (See **165.501**, chapter 2, for limits and regulations.)

(53)   **Lynnhaven Roads,** an open bight westward of Cape Henry, is protected from southerly winds and is sometimes used as an anchorage. The former dumping-ground area in the western part of the bight has shoals and obstructions with depths as little as 11 feet; elsewhere, general depths are 20 to 28 feet Eastward of Lynnhaven Inlet, the 18-foot curve is no more than 0.3 mile from shore; westward of the inlet, the shoaling is gradual and depths of 18 feet can be found 0.8 mile from shore.

(54)   There are two small-craft openings in the Chesapeake Bay Bridge-Tunnel south of Thimble Shoal Channel. Each fixed span has a clearance of 21 feet.

(55)   **Lynnhaven Inlet,** 4 miles westward of Cape Henry Light, is subject to continual change. The inlet is marked by a lighted buoy, daybeacons, and lights. The twin fixed highway bridges over the inlet have a clearance of 35 feet. Overhead power cables close southward of the bridges have clearances of 68 feet. **Lynnhaven Bay,** south of the inlet, has depths of 1 to 10 feet.

(56)   A dredged channel marked by a light and daybeacons leads eastward from the south end of the inlet to **Broad Bay.** In May-July 1988, the controlling depths were 5½ feet (8 feet in the midchannel) in the channel leading eastward from the south end of the inlet to Daybeacon 6, thence 7 feet to Light 14 at the west end of Broad Bay. Another dredged channel leads eastward from just south of the bridges around the north side of a small island and connects with the southerly channel southeast of the island near Daybeacon 6. In May-July 1988, the midchannel controlling

depth was 8½ feet in the northerly channel. The Great Neck Road fixed highway bridge over the channel 1.2 miles from the twin bridges over the inlet has a clearance of 35 feet; nearby overhead power and telephone cables have a clearance of 55 feet. In 1987, twin fixed highway bridges with a design clearance of 36 feet were under construction about 0.5 mile east of the Great Neck Road bridge.

(57)   **Caution.**–It is reported that this channel has very heavy boat traffic and is especially congested on summer weekends.

(58)   An alternate route to Broad Bay is through **Long Creek** which branches northeastward from the dredged channel in the vicinity of Daybeacon 11. In June 1988, the controlling depth was 8 feet in Long Creek. The 40-foot span of the Great Neck Road Bridge over Long Creek has a clearance of 20 feet. Nearby overhead cables have a clearance of 37 feet. In 1987, twin fixed highway bridges with a design clearance of 36 feet were under construction about 0.5 mile east of the Great Neck Road bridge.

(59)   Depths are about 7 feet in Broad Bay. A marked channel with a midchannel controlling depth of 5 feet in June 1987, leads southeastward through **The Narrows** to the southern end of **Linkhorn Bay** near Virginia Beach.

(60)   Small-craft facilities are inside Lynnhaven Inlet and in both forks of Linkhorn Bay.

(61)   **Little Creek** is entered between jetties 8 miles westward of Cape Henry Light. Most of the creek comprises the **U. S. Naval Amphibious Base,** but the Virginia and Maryland Railroad operates car floats from the south end terminal to the town of Cape Charles on the Delmarva Peninsula; small craft use the west arm.

(62)   A dredged channel in Little Creek leads to a basin off the railroad terminal, 1.2 miles south of the jetties. In June 1987, the reported controlling depth was 20 feet in the channel and in the basin. The channel is marked by a **177°30′** lighted entrance range and by lights. **Little Creek Coast Guard Station** is eastward of the railroad terminal.

(63)   **Fishermans Cove,** on the west side of Little Creek, has fuel and berthing facilities for small craft. **A speed limit** of 5 knots is prescribed for Fishermans Cove. (See **33 CFR 165.509(d)(9),** chapter 2.)

(64)   Naval **danger zones** and **restricted areas** extend northward from the vicinity of Little Creek to the edge of Thimble Shoal Channel. (See **334.310** and **334.370,** chapter 2, for limits and regulations.)

(65)   **Chart 12245.**–**Hampton Roads,** at the southwest corner of Chesapeake Bay, is entered 16 miles westward of the Virginia Capes. It includes the Port of Norfolk, encompassing the cities of Norfolk, Portsmouth, and Chesapeake, and the Port of Newport News, which takes in the cities of Newport News and Hampton.

(66)   Hampton Roads is the world's foremost bulk cargo harbor. Coal, petroleum products, grain, sand and gravel, tobacco, and fertilizer constitute more than 90 percent of the heavy traffic movement by water, although an increasing amount of general cargo is handled by the Hampton Roads ports.

(67)   **Channels.**–The approach to Hampton Roads is through the 55-foot Thimble Shoal Channel. There are natural depths of 80 to 20 feet in the main part of Hampton Roads, but the harbor shoals to less than 10 feet toward the shores. Dredged channels lead to the principal ports.

(68)   Two main Federal project channels, marked by buoys, lead through Hampton Roads. One channel leads southward along the waterfronts of Norfolk, Portsmouth, and Chesapeake to the first bridge across the Southern Branch of Elizabeth River; project depths are 50 feet through Entrance Reach; thence 55 feet through Craney Island Reach at Lamberts Point; thence 40 feet to the bridge. The other channel with a 55-foot project depth leads westward to the waterfront at Newport News at the entrance to James River. (See Notice to Mariners and latest editions of the charts for controlling depths.)

(69)   **Anchorages.**–Numerous general, explosives, naval, and small-craft anchorages are in Hampton Roads and Elizabeth River. (See **110.1 and 110.168,** chapter 2, for limits and regulations.) The areas are shown on charts 12245 and 12253.

(70)   **Tides.**–The mean range of tide is 2.5 feet in Hampton Roads. (See Tide Tables for daily predictions of tides at Sewells Point.)

(71)   **Currents.**–Information for several places in Hampton Roads and Elizabeth River is given in the Tidal Current Tables. The currents are influenced considerably by the winds and at times attain velocities in excess of the tabulated values. The current velocity is about 1.0 knot in Hampton Roads and about 0.6 knot in Elizabeth River.

(72)   **Ice.**–Hampton Roads is free of ice. In severe winters the upper part of Southern Branch, Elizabeth River, is sometimes closed for short periods.

(73)   **Weather.**–The National Weather Service maintains an office at Norfolk International Airport; **barometers** in the Hampton Roads area can be compared there or checked by telephone.

(74)   **Pilotage** for Hampton Roads ports. (See Pilotage at the beginning of this chapter and chapter 3.)

(75)   **Towage.**–Vessels usually proceed from Cape Henry to points in the Hampton Roads port area under their own power and without assistance. A large fleet of tugs is available at Norfolk and Newport News to assist in docking or undocking and in shifting within the harbor.

(76)   **Quarantine, customs, immigration, and agricultural quarantine.**–(See chapter 3, Vessel Arrival Inspections, and appendix for addresses.)

(77)   **Quarantine** is enforced in accordance with regulations of the U.S. Public Health Service. (See Public Health Service, chapter 1.) The **quarantine anchorage** is southwestward of Old Point Comfort. The U.S. Naval Hospital is in Portsmouth.

(78)   Hampton Roads is a **customs port of entry.**

(79)   **Coast Guard.**–A **Marine Safety Office** is in Norfolk. (See appendix for address.)

(80)   **Harbor regulations.**–Port regulations are principally concerned with grain, coal handling, port charges, and pilotage and stevedoring rates. Copies of these regulations may be obtained from the Hampton Roads Maritime Association, 236 East Plume Street, P.O. Box 3528, Norfolk, Va. 23514.

(81)   **Anchorage regulations** are given in **110.1 and 110.168,** chapter 2.

(82)   **Wharves.**–The Hampton Roads area has more than 200 piers and wharves along more than 30 miles of improved waterfront; only the major deepwater facilities are described. Included are coal piers; containerized-cargo berths; oil storage and bunkering facilities; general-cargo, grain, and ore piers; and marine railways and drydocks. Available depths are 22 to 42 feet at the general-cargo, ore, and grain piers; 36 to 45 feet at the coal piers; and 20 to 42 feet at the oil-storage and bunkering facilities. A 350-ton floating crane is available.

(83)   **Supplies.**–The principal coal-handling and bunkering piers are those of the Norfolk and Western Railway at Lamberts Point, Norfolk, and of the Chesapeake and Ohio Railway at Newport News. Bunker oil is available at Sewells

Point, in Southern Branch of Elizabeth River, and at Newport News, or it can be delivered from barges in the stream. Freshwater is available on the principal piers and can be supplied from barges. The area also has numerous ship chandlers and marine suppliers.

(84) **Repairs.**–Hampton Roads has extensive facilities for drydocking and making major repairs to large deep-draft vessels. The largest floating drydock at Norfolk has a capacity of 54,000 tons, and the largest marine railway can handle 6,000 tons. The shipyard at Newport News is one of the largest and best equipped in the United States; the principal graving dock has a length of 1,600 feet on the keel blocks. There are many other yards that are especially equipped to handle medium-sized and small vessels. More details on these repair facilities are given with the discussion of the waterway or port in which they are located.

(85) **Small-craft facilities.**–Complete services and repairs are available at Hampton Roads ports. There are marine railways up to 11 tons and mobile hoists up to 60 tons for repairs. (See small-craft facilities tabulations on charts 12205 and 12206 for services and supplies available.)

(86) **Communications.**–Hampton Roads ports are served by a terminal beltline, several large railroads, and by more than 50 motor carriers. In addition, over 90 steamship lines connect Hampton Roads with the principal U.S. and foreign ports; most of the lines have regular sailings, and others maintain frequent but irregular service. Three airlines offer prompt airfreight, express, and passenger service from Norfolk and Newport News to major U.S. cities with connecting service overseas.

(87) **Thimble Shoal Light** (37°00.9′N., 76°14.4′W.), 55 feet above the water, is shown from a red conical tower on a brown cylindrical pier on the eastern edge of the shoal; a fog signal is sounded from the station. The light is 12.3 miles from the Virginia Capes. Thimble Shoal is the southern edge of **Horseshoe**, described in chapter 11.

(88) The entrance to Hampton Roads is between Willoughby Spit and Old Point Comfort, 2 miles to the northward.

(89) **A bridge-tunnel complex** crosses Chesapeake Bay from Willoughby Spit to Hampton.

(90) **Old Point Comfort** is the site of historic **Fort Monroe.** The Chamberlin Hotel is an excellent landmark. **Old Point Comfort Light** (37°00.1′N., 76°18.4′W.), 54 feet above the water, is shown from a white tower. Only Government craft can tie up at the wharf on the south waterfront of Old Point Comfort.

(91) A naval **restricted area** extends eastward and southward of Old Point Comfort, and a **danger zone** of an army firing range extends to seaward from a point 1.5 miles northward of the point. (See **334.350,** and **334.360,** chapter 2, respectively, for limits and regulations.)

(92) **Hampton Bar** begins about 200 yards southwestward of Old Point Comfort and extends 2 miles southwestward; depths on the bar are 1 to 5 feet. The bar is marked by two lights and by buoys along its southern edge. These lights, together with one on Hampton Flats, aid vessels in mooring in the naval and other anchorages northward of the main channel.

(93) A dredged channel, marked by a light and daybeacons, leads along the west side of Old Point Comfort to the fish wharves at **Phoebus.** In September 1980, the channel had a controlling depth of 11 feet. The wharves have depths of 8 to 12 feet at their outer ends, but are in poor condition. Small craft can anchor in depths of 8 to 20 feet along the sides of the channel. The Fort Monroe yacht piers are on the east side of the channel 0.4 mile above Old Point Comfort.

(94) **Hampton River,** 1.5 miles westward of Old Point Comfort, is entered by a marked channel through Hampton Bar and Flats to a point just below the highway bridge at Hampton. Federal project depths are 12 feet. (See Notice to Mariners and latest editions of the charts for controlling depths.) Some small craft also enter west of Hampton Bar. **Hampton,** on the west side of the river 2 miles above the channel entrance, is an important seafood center. Traffic on the river consists of seafood and petroleum products, sand and gravel, and building materials. The residential and commercial areas of Hampton are on the west side of Hampton River; **Hampton Institute** and a Veterans Hospital are on the east side.

(95) **Sunset Creek,** on the west side just above the Hampton River mouth, is entered by a marked dredged channel leading westward from the channel in the river. In December 1980, the controlling depth was 12 feet to the head of the creek.

(96) The principal commercial wharves at Hampton, just below the bridge, have depths of 7 to 12 feet at their faces. The public landing 500 yards below the bridge has depths of 8 feet at the face; small boats anchor between the public landing and the bridge. The wharves along Sunset Creek have depths of 4 to 9 feet at their outer ends.

(97) Supplies and fuel are available at Hampton. A yacht club and several marinas here have berthing space. Repairs can be made; largest marine railway, 120 feet; lift, 35 tons.

(98) **Jones Creek,** on the east side of Hampton River 300 yards above the mouth, has depths of 8 to 11 feet. The bulkheads have depths of 3 to 10 feet alongside and are controlled by the Veterans Hospital on the south and Hampton Institute on the north.

(99) **Salters Creek,** 4 miles west-southwestward of Old Point Comfort, has a narrow unmarked approach channel with depths of 2 feet. The fixed highway bridge over the entrance has a channel width of 24 feet and a clearance of 9 feet. Numerous small craft moor above the bridge in a basin that has depths of about 5 feet.

(100) The 55-foot project channel to Newport News was discussed earlier. Depths along the edges of the dredged section are 19 to 25 feet. The currents do not always set fair with the channel, especially with strong winds, and deep-draft vessels sometimes find it difficult to stay in the channel.

(101) **Newport News Middle Ground Light** (36°56.7′N., 76°23.5′W.), 52 feet above the water, is shown from a red conical tower on a red cylindrical pier in 15 feet of water near the western end of the shoal; a seasonal fog signal is at the light.

(102) **Newport News Point** (36°57.8′N., 76°24.7′W.) on the north side of the entrance to James River, is 21.5 miles from the Virginia Capes. The city of **Newport News** extends several miles along the northeast bank of James River.

(103) **Newport News Creek,** just west of Newport News Point is a city-owned small-boat harbor used by fishing boats, pleasure craft, and petroleum barges. In January 1985, the controlling depth was 12 feet in the dredged channel for about 0.6 mile above the mouth. Fuel, supplies, and slips are available, and repairs can be made. A 75-ton marine railway and a 40-ton mobile hoist are available.

(104) Newport News Shipbuilding and Drydock Company is just below the James River Bridge on the east side of the river. A security zone is along the waterfront of the company property. (See **165.30, 165.33 and 165.504,** chapter 2, for limits and regulations.)

(105) **Wharves.**–The deepwater piers and wharves at Newport News extend from Newport News Point for 2.5 miles up James River. Only the major facilities are described. All

have access to highways and railroads, freshwater connections, and electric shore-power connections. Unless otherwise indicated, these facilities are owned by the Virginia Ports Authority. The alongside depths given for each facility described are reported depths. (For information on the latest depths, contact the operator.) For a complete description of the port facilities at Newport News, refer to Port Series No. 11, published and sold by the U.S. Army Corps of Engineers. (See appendix for address.)

(106) **Chart 12245:**
(107) **Newport News Marine Terminal Pier 2** (36°58′24″N., 76°26′00″W.): north and south sides 606 feet long; 32 feet along north side, 35 feet along south side; deck height, 8 feet; receipt and shipment of bulk cargo; operated by Virginia International Terminals.

(108) **Newport News Marine Terminal Pier B:** about 200 yards southeastward of Newport News Marine Terminal Pier 2; 543-foot face, north and south sides 620 feet long; 35 feet along north side, 40 feet along south side and face; deck height, 15 feet; 268,000 square feet covered storage; 8 acres of open storage; receipt and shipment of general and roll-on/roll-off cargo; operated by Virginia International Terminals.

(109) **Newport News Marine Terminal Pier C:** about 150 yards southeastward of Newport News Marine Terminal Pier B; 552-foot face, 35 feet alongside; north side, 755 feet long; 35 feet alongside; south side, 935 feet long; 40 feet alongside; 410,000 square feet covered storage; 200-ton-capacity container crane, 50-ton gantry crane; use of equipment from Pier B; receipt and shipment of general, containerized and roll-on/roll-off cargo; operated by Virginia International Terminals.

(110) **Pier 8 Terminal:** about 700 yards southeastward of Newport News Marine Terminal Pier 2; 213-foot face; north and south sides 818 feet long; 32 feet alongside; deck height, 15 feet; 138,000 square feet covered storage; 20-ton crane available, forklift trucks; receipt of general cargo; operated by Tidewater Stevedoring Corp.

(111) **Massey Coal Terminal Pier 9** (36°58′05″N., 76°25′44″W.): east and west sides 1,200 feet long; 46 feet alongside; deck height, 11½ feet; tandem in-line rotary car dumper with unloading rate of 5,000 tons per hour; traveling shiploader with loading rate of 8,000 tons per hour; receipt and shipment of coal; owned and operated by Massey Coal Terminal Corp.

(112) **C. & O. Pier 14:** about 0.75 mile southeastward of Pier 8 Terminal; east and west sides 1,090 feet long; 45 feet alongside; deck height, 11½ feet; two traveling coal-loading towers, 4,500-ton-per-hour capacity each; shipment of coal; owned and operated by the Chessie System.

(113) **C. & O. Pier 15:** eastward of C. & O. Pier 14: west side 1,000 feet long; 38 feet alongside; deck height, 9½ feet; one fixed coal-loading tower on each side of the pier, ship-positioning winches; shipment of coal; owned and operated by the Chessie System. East side is not used.

(114) **Koch Fuels, Inc. Tanker Dock:** about 200 yards eastward of C. & O. Pier 15; offshore wharf, 203 feet with platform; 35 feet alongside; deck height, 13 feet; storage tanks, 520,000-barrel capacity; receipt and shipment of petroleum products, bunkering vessels; operated by Koch Fuels, Inc.

(115) The facilities of the Newport News Shipbuilding and Drydock Co. begin 1.7 miles northwest of Newport News Point and extend 2 miles upriver. The company operates five outfitting piers; four drydocks, the largest being 862 feet long, 118 feet wide, and a depth of 31 feet over the sill; and three graving docks used for ship construction and repair, the largest being 1,600 feet long and 250 feet wide with a depth over the sill of 33 feet. Gantry cranes of 900 and 310 tons serve the graving docks. The shipyard also has two inclining shipways with lengths to 650 feet. The largest shaft produced by the shipyard is 76 feet by 60 inches. Most of the outfitting piers are equipped with cranes; largest has a capacity of 50 tons. Floating derricks up to 67-ton capacity are available at the yard.

(116) **Willoughby Spit,** on the south side of the entrance to Hampton Roads, is a narrow barrier beach 1.3 miles long in an east-west direction. About midway between the spit and Old Point Comfort, on the opposite side of the entrance, is **Fort Wool,** which is on the south edge of the main ship channel; a light is shown from a small gray house on the north side of the island.

(117) The 45-foot-wide small-boat openings in the south approach bridge to Hampton Roads Tunnel have clearances of 10 feet.

(118) **Willoughby Bank,** with depths of 3 to 7 feet, extends east-northeastward along the edge of the main channel for about 2.5 miles from Fort Wool.

(119) **Willoughby Bay,** on the inner side of Willoughby Spit, has general depths of 7 to 12 feet. On the south side of the bay are the prominent buildings of the Norfolk Naval Base and the Naval Air Station. A marked channel, 0.4 mile westward of Fort Wool, leads to a small-boat harbor behind the hook of Willoughby Spit. In September 1987, the controlling depth was 5½ feet. Some supplies, fuel, and berthing are available. Repairs can be made; largest marine railway, 40 feet.

(120) The western and southern part of Willoughby Bay is a **restricted area.** (See **334.300,** chapter 2, for limits and regulations.) The northern part of the bay is a **small-craft anchorage.** (See **110.1** and **110.168 (f)** and **(h)),** chapter 2, for limits and regulations.)

(121) A fixed highway bridge with a clearance of 25 feet crosses the yacht anchorage in the northern part of Willoughby Bay.

(122) **Charts 12245, 12253.–Norfolk Harbor** comprises a portion of the southern and eastern shores of Hampton Roads and both shores of **Elizabeth River** and its Eastern, Southern, and Western Branches, on which the cities of Norfolk, Portsmouth, and Chesapeake are located.

(123) The harbor extends from off Sewells Point south in Elizabeth River to the seventh bridge over Southern Branch, a distance of 15 miles; it extends 1.5 miles up Western Branch to a point 0.5 mile above the West Norfolk highway bridge, and up Eastern Branch for 2.5 miles to the Norfolk and Western Railway Bridge.

(124) The main part of Norfolk is on the east side of Elizabeth River north of Eastern Branch, with Berkley, a subdivision, to the southward between Eastern and Southern Branches. South of Berkley is the city of Chesapeake. Portsmouth is opposite Norfolk, and its waterfront extends along the west shore of Southern Branch and the south shore of Western Branch. These cities form practically a single community, united by the same commercial interests and served by the same ship channel.

(125) A **safety zone** is in effect in the Elizabeth River when a naval aircraft carrier transits the river to or from the Norfolk Naval Shipyard. (See **165.505,** chapter 2, for limits and regulations.)

(126) **Weather.–**Norfolk, with an average elevation of 13 feet above sea level and almost surrounded by water, has a modified marine climate. The city's geographic position with respect to the principal storm tracks is especially favorable, being south of the average path of storms originating in the higher latitudes and north of the usual

track of hurricanes and other tropical storms. These features combine to place Norfolk in one of the favored climatic regions of the world. The winters are mild, while autumn and spring seasons usually are delightful. Summers, though warm and long, frequently are tempered by cool periods, often associated with northeasterly winds off the Atlantic. Temperatures of 100° or higher are very infrequent. Cold waves seldom penetrate to this area. Occasional winters pass without a measurable amount of snowfall. Most of Norfolk's snow generally occurs in light falls, which usually melt and disappear within 24 hours. The average date of the last freezing temperature in the spring is March 23, while the average date of the first in autumn is November 18. The average annual amount of rainfall is about 45 inches, and considerably more than one-half of it falls in well-distributed amounts during April to October, inclusive. (See page T–4 **Norfolk climatological table.)**

(127)   **Chart 12245.–Sewells Point** (36°57.8′N., 76°19.6′W.), on the east side of the entrance to Elizabeth River, is 18 miles from the Virginia Capes. A breakwater, marked by a light on its outer end, extends about 0.3 mile westward from the point. The piers of the **Norfolk Naval Base** and its annex extend southward from the breakwater along the east bank of the river. Depths at the naval piers are 33 to 45 feet. A jettied basin at the naval base, 0.6 mile south of Sewells Point, affords protection for navy service craft in depths of 21 to 29 feet.

(128)   **Sewells Point Spit,** covered 3 to 6 feet, extends north-northeastward from the point for 1.4 miles to the outer end of Willoughby Channel.

(129)   A channel, marked by lights and daybeacons, extends eastward and southward through Sewells Point Spit for about 1.2 miles to an enclosed boat basin used by small navy boats. In May 1974, the channel had a controlling depth of 10 feet; depths of 7 to 10 feet were available in the basin.

(130)   The approach to the naval piers is a **restricted area.** (See **334.300(b)(1),** chapter 2, for limits and regulations.)

(131)   **Wharves.–**Norfolk Harbor has numerous wharves and piers of all types, the majority of which are privately owned and operated; only the major deepwater facilities are described. These facilities are southward of Sewells Point, between the Norfolk Naval Base and Tanner Point; on Lamberts Point; on Pinner Point; and on Eastern Branch and Southern Branch of Elizabeth River. All have freshwater connections and access to highways and railroads, and most have electrical shore-power connections. Cargo is generally handled by ship's tackle; special cargo-handling equipment, if available, is mentioned in the description of the particular facility. The alongside depths given for each facility described are reported depths. (For information on the latest depths, contact the operator.) For a complete description of the wharves and piers in Norfolk Harbor refer to Port Series No. 11, published and sold by the U.S. Army Corps of Engineers. (See appendix for address.)

(132)   **Facilities southward of Sewells Point, between Norfolk Naval Base and Tanner Point (chart 12245):**

(133)   **Continental Grain Co. Wharf** (36°55′57″N., 76°19′41″W.): face 1,035 feet; 40 feet alongside; deck height 9 feet; face of wharf in line and contiguous with Virginia Ports Authority Pier B to the westward; 3¼-million-bushel grain elevator; railroad car and truck dumpers; loading tower, marine leg, and conveyor system, combined loading rate 80,000 bushels per hour; receipt and shipment of grains; owned by Virginia Port Authority and operated by Continental Grain Co.

(134)   **Sewells Point Division, Piers A and B:** immediately westward of Continental Grain Co. Wharf; 498-foot face, 32 feet alongside; Pier B (north side) 1,211 feet long, 32 feet alongside; Pier A (south side) 1,193 feet long, 32 feet alongside; deck height, 9½ feet; 230,000 square feet covered storage; cranes up to 15-ton capacity; receipt and shipment of general cargo and shipment of scrap metal; owned by Virginia Ports Authority and operated by Lamberts Point Docks, Inc. A buoy marks a shoal just northward of Pier B.

(135)   **Lehigh Portland Cement Pier:** 150 yards southward of Virginia Ports Authority Piers; 40-foot face, 205 feet with dolphins; 33 feet alongside; deck height, 11½ feet; 33,000-ton storage capacity; unloading rate 600 tons per hour; receipt of bulk cement; owned and operated by Lehigh Portland Cement Co.

(136)   **Exxon Co., U.S.A. Pier** (36°55′39″N., 76°20′00″W.): about 0.2 mile southward of Sewells Point Division Piers; north and south sides 1,300 feet; north side, 40 feet alongside; south side, 20 to 30 feet alongside; deck height, 9 feet; storage tanks, 2½-million-barrel capacity; receipt and shipment of petroleum products, bunkering vessels; owned and operated by Exxon Co., U.S.A.

(137)   **Norfolk International Terminals:** 900,000 square feet covered storage; 300,000 cubic feet cold storage; 55 acres open storage; deck heights, 9½ feet; receipt and shipment of general and containerized cargo; receipt of logs; passengers; owned by Virginia Ports Authority and operated by Virginia International Terminals.

(138)   **Pier 2** (36°55′02″N., 76°19′56″W.): 334-foot face, north and south sides 1,328 feet long; 35 feet along north side, 42 feet along south side.

(139)   **North Berth:** immediately northward of Pier 2; 950-foot marginal wharf; 32 feet alongside; roll-on/roll-off berth.

(140)   **Pier 1:** about 200 yards southward of Pier 2; 308-foot face, north and south sides 1,320 feet long; 42 feet along north side, 35 feet along south side; fumigation chambers.

(141)   **Container Berths 1, 2, 3, and 4:** immediately southward of Pier 1; 2,688-foot marginal wharf; 35 to 41 feet alongside; one 30-ton and three 40-ton dual hoist cranes, three 40-ton traveling container carriers.

(142)   **Facilities at Lamberts Point (chart 12253):**

(143)   **Norfolk and Western Railway Co. Piers:** owned and operated by Norfolk and Western Railway Co.; shipment of coal.

(144)   **Pier 6** (36°52′45″N., 76°19′54″W.): 88-foot face; 45 feet alongside; north and south sides 1,600 feet, 1,850 feet with dolphins, 50 feet alongside; deck height, 11 feet; two electric shiploaders, loading rate 5,000 tons per hour each.

(145)   **Pier 5:** about 200 yards southward of Pier 6; 74-foot face; north and south sides 1850 feet; 36 feet alongside; deck height, 11 feet; one electric dumper with a loading capacity of 1,000 tons per hour; ship-positioning winches on south side.

(146)   **Virginia Ports Authority Terminal, Piers N, L, and P:** 1.5 million square feet covered storage; 100,000 cubic feet cold storage space; fumigation chambers; storage tanks, 10,000-ton capacity; forklift trucks and other portable mechanized cargo-handling equipment; cranes up to 25-ton capacity; receipt and shipment of general and containerized cargo; receipt of castor oil and shipment of soybean, palm and coconut oils; owned by Virginia Ports Authority and operated by Lamberts Point Docks, Inc.

(147)   **Pier N** (36°52′00″N., 76°19′06″W.): 390-foot face, 24 feet alongside; north and south sides 1,100 feet long, 32 feet alongside; deck height, 11½ feet.

(148)   **Pier L:** about 200 yards southeastward of Pier N; 243-foot face; north side 1,180 feet, south side 1,200 feet long; 32 feet alongside; deck height, 9 feet.

(149)   Pier P: about 600 yards southeastward of Pier N; 396-foot face; north and south sides 1,196 feet long; 32 feet alongside; deck height, 11 feet.

(150)   **Facilities at Port Norfolk (chart 12253):**

(151)   **Portsmouth Marine Terminal** (36°51′27″N., 76°19′27″W.): 2,536-foot face; 60-foot roll-on/roll-off ramp; 36 feet alongside except 31 feet near the west end; deck height, 12 feet; 200,000 square feet covered storage, 215 acres open storage; cranes to 110 tons, container cranes to 30 tons; fumigation chambers; receipt and shipment of general, containerized and roll-on/roll-off cargo; receipt of automobiles; shipment of tobacco; owned by Virginia Ports Authority and operated by Virginia International Terminals.

(152)   **Sea-Land Service Terminal** (36°51′28″N., 76°19′04″W.): 600-foot face, 1,000 feet with dolphins; 38 feet alongside; deck height, 12 feet; 30,000 square feet covered storage, open storage for 650 containers; two 30-ton container cranes; receipt and shipment of general and containerized cargo; owned and operated by Sea-Land Service, Inc.

(153)   **Facilities in Eastern Branch of Elizabeth River (chart 12253):**

(154)   **Norfolk, Baltimore, and Carolina Line Terminal:** 33,000 square feet covered storage area; receipt and shipment of containerized general cargo in the intracoastal trade; owned and operated by the Norfolk, Baltimore, and Carolina Line, Inc.

(155)   Pier No. 2 (36°50′33″N., 76°17′07″W.): 68-foot face; 20 feet alongside; deck height, 8 feet.

(156)   Pier No. 1: about 50 yards eastward of Pier 2; 46-foot face, 20 feet alongside; deck height, 8 feet.

(157)   **Chemphalt Wharf** (36°50′19″N., 76°16′19″W.): 50-foot offshore wharf with 300 feet of berthing space with dolphins; 35 feet alongside; deck height, 9 feet; storage tanks, 300,000-barrel capacity; receipt of asphalt, liquid fertilizer, and styrene monomer; owned and operated by Chemphalt of Carolina Corp.

(158)   **Facilities in Southern Branch of Elizabeth River, Berkley, Chesapeake, and Portsmouth (chart 12253):**

(159)   **U.S. Gypsum Co. Wharf** (36°49′18″N., 76°17′23″W.): 40-foot offshore wharf, 370 feet with dolphins; 27 feet alongside; deck height, 10 feet; storage shed, 47,000-ton capacity; open storage for 100,000 tons; receipt of gypsum rock; owned and operated by U. S. Gypsum Co.

(160)   **Crown Central Petroleum Corp. Wharf** (36°49′14″N., 76°17′24″W.): 40-foot T-head pier, 145 feet with dolphins; 30 feet alongside; deck height, 6 feet; 214,000-barrel storage capacity; receipt and shipment of petroleum products; operated by Crown Central Petroleum Corp.

(161)   **Mobil Oil Corp. Tanker Wharf** (36°49′11″N., 76°17′23″W.): 75-foot T-head wharf, 750 feet with dolphins; 36 feet alongside; deck height, 10 feet; receipt and shipment of petroleum products, bunkering vessels; 683,000-barrel storage facility; owned by Mobil Oil Corp., operated by Mobil Oil Corp., and Union Oil Co. of California.

(162)   **Gulf Oil Co. Wharf:** 200 yards south of Mobil Oil Wharf; 1,020-foot face, 30 to 32 feet alongside; deck height, 12 feet; receipt and shipment of petroleum products, bunkering vessels; 800,000-barrel storage facility; owned and operated by Gulf Oil Refining and Marketing Co.

(163)   **Lone Star Industries, Cement Wharf:** 100 yards south of Gulf Oil Co. Wharf; 27-foot platforms with 267 feet of berthing space; 35 feet alongside; deck height, 10 feet; silos, 37,000-ton capacity; receipt of cement clinker; owned and operated by Lone Star Industries, Inc.

(164)   **Royster Co. Wharf** (36°48′46″N., 76°17′24″W.): marginal type wharf, 450 feet with dolphins; 25 feet alongside; deck height, 9 feet; shipment of fertilizer products; owned and operated by Royster Co.

(165)   **Amoco Oil Co. Wharf** (36°48′21″N., 76°17′22″W.): 60-foot T-head pier, 235 feet with dolphins; 27 to 29 feet alongside; deck height, 11 feet; 655,000-barrel storage facility; receipt and shipment of petroleum products; receipt of asphalt; shipment of soybean oil; bunkering vessels; owned and operated by Amoco Oil Co.

(166)   **Cargill Grain South Elevator Dock** (36°48′06″N., 76°17′20″W.): 500-foot face 39 feet alongside; deck height, 10 feet; 6¾-million-bushel elevator; elevator loading rate 60,000 bushels per hour; shipment of grain and soybean meal; owned and operated by Cargill Inc.

(167)   **Texaco Oil Co. Wharf** (36°47′51″N., 76°17′29″W.): marginal wharf, 565 feet with dolphins; 32 feet alongside; deck height, 12 feet; 1½-million-barrel storage capacity; receipt and shipment of petroleum products; receipt of asphalt; bunkering vessels; owned and operated by Texaco Inc.

(168)   **Conoco Wharf** (36°47′44″N., 76°17′32″W.): 145-foot T-head wharf, 650 feet with dolphins; 31 feet alongside; deck height, 10 feet; receipt and shipment of petroleum products; 700,000-barrel storage facility; owned and operated by Conoco.

(169)   **Lone Star Industries Ulexite Plant Pier** (36°47′27″N., 76°17′50″W.): north side, 447 feet long; 36 feet alongside; deck height, 12 feet; open storage for 27,000 tons; receipt and shipment of pumice and ulexite, shipment of fertilizer; owned and operated by Lone Star Industries, Inc.

(170)   **Tenneco-Cities Service Pier** (36°47′22″N., 76°18′07″W.): 55-foot face, 208 feet with dolphins; 27 feet alongside; deck height, 8 feet; storage tanks, 350,000-barrel capacity; receipt and shipment of petroleum products; receipt of creosote and coal tar; owned and operated by Tenneco-Cities Service.

(171)   **Amerada Hess Corp. Tanker Dock** (36°47′06″N., 76°18′10″W.): 68-foot offshore wharf with berthing space for vessels to 700 feet; 35 feet alongside; deck height, 13½ feet; tanks, 500,000-barrel storage capacity; receipt and shipment of petroleum products; owned and operated by Amerada Hess Corp.

(172)   **Atlantic Cement Co. Wharf** (36°46′42″N., 76°18′22″W.): 465 feet long with dolphins; 30 to 31 feet alongside; deck height, 10½ feet; 31,000-ton capacity storage silos; receipt of bulk cement; owned and operated by Atlantic Cement Co.

(173)   **Elizabeth River Terminals, Piers 1 and 2** (36°46′40″N., 76°18′05″W.): Pier 1, 1200 feet long with dolphins; 35 feet alongside; deck height, 8½ feet; Pier 2, 750 feet long with dolphins; 14 feet alongside; deck height, 11 feet; 225,000 square feet covered storage; 350,000 square feet of open storage; 36,000 tons of tank storage; cranes to 50 tons; receipt and shipment of liquid sulfur; receipt of chemicals, scrap metals, and bulk materials; shipment of fertilizer and animal feed; owned and operated by Elizabeth River Terminals, Inc.

(174)   **Chilean Nitrate Wharf** (36°46.6′N., 76°17.7′W.): 350-foot offshore wharf, 395 feet with dolphins; 32 feet alongside; deck height, 11 feet; covered storage for 28,000 tons of fertilizer; receipt of bulk fertilizers; owned and operated by the Chilean Nitrate Sales Corp.

(175)   **Smith-Douglass Wharf** (36°46′25″N., 76°17′40″W.): 365-foot face, 500 feet long with dolphins; 30 feet alongside; deck height, 12 feet; covered storage for 65,000 tons of fertilizer; receipt of spent sulphuric acid; owned and operated by Smith-Douglass Division of Borden Chemical Co.

(176) **Hitch Terminal Tanker Wharf** (36°46′21″N., 76°17′51″W.): 30-foot offshore wharf, 200 feet long with dolphins; 30 feet alongside; deck height, 8 feet; tank storage for nitrogen, capacity 146,000 barrels, petroleum tank storage, capacity 323,000 barrels; receipt of liquid nitrogen; owned by Arthur Hitch, Jr.; operated by Hitch Terminal Corp. and Swift Nitrogen Terminal.

(177) **American Hoechst Corp. Wharf** (36°45′28″N., 76°17′37″W.): offshore wharf, 190 feet long with dolphins; 22 feet alongside; deck height, 10 feet; storage tanks for 120,000 barrels; receipt of styrene monomer; owned and operated by American Hoechst Corp.

(178) **Portsmouth Power Station Wharf** (36°46′11″N., 76°17′55″W.): 75-foot face, berthing space for vessels to 800 feet; 36 feet alongside; deck height, 10 feet; storage tanks for 475,000 barrels; receipt of fuel oils for plant consumption; owned and operated by Virginia Electric and Power Co.

(179) **Swann Oil Co. Wharf** (36°46′36″N., 76°18′25″W.): 50-foot T-head pier, 280 feet with dolphins; 35 feet alongside; deck height, 12 feet; 850,000-barrel storage facility; receipt of petroleum products; owned and operated by Swann Oil Co.

(180) **Atlantic Energy, Inc. Wharf** (36°46′43″N., 76°18′41″W.): 30-foot offshore wharf, 700 feet of berthing with dolphins; 32 feet alongside; storage tanks, 480,000-barrel capacity; receipt of liquified petroleum gases; owned and operated by Atlantic Energy, Inc.

(181) **Alcoa Transfer Station Pier** (39°47′54″N., 76°17′42″W.): 750 feet long; 42 feet alongside; deck height, 15 feet; 55,000-ton storage tank; unloading tower with unloading rate of 1,100 tons per hour; and conveyor system to storage tank; receipt of alumina; owned and operated by Aluminum Co. of America.

(182) **BP Oil Co. Wharf** (36°47′57″N., 76°17′45″W.): 317-foot offshore wharf, 360 feet of berthing with dolphins; 30 feet alongside; deck height, 12 feet; storage tanks, 410,000-barrel capacity; shipment of petroleum products; owned and operated by the BP Oil Co., Inc.

(183) **Allied Mills Wharf** (36°48′00″N., 76°17′45″W.): 81-foot face, 275 feet of berthing with dolphins; 25 feet alongside; deck height, 12 feet; receipt of bulk molasses; 2-million-gallon molasses storage tank; grain elevator, 375,000-bushel capacity; owned by Allied Mills Inc.; operated by Southgate Molasses Co. Inc.

(184) A disposal area, enclosed by levees, is in Hampton Roads on the north side of Craney Island. A smaller levee extends eastward from the lower east side of the disposal area to a dolphin 0.2 mile west of the ship channel; the section of the levee east of about 36°54.0′N., 76°20.8′W. covers at high water.

(185) **Lafayette River** empties into the east side of Elizabeth River 4 miles south of Sewells Point and 22 miles from the Virginia Capes. The river, used exclusively by pleasure and recreational craft, is entered by a marked dredged channel between **Tanner Point** and Lamberts Point, 1.5 miles to the southward. A light, 0.6 mile south of Tanner Point, marks the channel entrance. The dredged channel leads for 1.1 miles to a point about 0.3 mile westward of the Hampton Boulevard Bridge. From this point, a marked natural channel leads for about 2.4 miles to where the river divides into two forks. In August 1984, the controlling depth was 8 feet in the dredged section; thence depths of about 6 feet to the forks, and 2 to 4 feet up each fork; the chart is the best guide. The dredged channel turns sharply at the light off **Lawless Point,** a mile above the entrance, and vessels must be on the alert to avoid grounding. **General and small-craft anchorages** extend up Lafayette River to the first bridge.

(See **110.168 (c) and (h),** chapter 2, for limits and regulations.)

(186) **Hampton Boulevard Bridge,** 1.5 miles above the entrance to Lafayette River, has a fixed channel span with a clearance of 26 feet. A yacht club is just below the north end of the bridge.

(187) **Knitting Mill Creek,** is on the south side of Lafayette River about 3 miles above the mouth. In May 1985, the creek had a midchannel controlling depth of 4 feet to the head. Some supplies, gasoline, and berths are available within the creek. Repairs can be made; largest marine railway, 40 feet; lift, 10 tons.

(188) **East Haven,** on the south side of Lafayette River about 3.5 miles above the mouth, has a dredged channel that leads to a settling basin and boat ramp at the head. In January 1981, a controlling depth of 6 feet was in the channel and 8 feet in the basin.

(189) **Granby Street Bridge,** 3.5 miles above the entrance to Lafayette River, has a 40-foot fixed span with a clearance of 22 feet.

(190) Just above Granby Street Bridge (chart 12253), Lafayette River divides into two forks, both unmarked. A fixed highway bridge over the mouth of the north fork has a channel width of 30 feet and a clearance of 10 feet. In 1986, a replacement fixed bridge with a design clearance of 18 feet was under construction adjacent to the existing bridge. A fixed highway bridge over the south fork, a mile from Granby Street Bridge, has a channel width of 27 feet and a clearance of 9 feet; another fixed highway bridge 0.3 mile farther up the south fork has a channel width of 23 feet and a clearance of 4 feet.

(191) **Chart 12253.–Craney Island,** now a part of the mainland, is on the west side of Elizabeth River 4.5 miles south of Sewells Point. The low and thinly wooded area is the site of a navy fuel depot, and the offshore wharf and piers, all on the eastern side, are used only by Government vessels. Two daybeacons close off the northeast end of Craney Island mark submerged rocks. The offshore wharf and piers have depths of 22 to 47 feet alongside. A submerged water main crosses from Craney Island to the north side of Lamberts Point; vessels are cautioned not to anchor in the vicinity of the lighted range that marks the crossing. **Portsmouth Coast Guard Station** is on the west side of the entrance to Craney Island Creek.

(192) **Lamberts Point,** on the east side of Elizabeth River 5.3 miles south of Sewells Point, is the site of several deep-water piers. These facilities were described earlier in this chapter under Wharves, Norfolk Harbor.

(193) **Western Branch** (36°52.0′N., 76°19.7′W.) empties into the southwest side of Elizabeth River 5.8 miles south of Sewells Point and 23.8 miles from the capes. A marked channel leads from the main channel in Elizabeth River for 4.5 miles upstream. In June-July 1987, the midchannel controlling depth was 18 feet in the dredged channel to about 0.25 mile above the first bridge; then in 1980, about 7 feet could be carried to **Drum Point,** 0.5 mile above the third bridge.

(194) A 540-foot lighted pier about 1 mile above the entrance to Western Branch extends to the northern edge of the marked channel; mariners are advised to use caution in the area. A fixed highway bridge, about 1.2 miles above the entrance, has a clearance of 45 feet.

(195) **West Norfolk,** northward of the fixed bridge, has a shipyard and small-craft facilities. Supplies, fuel, and slips are available. Repairs can be made; largest marine railway, 220 feet.

(196) **Churchland** twin fixed highway bridges, 2.3 miles above the entrance to Western Branch, have clearances of 38 feet. The overhead power cable on the upper side of the bridge has a clearance of 45 feet; the transmission towers are marked by lights.

(197) A 280-foot fishing pier extends from the southeast shore about 1.4 miles above the Churchland bridges. An overhead power cable close upstream of the pier has a clearance of 47 feet. **Hodges Ferry** fixed highway bridge, 4.7 miles above the entrance, has a clearance of 18 feet. The overhead power cable on the upstream side of the Hodges Ferry bridge has a clearance of 37 feet.

(198) **Pinner Point** (36°51.3'N., 76°19.1'W.) is on the southwest side of Elizabeth River, 6.8 miles from Sewells Point. Most of the piers at the point have been destroyed by fire or are in poor condition; they are being razed or renovated. The Portsmouth Marine Terminals, Inc. operates the facilities at the Portsmouth Marine Terminal about 0.3 mile northwestward of Pinner Point. A marked dredged channel leads from Elizabeth River to a docking area at the terminal. In July 1979, the controlling depth to and in the docking area was 35 feet. The facilities of the Portsmouth Marine Terminal and those at Pinner Point were described earlier in this chapter under Wharves, Norfolk Harbor.

(199) **Scott Creek** (36°51.1'N., 76°18.5'W.), on the southwest side of Elizabeth River 7.3 miles from Sewells Point, is entered through a channel, marked by daybeacons, which had a controlling depth of 4½ feet in March 1971. The channel leads to old fishing wharves now used by pleasure craft. A marina with a 60-ton lift is on the S side of the creek about 0.4 mile above channel entrance. A marina is on the point on the south side of the creek, about 0.9 mile above the channel entrance. Berths, water, a 60-foot marine railway, and a 3½-ton fixed lift are available; hull repairs can be made.

(200) **Hospital Point,** on the southwest side of Elizabeth River 7.5 miles from Sewells Point, is the site of a U.S. Naval Hospital. The main hospital building, the largest structure along the southwest side of Elizabeth River, is visible for many miles. The hospital landing has depths of about 18 feet at the face.

(201) **Norfolk,** or parts of it, has been described at some length in the preceding text. The midpoint of the downtown section can be taken as the **City Wharf** (36°50.9'N., 76°17.8' W.) at the foot of West Main Street, which is on the northwest side of Elizabeth River 7.7 miles from Sewells Point and 25.7 miles from the Virginia Capes. City Wharf has depths of 15 feet at the face, but is in poor condition. The wharves northwest and southwest of West Main Street have depths of 14 to 20 feet alongside.

(202) (See page T–7 for **Norfolk climatological table.)** A **weather** summary for Norfolk is given in the preceding text under Norfolk Harbor.

(203) **Smith Creek,** opposite Hospital Point 7.5 miles from Sewells Point, has entrance depths of about 3 feet with deeper water inside, but the entrance is restricted by a 48-foot-wide fixed highway bridge with a clearance of 13 feet. **Small-craft anchorages** are in Smith Creek. (See **110.1 and 110.168 (d)(4) and (h),** chapter 2, for limits and regulations.)

(204) The **Atlantic Marine Center,** the Atlantic shipbase of the National Ocean Service, is on the east side of the entrance to Smith Creek. There are 243-, 251-, and 312-foot berths along the bulkhead wharf, which has depths of 20 feet alongside.

(205) **Waterside** is in the downtown area of **Town Point,** on Norfolk, the north side of the intersection between Elizabeth River and Eastern Branch. A municipal marina at this popular tourist stop has reported depths of about 16 feet at the

entrance, inside the marina, and alongside the berths. Transient berths are available year-round. A sewage pump-out station is at the marina. Electricity is at the berths; ice and provisions are available nearby. The marina staff monitors VHF-FM channels 16 and 68.

(206) **Eastern Branch** (36°50.5'N., 76°17.6'W.) empties into the east side of Elizabeth River 8 miles from Sewells Point and 26 miles from the Virginia Capes.

(207) A Federal project provides for a channel 25 feet deep to the Norfolk and Western Railway Bridge, 2.5 miles above the entrance. (See Notice to Mariners and latest edition of the charts for controlling depths.)

(208) Above the Norfolk and Western Railway Bridge, the natural channel has depths of 10 to 18 feet to the forks 3.3 miles from the entrance, and usually is marked by bush stakes.

(209) **General anchorages** are in Eastern Branch. (See **110.168 (e) and (h),** chapter 2, for limits and regulations.)

(210) Downtown Norfolk is on the north side of Eastern Branch, and **Berkley,** a subdivision, is on the south side. Traffic is fairly heavy as far as Campostella Bridge. Depths at most of the piers on both sides of the branch range from 14 to 25 feet.

(211) The highway bridge, 0.4 mile above the entrance to Eastern Branch, has a bascule span with a clearance of 48 feet. The Norfolk and Western Railway Bridge, 1 mile above the entrance, has a bascule span with a clearance of 4 feet. (See **117.1 through 117.49,** chapter 2, for drawbridge regulations.) An overhead power cable 200 yards east of this bridge has a clearance of 150 feet.

(212) **Campostella Bridge,** 1.4 miles above the entrance to Eastern Branch, has a fixed span with a clearance of 65 feet. The Norfolk and Western Railway Bridge, 2.5 miles above the entrance, has a swing span with a clearance of 6 feet. (See **117.1 through 117.59 and 117.1007(a),** chapter 2, for drawbridge regulations.)

(213) There are several shipyards along Eastern Branch: the largest floating drydock has a 3,200-ton capacity and handles vessels up to 316 feet; the largest marine railway has a 5,500-ton capacity and can handle vessels to 380 feet.

(214) **Southern Branch,** the continuation of Elizabeth River south of the junction with Eastern Branch, is a part of the **Intracoastal Waterway** route southward to Albemarle Sound. The waterway is described at length in **United States Coast Pilot 4, Atlantic Coast, Cape Henry to Key West.**

(215) The Federal project for Southern Branch provides for a channel 40 feet deep to the third bridge, thence 35 feet deep to the seventh bridge. The channel is maintained at or near project dimensions, and is well marked. (See Notice to Mariners and latest edition of the charts for controlling depths.)

(216) A **speed limit** of 6 knots is prescribed by **162.55,** chapter 2, for that part of Southern Branch between Eastern Branch and the first bridge.

(217) The Norfolk and Portsmouth Belt Line Railroad Bridge, 1.9 miles south of the junction with Eastern Branch and 9.9 miles from Sewells Point, has a vertical-lift span with a clearance of 6 feet down and 142 feet up. (See **117.1 through 117.49,** chapter 2, for drawbridge regulations.) State Route 337 highway bridge, 0.2 mile southward of the Norfolk and Portsmouth Belt Line Railroad Bridge, has a vertical lift span with a clearance of 15 feet down and 145 feet up. The Norfolk and Western Railway Bridge, 10.9 miles from Sewells Point, has a vertical lift span with a clearance of 10 feet down and 135 feet up. (See **117.1 through 117.59 and 117.997,** chapter 2, for drawbridge regulations.)

(218) U.S. Routes 13 and 460 highway bridge and the Norfolk and Western Railway Bridge, immediately to the southward, 13.1 miles from Sewells Point, have bascule spans with a least clearance of 7 feet. (See **117.1 through 117.49,** chapter 2, for drawbridge regulations.) Large vessels must exercise caution when making the turns to these bridges because of the current.

(219) The facilities on the east side of Southern Branch are mostly shipyards, oil terminals, and bulk-cargo piers, while Government installations front most of the west side.

(220) The port facilities on the Berkley side of Southern Branch were described earlier in this chapter under Wharves, Norfolk Harbor.

(221) The shipyard at Berkley has six piers that can accommodate vessels up to 1,200 feet. The largest floating drydock at the yard is 850 feet long over the keel blocks, 192 feet wide, 36 feet deep over the keel blocks, and has a lifting capacity of 54,250 tons. A marine railway with a capacity of 1,000 tons is available at the shipyard; cranes up to 67 tons are also available. The largest shaft the shipyard is able to produce is 100 feet by 30 inches.

(222) The **Norfolk Naval Shipyard** is on the **Portsmouth** side of Southern Branch, 3.5 miles from Lamberts Point, and occupies about 2 miles of waterfront. There are naval **restricted** areas along this reach. (See **334.290,** chapter 2, for limits and regulations.)

(223) Most of the oil terminals are at **Chesapeake,** on the east side of Southern Branch, 10 miles from Sewells Point and 28 miles from the Capes. These facilities, as well as the deep-draft bulk cargo, grain, chemical, and fertilizer piers and wharves, were described earlier in this chapter under Wharves, Norfolk Harbor.

11. CHESAPEAKE BAY, YORK AND RAPPAHANNOCK RIVERS

(1) This chapter describes the western shore of Chesapeake Bay from Old Point Comfort to the Potomac River including its principal tributaries Back, Poquoson, York, Piankatank, Rappahannock, and Great Wicomico Rivers, and Mobjack Bay. Also discussed are the ports of Yorktown, Fredericksburg, West Point, Tappahannock, Kilmarnock, and Reedville, as well as several of the smaller ports and landings on these waterways.

(2) **COLREGS Demarcation Lines.**–The lines established for Chesapeake Bay are described in **80.510**, chapter 2.

(3) **Charts 12221, 12225.**–The western shore of Chesapeake Bay from Old Point Comfort to the Potomac River is mostly low. York and Rappahannock Rivers are broad and deep at their entrances and are navigable for long distances.

(4) **Fishtraps** are thicker in this area than in any other part of the bay. Ice is seldom encountered this far south in the bay, but may be found in the upper parts of some of the tributaries.

(5) **Channels.**–The Federal project for Chesapeake Bay provides for depths of 50 feet in the main channel between the Virginia Capes and Fort McHenry, Baltimore. There are three dredged sections in the lower Chesapeake Bay: the first off Cape Henry, just above the Virginia Capes; the second off York Spit, 11 to 22 miles above the Capes; and the third off Rappahannock Spit, 40 to 46 miles above the Capes; they are well marked. (See Notice to Mariners and latest editions of the charts for controlling depths.)

(6) **York Spit Channel** begins 11 miles above the Capes and extends northward another 11 miles. The current velocity is about 1.0 knot in the channel.

(7) **Chart 12222.**–Horseshoe is a shoal that extends several miles out from the shore between Old Point Comfort and Back River, 6.5 miles to the northward. The southern edge of the shoal lies along the north side of the main channel into Hampton Roads; the eastern half has depths of 13 to 18 feet, and the western half, 6 to 11 feet. Local vessels drawing 7 feet or less use the lanes through the fishtraps on the Horseshoe when navigating between Hampton Roads and York River or Mobjack Bay. The tidal current velocity is 0.5 knot over the Horseshoe and is rotary, turning clockwise.

(8) A naval **restricted** area extends eastward and southward of Old Point Comfort, and a **danger zone** of the **Fort Monroe** firing range extends to seaward from a point 1.5 miles northward of the point. (See **334.350 and 334.360**, chapter 2, for limits and regulations, respectively.)

(9) **Salt Ponds** is entered through a privately dredged inlet on the west side of Chesapeake Bay about 4 miles north of Old Point Comfort. The entrance is marked by private aids. In 1980, the controlling depth just inside the inlet was 6½ feet. Sand dunes protect Salt Ponds from the open waters of the bay. A marina is on the east and west sides of Salt Ponds.

(10) **Back River** empties into the west side of Chesapeake Bay 7 miles northward of Old Point Comfort between **Northend Point** and **Plumtree Island**, 1 mile to the northward. A firing and bombing **danger zone** is north of the entrance to Back River. (See **334.340**, chapter 2, for limits and

regulations.) The approach to Back River, from southeastward through a lane in the fishtraps, is well marked. The mean range of tide is 2.3 feet at the entrance.

(11) About 2 miles above the mouth, Back River divides into **Northwest Branch** and **Southwest Branch**, which have general depths of 2 to 5 feet. The **Langley Field** hangars, water tanks, and wind tunnel back of Willoughby Point, between the branches, can be seen for many miles. In 1979, the marked channel that extends 3 miles from the mouth of the river to the Langley Field fuel pier on the west side of Southwest Branch had a controlling depth of about 12 feet. In August 1982, shoaling to 3 feet was reported on the south side of the channel about 150 yards east-northeastward of Light 9. In December 1985, a bare shoal was reported to extend about 60 feet north of Light 9. The Langley Yacht Club, just south of the fuel pier, has gasoline and supplies; the depth in the basin is about 4 feet. A marked side channel to the Langley Field boathouse, on the south side of Northwest Branch 3 miles above the river mouth, has a controlling depth of about 7 feet.

(12) A marina on the south side of Back River, just east of **Windmill Point** 1 mile above the mouth, has gasoline, diesel fuel, and supplies; marine railways can handle boats up to 40 feet. The reported depth to the marina is about 6½ feet.

(13) **Harris River,** on the south side of Back River west of **Windmill Point**, has depths of 6 feet in a marked channel that leads to a marina inside **Stony Point.** Some supplies, gasoline, diesel fuel, and berths are available. Repairs can be made; mobile lift, 20 tons.

(14) **Messick Point** is on the north side of Back River, 1.5 miles above the mouth.

(15) The side-by-side highway and rail bridges over Southwest Branch, 1.5 miles above Willoughby Point, have fixed spans with a minimum width of 18 feet and a clearance of 6 feet.

(16) Between Back River and Poquoson River are shoals that extend 1 to 3 miles from shore; on the shoals are scattered oyster rocks that bare, or nearly bare, at low water. Strangers should stay outside the 6-foot curve. A buoyed lane, about 0.6 mile outside the 6-foot curve, extends northwestward through a fishtrap area from about 2.4 miles east-southeast of Northend Point to about 1.6 miles west-southwest of York Spit Light. In September 1980, poles were reported in the lane in about 37°09′54″N., 76°16′21″W., 37°10′45″N., 76°16′42″W., and 37°10′51″N., 76°16′48″W.

(17) **Chart 12238.**–Poquoson River, which empties into Chesapeake Bay 5 miles northwest of Back River, has depths of 7 feet to the village of **Yorkville**, on the west side 2.5 miles above the mouth. The marked approach to the river is from northeastward and is clear of fishtraps for a width of 400 yards. There is a light on either side of the entrance. The mean range of tide is 2.4 feet.

(18) **Bennett Creek,** on the southeast side of the Poquoson River mouth, has depths of 6 feet or more for 1.3 miles to **Easton Cove,** which makes off to the eastward. The channel is marked as far as White House Cove, on the west side of Bennett Creek 0.8 mile above the mouth; the channel in White House Cove is marked by daybeacons and has depths of 8 to 2 feet for 0.7 mile above the mouth. A 50-ton mobile hoist at the basin on the north side of the cove entrance can handle boats for hull repairs. Gasoline and diesel fuel are

available at a marina near the south end of the cove. A "no wake" **speed limit** is in effect in White House Cove.

(19)   **Chisman Creek,** on the north side of the Poquoson River mouth, has depths of 9 feet or more in a narrow channel for 1.3 miles above its entrance. There are boatyards on the south side, 1 mile above the entrance; gasoline is available; the largest marine railway can handle boats up to 100 feet for hull repairs. The creek is marked by daybeacons and a light.

(20)   **Back Creek,** 1.5 miles south of York River, has depths of 7 feet for 2 miles. The entrance is marked by lights and daybeacons. The creek is used by oystering and fishing boats. A State-owned wharf on the south side, 1.4 miles above the mouth, has a depth of about 9 feet at the face. Gasoline, diesel fuel, limited berthing, and some supplies are available at a marina on the south side, 1.8 miles above the mouth; repairs can be made.

(21)   Passage northward from Back Creek to York River can be made through the **Thorofare,** about 0.8 mile from the mouth of Back Creek. In January-February 1980, the dredged channel, marked by lights and daybeacons, had a midchannel controlling depth of 3½ feet.

(22)   **Charts 12238, 12241, 12243.–York River** formed by the junction of Mattaponi and Pamunkey Rivers 29 miles about the mouth, is 15 miles northward of Old Point Comfort and 26 miles by the main channel from Cape Henry. Traffic on York River consists chiefly of pulpwood, petroleum products, military supplies, and shellfish. Drafts of vessels using the river are mostly 18 feet or less, but deep-draft vessels navigate the lower reaches.

(23)   York River has a broad and fairly straight channel, is well marked and easily followed. Depths are as much as 80 feet off Yorktown. In 1982, the controlling depth in the dredged sections of the river was 18 feet to West Point. Vessels can anchor in the wider parts of York River channel aside from the naval areas described later.

(24)   The mean range of tide is 2.2 feet at the entrance to York River, 2.4 feet at Yorktown, and 2.8 feet at West Point. The currents in York River follow the general direction of the channel except in the narrowest parts where there is a tendency to set a vessel onto the shoals. The velocity varies throughout the river; the times of slack water and strengths of current become later going up the river. The normal conditions are subject to change by winds and freshets.

(25)   **Ice** sometimes interferes with navigation of York River for short periods during severe winters, but in ordinary winters there is no interruption below West Point.

(26)   **Caution.**–Ships and craft underway in York River are to proceed at reduced speed and exercise extreme caution in order to reduce generated water motion and to prevent damage to the Virginia Fisheries Laboratory equipment and facilities located downstream from the Coleman Memorial Bridge, in the vicinity of Gloucester Point, ships and craft loading volatile fuels at the American Oil Co. refinery pier, and other craft and property close to the shores of the river. In no instance should the **speed** of ships underway upriver from the Tue Marshes Light exceed 12 knots.

(27)   **Pilotage** on the York River is compulsory for all foreign vessels and for U.S. vessels under register in the foreign trade. Pilotage is optional for U.S. vessels in the coastwise trade which have on board a pilot licensed by the Federal Government to operate in these waters.

(28)   The Chesapeake and Interstate Pilots Association offers pilot services to U.S. vessels, engaged in the coastwise trade, and public vessels to any port or place on the York River. Arrangements for pilots may be made through ships'

agents or the pilot office in Norfolk (telephone, 804-855-2733; cable, CINPILOT). Pilots will meet vessels entering from sea at Cape Henry (discussed in chapter 9), and will meet a vessel at its port if it is on the Chesapeake Bay and its tributaries or Delaware Bay and River and provide pilot services directly to the York River. The Virginia Pilots Association offers pilotage to all vessels. Pilot service above Cheatham Annex is available only during daylight. (See Pilotage, chapters 3 and 9.)

(29)   **Supplies** are available at Yorktown, West Point, and at other places described in this chapter. **Repairs** can be made to small vessels in Perrin River, Sarah Creek, and at other places.

(30)   **Chart 12238.–York Spit** extends outward along the northeast side of the York River approach channel for 7 miles from Guinea Marshes; the inner half of the spit has depths of 1 to 6 feet, and the outer half 10 to 20 feet.

(31)   **York Spit Light** (37°12.6′N., 76°15.3′ W.), 30 feet above the water, is shown from a pile with a red and white diamond-shaped daymark, in depths of 12 feet near the outer end of the spit. The light is 19.8 miles above Cape Charles.

(32)   The York River approach channel, extending from about 7 miles southeast of York Spit Light to about 3 miles northwest of the light, has a controlling depth of about 37 feet and is well marked. There are natural depths in excess of 37 feet from the north end of the dredged section to the naval installation 5 miles above Yorktown bridge.

(33)   About 1.5 miles northwest of York Spit Light, a buoyed lane extends northeastward through the fishtraps. The lane has depths of 15 feet or more and can be used by medium-draft vessels approaching York River from northward.

(34)   The swash channel through York Spit about 5 miles northwest of York Spit Light has a controlling depth of about 7 feet; it is marked by a light and daybeacons. The channel shows up well on a bright day.

(35)   **Chart 12241.**–The entrance to York River is between **Tue Point** and **Guinea Marshes,** 25.9 miles above the Virginia Capes.

(36)   **Tue Marshes Light** (37°14.1′N., 76°23.2′W.), 41 feet above the water, is shown from a pile with a green and white diamond-shaped daymark, in depths of 4 feet 0.3 mile north of Tue Point.

(37)   **Perrin River,** on the north side of York River 2 miles above the mouth, has depths of 6 feet or more in the approach and through a narrow marked channel to the wharf at **Perrin,** on the north side 0.3 mile above the entrance. A marina on the east side has gasoline, diesel fuel, some supplies, and a 20-ton mobile hoist; hull and engine repairs can be made. Gasoline and diesel fuel can be obtained at several of the oysterhouse wharves, on the east side of the river entrance; depths of 4 to 7 feet are alongside the wharves.

(38)   The Amoco offshore pier, on the south side of York River 3.3 miles above the mouth, has reported depths of 40 feet along the 1,240-foot outer face. The pier, connected to shore by a 0.5 mile long catwalk, is marked at its easterly end by a private light.

(39)   The intake for an electric powerplant, on the south side of the river 4.2 miles above the mouth, is marked by two lights.

(40)   **Wormley Creek** and **West Branch** have a common entrance on the south side of York River, 4.5 miles above the mouth; a light marks the entrance. A privately dredged channel leads through the entrance to the Coast Guard Reserve Training Center basin and pier on the north side of

West Branch 0.8 mile above the entrance light. In October 1984, the channel, marked by a light, buoys, and daybeacons, had a centerline controlling depth of 5 feet to the Coast Guard basin. Local knowledge is advised. Gasoline diesel fuel, berths, water, electricity, a 37-ton mobile lift, and marine supplies can be obtained at a marina on the east side of Wormley Creek just above the entrance; hull and engine repairs can be made.

(41)   The Coast Guard T-pier (37°13.6'N., 76°28.7'W.), on the south side of York River 5 miles above the mouth, has depths of 30 feet reported at the outer end.

(42)   A **naval explosives handling berth** is northward of the Coast Guard pier. (See **334.260**, chapter 2, for limits and regulations.)

(43)   **Sarah Creek,** on the north side of York River 6 miles above the mouth, has depths of 7 feet through the marked entrance channel and for about 0.8 mile up both its branches. A large yacht haven, on the west side 0.3 mile above the entrance, has supplies, gasoline, diesel fuel, a 35-ton lift, a pumpout station and numerous berths. Repairs can be made at a boatyard 0.3 mile up Northwest Branch; marine railway, 76 feet; largest lift, 60 tons.

(44)   A fixed highway bridge with a clearance of 6 feet and channel width of 47 feet crosses Northwest Branch about 0.8 mile above its mouth.

(45)   **Yorktown,** the historic Revolutionary War town, is on the southwest side of York River 6.7 miles above the mouth. High on the bluff in the southerly part is the **York-town Monument,** and a group of buildings is prominent on the shore back of the wharves. The main part of the town is not visible from the river. **George P. Coleman Memorial Bridge,** from Yorktown to Gloucester Point, has twin spans with clearance of 60 feet; the two spans open clockwise simultaneously. The bridgetender monitors VHF-FM channel 13; call sign KQ-7166. (See **117.1 through 117.49,** chapter 2, for drawbridge regulations.)

(46)   The public wharf at the Yorktown end of the bridge has depths of 6 feet at its face, but depths of 20 feet or more are only 5 feet off of it. The post office is at the wharf. Supplies are available nearby.

(47)   Permission to use the wharf facilities may be obtained from the Board of Trustees, P.O. Box 512, Yorktown, Va. 23690.

(48)   **Gloucester Point** is a village at the northeast end of Coleman Bridge. There are several piers and buildings on the low point, and the red brick building of the Virginia Institute of Marine Science is about 500 yards northeastward. The long T-head pier (37°14'46"N., 76°30'02"W.), owned by the Institute, has reported depths of 8 feet at the face. A shorter pier of the Institute is about 150 yards to the northward; depths of 6 feet are reported at the face.

(49)   The **Yorktown Naval Weapons Station** piers on the southwest side of York River, 8 miles above the mouth, have depths of about 39 feet at their outer ends. A **prohibited area** and a **restricted area** for mine service testing are off the piers. (See **334.260**, chapter 2, for limits and regulations.) A **naval anchorage** begins off the Naval Weapons Station piers and extends upriver about 4 miles. (See **110.166**, chapter 2, for limits and regulations.)

(50)   The **Naval Supply Center** piers at **Cheatham Annex Depot,** on the southwest side of York River 11.5 miles above the mouth, have reported depths of 22 feet at the southeasterly T-pier and 14 feet at the northwesterly L-pier; greater depths were reported close off the pier faces. The piers are within a **naval restricted area.** (See **334.270,** chapter 2, for limits and regulations.)

(51)   **Chart 12243.–Queen Creek** (37°18.1'N., 76°36.9'W.), on the southwest side of York River 13 miles above the mouth, has depths of about 5 feet with local knowledge through a marked channel across the flats at the entrance and deeper water through a narrow channel inside for 2.7 miles to **Hawtree Landing.** The channel inside is marked by daybeacons to a point about 0.6 mile below Hawtree Landing. Stakes on either side of the entrance mark the limits of the State's experimental oyster beds.

(52)   **Aberdeen Creek,** on the northeast side of York River 14 miles above the mouth, has a marked dredged channel leading to a turning basin and public landing 0.4 mile above the entrance. In 1982-March 1983, the controlling depth was 2 feet at midchannel to the basin, thence 3 feet in the basin. Gasoline and diesel fuel are available at a seafood company wharf just north of the public landing.

(53)   The ruins of a long T-head pier are at **Clay Bank,** on the northeast side of York River 15 miles above the mouth.

(54)   **Poropotank Bay,** on the northeast side of York River 22 miles above the mouth, has depths of 5 feet at the entrance; the best water favors the eastern side which is marked by bush stakes. From the entrance, depths of about 5 feet can be carried 4 miles through **Morris Bay** and **Poropotank River** to **Miller Landing.** There are several other landings along the river. The channel is usually marked by bush stakes, but is crooked and narrow in places and difficult to navigate without local knowledge.

(55)   **West Point,** at the junction of Mattaponi and Pamunkey Rivers 29 miles above the mouth of York River, has waterborne commerce in pulpwood, paper products, and petroleum. The town is the terminus of a Southern Railway branch line. The pulp, paper, and paperboard wharves just above the Eltham Bridge have reported depths of 16 feet alongside.

(56)   At West Point, the maximum current velocity is 0.8 knots on the flood in Mattaponi River, and 0.9 knots on the ebb in Pamunkey River. Broken-off piling extends off the south side of West Point.

(57)   A public pier is at the southeast end of West Point, at the mouth of Mattaponi River. Gasoline is available at an oil wharf with depths of 5 to 15 feet alongside 0.4 mile south of the Lord Delaware Bridge; diesel fuel can be delivered by truck. An oil pier 0.2 mile above the bridge has depths of 18 feet alongside. Supplies can be obtained in town.

(58)   **Chart 12243.–Mattaponi River,** which empties into York River eastward of West Point (37°31.7'N., 76°47.7'W.), is one of two tributaries that combine to form York River. Traffic on Mattaponi River consists chiefly of pulpwood. Drafts of vessels using the river above West Point usually do not exceed 10 feet.

(59)   Controlling depths in Mattaponi River are as follows: 12 feet to **Courthouse Landing,** 13 miles above the mouth; thence 9 feet for 10 miles to **Locust Grove;** and thence 2 feet to **Aylett,** 32 miles above the mouth.

(60)   The channel in Mattaponi River is unmarked and is difficult to navigate without local knowledge. The mean range of tide is 2.8 feet at West Point and 3.9 feet at Walkerton. Freshets occur at irregular intervals, being more severe in March and April, and have reached a height of 17 feet above low water at Aylett, though this is exceptional; the freshet rise is negligible at and below West Point.

(61)   The Lord Delaware Bridge over Mattaponi River at West Point has a swing span with a clearance of 12 feet; the eastern opening is used as there are no fenders on the western opening. (See **117.1 through 117.59 and 117.1015,** chapter 2, for drawbridge regulations.) Overhead power cables

about 1.8 and 13 miles above the mouth have clearances of 62 feet and 90 feet, respectively.

(62)   The **Walkerton** highway bridge, 24.5 miles above the mouth of Mattaponi River, has a swing span with a clearance of 6 feet through the southerly opening which has fenders. (See **117.1 through 117.59 and 117.1015**, chapter 2, for drawbridge regulations.) Two fixed bridges cross the river at Aylett, 32 miles above the mouth; minimum clearance is 20 feet. The minimum clearance of the overhead power cables between the bridges at Walkerton and Aylett is 42 feet.

(63)   **Pamunkey River,** the westerly of the two tributaries that form York River, has many landings along its banks. Traffic on the river consists chiefly of pulpwood; there is a grain elevator platform at **Port Richmond,** 2 miles above the mouth. Vessels with drafts up to 12 feet navigate the river to Port Richmond.

(64)   Controlling depths in Pamunkey River are about 12 feet from the mouth to **Cumberland Landing,** 20 miles above the mouth, thence 8 feet to **White House,** 28 miles above the mouth, and 4 feet to the Newcastle Bridges 46 miles above the mouth. The mean range of tide is 2.7 feet at **Sweet Hall Landing,** 15 miles above the mouth, and 3.3 feet at **Northbury,** 35 miles above the mouth. Freshets occur at irregular intervals, being more severe in March and April.

(65)   Pamunkey River is easy to navigate as far as **Brickhouse Landing,** 16 miles above the mouth; farther up, navigation is difficult without local knowledge. Freshwater is available at some of the landings, and the river water is fresh above Cumberland Landing. Several narrow cutoffs have depths enough for small boats, but their use requires local knowledge. Above **Retreat,** 36 miles above the mouth, the river is covered with floating debris and snags.

(66)   The Eltham Bridge over Pamunkey River at West Point has a swing span with a clearance of 10 feet; the southwest opening is preferred, as there are no fenders along the northeast opening. The bridgetender monitors VHF-FM channel 13; call sign KQ-7168. Power cables crossing the river about 2 and 14.6 miles above the mouth have clearances of 60 and 90 feet, respectively. The railroad bridge at White House has a swing span with a clearance of 4 feet; the easterly opening is used. (See **117.1 through 117.49,** chapter 2, for drawbridge regulations.)

(67)   **Chart 12238.–Mobjack Bay,** which is entered between Guinea Marshes at the shore end of York Spit, and New Point Comfort, 4 miles east-northeastward, includes several tributaries, the most important being East, North, Ware, and Severn Rivers. The bay is obstructed by extensive shoals, but has depths of 22 feet in the entrance and 15 feet for considerable distances into the tributaries. Many of the shoals are marked by lights and buoys.

(68)   The only prominent marks in the approach to Mobjack Bay are York Spit Light on the south and the white tower of the abandoned lighthouse on New Point Comfort on the north. The approach channel extends between fishtrap buoys; numerous crab pots exist shoreward of these buoys. Good anchorage, sheltered from all but southerly and southeasterly winds, can be found in the bay. Small craft find safe anchorage in the bight westward of New Point Comfort and in the rivers and creeks. The mean range of tide is 2.3 feet at the entrance.

(69)   **New Point Comfort** is the south end of a low, partly wooded island which is separated from the mainland by **Deep Creek,** a crooked and unmarked natural channel. The pile remains of **Bayside Wharf,** visible at high water 1.5 miles northwest of New Point Comfort, extend about 0.4 mile channelward.

(70)   **Davis Creek,** 1.6 miles northwest of New Point Comfort, has a marked dredged channel leading to a public landing in the western arm about 0.8 mile above the entrance. In October 1986, the controlling depth was 7 feet in the east half of the channel from Light 1 to Light 8, thence 9 feet to the turning basin with 10 feet in the basin. Depths of 8½ to 10 feet are alongside the face of the public landing. Several wharves are on the shore in the upper part of the creek; gasoline and diesel fuel are available.

(71)   **Pepper Creek,** 3 miles northwest of New Point Comfort, has depths of 4 feet for about 0.7 mile above the entrance. The approach is marked by daybeacons.

(72)   **East River,** 5 miles northwest of New Point Comfort, has a marked narrow channel with depths of 10 feet for 3.5 miles above the entrance, and thence 4 feet for another 2 miles to the head. Shoals, sometimes marked by bush stakes, extend for some distance off many of the points above the entrance, but the midchannel is clear.

(73)   **Diggs Wharf,** on the east side of East River just inside the entrance, is in ruins. There are no commercial facilities at **Mobjack** opposite Diggs Wharf.

(74)   **Williams Wharf,** on the northeast side of East River about 2.5 miles above the entrance, has reported depths of 6 to 8 feet alongside the abandoned oysterhouse bulkhead. A boatyard on the western shore opposite Williams Wharf has a 50-foot marine railway; repairs can be made.

(75)   **North River,** which empties into the head of Mobjack Bay from northward, is wide, but has long shoals making off from many of the points. The channel has depths of 12 feet for 4 miles and is well marked; depths of 7 feet can be carried 2 miles farther. **Blackwater Creek** empties into North River 3 miles above the mouth. The entrance is marked by a light and depths of 7 feet can be carried for 0.5 mile to a boatyard and a marina just inside the entrance of **Greenmansion Cove;** gasoline, diesel fuel, and some supplies are available. The depth at the face of the dock is 5 feet. Hull and engine repairs can be made; marine railway, 50 feet; mobile hoist, 6 tons.

(76)   **Ware River,** which flows into the head of Mobjack Bay from northwestward, has depths of 15 feet to the mouth of **Wilson Creek,** on the west side 3 miles above the entrance, and 7 feet for another 2 miles. Long shoals, some of which are marked by lights and daybeacons, extend off many of the points. The only commercial landing on Ware River is the J. C. Brown Co. wharf, on the east side about 4 miles above the entrance, which has a depth of about 5 feet off the end; gasoline is available. **Schley,** 0.5 mile inland from the wharf, has a store.

(77)   **Severn River,** on the west side of Mobjack Bay, has depths of 18 feet to the junction with **Northwest Branch** and **Southwest Branch,** 8 feet for 1.3 miles in Southwest Branch, and 8 feet for 1.8 miles in Northwest Branch. The most prominent shoals are marked by lights or daybeacons.

(78)   A wharf at **Glass,** on the north side of Southwest Branch 1.1 miles above the fork, has depths of about 7 feet to the outer end. Mariners are advised to stay within the marked channel to avoid the 1-foot shoal extending from the point 0.4 mile eastward of the wharf. Gasoline, diesel fuel, and marine supplies are available. Hull and engine repairs can be made; marine railway, 60 feet. A marina on the west side of **Rowes Creek,** 0.5 mile southeast of the Glass Wharf, has gasoline, diesel fuel, marine supplies, and a 10-ton mobile hoist.

(79)   **Browns Bay,** 1 mile south of Severn River, is marked by lights at the entrance and by bush stakes inside. Gasoline and diesel fuel are available at a wharf, with a depth of 4 feet at the end, at the head of the bay. A store is at **Severn,** about 1 mile westward of the wharf.

(80) **Dyer Creek,** which empties into Chesapeake Bay 2 miles north of New Point Comfort, has depths of 3 feet in the entrance and 4 to 5 feet inside. The creek is bush-staked, but local knowledge is essential. Overhead power cables across the creek have a least clearance of 17 feet.

(81) **Horn Harbor** is entered through a dredged channel marked by lights 2.4 miles northward of New Point Comfort; lights and daybeacons mark the channel in the upper part of the harbor. In January-February 1990, the controlling depth was 7 feet in the dredged channel, thence in 1977, about 5 feet to a point 3.5 miles above the entrance. In April 1982, a 3-foot shoal was reported on the northeast edge of the channel at the bend opposite Horn Harbor Light 3. A cluster of submerged piling of a former fishhouse is on the east side of the channel about 1 mile above the entrance. Traffic consists chiefly of fish, shellfish, and pleasure craft.

(82) The ruins of a fish wharf are at **New Point,** 0.7 mile above the Horn Harbor entrance. A marina, 3.5 miles above the entrance, has gasoline, diesel fuel, and some supplies. An 80-foot marine railway can haul out boats for repairs.

(83) **Winter Harbor** is entered through a dredged channel marked by lights and daybeacons 4.3 miles north-northeast of New Point Comfort. The channel leads to a turning basin and public landing 1.5 miles above the entrance. In December 1990-January 1991, the controlling depth was less than 1 foot to the turning basin with 1 to 3 feet available in the basin, except for shoaling to bare along the north edge. Commerce in the harbor consists chiefly of fish and shellfish.

(84) **Wolf Trap,** the area of broken ground 6 miles northward of New Point Comfort, has numerous shoal spots 5 to 10 feet deep which extend as much as 3 miles from the western shore of Chesapeake Bay. All the shoal area lies in the fishtrap limits. **Wolf Trap Light** (37°23.4′N., 76°11.4′ W.), 52 feet above the water, is shown from an octagonal red-brick dwelling with a square tower on a brown cylinder, in depths of 16 feet near the outer end of the shoal area. The light is 5 miles due west of a point in the main channel 28.8 miles above the Capes.

(85) **Chart 12225.–**The **danger zone** of a naval firing range begins about 4 miles north-northeastward of Wolf Trap Light and extends northward to Tangier Sound Light, just south of **Tangier Island.** (See **334.220,** chapter 2, for limits and regulations.) The danger zone also contains a designated hurricane anchorage for shallow and deep-draft naval vessels. During hurricane warnings, naval ships may be anchored in the fairway; caution is advised.

(86) The ruins of a former degaussing range control tower, 6.2 miles eastward of Wolf Trap Light, are covered 3½ feet. A lighted bell buoy, 150 yards to westward, marks the obstruction.

(87) **Chart 12235.–Piankatank River** is 11 miles northward of Wolf Trap Light. The entrance is between **Cherry Point** (37°31.0′N., 76°17.8′W.), at the north end of **Gwynn Island,** and **Stingray Point,** 2.5 miles to the northward. The entrance point is 45.3 miles above the Virginia Capes. **Stingray Point Light** (37°33.7′N., 76°16.2′W.), 34 feet above the water, is shown from a pile with a green and white diamond-shaped daymark on piles in depths of 6 feet 1.3 miles east of the point.

(88) Traffic on Piankatank River consists of fish, shellfish, and shells. Drafts of vessels using the river are mostly 6 feet, but drafts up to 11 feet are on record. The river has depths of about 18 feet in the approach from northeastward through a buoyed lane in the fishtraps, 16 feet or more to the fixed bridge 9 miles above the mouth, and 7 feet to Freeport, 13.5 miles above the mouth. Lights and buoys mark the lower 6 miles of the river channel.

(89) The mean range of tide is 1.2 feet in the lower part of Piankatank River. During severe winters, the river is sometimes closed by ice for short periods. Hull repairs can be made to medium-size vessels in Fishing Bay; gasoline and diesel fuel are available.

(90) **Jackson Creek,** on the north side of Piankatank River 1 mile above the mouth, has a dredged entrance channel marked by a light and daybeacons. The controlling depth in August 1987 was 8 feet in the entrance, with natural depths of 8 to 10 feet inside. In August 1987, a shoal spot less than 1 foot was reported to be in the channel about 20 yards downstream from Daybeacon 5. Stakes usually define the channel edges. **Deltaville** is at the head of the north arm.

(91) There is a marina along Jackson Creek where fuel, supplies, and berths can be obtained. The largest lift can handle boats to 35 tons feet for hull and engine repairs.

(92) **Hills Bay,** on the south side of Piankatank River 2 miles above the mouth, has general depths of 14 to 20 feet, and is the approach to Queens Creek and Milford Haven.

(93) **Queens Creek,** at the head of Hills Bay, is entered by a dredged channel that leads across the bar at the entrance and thence to a turning basin about 0.6 mile above the entrance. In February-March 1989, the controlling depth was 1 foot in the entrance channel to Light 5, thence 3½ feet at midchannel to the turning basin, and 5½ feet in the basin. The channel across the bar and to the turning basin is marked by lights and daybeacons. A few broken piles that remain of the wooden jetty on the north side of the entrance are marked at the outer end by a daybeacon.

(94) **Milford Haven,** the strait between Gwynn Island and the mainland to the southwestward, is entered from the head of Hills Bay. Traffic on the waterway consists chiefly of fish and shellfish carried in vessels drawing up to 7 feet. A marked channel with a controlling depth of 7½ feet (9½ feet at midchannel) in August 1987 leads from Hills Bay to natural depths of 15 to 8 feet in Milford Haven.

(95) The jetty on **Narrows Point,** at the north side of the Hills Bay entrance to Milford Haven, is marked by a light. The highway bridge from the mainland to Gwynn Island has a swing span with a clearance of 12 feet in the north opening. (See **117.1 through 117.49,** chapter 2, for drawbridge regulations.)

(96) A marina on Gwynn Island just west of the bridge has gasoline, diesel fuel, supplies, and berths; Hull and Engine repairs can be made; lift, 40 tons, railway, 60-foot long. A public landing pier is on Gwynn Island just east of the bridge. **Milford Haven Coast Guard Station** is 0.2 mile east of the south end of the bridge.

(97) **Callis Wharf** at **Grimstead,** on the Gwynn Island side of Milford Haven 0.7 mile from the jetty, has depths of 9 feet at the face. Gasoline, diesel fuel, and some other supplies are available. A marine railway on the southeast side of the entrance to **Edwards Creek,** 0.5 mile eastward of Callis Wharf, can handle boats up to 35 feet for hull repairs.

(98) A wharf at **Cricket Hill,** on the west side of **Lanes Creek,** opposite Edwards Creek, has gasoline, diesel fuel, and ice; depths of 8 feet are reported at the face.

(99) Milford Haven can also be entered from Chesapeake Bay at the south end of Gwynn Island. This passage, known as **The Hole in the Wall** has a reported controlling depth of about 4 feet and is used by small local boats, but is exposed to heavy seas. The passage is marked by lights, daybeacons, and a buoy. Local knowledge is recommended when transiting the passage.

(THIS PAGE INTENTIONALLY LEFT BLANK)

14. CHESAPEAKE BAY, EASTERN SHORE

(1) This chapter describes the Eastern Shore of Chesapeake Bay from Cape Charles to Swan Point, about 6 miles northward of the entrance to Chester River, and several bodies of water and their tributaries that empty into this part of the bay. Included are Pocomoke Sound, Pocomoke River, Tangier Sound, Wicomico River, Nanticoke River, Little Choptank River, Choptank River, Eastern Bay, and Chester River, and the off-lying islands of Tangier, Smith, Hooper, and Tilghman.

(2) Also described are the ports of Cape Charles, Pocomoke City, Tangier, Crisfield, Salisbury, Easton, Cambridge, St. Michaels, and several smaller ports and landings.

(3) **COLREGS Demarcation Lines.**–The lines established for Chesapeake Bay are described in **80.510**, chapter 2.

(4) During the ice navigation season, the Maryland waters of Chesapeake Bay described in this chapter are a **regulated navigation area.** (See **165.503**, chapter 2, for limits and regulations.)

(5) **Charts 12221, 12225, 12230, 12263, 12273.**– The Eastern Shore of Chesapeake Bay, from Cape Charles to Chester River, is mostly low and has few prominent natural features. The mainland and the islands are subject to erosion, and many of the islands and points have completely washed away. **Fishtrap** limits are shown on the charts and usually are marked by black and white horizontal-banded buoys. In the tributaries of Pocomoke Sound, ice sufficient to interfere with the navigation of small vessels may be encountered at any time from January through March. The ice from Pocomoke Sound does not interfere with the larger vessels in the bay, but the smaller oyster and fishing boats frequently are held up and sometimes require assistance, especially in Kedges and Hooper Straits.

(6) **Charts 12224.**–Wise Point (37°07.0′N., 75°58.3′W.), the mainland tip of Cape Charles, is included in chapter 9, which also describes Fishermans Island, Cape Charles Light on Smith Island, and the Atlantic entrance to Chesapeake Bay.

(7) **Kiptopeke Beach,** 3.2 miles northward of Wise Point, is the site of a former ferry terminal. The offshore breakwaters are obsolete ships filled with sand and sunk end-to-end. Just northward of the abandoned terminal is **Butlers Bluff,** which has steep bare faces conspicuous from the bay.

(8) **Old Plantation Creek,** 7 miles northward of Wise Point, has depths of about a foot. Many of the bars and middle grounds are marked by discolored water, and the channel usually is marked by bush stakes, but it is narrow and difficult to navigate without local knowledge. The opening in the thick woods at the mouth is visible from outside. No supplies are available along the creek.

(9) **Old Plantation Flats Light** (37°13.7′N., 76°02.8′W.), 39 feet above the water, is shown from a pile with a black and white diamond-shaped daymark in 11 feet on the north end of the flats about 1.5 miles from shore. The current velocity is about 1.3 knots 0.5 mile west of the light.

(10) **Cape Charles Harbor,** 9 miles northward of Wise Point, is a dredged basin on the south side of the town of **Cape Charles.** A well-marked dredged channel just north of Old Plantation Flats Light leads to the harbor between sand flats on the south and a stone jetty on the north. Two small dredged basins are eastward of the main harbor basin. The northerly basin is known as the Harbor of Refuge, and the southerly basin as Mud Creek Basin. In December 1987-February 1988, the dredged channel to Cape Charles Harbor had a controlling depth of 17 feet at midchannel with 18 feet available in the harbor basin; thence in December 1988, depths of 4 to 6½ feet were available in the Harbor of Refuge Basin. In May 1987-January 1988, depths of 6½ to 10 feet were available in Mud Creek Basin except for shoaling to bare at the NE corner.

(11) **Cape Charles Coast Guard Station** is on the spit between Mud Creek and the Harbor of Refuge.

(12) The mean range of tide is 2.4 feet at Cape Charles. The tidal currents set across the entrance to and across the southwest section of the dredged channel, but farther north they follow the general direction of the axis. The channel is exposed to westerly winds, but is partially protected by the flats to the westward, and seldom is too rough for motorboats. However, during severe W weather heavy surges may occur in the harbor. Ice may hinder navigation in the harbor during severe winters. Because of the limited space in the channel and harbor, the larger vessels and tows occasionally are somewhat of a hazard to small boats.

(13) Cape Charles is a **customs port of entry.**

(14) Cape Charles Harbor is a terminus of the Eastern Shore Railroad. The railroad operates floats to Little Creek. Floats are usually brought into the harbor in the late afternoon, although there are also occasional early morning arrivals. Due to the limited maneuvering room in the channel and the harbor, larger vessels and tows are sometimes a hazard to small craft. The tugs that handle the floats monitor VHF-FM channels 13 and 16.

(15) There is public access to the bulkheads and slips at the eastern end of the harbor. Anchoring is forbidden in any part of the harbor or the basins. A "no-wake" **speed limit** is enforced. A **harbormaster** enforces harbor regulations, and a **dockmaster** supervises docking at the municipal facilities. Gasoline, diesel fuel, and water are available. Some marine supplies may be obtained in town.

(16) **Cherrystone Channel** is a passage inside Old Plantation Flats that leads from deep water 2 miles south-southeastward of Old Plantation Flats Light northward to Kings Creek and Cherrystone Inlet. The route follows part of the dredged channel to Cape Charles Harbor for about 1 mile. That part of Cherrystone Channel southward of the dredged channel to Cape Charles Harbor is unmarked and little used. Cherrystone Channel above Cape Charles Harbor is marked by lights and daybeacons to the vicinity of **Sandy Island.** This part of the channel has depths of about 10 feet, but is narrow in places, and local knowledge is required to carry the best water. The recommended southerly approach to Kings Creek and Cherrystone Inlet is via the marked dredged channel to Cape Charles Harbor, which was discussed earlier in this chapter.

(17) **Kings Creek,** about 1 mile northward of Cape Charles Harbor and eastward of Sandy Island, has depths of 3½ feet for 1 mile upstream. The shoal that extends out from the north side of the entrance bares at low water; lights and daybeacons mark the entrance. The creek is used extensively by fishermen and pleasure craft. Gasoline, berths, and some marine supplies are available at a marina just inside the entrance; a marine railway can haul out boats up to 60 feet for minor repairs.

ATLANTIC OCEAN DISTANCES
MONTREAL, CANADA, TO PANAMA CANAL ZONE
(Nautical Miles)

Figure at intersection of columns opposite ports in question is the nautical mileage between the two. Example: New York, N. Y., is 1399 nautical miles from San Juan, P. R.

Ports (with coordinates):

- MONTREAL, CANADA* (St. Lambert Lock)
- Cabot Strait — 47°07.0'N., 60°17.0'W.
- Cut of Canso (Lock) — 45°19.0'N., 61°25.0'W.
- Portland, Maine — 43°39.4'N., 70°14.7'W.
- Boston, Mass. — 42°22.0'N., 70°14.7'W.
- NANTUCKET SHOALS — 42°20.0'N., 71°03.0'W.
- NEW YORK, N.Y. — 40°30.0'N., 69°25.0'W.
- Philadelphia, Pa. — 40°42.0'N., 74°01.0'W.
- Baltimore, Md. — 39°56.8'N., 75°08.3'W.
- CHESAPEAKE BAY ENT. — 39°16.0'N., 76°34.5'W.
- Norfolk, Va. — 36°56.5'N., 75°58.6'W.
- DIAMOND SHOALS — 36°50.9'N., 76°19.9'W.
- Wilmington, N.C. — 35°08.0'N., 75°15.0'W.
- Charleston, S.C. — 34°14.0'N., 77°57.0'W.
- Savannah, Ga. — 32°05.0'N., 81°05.1'W.
- Jacksonville, Fla. — 30°19.2'N., 81°39.0'W.
- Key West, Fla. — 24°33.7'N., 81°48.5'W.
- STRAITS OF FLORIDA — 24°25.0'N., 83°00.0'W.
- Tampa, Fla. — 27°56.5'N., 82°26.7'W.
- Pensacola, Fla. — 30°24.0'N., 87°13.0'W.
- Mobile, Ala. — 30°42.5'N., 88°02.5'W.
- NEW ORLEANS, La. (via SW Pass) — 29°57.0'N., 90°03.7'W.
- Port Arthur, Tex. — 29°49.5'N., 93°57.6'W.
- Galveston, Tex. — 29°19.0'N., 94°47.0'W.
- Corpus Christi, Tex. — 27°48.9'N., 97°24.0'W.
- San Juan, P.R. — 18°27.8'N., 66°06.7'W.
- YUCATAN CHANNEL — 21°50.0'N., 85°03.0'W.
- Panama Canal (Atlantic Ent.) — 9°23.5'N., 79°55.3'W.
- PANAMA CANAL (Pacific Ent.) — 8°53.0'N., 79°31.0'W.

Distance between consecutive listed ports (nautical miles, from diagonal of table):

Port pair	Distance
Montreal – Cabot Strait	681
Cabot Strait – Cut of Canso	120
Cut of Canso – Portland	100
Portland – Boston	163
Boston – Nantucket Shoals	223
Nantucket Shoals – New York	240
New York – Philadelphia	392
Philadelphia – Baltimore	150
Baltimore – Chesapeake Bay Ent.	27
Chesapeake Bay Ent. – Norfolk	144
Norfolk – Diamond Shoals	219
Diamond Shoals – Wilmington	151
Wilmington – Charleston	102
Charleston – Savannah	145
Savannah – Jacksonville	462
Jacksonville – Key West	73
Key West – Straits of Florida	232
Straits of Florida – Tampa	347
Tampa – Pensacola	89
Pensacola – Mobile	269
Mobile – New Orleans	441
New Orleans – Port Arthur	89
Port Arthur – Galveston	207
Galveston – Corpus Christi	1824
Corpus Christi – San Juan	1111
San Juan – Yucatan Channel	609
Yucatan Channel – Panama Canal (Atl.)	46

Distances from principal origins (nautical miles):

Destination	Montreal	Cabot Strait	Cut of Canso
Cabot Strait	681	—	—
Cut of Canso	717	120	—
Portland, Maine	1276	595	—
Boston, Mass.	1310	637	526
Nantucket Shoals	1311	630	519
New York, N.Y.	1534	653	742
Philadelphia, Pa.	1682	1001	890
Baltimore, Md.	1830	1157	1046
Chesapeake Bay Ent.	1689	1008	896
Norfolk, Va.	1716	1035	923
Diamond Shoals	1729	1048	936
Wilmington, N.C.	1946	1267	1155
Charleston, S.C.	2014	1333	1221
Savannah, Ga.	2088	1407	1295
Jacksonville, Fla.	2172	1491	1379
Key West, Fla.	2479	1796	1690
Straits of Florida	2540	1859	1751
Tampa, Fla.	2772	2091	1983
Pensacola, Fla.	2977	2296	2188
Mobile, Ala.	3011	2330	2222
New Orleans, La.	3080	2399	2291
Port Arthur, Tex.	3240	2559	2451
Galveston, Tex.	3242	2561	2453
Corpus Christi, Tex.	3347	2666	2558
San Juan, P.R.	2445	1784	1669
Yucatan Channel	2730	2049	1937
Panama Canal (Atlantic)	3203	2522	2410
Panama Canal (Pacific)	3249	2566	2465

*Quebec, Canada - SUBTRACT 139 miles

All tabular distances are by outside routes which can be used by the deepest-draft vessel that the listed ports can accommodate. Lighter-draft vessels can save considerable mileage by transiting Canso Lock (Canada), the Cape Cod Canal (Massachusetts), and the Chesapeake and Delaware Canal (Delaware-Maryland); see the detailed tables. Gulf of Mexico distances are through the Shipping Safety Fairways.

COASTWISE DISTANCES
NEW YORK, N.Y., TO CHESAPEAKE BAY ENTRANCE, VA.
(Nautical Miles)

Figure at intersection of columns opposite ports in question is the nautical mileage between the two. Example: New York, N.Y., is 240 nautical miles from Philadelphia, Pa.

Port key (with coordinates):

1. NANTUCKET SHOALS — 40°30.0'N. 69°25.0'W.
2. MONTAUK POINT, N.Y. — 41°01.7'N. 71°47.3'W.
3. NEW YORK, N.Y. — 40°42.0'N. 74°01.0'W.
4. Manasquan Inlet, N.J. — 40°06.1'N. 74°01.9'W.
5. Barnegat Inlet, N.J. — 39°46.0'N. 74°06.3'W.
6. Atlantic City, N.J. — 39°22.6'N. 74°24.9'W.
7. Cape May Harbor, N.J. — 38°57.1'N. 74°52.6'W.
8. DELAWARE BAY ENTRANCE — 38°50.5'N. 75°03.3'W.
9. Harbor of Refuge, Del. — 38°49.0'N. 75°05.2'W.
10. CHES. & DEL. CANAL E. ENT. — 39°33.8'N. 75°32.8'W.
11. Wilmington, Del. — 39°43.2'N. 75°31.5'W.
12. Marcus Hook, Pa. — 39°48.2'N. 75°25.2'W.
13. Chester, Pa. — 39°50.0'N. 75°22.0'W.
14. Philadelphia, Pa. — 39°56.8'N. 75°08.3'W.
15. U.S. Steel Basin, Pa. — 40°08.2'N. 74°43.3'W.
16. Trenton, N.J. — 40°11.4'N. 74°45.4'W.
17. Indian River Inlet, Del. — 38°36.5'N. 75°03.6'W.
18. Ocean City, Md. — 38°19.6'N. 75°05.6'W.
19. Chincoteague, Va. — 37°56.1'N. 75°22.8'W.
20. CHESAPEAKE BAY ENT. — 36°56.3'N. 75°58.6'W.

Distance matrix (from port = row; to port = column number):

From \ To	2	3	4	5	6	7	8	9	10	11	12	13	14	15	16	17	18	19	20
1	113	223	212	221	242	271	285	285	336	347	353	356	372	395	400	285	295	328	381
2		122	117	131	159	192	212	212	263	274	280	283	299	322	327	209	227	262	322
3			40	63	94	128	153	153	204	215	221	224	240	263	268	145	161	201	267
4				22	52	85	97	98	148	159	165	169	184	207	212	105	121	161	219
5					32	65	78	79	129	140	146	150	165	188	193	86	101	141	199
6						37	49	50	100	111	117	121	136	159	164	57	73	113	171
7							16	17	67	78	84	88	103	126	131	24	40	80	141
8								2	51	62	68	72	87	110	115	15	32	72	155
9									52	63	69	73	88	111	116	14	31	71	155
10										11	17	21	36	59	64	66	83	123	206
11											8	11	26	49	54	77	95	134	218
12												3	18	41	46	83	101	140	224
13													15	38	43	86	104	144	227
14														23	28	101	119	159	242
15															5	124	142	182	265
16																129	147	187	270
17																	20	60	118
18																		41	100
19																			69

Ambrose Light (40°27.6'N., 73°49.9'W.) to New York, 20.7 miles.
Five Fathom Bank Lighted Horn Buoy F(LNB) (38°47.3'N., 74°34.6'W.) to Philadelphia, 111 miles.
Delaware Lighted Horn Buoy D (38°27.3'N., 74°41.8'W.) to Philadelphia, 116 miles.
Chesapeake Light (36°54.3'N., 75°42.8'W.) to Norfolk, 42 miles; Baltimore, 165 miles.

DISTANCES BY INTRACOASTAL WATERWAY
MANASQUAN INLET, N.J., TO CAPE MAY CANAL, N.J.
(Nautical Miles)

Figure at intersection of columns opposite ports in question is the nautical mileage between the two. Example: Atlantic City N.J., is 13 nautical miles from Ocean City, N.J.

Ports (with coordinates):

- CHES. & DEL CANAL E ENT. 39°33.8'N., 75°32.8'W.
- Cape May Canal W. Ent. 38°58.0'N. 74°58.0'W.
- Cape May Harbor 38°57.1'N. 74°52.6'W.
- Wildwood 39°00.5'N. 74°49.8'W.
- Stone Harbor 39°03.4'N. 74°46.0'W.
- Avalon 39°06.6'N. 74°44.0'W.
- Sea Isle City 39°09.4'N. 74°42.0'W.
- Ocean City 39°17.3'N. 74°34.4'W.
- Mays Landing 39°26.9'N. 74°43.4'W.
- Atlantic City 39°22.6'N. 74°24.9'W.
- Beach Haven 39°34.0'N. 74°14.8'W.
- Barnegat Inlet 39°46.0'N. 74°06.3'W.
- Forked River (town) 39°50.1'N. 74°11.7'W.
- Seaside Park 39°55.3'N. 74°05.0'W.
- Toms River (town) 39°56.9'N. 74°11.8'W.
- Mantoloking 40°02.2'N. 74°03.4'W.
- Bay Head 40°03.8'N. 74°03.1'W.
- Manasquan Inlet 40°06.1'N. 74°01.9'W.
- Snark River Inlet 40°11.2'N. 74°00.5'W.
- NEW YORK, N.Y. (The Battery) 40°42.0'N. 74°01.0'W.

Distance matrix (nautical miles):

From \ (cumulative columns)																			
Cape May Canal W. Ent.	48																	
Cape May Harbor	4	52																
Wildwood	5	9	57															
Stone Harbor	5	9	14	62														
Avalon	5	10	15	19	67													
Sea Isle City	4	9	14	18	23	71												
Ocean City	11	15	20	25	30	34	82											
Mays Landing	18	29	33	38	43	47	52	100										
Atlantic City	30	13	25	28	34	39	43	47	95									
Beach Haven	18	45	29	40	44	49	54	59	63	111								
Barnegat Inlet	20	38	65	49	60	64	69	74	79	83	131							
Forked River (town)	8	21	39	66	50	61	65	70	75	80	84	132						
Seaside Park	10	13	26	44	71	55	66	70	75	80	85	89	137					
Toms River (town)	7	15	18	31	49	77	60	72	75	81	86	90	94	142				
Mantoloking	12	9	17	20	33	51	79	63	74	77	83	88	92	96	144			
Bay Head	2	14	10	19	22	35	53	80	64	76	79	85	89	94	98	146		
Manasquan Inlet	4	6	18	14	23	26	39	57	84	68	79	83	88	93	98	102	150	
Snark River Inlet	6	9	11	23	20	29	32	45	62	90	74*	85	89	94	99	103	108	156
NEW YORK, N.Y. (The Battery)	34	40	44	46	58	54	63	66	79	97	124	108	119	123	128	133	138	142	190

DISTANCES ON DELAWARE BAY AND RIVER
(Nautical Miles)

Figure at intersection of columns opposite ports in question is the nautical mileage between the two. Example: Salem, N.J., is 41 nautical miles from Philadelphia, Pa.

Ports (with coordinates):

1. Trenton, N.J. — 40°11.4'N., 74°45.4'W.
2. Bordentown, N.J. — 40°09.1'N., 74°43.0'W.
3. U.S Steel Basin, Pa — 40°08.2'N., 74°45.3'W.
4. Burlington, N.J. — 40°04.9'N., 74°51.8'W.
5. Philadelphia, Pa — 39°56.8'N., 75°06.3'W.
6. Schuylkill River Mouth, Pa — 39°52.8'N., 75°11.9'W.
7. Chester, Pa — 39°50.0'N., 75°22.0'W.
8. Bridgeport, N.J — 39°48.0'N., 75°21.3'W.
9. Marcus Hook, Pa — 39°48.2'N., 75°25.2'W.
10. Wilmington, Del. — 39°43.2'N., 75°31.5'W.
11. New Castle, Del. — 39°39.4'N., 75°33.6'W.
12. CHES & DEL CANAL E. ENT. — 39°33.8'N., 75°32.8'W.
13. Salem, N.J. — 39°34.6'N., 75°28.7'W.
14. Smyrna River Mouth, Del. — 39°22.2'N., 75°30.2'W.
15. Bridgeton, N.J. — 39°25.5'N., 75°14.2'W.
16. Mauricetown, N.J. — 39°17.1'N., 74°59.5'W.
17. St. Jones River Mouth, Del. — 39°04.0'N., 75°22.5'W.
18. Cape May Canal W Ent., N.J — 38°58.0'N., 74°58.0'W.
19. Roosevelt Inlet, Del. — 38°47.7'N., 75°09.4'W.
20. DELAWARE BAY ENT. — 38°50.5'N., 75°03.3'W.

Distance table (row/column numbers correspond to the ports listed above):

Port	1	2	3	4	5	6	7	8	9	10	11	12	13	14	15	16	17	18	19
2 Bordentown	4																		
3 U.S Steel Basin	5	2																	
4 Burlington	12	9	7																
5 Philadelphia	28	25	23	16															
6 Schuylkill River Mouth	34	31	29	23	7														
7 Chester	43	40	38	31	15	9													
8 Bridgeport	49	46	44	37	22	14	6												
9 Marcus Hook	46	43	41	34	18	12	3	4											
10 Wilmington	54	51	49	42	26	19	11	11	8										
11 New Castle	58	55	53	46	30	23	15	15	12	5									
12 CHES & DEL CANAL E. ENT.	64	61	59	52	36	29	21	21	17	11	7								
13 Salem	69	66	64	57	41	34	26	26	22	16	12	5							
14 Smyrna River Mouth	77	74	72	65	49	42	34	34	30	24	20	13	16						
15 Bridgeton	100	97	95	88	72	65	57	57	53	47	43	36	39	25					
16 Mauricetown	115	112	110	103	87	80	72	72	68	62	58	51	54	39	51				
17 St. Jones River Mouth	97	94	92	85	69	63	55	55	51	45	40	34	36	21	35	30			
18 Cape May Canal W Ent.	112	109	107	100	84	77	69	69	65	59	55	48	51	36	47	26	21		
19 Roosevelt Inlet	116	113	111	104	88	81	73	73	69	63	59	52	55	40	52	37	20	14	
20 DELAWARE BAY ENT.	115	112	110	103	87	80	72	72	68	62	58	51	54	39	51	33	20	9	6

CHESAPEAKE BAY DISTANCES
(Nautical Miles)

Figure at intersection of columns opposite ports in question is the nautical mileage between the two. Example: Washington, D.C., is 155 nautical miles from Annapolis, Md.

Ports and coordinates

Port	Latitude / Longitude
CHESAPEAKE BAY ENT.	36°56.3'N. 75°58.6'W.
Norfolk, Va	36°50.9'N. 76°17.9'W.
Richmond, Va	37°31.4'N. 77°25.2'W.
Petersburg Va	37°14.1'N. 77°24.0'W.
Hopewell, Va	37°19.0'N. 77°16.4'W.
Suffolk, Va	36°44.3'N. 76°35.0'W.
Newport News, Va	36°58.0'N. 76°26.0'W.
West Point, Va	37°31.6'N. 76°48.1'W.
Yorktown, Va	37°14.4'N. 76°30.5'W.
Cape Charles Va	37°15.9'N. 76°01.4'W.
Fredericksburg Va	38°17.8'N. 77°27.2'W.
Crisfield, Md	37°58.6'N. 75°51.9'W.
Washington, D.C	38°52.4'N. 77°01.4'W.
Potomac River Mouth	37°57.7'N. 76°16.7'W.
Salisbury, Md	38°21.9'N. 75°36.3'W.
Solomons, Md	38°19.2'N. 76°27.4'W.
Cambridge, Md	38°34.4'N. 76°04.3'W.
St. Michaels, Md	38°47.2'N. 76°13.2'W.
Annapolis, Md	38°59.0'N. 76°28.6'W.
Chestertown, Md	39°12.4'N. 76°03.8'W.
Baltimore, Md	39°16.0'N. 76°34.5'W.
Havre de Grace, Md	39°32.7'N. 76°05.0'W.
Chesapeake City, Md	39°31.6'N. 75°48.9'W.
CHES. & DEL. CANAL E. ENT.	39°33.8'N. 75°32.8'W.

Distance matrix (nautical miles)

Column abbreviations: CBE = Chesapeake Bay Ent., Norf = Norfolk, Rich = Richmond, Pet = Petersburg, Hope = Hopewell, Suff = Suffolk, NN = Newport News, WP = West Point, York = Yorktown, CC = Cape Charles, Fred = Fredericksburg, Cris = Crisfield, Wash = Washington D.C., Pot = Potomac River Mouth, Sal = Salisbury, Sol = Solomons, Camb = Cambridge, StM = St. Michaels, Anna = Annapolis, Chest = Chestertown, Balt = Baltimore, HdG = Havre de Grace, CheCity = Chesapeake City

From	CBE	Norf	Rich	Pet	Hope	Suff	NN	WP	York	CC	Fred	Cris	Wash	Pot	Sal	Sol	Camb	StM	Anna	Chest	Balt	HdG	CheCity
Norfolk	27																						
Richmond	101	90																					
Petersburg	92	80	28																				
Hopewell	82	70	19	10																			
Suffolk	42	29	89	79																			
Newport News	24	12	77	68	58	21																	
West Point	56	66	140	123	122	78	63																
Yorktown	34	58	132	101	114	55	55	22															
Cape Charles	21	32	106	97	88	48	29	50	28														
Fredericksburg	136	146	220	211	201	161	143	154	132	122													
Crisfield	67	77	151	142	132	92	74	86	64	51	129												
Washington, D.C	163	185	259	233	240	185	182	186	164	146	221	121											
Potomac River Mouth	67	89	163	137	144	89	86	90	68	50	125	27	96										
Salisbury	103	113	187	178	168	128	110	122	100	87	165	43	141	49									
Solomons	92	100	174	165	155	115	97	109	87	76	150	42	118	27	51								
Cambridge	123	132	206	197	187	147	129	140	117	107	182	72	149	58	81	39							
St. Michaels	132	141	215	206	196	156	138	149	126	116	190	80	156	65	89	48	36						
Annapolis	129	140	213	204	194	152	136	152	130	112	166	77	155	64	86	45	39	25					
Chestertown	162	170	244	235	225	185	167	178	156	146	219	110	187	96	119	78	72	59	40				
Baltimore	150	173	247	222	228	172	170	174	155	132	206	98	175	84	107	66	60	45	28	45			
Havre de Grace	166	175	249	240	230	190	172	165	163	149	224	115	192	101	124	84	78	62	45	61	41		
Chesapeake City	174	196	271	246	252	196	201	194	179	156	230	121	200	109	130	90	85	70	52	65	49	20	
CHES. & DEL. CANAL E. ENT.	187	209	271	284	259	265	230	243	169	192	214	207	134	213	122	143	103	98	83	65	78	62	13

DISTANCES ON POTOMAC RIVER
(Nautical Miles)

Figure at intersection of columns opposite ports in question is the nautical mileage between the two. Example: Colonial Beach, Va., is 63 nautical miles from Washington, D.C.

Ports (with coordinates):

- Chain Bridge — 38°55.7'N, 77°07.0'W
- Key Bridge — 38°54.1'N, 77°04.2'W
- Washington, D.C. — 38°52.4'N, 77°01.4'W
- Bladensburg, Md. — 38°56.1'N, 76°56.4'W
- Alexandria, Va. — 38°48.2'N, 77°02.3'W
- Mount Vernon, Va. — 38°42.3'N, 77°05.3'W
- Marshall Hall, Md. — 38°41.2'N, 77°06.2'W
- Indian Head, Md. — 38°36.4'N, 77°10.1'W
- Occoquan, Va. — 38°41.0'N, 77°15.4'W
- Quantico, Va. — 38°31.2'N, 76°17.2'W
- Potomac River (U.S. 301) Bridge — 38°21.7'N, 76°59.4'W
- Dahlgren, Va. — 38°19.1'N, 77°02.1'W
- Colonial Beach, Va. — 38°14.4'N, 76°57.9'W
- Wicomico River mouth, Md. — 38°14.5'N, 76°49.1'W
- Breton Bay Entrance, Md. — 38°14.0'N, 76°43.4'W
- Nomini Bay, Va. — 38°08.6'N, 76°43.4'W
- Lower Machodoc Creek, Va. — 38°06.5'N, 76°39.1'W
- Piney Point, Md. — 38°08.0'N, 76°32.0'W
- Yeocomico River Mouth, Va. — 38°02.1'N, 76°31.0'W
- St. Marys River Mouth, Md. — 38°06.2'N, 76°26.3'W
- Smith Creek Mouth, Md. — 38°05.8'N, 76°24.0'W
- Coan River Mouth, Va. — 37°58.7'N, 76°27.1'W
- Potomac River Mouth — 37°57.7'N, 76°16.7'W

(Triangular distance chart – nautical miles between ports)

INDEX

The numbers of the largest scale charts on which the names appear follow the indexed items. Some geographic names are indexed more than once when more than one place has the same geographic name. Charts published by the Defense Mapping Agency Hydrographic/Topographic Service are indicated by an asterisk.

* U.S. GOVERNMENT PRINTING OFFICE : 1993 O - 362-144

U.S. Department
of Transportation

**United States
Coast Guard**

**Merchant Marine Deck
Examination Reference Material**

Reprints from the

1983
TIDE TABLES and
TIDAL CURRENT TABLES

This publication contains information to be used in
examinations for Merchant Marine Licenses

NOT TO BE USED FOR NAVIGATION

COMDTPUB P16721.46

U.S. Department of Transportation

United States Coast Guard

Commandant
United States Coast Guard

2100 Second St. S.W.
Washington, DC 20593-0001
Staff Symbol: NMC
Phone: (703) 235-0018

COMDTPUB P16721.46

AUG 16 1996

COMMANDANT PUBLICATION P16721.46

Subj: MERCHANT MARINE DECK EXAMINATION REFERENCE MATERIAL,
REPRINTS FROM THE TIDE TABLES AND TIDAL CURRENT TABLES

1. PURPOSE. This publication contains reference material for
    use during an examination for a merchant marine deck
    license. It contains excerpts from the Tide Tables and the
    Tidal Current Tables. This manual is current with the
    problems used in the examinations.

2. PROCEDURES. This publication is available to applicants
    taking a deck merchant marine examination. The covers
    available for sale from the Government Printing Office
    (GPO) are printed with red ink. The covers used in
    Regional Examination Centers are printed with green ink.
    Applicants who purchase copies of this publication from the
    GPO may not use their personal copies during examinations.

3. DISCUSSION. Applicants for merchant marine deck licenses
    are tested to ensure their professional qualification.
    Tide and current problems require the use of data contained
    in this publication.

4. ORDERING INFORMATION.

    a. Regional Examination Centers will be provided with an
        initial supply of this publication. Replacement and
        additional copies are available through standard
        distribution sources.

DISTRIBUTION - SDL No. 134

	a	b	c	d	e	f	g	h	i	j	k	l	m	n	o	p	q	r	s	t	u	v	w	x	y	z
A																										
B		1	1		1		1	1						1				1								
C					*								*		.											
D																										
E																										
F																										
G																										
H																										

NON-STANDARD DISTRIBUTION (See page 2.)

b. The public and other Coast Guard units may order copies of this publication from the GPO at the following address:

        Superintendent of Documents
        U.S. Government Printing Office
        Washington, DC 20402

This book may also be ordered by telephone and charged to a national credit card by calling (202) 783-3238.

                    NORMAN W. LEMLEY
            Director, National Maritime Center

NON-STANDARD DISTRIBUTION:

C:e Toledo (350); Miami (225): New Orleans (150); Baltimore (100); Boston, San Francisco, Long Beach, Anchorage, Houston (75); Charleston; Portland, OR; Memphis, Puget Sound (30); Honolulu (20); St Louis (15); Norfolk, Guam, Juneau, San Juan, Ketchikan (10) (only)

C:m New York (250) (only)

INSTRUCTIONS

1.   This reference contains extracts of the TIDE TABLES and TIDAL
CURRENT TABLES.   Some navigation problems require determining the
tide or tidal current for a specific time of day.   The data
necessary for solving these problems is contained in this manual.

2.   This manual is in two parts.   Part one contains the
information referring to tides.   Part two contains the
information referring to tidal currents.

3.   Applicants who wish to comment on any material in this
publication should complete a Comment/Protest form for the
question involved and give it to the examiner.

4.   Individuals not taking an examination who wish to make a
comment about this publicaiton should send a written comment,
citing this publication and the appropriate page and paragraph
to:

                    Director, National Maritime Center (NMC-4B)
                    U.S. Coast Guard
                    REPRINTS from TIDE and TIDAL CURRENT TABLES
                    4200 Wilson Blvd., Suite 510
                    Arlington, VA 22203-1804

All comments are welcomed and will be acknowledged.   Valid
comments will be incorporated into this publication.

**Merchant Marine Deck
Examination Reference Material**

Reprints from the

TIDE TABLES and

TIDAL CURRENT TABLES

PART ONE. 1983 TIDE TABLES

PART TWO. 1983 TIDAL CURRENT TABLES

MERCHANT MARINE DECK EXAMINATION REFERENCE MATERIAL

PART ONE

1983
TIDE TABLES

High and low water predictions

EAST COAST of NORTH and SOUTH AMERICA

including GREENLAND

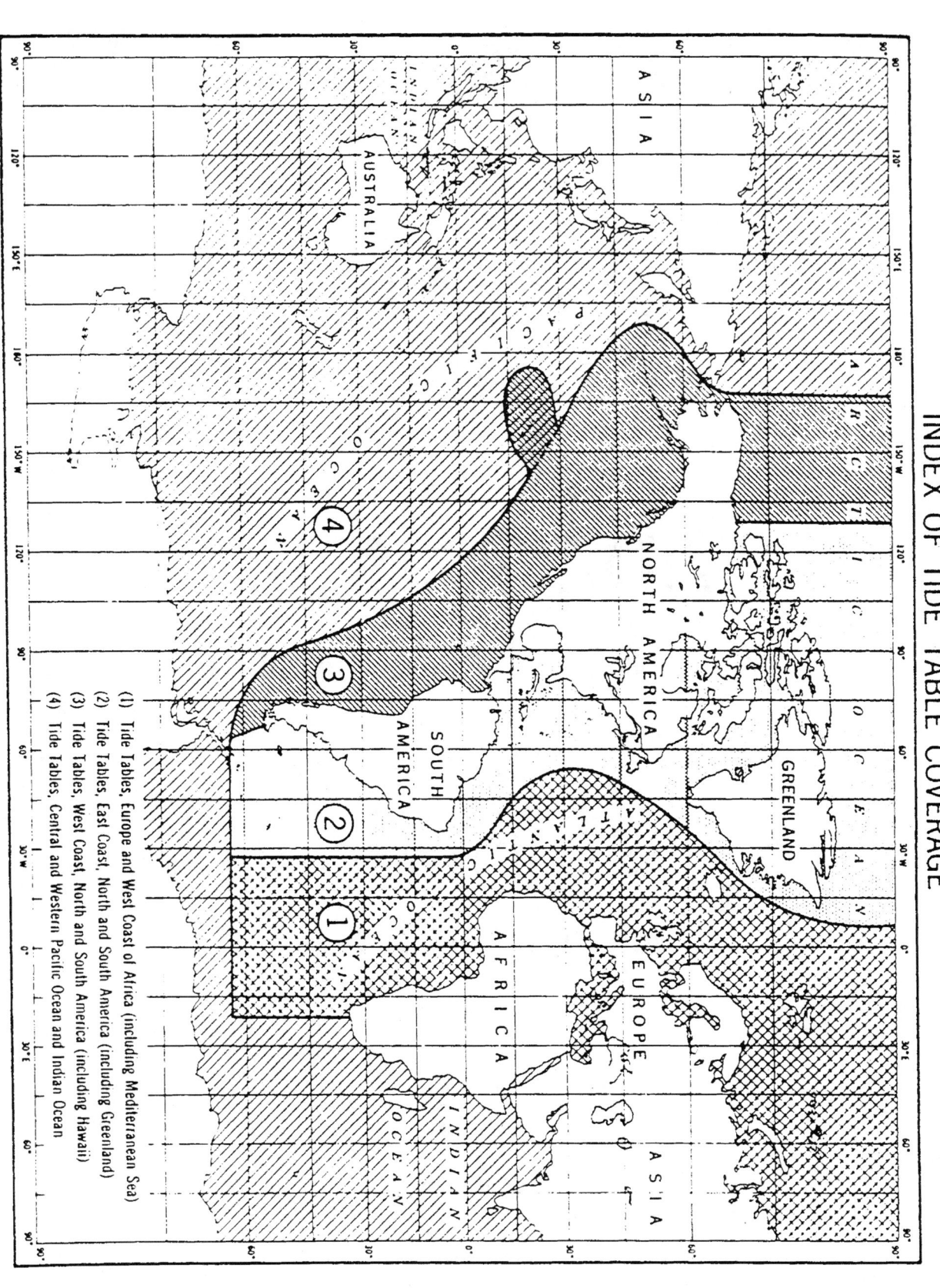

INDEX OF TIDE TABLE COVERAGE

(1) Tide Tables, Europe and West Coast of Africa (including Mediterranean Sea)
(2) Tide Tables, East Coast, North and South America (including Greenland)
(3) Tide Tables, West Coast, North and South America (including Hawaii)
(4) Tide Tables, Central and Western Pacific Ocean and Indian Ocean

CONTENTS

———

IMPORTANT NOTICE

For the most part, tide predictions for U.S. reference stations are based upon analyses of tide observations for periods of at least one year. Since the extremes of meteorological conditions have been excluded from the analyses and predictions, the predicted tidal heights should be considered those expected under average weather conditions. The mariner must be cautioned that during times when weather conditions differ from what is considered average for the area, corresponding differences between predicted levels and those actually observed will be noted. Generally, prolonged onshore winds or a low barometric pressure can produce higher levels than predicted, while the opposite can result in lower levels than those predicted.

Exclusive of weather conditions, the astronomical tide is subject to range variations which should be noted. Decreased ranges may be expected near the times when the Moon is in apogee (apogean tides) or in quadrature (neap tides) and increased ranges when the Moon is in perigee (perigean tides) or in a new or full position (spring tides). A larger diurnal range may also result when the Moon is in its maximum declination (tropic tides). The actual range will depend upon the extent to which combinations of these positions reinforce or detract one from the other. The effect of these astronomical lineups is included in the predictions and may be apparent upon inspection.

The mariner may be kept aware of the times of these astronomical events by referring to the astronomical data listed in this book. He should realize, however, that there is generally a time lag from a few hours to several days from the time of the astronomical event to the time of the resultant tide. During times of storm surges or when extreme weather conditions are imminent, it would be prudent for the mariner to keep closely advised by local weather forecasts as they relate to the effects upon the tide levels.

TIDE TABLES

INTRODUCTION

Tide tables for the use of mariners have been published by the National Ocean Survey (formerly the Coast and Geodetic Survey) since 1853. For a number of years these tables appeared as appendixes to the annual reports of the Superintendent of the Survey, and consisted of more or less elaborated means for enabling the mariner to make his own prediction of tides as occasion arose.

The first tables to give predictions for each day were those for the year 1867. They gave the times and heights of high waters only and were published in two separate parts, one for the Atlantic coast and the other for the Pacific coast of the United States. Together they contained daily predictions for 19 stations and tidal differences for 124 stations. A few years later predictions for the low waters were also included, and for the year 1896 the tables were extended to include the entire maritime world, with full predictions for 70 ports and tidal differences for about 3,000 stations.

The tide tables are now issued in four volumes, as follows: *Europe and West Coast of Africa (including the Mediterranean Sea); East Coast of North and South America (including Greenland); West Coast of North and South America (including the Hawaiian Islands); Central and Western Pacific Ocean and Indian Ocean.* Together, they contain daily predictions for 198 reference ports and differences and other constants for about 6,000 stations.

This edition of the *Tide Tables, East Coast of North and South America* contains full daily predictions for 48 reference ports and differences and other constants for about 2,000 stations in North America, South America, and Greenland. It also contains a table for obtaining the approximate height of the tide at any time, a table of local mean time of sunrise and sunset for every 5th day of the year for different latitudes, a table for the reduction of local mean time to standard time, a table of moonrise and moonset for 8 places, a table of the Greenwich mean time of the Moon's phases, apogee, perigee, greatest north and south and zero declination, and the time of the solar equinoxes and solstices, and a glossary of terms.

Up to and including the tide tables for the year 1884, all the tide predictions were computed by means of auxiliary tables and curves constructed from the results of tide observations at the different ports. From 1885 to 1911, inclusive, the predictions were generally made by means of the Ferrel tide-predicting machine. From 1912 to 1965, inclusive, they were made by means of the Coast and Geodetic Survey tide predicting machine No. 2. Since 1966, predictions have been made by electronic computer.

In the preparation of these tables all available observations were used. In some cases, however, the observations were insufficient for obtaining final results, and as further information becomes available it will be included in subsequent editions. All persons using these tables are invited to send information or suggestions for increasing their usefulness to the Director, National Ocean Survey, Rockville, MD 20852, U.S.A.

In accordance with cooperative arrangements for the exchange of tide predictions, the authorities given below have furnished the predictions for the following stations in the present issue:

Canadian Hydrographic Service.—Harrington Harbour, Quebec, Halifax, St. John, Pictou, and Argentia.

Directoria de Hidrografia e Navegacao, Brazil.—Recife, Rio de Janeiro, and Santos.

Servicio Hidrografico, Argentina.—Buenos Aires, Puerto Belgrano, Comodoro Rivadavia, and Punta Loyola.

LIST OF REFERENCE STATIONS

Name of Station	Datum below mean sea level	Page	Name of Station	Datum below mean sea level	Page
	Feet			Feet	
Albany, N.Y.........................	*2.5	60	Pensacola, Fla.....................	0.6	128
Amuay, Venezuela...................	0.6	156	Philadelphia, Pa...................	*3.2	76
Argentia, Newfoundland.............	4.3	4	Pictou, Nova Scotia................	3.9	8
Baltimore, Md......................	0.6	80	Portland, Maine....................	4.5	32
Boston, Mass.......................	4.9	36	Puerto Belgrano, Argentina.........	8.0	184
Breakwater Harbor, Del.............	2.1	68	Punta Gorda, Venezuela.............	3.3	160
Bridgeport, Conn...................	3.4	48	Punta Loyola, Argentina............	20.3	192
Buenos Aires, Argentina............	2.6	180	Quebec, Quebec.....................	*8.5	16
Charleston, S.C....................	2.7	96	Recife, Brazil.....................	3.7	168
Comodoro Rivadavia, Argentina......	10.3	188	Reedy Point, Del...................	2.8	72
Cristobal, Panama..................	0.4	144	Rio de Janeiro, Brazil.............	2.2	172
Eastport, Maine....................	9.2	28	St. John, New Brunswick............	14.5	24
Galveston, Tex.....................	0.8	136	St. Marks River Entrance, Fla.....	1.8	124
Halifax, Nova Scotia...............	4.3	20	St. Petersburg, Fla................	1.2	120
Hampton Roads, Va..................	1.2	88	Sandy Hook, N.J....................	2.3	64
Harrington Harbour, Quebec.........	3.5	12	San Juan, Puerto Rico..............	0.6	148
Isla Zapara, Venezuela.............	2.7	152	Santos, Brazil.....................	2.5	176
Key West, Fla......................	0.9	116	Savannah, Ga.......................	*4.0	104
Mayport, Fla.......................	2.3	108	Savannah River Entrance, Ga.......	3.6	100
Miami Harbor Entrance, Fla........	1.3	112	Suriname Rivier, Surinam..........	4.3	164
Mobile, Ala........................	0.8	132	Tampico Harbor, Mexico.............	0.8	140
New London, Conn...................	1.3	44	Washington, D.C....................	*1.4	84
Newport, R.I.......................	1.6	40	Willets Point, N.Y.................	3.6	52
New York, N.Y......................	2.3	56	Wilmington, N.C....................	*2.2	92

* Datum below mean river level.

Each datum figure above represents the difference in elevation between the local mean sea (or river) level and the reference level from which the predicted heights in table 1 were calculated.

Local mean sea level datum should not be confused with the National Geodetic Vertical Datum which is the datum of the geodetic level net of the United States. Relationships between geodetic and local tidal datums are published in connection with the tidal bench mark data of the National Ocean Survey.

TABLE 1.—DAILY TIDE PREDICTIONS
EXPLANATION OF TABLE

This table contains the predicted times and heights of the high and low waters for each day of the year at a number of places which are designated as *reference stations*. By using tidal differences from table 2, one can calculate the approximate times and heights of the tide at many other places which are called subordinate stations. Instructions on the use of the tidal differences are found in the explanation of table 2.

High water is the maximum height reached by each rising tide, and low water is the minimum height reached by each falling tide. High and low waters can be selected from the predictions by the comparison of consecutive heights. Because of diurnal inequality at certain places, however, there may be a difference of only a few tenths of a foot between one high water and low water of a day, but a marked difference in height between the other high water and low water. It is essential, therefore, in using the tide tables to note carefully the heights as well as the times of the tides.

Time.—The kind of time used for the predictions at each reference station is indicated by the time meridian at the bottom of each page. Daylight saving time is not used in this publication.

Datum.—The datum from which the predicted heights are reckoned is the same as that used for the charts of the locality. The datum for the Atlantic coast of the United States is mean low water. For foreign coasts a datum approximating to mean low water springs, Indian spring low water, or the lowest possible low water is generally used. The depression of the datum below mean sea level for each of the reference stations of this volume is given on the preceding page.

Depth of water.—The nautical charts published by the United States and other maritime nations show the depth of water as referred to a low water datum corresponding to that from which the predicted tidal heights are reckoned. To find the actual depth of water at any time the height of the tide should be added to the charted depth. If the height of the tide is negative—that is, if there is a minus sign (—) before the tabular height—it should be subtracted from the charted depth. For any time between high and low water, the height of the tide may be estimated from the heights of the preceding and following tides, or table 3 may be used. The reference stations in table 1 now contain the heights in meters as well as feet.

Variation in sea level.—Changes in winds and barometric conditions cause variations in sea level from day to day. In general, with onshore winds or a low barometer the heights of both the high and low waters will be higher than predicted while with offshore winds or a high barometer they will be lower. There are also seasonal variations in sea level, but these variations have been included in the predictions for each station. At ocean stations the seasonal variation in sea level is usually less than half a foot.

At stations on tidal rivers the average seasonal variation in river level due to freshets and droughts may be considerably more than a foot. The predictions for these stations include an allowance for this seasonal variation representing average freshet and drought conditions. Unusual freshets or droughts, however, will cause the tides to be higher or lower, respectively, than predicted.

Number of tides.—There are usually two high and two low waters in a day. Tides follow the Moon more closely than they do the Sun, and the lunar or tidal day is about 50 minutes longer than the solar day. This causes the tide to occur later each day, and a tide that has occurred near the end of one calendar day will be followed by a corresponding tide that may skip the next day and occur in the early morning of the third day. Thus on certain days of each month only a single high or a single low water occurs. At some stations, during portions of each month, the tide becomes diurnal—that is, only one high and one low water will occur during the period of a lunar day.

Relation of tide to current.—In using these tables of tide predictions it must be borne in mind that they give the times and heights of high and low waters and *not* the times of turning of the current or slack water. For stations on the outer coast there is usually but little difference between the time of high or low water and the beginning of ebb or flood current, but for places in narrow channels, landlocked harbors, or on tidal rivers, the time of slack water may differ by several hours from the time of high or low water stand. The relation of the times of high and low water to the turning of the current depends upon a number of factors, so that no simple or general rule can be given. For the predicted times of slack water reference should be made to the tidal current tables published by the National Ocean Survey in two separate volumes, one for the Atlantic coast of North America and the other for the Pacific coast of North America and Asia.

Typical tide curves.—The variations in the tide from day to day and from place to place are illustrated on the opposite page by the tide curves for representative ports along the Atlantic and Gulf coasts of the United States. It will be noted that the range of tide for stations along the Atlantic coast varies from place to place but that the type is uniformly semi-diurnal with the principal variations following the changes in the Moon's distance and phase. In the Gulf of Mexico, however, the range of tide is uniformly small but the type of tide differs considerably. At certain ports such as Pensacola there is usually but one high and one low water a day while at other ports such as Galveston the inequality is such that the tide is semidiurnal around the times the Moon is on the Equator but becomes diurnal around the times of maximum north or south declination of the Moon. In the Gulf of Mexico, consequently, the principal variations in the tide are due to the changing declination of the Moon. Key West, at the entrance to the Gulf of Mexico, has a type of tide which is a mixture of semidaily and daily types. Here the tide is semidiurnal but there is considerable inequality in the heights of high and low waters. By reference to the curves it will be seen that where the inequality is large there are times when there is but a few tenths of a foot difference between high water and low water.

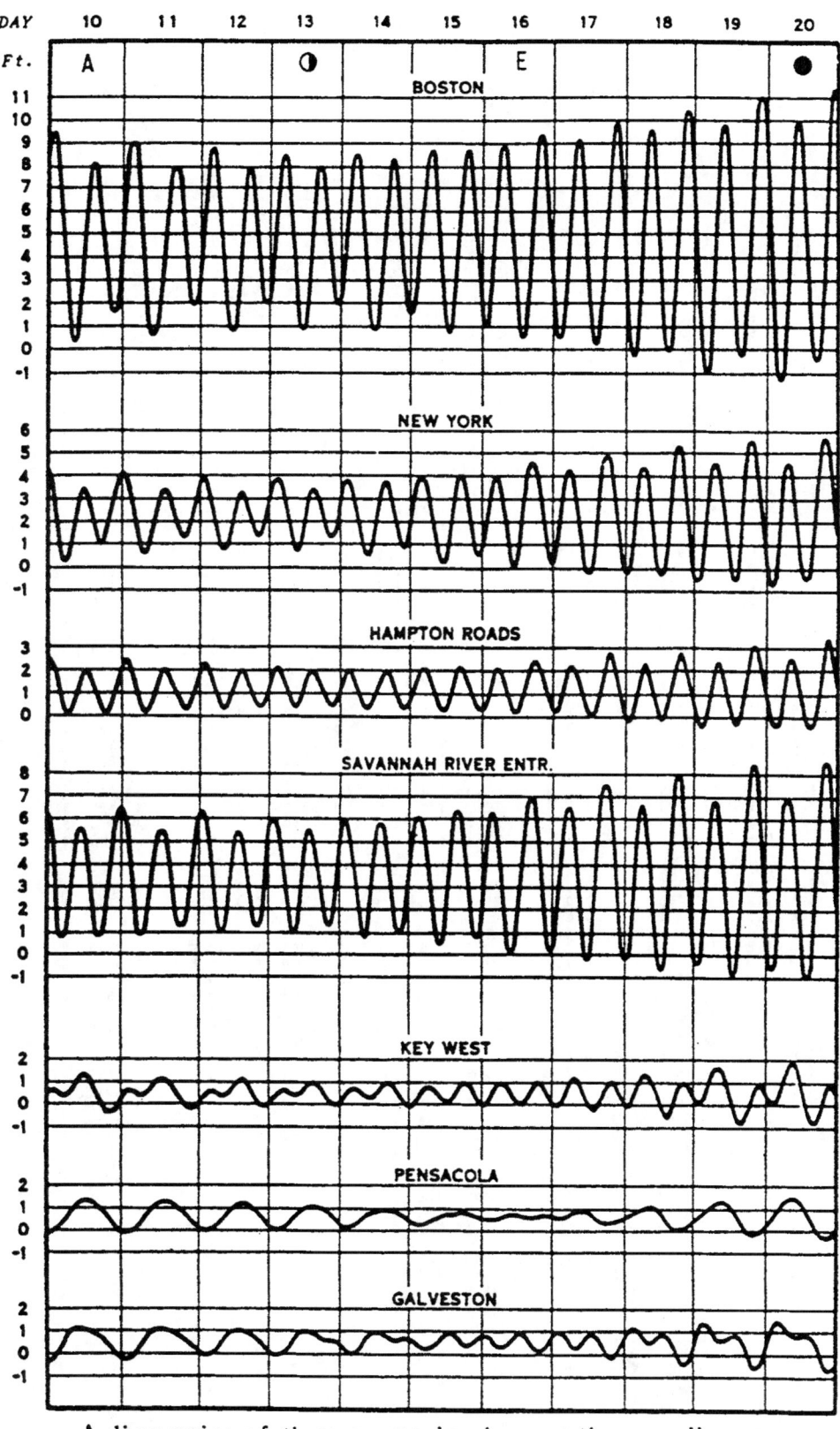

A discussion of these curves is given on the preceding page.

Lunar data: A - Moon in apogee
    ☾ - last quarter
    E - Moon on Equator
    ● - new Moon

ARGENTIA, NEWFOUNDLAND, 1983
Times and Heights of High and Low Waters

JANUARY

Day	Time h m	Height ft	Height m	Day	Time h m	Height ft	Height m
1 Sa	0240	1.2	0.4	16 Su	0255	2.2	0.7
	0930	8.7	2.7		0935	7.8	2.4
	1525	1.5	0.5		1530	2.2	0.7
	2210	7.0	2.1		2135	6.7	2.0
2 Su	0330	1.3	0.4	17 M	0335	2.2	0.7
	1030	8.5	2.6		1000	7.7	2.3
	1610	1.7	0.5		1610	2.2	0.7
	2300	6.9	2.1		2215	6.6	2.0
3 M	0415	1.5	0.5	18 Tu	0410	2.2	0.7
	1115	8.2	2.5		1050	7.4	2.3
	1650	1.9	0.6		1635	2.3	0.7
	2355	6.7	2.0		2255	6.6	2.0
4 Tu	0510	1.8	0.5	19 W	0435	2.3	0.7
	1220	7.7	2.3		1125	7.2	2.2
	1730	2.3	0.7		1705	2.3	0.7
					2345	6.6	2.0
5 W	0050	6.6	2.0	20 Th	0510	2.4	0.7
	0555	2.2	0.7		1200	6.8	2.1
	1315	7.2	2.2		1730	2.4	0.7
	1825	2.7	0.8				
6 Th	0150	6.5	2.0	21 F	0015	6.7	2.0
	0700	2.6	0.8		0555	2.6	0.8
	1425	6.7	2.0		1240	6.5	2.0
	1920	3.0	0.9		1815	2.4	0.7
7 F	0255	6.5	2.0	22 Sa	0115	6.7	2.0
	0900	2.9	0.9		0650	2.8	0.9
	1515	6.3	1.9		1340	6.2	1.9
	2145	3.1	0.9		1915	2.5	0.8
8 Sa	0350	6.6	2.0	23 Su	0215	6.8	2.1
	1020	2.9	0.9		0800	3.0	0.9
	1615	6.1	1.9		1450	6.1	1.9
	2230	3.0	0.9		2020	2.5	0.8
9 Su	0445	6.7	2.0	24 M	0335	7.0	2.1
	1100	2.9	0.9		0925	3.0	0.9
	1710	6.0	1.8		1625	6.2	1.9
	2255	2.9	0.9		2145	2.4	0.7
10 M	0540	6.9	2.1	25 Tu	0455	7.3	2.2
	1150	2.8	0.9		1115	2.6	0.8
	1800	6.1	1.9		1720	6.5	2.0
	2340	2.8	0.9		2300	2.1	0.6
11 Tu	0620	7.1	2.2	26 W	0545	7.7	2.3
	1230	2.7	0.8		1225	2.2	0.7
	1835	6.3	1.9		1815	6.8	2.1
12 W	0010	2.6	0.8	27 Th	0000	1.8	0.5
	0710	7.4	2.3		0655	8.1	2.5
	1310	2.6	0.8		1320	1.9	0.6
	1910	6.4	2.0		1920	7.1	2.2
13 Th	0050	2.5	0.8	28 F	0055	1.6	0.5
	0745	7.6	2.3		0745	8.5	2.6
	1345	2.4	0.7		1410	1.5	0.5
	1955	6.6	2.0		2005	7.2	2.2
14 F	0130	2.4	0.7	29 Sa	0200	1.4	0.4
	0825	7.7	2.3		0830	8.7	2.7
	1430	2.3	0.7		1450	1.4	0.4
	2020	6.7	2.0		2100	7.3	2.2
15 Sa	0220	2.3	0.7	30 Su	0240	1.2	0.4
	0855	7.8	2.4		0925	8.6	2.6
	1510	2.2	0.7		1515	1.3	0.4
	2100	6.7	2.0		2155	7.3	2.2
				31 M	0320	1.2	0.4
					1015	8.4	2.6
					1600	1.4	0.4
					2235	7.2	2.2

FEBRUARY

Day	Time h m	Height ft	Height m	Day	Time h m	Height ft	Height m
1 Tu	0405	1.1	0.3	16 W	0355	1.6	0.5
	1100	8.1	2.5		1015	7.4	2.3
	1625	1.5	0.5		1610	1.7	0.5
	2325	7.0	2.1		2225	7.1	2.2
2 W	0455	1.3	0.4	17 Th	0420	1.7	0.5
	1150	7.5	2.3		1050	7.1	2.2
	1710	1.8	0.5		1640	1.6	0.5
					2300	7.1	2.2
3 Th	0025	6.8	2.1	18 F	0455	1.8	0.5
	0525	1.8	0.5		1130	6.8	2.1
	1235	6.9	2.1		1715	1.7	0.5
	1750	2.2	0.7		2355	7.0	2.1
4 F	0120	6.7	2.0	19 Sa	0540	2.0	0.6
	0625	2.3	0.7		1215	6.4	2.0
	1330	6.4	2.0		1745	1.8	0.5
	1825	2.7	0.8				
5 Sa	0215	6.5	2.0	20 Su	0055	6.9	2.1
	0720	2.8	0.9		0620	2.3	0.7
	1435	5.9	1.8		1310	6.1	1.9
	1915	3.0	0.9		1840	2.0	0.6
6 Su	0310	6.4	2.0	21 M	0145	6.9	2.1
	0905	3.2	1.0		0720	2.7	0.8
	1530	5.6	1.7		1430	5.9	1.8
	2055	3.2	1.0		1950	2.3	0.7
7 M	0405	6.4	2.0	22 Tu	0305	6.9	2.1
	1025	3.3	1.0		0855	2.9	0.9
	1630	5.6	1.7		1545	5.9	1.8
	2200	3.2	1.0		2105	2.4	0.7
8 Tu	0505	6.5	2.0	23 W	0420	7.0	2.1
	1125	3.2	1.0		1100	2.6	0.8
	1735	5.7	1.7		1710	6.1	1.9
	2310	3.1	0.9		2230	2.3	0.7
9 W	0610	6.7	2.0	24 Th	0540	7.4	2.3
	1220	3.0	0.9		1210	2.2	0.7
	1820	6.0	1.8		1810	6.6	2.0
	2355	2.9	0.9		2355	2.0	0.6
10 Th	0655	7.0	2.1	25 F	0635	7.8	2.4
	1255	2.7	0.8		1310	1.7	0.5
	1855	6.3	1.9		1905	7.0	2.1
11 F	0050	2.6	0.8	26 Sa	0055	1.6	0.5
	0725	7.3	2.2		0740	8.2	2.5
	1335	2.4	0.7		1345	1.3	0.4
	1930	6.6	2.0		1955	7.3	2.2
12 Sa	0130	2.3	0.7	27 Su	0150	1.2	0.4
	0805	7.6	2.3		0815	8.4	2.6
	1415	2.2	0.7		1430	1.1	0.3
	2005	6.8	2.1		2045	7.5	2.3
13 Su	0215	2.1	0.6	28 M	0230	0.9	0.3
	0845	7.8	2.4		0900	8.4	2.6
	1435	2.0	0.6		1455	1.0	0.3
	2035	7.0	2.1		2125	7.5	2.3
14 M	0245	1.9	0.6				
	0900	7.8	2.4				
	1500	1.8	0.5				
	2110	7.1	2.2				
15 Tu	0315	1.7	0.5				
	0945	7.7	2.3				
	1530	1.7	0.5				
	2145	7.1	2.2				

MARCH

Day	Time h m	Height ft	Height m	Day	Time h m	Height ft	Height m
1 Tu	0305	0.8	0.2	16 W	0300	1.4	0.4
	0945	8.1	2.5		0925	7.4	2.3
	1525	1.1	0.3		1500	1.3	0.4
	2215	7.4	2.3		2125	7.4	2.3
2 W	0355	0.8	0.2	17 Th	0325	1.3	0.4
	1030	7.7	2.3		0955	7.2	2.2
	1605	1.3	0.4		1545	1.3	0.4
	2305	7.2	2.2		2215	7.4	2.3
3 Th	0420	1.1	0.3	18 F	0355	1.3	0.4
	1120	7.1	2.2		1030	6.9	2.1
	1640	1.6	0.5		1610	1.1	0.3
	2355	7.0	2.1		2255	7.4	2.3
4 F	0515	1.6	0.5	19 Sa	0430	1.4	0.4
	1215	6.5	2.0		1105	6.6	2.0
	1700	2.0	0.6		1645	1.3	0.4
					2335	7.2	2.2
5 Sa	0040	6.7	2.0	20 Su	0515	1.6	0.5
	0555	2.1	0.6		1155	6.2	1.9
	1310	6.0	1.8		1725	1.4	0.4
	1745	2.4	0.7				
6 Su	0140	6.4	2.0	21 M	0020	7.0	2.1
	0630	2.8	0.9		0550	2.0	0.6
	1355	5.6	1.7		1255	5.9	1.8
	1835	3.0	0.9		1800	1.8	0.5
7 M	0235	6.2	1.9	22 Tu	0125	6.8	2.1
	0830	3.3	1.0		0645	2.5	0.8
	1500	5.3	1.6		1405	5.7	1.7
	1930	3.3	1.0		1900	2.3	0.7
8 Tu	0335	6.0	1.8	23 W	0235	6.6	2.0
	1030	3.4	1.0		0815	2.8	0.9
	1610	5.3	1.6		1535	5.7	1.7
	2205	3.4	1.0		2030	2.6	0.8
9 W	0445	6.1	1.9	24 Th	0410	6.7	2.0
	1125	3.2	1.0		1115	2.4	0.7
	1710	5.5	1.7		1655	6.0	1.8
	2305	3.3	1.0		2300	2.4	0.7
10 Th	0545	6.4	2.0	25 F	0525	7.0	2.1
	1200	2.9	0.9		1200	1.9	0.6
	1755	5.8	1.8		1805	6.5	2.0
11 F	0000	2.9	0.9	26 Sa	0015	1.9	0.6
	0630	6.7	2.0		0630	7.4	2.3
	1245	2.6	0.8		1245	1.5	0.5
	1830	6.2	1.9		1855	7.0	2.1
12 Sa	0045	2.6	0.8	27 Su	0055	1.4	0.4
	0715	7.1	2.2		0725	7.7	2.3
	1315	2.3	0.7		1325	1.2	0.4
	1905	6.6	2.0		1940	7.4	2.3
13 Su	0125	2.2	0.7	28 M	0140	1.0	0.3
	0745	7.3	2.2		0800	7.9	2.4
	1355	2.0	0.6		1400	1.0	0.3
	1950	6.9	2.1		2020	7.6	2.3
14 M	0155	1.8	0.5	29 Tu	0225	0.7	0.2
	0815	7.5	2.3		0855	7.8	2.?
	1415	1.7	0.5		1430	0.9	0.
	2020	7.2	2.2		2100	7.7	2
15 Tu	0230	1.6	0.5	30 W	0255	0.7	
	0855	7.6	2.3		0935	7.5	
	1445	1.5	0.5		1505	1.r	
	2050	7.4	2.3		2155	7.	
				31 Th	0335		
					1015		
					1540		
					223		

Time meridian 52° 30' W. 0000 is midnight. 1200 is noon.
Heights are referred to the Canadian chart datum of soundings. Subtract 1.7 feet (0.5 meter) to refer ‘
to the datum of N.O.S. charts.

Times and Heights of High and Low Waters

APRIL

Day	Time (h m)	ft	m	Day	Time (h m)	ft	m
1 F	0415	1.0	0.3	16 Sa	0350	1.0	0.3
	1045	6.6	2.0		1010	6.7	2.0
	1600	1.3	0.4		1545	0.8	0.2
	2315	7.0	2.1		2240	7.5	2.3
2 Sa	0450	1.4	0.4	17 Su	0420	1.2	0.4
	1130	6.1	1.9		1055	6.3	1.9
	1655	1.7	0.5		1620	1.0	0.3
					2325	7.3	2.2
3 Su	0010	6.7	2.0	18 M	0455	1.4	0.4
	0525	1.9	0.6		1150	5.9	1.8
	1220	5.6	1.7		1710	1.3	0.4
	1725	2.2	0.7				
4 M	0100	6.3	1.9	19 Tu	0015	7.0	2.1
	0615	2.6	0.8		0540	1.9	0.6
	1335	5.3	1.6		1250	5.6	1.7
	1805	2.8	0.9		1755	1.8	0.5
5 Tu	0200	6.0	1.8	20 W	0115	6.7	2.0
	0715	3.2	1.0		0630	2.4	0.7
	1445	5.2	1.6		1420	5.5	1.7
	1910	3.3	1.0		1900	2.4	0.7
6 W	0305	5.9	1.8	21 Th	0230	6.5	2.0
	0945	3.2	1.0		1000	2.5	0.8
	1545	5.2	1.6		1540	5.7	1.7
	2150	3.4	1.0		2130	2.5	0.8
7 Th	0410	5.9	1.8	22 F	0345	6.5	2.0
	1055	3.1	0.9		1100	2.2	0.7
	1635	5.4	1.6		1640	6.1	1.9
	2250	3.2	1.0		2300	2.1	0.6
8 F	0500	6.0	1.8	23 Sa	0500	6.6	2.0
	1125	2.9	0.9		1140	1.8	0.5
	1730	5.7	1.7		1745	6.5	2.0
	2335	2.8	0.9		2345	1.7	0.5
9 Sa	0600	6.3	1.9	24 Su	0615	6.8	2.1
	1200	2.5	0.8		1220	1.5	0.5
	1800	6.2	1.9		1840	7.0	2.1
10 Su	0015	2.4	0.7	25 M	0040	1.3	0.4
	0645	6.6	2.0		0705	7.1	2.2
	1245	2.2	0.7		1255	1.3	0.4
	1855	6.6	2.0		1925	7.4	2.3
11 M	0055	2.0	0.6	26 Tu	0120	0.9	0.3
	0715	7.0	2.1		0750	7.2	2.2
	1315	1.8	0.5		1330	1.1	0.3
	1920	7.0	2.1		2000	7.6	2.3
12 Tu	0130	1.5	0.5	27 W	0205	0.7	0.2
	0755	7.1	2.2		0835	7.1	2.2
	1355	1.4	0.4		1405	1.0	0.3
	2000	7.3	2.2		2050	7.6	2.3
13 W	0205	1.2	0.4	28 Th	0230	0.7	0.2
	0830	7.2	2.2		0905	6.9	2.1
	1415	1.2	0.4		1440	1.0	0.3
	2030	7.5	2.3		2120	7.5	2.3
14 Th	0240	1.0	0.3	29 F	0305	0.8	0.2
	0905	7.1	2.2		0945	6.6	2.0
	1450	1.0	0.3		1515	1.1	0.3
	2110	7.6	2.3		2210	7.3	2.2
15 F	0305	1.0	0.3	30 Sa	0350	1.1	0.3
	0935	6.9	2.1		1025	6.2	1.9
	1515	0.8	0.2		1545	1.4	0.4
	2150	7.6	2.3		2240	7.0	2.1

MAY

Day	Time (h m)	ft	m	Day	Time (h m)	ft	m
1 Su	0425	1.4	0.4	16 M	0405	1.1	0.3
	1110	5.9	1.8		1045	6.2	1.9
	1620	1.7	0.5		1615	0.9	0.3
	2325	6.7	2.0		2315	7.4	2.3
2 M	0500	2.0	0.6	17 Tu	0445	1.4	0.4
	1145	5.5	1.7		1140	5.9	1.8
	1655	2.2	0.7		1650	1.2	0.4
3 Tu	0025	6.4	2.0	18 W	0015	7.1	2.2
	0545	2.5	0.8		0520	1.8	0.5
	1250	5.2	1.6		1255	5.7	1.7
	1730	2.7	0.8		1750	1.7	0.5
4 W	0130	6.1	1.9	19 Th	0130	6.8	2.1
	0630	3.0	0.9		0620	2.2	0.7
	1355	5.1	1.6		1400	5.7	1.7
	1820	3.1	0.9		1905	2.2	0.7
5 Th	0230	5.9	1.8	20 F	0220	6.5	2.0
	0905	3.1	0.9		0945	2.2	0.7
	1450	5.2	1.6		1510	5.8	1.8
	2105	3.3	1.0		2140	2.2	0.7
6 F	0315	5.8	1.8	21 Sa	0335	6.3	1.9
	1000	2.9	0.9		1035	2.0	0.6
	1600	5.4	1.6		1620	6.1	1.9
	2210	3.1	0.9		2245	1.9	0.6
7 Sa	0420	5.8	1.8	22 Su	0445	6.2	1.9
	1050	2.7	0.8		1115	1.9	0.6
	1645	5.7	1.7		1730	6.5	2.0
	2310	2.7	0.8		2340	1.6	0.5
8 Su	0520	5.9	1.8	23 M	0545	6.4	2.0
	1140	2.4	0.7		1150	1.6	0.5
	1735	6.1	1.9		1815	6.9	2.1
	2345	2.3	0.7				
9 M	0600	6.2	1.9	24 Tu	0030	1.3	0.4
	1205	2.0	0.6		0650	6.5	2.0
	1820	6.6	2.0		1225	1.5	0.5
					1905	7.2	2.2
10 Tu	0030	1.8	0.5	25 W	0105	1.1	0.3
	0645	6.5	2.0		0725	6.5	2.0
	1245	1.7	0.5		1300	1.4	0.4
	1855	7.0	2.1		1940	7.4	2.3
11 W	0115	1.4	0.4	26 Th	0145	1.0	0.3
	0730	6.7	2.0		0810	6.5	2.0
	1315	1.3	0.4		1340	1.3	0.4
	1930	7.4	2.3		2025	7.4	2.3
12 Th	0155	1.1	0.3	27 F	0225	1.0	0.3
	0815	6.9	2.1		0835	6.4	2.0
	1350	1.0	0.3		1400	1.2	0.4
	2015	7.7	2.3		2055	7.4	2.3
13 F	0230	1.0	0.3	28 Sa	0250	1.1	0.3
	0840	6.9	2.1		0910	6.2	1.9
	1420	0.8	0.2		1450	1.3	0.4
	2055	7.8	2.4		2140	7.2	2.2
14 Sa	0250	0.9	0.3	29 Su	0325	1.3	0.4
	0920	6.8	2.1		0955	6.1	1.9
	1450	0.7	0.2		1525	1.5	0.5
	2135	7.8	2.4		2220	7.0	2.1
15 Su	0325	0.9	0.3	30 M	0410	1.6	0.5
	1000	6.5	2.0		1025	5.8	1.8
	1530	0.7	0.2		1600	1.8	0.5
	2215	7.6	2.3		2305	6.8	2.1
				31 Tu	0445	1.9	0.6
					1120	5.6	1.7
					1635	2.1	0.6
					2345	6.5	2.0

JUNE

Day	Time (h m)	ft	m	Day	Time (h m)	ft	m
1 W	0525	2.2	0.7	16 Th	0005	7.3	2.2
	1210	5.4	1.6		0520	1.5	0.5
	1730	2.3	0.7		1230	6.0	1.8
					1745	1.4	0.4
2 Th	0020	6.2	1.9	17 F	0100	6.8	2.1
	0605	2.5	0.8		0620	1.9	0.6
	1250	5.3	1.6		1340	5.9	1.8
	1805	2.7	0.8		1845	1.8	0.5
3 F	0115	5.9	1.8	18 Sa	0200	6.4	2.0
	0700	2.8	0.9		0720	2.2	0.7
	1350	5.3	1.6		1450	6.0	1.8
	1910	2.9	0.9		2020	2.0	0.6
4 Sa	0200	5.7	1.7	19 Su	0305	6.1	1.9
	0835	2.9	0.9		0945	2.3	0.7
	1445	5.4	1.6		1555	6.1	1.9
	2050	2.9	0.9		2205	2.0	0.6
5 Su	0310	5.5	1.7	20 M	0425	5.9	1.8
	0950	2.7	0.8		1035	2.2	0.7
	1550	5.6	1.7		1655	6.3	1.9
	2200	2.7	0.8		2300	1.9	0.6
6 M	0430	5.6	1.7	21 Tu	0525	5.8	1.8
	1035	2.4	0.7		1110	2.0	0.6
	1645	6.0	1.8		1740	6.5	2.0
	2300	2.3	0.7		2355	1.8	0.5
7 Tu	0525	5.8	1.8	22 W	0605	5.8	1.8
	1110	2.0	0.6		1145	1.9	0.6
	1740	6.5	2.0		1830	6.7	2.0
	2350	1.9	0.6				
8 W	0610	6.1	1.9	23 Th	0025	1.7	0.5
	1155	1.6	0.5		0650	5.9	1.8
	1825	7.0	2.1		1215	1.8	0.5
					1915	6.9	2.1
9 Th	0030	1.6	0.5	24 F	0110	1.6	0.5
	0700	6.4	2.0		0730	6.0	1.8
	1225	1.2	0.4		1255	1.6	0.5
	1910	7.4	2.3		1950	7.0	2.1
10 F	0110	1.3	0.4	25 Sa	0150	1.6	0.5
	0735	6.5	2.0		0815	6.0	1.8
	1315	0.9	0.3		1335	1.6	0.5
	1945	7.7	2.3		2035	7.1	2.2
11 Sa	0150	1.1	0.3	26 Su	0225	1.6	0.5
	0810	6.6	2.0		0840	6.0	1.8
	1355	0.7	0.2		1425	1.5	0.5
	2030	7.9	2.4		2110	7.1	2.2
12 Su	0240	0.9	0.3	27 M	0300	1.5	0.5
	0900	6.6	2.0		0920	6.0	1.8
	1435	0.6	0.2		1505	1.6	0.5
	2120	7.9	2.4		2155	7.1	2.2
13 M	0320	0.9	0.3	28 Tu	0350	1.6	0.5
	0950	6.4	2.0		0955	5.9	1.8
	1520	0.7	0.2		1545	1.7	0.5
	2215	7.8	2.4		2225	7.0	2.1
14 Tu	0400	1.0	0.3	29 W	0425	1.7	0.5
	1035	6.2	1.9		1045	5.8	1.8
	1605	0.8	0.2		1625	1.8	0.5
	2300	7.6	2.3		2310	6.8	2.1
15 W	0440	1.3	0.4	30 Th	0450	1.9	0.6
	1130	6.1	1.9		1115	5.7	1.7
	1650	1.1	0.3		1655	2.0	0.6
					2345	6.5	2.0

Time meridian 52° 30' W.   0000 is midnight.   1200 is noon.
Heights are referred to the Canadian chart datum of soundings.   Subtract 1.7 feet (0.5 meter) to refer these levels to the datum of N.O.S. charts.

6

ARGENTIA, NEWFOUNDLAND, 1983

Times and Heights of High and Low Waters

JULY

Day	Time h m	ft	m	Day	Time h m	ft	m
1 F	0520	2.1	0.6	16 Sa	0030	6.9	2.1
	1205	5.7	1.7		0550	1.7	0.5
	1730	2.2	0.7		1320	6.2	1.9
					1820	1.6	0.5
2 Sa	0025	6.2	1.9	17 Su	0130	6.4	2.0
	0600	2.3	0.7		0645	2.1	0.6
	1245	5.7	1.7		1420	6.1	1.9
	1810	2.4	0.7		1930	2.1	0.6
3 Su	0100	5.8	1.8	18 M	0240	5.9	1.8
	0645	2.5	0.8		0815	2.4	0.7
	1335	5.7	1.7		1515	6.1	1.9
	1905	2.6	0.8		2145	2.2	0.7
4 M	0205	5.6	1.7	19 Tu	0350	5.5	1.7
	0730	2.5	0.8		0945	2.5	0.8
	1445	5.9	1.8		1620	6.1	1.9
	2015	2.6	0.8		2245	2.3	0.7
5 Tu	0310	5.4	1.6	20 W	0450	5.4	1.6
	0905	2.4	0.7		1045	2.5	0.8
	1550	6.1	1.9		1710	6.2	1.9
	2200	2.5	0.8		2330	2.3	0.7
6 W	0425	5.5	1.7	21 Th	0535	5.4	1.6
	1005	2.1	0.6		1125	2.4	0.7
	1655	6.5	2.0		1815	6.4	2.0
	2305	2.2	0.7				
7 Th	0520	5.8	1.8	22 F	0020	2.3	0.7
	1105	1.7	0.5		0620	5.6	1.7
	1750	6.9	2.1		1205	2.3	0.7
					1850	6.6	2.0
8 F	0010	1.9	0.6	23 Sa	0100	2.2	0.7
	0620	6.1	1.9		0710	5.8	1.8
	1145	1.3	0.4		1245	2.1	0.6
	1840	7.4	2.3		1930	6.9	2.1
9 Sa	0055	1.6	0.5	24 Su	0145	2.1	0.6
	0700	6.4	2.0		0740	6.0	1.8
	1235	1.1	0.3		1330	2.0	0.6
	1940	7.7	2.3		2010	7.0	2.1
10 Su	0145	1.3	0.4	25 M	0225	1.9	0.6
	0755	6.6	2.0		0815	6.1	1.9
	1335	0.9	0.3		1410	1.8	0.5
	2020	8.0	2.4		2055	7.2	2.2
11 M	0230	1.1	0.3	26 Tu	0250	1.8	0.5
	0850	6.6	2.0		0845	6.2	1.9
	1415	0.7	0.2		1445	1.7	0.5
	2115	8.1	2.5		2120	7.2	2.2
12 Tu	0315	1.0	0.3	27 W	0320	1.7	0.5
	0930	6.6	2.0		0925	6.2	1.9
	1510	0.7	0.2		1525	1.7	0.5
	2210	8.1	2.5		2200	7.1	2.2
13 W	0350	1.0	0.3	28 Th	0355	1.7	0.5
	1025	6.5	2.0		1005	6.2	1.9
	1600	0.7	0.2		1600	1.7	0.5
	2250	7.8	2.4		2235	6.9	2.1
14 Th	0425	1.1	0.3	29 F	0415	1.7	0.5
	1115	6.4	2.0		1040	6.2	1.9
	1640	0.9	0.3		1625	1.8	0.5
	2345	7.4	2.3		2315	6.7	2.0
15 F	0505	1.4	0.4	30 Sa	0445	1.9	0.6
	1225	6.3	1.9		1120	6.1	1.9
	1720	1.2	0.4		1700	1.9	0.6
					2335	6.3	1.9
				31 Su	0520	1.9	0.6
					1200	6.1	1.9
					1730	2.0	0.6

AUGUST

Day	Time h m	ft	m	Day	Time h m	ft	m
1 M	0020	6.0	1.8	16 Tu	0210	5.7	1.7
	0610	1.9	0.6		0710	2.4	0.7
	1255	6.2	1.9		1440	6.1	1.9
	1830	2.2	0.7		2020	2.6	0.8
2 Tu	0115	5.7	1.7	17 W	0310	5.4	1.6
	0650	2.0	0.6		0810	2.7	0.8
	1350	6.2	1.9		1550	6.0	1.8
	1925	2.4	0.7		2230	2.9	0.9
3 W	0215	5.6	1.7	18 Th	0410	5.2	1.6
	0755	2.1	0.6		0930	2.8	0.9
	1455	6.3	1.9		1645	6.1	1.9
	2045	2.6	0.8		2340	2.9	0.9
4 Th	0325	5.5	1.7	19 F	0510	5.3	1.6
	0900	2.0	0.6		1055	2.7	0.8
	1600	6.6	2.0		1800	6.3	1.9
	2215	2.4	0.7				
5 F	0445	5.7	1.7	20 Sa	0010	2.7	0.8
	1015	1.8	0.5		0605	5.6	1.7
	1715	6.9	2.1		1155	2.5	0.8
	2340	2.1	0.6		1835	6.6	2.0
6 Sa	0550	6.1	1.9	21 Su	0050	2.5	0.8
	1125	1.5	0.5		0640	5.8	1.8
	1820	7.4	2.3		1240	2.3	0.7
					1915	6.9	2.1
7 Su	0045	1.6	0.5	22 M	0120	2.2	0.7
	0645	6.5	2.0		0715	6.1	1.9
	1235	1.2	0.4		1310	2.0	0.6
	1925	7.9	2.4		1955	7.2	2.2
8 M	0135	1.2	0.4	23 Tu	0145	1.9	0.6
	0740	6.8	2.1		0745	6.4	2.0
	1325	0.9	0.3		1350	1.6	0.5
	2005	8.2	2.5		2025	7.3	2.2
9 Tu	0215	0.9	0.3	24 W	0215	1.7	0.5
	0830	6.9	2.1		0815	6.6	2.0
	1415	0.7	0.2		1430	1.6	0.5
	2100	8.2	2.5		2055	7.3	2.2
10 W	0250	0.8	0.2	25 Th	0250	1.6	0.5
	0920	7.0	2.1		0855	6.7	2.0
	1500	0.5	0.2		1505	1.5	0.5
	2150	8.1	2.5		2130	7.2	2.2
11 Th	0330	0.8	0.2	26 F	0315	1.5	0.5
	1005	6.9	2.1		0935	6.7	2.0
	1545	0.5	0.2		1540	1.4	0.4
	2240	7.8	2.4		2205	7.0	2.1
12 F	0415	0.9	0.3	27 Sa	0345	1.5	0.5
	1105	6.8	2.1		1105	6.8	2.1
	1620	0.7	0.2		1610	1.4	0.4
	2325	7.4	2.3		2230	6.7	2.0
13 Sa	0450	1.2	0.4	28 Su	0420	1.5	0.5
	1155	6.6	2.0		1045	6.7	2.0
	1700	1.0	0.3		1635	1.6	0.5
					2310	6.4	2.0
14 Su	0025	6.8	2.1	29 M	0450	1.5	0.5
	0515	1.5	0.5		1140	6.7	2.0
	1255	6.5	2.0		1710	1.8	0.5
	1755	1.5	0.5		2350	6.1	1.9
15 M	0110	6.2	1.9	30 Tu	0525	1.7	0.5
	0615	2.0	0.6		1230	6.6	2.0
	1345	6.3	1.9		1755	2.1	0.6
	1900	2.1	0.6				
				31 W	0040	5.8	1.8
					0605	1.8	0.5
					1320	6.5	2.0
					1855	2.4	0.7

SEPTEMBER

Day	Time h m	ft	m	Day	Time h m	ft	m
1 Th	0140	5.6	1.7	16 F	0400	5.3	1.6
	0715	2.1	0.6		1015	3.2	1.0
	1415	6.5	2.0		1640	6.1	1.9
	2005	2.8	0.9		2315	3.1	0.9
2 F	0305	5.5	1.7	17 Sa	0500	5.4	1.6
	0820	2.2	0.7		1105	3.0	0.9
	1545	6.6	2.0		1725	6.3	1.9
	2250	2.7	0.8		2350	2.9	0.9
3 Sa	0430	5.7	1.7	18 Su	0535	5.8	1.8
	1010	2.2	0.7		1155	2.7	0.8
	1710	6.9	2.1		1810	6.6	2.0
	2355	2.2	0.7				
4 Su	0540	6.2	1.9	19 M	0020	2.6	0.8
	1130	1.9	0.6		0620	6.1	1.9
	1805	7.4	2.3		1220	2.4	0.7
					1850	6.9	2.1
5 M	0040	1.7	0.5	20 Tu	0100	2.3	0.7
	0635	6.7	2.0		0650	6.5	2.0
	1235	1.4	0.4		1305	2.1	0.6
	1910	7.9	2.4		1925	7.2	2.2
6 Tu	0115	1.2	0.4	21 W	0130	2.1	0.6
	0725	7.0	2.1		0725	6.8	2.1
	1325	1.0	0.3		1335	1.8	0.5
	1955	8.2	2.5		2000	7.4	2.3
7 W	0200	0.9	0.3	22 Th	0200	1.8	0.5
	0815	7.3	2.2		0800	7.0	2.1
	1415	0.7	0.2		1405	1.6	0.5
	2045	8.2	2.5		2035	7.4	2.3
8 Th	0240	0.8	0.2	23 F	0225	1.6	0.5
	0910	7.4	2.3		0840	7.2	2.2
	1455	0.5	0.2		1445	1.5	0.5
	2130	8.0	2.4		2110	7.3	2.2
9 F	0300	0.8	0.2	24 Sa	0250	1.5	0.5
	0955	7.4	2.3		0905	7.2	2.2
	1525	0.6	0.2		1505	1.4	0.4
	2220	7.7	2.3		2135	7.1	2.2
10 Sa	0345	1.0	0.3	25 Su	0325	1.4	0.4
	1035	7.2	2.2		0955	7.3	2.2
	1600	0.8	0.2		1540	1.5	0.5
	2310	7.2	2.2		2205	6.8	2.1
11 Su	0420	1.3	0.4	26 M	0345	1.4	0.4
	1130	7.0	2.1		1025	7.2	2.2
	1655	1.2	0.4		1605	1.6	0.5
	2355	6.6	2.0		2255	6.5	2.0
12 M	0455	1.6	0.5	27 Tu	0425	1.4	0.4
	1225	6.7	2.0		1110	7.1	2.2
	1725	1.8	0.5		1645	1.9	0.6
					2330	6.2	1.9
13 Tu	0040	6.0	1.8	28 W	0500	1.5	0.5
	0530	2.1	0.6		1205	7.0	2.1
	1320	6.4	2.0		1730	2.2	0.7
	1815	2.5	0.8				
14 W	0140	5.6	1.7	29 Th	0025	5.9	1.8
	0615	2.6	0.8		0550	1.8	0.5
	1425	6.2	1.9		1300	6.8	2.1
	1920	3.1	0.9		1815	2.6	0.8
15 Th	0250	5.3	1.6	30 F	0120	5.7	1.7
	0725	3.1	0.9		0635	2.2	0.7
	1530	6.0	1.8		1405	6.7	2.0
	2230	3.2	1.0		1925	2.9	0.9

Time meridian 52° 30′ W. 0000 is midnight. 1200 is noon.
Heights are referred to the Canadian chart datum of soundings. Subtract 1.7 feet (0.5 meter) to refer these levels to the datum of N.O.S. charts.

ARGENTIA, NEWFOUNDLAND, 1983

Times and Heights of High and Low Waters

OCTOBER

Day	Time h m	Height ft	Height m	Day	Time h m	Height ft	Height m
1 Sa	0315	5.7	1.7	16 Su	0420	5.6	1.7
	0825	2.6	0.8		1035	3.2	1.0
	1530	6.7	2.0		1650	6.4	2.0
	2245	2.7	0.8		2320	3.0	0.9
2 Su	0415	6.0	1.8	17 M	0505	5.9	1.8
	1020	2.4	0.7		1115	2.9	0.9
	1655	7.0	2.1		1745	6.6	2.0
	2340	2.2	0.7		2350	2.7	0.8
3 M	0525	6.5	2.0	18 Tu	0550	6.3	1.9
	1115	2.0	0.6		1200	2.6	0.8
	1750	7.4	2.3		1825	6.8	2.1
4 Tu	0015	1.7	0.5	19 W	0020	2.4	0.7
	0620	7.0	2.1		0635	6.7	2.0
	1225	1.5	0.5		1235	2.2	0.7
	1850	7.7	2.3		1910	7.1	2.2
5 W	0050	1.3	0.4	20 Th	0055	2.1	0.6
	0720	7.4	2.3		0715	7.1	2.2
	1300	1.0	0.3		1315	1.9	0.6
	1945	8.0	2.4		1935	7.2	2.2
6 Th	0135	1.0	0.3	21 F	0125	1.8	0.5
	0805	7.7	2.3		0740	7.4	2.3
	1345	0.7	0.2		1345	1.6	0.5
	2030	8.0	2.4		2005	7.3	2.2
7 F	0200	0.9	0.3	22 Sa	0155	1.6	0.5
	0850	7.8	2.4		0815	7.6	2.3
	1435	0.6	0.2		1415	1.5	0.5
	2110	7.8	2.4		2045	7.2	2.2
8 Sa	0240	1.0	0.3	23 Su	0225	1.4	0.4
	0925	7.8	2.4		0850	7.7	2.3
	1505	0.7	0.2		1450	1.5	0.5
	2145	7.4	2.3		2115	7.0	2.1
9 Su	0315	1.1	0.3	24 M	0255	1.3	0.4
	1010	7.6	2.3		0935	7.7	2.3
	1555	1.0	0.3		1520	1.5	0.5
	2235	6.9	2.1		2145	6.8	2.1
10 M	0350	1.4	0.4	25 Tu	0325	1.3	0.4
	1100	7.2	2.2		1005	7.7	2.3
	1620	1.5	0.5		1600	1.7	0.5
	2320	6.4	2.0		2225	6.5	2.0
11 Tu	0425	1.8	0.5	26 W	0405	1.4	0.4
	1150	6.9	2.1		1055	7.5	2.3
	1710	2.1	0.6		1640	2.0	0.6
					2310	6.2	1.9
12 W	0015	5.9	1.8	27 Th	0450	1.7	0.5
	0515	2.3	0.7		1155	7.3	2.2
	1250	6.6	2.0		1710	2.3	0.7
	1800	2.8	0.9				
13 Th	0130	5.5	1.7	28 F	0015	5.9	1.8
	0545	2.8	0.9		0525	2.1	0.6
	1355	6.4	2.0		1250	7.0	2.1
	1920	3.4	1.0		1810	2.7	0.8
14 F	0235	5.4	1.6	29 Sa	0140	5.8	1.8
	0710	3.3	1.0		0615	2.5	0.8
	1455	6.3	1.9		1405	6.9	2.1
	2145	3.4	1.0		1900	3.1	0.9
15 Sa	0330	5.4	1.6	30 Su	0255	6.0	1.8
	0945	3.4	1.0		0820	2.8	0.9
	1555	6.3	1.9		1525	6.9	2.1
	2240	3.3	1.0		2230	2.6	0.8
				31 M	0410	6.4	2.0
					1020	2.5	0.8
					1630	7.0	2.1
					2315	2.2	0.7

NOVEMBER

Day	Time h m	Height ft	Height m	Day	Time h m	Height ft	Height m
1 Tu	0505	6.8	2.1	16 W	0515	6.5	2.0
	1125	2.0	0.6		1130	2.8	0.9
	1730	7.3	2.2		1755	6.7	2.0
	2350	1.8	0.5		2350	2.5	0.8
2 W	0600	7.3	2.2	17 Th	0600	6.9	2.1
	1210	1.6	0.5		1215	2.4	0.7
	1840	7.5	2.3		1835	6.9	2.1
3 Th	0035	1.5	0.5	18 F	0020	2.2	0.7
	0655	7.7	2.3		0635	7.4	2.3
	1255	1.3	0.4		1250	2.1	0.6
	1920	7.6	2.3		1900	7.1	2.2
4 F	0110	1.3	0.4	19 Sa	0050	1.9	0.6
	0740	8.0	2.4		0720	7.7	2.3
	1330	1.0	0.3		1335	1.9	0.6
	2010	7.6	2.3		1945	7.2	2.2
5 Sa	0135	1.2	0.4	20 Su	0120	1.6	0.5
	0815	8.1	2.5		0755	8.0	2.4
	1415	1.0	0.3		1410	1.7	0.5
	2045	7.4	2.3		2020	7.2	2.2
6 Su	0210	1.3	0.4	21 M	0155	1.5	0.5
	0845	8.1	2.5		0840	8.2	2.5
	1450	1.1	0.3		1440	1.7	0.5
	2115	7.1	2.2		2050	7.1	2.2
7 M	0300	1.4	0.4	22 Tu	0230	1.4	0.4
	0915	7.8	2.4		0910	8.2	2.5
	1525	1.5	0.5		1500	1.7	0.5
	2205	6.7	2.0		2130	6.9	2.1
8 Tu	0320	1.7	0.5	23 W	0310	1.3	0.4
	1025	7.5	2.3		1000	8.1	2.5
	1615	1.9	0.6		1545	1.9	0.6
	2245	6.2	1.9		2210	6.6	2.0
9 W	0405	2.0	0.6	24 Th	0350	1.5	0.5
	1115	7.2	2.2		1050	7.9	2.4
	1645	2.4	0.7		1620	2.1	0.6
	2345	5.9	1.8		2305	6.4	2.0
10 Th	0440	2.5	0.8	25 F	0425	1.8	0.5
	1235	6.9	2.1		1140	7.7	2.3
	1720	2.9	0.9		1705	2.3	0.7
11 F	0100	5.7	1.7	26 Sa	0015	6.2	1.9
	0525	3.0	0.9		0515	2.2	0.7
	1320	6.6	2.0		1250	7.4	2.3
	1825	3.4	1.0		1800	2.7	0.8
12 Sa	0145	5.7	1.7	27 Su	0130	6.2	1.9
	0645	3.4	1.0		0620	2.6	0.8
	1425	6.5	2.0		1345	7.2	2.2
	2105	3.5	1.1		1925	2.9	0.9
13 Su	0255	5.7	1.7	28 M	0240	6.4	2.0
	0850	3.6	1.1		0840	2.7	0.8
	1500	6.4	2.0		1455	7.0	2.1
	2155	3.3	1.0		2145	2.6	0.8
14 M	0340	5.8	1.8	29 Tu	0345	6.7	2.0
	0955	3.4	1.0		1005	2.5	0.8
	1610	6.4	2.0		1610	6.9	2.1
	2240	3.1	0.9		2250	2.3	0.7
15 Tu	0425	6.1	1.9	30 W	0450	7.0	2.1
	1055	3.1	0.9		1105	2.1	0.6
	1700	6.5	2.0		1715	6.9	2.1
	2320	2.9	0.9		2330	2.1	0.6

DECEMBER

Day	Time h m	Height ft	Height m	Day	Time h m	Height ft	Height m
1 Th	0540	7.4	2.3	16 F	0515	6.9	2.1
	1140	1.9	0.6		1140	2.7	0.8
	1805	7.0	2.1		1750	6.4	2.0
	2350	1.9	0.6		2330	2.4	0.7
2 F	0630	7.7	2.3	17 Sa	0600	7.4	2.3
	1220	1.7	0.5		1210	2.4	0.7
	1850	7.0	2.1		1825	6.7	2.0
3 Sa	0015	1.8	0.5	18 Su	0010	2.0	0.6
	0715	7.9	2.4		0645	7.8	2.4
	1315	1.6	0.5		1250	2.2	0.7
	1940	7.0	2.1		1900	7.0	2.1
4 Su	0100	1.7	0.5	19 M	0045	1.7	0.5
	0750	8.0	2.4		0725	8.2	2.5
	1350	1.6	0.5		1335	2.0	0.6
	2010	6.9	2.1		1955	7.1	2.2
5 M	0135	1.7	0.5	20 Tu	0120	1.5	0.5
	0840	8.0	2.4		0810	8.4	2.6
	1420	1.7	0.5		1415	1.8	0.5
	2055	6.7	2.0		2030	7.0	2.1
6 Tu	0220	1.8	0.5	21 W	0215	1.4	0.4
	0920	7.8	2.4		0900	8.5	2.6
	1515	1.9	0.6		1455	1.8	0.5
	2125	6.5	2.0		2115	7.0	2.1
7 W	0300	1.9	0.6	22 Th	0250	1.3	0.4
	1005	7.7	2.3		0955	8.4	2.6
	1550	2.2	0.7		1530	1.8	0.5
	2210	6.3	1.9		2215	6.8	2.1
8 Th	0345	2.2	0.7	23 F	0335	1.4	0.4
	1050	7.4	2.3		1030	8.3	2.5
	1620	2.5	0.8		1620	1.9	0.6
	2305	6.1	1.9		2305	6.7	2.0
9 F	0420	2.5	0.8	24 Sa	0420	1.6	0.5
	1135	7.2	2.2		1130	8.0	2.4
	1700	2.8	0.9		1705	2.0	0.6
	2350	5.9	1.8				
10 Sa	0515	2.9	0.9	25 Su	0010	6.6	2.0
	1220	6.9	2.1		0510	1.9	0.6
	1800	3.1	0.9		1215	7.7	2.3
					1800	2.3	0.7
11 Su	0050	5.8	1.8	26 M	0100	6.5	2.0
	0600	3.2	1.0		0600	2.2	0.7
	1310	6.6	2.0		1315	7.3	2.2
	1850	3.4	1.0		1840	2.6	0.8
12 M	0140	5.8	1.8	27 Tu	0210	6.6	2.0
	0700	3.5	1.0		0720	2.5	0.8
	1355	6.3	1.9		1425	6.8	2.1
	2020	3.5	1.1		2025	2.7	0.8
13 Tu	0235	5.9	1.8	28 W	0325	6.7	2.0
	0840	3.6	1.1		0930	2.7	0.8
	1455	6.1	1.9		1530	6.5	2.0
	2140	3.3	1.0		2150	2.7	0.8
14 W	0330	6.2	1.9	29 Th	0420	6.9	2.1
	0945	3.4	1.0		1035	2.5	0.8
	1600	6.1	1.9		1645	6.4	2.0
	2215	3.1	0.9		2230	2.5	0.8
15 Th	0425	6.5	2.0	30 F	0510	7.2	2.2
	1055	3.0	0.9		1125	2.4	0.7
	1655	6.2	1.9		1740	6.4	2.0
	2245	2.7	0.8		2315	2.3	0.7
				31 Sa	0610	7.5	2.3
					1215	2.3	0.7
					1830	6.4	2.0
					2355	2.3	0.7

Time meridian 52° 30' W. 0000 is midnight. 1200 is noon.
Heights are referred to the Canadian chart datum of soundings. Subtract 1.7 feet (0.5 meter) to refer these levels to the datum of N.O.S. charts.

EASTPORT, MAINE, 1983

Times and Heights of High and Low Waters

JANUARY

Day	Time h m	Height ft	m	Day	Time h m	Height ft	m
1 Sa	0553	-1.5	-0.5	16 Su	0614	1.2	0.4
	1157	21.3	6.5		1212	18.1	5.5
	1827	-3.1	-0.9		1839	0.1	0.0
2 Su	0030	19.7	6.0	17 M	0038	17.0	5.2
	0647	-1.5	-0.5		0652	1.2	0.4
	1251	21.0	6.4		1249	18.0	5.5
	1920	-2.8	-0.9		1917	0.2	0.1
3 M	0125	19.5	5.9	18 Tu	0115	17.1	5.2
	0741	-1.2	-0.4		0731	1.3	0.4
	1345	20.3	6.2		1329	17.8	5.4
	2013	-2.2	-0.7		1955	0.5	0.2
4 Tu	0219	19.1	5.8	19 W	0155	17.1	5.2
	0837	-0.8	-0.2		0813	1.4	0.4
	1441	19.4	5.9		1411	17.5	5.3
	2107	-1.4	-0.4		2035	0.7	0.2
5 W	0315	18.7	5.7	20 Th	0237	17.1	5.2
	0935	-0.2	-0.1		0858	1.5	0.5
	1540	18.5	5.6		1457	17.1	5.2
	2203	-0.6	-0.2		2120	1.0	0.3
6 Th	0414	18.2	5.5	21 F	0325	17.1	5.2
	1034	0.3	0.1		0945	1.6	0.5
	1641	17.6	5.4		1545	16.8	5.1
	2300	0.2	0.1		2207	1.3	0.4
7 F	0513	17.9	5.5	22 Sa	0413	17.2	5.2
	1135	0.6	0.2		1039	1.5	0.5
	1742	16.9	5.2		1640	16.5	5.0
	2359	0.8	0.2		2300	1.5	0.5
8 Sa	0610	17.6	5.4	23 Su	0508	17.4	5.3
	1235	0.8	0.2		1136	1.2	0.4
	1842	16.5	5.0		1739	16.5	5.0
					2358	1.5	0.5
9 Su	0056	1.2	0.4	24 M	0607	17.8	5.4
	0708	17.6	5.4		1235	0.7	0.2
	1333	0.7	0.2		1840	16.7	5.1
	1940	16.4	5.0				
10 M	0152	1.4	0.4	25 Tu	0057	1.3	0.4
	0801	17.6	5.4		0706	18.4	5.6
	1426	0.6	0.2		1336	0.0	0.0
	2033	16.4	5.0		1943	17.2	5.2
11 Tu	0242	1.5	0.5	26 W	0158	0.7	0.2
	0849	17.7	5.4		0805	19.2	5.9
	1515	0.4	0.1		1436	-0.9	-0.3
	2120	16.5	5.0		2041	18.0	5.5
12 W	0331	1.4	0.4	27 Th	0255	-0.1	0.0
	0933	17.9	5.5		0903	20.1	6.1
	1601	0.2	0.1		1534	-1.9	-0.6
	2203	16.6	5.1		2137	18.8	5.7
13 Th	0414	1.3	0.4	28 F	0353	-0.9	-0.3
	1015	18.0	5.5		0958	20.9	6.4
	1643	0.0	0.0		1627	-2.7	-0.8
	2243	16.7	5.1		2232	19.5	5.9
14 F	0456	1.2	0.4	29 Sa	0446	-1.6	-0.5
	1055	18.1	5.5		1052	21.4	6.5
	1722	0.0	0.0		1720	-3.2	-1.0
	2322	16.9	5.2		2324	20.1	6.1
15 Sa	0535	1.2	0.4	30 Su	0539	-2.1	-0.6
	1133	18.1	5.5		1144	21.5	6.6
	1801	0.0	0.0		1811	-3.4	-1.0
	2359	17.0	5.2				
				31 M	0015	20.3	6.2
					0630	-2.2	-0.7
					1235	21.3	6.5
					1900	-3.1	-0.9

FEBRUARY

Day	Time h m	Height ft	m	Day	Time h m	Height ft	m
1 Tu	0105	20.2	6.2	16 W	0046	18.0	5.5
	0723	-2.0	-0.6		0704	0.4	0.1
	1326	20.6	6.3		1302	18.3	5.6
	1950	-2.4	-0.7		1923	0.0	0.0
2 W	0155	19.8	6.0	17 Th	0123	18.0	5.5
	0814	-1.4	-0.4		0742	0.4	0.1
	1419	19.6	6.0		1342	18.0	5.5
	2040	-1.5	-0.5		2003	0.3	0.1
3 Th	0248	19.1	5.8	18 F	0204	18.0	5.5
	0907	-0.7	-0.2		0824	0.6	0.2
	1512	18.4	5.6		1424	17.6	5.4
	2133	-0.4	-0.1		2045	0.7	0.2
4 F	0340	18.4	5.6	19 Sa	0248	17.9	5.5
	1002	0.2	0.1		0912	0.8	0.2
	1607	17.3	5.3		1514	17.1	5.2
	2226	0.7	0.2		2133	1.2	0.4
5 Sa	0435	17.6	5.4	20 Su	0338	17.7	5.4
	1100	0.9	0.3		1005	1.0	0.3
	1708	16.3	5.0		1609	16.7	5.1
	2322	1.6	0.5		2227	1.6	0.5
6 Su	0534	17.0	5.2	21 M	0434	17.6	5.4
	1159	1.4	0.4		1105	1.0	0.3
	1808	15.7	4.8		1710	16.4	5.0
					2328	1.8	0.5
7 M	0022	2.2	0.7	22 Tu	0537	17.7	5.4
	0635	16.7	5.1		1210	0.8	0.2
	1259	1.6	0.5		1816	16.4	5.0
	1908	15.5	4.7				
8 Tu	0119	2.4	0.7	23 W	0033	1.6	0.5
	0730	16.7	5.1		0642	18.1	5.5
	1357	1.4	0.4		1315	0.2	0.1
	2004	15.6	4.8		1922	17.0	5.2
9 W	0215	2.3	0.7	24 Th	0138	1.0	0.3
	0822	16.9	5.2		0748	18.9	5.8
	1449	1.1	0.3		1418	-0.7	-0.2
	2054	15.9	4.8		2025	17.8	5.4
10 Th	0304	1.9	0.6	25 F	0241	0.0	0.0
	0910	17.3	5.3		0847	19.8	6.0
	1536	0.7	0.2		1516	-1.7	-0.5
	2139	16.3	5.0		2122	18.8	5.7
11 F	0350	1.5	0.5	26 Sa	0339	-1.0	-0.3
	0953	17.7	5.4		0945	20.6	6.3
	1618	0.3	0.1		1611	-2.6	-0.8
	2220	16.8	5.1		2216	19.8	6.0
12 Sa	0432	1.1	0.3	27 Su	0432	-1.9	-0.6
	1032	18.1	5.5		1037	21.2	6.5
	1658	0.0	0.0		1702	-3.1	-0.9
	2257	17.2	5.2		2307	20.4	6.2
13 Su	0512	0.8	0.2	28 M	0523	-2.5	-0.8
	1111	18.4	5.6		1128	21.3	6.5
	1736	-0.2	-0.1		1751	-3.2	-1.0
	2334	17.5	5.3		2355	20.7	6.3
14 M	0548	0.5	0.2				
	1147	18.5	5.6				
	1812	-0.3	-0.1				
15 Tu	0009	17.8	5.4				
	0625	0.4	0.1				
	1224	18.5	5.6				
	1847	-0.2	-0.1				

MARCH

Day	Time h m	Height ft	m	Day	Time h m	Height ft	m
1 Tu	0613	-2.6	-0.8	16 W	0559	-0.4	-0.1
	1217	21.0	6.4		1158	18.8	5.7
	1837	-2.9	-0.9		1817	-0.5	-0.2
2 W	0041	20.5	6.2	17 Th	0016	18.8	5.7
	0700	-2.4	-0.7		0636	-0.5	-0.2
	1305	20.3	6.2		1235	18.7	5.7
	1924	-2.1	-0.6		1854	-0.3	-0.1
3 Th	0128	20.0	6.1	18 F	0053	18.9	5.8
	0750	-1.7	-0.5		0716	-0.5	-0.2
	1352	19.3	5.9		1316	18.4	5.6
	2011	-1.0	-0.3		1933	0.1	0.0
4 F	0216	19.2	5.9	19 Sa	0135	18.8	5.7
	0837	-0.8	-0.2		0758	-0.3	-0.1
	1442	18.0	5.5		1358	17.9	5.5
	2101	0.2	0.1		2016	0.6	0.2
5 Sa	0305	18.2	5.5	20 Su	0221	18.5	5.6
	0929	0.3	0.1		0847	0.0	0.0
	1533	16.8	5.1		1450	17.3	5.3
	2152	1.4	0.4		2107	1.1	0.3
6 Su	0359	17.2	5.2	21 M	0312	18.1	5.5
	1024	1.2	0.4		0941	0.5	0.2
	1629	15.8	4.8		1546	16.7	5.1
	2247	2.3	0.7		2205	1.6	0.5
7 M	0455	16.4	5.0	22 Tu	0412	17.7	5.4
	1124	1.9	0.6		1044	0.8	0.2
	1729	15.1	4.6		1650	16.4	5.0
	2346	2.9	0.9		2309	1.9	0.6
8 Tu	0555	16.0	4.9	23 W	0517	17.6	5.4
	1224	2.2	0.7		1150	0.7	0.2
	1832	14.9	4.5		1759	16.5	5.0
9 W	0046	3.0	0.9	24 Th	0017	1.6	0.5
	0655	16.1	4.9		0626	17.9	5.5
	1324	2.0	0.6		1258	0.2	0.1
	1931	15.2	4.6		1908	17.1	5.2
10 Th	0143	2.7	0.8	25 F	0124	0.9	0.3
	0751	16.4	5.0		0732	18.6	5.7
	1417	1.6	0.5		1401	-0.6	-0.2
	2023	15.7	4.8		2009	18.0	5.5
11 F	0234	2.1	0.6	26 Sa	0225	-0.1	0.0
	0841	17.0	5.2		0833	19.4	5.9
	1505	1.0	0.3		1500	-1.5	-0.5
	2109	16.4	5.0		2105	19.1	5.8
12 Sa	0321	1.4	0.4	27 Su	0323	-1.2	-0.4
	0924	17.6	5.4		0929	20.2	6.2
	1547	0.4	0.1		1553	-2.2	-0.7
	2150	17.0	5.2		2158	20.0	6.1
13 Su	0404	0.8	0.2	28 M	0415	-2.1	-0.6
	1006	18.1	5.5		1021	20.6	6.3
	1627	0.0	0.0		1641	-2.6	-0.8
	2227	17.7	5.4		2246	20.5	6.2
14 M	0443	0.3	0.1	29 Tu	0505	-2.6	-0.8
	1043	18.5	5.6		1108	20.7	6.3
	1705	-0.4	-0.1		1728	-2.5	-0.8
	2304	18.2	5.5		2331	20.6	6.3
15 Tu	0521	-0.1	0.0	30 W	0552	-2.6	-0.8
	1121	18.7	5.7		1154	20.3	6.2
	1740	-0.5	-0.2		1812	-2.1	-0.6
	2340	18.6	5.7				
				31 Th	0016	20.4	6.2
					0636	-2.2	-0.7
					1240	19.6	6.0
					1857	-1.2	-0.4

Time meridian 75° W. 0000 is midnight. 1200 is noon.
Heights are referred to mean low water which is the chart datum of soundings.

Times and Heights of High and Low Waters

APRIL

Day	Time (h m)	ft	m
1 F	0059	19.7	6.0
	0722	-1.5	-0.5
	1326	18.6	5.7
	1942	-0.2	-0.1
2 Sa	0145	18.8	5.7
	0810	-0.5	-0.2
	1411	17.5	5.3
	2029	0.9	0.3
3 Su	0230	17.8	5.4
	0859	0.5	0.2
	1501	16.4	5.0
	2117	1.9	0.6
4 M	0320	16.9	5.2
	0950	1.4	0.4
	1554	15.5	4.7
	2212	2.7	0.8
5 Tu	0417	16.1	4.9
	1045	2.1	0.6
	1653	15.0	4.6
	2308	3.2	1.0
6 W	0515	15.7	4.8
	1145	2.4	0.7
	1753	14.9	4.5
7 Th	0008	3.2	1.0
	0616	15.8	4.8
	1242	2.2	0.7
	1850	15.2	4.6
8 F	0106	2.8	0.9
	0711	16.2	4.9
	1338	1.8	0.5
	1943	15.8	4.8
9 Sa	0159	2.1	0.6
	0804	16.8	5.1
	1426	1.2	0.4
	2030	16.6	5.1
10 Su	0247	1.3	0.4
	0849	17.4	5.3
	1510	0.6	0.2
	2113	17.4	5.3
11 M	0331	0.5	0.2
	0931	18.0	5.5
	1552	0.1	0.0
	2153	18.2	5.5
12 Tu	0411	-0.2	-0.1
	1011	18.5	5.6
	1631	-0.3	-0.1
	2230	18.8	5.7
13 W	0451	-0.7	-0.2
	1051	18.8	5.7
	1708	-0.5	-0.2
	2308	19.2	5.9
14 Th	0530	-1.1	-0.3
	1130	18.9	5.8
	1747	-0.5	-0.2
	2347	19.5	5.9
15 F	0610	-1.2	-0.4
	1210	18.8	5.7
	1827	-0.4	-0.1
16 Sa	0027	19.6	6.0
	0652	-1.2	-0.4
	1252	18.6	5.7
	1910	0.0	0.0
17 Su	0110	19.4	5.9
	0737	-0.9	-0.3
	1339	18.1	5.5
	1957	0.5	0.2
18 M	0200	19.0	5.8
	0830	-0.5	-0.2
	1433	17.5	5.3
	2051	1.0	0.3
19 Tu	0253	18.4	5.6
	0927	0.0	0.0
	1533	17.0	5.2
	2149	1.5	0.5
20 W	0357	18.0	5.5
	1029	0.3	0.1
	1637	16.7	5.1
	2255	1.6	0.5
21 Th	0504	17.7	5.4
	1135	0.4	0.1
	1746	16.9	5.2
22 F	0003	1.3	0.4
	0613	17.9	5.5
	1240	0.0	0.0
	1851	17.5	5.3
23 Sa	0109	0.6	0.2
	0716	18.4	5.6
	1343	-0.6	-0.2
	1951	18.4	5.6
24 Su	0210	-0.4	-0.1
	0817	19.0	5.8
	1438	-1.1	-0.3
	2046	19.2	5.9
25 M	0305	-1.2	-0.4
	0910	19.5	5.9
	1531	-1.6	-0.5
	2137	19.9	6.1
26 Tu	0357	-1.9	-0.6
	1001	19.7	6.0
	1619	-1.7	-0.5
	2224	20.2	6.2
27 W	0444	-2.2	-0.7
	1049	19.6	6.0
	1704	-1.4	-0.4
	2308	20.1	6.1
28 Th	0529	-2.1	-0.6
	1133	19.2	5.9
	1747	-0.9	-0.3
	2350	19.8	6.0
29 F	0615	-1.6	-0.5
	1215	18.5	5.6
	1831	-0.2	-0.1
30 Sa	0032	19.1	5.8
	0657	-1.0	-0.3
	1300	17.8	5.4
	1915	0.6	0.2

MAY

Day	Time (h m)	ft	m
1 Su	0115	18.3	5.6
	0742	-0.2	-0.1
	1343	16.9	5.2
	1958	1.5	0.5
2 M	0158	17.5	5.3
	0829	0.7	0.2
	1430	16.2	4.9
	2047	2.2	0.7
3 Tu	0247	16.8	5.1
	0917	1.4	0.4
	1520	15.5	4.7
	2138	2.8	0.9
4 W	0338	16.2	4.9
	1010	1.9	0.6
	1615	15.2	4.6
	2231	3.1	0.9
5 Th	0434	15.8	4.8
	1105	2.2	0.7
	1711	15.2	4.6
	2329	3.1	0.9
6 F	0532	15.8	4.8
	1200	2.1	0.6
	1806	15.5	4.7
7 Sa	0025	2.7	0.8
	0629	16.1	4.9
	1253	1.8	0.5
	1858	16.1	4.9
8 Su	0117	2.0	0.6
	0721	16.6	5.1
	1343	1.3	0.4
	1948	16.9	5.2
9 M	0207	1.2	0.4
	0809	17.2	5.2
	1428	0.8	0.2
	2031	17.8	5.4
10 Tu	0254	0.4	0.1
	0854	17.7	5.4
	1513	0.3	0.1
	2114	18.5	5.6
11 W	0337	-0.4	-0.1
	0938	18.2	5.5
	1555	-0.1	0.0
	2156	19.2	5.9
12 Th	0419	-1.0	-0.3
	1020	18.6	5.7
	1636	-0.4	-0.1
	2236	19.7	6.0
13 F	0503	-1.5	-0.5
	1104	18.9	5.8
	1720	-0.5	-0.2
	2321	20.1	6.1
14 Sa	0546	-1.8	-0.5
	1149	18.9	5.8
	1803	-0.4	-0.1
15 Su	0004	20.1	6.1
	0633	-1.8	-0.5
	1235	18.7	5.7
	1851	-0.2	-0.1
16 M	0052	19.9	6.1
	0723	-1.5	-0.5
	1326	18.3	5.6
	1942	0.2	0.1
17 Tu	0145	19.5	5.9
	0816	-1.1	-0.3
	1422	17.9	5.5
	2037	0.6	0.2
18 W	0242	18.9	5.8
	0914	-0.7	-0.2
	1520	17.5	5.3
	2138	0.9	0.3
19 Th	0344	18.4	5.6
	1015	-0.3	-0.1
	1625	17.4	5.3
	2242	1.0	0.3
20 F	0449	18.0	5.5
	1118	-0.1	0.0
	1729	17.6	5.4
	2348	0.7	0.2
21 Sa	0555	17.9	5.5
	1221	-0.2	-0.1
	1831	18.0	5.5
22 Su	0051	0.2	0.1
	0659	18.1	5.5
	1319	-0.4	-0.1
	1930	18.6	5.7
23 M	0151	-0.4	-0.1
	0759	18.3	5.6
	1415	-0.5	-0.2
	2025	19.1	5.8
24 Tu	0246	-1.0	-0.3
	0853	18.5	5.6
	1508	-0.6	-0.2
	2113	19.4	5.9
25 W	0337	-1.3	-0.4
	0941	18.5	5.6
	1555	-0.5	-0.2
	2159	19.5	5.9
26 Th	0426	-1.4	-0.4
	1027	18.3	5.6
	1641	-0.2	-0.1
	2243	19.3	5.9
27 F	0509	-1.3	-0.4
	1112	18.0	5.5
	1725	0.2	0.1
	2325	19.0	5.8
28 Sa	0552	-0.9	-0.3
	1155	17.6	5.4
	1807	0.7	0.2
29 Su	0007	18.5	5.6
	0635	-0.4	-0.1
	1236	17.1	5.2
	1849	1.3	0.4
30 M	0048	18.0	5.5
	0718	0.1	0.0
	1318	16.6	5.1
	1931	1.8	0.5
31 Tu	0131	17.4	5.3
	0800	0.7	0.2
	1401	16.2	4.9
	2016	2.2	0.7

JUNE

Day	Time (h m)	ft	m
1 W	0216	16.9	5.2
	0845	1.2	0.4
	1448	15.8	4.8
	2104	2.6	0.8
2 Th	0304	16.5	5.0
	0933	1.6	0.5
	1538	15.7	4.8
	2154	2.7	0.8
3 F	0356	16.2	4.9
	1023	1.8	0.5
	1629	15.7	4.8
	2247	2.7	0.8
4 Sa	0449	16.1	4.9
	1115	1.8	0.5
	1722	16.0	4.9
	2342	2.4	0.7
5 Su	0543	16.1	4.9
	1205	1.7	0.5
	1813	16.5	5.0
6 M	0034	1.9	0.6
	0635	16.4	5.0
	1256	1.4	0.4
	1903	17.2	5.2
7 Tu	0124	1.2	0.4
	0727	16.9	5.2
	1346	1.1	0.3
	1951	18.0	5.5
8 W	0215	0.4	0.1
	0817	17.4	5.3
	1433	0.6	0.2
	2038	18.7	5.7
9 Th	0303	-0.5	-0.2
	0906	17.9	5.5
	1520	0.2	0.1
	2124	19.5	5.9
10 F	0350	-1.2	-0.4
	0953	18.4	5.6
	1607	-0.2	-0.1
	2210	20.1	6.1
11 Sa	0438	-1.8	-0.5
	1040	18.8	5.7
	1654	-0.5	-0.2
	2257	20.5	6.2
12 Su	0527	-2.2	-0.7
	1129	19.0	5.8
	1744	-0.7	-0.2
	2347	20.6	6.3
13 M	0617	-2.3	-0.7
	1220	19.0	5.8
	1835	-0.7	-0.2
14 Tu	0038	20.5	6.2
	0709	-2.2	-0.7
	1312	18.9	5.8
	1929	-0.5	-0.2
15 W	0131	20.1	6.1
	0803	-1.9	-0.6
	1408	18.6	5.7
	2024	-0.2	-0.1
16 Th	0230	19.5	5.9
	0859	-1.4	-0.4
	1507	18.4	5.6
	2124	0.0	0.0
17 F	0330	18.8	5.7
	0956	-0.9	-0.3
	1607	18.2	5.5
	2226	0.2	0.1
18 Sa	0431	18.2	5.5
	1055	-0.4	-0.1
	1707	18.2	5.5
	2328	0.3	0.1
19 Su	0535	17.8	5.4
	1156	-0.1	0.0
	1808	18.3	5.6
20 M	0030	0.1	0.0
	0637	17.6	5.4
	1255	0.2	0.1
	1906	18.4	5.6
21 Tu	0129	-0.1	0.0
	0736	17.5	5.3
	1351	0.3	0.1
	2001	18.6	5.7
22 W	0225	-0.3	-0.1
	0832	17.4	5.3
	1443	0.4	0.1
	2051	18.7	5.7
23 Th	0316	-0.5	-0.2
	0923	17.4	5.3
	1532	0.6	0.2
	2139	18.7	5.7
24 F	0404	-0.6	-0.2
	1008	17.3	5.3
	1619	0.8	0.2
	2222	18.5	5.6
25 Sa	0448	-0.5	-0.2
	1051	17.1	5.2
	1702	1.0	0.3
	2302	18.4	5.6
26 Su	0530	-0.3	-0.1
	1130	17.0	5.2
	1744	1.2	0.4
	2343	18.2	5.5
27 M	0611	-0.1	0.0
	1211	16.8	5.1
	1825	1.4	0.4
28 Tu	0024	17.9	5.5
	0652	0.2	0.1
	1252	16.6	5.1
	1906	1.6	0.5
29 W	0104	17.6	5.4
	0733	0.5	0.2
	1333	16.5	5.0
	1947	1.8	0.5
30 Th	0145	17.3	5.3
	0814	0.8	0.2
	1415	16.4	5.0
	2032	2.0	0.6

Time meridian 75° W. 0000 is midnight. 1200 is noon.
Heights are referred to mean low water which is the chart datum of soundings.

EASTPORT, MAINE, 1983

Times and Heights of High and Low Waters

JULY

Day	Time h m	Height ft	Height m	Day	Time h m	Height ft	Height m
1 F	0230	17.0	5.2	16 Sa	0309	19.1	5.8
	0858	1.1	0.3		0933	-1.2	-0.4
	1459	16.3	5.0		1542	18.8	5.7
	2117	2.1	0.6		2203	-0.3	-0.1
2 Sa	0317	16.6	5.1	17 Su	0410	18.2	5.5
	0944	1.4	0.4		1030	-0.4	-0.1
	1546	16.4	5.0		1641	18.4	5.6
	2205	2.2	0.7		2303	0.1	0.0
3 Su	0405	16.4	5.0	18 M	0510	17.4	5.3
	1031	1.6	0.5		1127	0.4	0.1
	1636	16.6	5.1		1740	18.1	5.5
	2259	2.0	0.6				
4 M	0458	16.3	5.0	19 Tu	0004	0.4	0.1
	1119	1.7	0.5		0612	16.9	5.2
	1726	16.9	5.2		1227	0.9	0.3
	2351	1.7	0.5		1839	17.9	5.5
5 Tu	0554	16.3	5.0	20 W	0104	0.5	0.2
	1213	1.6	0.5		0714	16.6	5.1
	1818	17.4	5.3		1324	1.3	0.4
					1936	17.8	5.4
6 W	0045	1.2	0.4	21 Th	0201	0.4	0.1
	0647	16.6	5.1		0809	16.5	5.0
	1303	1.4	0.4		1420	1.4	0.4
	1911	18.0	5.5		2028	17.8	5.4
7 Th	0138	0.4	0.1	22 F	0255	0.3	0.1
	0743	17.0	5.2		0900	16.5	5.0
	1359	0.9	0.3		1511	1.4	0.4
	2004	18.7	5.7		2117	17.9	5.5
8 F	0233	-0.4	-0.1	23 Sa	0342	0.2	0.1
	0836	17.6	5.4		0947	16.6	5.1
	1451	0.4	0.1		1558	1.3	0.4
	2056	19.5	5.9		2200	18.0	5.5
9 Sa	0327	-1.2	-0.4	24 Su	0428	0.0	0.0
	0929	18.3	5.6		1030	16.7	5.1
	1543	-0.2	-0.1		1640	1.2	0.4
	2147	20.3	6.2		2242	18.1	5.5
10 Su	0418	-2.0	-0.6	25 M	0509	0.0	0.0
	1021	18.8	5.7		1109	16.9	5.2
	1636	-0.8	-0.2		1722	1.1	0.3
	2240	20.8	6.3		2321	18.1	5.5
11 M	0509	-2.5	-0.8	26 Tu	0548	0.0	0.0
	1113	19.3	5.9		1146	17.0	5.2
	1728	-1.2	-0.4		1800	1.1	0.3
	2332	21.1	6.4		2359	18.1	5.5
12 Tu	0600	-2.8	-0.9	27 W	0626	0.1	0.0
	1204	19.6	6.0		1225	17.0	5.2
	1820	-1.4	-0.4		1840	1.1	0.3
13 W	0024	21.0	6.4	28 Th	0038	18.0	5.5
	0652	-2.8	-0.9		0703	0.3	0.1
	1257	19.7	6.0		1302	17.1	5.2
	1913	-1.4	-0.4		1918	1.2	0.4
14 Th	0118	20.7	6.3	29 F	0115	17.7	5.4
	0745	-2.5	-0.8		0742	0.5	0.2
	1350	19.5	5.9		1342	17.1	5.2
	2008	-1.2	-0.4		1958	1.3	0.4
15 F	0213	20.0	6.1	30 Sa	0157	17.4	5.3
	0838	-1.9	-0.6		0821	0.8	0.2
	1445	19.2	5.9		1422	17.1	5.2
	2104	-0.8	-0.2		2042	1.5	0.5
				31 Su	0240	17.1	5.2
					0903	1.1	0.3
					1505	17.0	5.2
					2125	1.6	0.5

AUGUST

Day	Time h m	Height ft	Height m	Day	Time h m	Height ft	Height m
1 M	0325	16.7	5.1	16 Tu	0442	16.8	5.1
	0948	1.5	0.5		1057	1.2	0.4
	1552	17.0	5.2		1709	17.5	5.3
	2217	1.6	0.5		2335	0.9	0.3
2 Tu	0419	16.4	5.0	17 W	0544	16.1	4.9
	1038	1.7	0.5		1158	1.8	0.5
	1644	17.1	5.2		1810	17.1	5.2
	2310	1.5	0.5				
3 W	0513	16.2	4.9	18 Th	0037	1.2	0.4
	1133	1.8	0.5		0647	15.8	4.8
	1740	17.4	5.3		1258	2.1	0.6
					1909	16.9	5.2
4 Th	0008	1.2	0.4	19 F	0135	1.2	0.4
	0613	16.3	5.0		0746	15.8	4.8
	1229	1.7	0.5		1356	2.1	0.6
	1839	17.9	5.5		2003	17.1	5.2
5 F	0108	0.6	0.2	20 Sa	0230	1.0	0.3
	0714	16.8	5.1		0838	16.0	4.9
	1330	1.2	0.4		1449	1.8	0.5
	1938	18.6	5.7		2054	17.4	5.3
6 Sa	0207	-0.3	-0.1	21 Su	0319	0.6	0.2
	0812	17.4	5.3		0923	16.4	5.0
	1428	0.5	0.2		1534	1.4	0.4
	2034	19.5	5.9		2139	17.7	5.4
7 Su	0305	-1.2	-0.4	22 M	0403	0.3	0.1
	0908	18.3	5.6		1006	16.8	5.1
	1524	-0.4	-0.1		1616	1.0	0.3
	2130	20.4	6.2		2219	18.1	5.5
8 M	0358	-2.1	-0.6	23 Tu	0443	0.0	0.0
	1003	19.2	5.9		1042	17.2	5.2
	1619	-1.3	-0.4		1656	0.7	0.2
	2224	21.1	6.4		2256	18.3	5.6
9 Tu	0451	-2.9	-0.9	24 W	0520	-0.2	-0.1
	1055	19.9	6.1		1119	17.5	5.3
	1711	-1.9	-0.6		1734	0.5	0.2
	2316	21.5	6.6		2333	18.4	5.6
10 W	0542	-3.2	-1.0	25 Th	0556	-0.2	-0.1
	1147	20.3	6.2		1154	17.7	5.4
	1803	-2.3	-0.7		1812	0.4	0.1
11 Th	0007	21.4	6.5	26 F	0009	18.3	5.6
	0633	-3.2	-1.0		0632	0.0	0.0
	1237	20.5	6.2		1230	17.8	5.4
	1856	-2.3	-0.7		1849	0.4	0.1
12 F	0059	21.0	6.4	27 Sa	0046	18.1	5.5
	0723	-2.8	-0.9		0708	0.2	0.1
	1329	20.3	6.2		1306	17.9	5.5
	1947	-2.0	-0.6		1927	0.6	0.2
13 Sa	0152	20.1	6.1	28 Su	0123	17.8	5.4
	0814	-2.0	-0.6		0745	0.6	0.2
	1420	19.7	6.0		1345	17.8	5.4
	2040	-1.3	-0.4		2008	0.8	0.2
14 Su	0245	19.0	5.8	29 M	0206	17.4	5.3
	0906	-0.9	-0.3		0826	1.0	0.3
	1514	19.0	5.8		1427	17.6	5.4
	2136	-0.5	-0.2		2051	1.0	0.3
15 M	0343	17.9	5.5	30 Tu	0251	16.9	5.2
	1001	0.2	0.1		0909	1.5	0.5
	1610	18.2	5.5		1515	17.4	5.3
	2234	0.3	0.1		2141	1.2	0.4
				31 W	0345	16.4	5.0
					1002	1.9	0.6
					1609	17.3	5.3
					2237	1.3	0.4

SEPTEMBER

Day	Time h m	Height ft	Height m	Day	Time h m	Height ft	Height m
1 Th	0442	16.1	4.9	16 F	0005	1.8	0.5
	1100	2.1	0.6		0616	15.2	4.6
	1708	17.3	5.3		1228	2.7	0.8
	2341	1.2	0.4		1837	16.3	5.0
2 F	0546	16.2	4.9	17 Sa	0105	1.7	0.5
	1204	1.9	0.6		0716	15.4	4.7
	1813	17.7	5.4		1327	2.5	0.8
					1935	16.5	5.1
3 Sa	0045	0.6	0.2	18 Su	0201	1.4	0.4
	0651	16.6	5.1		0809	15.9	4.8
	1308	1.3	0.4		1419	1.9	0.6
	1916	18.4	5.6		2025	17.1	5.2
4 Su	0148	-0.2	-0.1	19 M	0249	0.9	0.3
	0753	17.5	5.3		0854	16.5	5.0
	1409	0.4	0.1		1505	1.3	0.4
	2017	19.4	5.9		2110	17.6	5.4
5 M	0246	-1.3	-0.4	20 Tu	0332	0.4	0.1
	0852	18.6	5.7		0934	17.2	5.2
	1508	-0.8	-0.2		1547	0.7	0.2
	2114	20.4	6.2		2150	18.1	5.5
6 Tu	0341	-2.3	-0.7	21 W	0411	0.0	0.0
	0945	19.7	6.0		1011	17.7	5.4
	1603	-1.8	-0.5		1627	0.2	0.1
	2208	21.1	6.4		2227	18.4	5.6
7 W	0433	-3.0	-0.9	22 Th	0448	-0.2	-0.1
	1037	20.5	6.2		1048	18.1	5.5
	1654	-2.6	-0.8		1706	-0.1	0.0
	2259	21.5	6.6		2304	18.5	5.6
8 Th	0522	-3.3	-1.0	23 F	0525	-0.3	-0.1
	1126	20.9	6.4		1123	18.4	5.6
	1744	-2.9	-0.9		1742	-0.3	-0.1
	2349	21.3	6.5		2340	18.5	5.6
9 F	0611	-3.1	-0.9	24 Sa	0559	-0.2	-0.1
	1214	21.0	6.4		1158	18.6	5.7
	1835	-2.8	-0.9		1820	-0.3	-0.1
10 Sa	0038	20.7	6.3	25 Su	0017	18.3	5.6
	0659	-2.5	-0.8		0636	0.1	0.0
	1302	20.5	6.2		1234	18.6	5.7
	1923	-2.3	-0.7		1857	-0.2	-0.1
11 Su	0128	19.8	6.0	26 M	0057	18.0	5.5
	0747	-1.5	-0.5		0713	0.5	0.2
	1352	19.7	6.0		1313	18.4	5.6
	2014	-1.4	-0.4		1938	0.1	0.0
12 M	0218	18.6	5.7	27 Tu	0138	17.6	5.4
	0837	-0.3	-0.1		0754	1.0	0.3
	1443	18.7	5.7		1355	18.1	5.5
	2109	-0.3	-0.1		2022	0.4	0.1
13 Tu	0314	17.3	5.3	28 W	0224	17.0	5.2
	0930	0.9	0.3		0843	1.5	0.5
	1536	17.7	5.4		1443	17.8	5.4
	2205	0.7	0.2		2115	0.8	0.2
14 W	0412	16.2	4.9	29 Th	0317	16.5	5.0
	1027	1.9	0.6		0935	2.0	0.6
	1636	16.8	5.1		1541	17.4	5.3
	2304	1.4	0.4		2213	1.1	0.3
15 Th	0514	15.5	4.7	30 F	0420	16.2	4.9
	1128	2.6	0.8		1039	2.2	0.7
	1737	16.3	5.0		1646	17.3	5.3
					2319	1.0	0.3

Time meridian 75° W. 0000 is midnight. 1200 is noon.
Heights are referred to mean low water which is the chart datum of soundings.

Times and Heights of High and Low Waters

| OCTOBER | | | | NOVEMBER | | | | DECEMBER | | | |

Day	Time h m	Height ft	m	Day	Time h m	Height ft	m	Day	Time h m	Height ft	m
1 Sa	0527 1145 1754	16.2 1.9 17.6	4.9 0.6 5.4	16 Su	0029 0639 1253 1858	2.0 15.4 2.7 16.2	0.6 4.7 0.8 4.9	1 Tu	0108 0719 1338 1944	-0.4 18.3 -0.2 18.9	-0.1 5.6 -0.1 5.8
2 Su	0026 0634 1251 1859	0.5 16.8 1.2 18.3	0.2 5.1 0.4 5.6	17 M	0122 0730 1345 1949	1.6 16.0 2.0 16.7	0.5 4.9 0.6 5.1	2 W	0207 0815 1434 2041	-1.1 19.3 -1.3 19.5	-0.3 5.9 -0.4 5.9
3 M	0128 0736 1354 2001	-0.3 17.9 0.1 19.2	-0.1 5.5 0.0 5.9	18 Tu	0212 0817 1431 2036	1.1 16.7 1.2 17.3	0.3 5.1 0.4 5.3	3 Th	0300 0907 1529 2132	-1.6 20.1 -2.1 19.9	-0.5 6.1 -0.6 6.1
4 Tu	0226 0833 1452 2058	-1.3 19.0 -1.1 20.1	-0.4 5.8 -0.3 6.1	19 W	0254 0857 1516 2116	0.6 17.5 0.5 17.9	0.2 5.3 0.2 5.5	4 F	0350 0955 1617 2222	-1.9 20.6 -2.6 19.9	-0.6 6.3 -0.8 6.1
5 W	0321 0926 1545 2150	-2.1 20.1 -2.2 20.7	-0.6 6.1 -0.7 6.3	20 Th	0335 0937 1555 2155	0.2 18.1 -0.1 18.2	0.1 5.5 0.0 5.5	5 Sa	0437 1042 1705 2309	-1.8 20.7 -2.6 19.6	-0.5 6.3 -0.8 6.0
6 Th	0411 1016 1636 2240	-2.7 20.8 -2.8 20.9	-0.8 6.3 -0.9 6.4	21 F	0414 1013 1635 2234	-0.1 18.7 -0.5 18.5	0.0 5.7 -0.2 5.6	6 Su	0523 1126 1751 2355	-1.4 20.4 -2.3 19.0	-0.4 6.2 -0.7 5.8
7 F	0459 1104 1725 2329	-2.8 21.1 -3.1 20.7	-0.9 6.4 -0.9 6.3	22 Sa	0451 1050 1713 2313	-0.2 19.0 -0.8 18.5	-0.1 5.8 -0.2 5.6	7 M	0609 1209 1837	-0.7 19.7 -1.6	-0.2 6.0 -0.5
8 Sa	0547 1150 1813	-2.4 20.9 -2.8	-0.7 6.4 -0.9	23 Su	0528 1127 1750 2350	-0.1 19.2 -0.9 18.4	0.0 5.9 -0.3 5.6	8 Tu	0041 0654 1256 1923	18.2 0.2 18.9 -0.7	5.5 0.1 5.8 -0.2
9 Su	0016 0633 1236 1900	20.0 -1.7 20.3 -2.1	6.1 -0.5 6.2 -0.6	24 M	0606 1205 1832	0.1 19.2 -0.8	0.0 5.9 -0.2	9 W	0126 0742 1342 2011	17.3 1.1 18.0 0.2	5.3 0.3 5.5 0.1
10 M	0104 0720 1321 1948	19.0 -0.6 19.4 -1.1	5.8 -0.2 5.9 -0.3	25 Tu	0032 0646 1246 1914	18.1 0.4 19.0 -0.5	5.5 0.1 5.8 -0.2	10 Th	0214 0830 1430 2101	16.4 2.0 17.1 1.1	5.0 0.6 5.2 0.3
11 Tu	0152 0807 1411 2039	17.9 0.5 18.3 0.0	5.5 0.2 5.6 0.0	26 W	0115 0728 1332 2003	17.7 0.9 18.7 -0.2	5.4 0.3 5.7 -0.1	11 F	0305 0922 1522 2154	15.7 2.6 16.3 1.7	4.8 0.8 5.0 0.5
12 W	0243 0858 1502 2133	16.8 1.6 17.2 1.0	5.1 0.5 5.2 0.3	27 Th	0205 0821 1424 2056	17.2 1.3 18.2 0.2	5.2 0.4 5.5 0.1	12 Sa	0400 1018 1620 2250	15.3 3.0 15.9 2.0	4.7 0.9 4.8 0.6
13 Th	0338 0953 1600 2229	15.8 2.5 16.4 1.8	4.8 0.8 5.0 0.5	28 F	0301 0919 1524 2157	16.8 1.7 17.8 0.5	5.1 0.5 5.4 0.2	13 Su	0456 1114 1719 2344	15.2 3.0 15.8 2.1	4.6 0.9 4.8 0.6
14 F	0439 1054 1700 2330	15.2 3.0 15.9 2.1	4.6 0.9 4.8 0.6	29 Sa	0404 1023 1629 2301	16.5 1.8 17.5 0.6	5.0 0.5 5.3 0.2	14 M	0552 1210 1814	15.5 2.7 16.0	4.7 0.8 4.9
15 Sa	0540 1154 1802	15.1 3.0 15.9	4.6 0.9 4.8	30 Su	0511 1130 1737	16.7 1.5 17.7	5.1 0.5 5.4	15 Tu	0037 0645 1303 1906	1.8 16.1 2.1 16.4	0.5 4.9 0.6 5.0
				31 M	0005 0617 1234 1843	0.2 17.4 0.8 18.2	0.1 5.3 0.2 5.5				

Day	Time h m	Height ft	m	Day	Time h m	Height ft	m
16 W	0127 0732 1353 1954	1.4 16.8 1.3 16.9	0.4 5.1 0.4 5.2	16 F	0128 0733 1359 2001	1.5 17.5 0.8 16.8	0.5 5.3 0.2 5.1
17 Th	0212 0817 1438 2039	1.0 17.6 0.6 17.4	0.3 5.4 0.2 5.3	17 Sa	0215 0820 1446 2047	1.1 18.2 0.1 17.3	0.3 5.5 0.0 5.3
18 F	0257 0857 1521 2121	0.6 18.3 -0.1 17.9	0.2 5.6 0.0 5.7	18 Su	0302 0905 1533 2134	0.7 18.9 -0.6 17.8	0.2 5.8 -0.2 5.4
19 Sa	0339 0939 1603 2203	0.2 18.9 -0.7 18.2	0.1 5.8 -0.2 5.5	19 M	0349 0951 1619 2220	0.3 19.5 -1.2 18.3	0.1 5.9 -0.4 5.6
20 Su	0418 1019 1644 2246	0.0 19.4 -1.1 18.4	0.0 5.9 -0.3 5.6	20 Tu	0435 1037 1706 2307	-0.1 20.0 -1.7 18.6	0.0 6.1 -0.5 5.7
21 M	0500 1059 1726 2327	-0.1 19.6 -1.3 18.5	0.0 6.0 -0.4 5.6	21 W	0523 1123 1753 2356	-0.4 20.3 -2.0 18.8	-0.1 6.2 -0.6 5.7
22 Tu	0542 1142 1811	0.0 19.7 -1.4	0.0 6.0 -0.4	22 Th	0610 1212 1842	-0.5 20.4 -2.1	-0.2 6.2 -0.6
23 W	0011 0625 1227 1857	18.4 0.1 19.6 -1.2	5.6 0.0 6.0 -0.4	23 F	0044 0700 1302 1933	18.8 -0.5 20.2 -1.9	5.7 -0.2 6.2 -0.6
24 Th	0059 0713 1316 1947	18.1 0.4 19.3 -0.9	5.5 0.1 5.9 -0.3	24 Sa	0137 0754 1357 2027	18.7 -0.3 19.7 -1.5	5.7 -0.1 6.0 -0.5
25 F	0150 0807 1411 2042	17.8 0.7 18.9 -0.6	5.4 0.2 5.8 -0.2	25 Su	0232 0851 1455 2122	18.6 -0.1 19.1 -1.0	5.7 0.0 5.8 -0.3
26 Sa	0248 0904 1509 2141	17.5 1.0 18.4 -0.2	5.3 0.3 5.6 -0.1	26 M	0330 0950 1554 2220	18.4 0.1 18.4 -0.5	5.6 0.0 5.5 -0.2
27 Su	0349 1007 1613 2242	17.3 1.1 18.0 0.0	5.3 0.3 5.5 0.0	27 Tu	0431 1052 1659 2321	18.3 0.2 17.9 -0.1	5.6 0.1 5.5 0.0
28 M	0452 1113 1719 2345	17.5 0.9 17.8 -0.1	5.3 0.3 5.4 0.0	28 W	0532 1155 1802	18.3 0.2 17.5	5.6 0.1 5.3
29 Tu	0557 1217 1824	17.9 0.4 18.0	5.5 0.1 5.5	29 Th	0021 0633 1258 1905	0.2 18.4 0.0 17.4	0.1 5.6 0.0 5.3
30 W	0046 0657 1319 1926	-0.2 18.6 -0.3 18.2	-0.1 5.7 -0.1 5.5	30 F	0119 0732 1357 2004	0.4 18.6 -0.3 17.4	0.1 5.7 -0.1 5.3
				31 Sa	0218 0826 1452 2100	0.4 18.8 -0.6 17.5	0.1 5.7 -0.2 5.3

Time meridian 75° W. 0000 is midnight. 1200 is noon.
Heights are referred to mean low water which is the chart datum of soundings.

PORTLAND, MAINE, 1983

Times and Heights of High and Low Waters

JANUARY

Day	Time h m	Height ft	Height m	Day	Time h m	Height ft	Height m
1 Sa	0549	-0.7	-0.2	16 Su	0022	8.2	2.5
	1204	11.3	3.4		0613	0.7	0.2
	1833	-2.1	-0.6		1224	9.3	2.8
					1847	-0.2	-0.1
2 Su	0047	9.6	2.9	17 M	0055	8.2	2.5
	0643	-0.6	-0.2		0649	0.8	0.2
	1258	11.0	3.4		1259	9.1	2.8
	1927	-1.8	-0.5		1920	-0.1	0.0
3 M	0143	9.5	2.9	18 Tu	0129	8.2	2.5
	0743	-0.4	-0.1		0727	0.8	0.2
	1356	10.5	3.2		1334	8.9	2.7
	2022	-1.4	-0.4		1956	0.1	0.0
4 Tu	0240	9.4	2.9	19 W	0206	8.3	2.5
	0843	-0.1	0.0		0808	0.8	0.2
	1457	9.9	3.0		1415	8.7	2.7
	2118	-0.9	-0.3		2033	0.2	0.1
5 W	0339	9.3	2.8	20 Th	0243	8.3	2.5
	0947	0.1	0.0		0853	0.7	0.2
	1559	9.3	2.8		1457	8.4	2.6
	2218	-0.4	-0.1		2115	0.3	0.1
6 Th	0441	9.1	2.8	21 F	0329	8.5	2.6
	1053	0.3	0.1		0943	0.6	0.2
	1707	8.7	2.7		1547	8.2	2.5
	2318	0.0	0.0		2201	0.4	0.1
7 F	0544	9.1	2.8	22 Sa	0416	8.6	2.6
	1200	0.3	0.1		1036	0.5	0.2
	1813	8.3	2.5		1643	8.0	2.4
					2252	0.5	0.2
8 Sa	0018	0.3	0.1	23 Su	0510	8.8	2.7
	0642	9.1	2.8		1134	0.2	0.1
	1304	0.2	0.1		1743	7.9	2.4
	1917	8.1	2.5		2348	0.5	0.2
9 Su	0117	0.5	0.2	24 M	0607	9.2	2.8
	0741	9.1	2.8		1237	-0.2	-0.1
	1400	0.0	0.0		1848	8.0	2.4
	2015	8.0	2.4				
10 M	0210	0.6	0.2	25 Tu	0048	0.4	0.1
	0831	9.2	2.8		0707	9.6	2.9
	1455	-0.2	-0.1		1339	-0.6	-0.2
	2108	8.0	2.4		1951	8.2	2.5
11 Tu	0300	0.6	0.2	26 W	0148	0.1	0.0
	0917	9.3	2.8		0807	10.1	3.1
	1541	-0.3	-0.1		1439	-1.1	-0.3
	2154	8.1	2.5		2052	8.6	2.6
12 W	0345	0.7	0.2	27 Th	0248	-0.2	-0.1
	0959	9.3	2.8		0906	10.6	3.2
	1623	-0.4	-0.1		1537	-1.6	-0.5
	2236	8.1	2.5		2149	9.1	2.8
13 Th	0423	0.7	0.2	28 F	0346	-0.5	-0.2
	1038	9.4	2.9		0943	11.1	3.4
	1702	-0.4	-0.1		1633	-1.9	-0.6
	2314	8.1	2.5		2245	9.5	2.9
14 F	0502	0.7	0.2	29 Sa	0442	-0.8	-0.2
	1116	9.4	2.9		1058	11.3	3.4
	1737	-0.3	-0.1		1726	-2.1	-0.6
	2349	8.2	2.5		2338	9.8	3.0
15 Sa	0537	0.7	0.2	30 Su	0537	-1.0	-0.3
	1149	9.4	2.9		1153	11.3	3.4
	1813	-0.3	-0.1		1818	-2.1	-0.6
				31 M	0030	9.9	3.0
					0632	-1.0	-0.3
					1246	11.0	3.4
					1908	-1.9	-0.6

FEBRUARY

Day	Time h m	Height ft	Height m	Day	Time h m	Height ft	Height m
1 Tu	0124	9.9	3.0	16 W	0056	8.7	2.7
	0727	-0.9	-0.3		0700	0.1	0.0
	1339	10.4	3.2		1308	9.1	2.8
	2001	-1.5	-0.5		1922	-0.3	-0.1
2 W	0216	9.8	3.0	17 Th	0132	8.8	2.7
	0822	-0.6	-0.2		0740	0.0	0.0
	1434	9.7	3.0		1345	8.8	2.7
	2051	-0.9	-0.3		1959	-0.2	-0.1
3 Th	0310	9.5	2.9	18 F	0209	8.9	2.7
	0920	-0.3	-0.1		0822	0.0	0.0
	1533	9.0	2.7		1428	8.6	2.6
	2146	-0.3	-0.1		2041	0.0	0.0
4 F	0406	9.1	2.8	19 Sa	0254	9.0	2.7
	1021	0.0	0.0		0910	-0.1	0.0
	1635	8.3	2.5		1518	8.3	2.5
	2243	0.2	0.1		2127	0.2	0.1
5 Sa	0506	8.8	2.7	20 Su	0342	9.0	2.7
	1126	0.3	0.1		1005	0.0	0.0
	1739	7.8	2.4		1613	8.0	2.4
	2342	0.7	0.2		2217	0.5	0.2
6 Su	0606	8.6	2.6	21 M	0436	9.1	2.8
	1230	0.4	0.1		1106	0.0	0.0
	1848	7.5	2.3		1715	7.9	2.4
					2319	0.6	0.2
7 M	0044	1.0	0.3	22 Tu	0539	9.3	2.8
	0707	8.6	2.6		1213	-0.2	-0.1
	1331	0.4	0.1		1824	7.9	2.4
	1949	7.5	2.3				
8 Tu	0140	1.1	0.3	23 W	0024	0.6	0.2
	0802	8.7	2.7		0646	9.6	2.9
	1427	0.3	0.1		1320	-0.4	-0.1
	2042	7.6	2.3		1933	8.2	2.5
9 W	0231	1.1	0.3	24 Th	0131	0.4	0.1
	0854	8.8	2.7		0752	10.0	3.0
	1516	0.2	0.1		1423	-0.8	-0.2
	2131	7.8	2.4		2039	8.7	2.7
10 Th	0321	1.0	0.3	25 F	0236	0.0	0.0
	0937	9.0	2.7		0855	10.5	3.2
	1559	0.0	0.0		1524	-1.3	-0.4
	2212	8.0	2.4		2137	9.2	2.8
11 F	0401	0.8	0.2	26 Sa	0335	-0.5	-0.2
	1017	9.2	2.8		0953	10.9	3.3
	1638	-0.1	0.0		1619	-1.6	-0.5
	2249	8.2	2.5		2233	9.7	3.0
12 Sa	0439	0.7	0.2	27 Su	0433	-0.9	-0.3
	1054	9.3	2.8		1049	11.1	3.4
	1713	-0.2	-0.1		1709	-1.9	-0.6
	2321	8.3	2.5		2322	10.1	3.1
13 Su	0515	0.5	0.2	28 M	0526	-1.2	-0.4
	1127	9.4	2.9		1141	11.0	3.4
	1745	-0.2	-0.1		1758	-1.9	-0.6
	2353	8.5	2.6				
14 M	0550	0.4	0.1				
	1159	9.3	2.8				
	1818	-0.3	-0.1				
15 Tu	0024	8.6	2.6				
	0625	0.2	0.1				
	1233	9.2	2.8				
	1850	-0.3	-0.1				

MARCH

Day	Time h m	Height ft	Height m	Day	Time h m	Height ft	Height m
1 Tu	0011	10.3	3.1	16 W	0558	-0.3	-0.1
	0618	-1.3	-0.4		1206	9.3	2.8
	1231	10.7	3.3		1816	-0.4	-0.1
	1846	-1.6	-0.5				
2 W	0100	10.2	3.1	17 Th	0025	9.3	2.8
	0708	-1.3	-0.4		0635	-0.5	-0.2
	1321	10.1	3.1		1243	9.1	2.8
	1932	-1.2	-0.4		1852	-0.4	-0.1
3 Th	0148	9.9	3.0	18 F	0101	9.4	2.9
	0800	-1.0	-0.3		0715	-0.7	-0.2
	1412	9.4	2.9		1323	9.0	2.7
	2020	-0.7	-0.2		1929	-0.2	-0.1
4 F	0236	9.5	2.9	19 Sa	0140	9.5	2.9
	0851	-0.6	-0.2		0758	-0.7	-0.2
	1505	8.7	2.7		1408	8.7	2.7
	2109	0.0	0.0		2012	0.0	0.0
5 Sa	0328	9.1	2.8	20 Su	0225	9.5	2.9
	0949	-0.1	0.0		0849	-0.5	-0.2
	1600	8.0	2.4		1457	8.4	2.6
	2203	0.6	0.2		2102	0.3	0.1
6 Su	0423	8.6	2.6	21 M	0315	9.4	2.9
	1047	0.4	0.1		0944	-0.3	-0.1
	1703	7.5	2.3		1555	8.1	2.5
	2300	1.2	0.4		2158	0.6	0.2
7 M	0523	8.3	2.5	22 Tu	0415	9.3	2.8
	1150	0.7	0.2		1047	-0.1	0.0
	1808	7.3	2.2		1700	8.0	2.4
					2302	0.9	0.3
8 Tu	0003	1.5	0.5	23 W	0521	9.4	2.9
	0624	8.2	2.5		1155	-0.1	0.0
	1252	0.9	0.3		1812	8.1	2.5
	1910	7.3	2.2				
9 W	0104	1.6	0.5	24 Th	0012	0.9	0.3
	0727	8.3	2.5		0631	9.5	2.9
	1352	0.8	0.2		1305	-0.2	-0.1
	2007	7.4	2.3		1922	8.5	2.6
10 Th	0200	1.5	0.5	25 F	0122	0.6	0.2
	0819	8.5	2.6		0741	9.8	3.0
	1443	0.7	0.2		1410	-0.5	-0.2
	2057	7.7	2.3		2026	9.0	2.7
11 F	0250	1.3	0.4	26 Sa	0227	0.1	0.0
	0906	8.8	2.7		0844	10.2	3.1
	1527	0.5	0.2		1508	-0.9	-0.3
	2138	8.0	2.4		2124	9.6	2.9
12 Sa	0332	1.0	0.3	27 Su	0327	-0.5	-0.2
	0947	9.1	2.8		0943	10.5	3.2
	1606	0.3	0.1		1601	-1.2	-0.4
	2215	8.3	2.5		2215	10.0	3.0
13 Su	0412	0.6	0.2	28 M	0422	-1.0	-0.3
	1025	9.2	2.8		1036	10.6	3.2
	1639	0.1	0.0		1651	-1.4	-0.4
	2248	8.6	2.6		2303	10.3	3.1
14 M	0448	0.3	0.1	29 Tu	0512	-1.3	-0.4
	1058	9.3	2.8		1125	10.5	3.2
	1711	-0.1	0.0		1737	-1.4	-0.4
	2320	8.9	2.7		2349	10.4	3.2
15 Tu	0522	0.0	0.0	30 W	0601	-1.4	-0.4
	1132	9.3	2.8		1214	10.1	3.1
	1743	-0.3	-0.1		1821	-1.1	-0.3
	2349	9.1	2.8	31 Th	0034	10.3	3.1
					0649	-1.3	-0.4
					1301	9.6	2.9
					1905	-0.7	-0.2

Time meridian 75° W. 0000 is midnight. 1200 is noon.
Heights are referred to mean low water which is the chart datum of soundings.

Times and Heights of High and Low Waters

APRIL

Day	h m	ft	m	Day	h m	ft	m
1 F	0116	9.9	3.0	16 Sa	0032	10.0	3.0
	0735	-1.0	-0.3		0655	-1.2	-0.4
	1348	9.1	2.8		1304	9.0	2.7
	1949	-0.2	-0.1		1905	-0.2	-0.1
2 Sa	0202	9.5	2.9	17 Su	0116	10.0	3.0
	0824	-0.6	-0.2		0742	-1.1	-0.3
	1435	8.5	2.6		1353	8.9	2.7
	2035	0.4	0.1		1952	0.1	0.0
3 Su	0249	9.0	2.7	18 M	0204	10.0	3.0
	0912	0.0	0.0		0833	-0.8	-0.2
	1528	7.9	2.4		1446	8.6	2.6
	2126	1.0	0.3		2045	0.5	0.2
4 M	0340	8.6	2.6	19 Tu	0259	9.8	3.0
	1007	0.5	0.2		0931	-0.5	-0.2
	1624	7.5	2.3		1544	8.4	2.6
	2221	1.5	0.5		2145	0.8	0.2
5 Tu	0439	8.2	2.5	20 W	0400	9.6	2.9
	1108	0.9	0.3		1035	-0.2	-0.1
	1726	7.3	2.2		1652	8.4	2.6
	2320	1.8	0.5		2253	1.0	0.3
6 W	0540	8.1	2.5	21 Th	0510	9.5	2.9
	1208	1.2	0.4		1142	-0.1	0.0
	1829	7.3	2.2		1803	8.5	2.6
7 Th	0022	1.9	0.6	22 F	0006	0.9	0.3
	0640	8.1	2.5		0622	9.5	2.9
	1307	1.2	0.4		1250	-0.1	0.0
	1925	7.5	2.3		1912	8.9	2.7
8 F	0120	1.8	0.5	23 Sa	0115	0.6	0.2
	0736	8.3	2.5		0731	9.6	2.9
	1359	1.1	0.3		1354	-0.3	-0.1
	2013	7.8	2.4		2013	9.4	2.9
9 Sa	0210	1.5	0.5	24 Su	0219	0.1	0.0
	0826	8.6	2.6		0834	9.8	3.0
	1442	0.9	0.3		1450	-0.5	-0.2
	2055	8.2	2.5		2107	9.9	3.0
10 Su	0256	1.0	0.3	25 M	0316	-0.5	-0.2
	0911	8.8	2.7		0930	9.9	3.0
	1521	0.6	0.2		1541	-0.7	-0.2
	2132	8.6	2.6		2156	10.2	3.1
11 M	0337	0.5	0.2	26 Tu	0409	-0.9	-0.3
	0948	9.0	2.7		1022	9.9	3.0
	1557	0.3	0.1		1628	-0.8	-0.2
	2206	9.0	2.7		2242	10.4	3.2
12 Tu	0415	0.0	0.0	27 W	0459	-1.2	-0.4
	1025	9.1	2.8		1110	9.8	3.0
	1633	0.0	0.0		1713	-0.7	-0.2
	2241	9.3	2.8		2327	10.3	3.1
13 W	0452	-0.4	-0.1	28 Th	0542	-1.3	-0.4
	1102	9.2	2.8		1156	9.5	2.9
	1706	-0.2	-0.1		1756	-0.4	-0.1
	2315	9.6	2.9				
14 Th	0532	-0.8	-0.2	29 F	0008	10.1	3.1
	1141	9.2	2.8		0628	-1.2	-0.4
	1744	-0.3	-0.1		1242	9.1	2.8
	2351	9.9	3.0		1837	-0.1	0.0
15 F	0610	-1.1	-0.3	30 Sa	0050	9.8	3.0
	1219	9.2	2.8		0710	-0.8	-0.2
	1823	-0.3	-0.1		1324	8.7	2.7
					1919	0.4	0.1

MAY

Day	h m	ft	m	Day	h m	ft	m
1 Su	0132	9.4	2.9	16 M	0058	10.5	3.2
	0756	-0.4	-0.1		0727	-1.3	-0.4
	1409	8.3	2.5		1340	9.1	2.8
	2004	0.9	0.3		1939	0.2	0.1
2 M	0217	9.0	2.7	17 Tu	0150	10.4	3.2
	0841	0.1	0.0		0822	-1.1	-0.3
	1457	7.9	2.4		1437	8.9	2.7
	2051	1.3	0.4		2035	0.5	0.2
3 Tu	0305	8.7	2.7	18 W	0249	10.1	3.1
	0931	0.6	0.2		0921	-0.7	-0.2
	1547	7.7	2.3		1538	8.8	2.7
	2142	1.7	0.5		2139	0.7	0.2
4 W	0355	8.4	2.6	19 Th	0352	9.8	3.0
	1024	1.0	0.3		1024	-0.4	-0.1
	1641	7.5	2.3		1645	8.9	2.7
	2237	2.0	0.6		2246	0.8	0.2
5 Th	0451	8.2	2.5	20 F	0501	9.5	2.9
	1119	1.2	0.4		1128	-0.2	-0.1
	1738	7.6	2.3		1751	9.0	2.7
	2334	2.0	0.6		2357	0.7	0.2
6 F	0549	8.1	2.5	21 Sa	0611	9.4	2.9
	1211	1.3	0.4		1232	-0.1	0.0
	1832	7.8	2.4		1854	9.3	2.8
7 Sa	0032	1.8	0.5	22 Su	0106	0.4	0.1
	0644	8.2	2.5		0719	9.3	2.8
	1301	1.2	0.4		1333	-0.1	0.0
	1920	8.1	2.5		1954	9.7	3.0
8 Su	0123	1.5	0.5	23 M	0207	0.0	0.0
	0736	8.3	2.5		0821	9.3	2.8
	1349	1.0	0.3		1427	-0.2	-0.1
	2002	8.4	2.6		2047	10.0	3.0
9 M	0212	1.0	0.3	24 Tu	0303	-0.5	-0.2
	0821	8.5	2.6		0916	9.3	2.8
	1431	0.7	0.2		1519	-0.2	-0.1
	2044	8.9	2.7		2135	10.1	3.1
10 Tu	0255	0.4	0.1	25 W	0353	-0.8	-0.2
	0907	8.7	2.7		1007	9.2	2.8
	1511	0.4	0.1		1606	-0.1	0.0
	2121	9.3	2.8		2221	10.1	3.1
11 W	0339	-0.2	-0.1	26 Th	0441	-1.0	-0.3
	0948	8.9	2.7		1054	9.0	2.7
	1551	0.1	0.0		1649	0.0	0.0
	2202	9.7	3.0		2303	10.1	3.1
12 Th	0421	-0.7	-0.2	27 F	0526	-1.0	-0.3
	1030	9.0	2.7		1139	8.9	2.7
	1630	-0.1	0.0		1731	0.2	0.1
	2240	10.1	3.1		2345	9.9	3.0
13 F	0503	-1.2	-0.4	28 Sa	0608	-0.8	-0.2
	1114	9.1	2.8		1222	8.6	2.6
	1713	-0.2	-0.1		1812	0.5	0.2
	2325	10.4	3.2				
14 Sa	0549	-1.4	-0.4	29 Su	0026	9.6	2.9
	1159	9.2	2.8		0649	-0.5	-0.2
	1758	-0.2	-0.1		1303	8.4	2.6
					1854	0.8	0.2
15 Su	0009	10.5	3.2	30 M	0105	9.4	2.9
	0636	-1.5	-0.5		0731	-0.2	-0.1
	1247	9.2	2.8		1345	8.2	2.5
	1846	-0.1	0.0		1935	1.1	0.3
				31 Tu	0145	9.1	2.8
					0812	0.2	0.1
					1427	8.0	2.4
					2020	1.4	0.4

JUNE

Day	h m	ft	m	Day	h m	ft	m
1 W	0230	8.9	2.7	16 Th	0239	10.3	3.1
	0857	0.6	0.2		0907	-0.9	-0.3
	1513	7.9	2.4		1526	9.3	2.8
	2106	1.7	0.5		2128	0.4	0.1
2 Th	0317	8.6	2.6	17 F	0342	9.9	3.0
	0942	0.9	0.3		1008	-0.6	-0.2
	1558	7.8	2.4		1630	9.3	2.8
	2155	1.8	0.5		2235	0.4	0.1
3 F	0405	8.4	2.6	18 Sa	0449	9.5	2.9
	1030	1.1	0.3		1109	-0.3	-0.1
	1647	7.9	2.4		1733	9.4	2.9
	2248	1.8	0.5		2343	0.4	0.1
4 Sa	0457	8.2	2.5	19 Su	0556	9.1	2.8
	1118	1.1	0.3		1210	-0.1	0.0
	1734	8.1	2.5		1835	9.5	2.9
	2342	1.6	0.5				
5 Su	0551	8.1	2.5	20 M	0051	0.2	0.1
	1204	1.1	0.3		0701	8.8	2.7
	1823	8.3	2.5		1309	0.1	0.0
					1933	9.7	3.0
6 M	0037	1.2	0.4	21 Tu	0152	-0.1	0.0
	0641	8.1	2.5		0803	8.7	2.7
	1252	1.0	0.3		1405	0.2	0.1
	1909	8.7	2.7		2024	9.8	3.0
7 Tu	0125	0.7	0.2	22 W	0247	-0.3	-0.1
	0733	8.2	2.5		0900	8.6	2.6
	1338	0.7	0.2		1456	0.3	0.1
	1955	9.1	2.8		2114	9.8	3.0
8 W	0215	0.2	0.1	23 Th	0337	-0.5	-0.2
	0823	8.4	2.6		0951	8.6	2.6
	1423	0.5	0.2		1543	0.4	0.1
	2039	9.6	2.9		2201	9.8	3.0
9 Th	0303	-0.4	-0.1	24 F	0425	-0.6	-0.2
	0914	8.6	2.6		1038	8.5	2.6
	1511	0.2	0.1		1628	0.5	0.2
	2124	10.1	3.1		2243	9.7	3.0
10 F	0351	-1.0	-0.3	25 Sa	0508	-0.6	-0.2
	1001	8.9	2.7		1122	8.4	2.6
	1557	0.0	0.0		1710	0.7	0.2
	2212	10.5	3.2		2324	9.7	3.0
11 Sa	0440	-1.4	-0.4	26 Su	0548	-0.4	-0.1
	1051	9.1	2.8		1201	8.3	2.5
	1646	-0.2	-0.1		1751	0.8	0.2
	2301	10.8	3.3				
12 Su	0529	-1.6	-0.5	27 M	0002	9.5	2.9
	1142	9.3	2.8		0628	-0.2	-0.1
	1737	-0.2	-0.1		1241	8.3	2.5
	2351	10.9	3.3		1828	1.0	0.3
13 M	0620	-1.7	-0.5	28 Tu	0042	9.4	2.9
	1234	9.3	2.8		0706	0.0	0.0
	1830	-0.2	-0.1		1318	8.2	2.5
					1909	1.1	0.3
14 Tu	0044	10.9	3.3	29 W	0119	9.2	2.8
	0715	-1.5	-0.5		0743	0.2	0.1
	1329	9.4	2.9		1356	8.1	2.5
	1926	0.0	0.0		1950	1.3	0.4
15 W	0140	10.7	3.3	30 Th	0200	9.0	2.7
	0809	-1.3	-0.4		0822	0.4	0.1
	1425	9.3	2.8		1435	8.1	2.5
	2025	0.2	0.1		2032	1.4	0.4

Time meridian 75° W. 0000 is midnight. 1200 is noon.
Heights are referred to mean low water which is the chart datum of soundings.

PORTLAND, MAINE, 1983

Times and Heights of High and Low Waters

JULY

Day	Time (h m)	Height (ft)	Height (m)	Day	Time (h m)	Height (ft)	Height (m)
1 F	0241	8.7	2.7	16 Sa	0326	9.8	3.0
	0902	0.6	0.2		0947	-0.7	-0.2
	1515	8.1	2.5		1608	9.6	2.9
	2118	1.4	0.4		2219	0.0	0.0
2 Sa	0323	8.5	2.6	17 Su	0431	9.2	2.8
	0944	0.7	0.2		1044	-0.2	-0.1
	1558	8.2	2.5		1707	9.5	2.9
	2205	1.3	0.4		2325	0.1	0.0
3 Su	0411	8.2	2.5	18 M	0536	8.7	2.7
	1027	0.8	0.2		1144	0.1	0.0
	1642	8.4	2.6		1808	9.4	2.9
	2256	1.2	0.4				
4 M	0502	8.1	2.5	19 Tu	0029	0.1	0.0
	1114	0.9	0.3		0641	8.3	2.5
	1730	8.6	2.6		1243	0.4	0.1
	2349	0.8	0.2		1907	9.4	2.9
5 Tu	0555	8.0	2.4	20 W	0130	0.0	0.0
	1203	0.8	0.2		0745	8.2	2.5
	1821	8.9	2.7		1341	0.6	0.2
					2003	9.4	2.9
6 W	0044	0.4	0.1	21 Th	0227	-0.1	0.0
	0649	8.0	2.4		0841	8.1	2.5
	1253	0.7	0.2		1436	0.8	0.2
	1912	9.3	2.8		2055	9.5	2.9
7 Th	0138	-0.1	0.0	22 F	0318	-0.2	-0.1
	0746	8.2	2.5		0932	8.2	2.5
	1345	0.5	0.2		1524	0.8	0.2
	2003	9.8	3.0		2141	9.5	2.9
8 F	0231	-0.6	-0.2	23 Sa	0404	-0.2	-0.1
	0842	8.5	2.6		1018	8.2	2.5
	1439	0.2	0.1		1609	0.8	0.2
	2055	10.3	3.1		2225	9.5	2.9
9 Sa	0327	-1.1	-0.3	24 Su	0446	-0.2	-0.1
	0937	8.8	2.7		1100	8.3	2.5
	1532	0.0	0.0		1649	0.9	0.3
	2148	10.8	3.3		2304	9.5	2.9
10 Su	0418	-1.5	-0.5	25 M	0527	-0.1	0.0
	1031	9.2	2.8		1138	8.3	2.5
	1626	-0.3	-0.1		1727	0.9	0.3
	2241	11.1	3.4		2341	9.5	2.9
11 M	0512	-1.7	-0.5	26 Tu	0603	-0.1	0.0
	1123	9.4	2.9		1213	8.3	2.5
	1720	-0.4	-0.1		1804	0.9	0.3
	2336	11.2	3.4				
12 Tu	0605	-1.8	-0.5	27 W	0017	9.4	2.9
	1219	9.7	3.0		0638	0.0	0.0
	1816	-0.5	-0.2		1247	8.4	2.6
					1842	0.9	0.3
13 W	0031	11.1	3.4	28 Th	0052	9.2	2.8
	0659	-1.7	-0.5		0711	0.1	0.0
	1313	9.8	3.0		1321	8.4	2.6
	1913	-0.4	-0.1		1919	0.9	0.3
14 Th	0127	10.8	3.3	29 F	0128	9.0	2.7
	0753	-1.5	-0.5		0747	0.3	0.1
	1409	9.8	3.0		1356	8.4	2.6
	2012	-0.3	-0.1		2000	0.9	0.3
15 F	0225	10.4	3.2	30 Sa	0206	8.8	2.7
	0848	-1.1	-0.3		0823	0.4	0.1
	1507	9.7	3.0		1433	8.4	2.6
	2115	-0.1	0.0		2040	0.8	0.2
				31 Su	0246	8.5	2.6
					0901	0.5	0.2
					1514	8.5	2.6
					2126	0.8	0.2

AUGUST

Day	Time (h m)	Height (ft)	Height (m)	Day	Time (h m)	Height (ft)	Height (m)
1 M	0332	8.2	2.5	16 Tu	0514	8.3	2.5
	0944	0.6	0.2		1115	0.6	0.2
	1557	8.6	2.6		1738	9.1	2.8
	2216	0.7	0.2				
2 Tu	0421	8.0	2.4	17 W	0003	0.2	0.1
	1032	0.7	0.2		0619	7.9	2.4
	1646	8.8	2.7		1215	0.9	0.3
	2309	0.5	0.2		1839	9.0	2.7
3 W	0515	7.9	2.4	18 Th	0106	0.3	0.1
	1123	0.7	0.2		0722	7.8	2.4
	1739	9.1	2.8		1317	1.1	0.3
					1939	9.0	2.7
4 Th	0007	0.2	0.1	19 F	0205	0.3	0.1
	0615	8.0	2.4		0821	7.9	2.4
	1219	0.7	0.2		1411	1.1	0.3
	1837	9.5	2.9		2032	9.1	2.8
5 F	0106	-0.2	-0.1	20 Sa	0255	0.2	0.1
	0717	8.2	2.5		0911	8.0	2.4
	1317	0.5	0.2		1502	1.1	0.3
	1934	9.9	3.0		2121	9.3	2.8
6 Sa	0207	-0.6	-0.2	21 Su	0341	0.2	0.1
	0818	8.5	2.6		0953	8.2	2.5
	1415	0.2	0.1		1546	1.0	0.3
	2034	10.4	3.2		2202	9.4	2.9
7 Su	0306	-1.0	-0.3	22 M	0425	0.1	0.0
	0916	9.0	2.7		1034	8.4	2.6
	1514	-0.1	0.0		1625	0.8	0.2
	2132	10.9	3.3		2241	9.5	2.9
8 M	0401	-1.4	-0.4	23 Tu	0459	0.1	0.0
	1012	9.4	2.9		1108	8.5	2.6
	1610	-0.5	-0.2		1702	0.7	0.2
	2228	11.2	3.4		2316	9.5	2.9
9 Tu	0455	-1.7	-0.5	24 W	0533	0.1	0.0
	1107	9.8	3.0		1142	8.6	2.6
	1707	-0.8	-0.2		1738	0.6	0.2
	2323	11.3	3.4		2349	9.4	2.9
10 W	0548	-1.8	-0.5	25 Th	0605	0.1	0.0
	1200	10.1	3.1		1212	8.7	2.7
	1802	-0.9	-0.3		1813	0.5	0.2
11 Th	0017	11.1	3.4	26 F	0023	9.2	2.8
	0640	-1.7	-0.5		0636	0.1	0.0
	1254	10.2	3.1		1242	8.7	2.7
	1858	-0.9	-0.3		1849	0.4	0.1
12 F	0111	10.7	3.3	27 Sa	0056	9.0	2.7
	0731	-1.5	-0.5		0709	0.1	0.0
	1347	10.1	3.1		1318	8.8	2.7
	1956	-0.8	-0.2		1927	0.3	0.1
13 Sa	0208	10.1	3.1	28 Su	0135	8.7	2.7
	0824	-1.0	-0.3		0744	0.3	0.1
	1441	9.9	3.0		1353	8.8	2.7
	2054	-0.6	-0.2		2008	0.2	0.1
14 Su	0305	9.5	2.9	29 M	0214	8.5	2.6
	0918	-0.5	-0.2		0822	0.4	0.1
	1538	9.6	2.9		1433	8.9	2.7
	2155	-0.3	-0.1		2053	0.2	0.1
15 M	0408	8.8	2.7	30 Tu	0258	8.3	2.5
	1015	0.1	0.0		0907	0.6	0.2
	1637	9.3	2.8		1518	8.9	2.7
	2257	0.0	0.0		2144	0.2	0.1
				31 W	0350	8.1	2.5
					0956	0.8	0.2
					1612	9.1	2.8
					2240	0.2	0.1

SEPTEMBER

Day	Time (h m)	Height (ft)	Height (m)	Day	Time (h m)	Height (ft)	Height (m)
1 Th	0449	8.0	2.4	16 F	0036	0.7	0.2
	1051	0.9	0.3		0655	7.7	2.3
	1709	9.2	2.8		1248	1.5	0.5
	2341	0.1	0.0		1909	8.7	2.7
2 F	0551	8.0	2.4	17 Sa	0135	0.7	0.2
	1154	0.9	0.3		0751	7.8	2.4
	1813	9.5	2.9		1345	1.4	0.4
					2005	8.9	2.7
3 Sa	0045	-0.1	0.0	18 Su	0226	0.6	0.2
	0659	8.3	2.5		0839	8.1	2.5
	1259	0.7	0.2		1436	1.2	0.4
	1917	10.0	3.0		2051	9.1	2.8
4 Su	0149	-0.5	-0.2	19 M	0309	0.5	0.2
	0802	8.8	2.7		0923	8.4	2.6
	1400	0.3	0.1		1519	1.0	0.3
	2018	10.4	3.2		2133	9.2	2.8
5 M	0248	-0.9	-0.3	20 Tu	0349	0.4	0.1
	0901	9.3	2.8		1000	8.6	2.6
	1501	-0.2	-0.1		1557	0.7	0.2
	2119	10.8	3.3		2212	9.3	2.8
6 Tu	0344	-1.3	-0.4	21 W	0425	0.2	0.1
	0956	9.8	3.0		1033	8.8	2.7
	1559	-0.7	-0.2		1633	0.4	0.1
	2215	11.1	3.4		2246	9.3	2.8
7 W	0436	-1.6	-0.5	22 Th	0457	0.1	0.0
	1049	10.3	3.1		1104	8.9	2.7
	1654	-1.1	-0.3		1709	0.2	0.1
	2308	11.1	3.4		2319	9.2	2.8
8 Th	0527	-1.7	-0.5	23 F	0528	0.1	0.0
	1140	10.5	3.2		1134	9.1	2.8
	1748	-1.3	-0.4		1744	0.0	0.0
					2351	9.1	2.8
9 F	0001	10.9	3.3	24 Sa	0601	0.1	0.0
	0616	-1.6	-0.5		1205	9.2	2.8
	1230	10.5	3.2		1819	-0.2	-0.1
	1842	-1.4	-0.4				
10 Sa	0054	10.4	3.2	25 Su	0026	8.9	2.7
	0705	-1.2	-0.4		0633	0.1	0.0
	1319	10.3	3.1		1242	9.2	2.8
	1934	-1.2	-0.4		1857	-0.3	-0.1
11 Su	0148	9.7	3.0	26 M	0103	8.7	2.7
	0756	-0.7	-0.2		0710	0.2	0.1
	1412	10.0	3.0		1319	9.3	2.8
	2027	-0.8	-0.2		1937	-0.3	-0.1
12 M	0243	9.0	2.7	27 Tu	0147	8.5	2.6
	0849	-0.1	0.0		0750	0.4	0.1
	1504	9.5	2.9		1401	9.3	2.8
	2126	-0.3	-0.1		2025	-0.2	-0.1
13 Tu	0341	8.4	2.6	28 W	0233	8.3	2.5
	0944	0.5	0.2		0838	0.7	0.2
	1603	9.1	2.8		1451	9.3	2.8
	2227	0.1	0.0		2118	-0.1	0.0
14 W	0445	7.9	2.4	29 Th	0328	8.1	2.5
	1043	1.1	0.3		0930	0.9	0.3
	1704	8.7	2.7		1547	9.3	2.8
	2332	0.5	0.2		2215	0.1	0.0
15 Th	0551	7.7	2.3	30 F	0429	8.1	2.5
	1146	1.4	0.4		1033	1.1	0.3
	1809	8.6	2.6		1648	9.3	2.8
					2322	0.1	0.0

Time meridian 75° W. 0000 is midnight. 1200 is noon.
Heights are referred to mean low water which is the chart datum of soundings.

Times and Heights of High and Low Waters

OCTOBER

Day	Time h m	Height ft	Height m
1 Sa	0538	8.2	2.5
	1138	1.0	0.3
	1757	9.5	2.9
2 Su	0029	-0.1	0.0
	0646	8.6	2.6
	1246	0.7	0.2
	1903	9.9	3.0
3 M	0133	-0.4	-0.1
	0749	9.1	2.8
	1352	0.2	0.1
	2009	10.2	3.1
4 Tu	0231	-0.8	-0.2
	0847	9.7	3.0
	1452	-0.4	-0.1
	2108	10.6	3.2
5 W	0325	-1.1	-0.3
	0940	10.2	3.1
	1548	-1.0	-0.3
	2202	10.7	3.3
6 Th	0417	-1.3	-0.4
	1030	10.6	3.2
	1641	-1.4	-0.4
	2255	10.6	3.2
7 F	0504	-1.3	-0.4
	1118	10.7	3.3
	1732	-1.6	-0.5
	2344	10.3	3.1
8 Sa	0551	-1.2	-0.4
	1204	10.6	3.2
	1822	-1.5	-0.5
9 Su	0034	9.8	3.0
	0638	-0.8	-0.2
	1252	10.3	3.1
	1911	-1.3	-0.4
10 M	0124	9.3	2.8
	0727	-0.2	-0.1
	1340	9.9	3.0
	2001	-0.8	-0.2
11 Tu	0217	8.7	2.7
	0815	0.4	0.1
	1429	9.3	2.8
	2057	-0.2	-0.1
12 W	0313	8.1	2.5
	0910	1.0	0.3
	1525	8.9	2.7
	2152	0.3	0.1
13 Th	0413	7.7	2.3
	1008	1.5	0.5
	1627	8.5	2.6
	2255	0.8	0.2
14 F	0516	7.6	2.3
	1111	1.8	0.5
	1730	8.4	2.6
	2357	1.0	0.3
15 Sa	0619	7.6	2.3
	1212	1.8	0.5
	1832	8.4	2.6
16 Su	0053	1.0	0.3
	0715	7.9	2.4
	1312	1.7	0.5
	1927	8.6	2.6
17 M	0146	1.0	0.3
	0802	8.2	2.5
	1402	1.3	0.4
	2016	8.7	2.7
18 Tu	0229	0.8	0.2
	0844	8.5	2.6
	1444	0.9	0.3
	2058	8.9	2.7
19 W	0308	0.6	0.2
	0921	8.8	2.7
	1525	0.5	0.2
	2137	9.0	2.7
20 Th	0343	0.4	0.1
	0953	9.1	2.8
	1602	0.1	0.0
	2212	9.0	2.7
21 F	0417	0.2	0.1
	1025	9.3	2.8
	1637	-0.3	-0.1
	2247	9.0	2.7
22 Sa	0449	0.1	0.0
	1057	9.5	2.9
	1713	-0.6	-0.2
	2322	9.0	2.7
23 Su	0523	0.0	0.0
	1131	9.6	2.9
	1751	-0.8	-0.2
	2359	8.9	2.7
24 M	0600	0.1	0.0
	1209	9.8	3.0
	1831	-0.8	-0.2
25 Tu	0041	8.8	2.7
	0640	0.2	0.1
	1250	9.8	3.0
	1915	-0.8	-0.2
26 W	0126	8.6	2.6
	0726	0.4	0.1
	1337	9.7	3.0
	2003	-0.6	-0.2
27 Th	0217	8.5	2.6
	0817	0.7	0.2
	1428	9.6	2.9
	2059	-0.3	-0.1
28 F	0313	8.3	2.5
	0913	1.0	0.3
	1528	9.5	2.9
	2200	-0.1	0.0
29 Sa	0418	8.3	2.5
	1019	1.1	0.3
	1635	9.4	2.9
	2307	0.0	0.0
30 Su	0527	8.5	2.6
	1129	1.0	0.3
	1745	9.4	2.9
31 M	0014	-0.1	0.0
	0635	8.9	2.7
	1239	0.6	0.2
	1855	9.6	2.9

NOVEMBER

Day	Time h m	Height ft	Height m
1 Tu	0117	-0.3	-0.1
	0736	9.5	2.9
	1344	0.1	0.0
	1957	9.8	3.0
2 W	0214	-0.6	-0.2
	0831	10.0	3.0
	1444	-0.4	-0.2
	2056	10.0	3.0
3 Th	0307	-0.8	-0.2
	0922	10.4	3.2
	1537	-1.1	-0.3
	2150	10.0	3.0
4 F	0356	-0.9	-0.3
	1011	10.6	3.2
	1628	-1.5	-0.5
	2241	9.9	3.0
5 Sa	0442	-0.9	-0.3
	1057	10.7	3.3
	1716	-1.6	-0.5
	2330	9.6	2.9
6 Su	0527	-0.6	-0.2
	1141	10.5	3.2
	1804	-1.5	-0.5
7 M	0016	9.3	2.8
	0613	-0.2	-0.1
	1225	10.1	3.1
	1850	-1.1	-0.3
8 Tu	0103	8.8	2.7
	0658	0.2	0.1
	1312	9.7	3.0
	1937	-0.7	-0.2
9 W	0153	8.4	2.6
	0745	0.8	0.2
	1400	9.3	2.8
	2027	-0.1	0.0
10 Th	0241	8.0	2.4
	0836	1.3	0.4
	1449	8.8	2.7
	2118	0.4	0.1
11 F	0337	7.7	2.3
	0930	1.7	0.5
	1544	8.5	2.6
	2213	0.9	0.3
12 Sa	0434	7.6	2.3
	1027	1.9	0.6
	1643	8.2	2.5
	2309	1.1	0.3
13 Su	0533	7.6	2.3
	1119	1.9	0.6
	1742	8.1	2.5
14 M	0005	1.2	0.4
	0625	7.8	2.4
	1227	1.7	0.5
	1837	8.2	2.5
15 Tu	0054	1.1	0.3
	0714	8.1	2.5
	1318	1.4	0.4
	1930	8.3	2.5
16 W	0139	1.0	0.3
	0754	8.5	2.6
	1405	0.9	0.3
	2015	8.4	2.6
17 Th	0221	0.8	0.2
	0834	8.8	2.7
	1447	0.4	0.1
	2057	8.5	2.6
18 F	0258	0.5	0.2
	0911	9.2	2.8
	1527	-0.1	0.0
	2136	8.6	2.6
19 Sa	0335	0.3	0.1
	0945	9.5	2.9
	1606	-0.6	-0.2
	2215	8.7	2.7
20 Su	0413	0.1	0.0
	1022	9.8	3.0
	1647	-1.0	-0.3
	2255	8.8	2.7
21 M	0452	0.0	0.0
	1102	10.1	3.1
	1726	-1.2	-0.4
	2338	8.9	2.7
22 Tu	0533	0.0	0.0
	1144	10.3	3.1
	1811	-1.3	-0.4
23 W	0021	8.9	2.7
	0617	0.1	0.0
	1229	10.3	3.1
	1858	-1.2	-0.4
24 Th	0111	8.8	2.7
	0708	0.3	0.1
	1320	10.2	3.1
	1950	-1.0	-0.3
25 F	0203	8.7	2.7
	0801	0.5	0.2
	1414	10.0	3.0
	2046	-0.7	-0.2
26 Sa	0302	8.7	2.7
	0902	0.7	0.2
	1515	9.7	3.0
	2147	-0.4	-0.1
27 Su	0407	8.7	2.7
	1009	0.8	0.2
	1621	9.4	2.9
	2250	-0.2	-0.1
28 M	0513	8.9	2.7
	1119	0.7	0.2
	1733	9.2	2.8
	2356	-0.2	-0.1
29 Tu	0617	9.2	2.8
	1229	0.4	0.1
	1842	9.2	2.8
30 W	0057	-0.2	-0.1
	0718	9.6	2.9
	1334	-0.1	0.0
	1946	9.2	2.8

DECEMBER

Day	Time h m	Height ft	Height m
1 Th	0154	-0.3	-0.1
	0815	10.0	3.0
	1434	-0.7	-0.2
	2045	9.2	2.8
2 F	0247	-0.4	-0.1
	0906	10.3	3.1
	1525	-1.1	-0.3
	2138	9.2	2.8
3 Sa	0338	-0.4	-0.1
	0953	10.4	3.2
	1615	-1.3	-0.4
	2229	9.1	2.8
4 Su	0425	-0.3	-0.1
	1039	10.3	3.1
	1702	-1.4	-0.4
	2315	9.0	2.7
5 M	0509	-0.1	0.0
	1121	10.2	3.1
	1748	-1.2	-0.4
6 Tu	0000	8.8	2.7
	0552	0.2	0.1
	1206	9.9	3.0
	1830	-0.9	-0.3
7 W	0043	8.5	2.6
	0634	0.5	0.2
	1247	9.6	2.9
	1913	-0.5	-0.2
8 Th	0127	8.3	2.5
	0719	0.9	0.3
	1329	9.3	2.8
	1958	-0.1	0.0
9 F	0211	8.0	2.4
	0804	1.2	0.4
	1414	8.9	2.7
	2041	0.3	0.1
10 Sa	0257	7.8	2.4
	0853	1.5	0.5
	1502	8.5	2.6
	2128	0.7	0.2
11 Su	0347	7.7	2.3
	0942	1.7	0.5
	1554	8.2	2.5
	2218	1.0	0.3
12 M	0435	7.7	2.3
	1037	1.7	0.5
	1646	8.0	2.4
	2306	1.1	0.3
13 Tu	0526	7.8	2.4
	1132	1.6	0.5
	1741	7.8	2.4
	2354	1.1	0.3
14 W	0614	8.1	2.5
	1227	1.3	0.4
	1834	7.8	2.4
15 Th	0041	1.0	0.3
	0659	8.4	2.6
	1318	0.8	0.2
	1923	7.8	2.4
16 F	0128	0.9	0.3
	0742	8.8	2.7
	1405	0.3	0.1
	2013	8.0	2.4
17 Sa	0213	0.6	0.2
	0827	9.2	2.8
	1450	-0.2	-0.1
	2059	8.2	2.5
18 Su	0255	0.4	0.1
	0908	9.7	3.0
	1536	-0.8	-0.2
	2145	8.5	2.6
19 M	0341	0.1	0.0
	0953	10.1	3.1
	1620	-1.2	-0.4
	2230	8.8	2.7
20 Tu	0424	-0.1	0.0
	1038	10.5	3.2
	1706	-1.5	-0.5
	2318	9.0	2.7
21 W	0513	-0.2	-0.1
	1124	10.7	3.3
	1755	-1.6	-0.5
22 Th	0005	9.1	2.8
	0601	-0.2	-0.1
	1214	10.7	3.3
	1844	-1.6	-0.5
23 F	0056	9.2	2.8
	0655	-0.2	-0.1
	1308	10.6	3.2
	1937	-1.4	-0.4
24 Sa	0150	9.2	2.8
	0750	0.0	0.0
	1404	10.3	3.1
	2030	-1.1	-0.3
25 Su	0248	9.2	2.8
	0851	0.2	0.1
	1504	9.8	3.0
	2130	-0.8	-0.2
26 M	0350	9.2	2.8
	0957	0.3	0.1
	1608	9.3	2.8
	2229	-0.4	-0.1
27 Tu	0452	9.2	2.8
	1105	0.3	0.1
	1718	8.9	2.7
	2333	-0.2	-0.1
28 W	0557	9.3	2.8
	1214	0.1	0.0
	1827	8.6	2.6
29 Th	0035	0.0	0.0
	0659	9.5	2.9
	1320	-0.2	-0.1
	1933	8.5	2.6
30 F	0133	0.1	0.0
	0757	9.7	3.0
	1421	-0.6	-0.2
	2033	8.5	2.6
31 Sa	0230	0.1	0.0
	0850	9.9	3.0
	1514	-0.8	-0.2
	2128	8.5	2.6

Time meridian 75° W.   0000 is midnight.   1200 is noon.
Heights are referred to mean low water which is the chart datum of soundings.

BOSTON, MASS., 1983

Times and Heights of High and Low Waters

JANUARY

Day	Time (h m)	Height (ft)	Height (m)	Day	Time (h m)	Height (ft)	Height (m)
1 Sa	0009	10.0	3.0	16 Su	0028	8.6	2.6
	0608	-0.9	-0.3		0624	0.6	0.2
	1223	11.7	3.6		1237	9.7	3.0
	1847	-2.2	-0.7		1855	-0.4	-0.1
2 Su	0102	10.1	3.1	17 M	0106	8.6	2.6
	0701	-0.9	-0.3		0703	0.6	0.2
	1318	11.5	3.5		1315	9.6	2.9
	1940	-2.0	-0.6		1935	-0.3	-0.1
3 M	0156	10.0	3.0	18 Tu	0145	8.7	2.7
	0756	-0.7	-0.2		0745	0.7	0.2
	1413	11.0	3.4		1356	9.4	2.9
	2033	-1.6	-0.5		2014	-0.1	0.0
4 Tu	0252	9.9	3.0	19 W	0227	8.7	2.7
	0854	-0.4	-0.1		0830	0.7	0.2
	1510	10.4	3.2		1438	9.2	2.8
	2129	-1.1	-0.3		2056	0.1	0.0
5 W	0349	9.7	3.0	20 Th	0310	8.8	2.7
	0955	-0.1	0.0		0917	0.7	0.2
	1608	9.8	3.0		1526	8.9	2.7
	2224	-0.5	-0.2		2140	0.3	0.1
6 Th	0446	9.6	2.9	21 F	0355	8.9	2.7
	1056	0.2	0.1		1007	0.7	0.2
	1710	9.2	2.8		1616	8.7	2.7
	2322	0.0	0.0		2229	0.4	0.1
7 F	0543	9.5	2.9	22 Sa	0444	9.1	2.8
	1201	0.3	0.1		1103	0.6	0.2
	1811	8.7	2.7		1709	8.5	2.6
					2321	0.6	0.2
8 Sa	0019	0.4	0.1	23 Su	0536	9.3	2.8
	0641	9.5	2.9		1200	0.3	0.1
	1301	0.3	0.1		1808	8.4	2.6
	1913	8.4	2.6				
9 Su	0115	0.6	0.2	24 M	0017	0.6	0.2
	0734	9.5	2.9		0632	9.7	3.0
	1357	0.2	0.1		1259	-0.1	0.0
	2010	8.2	2.5		1908	8.5	2.6
10 M	0206	0.8	0.2	25 Tu	0115	0.4	0.1
	0827	9.5	2.9		0731	10.1	3.1
	1451	0.1	0.0		1400	-0.6	-0.2
	2103	8.2	2.5		2008	8.8	2.7
11 Tu	0255	0.8	0.2	26 W	0213	0.1	0.0
	0914	9.6	2.9		0827	10.6	3.2
	1538	0.0	0.0		1458	-1.1	-0.3
	2148	8.3	2.5		2106	9.1	2.8
12 W	0340	0.8	0.2	27 Th	0311	-0.3	-0.1
	0957	9.7	3.0		0924	11.1	3.4
	1620	-0.2	-0.1		1554	-1.6	-0.5
	2233	8.3	2.5		2204	9.5	2.9
13 Th	0423	0.7	0.2	28 F	0405	-0.7	-0.2
	1039	9.7	3.0		1020	11.5	3.5
	1700	-0.3	-0.1		1646	-2.0	-0.6
	2311	8.4	2.6		2259	9.9	3.0
14 F	0504	0.7	0.2	29 Sa	0500	-1.0	-0.3
	1119	9.8	3.0		1115	11.7	3.6
	1737	-0.4	-0.1		1738	-2.3	-0.7
	2351	8.5	2.6		2352	10.2	3.1
15 Sa	0544	0.6	0.2	30 Su	0553	-1.2	-0.4
	1158	9.8	3.0		1209	11.7	3.6
	1816	-0.4	-0.1		1829	-2.2	-0.7
				31 M	0044	10.4	3.2
					0645	-1.3	-0.4
					1302	11.4	3.5
					1919	-2.0	-0.6

FEBRUARY

Day	Time (h m)	Height (ft)	Height (m)	Day	Time (h m)	Height (ft)	Height (m)
1 Tu	0135	10.4	3.2	16 W	0116	9.2	2.8
	0738	-1.1	-0.3		0719	0.1	0.0
	1354	10.9	3.3		1329	9.6	2.9
	2009	-1.6	-0.5		1943	-0.3	-0.1
2 W	0227	10.3	3.1	17 Th	0153	9.3	2.8
	0833	-0.8	-0.2		0801	0.1	0.0
	1449	10.3	3.1		1411	9.4	2.9
	2059	-1.0	-0.3		2024	-0.1	0.0
3 Th	0318	10.0	3.0	18 F	0235	9.4	2.9
	0929	-0.4	-0.1		0847	0.1	0.0
	1542	9.6	2.9		1456	9.1	2.8
	2152	-0.3	-0.1		2105	0.2	0.1
4 F	0413	9.7	3.0	19 Sa	0321	9.4	2.9
	1027	0.0	0.0		0938	0.1	0.0
	1639	8.9	2.7		1547	8.8	2.7
	2245	0.3	0.1		2156	0.4	0.1
5 Sa	0507	9.4	2.9	20 Su	0410	9.5	2.9
	1126	0.4	0.1		1032	0.2	0.1
	1739	8.3	2.5		1643	8.5	2.6
	2341	0.8	0.2		2249	0.6	0.2
6 Su	0603	9.2	2.8	21 M	0506	9.6	2.9
	1227	0.6	0.2		1131	0.1	0.0
	1838	7.9	2.4		1742	8.4	2.6
					2348	0.7	0.2
7 M	0038	1.1	0.3	22 Tu	0606	9.7	3.0
	0700	9.0	2.7		1235	-0.1	0.0
	1326	0.6	0.2		1845	8.4	2.6
	1939	7.8	2.4				
8 Tu	0136	1.3	0.4	23 W	0051	0.6	0.2
	0755	9.0	2.7		0707	10.0	3.0
	1421	0.5	0.2		1339	-0.4	-0.1
	2035	7.8	2.4		1949	8.7	2.7
9 W	0228	1.2	0.4	24 Th	0154	0.3	0.1
	0846	9.1	2.8		0810	10.4	3.2
	1509	0.4	0.1		1439	-0.9	-0.3
	2124	8.0	2.4		2050	9.1	2.8
10 Th	0316	1.0	0.3	25 F	0255	-0.2	-0.1
	0932	9.3	2.8		0911	10.9	3.3
	1554	0.1	0.0		1535	-1.4	-0.4
	2207	8.2	2.5		2148	9.6	2.9
11 F	0359	0.8	0.2	26 Sa	0351	-0.7	-0.2
	1015	9.5	2.9		1007	11.2	3.4
	1634	-0.1	0.0		1628	-1.8	-0.5
	2246	8.4	2.6		2242	10.1	3.1
12 Sa	0441	0.6	0.2	27 Su	0445	-1.2	-0.4
	1054	9.7	3.0		1102	11.5	3.5
	1713	-0.3	-0.1		1719	-2.0	-0.6
	2324	8.7	2.7		2333	10.5	3.2
13 Su	0521	0.4	0.1	28 M	0537	-1.5	-0.5
	1134	9.8	3.0		1152	11.4	3.5
	1750	-0.4	-0.1		1808	-2.0	-0.6
14 M	0002	8.9	2.7				
	0600	0.2	0.1				
	1211	9.8	3.0				
	1828	-0.5	-0.2				
15 Tu	0038	9.0	2.7				
	0639	0.1	0.0				
	1250	9.8	3.0				
	1905	-0.4	-0.1				

MARCH

Day	Time (h m)	Height (ft)	Height (m)	Day	Time (h m)	Height (ft)	Height (m)
1 Tu	0023	10.7	3.3	16 W	0005	9.6	2.9
	0627	-1.5	-0.5		0614	-0.4	-0.1
	1243	11.2	3.4		1224	9.9	3.0
	1855	-1.7	-0.5		1834	-0.4	-0.1
2 W	0110	10.7	3.3	17 Th	0045	9.8	3.0
	0718	-1.4	-0.4		0654	-0.5	-0.2
	1332	10.7	3.3		1303	9.7	3.0
	1942	-1.2	-0.4		1913	-0.3	-0.1
3 Th	0157	10.5	3.2	18 F	0122	9.9	3.0
	0807	-1.0	-0.3		0737	-0.5	-0.2
	1423	10.0	3.0		1347	9.5	2.9
	2029	-0.6	-0.2		1954	-0.1	0.0
4 F	0246	10.2	3.1	19 Sa	0204	10.0	3.0
	0859	-0.5	-0.2		0823	-0.5	-0.2
	1515	9.3	2.8		1433	9.2	2.8
	2118	0.1	0.0		2039	0.2	0.1
5 Sa	0334	9.7	3.0	20 Su	0252	9.9	3.0
	0952	0.0	0.0		0913	-0.3	-0.1
	1606	8.6	2.6		1525	8.9	2.7
	2208	0.7	0.2		2128	0.5	0.2
6 Su	0429	9.3	2.8	21 M	0345	9.8	3.0
	1048	0.5	0.2		1010	-0.1	0.0
	1702	8.1	2.5		1622	8.6	2.6
	2304	1.3	0.4		2227	0.8	0.2
7 M	0523	8.9	2.7	22 Tu	0442	9.7	3.0
	1148	0.8	0.2		1111	0.0	0.0
	1802	7.7	2.3		1723	8.4	2.6
					2328	0.9	0.3
8 Tu	0002	1.6	0.5	23 W	0545	9.7	3.0
	0621	8.7	2.7		1216	-0.1	0.0
	1249	1.0	0.3		1828	8.5	2.6
	1901	7.6	2.3				
9 W	0101	1.6	0.5	24 Th	0035	0.7	0.2
	0720	8.7	2.7		0651	9.9	3.0
	1344	0.9	0.3		1320	-0.3	-0.1
	2000	7.7	2.3		1933	8.8	2.7
10 Th	0157	1.5	0.5	25 F	0139	0.4	0.1
	0812	8.8	2.7		0755	10.2	3.1
	1435	0.7	0.2		1421	-0.7	-0.2
	2050	8.0	2.4		2034	9.4	2.9
11 F	0247	1.2	0.4	26 Sa	0240	-0.2	-0.1
	0903	9.1	2.8		0855	10.6	3.2
	1521	0.4	0.1		1517	-1.1	-0.3
	2135	8.3	2.5		2132	9.9	3.0
12 Sa	0332	0.8	0.2	27 Su	0338	-0.7	-0.2
	0946	9.3	2.8		0952	10.9	3.3
	1604	0.1	0.0		1609	-1.4	-0.4
	2215	8.6	2.6		2223	10.4	3.2
13 Su	0415	0.5	0.2	28 M	0431	-1.2	-0.4
	1028	9.6	2.9		1046	11.0	3.4
	1642	-0.2	-0.1		1657	-1.5	-0.5
	2254	9.0	2.7		2312	10.8	3.3
14 M	0454	0.1	0.0	29 Tu	0520	-1.5	-0.5
	1107	9.8	3.0		1135	10.9	3.3
	1719	-0.3	-0.1		1744	-1.4	-0.4
	2330	9.3	2.8		2358	10.9	3.3
15 Tu	0534	-0.2	-0.1	30 W	0608	-1.5	-0.5
	1145	9.9	3.0		1223	10.6	3.2
	1757	-0.4	-0.1		1827	-1.1	-0.3
				31 Th	0041	10.9	3.3
					0655	-1.3	-0.4
					1309	10.2	3.1
					1912	-0.6	-0.2

Time meridian 75° W. 0000 is midnight. 1200 is noon.
Heights are referred to mean low water which is the chart datum of soundings.

APRIL

Day	Time h m	Height ft	Height m	Day	Time h m	Height ft	Height m
1 F	0127	10.6	3.2	16 Sa	0054	10.6	3.2
	0741	-1.0	-0.3		0715	-1.0	-0.3
	1355	9.6	2.9		1326	9.6	2.9
	1958	0.0	0.0		1929	0.0	0.0
2 Sa	0212	10.2	3.1	17 Su	0140	10.5	3.2
	0827	-0.5	-0.2		0804	-0.9	-0.3
	1444	9.0	2.7		1415	9.3	2.8
	2044	0.6	0.2		2017	0.3	0.1
3 Su	0300	9.7	3.0	18 M	0230	10.4	3.2
	0918	0.1	0.0		0857	-0.7	-0.2
	1534	8.5	2.6		1509	9.0	2.7
	2134	1.1	0.3		2111	0.6	0.2
4 M	0350	9.2	2.8	19 Tu	0326	10.2	3.1
	1011	0.6	0.2		0953	-0.4	-0.1
	1627	8.0	2.4		1608	8.8	2.7
	2227	1.6	0.5		2211	0.8	0.2
5 Tu	0443	8.8	2.7	20 W	0427	9.9	3.0
	1107	0.9	0.3		1055	-0.2	-0.1
	1723	7.7	2.3		1711	8.7	2.7
	2323	1.8	0.5		2315	0.9	0.3
6 W	0541	8.5	2.6	21 Th	0531	9.8	3.0
	1205	1.1	0.3		1159	-0.2	-0.1
	1822	7.7	2.3		1816	8.9	2.7
7 Th	0022	1.8	0.5	22 F	0021	0.7	0.2
	0637	8.5	2.6		0638	9.8	3.0
	1302	1.1	0.3		1301	-0.3	-0.1
	1917	7.8	2.4		1918	9.2	2.8
8 F	0119	1.6	0.5	23 Sa	0127	0.3	0.1
	0733	8.6	2.6		0741	10.0	3.0
	1355	0.9	0.3		1402	-0.5	-0.2
	2009	8.1	2.5		2018	9.7	3.0
9 Sa	0213	1.3	0.4	24 Su	0227	-0.2	-0.1
	0825	8.9	2.7		0840	10.2	3.1
	1442	0.6	0.2		1456	-0.7	-0.2
	2055	8.5	2.6		2111	10.1	3.1
10 Su	0258	0.8	0.2	25 M	0324	-0.7	-0.2
	0911	9.2	2.8		0937	10.3	3.1
	1525	0.3	0.1		1546	-0.8	-0.2
	2136	9.0	2.7		2202	10.6	3.2
11 M	0343	0.3	0.1	26 Tu	0414	-1.1	-0.3
	0954	9.5	2.9		1028	10.3	3.1
	1606	0.0	0.0		1633	-0.8	-0.2
	2215	9.5	2.9		2248	10.8	3.3
12 Tu	0425	-0.1	0.0	27 W	0502	-1.3	-0.4
	1036	9.7	3.0		1116	10.2	3.1
	1645	-0.2	-0.1		1718	-0.6	-0.2
	2254	9.9	3.0		2332	10.9	3.3
13 W	0506	-0.5	-0.2	28 Th	0547	-1.3	-0.4
	1116	9.8	3.0		1202	10.0	3.0
	1725	-0.3	-0.1		1801	-0.3	-0.1
	2333	10.2	3.1				
14 Th	0548	-0.8	-0.2	29 F	0015	10.7	3.3
	1158	9.8	3.0		0631	-1.1	-0.3
	1804	-0.3	-0.1		1247	9.6	2.9
					1844	0.0	0.0
15 F	0012	10.5	3.2	30 Sa	0058	10.5	3.2
	0630	-1.0	-0.3		0716	-0.8	-0.2
	1241	9.8	3.0		1330	9.2	2.8
	1845	-0.2	-0.1		1927	0.5	0.2

MAY

Day	Time h m	Height ft	Height m	Day	Time h m	Height ft	Height m
1 Su	0142	10.1	3.1	16 M	0122	11.0	3.4
	0801	-0.3	-0.1		0746	-1.3	-0.4
	1416	8.8	2.7		1401	9.5	2.9
	2011	0.9	0.3		2001	0.2	0.1
2 M	0225	9.6	2.9	17 Tu	0215	10.8	3.3
	0847	0.1	0.0		0841	-1.0	-0.3
	1503	8.4	2.6		1457	9.3	2.8
	2100	1.4	0.4		2057	0.4	0.1
3 Tu	0315	9.2	2.8	18 W	0313	10.5	3.2
	0937	0.6	0.2		0937	-0.7	-0.2
	1553	8.1	2.5		1555	9.2	2.8
	2151	1.7	0.5		2157	0.6	0.2
4 W	0406	8.8	2.7	19 Th	0414	10.1	3.1
	1030	0.9	0.3		1039	-0.5	-0.2
	1647	7.9	2.4		1658	9.2	2.8
	2247	1.9	0.6		2303	0.7	0.2
5 Th	0459	8.6	2.6	20 F	0517	9.9	3.0
	1123	1.1	0.3		1140	-0.3	-0.1
	1740	7.9	2.4		1800	9.4	2.9
	2344	1.9	0.6				
6 F	0555	8.5	2.6	21 Sa	0009	0.5	0.2
	1219	1.1	0.3		0623	9.7	3.0
	1834	8.1	2.5		1242	-0.2	-0.1
					1900	9.7	3.0
7 Sa	0040	1.6	0.5	22 Su	0113	0.2	0.1
	0650	8.6	2.6		0725	9.7	3.0
	1309	0.9	0.3		1339	-0.2	-0.1
	1923	8.4	2.6		1957	10.0	3.0
8 Su	0133	1.3	0.4	23 M	0213	-0.1	0.0
	0742	8.8	2.7		0824	9.6	2.9
	1358	0.7	0.2		1432	-0.2	-0.1
	2010	8.9	2.7		2051	10.3	3.1
9 M	0222	0.8	0.2	24 Tu	0306	-0.5	-0.2
	0832	9.0	2.7		0919	9.6	2.9
	1443	0.5	0.2		1522	-0.2	-0.1
	2055	9.4	2.9		2138	10.6	3.2
10 Tu	0309	0.2	0.1	25 W	0356	-0.8	-0.2
	0918	9.3	2.8		1009	9.6	2.9
	1527	0.2	0.1		1609	-0.1	0.0
	2136	9.9	3.0		2223	10.7	3.3
11 W	0355	-0.3	-0.1	26 Th	0442	-0.9	-0.3
	1002	9.5	2.9		1056	9.5	2.9
	1609	0.0	0.0		1651	0.1	0.0
	2219	10.4	3.2		2307	10.6	3.2
12 Th	0438	-0.8	-0.2	27 F	0526	-0.9	-0.3
	1047	9.7	3.0		1141	9.3	2.8
	1651	-0.2	-0.1		1735	0.3	0.1
	2301	10.7	3.3		2349	10.5	3.2
13 F	0523	-1.2	-0.4	28 Sa	0609	-0.7	-0.2
	1133	9.8	3.0		1223	9.1	2.8
	1736	-0.2	-0.1		1817	0.6	0.2
	2343	11.0	3.4				
14 Sa	0609	-1.4	-0.4	29 Su	0031	10.2	3.1
	1219	9.8	3.0		0651	-0.5	-0.2
	1820	-0.2	-0.1		1305	8.9	2.7
					1859	0.8	0.2
15 Su	0032	11.1	3.4	30 M	0114	9.9	3.0
	0655	-1.4	-0.4		0733	-0.2	-0.1
	1309	9.7	3.0		1350	8.6	2.6
	1909	-0.1	0.0		1942	1.1	0.3
				31 Tu	0156	9.6	2.9
					0817	0.1	0.0
					1433	8.4	2.6
					2028	1.4	0.4

JUNE

Day	Time h m	Height ft	Height m	Day	Time h m	Height ft	Height m
1 W	0241	9.3	2.8	16 Th	0259	10.7	3.3
	0904	0.4	0.1		0921	-1.0	-0.3
	1521	8.3	2.5		1541	9.7	3.0
	2118	1.6	0.5		2144	0.2	0.1
2 Th	0331	9.0	2.7	17 F	0358	10.3	3.1
	0952	0.7	0.2		1019	-0.7	-0.2
	1608	8.2	2.5		1640	9.7	3.0
	2210	1.7	0.5		2247	0.3	0.1
3 F	0420	8.8	2.7	18 Sa	0500	9.9	3.0
	1042	0.8	0.2		1118	-0.3	-0.1
	1659	8.3	2.5		1739	9.8	3.0
	2303	1.7	0.5		2351	0.3	0.1
4 Sa	0512	8.6	2.6	19 Su	0604	9.5	2.9
	1133	0.9	0.3		1216	0.0	0.0
	1748	8.5	2.6		1838	9.9	3.0
	2358	1.5	0.5				
5 Su	0606	8.6	2.6	20 M	0053	0.2	0.1
	1223	0.9	0.3		0705	9.2	2.8
	1838	8.8	2.7		1312	0.2	0.1
					1934	10.1	3.1
6 M	0053	1.1	0.3	21 Tu	0154	0.0	0.0
	0658	8.6	2.6		0806	9.1	2.8
	1312	0.8	0.2		1407	0.3	0.1
	1926	9.2	2.8		2026	10.2	3.1
7 Tu	0144	0.7	0.2	22 W	0248	-0.2	-0.1
	0749	8.8	2.7		0901	9.0	2.7
	1402	0.6	0.2		1458	0.4	0.1
	2013	9.7	3.0		2116	10.3	3.1
8 W	0234	0.1	0.0	23 Th	0337	-0.3	-0.1
	0840	9.0	2.7		0951	8.9	2.7
	1448	0.4	0.1		1544	0.5	0.2
	2058	10.2	3.1		2202	10.3	3.1
9 Th	0322	-0.5	-0.2	24 F	0424	-0.4	-0.1
	0930	9.3	2.8		1038	8.9	2.7
	1535	0.1	0.0		1628	0.6	0.2
	2145	10.7	3.3		2244	10.3	3.1
10 F	0411	-1.0	-0.3	25 Sa	0506	-0.4	-0.1
	1019	9.5	2.9		1120	8.8	2.7
	1621	-0.1	0.0		1711	0.7	0.2
	2234	11.1	3.4		2326	10.2	3.1
11 Sa	0459	-1.4	-0.4	26 Su	0545	-0.3	-0.1
	1110	9.7	3.0		1202	8.8	2.7
	1709	-0.3	-0.1		1752	0.8	0.2
	2322	11.4	3.5				
12 Su	0548	-1.6	-0.5	27 M	0007	10.0	3.0
	1200	9.8	3.0		0628	-0.2	-0.1
	1759	-0.3	-0.1		1240	8.7	2.7
					1834	0.9	0.3
13 M	0013	11.5	3.5	28 Tu	0049	9.9	3.0
	0639	-1.7	-0.5		0708	-0.1	0.0
	1253	9.8	3.0		1322	8.6	2.6
	1851	-0.3	-0.1		1916	1.1	0.3
14 Tu	0106	11.4	3.5	29 W	0130	9.7	3.0
	0730	-1.6	-0.5		0749	0.1	0.0
	1346	9.8	3.0		1404	8.6	2.6
	1945	-0.2	-0.1		1959	1.2	0.4
15 W	0201	11.1	3.4	30 Th	0213	9.4	2.9
	0825	-1.3	-0.4		0832	0.2	0.1
	1441	9.8	3.0		1446	8.6	2.6
	2043	0.0	0.0		2046	1.3	0.4

Time meridian 75° W.   0000 is midnight.   1200 is noon.
Heights are referred to mean low water which is the chart datum of soundings.

BOSTON, MASS., 1983

Times and Heights of High and Low Waters

JULY

Day	Time h m	ft	m	Day	Time h m	ft	m
1 F	0257	9.2	2.8	16 Sa	0339	10.3	3.1
	0915	0.4	0.1		0955	-0.7	-0.2
	1531	8.6	2.6		1615	10.1	3.1
	2134	1.4	0.4		2226	0.0	0.0
2 Sa	0345	8.9	2.7	17 Su	0440	9.7	3.0
	1000	0.6	0.2		1051	-0.1	0.0
	1618	8.6	2.6		1713	10.0	3.0
	2224	1.4	0.4		2328	0.2	0.1
3 Su	0432	8.7	2.7	18 M	0540	9.2	2.8
	1050	0.8	0.2		1148	0.3	0.1
	1705	8.8	2.7		1810	9.9	3.0
	2318	1.2	0.4				
4 M	0523	8.6	2.6	19 Tu	0030	0.3	0.1
	1138	0.9	0.3		0642	8.8	2.7
	1752	9.1	2.8		1246	0.7	0.2
					1908	9.9	3.0
5 Tu	0011	0.9	0.3	20 W	0130	0.3	0.1
	0618	8.6	2.6		0742	8.6	2.6
	1229	0.9	0.3		1342	0.9	0.3
	1843	9.5	2.9		2001	9.8	3.0
6 W	0106	0.5	0.2	21 Th	0226	0.2	0.1
	0712	8.6	2.6		0840	8.5	2.6
	1320	0.7	0.2		1433	1.0	0.3
	1933	9.9	3.0		2052	9.9	3.0
7 Th	0200	0.0	0.0	22 F	0317	0.1	0.0
	0806	8.8	2.7		0932	8.5	2.6
	1414	0.5	0.2		1522	1.0	0.3
	2026	10.4	3.2		2140	9.9	3.0
8 F	0255	-0.5	-0.2	23 Sa	0401	0.0	0.0
	0901	9.1	2.8		1015	8.5	2.6
	1506	0.2	0.1		1606	0.9	0.3
	2119	10.9	3.3		2224	9.9	3.0
9 Sa	0346	-1.1	-0.3	24 Su	0445	-0.1	0.0
	0956	9.4	2.9		1057	8.6	2.6
	1556	-0.1	0.0		1649	0.9	0.3
	2210	11.3	3.4		2306	9.9	3.0
10 Su	0437	-1.5	-0.5	25 M	0524	-0.1	0.0
	1049	9.7	3.0		1138	8.7	2.7
	1648	-0.4	-0.1		1729	0.8	0.2
	2303	11.6	3.5		2345	9.9	3.0
11 M	0529	-1.8	-0.5	26 Tu	0603	-0.1	0.0
	1142	10.0	3.0		1215	8.8	2.7
	1741	-0.6	-0.2		1810	0.8	0.2
	2356	11.8	3.6				
12 Tu	0621	-1.9	-0.6	27 W	0023	9.9	3.0
	1235	10.2	3.1		0642	-0.1	0.0
	1835	-0.7	-0.2		1253	8.8	2.7
					1850	0.8	0.2
13 W	0051	11.7	3.6	28 Th	0103	9.8	3.0
	0713	-1.8	-0.5		0719	0.0	0.0
	1329	10.3	3.1		1332	8.9	2.7
	1930	-0.6	-0.2		1932	0.8	0.2
14 Th	0146	11.4	3.5	29 F	0143	9.6	2.9
	0806	-1.6	-0.5		0759	0.1	0.0
	1423	10.3	3.1		1411	8.9	2.7
	2027	-0.5	-0.2		2015	0.9	0.3
15 F	0242	10.9	3.3	30 Sa	0225	9.4	2.9
	0900	-1.2	-0.4		0840	0.3	0.1
	1518	10.2	3.1		1453	9.0	2.7
	2125	-0.2	-0.1		2100	0.9	0.3
				31 Su	0308	9.1	2.8
					0921	0.5	0.2
					1536	9.1	2.8
					2148	0.9	0.3

AUGUST

Day	Time h m	ft	m	Day	Time h m	ft	m
1 M	0357	8.8	2.7	16 Tu	0514	8.8	2.7
	1008	0.8	0.2		1117	0.8	0.2
	1622	9.2	2.8		1739	9.7	3.0
	2240	0.9	0.3				
2 Tu	0448	8.6	2.6	17 W	0002	0.5	0.2
	1058	0.9	0.3		0616	8.4	2.6
	1712	9.4	2.9		1217	1.2	0.4
	2335	0.7	0.2		1836	9.5	2.9
3 W	0542	8.5	2.6	18 Th	0103	0.6	0.2
	1150	1.0	0.3		0717	8.2	2.5
	1807	9.6	2.9		1313	1.3	0.4
					1936	9.4	2.9
4 Th	0032	0.4	0.1	19 F	0202	0.6	0.2
	0639	8.5	2.6		0816	8.2	2.5
	1248	0.9	0.3		1408	1.3	0.4
	1902	10.0	3.0		2029	9.4	2.9
5 F	0130	0.0	0.0	20 Sa	0253	0.5	0.2
	0739	8.7	2.7		0907	8.3	2.5
	1344	0.6	0.2		1459	1.2	0.4
	2000	10.5	3.2		2116	9.5	2.9
6 Sa	0229	-0.5	-0.2	21 Su	0338	0.3	0.1
	0837	9.0	2.7		0951	8.5	2.6
	1442	0.2	0.1		1543	1.0	0.3
	2056	10.9	3.3		2201	9.7	3.0
7 Su	0324	-1.1	-0.3	22 M	0418	0.2	0.1
	0935	9.5	2.9		1031	8.7	2.7
	1537	-0.3	-0.1		1625	0.8	0.2
	2152	11.4	3.5		2241	9.8	3.0
8 M	0418	-1.5	-0.5	23 Tu	0457	0.0	0.0
	1029	9.9	3.0		1110	8.9	2.7
	1631	-0.7	-0.2		1706	0.6	0.2
	2247	11.7	3.6		2319	9.9	3.0
9 Tu	0510	-1.9	-0.6	24 W	0535	-0.1	0.0
	1123	10.3	3.1		1146	9.1	2.8
	1726	-1.0	-0.3		1746	0.4	0.1
	2341	11.8	3.6		2358	9.9	3.0
10 W	0602	-2.0	-0.6	25 Th	0611	-0.1	0.0
	1216	10.6	3.2		1223	9.2	2.8
	1818	-1.2	-0.4		1824	0.4	0.1
11 Th	0035	11.7	3.6	26 F	0035	9.8	3.0
	0652	-1.9	-0.6		0648	-0.1	0.0
	1307	10.8	3.3		1300	9.3	2.8
	1912	-1.1	-0.3		1904	0.3	0.1
12 F	0127	11.4	3.5	27 Sa	0114	9.7	3.0
	0743	-1.5	-0.5		0724	0.1	0.0
	1358	10.8	3.3		1337	9.4	2.9
	2006	-0.9	-0.3		1943	0.3	0.1
13 Sa	0222	10.8	3.3	28 Su	0155	9.4	2.9
	0833	-1.0	-0.3		0804	0.3	0.1
	1452	10.6	3.2		1415	9.4	2.9
	2102	-0.6	-0.2		2028	0.4	0.1
14 Su	0316	10.1	3.1	29 M	0237	9.2	2.8
	0926	-0.4	-0.1		0846	0.5	0.2
	1545	10.3	3.1		1500	9.5	2.9
	2158	-0.2	-0.1		2115	0.4	0.1
15 M	0414	9.4	2.9	30 Tu	0325	8.9	2.7
	1020	0.2	0.1		0932	0.8	0.2
	1640	10.0	3.0		1547	9.5	2.9
	2300	0.2	0.1		2206	0.5	0.2
				31 W	0418	8.6	2.6
					1023	1.0	0.3
					1639	9.5	2.9
					2305	0.5	0.2

SEPTEMBER

Day	Time h m	ft	m	Day	Time h m	ft	m
1 Th	0514	8.4	2.6	16 F	0029	0.9	0.3
	1121	1.1	0.3		0647	8.0	2.4
	1737	9.7	3.0		1243	1.7	0.5
					1901	9.0	2.7
2 F	0005	0.3	0.1	17 Sa	0128	0.9	0.3
	0615	8.5	2.6		0743	8.0	2.4
	1221	1.0	0.3		1341	1.6	0.5
	1837	10.0	3.0		1957	9.0	2.7
3 Sa	0107	0.0	0.0	18 Su	0221	0.8	0.2
	0717	8.7	2.7		0837	8.3	2.5
	1324	0.7	0.2		1432	1.3	0.4
	1939	10.4	3.2		2047	9.2	2.8
4 Su	0208	-0.5	-0.2	19 M	0306	0.5	0.2
	0819	9.2	2.8		0920	8.6	2.6
	1424	0.2	0.1		1519	1.0	0.3
	2039	10.8	3.3		2133	9.5	2.9
5 M	0306	-1.0	-0.3	20 Tu	0348	0.3	0.1
	0916	9.7	3.0		1001	8.9	2.7
	1521	-0.4	-0.1		1601	0.6	0.2
	2136	11.3	3.4		2212	9.7	3.0
6 Tu	0359	-1.5	-0.5	21 W	0425	0.1	0.0
	1010	10.3	3.1		1038	9.2	2.8
	1617	-1.0	-0.3		1640	0.3	0.1
	2231	11.6	3.5		2252	9.8	3.0
7 W	0449	-1.8	-0.5	22 Th	0503	-0.1	0.0
	1102	10.8	3.3		1114	9.5	2.9
	1709	-1.4	-0.4		1718	0.1	0.0
	2324	11.7	3.6		2330	9.8	3.0
8 Th	0540	-1.8	-0.5	23 F	0539	-0.1	0.0
	1153	11.1	3.4		1149	9.7	3.0
	1800	-1.6	-0.5		1757	-0.1	0.0
9 F	0016	11.5	3.5	24 Sa	0008	9.8	3.0
	0628	-1.6	-0.5		0616	-0.1	0.0
	1242	11.2	3.4		1226	9.8	3.0
	1852	-1.5	-0.5		1836	-0.2	-0.1
10 Sa	0108	11.1	3.4	25 Su	0046	9.7	3.0
	0716	-1.2	-0.4		0653	0.1	0.0
	1332	11.0	3.4		1302	9.9	3.0
	1943	-1.2	-0.4		1917	-0.2	-0.1
11 Su	0159	10.5	3.2	26 M	0127	9.4	2.9
	0804	-0.6	-0.2		0732	0.3	0.1
	1421	10.7	3.3		1344	9.9	3.0
	2036	-0.8	-0.2		2001	-0.2	-0.1
12 M	0251	9.8	3.0	27 Tu	0212	9.2	2.8
	0854	0.0	0.0		0816	0.6	0.2
	1513	10.3	3.1		1427	9.9	3.0
	2131	-0.2	-0.1		2049	0.0	0.0
13 Tu	0347	9.1	2.8	28 W	0300	8.9	2.7
	0947	0.7	0.2		0903	0.9	0.3
	1606	9.8	3.0		1516	9.8	3.0
	2227	0.3	0.1		2142	0.1	0.0
14 W	0443	8.5	2.6	29 Th	0354	8.6	2.6
	1044	1.3	0.4		0954	1.1	0.3
	1704	9.3	2.8		1613	9.7	3.0
	2328	0.7	0.2		2240	0.2	0.1
15 Th	0544	8.1	2.5	30 F	0454	8.5	2.6
	1143	1.6	0.5		1059	1.2	0.4
	1804	9.0	2.7		1714	9.7	3.0
					2343	0.2	0.1

Time meridian 75° W. 0000 is midnight. 1200 is noon.
Heights are referred to mean low water which is the chart datum of soundings.

BOSTON, MASS., 1983

Times and Heights of High and Low Waters

OCTOBER

Day	Time h m	ft	m	Day	Time h m	ft	m
1 Sa	0557	8.6	2.6	16 Su	0048	1.1	0.3
	1203	1.0	0.3		0704	8.0	2.4
	1817	9.9	3.0		1307	1.7	0.5
					1920	8.7	2.7
2 Su	0049	-0.1	0.0	17 M	0141	0.9	0.3
	0701	8.9	2.7		0755	8.3	2.5
	1307	0.6	0.2		1358	1.3	0.4
	1923	10.2	3.1		2012	8.9	2.7
3 M	0149	-0.4	-0.1	18 Tu	0227	0.7	0.2
	0802	9.4	2.9		0842	8.7	2.7
	1410	0.0	0.0		1447	0.9	0.3
	2024	10.6	3.2		2058	9.2	2.8
4 Tu	0245	-0.9	-0.3	19 W	0309	0.4	0.1
	0859	10.0	3.0		0922	9.1	2.8
	1507	-0.6	-0.2		1530	0.5	0.2
	2122	10.9	3.3		2140	9.4	2.9
5 W	0338	-1.2	-0.4	20 Th	0351	0.2	0.1
	0951	10.6	3.2		1001	9.5	2.9
	1601	-1.2	-0.4		1610	0.0	0.0
	2216	11.1	3.4		2220	9.5	2.9
6 Th	0428	-1.4	-0.4	21 F	0428	0.0	0.0
	1041	11.1	3.4		1037	9.9	3.0
	1652	-1.6	-0.5		1650	-0.3	-0.1
	2306	11.1	3.4		2301	9.6	2.9
7 F	0516	-1.4	-0.4	22 Sa	0505	0.0	0.0
	1129	11.3	3.4		1115	10.1	3.1
	1742	-1.7	-0.5		1729	-0.6	-0.2
	2357	10.9	3.3		2340	9.6	2.9
8 Sa	0603	-1.2	-0.4	23 Su	0544	0.0	0.0
	1217	11.3	3.4		1153	10.3	3.1
	1830	-1.6	-0.5		1811	-0.8	-0.2
9 Su	0045	10.5	3.2	24 M	0020	9.6	2.9
	0648	-0.7	-0.2		0623	0.1	0.0
	1303	11.1	3.4		1233	10.4	3.2
	1919	-1.3	-0.4		1853	-0.8	-0.2
10 M	0135	10.0	3.0	25 Tu	0105	9.4	2.9
	0735	-0.2	-0.1		0705	0.3	0.1
	1351	10.6	3.2		1316	10.4	3.2
	2007	-0.8	-0.2		1938	-0.7	-0.2
11 Tu	0225	9.4	2.9	26 W	0151	9.2	2.8
	0822	0.5	0.2		0751	0.5	0.2
	1440	10.1	3.1		1403	10.3	3.1
	2059	-0.2	-0.1		2028	-0.5	-0.2
12 W	0317	8.8	2.7	27 Th	0242	8.9	2.7
	0915	1.1	0.3		0842	0.7	0.2
	1531	9.5	2.9		1456	10.1	3.1
	2154	0.4	0.1		2123	-0.3	-0.1
13 Th	0411	8.3	2.5	28 F	0337	8.7	2.7
	1011	1.5	0.5		0939	1.0	0.3
	1627	9.0	2.7		1554	9.9	3.0
	2251	0.8	0.2		2222	-0.1	0.0
14 F	0509	8.0	2.4	29 Sa	0438	8.7	2.7
	1108	1.8	0.5		1042	1.0	0.3
	1726	8.7	2.7		1657	9.7	3.0
	2350	1.1	0.3		2325	-0.1	0.0
15 Sa	0609	7.9	2.4	30 Su	0542	8.8	2.7
	1208	1.9	0.6		1147	0.9	0.3
	1824	8.6	2.6		1802	9.7	3.0
				31 M	0028	-0.2	-0.1
					0645	9.2	2.8
					1254	0.5	0.2
					1907	9.9	3.0

NOVEMBER

Day	Time h m	ft	m	Day	Time h m	ft	m
1 Tu	0128	-0.4	-0.1	16 W	0144	0.8	0.2
	0744	9.7	3.0		0757	8.8	2.7
	1357	-0.1	0.0		1410	0.8	0.2
	2008	10.1	3.1		2018	8.8	2.7
2 W	0224	-0.7	-0.2	17 Th	0227	0.6	0.2
	0840	10.3	3.1		0840	9.3	2.8
	1453	-0.7	-0.2		1455	0.3	0.1
	2106	10.3	3.1		2103	9.0	2.7
3 Th	0316	-0.9	-0.3	18 F	0309	0.4	0.1
	0932	10.8	3.3		0922	9.7	3.0
	1546	-1.2	-0.4		1538	-0.2	-0.1
	2159	10.4	3.2		2146	9.2	2.8
4 F	0406	-0.9	-0.3	19 Sa	0351	0.2	0.1
	1020	11.1	3.4		1002	10.1	3.1
	1636	-1.5	-0.5		1621	-0.6	-0.2
	2249	10.4	3.2		2231	9.3	2.8
5 Sa	0452	-0.8	-0.2	20 Su	0433	0.0	0.0
	1106	11.2	3.4		1041	10.5	3.2
	1724	-1.6	-0.5		1703	-1.0	-0.3
	2338	10.2	3.1		2312	9.4	2.9
6 Su	0537	-0.6	-0.2	21 M	0514	0.0	0.0
	1152	11.1	3.4		1124	10.7	3.3
	1810	-1.5	-0.5		1747	-1.2	-0.4
					2359	9.5	2.9
7 M	0024	9.9	3.0	22 Tu	0558	0.0	0.0
	0623	-0.2	-0.1		1208	10.8	3.3
	1236	10.8	3.3		1831	-1.3	-0.4
	1855	-1.1	-0.3				
8 Tu	0111	9.4	2.9	23 W	0045	9.4	2.9
	0706	0.2	0.1		0643	0.0	0.0
	1322	10.4	3.2		1255	10.8	3.3
	1942	-0.7	-0.2		1920	-1.2	-0.4
9 W	0159	9.0	2.7	24 Th	0132	9.3	2.8
	0752	0.7	0.2		0732	0.2	0.1
	1409	9.9	3.0		1345	10.6	3.2
	2029	-0.2	-0.1		2012	-1.0	-0.3
10 Th	0246	8.5	2.6	25 F	0226	9.2	2.8
	0843	1.2	0.4		0827	0.4	0.1
	1457	9.4	2.9		1441	10.4	3.2
	2120	0.3	0.1		2105	-0.8	-0.2
11 F	0338	8.2	2.5	26 Sa	0323	9.1	2.8
	0934	1.6	0.5		0923	0.6	0.2
	1550	8.9	2.7		1539	10.1	3.1
	2214	0.7	0.2		2204	-0.5	-0.2
12 Sa	0432	8.0	2.4	27 Su	0422	9.1	2.8
	1030	1.8	0.5		1027	0.6	0.2
	1643	8.6	2.6		1642	9.8	3.0
	2306	1.0	0.3		2305	-0.4	-0.1
13 Su	0525	8.0	2.4	28 M	0524	9.2	2.8
	1128	1.8	0.5		1133	0.5	0.2
	1741	8.5	2.6		1746	9.6	2.9
14 M	0002	1.0	0.3	29 Tu	0006	-0.3	-0.1
	0620	8.1	2.5		0626	9.5	2.9
	1225	1.6	0.5		1238	0.2	0.1
	1837	8.4	2.6		1849	9.5	2.9
15 Tu	0054	0.9	0.3	30 W	0105	-0.3	-0.1
	0711	8.4	2.6		0725	9.9	3.0
	1320	1.3	0.4		1341	-0.2	-0.1
	1929	8.6	2.6		1952	9.5	2.9

DECEMBER

Day	Time h m	ft	m	Day	Time h m	ft	m
1 Th	0202	-0.3	-0.1	16 F	0144	0.7	0.2
	0821	10.3	3.1		0756	9.3	2.8
	1439	-0.7	-0.2		1418	0.3	0.1
	2050	9.6	2.9		2024	8.5	2.6
2 F	0255	-0.4	-0.1	17 Sa	0231	0.5	0.2
	0911	10.6	3.2		0842	9.8	3.0
	1532	-1.0	-0.3		1506	-0.3	-0.1
	2143	9.6	2.9		2114	8.8	2.7
3 Sa	0344	-0.3	-0.1	18 Su	0316	0.3	0.1
	0959	10.8	3.3		0928	10.2	3.1
	1620	-1.2	-0.4		1552	-0.8	-0.2
	2233	9.5	2.9		2201	9.0	2.7
4 Su	0430	-0.2	-0.1	19 M	0401	0.1	0.0
	1045	10.8	3.3		1015	10.6	3.2
	1707	-1.3	-0.4		1639	-1.2	-0.4
	2321	9.4	2.9		2248	9.3	2.8
5 M	0513	0.0	0.0	20 Tu	0448	-0.2	-0.1
	1129	10.7	3.3		1101	11.0	3.4
	1750	-1.1	-0.3		1726	-1.5	-0.5
					2338	9.4	2.9
6 Tu	0004	9.2	2.8	21 W	0536	-0.3	-0.1
	0558	0.2	0.1		1148	11.2	3.4
	1213	10.5	3.2		1815	-1.7	-0.5
	1834	-0.9	-0.3				
7 W	0050	9.0	2.7	22 Th	0026	9.6	2.9
	0641	0.5	0.2		0624	-0.4	-0.1
	1255	10.1	3.1		1239	11.2	3.4
	1916	-0.6	-0.2		1903	-1.7	-0.5
8 Th	0132	8.7	2.7	23 F	0116	9.6	2.9
	0727	0.8	0.2		0716	-0.4	-0.1
	1340	9.8	3.0		1332	11.0	3.4
	2001	-0.2	-0.1		1955	-1.5	-0.5
9 F	0217	8.5	2.6	24 Sa	0211	9.6	2.9
	0812	1.1	0.3		0812	-0.2	-0.1
	1426	9.4	2.9		1425	10.7	3.3
	2046	0.1	0.0		2048	-1.3	-0.4
10 Sa	0304	8.3	2.5	25 Su	0307	9.6	2.9
	0900	1.3	0.4		0909	-0.1	0.0
	1513	9.0	2.7		1523	10.3	3.1
	2134	0.4	0.1		2145	-0.9	-0.3
11 Su	0352	8.2	2.5	26 M	0403	9.6	2.9
	0953	1.5	0.5		1011	0.1	0.0
	1603	8.7	2.7		1625	9.8	3.0
	2224	0.7	0.2		2242	-0.6	-0.2
12 M	0442	8.2	2.5	27 Tu	0503	9.7	3.0
	1046	1.6	0.5		1115	0.1	0.0
	1656	8.4	2.6		1727	9.4	2.9
	2315	0.8	0.2		2341	-0.3	-0.1
13 Tu	0532	8.3	2.5	28 W	0603	9.8	3.0
	1141	1.5	0.5		1220	0.0	0.0
	1748	8.3	2.5		1832	9.1	2.8
14 W	0006	0.9	0.3	29 Th	0041	0.0	0.0
	0621	8.5	2.6		0701	9.9	3.0
	1235	1.2	0.4		1323	-0.2	-0.1
	1843	8.3	2.5		1933	8.9	2.7
15 Th	0056	0.9	0.3	30 F	0138	0.1	0.0
	0710	8.9	2.7		0757	10.1	3.1
	1328	0.8	0.2		1421	-0.4	-0.1
	1934	8.4	2.6		2034	8.7	2.7
				31 Sa	0233	0.2	0.1
					0851	10.2	3.1
					1514	-0.6	-0.2
					2128	8.8	2.7

Time meridian 75° W. 0000 is midnight. 1200 is noon.
Heights are referred to mean low water which is the chart datum of soundings.

NEWPORT, R.I., 1983

Times and Heights of High and Low Waters

JANUARY

Day	Time (h m)	Height (ft)	Height (m)	Day	Time (h m)	Height (ft)	Height (m)
1 Sa	0209	-1.0	-0.3	16 Su	0204	-0.2	-0.1
	0857	4.6	1.4		0903	3.5	1.1
	1500	-0.9	-0.3		1440	-0.1	0.0
	2125	3.8	1.2		2124	3.0	0.9
2 Su	0305	-0.9	-0.3	17 M	0241	-0.1	0.0
	0951	4.4	1.3		0942	3.4	1.0
	1551	-0.7	-0.2		1513	-0.1	0.0
	2219	3.7	1.1		2206	3.0	0.9
3 M	0400	-0.6	-0.2	18 Tu	0320	-0.1	0.0
	1043	4.1	1.2		1022	3.2	1.0
	1641	-0.5	-0.2		1548	-0.1	0.0
	2315	3.6	1.1		2249	2.9	0.9
4 Tu	0459	-0.4	-0.1	19 W	0400	0.0	0.0
	1142	3.7	1.1		1105	3.0	0.9
	1736	-0.3	-0.1		1625	-0.1	0.0
					2333	2.9	0.9
5 W	0011	3.5	1.1	20 Th	0446	0.1	0.0
	0605	-0.1	0.0		1152	2.8	0.9
	1238	3.4	1.0		1710	0.0	0.0
	1833	-0.1	0.0				
6 Th	0111	3.4	1.0	21 F	0024	2.9	0.9
	0720	0.1	0.0		0539	0.2	0.1
	1337	3.1	0.9		1244	2.7	0.8
	1933	0.1	0.0		1758	0.0	0.0
7 F	0210	3.4	1.0	22 Sa	0117	3.0	0.9
	0843	0.3	0.1		0639	0.2	0.1
	1435	2.9	0.9		1341	2.7	0.8
	2038	0.1	0.0		1855	-0.1	0.0
8 Sa	0309	3.4	1.0	23 Su	0217	3.2	1.0
	0957	0.3	0.1		0745	0.2	0.1
	1531	2.8	0.9		1445	2.7	0.8
	2138	0.2	0.1		1958	-0.1	0.0
9 Su	0402	3.5	1.1	24 M	0318	3.5	1.1
	1053	0.2	0.1		0859	0.0	0.0
	1623	2.8	0.9		1545	2.9	0.9
	2226	0.1	0.0		2107	-0.3	-0.1
10 M	0452	3.5	1.1	25 Tu	0417	3.8	1.2
	1140	0.2	0.1		1013	-0.2	-0.1
	1711	2.8	0.9		1644	3.1	0.9
	2308	0.0	0.0		2213	-0.5	-0.2
11 Tu	0537	3.6	1.1	26 W	0514	4.1	1.2
	1215	0.1	0.0		1116	-0.5	-0.2
	1757	2.9	0.9		1738	3.4	1.0
	2346	0.0	0.0		2316	-0.8	-0.2
12 W	0620	3.7	1.1	27 Th	0607	4.4	1.3
	1247	0.0	0.0		1207	-0.7	-0.2
	1839	3.0	0.9		1833	3.7	1.1
13 Th	0020	-0.1	0.0	28 F	0014	-1.0	-0.3
	0702	3.7	1.1		0659	4.6	1.4
	1315	0.0	0.0		1305	-0.9	-0.3
	1923	3.1	0.9		1924	3.9	1.2
14 F	0054	-0.2	-0.1	29 Sa	0110	-1.1	-0.3
	0743	3.7	1.1		0750	4.6	1.4
	1341	-0.1	0.0		1354	-1.0	-0.3
	2003	3.1	0.9		2015	4.0	1.2
15 Sa	0129	-0.2	-0.1	30 Su	0204	-1.1	-0.3
	0823	3.7	1.1		0840	4.5	1.4
	1410	-0.1	0.0		1442	-1.0	-0.3
	2044	3.1	0.9		2106	4.1	1.2
				31 M	0256	-1.0	-0.3
					0932	4.3	1.3
					1527	-0.9	-0.3
					2156	4.0	1.2

FEBRUARY

Day	Time (h m)	Height (ft)	Height (m)	Day	Time (h m)	Height (ft)	Height (m)
1 Tu	0345	-0.8	-0.2	16 W	0300	-0.3	-0.1
	1022	4.0	1.2		0956	3.3	1.0
	1612	-0.7	-0.2		1519	-0.3	-0.1
	2248	3.8	1.2		2214	3.3	1.0
2 W	0438	-0.5	-0.2	17 Th	0340	-0.3	-0.1
	1113	3.6	1.1		1035	3.1	0.9
	1659	-0.4	-0.1		1556	-0.3	-0.1
	2340	3.6	1.1		2257	3.2	1.0
3 Th	0534	-0.2	-0.1	18 F	0424	-0.2	-0.1
	1206	3.2	1.0		1120	2.9	0.9
	1747	-0.1	0.0		1638	-0.2	-0.1
					2347	3.2	1.0
4 F	0036	3.4	1.0	19 Sa	0514	-0.1	0.0
	0635	0.2	0.1		1211	2.7	0.8
	1301	2.9	0.9		1726	-0.2	-0.1
	1836	0.1	0.0				
5 Sa	0135	3.2	1.0	20 Su	0043	3.2	1.0
	0752	0.4	0.1		0611	0.1	0.0
	1359	2.6	0.8		1311	2.6	0.8
	1936	0.3	0.1		1824	-0.1	0.0
6 Su	0233	3.1	0.9	21 M	0148	3.3	1.0
	0920	0.5	0.2		0719	0.1	0.0
	1457	2.5	0.8		1417	2.6	0.8
	2045	0.4	0.1		1929	-0.1	0.0
7 M	0331	3.1	0.9	22 Tu	0253	3.4	1.0
	1031	0.5	0.2		0839	0.1	0.0
	1554	2.5	0.8		1525	2.8	0.9
	2154	0.4	0.1		2045	-0.2	-0.1
8 Tu	0423	3.2	1.0	23 W	0357	3.7	1.1
	1124	0.4	0.1		0957	-0.1	0.0
	1646	2.6	0.8		1626	3.1	0.9
	2246	0.3	0.1		2200	-0.4	-0.1
9 W	0512	3.3	1.0	24 Th	0455	4.0	1.2
	1159	0.3	0.1		1103	-0.4	-0.1
	1733	2.8	0.9		1722	3.5	1.1
	2332	0.1	0.0		2308	-0.7	-0.2
10 Th	0557	3.4	1.0	25 F	0551	4.2	1.3
	1227	0.1	0.0		1159	-0.7	-0.2
	1817	3.0	0.9		1815	3.8	1.2
11 F	0007	0.0	0.0	26 Sa	0009	-0.9	-0.3
	0641	3.5	1.1		0643	4.4	1.3
	1252	0.0	0.0		1249	-0.9	-0.3
	1859	3.1	0.9		1906	4.1	1.2
12 Sa	0041	-0.2	-0.1	27 Su	0103	-1.1	-0.3
	0721	3.6	1.1		0732	4.4	1.3
	1318	-0.1	0.0		1335	-1.0	-0.3
	1940	3.2	1.0		1955	4.3	1.3
13 Su	0115	-0.3	-0.1	28 M	0152	-1.1	-0.3
	0759	3.6	1.1		0821	4.4	1.3
	1344	-0.2	-0.1		1418	-1.0	-0.3
	2019	3.3	1.0		2043	4.3	1.3
14 M	0149	-0.3	-0.1				
	0838	3.6	1.1				
	1414	-0.3	-0.1				
	2058	3.3	1.0				
15 Tu	0224	-0.4	-0.1				
	0916	3.5	1.1				
	1446	-0.3	-0.1				
	2135	3.3	1.0				

MARCH

Day	Time (h m)	Height (ft)	Height (m)	Day	Time (h m)	Height (ft)	Height (m)
1 Tu	0242	-1.0	-0.3	16 W	0203	-0.5	-0.2
	0908	4.1	1.2		0849	3.5	1.1
	1500	-0.9	-0.3		1417	-0.5	-0.2
	2129	4.2	1.3		2108	3.7	1.1
2 W	0327	-0.8	-0.2	17 Th	0242	-0.5	-0.2
	0956	3.8	1.2		0927	3.4	1.0
	1540	-0.6	-0.2		1452	-0.5	-0.2
	2219	4.0	1.2		2147	3.7	1.1
3 Th	0412	-0.5	-0.2	18 F	0321	-0.5	-0.2
	1043	3.4	1.0		1009	3.2	1.0
	1619	-0.4	-0.1		1531	-0.4	-0.1
	2307	3.7	1.1		2232	3.6	1.1
4 F	0457	-0.1	0.0	19 Sa	0407	-0.3	-0.1
	1133	3.1	0.9		1057	3.0	0.9
	1659	-0.1	0.0		1612	-0.3	-0.1
					2321	3.5	1.1
5 Sa	0000	3.4	1.0	20 Su	0457	-0.2	-0.1
	0547	0.2	0.1		1150	2.8	0.9
	1224	2.7	0.8		1704	-0.2	-0.1
	1742	0.2	0.1				
6 Su	0056	3.1	0.9	21 M	0019	3.4	1.0
	0643	0.5	0.2		0555	0.0	0.0
	1322	2.5	0.8		1254	2.7	0.8
	1832	0.4	0.1		1803	-0.1	0.0
7 M	0156	2.9	0.9	22 Tu	0125	3.4	1.0
	0807	0.7	0.2		0704	0.1	0.0
	1424	2.4	0.7		1400	2.7	0.8
	1937	0.6	0.2		1913	0.0	0.0
8 Tu	0256	2.9	0.9	23 W	0233	3.4	1.0
	0954	0.7	0.2		0824	0.1	0.0
	1522	2.4	0.7		1509	2.9	0.9
	2107	0.6	0.2		2035	0.0	0.0
9 W	0352	2.9	0.9	24 Th	0338	3.6	1.1
	1049	0.6	0.2		0942	-0.1	0.0
	1616	2.6	0.8		1610	3.3	1.0
	2221	0.5	0.2		2159	-0.3	-0.1
10 Th	0444	3.1	0.9	25 F	0437	3.8	1.2
	1124	0.4	0.1		1047	-0.3	-0.1
	1706	2.8	0.9		1706	3.7	1.1
	2311	0.3	0.1		2308	-0.6	-0.2
11 F	0529	3.2	1.0	26 Sa	0533	4.0	1.2
	1151	0.2	0.1		1141	-0.6	-0.2
	1751	3.1	0.9		1757	4.0	1.2
	2345	0.0	0.0				
12 Sa	0613	3.4	1.0	27 Su	0004	-0.8	-0.2
	1217	0.0	0.0		0625	4.2	1.3
	1833	3.3	1.0		1228	-0.8	-0.2
					1846	4.3	1.3
13 Su	0020	-0.2	-0.1	28 M	0054	-1.0	-0.3
	0654	3.5	1.1		0712	4.2	1.3
	1243	-0.2	-0.1		1310	-0.8	-0.2
	1911	3.5	1.1		1932	4.4	1.3
14 M	0054	-0.3	-0.1	29 Tu	0140	-1.0	-0.3
	0732	3.6	1.1		0759	4.1	1.2
	1312	-0.3	-0.1		1350	-0.8	-0.2
	1950	3.6	1.1		2018	4.4	1.3
15 Tu	0128	-0.5	-0.2	30 W	0224	-0.9	-0.3
	0810	3.6	1.1		0844	3.9	1.2
	1344	-0.4	-0.1		1427	-0.7	-0.2
	2028	3.7	1.1		2103	4.3	1.3
				31 Th	0303	-0.7	-0.2
					0927	3.6	1.1
					1503	-0.5	-0.2
					2148	4.0	1.2

Time meridian 75° W. 0000 is midnight. 1200 is noon.
Heights are referred to mean low water which is the chart datum of soundings.

Times and Heights of High and Low Waters

APRIL

Day	Time (h m)	Height (ft)	Height (m)
1 F	0345	-0.4	-0.1
	1013	3.3	1.0
	1540	-0.2	-0.1
	2235	3.7	1.1
2 Sa	0422	-0.1	0.0
	1100	3.0	0.9
	1617	0.0	0.0
	2323	3.4	1.0
3 Su	0503	0.3	0.1
	1152	2.7	0.8
	1657	0.3	0.1
4 M	0018	3.1	0.9
	0548	0.5	0.2
	1248	2.5	0.8
	1744	0.6	0.2
5 Tu	0116	2.9	0.9
	0644	0.7	0.2
	1349	2.4	0.7
	1845	0.7	0.2
6 W	0216	2.8	0.9
	0803	0.8	0.2
	1449	2.5	0.8
	2006	0.8	0.2
7 Th	0314	2.8	0.9
	0933	0.7	0.2
	1544	2.7	0.8
	2134	0.6	0.2
8 F	0407	2.9	0.9
	1021	0.5	0.2
	1634	2.9	0.9
	2231	0.4	0.1
9 Sa	0455	3.1	0.9
	1055	0.3	0.1
	1719	3.2	1.0
	2314	0.2	0.1
10 Su	0540	3.3	1.0
	1129	0.0	0.0
	1801	3.5	1.1
	2351	-0.1	0.0
11 M	0622	3.5	1.1
	1201	-0.2	-0.1
	1840	3.7	1.1
12 Tu	0029	-0.3	-0.1
	0702	3.6	1.1
	1233	-0.4	-0.1
	1920	3.9	1.2
13 W	0106	-0.5	-0.2
	0743	3.6	1.1
	1310	-0.5	-0.2
	1959	4.1	1.2
14 Th	0144	-0.6	-0.2
	0822	3.5	1.1
	1347	-0.5	-0.2
	2039	4.1	1.2
15 F	0224	-0.6	-0.2
	0906	3.4	1.0
	1426	-0.5	-0.2
	2124	4.1	1.2
16 Sa	0308	-0.6	-0.2
	0950	3.3	1.0
	1510	-0.5	-0.2
	2211	4.0	1.2
17 Su	0355	-0.4	-0.1
	1041	3.1	0.9
	1556	-0.3	-0.1
	2304	3.8	1.2
18 M	0446	-0.2	-0.1
	1139	3.0	0.9
	1649	-0.1	0.0
19 Tu	0003	3.6	1.1
	0546	0.0	0.0
	1240	2.9	0.9
	1755	0.1	0.0
20 W	0109	3.5	1.1
	0655	0.1	0.0
	1348	3.0	0.9
	1910	0.1	0.0
21 Th	0216	3.5	1.1
	0814	0.1	0.0
	1453	3.2	1.0
	2038	0.1	0.0
22 F	0320	3.6	1.1
	0928	-0.1	0.0
	1552	3.5	1.1
	2159	-0.1	0.0
23 Sa	0418	3.7	1.1
	1029	-0.2	-0.1
	1647	3.9	1.2
	2303	-0.4	-0.1
24 Su	0514	3.8	1.2
	1119	-0.4	-0.1
	1737	4.2	1.3
	2356	-0.6	-0.2
25 M	0602	3.9	1.2
	1201	-0.5	-0.2
	1823	4.4	1.3
26 Tu	0042	-0.7	-0.2
	0649	3.9	1.2
	1243	-0.6	-0.2
	1909	4.5	1.4
27 W	0124	-0.7	-0.2
	0734	3.8	1.2
	1319	-0.6	-0.2
	1953	4.5	1.4
28 Th	0205	-0.6	-0.2
	0818	3.6	1.1
	1356	-0.4	-0.1
	2037	4.3	1.3
29 F	0239	-0.4	-0.1
	0902	3.4	1.0
	1431	-0.3	-0.1
	2121	4.0	1.2
30 Sa	0316	-0.2	-0.1
	0945	3.2	1.0
	1506	-0.1	0.0
	2204	3.7	1.1

MAY

Day	Time (h m)	Height (ft)	Height (m)
1 Su	0351	0.1	0.0
	1030	3.0	0.9
	1542	0.2	0.1
	2251	3.4	1.0
2 M	0427	0.3	0.1
	1121	2.8	0.9
	1622	0.4	0.1
	2342	3.1	0.9
3 Tu	0507	0.5	0.2
	1216	2.6	0.8
	1707	0.6	0.2
4 W	0037	2.9	0.9
	0557	0.6	0.2
	1314	2.6	0.8
	1806	0.8	0.2
5 Th	0136	2.8	0.9
	0656	0.7	0.2
	1412	2.6	0.8
	1912	0.8	0.2
6 F	0233	2.8	0.9
	0759	0.7	0.2
	1507	2.8	0.9
	2031	0.8	0.2
7 Sa	0327	2.9	0.9
	0859	0.5	0.2
	1557	3.1	0.9
	2138	0.5	0.2
8 Su	0416	3.0	0.9
	0950	0.3	0.1
	1642	3.4	1.0
	2231	0.3	0.1
9 M	0503	3.2	1.0
	1034	0.1	0.0
	1725	3.7	1.1
	2316	0.0	0.0
10 Tu	0547	3.4	1.0
	1117	-0.1	0.0
	1807	4.0	1.2
	2359	-0.3	-0.1
11 W	0630	3.5	1.1
	1156	-0.3	-0.1
	1850	4.2	1.3
12 Th	0041	-0.5	-0.2
	0713	3.6	1.1
	1237	-0.5	-0.2
	1932	4.4	1.3
13 F	0123	-0.6	-0.2
	0759	3.6	1.1
	1322	-0.6	-0.2
	2018	4.4	1.3
14 Sa	0209	-0.7	-0.2
	0844	3.5	1.1
	1408	-0.5	-0.2
	2104	4.4	1.3
15 Su	0255	-0.6	-0.2
	0934	3.5	1.1
	1455	-0.4	-0.1
	2155	4.3	1.3
16 M	0345	-0.5	-0.2
	1028	3.4	1.0
	1548	-0.3	-0.1
	2249	4.1	1.2
17 Tu	0441	-0.3	-0.1
	1125	3.3	1.0
	1645	-0.1	0.0
	2350	3.9	1.2
18 W	0539	-0.1	0.0
	1227	3.3	1.0
	1752	0.1	0.0
19 Th	0053	3.7	1.1
	0645	0.0	0.0
	1332	3.4	1.0
	1912	0.2	0.1
20 F	0156	3.6	1.1
	0755	0.0	0.0
	1432	3.6	1.1
	2038	0.2	0.1
21 Sa	0259	3.5	1.1
	0904	0.0	0.0
	1530	3.8	1.2
	2152	0.0	0.0
22 Su	0357	3.5	1.1
	1002	-0.1	0.0
	1623	4.0	1.2
	2255	-0.2	-0.1
23 M	0450	3.6	1.1
	1050	-0.2	-0.1
	1714	4.2	1.3
	2345	-0.3	-0.1
24 Tu	0538	3.6	1.1
	1135	-0.2	-0.1
	1800	4.4	1.3
25 W	0028	-0.3	-0.1
	0626	3.6	1.1
	1214	-0.3	-0.1
	1846	4.4	1.3
26 Th	0108	-0.3	-0.1
	0709	3.5	1.1
	1250	-0.2	-0.1
	1928	4.4	1.3
27 F	0145	-0.2	-0.1
	0753	3.4	1.0
	1325	-0.2	-0.1
	2013	4.2	1.3
28 Sa	0218	-0.1	0.0
	0836	3.3	1.0
	1400	0.0	0.0
	2055	4.0	1.2
29 Su	0250	0.0	0.0
	0919	3.2	1.0
	1436	0.1	0.0
	2137	3.8	1.2
30 M	0323	0.2	0.1
	1005	3.0	0.9
	1514	0.3	0.1
	2222	3.5	1.1
31 Tu	0358	0.3	0.1
	1054	2.9	0.9
	1553	0.5	0.2
	2309	3.2	1.0

JUNE

Day	Time (h m)	Height (ft)	Height (m)
1 W	0436	0.4	0.1
	1142	2.8	0.9
	1638	0.7	0.2
	2358	3.0	0.9
2 Th	0518	0.5	0.2
	1237	2.8	0.9
	1731	0.8	0.2
3 F	0051	2.9	0.9
	0606	0.6	0.2
	1330	2.9	0.9
	1829	0.8	0.2
4 Sa	0146	2.8	0.9
	0701	0.5	0.2
	1423	3.0	0.9
	1935	0.8	0.2
5 Su	0241	2.9	0.9
	0756	0.5	0.2
	1514	3.2	1.0
	2043	0.6	0.2
6 M	0334	3.0	0.9
	0851	0.3	0.1
	1602	3.5	1.1
	2144	0.4	0.1
7 Tu	0423	3.1	0.9
	0944	0.1	0.0
	1648	3.9	1.2
	2239	0.1	0.0
8 W	0511	3.3	1.0
	1034	-0.1	0.0
	1735	4.2	1.3
	2329	-0.2	-0.1
9 Th	0559	3.4	1.0
	1124	-0.3	-0.1
	1822	4.5	1.4
10 F	0017	-0.4	-0.1
	0648	3.6	1.1
	1212	-0.5	-0.2
	1909	4.6	1.4
11 Sa	0106	-0.6	-0.2
	0736	3.7	1.1
	1302	-0.6	-0.2
	1957	4.7	1.4
12 Su	0155	-0.6	-0.2
	0826	3.7	1.1
	1352	-0.6	-0.2
	2047	4.7	1.4
13 M	0245	-0.6	-0.2
	0919	3.7	1.1
	1445	-0.5	-0.2
	2140	4.5	1.4
14 Tu	0337	-0.5	-0.2
	1012	3.7	1.1
	1540	-0.3	-0.1
	2235	4.3	1.3
15 W	0430	-0.4	-0.2
	1110	3.7	1.1
	1641	-0.1	0.0
	2333	4.1	1.2
16 Th	0526	-0.2	-0.1
	1208	3.7	1.1
	1750	0.1	0.0
17 F	0033	3.8	1.2
	0627	0.0	0.0
	1309	3.7	1.1
	1904	0.2	0.1
18 Sa	0133	3.6	1.1
	0730	0.1	0.0
	1409	3.8	1.2
	2025	0.3	0.1
19 Su	0235	3.4	1.0
	0832	0.1	0.0
	1507	3.9	1.2
	2139	0.2	0.1
20 M	0330	3.3	1.0
	0930	0.1	0.0
	1600	4.1	1.2
	2242	0.2	0.1
21 Tu	0424	3.3	1.0
	1021	0.1	0.0
	1650	4.2	1.3
	2332	0.1	0.0
22 W	0514	3.3	1.0
	1107	0.1	0.0
	1738	4.2	1.3
23 Th	0017	0.1	0.0
	0601	3.3	1.0
	1149	0.1	0.0
	1823	4.3	1.3
24 F	0053	0.0	0.0
	0646	3.3	1.0
	1225	0.1	0.0
	1907	4.2	1.3
25 Sa	0126	0.1	0.0
	0730	3.3	1.0
	1300	0.1	0.0
	1949	4.1	1.2
26 Su	0157	0.1	0.0
	0812	3.3	1.0
	1336	0.2	0.1
	2030	4.0	1.2
27 M	0226	0.1	0.0
	0856	3.3	1.0
	1413	0.2	0.1
	2113	3.8	1.2
28 Tu	0258	0.2	0.1
	0940	3.2	1.0
	1452	0.4	0.1
	2155	3.6	1.1
29 W	0332	0.3	0.1
	1024	3.1	0.9
	1532	0.5	0.2
	2238	3.4	1.0
30 Th	0404	0.3	0.1
	1110	3.1	0.9
	1612	0.6	0.2
	2322	3.2	1.0

Time meridian 75° W. 0000 is midnight. 1200 is noon.
Heights are referred to mean low water which is the chart datum of soundings.

NEWPORT, R.I., 1983

Times and Heights of High and Low Waters

JULY

Day	h m	ft	m
1 F	0443	0.4	0.1
	1158	3.0	0.9
	1659	0.7	0.2
2 Sa	0011	3.0	0.9
	0526	0.4	0.1
	1248	3.1	0.9
	1752	0.7	0.2
3 Su	0101	2.9	0.9
	0613	0.4	0.1
	1339	3.2	1.0
	1850	0.7	0.2
4 M	0156	2.9	0.9
	0704	0.4	0.1
	1432	3.4	1.0
	1954	0.6	0.2
5 Tu	0251	2.9	0.9
	0803	0.3	0.1
	1523	3.7	1.1
	2059	0.5	0.2
6 W	0346	3.0	0.9
	0901	0.1	0.0
	1615	4.0	1.2
	2205	0.2	0.1
7 Th	0441	3.2	1.0
	0959	-0.1	0.0
	1707	4.3	1.3
	2303	0.0	0.0
8 F	0533	3.4	1.0
	1058	-0.3	-0.1
	1757	4.6	1.4
	2357	-0.3	-0.1
9 Sa	0625	3.7	1.1
	1152	-0.4	-0.1
	1849	4.8	1.5
10 Su	0051	-0.5	-0.2
	0717	3.9	1.2
	1248	-0.6	-0.2
	1940	4.9	1.5
11 M	0141	-0.6	-0.2
	0808	4.0	1.2
	1343	-0.6	-0.2
	2031	4.9	1.5
12 Tu	0232	-0.7	-0.2
	0900	4.1	1.2
	1438	-0.5	-0.2
	2124	4.7	1.4
13 W	0321	-0.6	-0.2
	0954	4.1	1.2
	1535	-0.4	-0.1
	2217	4.5	1.4
14 Th	0412	-0.5	-0.2
	1049	4.1	1.2
	1633	-0.2	-0.1
	2312	4.2	1.3
15 F	0504	-0.3	-0.1
	1144	4.1	1.2
	1736	0.1	0.0
16 Sa	0008	3.8	1.2
	0558	-0.1	0.0
	1242	4.0	1.2
	1845	0.3	0.1
17 Su	0105	3.5	1.1
	0655	0.4	0.1
	1340	3.9	1.2
	2003	0.4	0.1
18 M	0205	3.3	1.0
	0755	0.3	0.1
	1439	3.9	1.2
	2122	0.5	0.2
19 Tu	0302	3.1	0.9
	0856	0.4	0.1
	1533	3.9	1.2
	2229	0.5	0.2
20 W	0359	3.1	0.9
	0954	0.4	0.1
	1626	4.0	1.2
	2323	0.4	0.1
21 Th	0450	3.1	0.9
	1044	0.4	0.1
	1716	4.0	1.2
22 F	0004	0.4	0.1
	0538	3.2	1.0
	1128	0.3	0.1
	1801	4.1	1.2
23 Sa	0041	0.3	0.1
	0624	3.3	1.0
	1209	0.3	0.1
	1845	4.1	1.2
24 Su	0106	0.3	0.1
	0708	3.4	1.0
	1244	0.2	0.1
	1926	4.1	1.2
25 M	0135	0.2	0.1
	0750	3.4	1.0
	1319	0.2	0.1
	2007	4.0	1.2
26 Tu	0202	0.2	0.1
	0831	3.5	1.1
	1354	0.2	0.1
	2047	3.9	1.2
27 W	0231	0.2	0.1
	0911	3.5	1.1
	1431	0.3	0.1
	2127	3.7	1.1
28 Th	0302	0.2	0.1
	0953	3.4	1.0
	1508	0.4	0.1
	2206	3.5	1.1
29 F	0334	0.2	0.1
	1035	3.4	1.0
	1548	0.4	0.1
	2248	3.3	1.0
30 Sa	0408	0.2	0.1
	1118	3.3	1.0
	1630	0.5	0.2
	2331	3.1	0.9
31 Su	0449	0.3	0.1
	1206	3.3	1.0
	1718	0.6	0.2

AUGUST

Day	h m	ft	m
1 M	0021	3.0	0.9
	0533	0.3	0.1
	1257	3.4	1.0
	1813	0.6	0.2
2 Tu	0114	2.9	0.9
	0624	0.3	0.1
	1353	3.5	1.1
	1917	0.6	0.2
3 W	0214	2.9	0.9
	0724	0.3	0.1
	1449	3.7	1.1
	2027	0.5	0.2
4 Th	0316	3.0	0.9
	0829	0.2	0.1
	1549	4.0	1.2
	2136	0.3	0.1
5 F	0416	3.2	1.0
	0934	0.0	0.0
	1644	4.3	1.3
	2244	0.0	0.0
6 Sa	0512	3.5	1.1
	1039	-0.2	-0.1
	1738	4.6	1.4
	2341	-0.3	-0.1
7 Su	0607	3.8	1.2
	1140	-0.4	-0.1
	1831	4.8	1.5
8 M	0036	-0.5	-0.2
	0658	4.1	1.2
	1239	-0.6	-0.2
	1922	4.9	1.5
9 Tu	0125	-0.7	-0.2
	0750	4.3	1.3
	1334	-0.7	-0.2
	2013	4.9	1.5
10 W	0213	-0.7	-0.2
	0840	4.5	1.4
	1428	-0.7	-0.2
	2103	4.7	1.4
11 Th	0300	-0.7	-0.2
	0932	4.5	1.4
	1522	-0.5	-0.2
	2154	4.5	1.4
12 F	0348	-0.5	-0.2
	1024	4.4	1.3
	1616	-0.3	-0.1
	2246	4.1	1.2
13 Sa	0433	-0.3	-0.1
	1116	4.3	1.3
	1712	0.0	0.0
	2339	3.7	1.1
14 Su	0521	0.0	0.0
	1212	4.1	1.2
	1815	0.4	0.1
15 M	0035	3.4	1.0
	0611	0.3	0.1
	1311	3.9	1.2
	1930	0.6	0.2
16 Tu	0135	3.1	0.9
	0653	0.3	0.1
	1409	3.7	1.1
	2059	0.7	0.2
17 W	0235	2.9	0.9
	0817	0.6	0.2
	1507	3.7	1.1
	2213	0.7	0.2
18 Th	0333	2.9	0.9
	0930	0.7	0.2
	1602	3.7	1.1
	2308	0.6	0.2
19 F	0426	3.0	0.9
	1031	0.6	0.2
	1652	3.7	1.1
	2346	0.5	0.2
20 Sa	0516	3.1	0.9
	1116	0.5	0.2
	1738	3.8	1.2
21 Su	0018	0.4	0.1
	0601	3.3	1.0
	1153	0.4	0.1
	1822	3.9	1.2
22 M	0044	0.3	0.1
	0644	3.5	1.1
	1230	0.3	0.1
	1902	4.0	1.2
23 Tu	0108	0.2	0.1
	0724	3.6	1.1
	1302	0.2	0.1
	1941	4.0	1.2
24 W	0133	0.1	0.0
	0804	3.7	1.1
	1336	0.1	0.0
	2020	3.9	1.2
25 Th	0159	0.0	0.0
	0842	3.7	1.1
	1409	0.1	0.0
	2058	3.8	1.2
26 F	0228	0.0	0.0
	0919	3.7	1.1
	1445	0.2	0.1
	2137	3.6	1.1
27 Sa	0300	0.0	0.0
	1001	3.6	1.1
	1522	0.2	0.1
	2214	3.4	1.0
28 Su	0336	0.1	0.0
	1041	3.6	1.1
	1604	0.3	0.1
	2257	3.2	1.0
29 M	0414	0.1	0.0
	1127	3.5	1.1
	1651	0.4	0.1
	2344	3.0	0.9
30 Tu	0459	0.2	0.1
	1219	3.5	1.1
	1744	0.5	0.2
31 W	0043	2.8	0.9
	0552	0.3	0.1
	1319	3.6	1.1
	1848	0.6	0.2

SEPTEMBER

Day	h m	ft	m
1 Th	0147	2.8	0.9
	0653	0.3	0.1
	1423	3.7	1.1
	2000	0.5	0.2
2 F	0253	3.0	0.9
	0804	0.3	0.1
	1525	3.9	1.2
	2117	0.3	0.1
3 Sa	0357	3.3	1.0
	0920	0.1	0.0
	1626	4.2	1.3
	2229	0.0	0.0
4 Su	0453	3.6	1.1
	1031	-0.2	-0.1
	1720	4.5	1.4
	2325	-0.3	-0.1
5 M	0548	4.0	1.2
	1135	-0.5	-0.2
	1814	4.7	1.4
6 Tu	0017	-0.6	-0.2
	0639	4.4	1.3
	1230	-0.7	-0.2
	1903	4.8	1.5
7 W	0105	-0.7	-0.2
	0729	4.6	1.4
	1323	-0.8	-0.2
	1953	4.8	1.5
8 Th	0150	-0.8	-0.2
	0818	4.7	1.4
	1414	-0.7	-0.2
	2041	4.6	1.4
9 F	0234	-0.7	-0.2
	0906	4.7	1.4
	1503	-0.6	-0.2
	2129	4.3	1.3
10 Sa	0316	-0.5	-0.2
	0956	4.5	1.4
	1551	-0.3	-0.1
	2219	3.9	1.2
11 Su	0358	-0.3	-0.1
	1046	4.3	1.3
	1641	0.1	0.0
	2310	3.5	1.1
12 M	0441	0.1	0.0
	1140	4.0	1.2
	1737	0.4	0.1
13 Tu	0005	3.2	1.0
	0528	0.4	0.1
	1237	3.7	1.1
	1844	0.7	0.2
14 W	0103	2.9	0.9
	0619	0.6	0.2
	1336	3.5	1.1
	2020	0.9	0.3
15 Th	0205	2.8	0.9
	0728	0.8	0.2
	1437	3.4	1.0
	2146	0.9	0.3
16 F	0305	2.8	0.9
	0901	0.9	0.3
	1534	3.4	1.0
	2239	0.8	0.2
17 Sa	0400	2.9	0.9
	1015	0.8	0.2
	1624	3.5	1.1
	2322	0.6	0.2
18 Su	0450	3.1	0.9
	1100	0.6	0.2
	1711	3.6	1.1
	2347	0.0	0.0
19 M	0535	3.3	1.0
	1137	0.4	0.1
	1753	3.7	1.1
20 Tu	0007	0.3	0.1
	0617	3.6	1.1
	1209	0.2	0.1
	1833	3.8	1.2
21 W	0030	0.1	0.0
	0655	3.8	1.2
	1241	0.1	0.0
	1914	3.9	1.2
22 Th	0057	0.0	0.0
	0733	3.9	1.2
	1313	0.0	0.0
	1951	3.8	1.2
23 F	0124	-0.1	0.0
	0812	3.9	1.2
	1346	-0.1	0.0
	2030	3.7	1.1
24 Sa	0157	-0.2	-0.1
	0848	3.9	1.2
	1422	-0.1	0.0
	2107	3.6	1.1
25 Su	0229	-0.2	-0.1
	0927	3.9	1.2
	1502	0.0	0.0
	2148	3.4	1.0
26 M	0306	-0.1	0.0
	1009	3.8	1.2
	1543	0.1	0.0
	2230	3.1	0.9
27 Tu	0345	0.0	0.0
	1057	3.7	1.1
	1630	0.2	0.1
	2321	2.9	0.9
28 W	0433	0.1	0.0
	1153	3.6	1.1
	1725	0.4	0.1
29 Th	0021	2.8	0.9
	0528	0.2	0.1
	1255	3.6	1.1
	1829	0.5	0.2
30 F	0129	2.8	0.9
	0636	0.3	0.1
	1403	3.7	1.1
	1946	0.4	0.1

Time meridian 75° W. 0000 is midnight. 1200 is noon.
Heights are referred to mean low water which is the chart datum of soundings.

Times and Heights of High and Low Waters

OCTOBER

Day	Time h m	Height ft	m	Day	Time h m	Height ft	m
1 Sa	0237	3.0	0.9	16 Su	0330	2.9	0.9
	0754	0.3	0.1		0936	0.8	0.2
	1508	3.8	1.2		1552	3.2	1.0
	2104	0.2	0.1		2229	0.6	0.2
2 Su	0341	3.4	1.0	17 M	0418	3.1	0.9
	0915	0.1	0.0		1031	0.6	0.2
	1607	4.0	1.2		1639	3.3	1.0
	2213	0.0	0.0		2255	0.4	0.1
3 M	0437	3.8	1.2	18 Tu	0503	3.4	1.0
	1029	-0.2	-0.1		1106	0.4	0.1
	1703	4.3	1.3		1722	3.5	1.1
	2308	-0.3	-0.1		2319	0.2	0.1
4 Tu	0529	4.2	1.3	19 W	0545	3.6	1.1
	1129	-0.5	-0.2		1137	0.2	0.1
	1755	4.4	1.3		1803	3.6	1.1
	2356	-0.6	-0.2		2348	0.0	0.0
5 W	0620	4.5	1.4	20 Th	0625	3.8	1.2
	1222	-0.7	-0.2		1212	0.0	0.0
	1844	4.5	1.4		1842	3.7	1.1
6 Th	0041	-0.7	-0.2	21 F	0018	-0.2	-0.1
	0707	4.8	1.5		0702	4.0	1.2
	1312	-0.8	-0.2		1247	-0.2	-0.1
	1931	4.4	1.3		1921	3.7	1.1
7 F	0124	-0.8	-0.2	22 Sa	0051	-0.3	-0.1
	0754	4.8	1.5		0742	4.1	1.2
	1358	-0.7	-0.2		1323	-0.3	-0.1
	2017	4.3	1.3		2000	3.6	1.1
8 Sa	0203	-0.7	-0.2	23 Su	0127	-0.4	-0.1
	0840	4.7	1.4		0821	4.2	1.3
	1442	-0.5	-0.2		1401	-0.3	-0.1
	2103	4.0	1.2		2042	3.5	1.1
9 Su	0244	-0.5	-0.2	24 M	0202	-0.4	-0.1
	0927	4.5	1.4		0901	4.1	1.2
	1527	-0.3	-0.1		1442	-0.2	-0.1
	2151	3.6	1.1		2123	3.3	1.0
10 M	0321	-0.2	-0.1	25 Tu	0242	-0.3	-0.1
	1017	4.2	1.3		0946	4.0	1.2
	1611	0.1	0.0		1526	-0.1	0.0
	2240	3.3	1.0		2211	3.1	0.9
11 Tu	0403	0.1	0.0	26 W	0327	-0.2	-0.1
	1107	3.8	1.2		1037	3.9	1.2
	1656	0.4	0.1		1616	0.0	0.0
	2331	3.0	0.9		2305	3.0	0.9
12 W	0444	0.4	0.1	27 Th	0417	0.0	0.0
	1202	3.5	1.1		1133	3.7	1.1
	1749	0.7	0.2		1713	0.2	0.1
13 Th	0031	2.7	0.8	28 F	0008	2.9	0.9
	0534	0.7	0.2		0518	0.1	0.0
	1259	3.2	1.0		1236	3.6	1.1
	1903	0.9	0.3		1819	0.3	0.1
14 F	0131	2.6	0.8	29 Sa	0115	3.0	0.9
	0639	0.9	0.3		0627	0.3	0.1
	1359	3.1	0.9		1343	3.6	1.1
	2050	0.9	0.3		1933	0.2	0.1
15 Sa	0235	2.7	0.8	30 Su	0220	3.2	1.0
	0808	0.9	0.3		0751	0.2	0.1
	1459	3.1	0.9		1449	3.7	1.1
	2154	0.8	0.2		2049	0.1	0.0
				31 M	0322	3.5	1.1
					0914	0.1	0.0
					1549	3.8	1.2
					2152	-0.1	0.0

NOVEMBER

Day	Time h m	Height ft	m	Day	Time h m	Height ft	m
1 Tu	0418	3.9	1.2	16 W	0427	3.3	1.0
	1023	-0.2	-0.1		1021	0.4	0.1
	1644	3.9	1.2		1645	3.2	1.0
	2247	-0.4	-0.1		2223	0.2	0.1
2 W	0511	4.3	1.3	17 Th	0511	3.6	1.1
	1122	-0.5	-0.2		1100	0.2	0.1
	1735	4.0	1.2		1729	3.3	1.0
	2332	-0.6	-0.2		2303	-0.1	0.0
3 Th	0559	4.5	1.4	18 F	0551	3.8	1.2
	1212	-0.6	-0.2		1140	-0.1	0.0
	1822	4.1	1.2		1812	3.4	1.0
					2340	-0.3	-0.1
4 F	0017	-0.7	-0.2	19 Sa	0633	4.1	1.2
	0646	4.7	1.4		1221	-0.3	-0.1
	1259	-0.7	-0.2		1854	3.5	1.1
	1908	4.0	1.2				
5 Sa	0056	-0.7	-0.2	20 Su	0020	-0.4	-0.1
	0732	4.7	1.4		0713	4.2	1.3
	1341	-0.6	-0.2		1303	-0.4	-0.1
	1954	3.9	1.2		1935	3.5	1.1
6 Su	0137	-0.6	-0.2	21 M	0059	-0.5	-0.2
	0817	4.6	1.4		0756	4.3	1.3
	1421	-0.4	-0.1		1344	-0.5	-0.2
	2038	3.7	1.1		2018	3.4	1.0
7 M	0213	-0.4	-0.1	22 Tu	0141	-0.6	-0.2
	0901	4.3	1.3		0841	4.3	1.3
	1501	-0.2	-0.1		1430	-0.5	-0.2
	2124	3.4	1.0		2106	3.4	1.0
8 Tu	0250	-0.2	-0.1	23 W	0226	-0.5	-0.2
	0947	4.0	1.2		0929	4.2	1.3
	1542	0.1	0.0		1516	-0.4	-0.1
	2212	3.1	0.9		2156	3.3	1.0
9 W	0327	0.1	0.0	24 Th	0316	-0.4	-0.1
	1036	3.7	1.1		1020	4.0	1.2
	1619	0.3	0.1		1606	-0.3	-0.1
	2301	2.9	0.9		2251	3.2	1.0
10 Th	0409	0.4	0.1	25 F	0409	-0.2	-0.1
	1126	3.3	1.0		1118	3.8	1.2
	1702	0.6	0.2		1702	-0.1	0.0
	2355	2.7	0.8		2352	3.1	0.9
11 F	0454	0.6	0.2	26 Sa	0513	0.0	0.0
	1221	3.1	0.9		1219	3.7	1.1
	1752	0.7	0.2		1806	0.0	0.0
12 Sa	0056	2.6	0.8	27 Su	0056	3.2	1.0
	0552	0.8	0.2		0624	0.1	0.0
	1320	2.9	0.9		1323	3.5	1.1
	1853	0.8	0.2		1914	0.0	0.0
13 Su	0155	2.6	0.8	28 M	0200	3.4	1.0
	0701	0.9	0.3		0746	0.1	0.0
	1416	2.9	0.9		1427	3.5	1.1
	2002	0.7	0.2		2024	0.0	0.0
14 M	0251	2.8	0.9	29 Tu	0301	3.6	1.1
	0821	0.8	0.2		0909	0.0	0.0
	1511	2.9	0.9		1526	3.5	1.1
	2101	0.6	0.2		2128	-0.2	-0.1
15 Tu	0341	3.0	0.9	30 W	0357	3.9	1.2
	0930	0.7	0.2		1018	-0.2	-0.1
	1600	3.0	0.9		1622	3.5	1.1
	2144	0.4	0.1		2221	-0.3	-0.1

DECEMBER

Day	Time h m	Height ft	m	Day	Time h m	Height ft	m
1 Th	0450	4.1	1.2	16 F	0434	3.5	1.1
	1114	-0.3	-0.1		1018	0.2	0.1
	1714	3.6	1.1		1655	3.0	0.9
	2311	-0.4	-0.1		2216	-0.1	0.0
2 F	0538	4.3	1.3	17 Sa	0519	3.8	1.2
	1203	-0.4	-0.1		1108	-0.1	0.0
	1801	3.6	1.1		1740	3.2	1.0
	2353	-0.5	-0.2		2303	-0.4	-0.1
3 Sa	0625	4.4	1.3	18 Su	0604	4.0	1.2
	1245	-0.5	-0.2		1156	-0.3	-0.1
	1847	3.6	1.1		1826	3.3	1.0
					2351	-0.6	-0.2
4 Su	0034	-0.5	-0.2	19 M	0649	4.3	1.3
	0711	4.4	1.3		1244	-0.5	-0.2
	1327	-0.4	-0.1		1913	3.4	1.0
	1931	3.5	1.1				
5 M	0112	-0.5	-0.2	20 Tu	0039	-0.7	-0.2
	0755	4.3	1.3		0736	4.4	1.3
	1404	-0.3	-0.1		1330	-0.7	-0.2
	2016	3.4	1.0		2001	3.5	1.1
6 Tu	0149	-0.4	-0.1	21 W	0128	-0.8	-0.2
	0839	4.1	1.2		0824	4.4	1.3
	1439	-0.2	-0.1		1417	-0.7	-0.2
	2059	3.2	1.0		2050	3.5	1.1
7 W	0226	-0.2	-0.1	22 Th	0218	-0.8	-0.2
	0922	3.8	1.2		0913	4.3	1.3
	1513	0.0	0.0		1506	-0.7	-0.2
	2145	3.0	0.9		2143	3.5	1.1
8 Th	0303	0.0	0.0	23 F	0310	-0.7	-0.2
	1006	3.6	1.1		1006	4.2	1.3
	1548	0.2	0.1		1556	-0.6	-0.2
	2232	2.9	0.9		2236	3.5	1.1
9 F	0343	0.2	0.1	24 Sa	0406	-0.5	-0.2
	1054	3.3	1.0		1102	3.9	1.2
	1625	0.3	0.1		1649	-0.4	-0.1
	2321	2.7	0.8		2334	3.5	1.1
10 Sa	0425	0.4	0.1	25 Su	0505	-0.3	-0.1
	1142	3.0	0.9		1200	3.7	1.1
	1705	0.4	0.1		1747	-0.3	-0.1
11 Su	0016	2.7	0.8	26 M	0033	3.5	1.1
	0513	0.6	0.2		0613	-0.1	0.0
	1235	2.8	0.9		1259	3.4	1.0
	1752	0.5	0.2		1847	-0.2	-0.1
12 M	0110	2.7	0.8	27 Tu	0135	3.5	1.1
	0608	0.7	0.2		0733	0.0	0.0
	1329	2.7	0.8		1401	3.3	1.0
	1843	0.5	0.2		1954	-0.1	0.0
13 Tu	0206	2.7	0.8	28 W	0235	3.6	1.1
	0712	0.7	0.2		0854	0.0	0.0
	1424	2.7	0.8		1501	3.2	1.0
	1940	0.4	0.1		2101	-0.1	0.0
14 W	0259	2.9	0.9	29 Th	0333	3.8	1.2
	0819	0.6	0.2		1006	0.0	0.0
	1517	2.8	0.9		1559	3.1	0.9
	2035	0.3	0.1		2157	-0.2	-0.1
15 Th	0347	3.2	1.0	30 F	0429	3.9	1.2
	0924	0.4	0.1		1106	-0.1	0.0
	1607	2.9	0.9		1652	3.1	0.9
	2128	0.1	0.0		2250	-0.2	-0.1
				31 Sa	0519	4.0	1.2
					1156	-0.2	-0.1
					1740	3.2	1.0
					2337	-0.3	-0.1

Time meridian 75° W. 0000 is midnight. 1200 is noon.
Heights are referred to mean low water which is the chart datum of soundings.

NEW LONDON, CONN., 1983

Times and Heights of High and Low Waters

JANUARY

Day	Time (h m)	Height (ft)	Height (m)
1 Sa	0424	-0.4	-0.1
	1024	3.3	1.0
	1712	-0.8	-0.2
	2306	2.4	0.7
2 Su	0521	-0.4	-0.1
	1120	3.1	0.9
	1806	-0.7	-0.2
3 M	0002	2.4	0.7
	0621	-0.3	-0.1
	1219	2.8	0.9
	1901	-0.6	-0.2
4 Tu	0101	2.4	0.7
	0725	-0.2	-0.1
	1320	2.5	0.8
	1956	-0.4	-0.1
5 W	0206	2.4	0.7
	0830	-0.1	0.0
	1425	2.2	0.7
	2053	-0.3	-0.1
6 Th	0306	2.5	0.8
	0935	-0.1	0.0
	1533	2.0	0.6
	2150	-0.2	-0.1
7 F	0411	2.5	0.8
	1037	-0.1	0.0
	1639	1.9	0.6
	2244	-0.1	0.0
8 Sa	0507	2.5	0.8
	1135	-0.1	0.0
	1740	1.8	0.5
	2335	0.0	0.0
9 Su	0558	2.6	0.8
	1230	-0.2	-0.1
	1830	1.7	0.5
10 M	0023	0.0	0.0
	0644	2.6	0.8
	1317	-0.2	-0.1
	1916	1.7	0.5
11 Tu	0109	0.0	0.0
	0726	2.6	0.8
	1400	-0.3	-0.1
	1958	1.8	0.5
12 W	0155	0.0	0.0
	0803	2.6	0.8
	1440	-0.3	-0.1
	2035	1.8	0.5
13 Th	0237	0.0	0.0
	0839	2.6	0.8
	1520	-0.3	-0.1
	2112	1.9	0.6
14 F	0319	0.0	0.0
	0916	2.6	0.8
	1602	-0.3	-0.1
	2150	1.9	0.6
15 Sa	0401	0.0	0.0
	0952	2.6	0.8
	1640	-0.3	-0.1
	2228	2.0	0.6
16 Su	0445	0.1	0.0
	1029	2.5	0.8
	1722	-0.3	-0.1
	2308	2.0	0.6
17 M	0531	0.1	0.0
	1108	2.4	0.7
	1803	-0.2	-0.1
	2347	2.0	0.6
18 Tu	0616	0.2	0.1
	1149	2.3	0.7
	1845	-0.1	0.0
19 W	0029	2.1	0.6
	0706	0.2	0.1
	1231	2.1	0.6
	1930	-0.1	0.0
20 Th	0113	2.1	0.6
	0800	0.2	0.1
	1319	2.0	0.6
	2015	0.0	0.0
21 F	0203	2.2	0.7
	0856	0.2	0.1
	1415	1.9	0.6
	2104	0.1	0.0
22 Sa	0255	2.3	0.7
	0955	0.1	0.0
	1517	1.8	0.5
	2153	0.1	0.0
23 Su	0350	2.5	0.8
	1052	-0.1	0.0
	1619	1.8	0.5
	2246	0.0	0.0
24 M	0447	2.7	0.8
	1146	-0.3	-0.1
	1721	1.8	0.5
	2341	-0.1	0.0
25 Tu	0542	2.9	0.9
	1239	-0.5	-0.2
	1820	1.9	0.6
26 W	0033	-0.2	-0.1
	0638	3.0	0.9
	1331	-0.7	-0.2
	1915	2.1	0.6
27 Th	0128	-0.4	-0.1
	0731	3.2	1.0
	1421	-0.8	-0.2
	2009	2.2	0.7
28 F	0221	-0.5	-0.2
	0826	3.2	1.0
	1511	-0.9	-0.3
	2102	2.4	0.7
29 Sa	0315	-0.6	-0.2
	0918	3.2	1.0
	1600	-0.9	-0.3
	2153	2.5	0.8
30 Su	0411	-0.6	-0.2
	1011	3.1	0.9
	1650	-0.9	-0.3
	2246	2.6	0.8
31 M	0507	-0.6	-0.2
	1106	2.9	0.9
	1741	-0.8	-0.2
	2339	2.6	0.8

FEBRUARY

Day	Time (h m)	Height (ft)	Height (m)
1 Tu	0604	-0.5	-0.2
	1159	2.6	0.8
	1832	-0.6	-0.2
2 W	0035	2.6	0.8
	0703	-0.4	-0.1
	1257	2.3	0.7
	1925	-0.4	-0.1
3 Th	0131	2.5	0.8
	0804	-0.3	-0.1
	1355	2.1	0.6
	2019	-0.2	-0.1
4 F	0231	2.5	0.8
	0908	-0.2	-0.1
	1459	1.8	0.5
	2115	-0.1	0.0
5 Sa	0333	2.4	0.7
	1008	-0.1	0.0
	1605	1.7	0.5
	2211	0.0	0.0
6 Su	0433	2.4	0.7
	1107	-0.1	0.0
	1709	1.6	0.5
	2305	0.1	0.0
7 M	0527	2.4	0.7
	1201	-0.1	0.0
	1805	1.6	0.5
	2358	0.1	0.0
8 Tu	0620	2.4	0.7
	1251	-0.1	0.0
	1852	1.7	0.5
9 W	0047	0.1	0.0
	0702	2.4	0.7
	1333	-0.2	-0.1
	1933	1.7	0.5
10 Th	0132	0.0	0.0
	0742	2.4	0.7
	1415	-0.2	-0.1
	2011	1.9	0.6
11 F	0216	0.0	0.0
	0819	2.5	0.8
	1454	-0.3	-0.1
	2049	2.0	0.6
12 Sa	0258	-0.1	0.0
	0855	2.5	0.8
	1532	-0.4	-0.1
	2125	2.1	0.6
13 Su	0339	-0.1	0.0
	0930	2.5	0.8
	1611	-0.4	-0.1
	2159	2.1	0.6
14 M	0420	-0.1	0.0
	1006	2.5	0.8
	1649	-0.3	-0.1
	2235	2.2	0.7
15 Tu	0503	-0.1	0.0
	1044	2.4	0.7
	1728	-0.3	-0.1
	2311	2.3	0.7
16 W	0547	-0.1	0.0
	1124	2.3	0.7
	1807	-0.2	-0.1
	2349	2.3	0.7
17 Th	0634	0.0	0.0
	1203	2.2	0.7
	1848	-0.1	0.0
18 F	0032	2.4	0.7
	0727	0.0	0.0
	1248	2.0	0.6
	1933	0.0	0.0
19 Sa	0120	2.4	0.7
	0823	0.0	0.0
	1343	1.9	0.6
	2022	0.1	0.0
20 Su	0215	2.5	0.8
	0922	0.0	0.0
	1446	1.8	0.5
	2118	0.1	0.0
21 M	0316	2.5	0.8
	1025	-0.1	0.0
	1553	1.7	0.5
	2219	0.1	0.0
22 Tu	0420	2.6	0.8
	1122	-0.2	-0.1
	1702	1.8	0.5
	2319	0.0	0.0
23 W	0524	2.8	0.9
	1218	-0.4	-0.1
	1804	1.9	0.6
24 Th	0018	-0.2	-0.1
	0623	2.9	0.9
	1312	-0.5	-0.2
	1900	2.0	0.7
25 F	0115	-0.4	-0.1
	0720	3.0	0.9
	1401	-0.7	-0.2
	1955	2.2	0.7
26 Sa	0211	-0.5	-0.2
	0814	3.0	0.9
	1450	-0.7	-0.2
	2046	2.6	0.8
27 Su	0304	-0.7	-0.2
	0752	3.0	0.9
	1537	-0.8	-0.2
	2134	2.7	0.8
28 M	0357	-0.7	-0.2
	0957	2.9	0.9
	1625	-0.7	-0.2
	2225	2.8	0.9

MARCH

Day	Time (h m)	Height (ft)	Height (m)
1 Tu	0451	-0.7	-0.2
	1047	2.7	0.8
	1712	-0.6	-0.2
	2314	2.8	0.9
2 W	0543	-0.6	-0.2
	1139	2.5	0.8
	1802	-0.4	-0.1
3 Th	0003	2.8	0.9
	0639	-0.4	-0.1
	1229	2.3	0.7
	1851	-0.3	-0.1
4 F	0056	2.7	0.8
	0735	-0.2	-0.1
	1325	2.0	0.6
	1944	-0.1	0.0
5 Sa	0151	2.5	0.8
	0834	-0.1	0.0
	1425	1.8	0.5
	2040	0.1	0.0
6 Su	0249	2.4	0.7
	0931	0.0	0.0
	1526	1.7	0.5
	2138	0.2	0.1
7 M	0353	2.3	0.7
	1031	0.1	0.0
	1631	1.6	0.5
	2235	0.3	0.1
8 Tu	0452	2.2	0.7
	1126	0.1	0.0
	1732	1.7	0.5
	2331	0.3	0.1
9 W	0545	2.3	0.7
	1217	0.0	0.0
	1822	1.8	0.5
10 Th	0022	0.2	0.1
	0633	2.3	0.7
	1302	0.0	0.0
	1907	1.9	0.6
11 F	0108	0.1	0.0
	0712	2.4	0.7
	1344	-0.1	0.0
	1942	2.1	0.6
12 Sa	0152	0.0	0.0
	0803	2.4	0.7
	1423	-0.2	-0.1
	2019	2.2	0.7
13 Su	0235	-0.1	0.0
	0829	2.5	0.8
	1500	-0.3	-0.1
	2052	2.3	0.7
14 M	0315	-0.2	-0.1
	0904	2.5	0.8
	1537	-0.3	-0.1
	2127	2.5	0.8
15 Tu	0356	-0.2	-0.1
	0941	2.5	0.8
	1614	-0.2	-0.1
	2200	2.6	0.8
16 W	0437	-0.2	-0.1
	1018	2.5	0.8
	1651	-0.2	-0.1
	2238	2.7	0.8
17 Th	0523	-0.2	-0.1
	1059	2.4	0.7
	1730	-0.1	0.0
	2318	2.7	0.8
18 F	0609	-0.2	-0.1
	1141	2.3	0.7
	1813	0.0	0.0
	2359	2.7	0.8
19 Sa	0701	-0.1	0.0
	1229	2.1	0.6
	1858	0.1	0.0
20 Su	0048	2.7	0.8
	0756	-0.1	0.0
	1324	2.0	0.6
	1953	0.2	0.1
21 M	0146	2.7	0.8
	0857	0.0	0.0
	1428	1.9	0.6
	2055	0.3	0.1
22 Tu	0251	2.7	0.8
	0959	-0.1	0.0
	1539	1.9	0.6
	2202	0.2	0.1
23 W	0400	2.7	0.8
	1101	-0.1	0.0
	1647	2.0	0.6
	2308	0.1	0.0
24 Th	0509	2.7	0.8
	1157	-0.2	-0.1
	1751	2.2	0.7
25 F	0009	-0.1	0.0
	0612	2.8	0.9
	1250	-0.3	-0.1
	1847	2.4	0.7
26 Sa	0105	-0.3	-0.1
	0710	2.8	0.9
	1339	-0.4	-0.1
	1939	2.7	0.8
27 Su	0200	-0.5	-0.2
	0803	2.9	0.9
	1427	-0.5	-0.2
	2026	2.9	0.9
28 M	0251	-0.6	-0.2
	0854	2.8	0.9
	1513	-0.5	-0.2
	2114	3.0	0.9
29 Tu	0342	-0.6	-0.2
	0940	2.7	0.8
	1558	-0.4	-0.1
	2200	3.1	0.9
30 W	0432	-0.6	-0.2
	1027	2.6	0.8
	1642	-0.3	-0.1
	2245	3.1	0.9
31 Th	0521	-0.5	-0.2
	1114	2.4	0.7
	1730	-0.2	-0.1
	2331	2.9	0.9

Time meridian 75° W. 0000 is midnight. 1200 is noon.
Heights are referred to mean low water which is the chart datum of soundings.

Times and Heights of High and Low Waters

APRIL

Day	Time (h m)	ft	m	Day	Time (h m)	ft	m
1 F	0613	-0.3	-0.1	16 Sa	0546	-0.3	-0.1
	1200	2.2	0.7		1123	2.4	0.7
	1818	0.0	0.0		1741	0.1	0.0
					2334	3.1	0.9
2 Sa	0019	2.8	0.9	17 Su	0639	-0.2	-0.1
	0704	-0.1	0.0		1213	2.2	0.7
	1253	2.0	0.6		1834	0.2	0.1
	1911	0.2	0.1				
3 Su	0110	2.6	0.8	18 M	0026	3.0	0.9
	0801	0.1	0.0		0736	-0.1	0.0
	1349	1.9	0.6		1314	2.1	0.6
	2007	0.4	0.1		1935	0.3	0.1
4 M	0205	2.4	0.7	19 Tu	0127	2.9	0.9
	0857	0.2	0.1		0837	-0.1	0.0
	1449	1.8	0.5		1420	2.1	0.6
	2105	0.5	0.2		2044	0.4	0.1
5 Tu	0305	2.3	0.7	20 W	0235	2.8	0.9
	0952	0.2	0.1		0938	0.0	0.0
	1554	1.8	0.5		1529	2.1	0.6
	2206	0.5	0.2		2152	0.3	0.1
6 W	0407	2.2	0.7	21 Th	0347	2.7	0.8
	1047	0.2	0.1		1037	0.0	0.0
	1657	1.9	0.6		1637	2.3	0.7
	2303	0.5	0.2		2258	0.2	0.1
7 Th	0505	2.2	0.7	22 F	0457	2.7	0.8
	1138	0.2	0.1		1135	-0.1	0.0
	1745	2.0	0.6		1737	2.5	0.8
	2353	0.4	0.1		2358	0.0	0.0
8 F	0554	2.3	0.7	23 Sa	0602	2.7	0.8
	1225	0.1	0.0		1227	-0.1	0.0
	1828	2.2	0.7		1832	2.7	0.8
9 Sa	0042	0.3	0.1	24 Su	0055	-0.2	-0.1
	0639	2.3	0.7		0658	2.7	0.8
	1307	0.0	0.0		1315	-0.2	-0.1
	1907	2.3	0.7		1921	2.9	0.9
10 Su	0126	0.1	0.0	25 M	0147	-0.3	-0.1
	0720	2.4	0.7		0750	2.7	0.8
	1345	0.0	0.0		1402	-0.2	-0.1
	1942	2.5	0.8		2007	3.1	0.9
11 M	0207	0.0	0.0	26 Tu	0237	-0.4	-0.1
	0757	2.5	0.8		0836	2.6	0.8
	1424	-0.1	0.0		1446	-0.2	-0.1
	2016	2.7	0.8		2051	3.2	1.0
12 Tu	0249	-0.2	-0.1	27 W	0325	-0.5	-0.2
	0836	2.6	0.8		0921	2.5	0.8
	1502	-0.1	0.0		1530	-0.1	0.0
	2053	2.9	0.9		2134	3.2	1.0
13 W	0330	-0.3	-0.1	28 Th	0412	-0.4	-0.1
	0916	2.6	0.8		1004	2.4	0.7
	1539	-0.1	0.0		1615	0.0	0.0
	2127	3.0	0.9		2216	3.1	0.9
14 Th	0413	-0.3	-0.1	29 F	0458	-0.3	-0.1
	0954	2.5	-0.8		1049	2.3	0.7
	1617	0.0	0.0		1701	0.1	0.0
	2206	3.1	0.9		2258	3.0	0.9
15 F	0458	-0.3	-0.1	30 Sa	0547	-0.1	0.0
	1039	2.5	0.8		1134	2.2	0.7
	1657	0.0	0.0		1747	0.3	0.1
	2248	3.1	0.9		2344	2.9	0.9

MAY

Day	Time (h m)	ft	m	Day	Time (h m)	ft	m
1 Su	0636	0.0	0.0	16 M	0621	-0.3	-0.1
	1221	2.1	0.6		1203	2.4	0.7
	1839	0.4	0.1		1819	0.3	0.1
2 M	0032	2.7	0.8	17 Tu	0011	3.2	1.0
	0725	0.2	0.1		0717	-0.2	-0.1
	1317	2.0	0.6		1304	2.3	0.7
	1935	0.6	0.2		1925	0.3	0.1
3 Tu	0124	2.5	0.8	18 W	0117	3.0	0.9
	0821	0.3	0.1		0816	-0.1	0.0
	1412	2.0	0.6		1410	2.3	0.7
	2033	0.7	0.2		2031	0.3	0.1
4 W	0221	2.3	0.7	19 Th	0223	2.8	0.9
	0914	0.3	0.1		0916	0.0	0.0
	1515	2.0	0.6		1516	2.4	0.7
	2132	0.7	0.2		2140	0.3	0.1
5 Th	0320	2.2	0.7	20 F	0335	2.6	0.8
	1007	0.3	0.1		1013	0.0	0.0
	1612	2.1	0.6		1622	2.6	0.8
	2229	0.6	0.2		2245	0.2	0.1
6 F	0419	2.2	0.7	21 Sa	0444	2.5	0.8
	1057	0.3	0.1		1110	0.0	0.0
	1703	2.2	0.7		1721	2.8	0.9
	2322	0.5	0.2		2345	0.0	0.0
7 Sa	0510	2.2	0.7	22 Su	0547	2.5	0.8
	1142	0.2	0.1		1201	0.0	0.0
	1745	2.4	0.7		1814	2.9	0.9
8 Su	0010	0.4	0.1	23 M	0042	-0.1	0.0
	0600	2.3	0.7		0643	2.5	0.8
	1225	0.2	0.1		1251	0.0	0.0
	1825	2.6	0.8		1902	3.1	0.9
9 M	0056	0.2	0.1	24 Tu	0133	-0.2	-0.1
	0642	2.4	0.7		0733	2.4	0.7
	1305	0.0	0.0		1336	0.0	0.0
	1905	2.8	0.9		1947	3.2	1.0
10 Tu	0139	0.0	0.0	25 W	0222	-0.3	-0.1
	0724	2.5	0.8		0819	2.4	0.7
	1346	0.1	0.0		1419	0.0	0.0
	1939	3.0	0.9		2029	3.2	1.0
11 W	0223	-0.2	-0.1	26 Th	0306	-0.3	-0.1
	0805	2.5	0.8		0901	2.3	0.7
	1424	0.0	0.0		1504	0.1	0.0
	2019	3.2	1.0		2110	3.2	1.0
12 Th	0305	-0.3	-0.1	27 F	0351	-0.2	-0.1
	0846	2.5	0.8		0942	2.3	0.7
	1505	0.0	0.0		1547	0.2	0.1
	2058	3.3	1.0		2151	3.1	0.9
13 F	0348	-0.4	-0.1	28 Sa	0437	-0.1	0.0
	0930	2.5	0.8		1024	2.2	0.7
	1546	0.0	0.0		1633	0.3	0.1
	2141	3.4	1.0		2231	3.0	0.9
14 Sa	0437	-0.4	-0.1	29 Su	0520	0.0	0.0
	1019	2.5	0.8		1107	2.2	0.7
	1632	0.1	0.0		1719	0.4	0.1
	2226	3.4	1.0		2312	2.9	0.9
15 Su	0526	-0.4	-0.1	30 M	0605	0.1	0.0
	1107	2.4	0.7		1155	2.2	0.7
	1721	0.2	0.1		1809	0.5	0.2
	2318	3.3	1.0		2355	2.7	0.8
				31 Tu	0655	0.2	0.1
					1245	2.1	0.6
					1904	0.6	0.2

JUNE

Day	Time (h m)	ft	m	Day	Time (h m)	ft	m
1 W	0044	2.5	0.8	16 Th	0104	3.0	0.9
	0743	0.2	0.1		0753	-0.2	-0.1
	1337	2.1	0.6		1354	2.6	0.8
	1959	0.7	0.2		2018	0.2	0.1
2 Th	0137	2.4	0.7	17 F	0211	2.7	0.8
	0834	0.3	0.1		0850	-0.1	0.0
	1433	2.2	0.7		1458	2.7	0.8
	2057	0.7	0.2		2124	0.2	0.1
3 F	0231	2.3	0.7	18 Sa	0320	2.5	0.8
	0925	0.3	0.1		0947	0.0	0.0
	1525	2.2	0.7		1600	2.8	0.9
	2153	0.7	0.2		2228	0.1	0.0
4 Sa	0330	2.2	0.7	19 Su	0426	2.4	0.7
	1013	0.3	0.1		1042	0.1	0.0
	1614	2.4	0.7		1659	2.9	0.9
	2247	0.6	0.2		2329	0.1	0.0
5 Su	0422	2.2	0.7	20 M	0531	2.3	0.7
	1059	0.3	0.1		1135	0.1	0.0
	1659	2.5	0.8		1753	3.0	0.9
	2337	0.4	0.1				
6 M	0514	2.2	0.7	21 Tu	0025	0.0	0.0
	1144	0.3	0.1		0627	2.2	0.7
	1742	2.7	0.8		1226	0.2	0.1
					1843	3.1	0.9
7 Tu	0023	0.2	0.1	22 W	0116	-0.1	0.0
	0603	2.3	0.7		0716	2.2	0.7
	1226	0.2	0.1		1312	0.2	0.1
	1822	3.0	0.9		1927	3.1	0.9
8 W	0109	0.0	0.0	23 Th	0203	-0.1	0.0
	0649	2.4	0.7		0759	2.2	0.7
	1307	0.2	0.1		1357	0.2	0.1
	1905	3.2	1.0		2008	3.1	0.9
9 Th	0155	-0.2	-0.1	24 F	0247	-0.1	0.0
	0736	2.4	0.7		0841	2.2	0.7
	1350	0.1	0.0		1440	0.2	0.1
	1947	3.4	1.0		2048	3.1	0.9
10 F	0240	-0.3	-0.1	25 Sa	0329	-0.1	0.0
	0821	2.5	0.8		0921	2.2	0.7
	1435	0.0	0.0		1524	0.3	0.1
	2032	3.5	1.1		2127	3.0	0.9
11 Sa	0327	-0.4	-0.1	26 Su	0411	0.0	0.0
	0909	2.5	0.8		1003	2.2	0.7
	1521	0.0	0.0		1608	0.3	0.1
	2120	3.6	1.1		2205	2.9	0.9
12 Su	0417	-0.5	-0.2	27 M	0454	0.0	0.0
	1000	2.6	0.8		1042	2.2	0.7
	1613	0.0	0.0		1654	0.4	0.1
	2210	3.6	1.1		2245	2.8	0.9
13 M	0507	-0.5	-0.2	28 Tu	0536	0.1	0.0
	1054	2.6	0.8		1126	2.2	0.7
	1708	0.1	0.0		1744	0.5	0.2
	2304	3.4	1.0		2326	2.7	0.8
14 Tu	0600	-0.4	-0.1	29 W	0621	0.1	0.0
	1151	2.6	0.8		1211	2.2	0.7
	1808	0.1	0.0		1832	0.6	0.2
15 W	0003	3.2	1.0	30 Th	0011	2.6	0.8
	0656	-0.3	-0.1		0707	0.2	0.1
	1250	2.6	0.8		1258	2.3	0.7
	1911	0.2	0.1		1925	0.6	0.2

Time meridian 75° W. 0000 is midnight. 1200 is noon.
Heights are referred to mean low water which is the chart datum of soundings.

NEW LONDON, CONN., 1983

Times and Heights of High and Low Waters

JULY

Day	Time (h m)	ft	m
1 F	0056	2.4	0.7
	0754	0.3	0.1
	1346	2.3	0.7
	2020	0.7	0.2
2 Sa	0147	2.3	0.7
	0841	0.3	0.1
	1434	2.4	0.7
	2114	0.6	0.2
3 Su	0239	2.2	0.7
	0928	0.4	0.1
	1523	2.5	0.8
	2207	0.5	0.2
4 M	0333	2.2	0.7
	1015	0.4	0.1
	1613	2.6	0.8
	2301	0.4	0.1
5 Tu	0429	2.1	0.6
	1101	0.3	0.1
	1700	2.8	0.9
	2350	0.2	0.1
6 W	0524	2.2	0.7
	1147	0.3	0.1
	1747	3.1	0.9
7 Th	0040	0.0	0.0
	0617	2.2	0.7
	1233	0.2	0.1
	1833	3.3	1.0
8 F	0129	-0.2	-0.1
	0708	2.3	0.7
	1321	0.1	0.0
	1923	3.5	1.1
9 Sa	0216	-0.4	-0.1
	0759	2.5	0.8
	1411	0.0	0.0
	2013	3.6	1.1
10 Su	0306	-0.5	-0.2
	0851	2.6	0.8
	1502	-0.1	0.0
	2104	3.6	1.1
11 M	0356	-0.5	-0.2
	0943	2.7	0.8
	1557	-0.1	0.0
	2156	3.6	1.1
12 Tu	0446	-0.5	-0.2
	1036	2.7	0.8
	1654	-0.1	0.0
	2252	3.4	1.0
13 W	0539	-0.5	-0.2
	1132	2.8	0.9
	1754	-0.1	0.0
	2349	3.2	1.0
14 Th	0632	-0.3	-0.1
	1231	2.8	0.9
	1856	0.0	0.0
15 F	0050	2.9	0.9
	0726	-0.2	-0.1
	1330	2.8	0.9
	1959	0.0	0.0
16 Sa	0152	2.7	0.8
	0822	-0.1	0.0
	1432	2.9	0.9
	2103	0.1	0.0
17 Su	0259	2.4	0.7
	0919	0.1	0.0
	1534	2.9	0.9
	2206	0.1	0.0
18 M	0403	2.2	0.7
	1015	0.2	0.1
	1634	2.9	0.9
	2306	0.1	0.0
19 Tu	0506	2.1	0.6
	1108	0.2	0.1
	1729	2.9	0.9
20 W	0005	0.1	0.0
	0606	2.1	0.6
	1201	0.3	0.1
	1822	3.0	0.9
21 Th	0054	0.1	0.0
	0656	2.1	0.6
	1248	0.3	0.1
	1906	3.0	0.9
22 F	0143	0.1	0.0
	0739	2.1	0.6
	1334	0.3	0.1
	1948	2.9	0.9
23 Sa	0225	0.0	0.0
	0822	2.1	0.6
	1420	0.3	0.1
	2029	2.9	0.9
24 Su	0306	0.0	0.0
	0859	2.2	0.7
	1503	0.3	0.1
	2105	2.9	0.9
25 M	0345	0.0	0.0
	0937	2.3	0.7
	1547	0.3	0.1
	2143	2.8	0.9
26 Tu	0425	0.0	0.0
	1016	2.3	0.7
	1631	0.4	0.1
	2219	2.8	0.9
27 W	0506	0.1	0.0
	1054	2.4	0.7
	1715	0.4	0.1
	2258	2.7	0.8
28 Th	0547	0.1	0.0
	1136	2.4	0.7
	1803	0.5	0.2
	2339	2.6	0.8
29 F	0629	0.2	0.1
	1216	2.4	0.7
	1850	0.5	0.2
30 Sa	0021	2.5	0.8
	0713	0.3	0.1
	1258	2.5	0.8
	1943	0.5	0.2
31 Su	0106	2.3	0.7
	0756	0.4	0.1
	1345	2.5	0.8
	2036	0.5	0.2

AUGUST

Day	Time (h m)	ft	m
1 M	0155	2.2	0.7
	0844	0.4	0.1
	1431	2.6	0.8
	2131	0.5	0.2
2 Tu	0251	2.1	0.6
	0931	0.5	0.2
	1524	2.7	0.8
	2226	0.4	0.1
3 W	0351	2.1	0.6
	1022	0.4	0.1
	1621	2.9	0.9
	2322	0.2	0.1
4 Th	0451	2.1	0.6
	1114	0.4	0.1
	1713	3.1	0.9
5 F	0015	0.0	0.0
	0550	2.2	0.7
	1209	0.2	0.1
	1809	3.2	1.0
6 Sa	0104	-0.2	-0.1
	0645	2.4	0.7
	1302	0.1	0.0
	1904	3.4	1.0
7 Su	0155	-0.3	-0.1
	0740	2.5	0.8
	1355	-0.1	0.0
	1957	3.5	1.1
8 M	0244	-0.4	-0.1
	0833	2.7	0.8
	1448	-0.2	-0.1
	2050	3.5	1.1
9 Tu	0333	-0.5	-0.2
	0925	2.9	0.9
	1544	-0.3	-0.1
	2144	3.5	1.1
10 W	0422	-0.5	-0.2
	1017	3.0	0.9
	1639	-0.3	-0.1
	2237	3.3	1.0
11 Th	0512	-0.4	-0.1
	1110	3.1	0.9
	1736	-0.3	-0.1
	2332	3.1	0.9
12 F	0603	-0.3	-0.1
	1203	3.1	0.9
	1835	-0.2	-0.1
13 Sa	0029	2.8	0.9
	0657	-0.1	0.0
	1301	3.0	0.9
	1935	0.0	0.0
14 Su	0130	2.6	0.8
	0752	0.0	0.0
	1401	3.0	0.9
	2038	0.1	0.0
15 M	0231	2.3	0.7
	0848	0.2	0.1
	1503	2.9	0.9
	2141	0.2	0.1
16 Tu	0336	2.1	0.6
	0945	0.3	0.1
	1604	2.8	0.9
	2241	0.2	0.1
17 W	0445	2.0	0.6
	1042	0.4	0.1
	1704	2.8	0.9
	2337	0.2	0.1
18 Th	0545	2.0	0.6
	1138	0.4	0.1
	1758	2.8	0.9
19 F	0030	0.2	0.1
	0636	2.1	0.6
	1227	0.4	0.1
	1846	2.8	0.9
20 Sa	0116	0.2	0.1
	0718	2.1	0.6
	1316	0.4	0.1
	1928	2.8	0.9
21 Su	0158	0.2	0.1
	0758	2.2	0.7
	1400	0.3	0.1
	2006	2.8	0.9
22 M	0237	0.1	0.0
	0833	2.3	0.7
	1443	0.3	0.1
	2042	2.8	0.9
23 Tu	0316	0.1	0.0
	0909	2.4	0.7
	1525	0.3	0.1
	2117	2.8	0.9
24 W	0355	0.1	0.0
	0944	2.5	0.8
	1606	0.3	0.1
	2153	2.8	0.9
25 Th	0433	0.1	0.0
	1019	2.6	0.8
	1649	0.3	0.1
	2231	2.7	0.8
26 F	0510	0.1	0.0
	1056	2.7	0.8
	1733	0.3	0.1
	2307	2.6	0.8
27 Sa	0549	0.2	0.1
	1133	2.7	0.8
	1819	0.3	0.1
	2347	2.5	0.8
28 Su	0631	0.3	0.1
	1214	2.7	0.8
	1906	0.4	0.1
29 M	0031	2.4	0.7
	0714	0.5	0.2
	1257	2.7	0.8
	2001	0.4	0.1
30 Tu	0121	2.2	0.7
	0802	0.5	0.2
	1346	2.8	0.9
	2058	0.3	0.1
31 W	0219	2.1	0.6
	0854	0.6	0.2
	1444	2.8	0.9
	2157	0.3	0.1

SEPTEMBER

Day	Time (h m)	ft	m
1 Th	0324	2.1	0.6
	0952	0.5	0.2
	1547	2.9	0.9
	2254	0.2	0.1
2 F	0429	2.1	0.6
	1052	0.4	0.1
	1650	3.0	0.9
	2350	0.1	0.0
3 Sa	0532	2.3	0.7
	1152	0.3	0.1
	1753	3.2	1.0
4 Su	0043	-0.1	0.0
	0630	2.5	0.8
	1248	0.1	0.0
	1849	3.3	1.0
5 M	0133	-0.2	-0.1
	0723	2.7	0.8
	1344	-0.1	0.0
	1944	3.4	1.0
6 Tu	0221	-0.3	-0.1
	0814	3.0	0.9
	1437	-0.3	-0.1
	2037	3.4	1.0
7 W	0309	-0.4	-0.1
	0905	3.1	0.9
	1530	-0.4	-0.1
	2129	3.3	1.0
8 Th	0356	-0.4	-0.1
	0954	3.3	1.0
	1623	-0.4	-0.1
	2221	3.1	0.9
9 F	0444	-0.3	-0.1
	1044	3.3	1.0
	1717	-0.4	-0.1
	2312	2.9	0.9
10 Sa	0534	-0.2	-0.1
	1136	3.3	1.0
	1812	-0.2	-0.1
11 Su	0005	2.7	0.8
	0624	0.0	0.0
	1229	3.1	0.9
	1911	0.0	0.0
12 M	0101	2.4	0.7
	0720	0.2	0.1
	1326	3.0	0.9
	2010	0.1	0.0
13 Tu	0202	2.2	0.7
	0815	0.4	0.1
	1425	2.8	0.9
	2109	0.3	0.1
14 W	0308	2.1	0.6
	0916	0.5	0.2
	1530	2.7	0.8
	2210	0.3	0.1
15 Th	0415	2.0	0.6
	1016	0.6	0.2
	1634	2.6	0.8
	2307	0.4	0.1
16 F	0516	2.1	0.6
	1113	0.6	0.2
	1729	2.6	0.8
	2358	0.3	0.1
17 Sa	0612	2.2	0.7
	1206	0.5	0.2
	1820	2.6	0.8
18 Su	0044	0.3	0.1
	0653	2.3	0.7
	1253	0.4	0.1
	1902	2.6	0.8
19 M	0126	0.2	0.1
	0729	2.4	0.7
	1339	0.3	0.1
	1939	2.7	0.8
20 Tu	0205	0.2	0.1
	0803	2.5	0.8
	1421	0.2	0.1
	2016	2.7	0.8
21 W	0242	0.1	0.0
	0839	2.7	0.8
	1501	0.2	0.1
	2051	2.8	0.9
22 Th	0319	0.1	0.0
	0911	2.8	0.9
	1540	0.1	0.0
	2127	2.7	0.8
23 F	0356	0.1	0.0
	0945	2.9	0.9
	1622	0.1	0.0
	2203	2.7	0.8
24 Sa	0433	0.2	0.1
	1018	2.9	0.9
	1704	0.1	0.0
	2241	2.6	0.8
25 Su	0510	0.3	0.1
	1054	3.0	0.9
	1749	0.1	0.0
	2321	2.5	0.8
26 M	0549	0.4	0.1
	1136	3.0	0.9
	1837	0.2	0.1
27 Tu	0007	2.4	0.7
	0634	0.5	0.2
	1221	3.0	0.9
	1931	0.3	0.1
28 W	0058	2.2	0.7
	0726	0.6	0.2
	1314	2.9	0.9
	2031	0.3	0.1
29 Th	0159	2.1	0.6
	0826	0.6	0.2
	1417	2.9	0.9
	2132	0.3	0.1
30 F	0308	2.1	0.6
	0934	0.6	0.2
	1524	2.9	0.9
	2231	0.2	0.1

Time meridian 75° W. 0000 is midnight. 1200 is noon.
Heights are referred to mean low water which is the chart datum of soundings.

Times and Heights of High and Low Waters

OCTOBER

Day	Time h m	ft	m	Day	Time h m	ft	m
1 Sa	0416	2.2	0.7	16 Su	0535	2.2	0.7
	1038	0.5	0.2		1142	0.5	0.2
	1636	2.9	0.9		1745	2.4	0.7
	2327	0.1	0.0				
2 Su	0519	2.4	0.7	17 M	0007	0.3	0.1
	1140	0.3	0.1		0617	2.4	0.7
	1739	3.0	0.9		1228	0.4	0.1
					1827	2.5	0.8
3 M	0020	0.0	0.0	18 Tu	0049	0.2	0.1
	0615	2.7	0.8		0655	2.5	0.8
	1238	0.0	0.0		1312	0.3	0.1
	1838	3.1	0.9		1908	2.5	0.8
4 Tu	0110	-0.2	-0.1	19 W	0128	0.2	0.1
	0707	2.9	0.9		0728	2.7	0.8
	1332	-0.2	-0.1		1354	0.2	0.1
	1932	3.1	0.9		1947	2.6	0.8
5 W	0158	-0.2	-0.1	20 Th	0206	0.1	0.0
	0756	3.2	1.0		0803	2.9	0.9
	1424	-0.4	-0.1		1433	0.0	0.0
	2024	3.1	0.9		2022	2.6	0.8
6 Th	0244	-0.3	-0.1	21 F	0243	0.1	0.0
	0844	3.4	1.0		0836	3.0	0.9
	1515	-0.5	-0.2		1515	-0.1	0.0
	2113	3.0	0.9		2058	2.6	0.8
7 F	0330	-0.2	-0.1	22 Sa	0320	0.1	0.0
	0930	3.4	1.0		0910	3.1	0.9
	1606	-0.5	-0.2		1555	-0.1	0.0
	2201	2.9	0.9		2136	2.6	0.8
8 Sa	0417	-0.2	-0.1	23 Su	0357	0.2	0.1
	1019	3.4	1.0		0947	3.2	1.0
	1656	-0.4	-0.1		1638	-0.1	0.0
	2249	2.7	0.8		2215	2.5	0.8
9 Su	0504	0.0	0.0	24 M	0435	0.2	0.1
	1106	3.3	1.0		1024	3.2	1.0
	1749	-0.2	-0.1		1724	-0.1	0.0
	2340	2.5	0.8		2259	2.4	0.7
10 M	0555	0.2	0.1	25 Tu	0516	0.3	0.1
	1155	3.1	0.9		1107	3.2	1.0
	1842	0.0	0.0		1813	0.0	0.0
					2347	2.3	0.7
11 Tu	0034	2.3	0.7	26 W	0605	0.4	0.1
	0648	0.4	0.1		1156	3.1	0.9
	1250	2.9	0.9		1906	0.0	0.0
	1938	0.2	0.1				
12 W	0130	2.2	0.7	27 Th	0042	2.2	0.7
	0746	0.5	0.2		0704	0.5	0.2
	1346	2.7	0.8		1253	3.0	0.9
	2037	0.3	0.1		2006	0.1	0.0
13 Th	0236	2.1	0.6	28 F	0146	2.2	0.7
	0846	0.6	0.2		0811	0.6	0.2
	1450	2.5	0.8		1358	2.8	0.9
	2135	0.4	0.1		2107	0.1	0.0
14 F	0341	2.1	0.6	29 Sa	0255	2.2	0.7
	0948	0.7	0.2		0920	0.5	0.2
	1554	2.4	0.7		1511	2.7	0.8
	2231	0.4	0.1		2207	0.1	0.0
15 Sa	0444	2.1	0.6	30 Su	0402	2.4	0.7
	1046	0.6	0.2		1026	0.4	0.1
	1652	2.4	0.7		1621	2.7	0.8
	2321	0.4	0.1		2303	0.0	0.0
				31 M	0505	2.6	0.8
					1129	0.1	0.0
					1727	2.7	0.8
					2356	0.0	0.0

NOVEMBER

Day	Time h m	ft	m	Day	Time h m	ft	m
1 Tu	0559	2.8	0.9	16 W	0009	0.2	0.1
	1227	-0.1	0.0		0614	2.6	0.8
	1825	2.7	0.8		1243	0.2	0.1
					1830	2.3	0.7
2 W	0046	-0.1	0.0	17 Th	0051	0.1	0.0
	0651	3.1	0.9		0651	2.7	0.8
	1320	-0.3	-0.1		1325	0.0	0.0
	1920	2.7	0.8		1911	2.3	0.7
3 Th	0134	-0.2	-0.1	18 F	0130	0.1	0.0
	0738	3.3	1.0		0726	2.9	0.9
	1411	-0.4	-0.1		1406	-0.1	0.0
	2009	2.7	0.8		1950	2.4	0.7
4 F	0219	-0.2	-0.1	19 Sa	0208	0.1	0.0
	0824	3.4	1.0		0800	3.1	0.9
	1501	-0.5	-0.2		1448	-0.3	-0.1
	2055	2.6	0.8		2029	2.4	0.7
5 Sa	0304	-0.1	0.0	20 Su	0245	0.0	0.0
	0909	3.4	1.0		0838	3.2	1.0
	1548	-0.5	-0.2		1531	-0.4	-0.1
	2142	2.6	0.8		2110	2.4	0.7
6 Su	0349	-0.1	0.0	21 M	0324	0.0	0.0
	0952	3.3	1.0		0918	3.3	1.0
	1636	-0.4	-0.1		1615	-0.4	-0.1
	2227	2.4	0.7		2154	2.4	0.7
7 M	0437	0.1	0.0	22 Tu	0408	0.1	0.0
	1038	3.2	1.0		1001	3.3	1.0
	1725	-0.2	-0.1		1702	-0.4	-0.1
	2315	2.3	0.7		2241	2.3	0.7
8 Tu	0525	0.2	0.1	23 W	0454	0.1	0.0
	1125	3.0	0.9		1046	3.2	1.0
	1815	-0.1	0.0		1751	-0.3	-0.1
					2333	2.3	0.7
9 W	0005	2.2	0.7	24 Th	0547	0.2	0.1
	0619	0.4	0.1		1139	3.1	0.9
	1215	2.8	0.9		1847	-0.3	-0.1
	1906	0.1	0.0				
10 Th	0101	2.1	0.6	25 F	0029	2.2	0.7
	0714	0.5	0.2		0650	0.3	0.1
	1306	2.6	0.8		1237	2.9	0.9
	2001	0.2	0.1		1943	-0.2	-0.1
11 F	0158	2.0	0.6	26 Sa	0133	2.3	0.7
	0815	0.6	0.2		0757	0.3	0.1
	1406	2.4	0.7		1345	2.7	0.8
	2057	0.3	0.1		2042	-0.1	0.0
12 Sa	0302	2.0	0.6	27 Su	0239	2.3	0.7
	0915	0.7	0.2		0907	0.3	0.1
	1507	2.2	0.7		1455	2.5	0.8
	2149	0.3	0.1		2142	-0.1	0.0
13 Su	0401	2.1	0.6	28 M	0345	2.5	0.8
	1015	0.6	0.2		1014	0.1	0.0
	1607	2.2	0.7		1606	2.4	0.7
	2239	0.3	0.1		2237	-0.1	0.0
14 M	0453	2.2	0.7	29 Tu	0447	2.7	0.8
	1108	0.5	0.2		1116	0.0	0.0
	1658	2.2	0.7		1713	2.4	0.7
	2326	0.2	0.1		2332	-0.1	0.0
15 Tu	0535	2.4	0.7	30 W	0542	2.8	0.9
	1158	0.4	0.1		1214	-0.2	-0.1
	1748	2.2	0.7		1812	2.3	0.7

DECEMBER

Day	Time h m	ft	m	Day	Time h m	ft	m
1 Th	0022	-0.1	0.0	16 F	0010	0.1	0.0
	0635	3.0	0.9		0609	2.7	0.8
	1307	-0.4	-0.1		1254	-0.1	0.0
	1905	2.3	0.7		1834	2.0	0.6
2 F	0110	-0.1	0.0	17 Sa	0052	0.0	0.0
	0721	3.1	0.9		0649	2.9	0.9
	1357	-0.4	-0.1		1339	-0.3	-0.1
	1955	2.3	0.7		1920	2.1	0.6
3 Sa	0156	-0.1	0.0	18 Su	0133	0.0	0.0
	0806	3.2	1.0		0731	3.0	0.9
	1445	-0.5	-0.2		1422	-0.5	-0.2
	2039	2.2	0.7		2003	2.2	0.7
4 Su	0241	-0.1	0.0	19 M	0215	-0.1	0.0
	0849	3.2	1.0		0813	3.2	1.0
	1530	-0.4	-0.1		1507	-0.6	-0.2
	2123	2.2	0.7		2048	2.2	0.7
5 M	0327	-0.1	0.0	20 Tu	0258	-0.2	-0.1
	0932	3.1	0.9		0857	3.3	1.0
	1616	-0.4	-0.1		1553	-0.7	-0.2
	2205	2.1	0.6		2135	2.3	0.7
6 Tu	0413	0.0	0.0	21 W	0347	-0.2	-0.1
	1014	3.0	0.9		0944	3.3	1.0
	1702	-0.3	-0.1		1640	-0.7	-0.2
	2251	2.1	0.6		2225	2.3	0.7
7 W	0459	0.2	0.1	22 Th	0439	-0.2	-0.1
	1056	2.8	0.9		1035	3.2	1.0
	1747	-0.2	-0.1		1731	-0.6	-0.2
	2336	2.0	0.6		2317	2.3	0.7
8 Th	0551	0.3	0.1	23 F	0536	-0.1	0.0
	1141	2.6	0.8		1129	3.0	0.9
	1834	-0.1	0.0		1824	-0.5	-0.2
9 F	0026	2.0	0.6	24 Sa	0013	2.3	0.7
	0645	0.4	0.1		0637	-0.1	0.0
	1230	2.4	0.7		1228	2.8	0.9
	1923	0.0	0.0		1919	-0.4	-0.1
10 Sa	0119	2.0	0.6	25 Su	0115	2.4	0.7
	0741	0.5	0.2		0742	0.0	0.0
	1319	2.2	0.7		1332	2.5	0.8
	2014	0.1	0.0		2017	-0.3	-0.1
11 Su	0215	2.0	0.6	26 M	0218	2.4	0.7
	0838	0.5	0.2		0849	-0.1	0.0
	1415	2.1	0.6		1440	2.3	0.7
	2105	0.2	0.1		2114	-0.2	-0.1
12 M	0309	2.1	0.6	27 Tu	0324	2.5	0.8
	0937	0.5	0.2		0956	-0.1	0.0
	1512	2.0	0.6		1549	2.1	0.6
	2156	0.2	0.1		2211	-0.2	-0.1
13 Tu	0401	2.2	0.7	28 W	0425	2.6	0.8
	1030	0.4	0.1		1058	-0.2	-0.1
	1609	1.9	0.6		1655	2.0	0.6
	2242	0.2	0.1		2305	-0.1	0.0
14 W	0447	2.3	0.7	29 Th	0524	2.7	0.8
	1121	0.3	0.1		1157	-0.3	-0.1
	1701	1.9	0.6		1756	2.0	0.6
	2327	0.1	0.0		2358	-0.1	0.0
15 Th	0530	2.5	0.8	30 F	0617	2.8	0.9
	1209	0.1	0.0		1251	-0.4	-0.1
	1748	2.0	0.6		1852	1.9	0.6
				31 Sa	0048	-0.1	0.0
					0705	2.9	0.9
					1342	-0.4	-0.1
					1939	1.9	0.6

Time meridian 75° W. 0000 is midnight. 1200 is noon.
Heights are referred to mean low water which is the chart datum of soundings.

BRIDGEPORT, CONN., 1983

Times and Heights of High and Low Waters

JANUARY

Day	Time h m	Height ft	m	Day	Time h m	Height ft	m
1 Sa	0004	6.8	2.1	16 Su	0016	6.2	1.9
	0612	-0.8	-0.2		0621	0.1	0.0
	1222	7.7	2.3		1227	6.8	2.1
	1849	-1.4	-0.4		1848	-0.3	-0.1
2 Su	0059	6.8	2.1	17 M	0051	6.3	1.9
	0707	-0.7	-0.2		0659	0.2	0.1
	1318	7.5	2.3		1302	6.7	2.0
	1944	-1.2	-0.4		1923	-0.2	-0.1
3 M	0155	6.8	2.1	18 Tu	0128	6.3	1.9
	0806	-0.6	-0.2		0736	0.2	0.1
	1415	7.1	2.2		1341	6.5	2.0
	2040	-0.9	-0.3		2000	-0.1	0.0
4 Tu	0251	6.7	2.0	19 W	0208	6.3	1.9
	0906	-0.4	-0.1		0819	0.3	0.1
	1514	6.7	2.0		1422	6.3	1.9
	2135	-0.6	-0.2		2040	0.0	0.0
5 W	0350	6.6	2.0	20 Th	0249	6.3	1.9
	1009	-0.3	-0.1		0904	0.3	0.1
	1615	6.3	1.9		1509	6.1	1.9
	2234	-0.4	-0.1		2122	0.1	0.0
6 Th	0449	6.5	2.0	21 F	0337	6.4	2.0
	1111	-0.2	-0.1		0954	0.3	0.1
	1718	6.0	1.8		1559	5.9	1.8
	2333	-0.1	0.0		2213	0.2	0.1
7 F	0549	6.5	2.0	22 Sa	0428	6.4	2.0
	1214	-0.2	-0.1		1055	0.3	0.1
	1820	5.8	1.8		1656	5.7	1.7
					2309	0.3	0.1
8 Sa	0032	0.0	0.0	23 Su	0527	6.5	2.0
	0648	6.6	2.0		1156	0.1	0.0
	1315	-0.2	-0.1		1759	5.6	1.7
	1919	5.7	1.7				
9 Su	0126	0.0	0.0	24 M	0009	0.2	0.1
	0740	6.6	2.0		0627	6.6	2.0
	1408	-0.3	-0.1		1300	-0.1	0.0
	2014	5.7	1.7		1904	5.7	1.7
10 M	0217	0.1	0.0	25 Tu	0111	0.1	0.0
	0831	6.7	2.0		0729	6.9	2.1
	1459	-0.4	-0.1		1401	-0.5	-0.2
	2102	5.8	1.8		2006	5.9	1.8
11 Tu	0305	0.1	0.0	26 W	0214	-0.2	-0.1
	0917	6.8	2.1		0828	7.2	2.2
	1544	-0.4	-0.1		1500	-0.8	-0.2
	2145	5.9	1.8		2105	6.2	1.9
12 W	0348	0.0	0.0	27 Th	0313	-0.5	-0.2
	0958	6.9	2.1		0927	7.4	2.3
	1624	-0.5	-0.2		1556	-1.2	-0.4
	2226	6.0	1.8		2203	6.5	2.0
13 Th	0429	0.1	0.0	28 F	0410	-0.8	-0.2
	1038	6.9	2.1		1022	7.6	2.3
	1701	-0.4	-0.1		1650	-1.5	-0.5
	2303	6.1	1.9		2256	6.8	2.1
14 F	0508	0.1	0.0	29 Sa	0505	-1.0	-0.3
	1114	6.9	2.1		1116	7.7	2.3
	1737	-0.4	-0.1		1741	-1.5	-0.5
	2340	6.2	1.9		2349	7.0	2.1
15 Sa	0544	0.1	0.0	30 Su	0558	-1.2	-0.4
	1150	6.9	2.1		1209	7.6	2.3
	1813	-0.3	-0.1		1832	-1.5	-0.5
				31 M	0041	7.1	2.2
					0653	-1.2	-0.4
					1302	7.4	2.3
					1923	-1.4	-0.4

FEBRUARY

Day	Time h m	Height ft	m	Day	Time h m	Height ft	m
1 Tu	0131	7.0	2.1	16 W	0057	6.6	2.0
	0747	-1.1	-0.3		0710	-0.3	-0.1
	1355	7.0	2.1		1313	6.6	2.0
	2014	-1.1	-0.3		1928	-0.3	-0.1
2 W	0224	6.9	2.1	17 Th	0134	6.6	2.0
	0842	-0.8	-0.2		0750	-0.2	-0.1
	1450	6.6	2.0		1352	6.4	2.0
	2106	-0.7	-0.2		2006	-0.2	-0.1
3 Th	0317	6.7	2.0	18 F	0216	6.6	2.0
	0941	-0.6	-0.2		0834	-0.1	0.0
	1546	6.1	1.9		1439	6.1	1.9
	2200	-0.3	-0.1		2048	0.0	0.0
4 F	0414	6.6	2.0	19 Sa	0303	6.6	2.0
	1039	-0.3	-0.1		0925	0.0	0.0
	1645	5.7	1.7		1530	5.9	1.8
	2258	0.0	0.0		2139	0.2	0.1
5 Sa	0513	6.3	1.9	20 Su	0357	6.5	2.0
	1141	-0.1	0.0		1025	0.1	0.0
	1746	5.5	1.7		1630	5.6	1.7
	2356	0.2	0.1		2238	0.4	0.1
6 Su	0610	6.2	1.9	21 M	0454	6.5	2.0
	1240	0.0	0.0		1101	0.1	0.0
	1847	5.4	1.6		1736	5.6	1.7
					2345	0.4	0.1
7 M	0052	0.4	0.1	22 Tu	0603	6.5	2.0
	0708	6.3	1.9		1239	0.0	0.0
	1337	0.1	0.0		1844	5.7	1.7
	1943	5.5	1.7				
8 Tu	0148	0.4	0.1	23 W	0055	0.3	0.1
	0801	6.4	2.0		0711	6.7	2.0
	1428	0.0	0.0		1344	-0.3	-0.1
	2033	5.6	1.7		1951	5.9	1.8
9 W	0238	0.3	0.1	24 Th	0201	0.0	0.0
	0851	6.5	2.0		0814	7.0	2.1
	1515	-0.1	0.0		1444	-0.6	-0.2
	2118	5.8	1.8		2051	6.3	1.9
10 Th	0323	0.2	0.1	25 F	0302	-0.4	-0.1
	0932	6.7	2.0		0915	7.3	2.2
	1556	-0.2	-0.1		1540	-1.0	-0.3
	2200	6.0	1.8		2147	6.7	2.0
11 F	0406	0.1	0.0	26 Sa	0358	-0.9	-0.3
	1012	6.8	2.1		1011	7.5	2.3
	1634	-0.3	-0.1		1633	-1.3	-0.4
	2237	6.2	1.9		2239	7.1	2.2
12 Sa	0443	0.0	0.0	27 Su	0453	-1.2	-0.4
	1051	6.8	2.1		1103	7.6	2.3
	1710	-0.4	-0.1		1722	-1.4	-0.4
	2313	6.4	2.0		2329	7.3	2.2
13 Su	0520	-0.1	0.0	28 M	0544	-1.4	-0.4
	1126	6.9	2.1		1153	7.5	2.3
	1745	-0.4	-0.1		1809	-1.4	-0.4
	2347	6.5	2.0				
14 M	0557	-0.2	-0.1				
	1202	6.8	2.1				
	1818	-0.4	-0.1				
15 Tu	0022	6.6	2.0				
	0633	-0.2	-0.1				
	1237	6.7	2.0				
	1853	-0.4	-0.1				

MARCH

Day	Time h m	Height ft	m	Day	Time h m	Height ft	m
1 Tu	0017	7.3	2.2	16 W	0606	-0.6	-0.2
	0634	-1.4	-0.4		1209	6.8	2.1
	1243	7.2	2.2		1821	-0.4	-0.1
	1857	-1.2	-0.4				
2 W	0105	7.3	2.2	17 Th	0027	7.0	2.1
	0725	-1.3	-0.4		0644	-0.6	-0.2
	1332	6.9	2.1		1249	6.6	2.0
	1944	-0.9	-0.3		1857	-0.3	-0.1
3 Th	0153	7.0	2.1	18 F	0105	7.0	2.1
	0815	-1.0	-0.3		0725	-0.5	-0.2
	1421	6.4	2.0		1332	6.4	2.0
	2034	-0.5	-0.2		1937	-0.1	0.0
4 F	0243	6.8	2.1	19 Sa	0150	7.0	2.1
	0908	-0.6	-0.2		0811	-0.4	-0.1
	1512	6.0	1.8		1418	6.2	1.9
	2125	-0.1	0.0		2023	0.1	0.0
5 Sa	0335	6.5	2.0	20 Su	0237	6.8	2.1
	1003	-0.2	-0.1		0904	-0.1	0.0
	1608	5.7	1.7		1512	5.9	1.8
	2220	0.3	0.1		2117	0.4	0.1
6 Su	0431	6.2	1.9	21 M	0333	6.7	2.0
	1101	0.2	0.1		1005	0.1	0.0
	1708	5.5	1.7		1614	5.8	1.8
	2317	0.6	0.2		2221	0.6	0.2
7 M	0531	6.1	1.9	22 Tu	0439	6.5	2.0
	1159	0.4	0.1		1114	0.2	0.1
	1807	5.4	1.6		1722	5.7	1.7
					2334	0.6	0.2
8 Tu	0017	0.8	0.2	23 W	0549	6.5	2.0
	0630	6.1	1.9		1223	0.1	0.0
	1259	0.5	0.2		1831	5.9	1.8
	1904	5.5	1.7				
9 W	0114	0.8	0.2	24 Th	0045	0.5	0.2
	0725	6.2	1.9		0658	6.6	2.0
	1352	0.4	0.1		1329	-0.1	0.0
	1957	5.7	1.7		1938	6.2	1.9
10 Th	0207	0.7	0.2	25 F	0152	0.1	0.0
	0817	6.4	2.0		0804	6.9	2.1
	1438	0.3	0.1		1428	-0.4	-0.1
	2044	6.0	1.8		2038	6.7	2.0
11 F	0254	0.5	0.2	26 Sa	0252	-0.4	-0.1
	0902	6.5	2.0		0903	7.1	2.2
	1521	0.1	0.0		1523	-0.7	-0.2
	2126	6.3	1.9		2131	7.1	2.2
12 Sa	0336	0.2	0.1	27 Su	0347	-0.9	-0.3
	0944	6.7	2.0		0956	7.3	2.2
	1600	-0.1	0.0		1612	-1.0	-0.3
	2204	6.5	2.0		2219	7.4	2.3
13 Su	0416	0.0	0.0	28 M	0438	-1.3	-0.4
	1021	6.8	2.1		1047	7.3	2.2
	1637	-0.2	-0.1		1701	-1.1	-0.3
	2241	6.7	2.0		2308	7.5	2.3
14 M	0453	-0.3	-0.1	29 Tu	0527	-1.4	-0.4
	1058	6.9	2.1		1136	7.2	2.2
	1712	-0.3	-0.1		1745	-1.0	-0.3
	2316	6.9	2.1		2353	7.5	2.3
15 Tu	0530	-0.4	-0.1	30 W	0614	-1.4	-0.4
	1133	6.9	2.1		1222	7.0	2.1
	1746	-0.4	-0.1		1831	-0.8	-0.2
	2351	7.0	2.1				
				31 Th	0038	7.4	2.3
					0700	-1.2	-0.4
					1307	6.7	2.0
					1915	-0.5	-0.2

Time meridian 75° W. 0000 is midnight. 1200 is noon.
Heights are referred to mean low water which is the chart datum of soundings.

BRIDGEPORT, CONN., 1983

Times and Heights of High and Low Waters

APRIL

Day	Time (h m)	Height (ft)	Height (m)	Day	Time (h m)	Height (ft)	Height (m)
1 F	0123	7.1	2.2	16 Sa	0041	7.4	2.3
	0747	-0.8	-0.2		0707	-0.7	-0.2
	1352	6.4	2.0		1313	6.5	2.0
	2000	-0.1	0.0		1917	0.1	0.0
2 Sa	0210	6.8	2.1	17 Su	0128	7.3	2.2
	0835	-0.4	-0.1		0757	-0.5	-0.2
	1442	6.0	1.8		1404	6.3	1.9
	2050	0.3	0.1		2008	0.3	0.1
3 Su	0259	6.5	2.0	18 M	0221	7.1	2.2
	0927	0.1	0.0		0852	-0.2	-0.1
	1533	5.8	1.8		1501	6.2	1.9
	2141	0.7	0.2		2108	0.6	0.2
4 M	0351	6.3	1.9	19 Tu	0320	6.8	2.1
	1020	0.5	0.2		0954	0.1	0.0
	1628	5.6	1.7		1605	6.1	1.9
	2238	1.0	0.3		2216	0.7	0.2
5 Tu	0447	6.1	1.9	20 W	0428	6.6	2.0
	1115	0.7	0.2		1100	0.2	0.1
	1724	5.6	1.7		1713	6.1	1.9
	2338	1.2	0.4		2328	0.7	0.2
6 W	0546	6.0	1.8	21 Th	0538	6.6	2.0
	1214	0.8	0.2		1208	0.2	0.1
	1823	5.8	1.8		1821	6.3	1.9
7 Th	0036	1.1	0.3	22 F	0037	0.4	0.1
	0642	6.1	1.9		0647	6.6	2.0
	1306	0.8	0.2		1311	0.0	0.0
	1915	6.0	1.8		1922	6.7	2.0
8 F	0129	0.9	0.3	23 Sa	0141	0.0	0.0
	0735	6.3	1.9		0751	6.8	2.1
	1356	0.6	0.2		1409	-0.2	-0.1
	2001	6.3	1.9		2020	7.0	2.1
9 Sa	0217	0.7	0.2	24 Su	0241	-0.5	-0.2
	0823	6.5	2.0		0849	6.9	2.1
	1441	0.4	0.1		1503	-0.4	-0.1
	2046	6.6	2.0		2111	7.4	2.3
10 Su	0302	0.3	0.1	25 M	0334	-0.9	-0.3
	0907	6.6	2.0		0940	7.0	2.1
	1521	0.2	0.1		1552	-0.6	-0.2
	2126	6.8	2.1		2159	7.6	2.3
11 M	0344	0.0	0.0	26 Tu	0422	-1.1	-0.3
	0947	6.8	2.1		1029	7.0	2.1
	1559	0.0	0.0		1636	-0.6	-0.2
	2203	7.1	2.2		2245	7.6	2.3
12 Tu	0422	-0.4	-0.1	27 W	0508	-1.2	-0.4
	1027	6.8	2.1		1115	6.9	2.1
	1636	-0.2	-0.1		1721	-0.6	-0.2
	2242	7.2	2.2		2329	7.6	2.3
13 W	0501	-0.6	-0.2	28 Th	0553	-1.1	-0.3
	1107	6.8	2.1		1158	6.7	2.0
	1714	-0.2	-0.1		1803	-0.4	-0.1
	2321	7.4	2.3				
14 Th	0540	-0.7	-0.2	29 F	0012	7.4	2.3
	1146	6.8	2.1		0636	-0.9	-0.3
	1753	-0.2	-0.1		1243	6.5	2.0
	2359	7.4	2.3		1847	-0.1	0.0
15 F	0622	-0.8	-0.2	30 Sa	0054	7.2	2.2
	1228	6.7	2.0		0720	-0.5	-0.2
	1832	-0.1	0.0		1326	6.3	1.9
					1930	0.3	0.1

MAY

Day	Time (h m)	Height (ft)	Height (m)	Day	Time (h m)	Height (ft)	Height (m)
1 Su	0138	6.9	2.1	16 M	0114	7.5	2.3
	0803	-0.1	0.0		0744	-0.6	-0.2
	1411	6.1	1.9		1355	6.6	2.0
	2016	0.7	0.2		1959	0.3	0.1
2 M	0224	6.7	2.0	17 Tu	0209	7.3	2.2
	0850	0.3	0.1		0843	-0.3	-0.1
	1458	6.0	1.8		1452	6.5	2.0
	2106	1.0	0.3		2101	0.5	0.2
3 Tu	0312	6.4	2.0	18 W	0312	7.0	2.1
	0940	0.6	0.2		0943	-0.1	0.0
	1549	5.9	1.8		1557	6.5	2.0
	2159	1.2	0.4		2210	0.6	0.2
4 W	0405	6.2	1.9	19 Th	0417	6.7	2.0
	1031	0.8	0.2		1046	0.1	0.0
	1641	6.0	1.8		1700	6.6	2.0
	2255	1.3	0.4		2319	0.5	0.2
5 Th	0500	6.1	1.9	20 F	0526	6.6	2.0
	1125	1.0	0.3		1150	0.1	0.0
	1734	6.1	1.9		1805	6.7	2.0
	2351	1.3	0.4				
6 F	0554	6.1	1.9	21 Sa	0025	0.3	0.1
	1216	0.9	0.3		0632	6.6	2.0
	1826	6.3	1.9		1252	0.1	0.0
					1905	7.0	2.1
7 Sa	0045	1.1	0.3	22 Su	0127	-0.1	0.0
	0648	6.2	1.9		0735	6.6	2.0
	1306	0.8	0.2		1348	0.1	0.0
	1916	6.5	2.0		2001	7.3	2.2
8 Su	0137	0.8	0.2	23 M	0225	-0.4	-0.1
	0737	6.3	1.9		0833	6.7	2.0
	1353	0.6	0.2		1441	-0.2	-0.1
	2001	6.8	2.1		2051	7.4	2.3
9 M	0222	0.4	0.1	24 Tu	0317	-0.7	-0.2
	0825	6.5	2.0		0923	6.7	2.0
	1438	0.4	0.1		1529	-0.2	-0.1
	2044	7.1	2.2		2138	7.5	2.3
10 Tu	0307	0.0	0.0	25 W	0404	-0.9	-0.3
	0911	6.6	2.0		1011	6.6	2.0
	1519	0.2	0.1		1614	-0.2	-0.1
	2126	7.3	2.2		2224	7.6	2.3
11 W	0351	-0.4	-0.1	26 Th	0448	-0.9	-0.3
	0954	6.7	2.0		1055	6.6	2.0
	1600	0.0	0.0		1658	-0.1	0.0
	2208	7.5	2.3		2306	7.5	2.3
12 Th	0435	-0.7	-0.2	27 F	0531	-0.8	-0.2
	1037	6.8	2.1		1138	6.5	2.0
	1643	-0.1	0.0		1740	0.1	0.0
	2251	7.7	2.3		2347	7.3	2.2
13 F	0518	-0.8	-0.2	28 Sa	0613	-0.6	-0.2
	1124	6.8	2.1		1219	6.4	2.0
	1726	-0.1	0.0		1820	0.3	0.1
	2337	7.7	2.3				
14 Sa	0603	-0.9	-0.3	29 Su	0028	7.2	2.2
	1210	6.7	2.0		0654	-0.3	-0.1
	1812	0.0	0.0		1259	6.3	1.9
					1902	0.6	0.2
15 Su	0024	7.7	2.3	30 M	0109	7.0	2.1
	0653	-0.8	-0.2		0734	0.0	0.0
	1300	6.7	2.0		1342	6.3	1.9
	1902	0.1	0.0		1947	0.8	0.2
				31 Tu	0150	6.8	2.1
					0816	0.3	0.1
					1424	6.2	1.9
					2032	1.1	0.3

JUNE

Day	Time (h m)	Height (ft)	Height (m)	Day	Time (h m)	Height (ft)	Height (m)
1 W	0235	6.6	2.0	16 Th	0300	7.1	2.2
	0901	0.6	0.2		0927	-0.3	-0.1
	1509	6.2	1.9		1541	6.9	2.1
	2120	1.2	0.4		2157	0.2	0.1
2 Th	0322	6.4	2.0	17 F	0404	6.8	2.1
	0948	0.8	0.2		1027	-0.1	0.0
	1559	6.3	1.9		1642	6.9	2.1
	2212	1.3	0.4		2303	0.2	0.1
3 F	0412	6.3	1.9	18 Sa	0508	6.6	2.0
	1036	0.9	0.3		1128	0.0	0.0
	1647	6.4	2.0		1743	7.0	2.1
	2305	1.2	0.4				
4 Sa	0506	6.2	1.9	19 Su	0007	0.0	0.0
	1126	0.9	0.3		0613	6.4	2.0
	1737	6.5	2.0		1227	0.1	0.0
	2359	1.0	0.3		1842	7.1	2.2
5 Su	0559	6.2	1.9	20 M	0109	-0.2	-0.1
	1215	0.8	0.2		0717	6.3	1.9
	1827	6.7	2.0		1324	0.1	0.0
					1938	7.2	2.2
6 M	0051	0.7	0.2	21 Tu	0206	-0.3	-0.1
	0652	6.2	1.9		0812	6.3	1.9
	1303	0.7	0.2		1417	0.1	0.0
	1916	6.9	2.1		2030	7.3	2.2
7 Tu	0141	0.4	0.1	22 W	0259	-0.5	-0.2
	0744	6.3	1.9		0904	6.3	1.9
	1352	0.5	0.2		1507	0.1	0.0
	2004	7.2	2.2		2118	7.4	2.3
8 W	0232	0.0	0.0	23 Th	0345	-0.5	-0.2
	0835	6.4	2.0		0952	6.3	1.9
	1441	0.3	0.1		1553	0.1	0.0
	2051	7.5	2.3		2203	7.4	2.3
9 Th	0321	-0.4	-0.1	24 F	0430	-0.5	-0.2
	0923	6.5	2.0		1035	6.3	1.9
	1527	0.1	0.0		1636	0.2	0.1
	2139	7.7	2.3		2245	7.3	2.2
10 F	0408	-0.7	-0.2	25 Sa	0512	-0.4	-0.1
	1012	6.7	2.0		1117	6.4	2.0
	1615	0.0	0.0		1718	0.3	0.1
	2227	7.9	2.4		2325	7.3	2.2
11 Sa	0457	-0.9	-0.3	26 Su	0550	-0.3	-0.1
	1103	6.8	2.1		1155	6.4	2.0
	1705	-0.1	0.0		1757	0.5	0.2
	2317	7.9	2.4				
12 Su	0546	-1.0	-0.3	27 M	0003	7.1	2.2
	1154	6.8	2.1		0628	-0.1	0.0
	1757	-0.1	0.0		1233	6.4	2.0
					1838	0.6	0.2
13 M	0008	7.9	2.4	28 Tu	0041	7.0	2.1
	0638	-0.9	-0.3		0707	0.1	0.0
	1246	6.9	2.1		1313	6.4	2.0
	1851	0.0	0.0		1917	0.8	0.2
14 Tu	0102	7.7	2.3	29 W	0120	6.9	2.1
	0731	-0.8	-0.2		0744	0.2	0.1
	1342	6.9	2.1		1352	6.5	2.0
	1950	0.1	0.0		1958	0.9	0.3
15 W	0200	7.4	2.3	30 Th	0200	6.7	2.0
	0827	-0.5	-0.2		0824	0.4	0.1
	1440	6.9	2.1		1431	6.5	2.0
	2053	0.2	0.1		2042	1.0	0.3

Time meridian 75° W. 0000 is midnight. 1200 is noon.
Heights are referred to mean low water which is the chart datum of soundings.

BRIDGEPORT, CONN., 1983

Times and Heights of High and Low Waters

JULY

Day	h m	ft	m	Day	h m	ft	m
1 F	0243	6.5	2.0	16 Sa	0343	6.7	2.0
	0904	0.5	0.2		1001	-0.2	-0.1
	1514	6.5	2.0		1617	7.1	2.2
	2128	1.0	0.3		2241	-0.1	0.0
2 Sa	0328	6.4	2.0	17 Su	0446	6.4	2.0
	0949	0.7	0.2		1101	0.0	0.0
	1602	6.6	2.0		1717	7.0	2.1
	2220	1.0	0.3		2343	0.0	0.0
3 Su	0420	6.2	1.9	18 M	0550	6.2	1.9
	1034	0.7	0.2		1200	0.2	0.1
	1651	6.7	2.0		1816	7.0	2.1
	2314	0.9	0.3				
4 M	0513	6.1	1.9	19 Tu	0046	-0.1	0.0
	1125	0.7	0.2		0652	6.1	1.9
	1742	6.8	2.1		1258	0.3	0.1
					1914	7.0	2.1
5 Tu	0007	0.7	0.2	20 W	0144	-0.1	0.0
	0607	6.0	1.8		0751	6.0	1.8
	1219	0.7	0.2		1353	0.4	0.1
	1834	7.0	2.1		2007	7.1	2.2
6 W	0103	0.4	0.1	21 Th	0238	-0.2	-0.1
	0706	6.1	1.9		0842	6.1	1.9
	1311	0.5	0.2		1444	0.4	0.1
	1929	7.2	2.2		2057	7.2	2.2
7 Th	0159	0.0	0.0	22 F	0324	-0.2	-0.1
	0801	6.2	1.9		0930	6.2	1.9
	1406	0.4	0.1		1531	0.4	0.1
	2021	7.5	2.3		2142	7.2	2.2
8 F	0252	-0.3	-0.1	23 Sa	0407	-0.2	-0.1
	0857	6.4	2.0		1012	6.3	1.9
	1501	0.2	0.1		1614	0.4	0.1
	2115	7.7	2.3		2224	7.2	2.2
9 Sa	0347	-0.6	-0.2	24 Su	0448	-0.2	-0.1
	0950	6.6	2.0		1052	6.4	2.0
	1555	0.0	0.0		1656	0.4	0.1
	2208	7.9	2.4		2301	7.2	2.2
10 Su	0438	-0.9	-0.3	25 M	0525	-0.1	0.0
	1045	6.9	2.1		1130	6.5	2.0
	1649	-0.2	-0.1		1734	0.4	0.1
	2301	8.0	2.4		2339	7.1	2.2
11 M	0529	-1.0	-0.3	26 Tu	0601	0.0	0.0
	1138	7.1	2.2		1206	6.6	2.0
	1743	-0.3	-0.1		1811	0.5	0.2
	2354	8.0	2.4				
12 Tu	0622	-1.1	-0.3	27 W	0015	7.1	2.2
	1230	7.2	2.2		0635	0.0	0.0
	1840	-0.4	-0.1		1241	6.7	2.0
					1849	0.5	0.2
13 W	0049	7.8	2.4	28 Th	0051	6.9	2.1
	0715	-1.0	-0.3		0710	0.1	0.0
	1325	7.2	2.2		1317	6.7	2.0
	1936	-0.4	-0.1		1926	0.6	0.2
14 Th	0145	7.5	2.3	29 F	0128	6.8	2.1
	0808	-0.8	-0.2		0747	0.2	0.1
	1421	7.2	2.2		1355	6.7	2.0
	2037	-0.3	-0.1		2008	0.6	0.2
15 F	0243	7.1	2.2	30 Sa	0208	6.6	2.0
	0904	-0.5	-0.2		0824	0.4	0.1
	1517	7.1	2.2		1435	6.8	2.1
	2138	-0.2	-0.1		2050	0.6	0.2
				31 Su	0253	6.4	2.0
					0904	0.5	0.2
					1516	6.8	2.1
					2138	0.7	0.2

AUGUST

Day	h m	ft	m	Day	h m	ft	m
1 M	0338	6.2	1.9	16 Tu	0521	6.0	1.8
	0950	0.6	0.2		1131	0.5	0.2
	1607	6.8	2.1		1746	6.8	2.1
	2231	0.7	0.2				
2 Tu	0432	6.0	1.8	17 W	0018	0.2	0.1
	1042	0.7	0.2		0623	5.9	1.8
	1659	6.8	2.1		1232	0.7	0.2
	2331	0.6	0.2		1846	6.8	2.1
3 W	0531	5.9	1.8	18 Th	0116	0.3	0.1
	1138	0.8	0.2		0723	5.9	1.8
	1757	7.0	2.1		1328	0.7	0.2
					1942	6.8	2.1
4 Th	0031	0.4	0.1	19 F	0210	0.2	0.1
	0634	6.0	1.8		0817	6.1	1.9
	1240	0.7	0.2		1421	0.7	0.2
	1859	7.2	2.2		2033	7.0	2.1
5 F	0131	0.1	0.0	20 Sa	0259	0.2	0.1
	0736	6.1	1.8		0905	6.3	1.9
	1341	0.5	0.2		1509	0.6	0.2
	1957	7.4	2.3		2118	7.1	2.2
6 Sa	0230	-0.2	-0.1	21 Su	0342	0.1	0.0
	0836	6.4	2.0		0946	6.5	2.0
	1441	0.2	0.1		1551	0.5	0.2
	2055	7.7	2.3		2200	7.1	2.2
7 Su	0326	-0.6	-0.2	22 M	0419	0.0	0.0
	0932	6.8	2.1		1023	6.6	2.0
	1539	-0.1	0.0		1632	0.4	0.1
	2152	7.9	2.4		2237	7.2	2.2
8 M	0419	-0.9	-0.3	23 Tu	0456	0.0	0.0
	1027	7.1	2.2		1100	6.8	2.1
	1636	-0.5	-0.2		1708	0.3	0.1
	2246	8.0	2.4		2313	7.2	2.2
9 Tu	0512	-1.1	-0.3	24 W	0530	0.0	0.0
	1119	7.4	2.3		1134	6.9	2.1
	1731	-0.7	-0.2		1743	0.2	0.1
	2340	8.0	2.4		2347	7.1	2.2
10 W	0602	-1.1	-0.3	25 Th	0604	0.0	0.0
	1211	7.5	2.3		1209	7.0	2.1
	1825	-0.8	-0.2		1820	0.2	0.1
11 Th	0033	7.8	2.4	26 F	0024	7.0	2.1
	0654	-1.1	-0.3		0638	0.1	0.0
	1303	7.6	2.3		1243	7.0	2.1
	1919	-0.8	-0.2		1856	0.2	0.1
12 F	0126	7.5	2.3	27 Sa	0057	6.8	2.1
	0744	-0.8	-0.2		0710	0.2	0.1
	1355	7.5	2.3		1319	7.0	2.1
	2016	-0.6	-0.2		1934	0.2	0.1
13 Sa	0221	7.0	2.1	28 Su	0136	6.6	2.0
	0837	-0.5	-0.2		0747	0.3	0.1
	1450	7.3	2.2		1357	7.0	2.1
	2113	-0.4	-0.1		2016	0.3	0.1
14 Su	0320	6.6	2.0	29 M	0219	6.4	2.0
	0932	-0.1	0.0		0826	0.5	0.2
	1546	7.1	2.2		1440	7.0	2.1
	2213	-0.2	-0.1		2105	0.4	0.1
15 M	0420	6.2	1.9	30 Tu	0306	6.2	1.9
	1031	0.2	0.1		0912	0.7	0.2
	1646	6.9	2.1		1528	6.9	2.1
	2316	0.1	0.0		2158	0.5	0.2
				31 W	0402	6.0	1.8
					1007	0.8	0.2
					1626	6.9	2.1
					2301	0.6	0.2

SEPTEMBER

Day	h m	ft	m	Day	h m	ft	m
1 Th	0506	5.9	1.8	16 F	0044	0.6	0.2
	1110	0.9	0.3		0652	5.9	1.8
	1731	6.9	2.1		1258	1.0	0.3
					1911	6.6	2.0
2 F	0006	0.5	0.2	17 Sa	0135	0.6	0.2
	0611	6.0	1.8		0745	6.2	1.9
	1220	0.8	0.2		1353	0.9	0.3
	1836	7.0	2.1		2001	6.9	2.1
3 Sa	0111	0.3	0.1	18 Su	0225	0.5	0.2
	0717	6.2	1.9		0830	6.4	2.0
	1327	0.6	0.2		1440	0.7	0.2
	1940	7.3	2.2		2049	6.9	2.1
4 Su	0211	-0.1	0.0	19 M	0307	0.4	0.1
	0820	6.6	2.0		0914	6.7	2.0
	1430	0.2	0.1		1523	0.5	0.2
	2041	7.5	2.3		2129	7.0	2.1
5 M	0307	-0.5	-0.2	20 Tu	0347	0.2	0.1
	0915	7.1	2.2		0951	6.9	2.1
	1527	-0.3	-0.1		1603	0.3	0.1
	2138	7.8	2.4		2207	7.1	2.2
6 Tu	0400	-0.8	-0.2	21 W	0422	0.1	0.0
	1008	7.4	2.3		1027	7.1	2.2
	1622	-0.7	-0.2		1640	0.1	0.0
	2232	7.9	2.4		2243	7.1	2.2
7 W	0451	-1.0	-0.3	22 Th	0457	0.0	0.0
	1100	7.7	2.3		1101	7.2	2.2
	1715	-1.0	-0.3		1715	0.0	0.0
	2323	7.8	2.4		2318	7.1	2.2
8 Th	0541	-1.1	-0.3	23 F	0529	0.0	0.0
	1149	7.8	2.4		1136	7.3	2.2
	1806	-1.1	-0.3		1752	-0.1	0.0
					2354	7.0	2.1
9 F	0015	7.6	2.3	24 Sa	0604	0.0	0.0
	0628	-1.0	-0.3		1209	7.3	2.2
	1238	7.8	2.4		1828	-0.1	0.0
	1857	-1.1	-0.3				
10 Sa	0105	7.3	2.2	25 Su	0031	6.8	2.1
	0718	-0.7	-0.2		0638	0.1	0.0
	1329	7.6	2.3		1246	7.3	2.2
	1951	-0.8	-0.2		1906	-0.1	0.0
11 Su	0158	6.9	2.1	26 M	0110	6.6	2.0
	0808	-0.3	-0.1		0715	0.3	0.1
	1419	7.3	2.2		1326	7.2	2.2
	2045	-0.5	-0.2		1950	0.1	0.0
12 M	0252	6.4	2.0	27 Tu	0154	6.4	2.0
	0901	0.1	0.0		0755	0.5	0.2
	1515	7.0	2.1		1411	7.1	2.2
	2143	-0.1	0.0		2037	0.2	0.1
13 Tu	0348	6.1	1.9	28 W	0245	6.2	1.9
	0957	0.5	0.2		0847	0.8	0.2
	1613	6.8	2.1		1503	7.0	2.1
	2242	0.3	0.1		2136	0.4	0.1
14 W	0450	5.9	1.8	29 Th	0341	6.0	1.8
	1058	0.9	0.3		0946	1.0	0.3
	1711	6.6	2.0		1605	6.9	2.1
	2344	0.5	0.2		2239	0.6	0.2
15 Th	0552	5.8	1.8	30 F	0447	6.0	1.8
	1201	1.0	0.3		1057	1.1	0.3
	1812	6.5	2.0		1713	6.8	2.1
					2347	0.5	0.2

Time meridian 75° W. 0000 is midnight. 1200 is noon.
Heights are referred to mean low water which is the chart datum of soundings.

Times and Heights of High and Low Waters

OCTOBER

Day	Time (h m)	Height (ft)	Height (m)	Day	Time (h m)	Height (ft)	Height (m)
1 Sa	0556	6.1	1.9	16 Su	0055	0.8	0.2
	1209	0.9	0.3		0704	6.2	1.9
	1823	6.9	2.1		1316	1.1	0.3
					1924	6.5	2.0
2 Su	0052	0.3	0.1	17 M	0143	0.7	0.2
	0702	6.5	2.0		0751	6.5	2.0
	1316	0.5	0.2		1405	0.8	0.2
	1928	7.1	2.2		2009	6.6	2.0
3 M	0154	0.0	0.0	18 Tu	0226	0.5	0.2
	0804	6.9	2.1		0833	6.8	2.1
	1420	0.0	0.0		1449	0.5	0.2
	2028	7.3	2.2		2053	6.8	2.1
4 Tu	0249	-0.4	-0.1	19 W	0307	0.3	0.1
	0859	7.3	2.2		0912	7.0	2.1
	1515	-0.5	-0.2		1529	0.2	0.1
	2123	7.5	2.3		2134	6.9	2.1
5 W	0342	-0.7	-0.2	20 Th	0344	0.2	0.1
	0950	7.7	2.3		0950	7.2	2.2
	1609	-0.9	-0.3		1608	-0.1	0.0
	2216	7.6	2.3		2211	6.9	2.1
6 Th	0430	-0.9	-0.3	21 F	0421	0.0	0.0
	1038	7.9	2.4		1026	7.4	2.3
	1659	-1.2	-0.4		1645	-0.3	-0.1
	2306	7.5	2.3		2248	6.9	2.1
7 F	0517	-0.9	-0.3	22 Sa	0457	0.0	0.0
	1127	7.9	2.4		1102	7.5	2.3
	1748	-1.3	-0.4		1725	-0.4	-0.1
	2355	7.3	2.2		2327	6.8	2.1
8 Sa	0604	-0.8	-0.2	23 Su	0532	0.0	0.0
	1213	7.8	2.4		1140	7.5	2.3
	1837	-1.1	-0.3		1802	-0.5	-0.2
9 Su	0043	7.0	2.1	24 M	0006	6.7	2.0
	0650	-0.5	-0.2		0611	0.1	0.0
	1300	7.6	2.3		1220	7.5	2.3
	1926	-0.8	-0.2		1843	-0.4	-0.1
10 M	0131	6.6	2.0	25 Tu	0049	6.6	2.0
	0739	-0.1	0.0		0649	0.3	0.1
	1349	7.3	2.2		1302	7.4	2.3
	2016	-0.4	-0.1		1930	-0.2	-0.1
11 Tu	0223	6.3	1.9	26 W	0136	6.4	2.0
	0829	0.4	0.1		0738	0.5	0.2
	1440	6.9	2.1		1350	7.2	2.2
	2109	0.1	0.0		2021	0.0	0.0
12 W	0317	6.0	1.8	27 Th	0229	6.2	1.9
	0925	0.8	0.2		0832	0.8	0.2
	1535	6.6	2.0		1448	7.0	2.1
	2205	0.5	0.2		2120	0.2	0.1
13 Th	0414	5.9	1.8	28 F	0330	6.1	1.9
	1023	1.1	0.3		0937	0.9	0.3
	1634	6.4	2.0		1549	6.8	2.1
	2304	0.8	0.2		2225	0.4	0.1
14 F	0514	5.9	1.8	29 Sa	0435	6.1	1.9
	1123	1.3	0.4		1048	0.9	0.3
	1733	6.3	1.9		1659	6.7	2.0
					2331	0.4	0.1
15 Sa	0001	0.9	0.3	30 Su	0544	6.3	1.9
	0610	6.0	1.8		1200	0.7	0.2
	1223	1.3	0.4		1808	6.7	2.0
	1831	6.4	2.0				
				31 M	0036	0.2	0.1
					0647	6.7	2.0
					1306	0.3	0.1
					1914	6.8	2.1

NOVEMBER

Day	Time (h m)	Height (ft)	Height (m)	Day	Time (h m)	Height (ft)	Height (m)
1 Tu	0135	-0.1	0.0	16 W	0140	0.6	0.2
	0746	7.1	2.2		0749	6.7	2.0
	1408	-0.2	-0.1		1409	0.5	0.2
	2014	7.0	2.1		2012	6.4	2.0
2 W	0230	-0.4	-0.1	17 Th	0223	0.4	0.1
	0841	7.4	2.3		0833	7.0	2.1
	1502	-0.7	-0.2		1454	0.1	0.0
	2110	7.1	2.2		2055	6.5	2.0
3 Th	0321	-0.6	-0.2	18 F	0305	0.2	0.1
	0931	7.7	2.3		0913	7.2	2.2
	1555	-1.0	-0.3		1536	-0.2	-0.1
	2201	7.1	2.2		2137	6.5	2.0
4 F	0409	-0.7	-0.2	19 Sa	0344	0.0	0.0
	1019	7.8	2.4		0952	7.4	2.3
	1643	-1.2	-0.4		1618	-0.5	-0.2
	2248	7.0	2.1		2219	6.6	2.0
5 Sa	0456	-0.7	-0.2	20 Su	0424	-0.1	0.0
	1105	7.8	2.4		1033	7.5	2.3
	1730	-1.2	-0.4		1657	-0.7	-0.2
	2335	6.9	2.1		2301	6.6	2.0
6 Su	0539	-0.5	-0.2	21 M	0505	-0.1	0.0
	1150	7.7	2.3		1114	7.6	2.3
	1815	-1.0	-0.3		1742	-0.7	-0.2
					2346	6.6	2.0
7 M	0021	6.6	2.0	22 Tu	0548	0.0	0.0
	0625	-0.2	-0.1		1159	7.6	2.3
	1235	7.5	2.3		1827	-0.7	-0.2
	1902	-0.7	-0.2				
8 Tu	0107	6.4	2.0	23 W	0033	6.5	2.0
	0710	0.1	0.0		0634	0.1	0.0
	1321	7.2	2.2		1246	7.5	2.3
	1949	-0.3	-0.1		1915	-0.6	-0.2
9 W	0155	6.2	1.9	24 Th	0123	6.4	2.0
	0758	0.5	0.2		0726	0.3	0.1
	1407	6.8	2.1		1338	7.3	2.2
	2035	0.1	0.0		2008	-0.3	-0.1
10 Th	0243	6.0	1.8	25 F	0218	6.4	2.0
	0849	0.9	0.3		0824	0.4	0.1
	1458	6.6	2.0		1435	7.0	2.1
	2126	0.5	0.2		2106	-0.1	0.0
11 F	0335	5.9	1.8	26 Sa	0317	6.3	1.9
	0944	1.1	0.3		0930	0.6	0.2
	1551	6.3	1.9		1539	6.7	2.0
	2220	0.7	0.2		2209	0.0	0.0
12 Sa	0430	5.9	1.8	27 Su	0423	6.4	2.0
	1041	1.3	0.4		1039	0.5	0.2
	1647	6.2	1.9		1646	6.5	2.0
	2312	0.9	0.3		2312	0.1	0.0
13 Su	0524	6.0	1.8	28 M	0527	6.5	2.0
	1138	1.3	0.4		1147	0.3	0.1
	1743	6.1	1.9		1754	6.4	2.0
14 M	0005	0.9	0.3	29 Tu	0015	0.0	0.0
	0616	6.2	1.9		0630	6.7	2.0
	1232	1.1	0.3		1252	0.0	0.0
	1836	6.2	1.9		1900	6.4	2.0
15 Tu	0055	0.8	0.2	30 W	0114	-0.1	0.0
	0705	6.5	2.0		0729	7.0	2.1
	1324	0.8	0.2		1353	-0.4	-0.1
	1924	6.3	1.9		1959	6.5	2.0

DECEMBER

Day	Time (h m)	Height (ft)	Height (m)	Day	Time (h m)	Height (ft)	Height (m)
1 Th	0211	-0.3	-0.1	16 F	0137	0.4	0.1
	0823	7.3	2.2		0749	6.8	2.1
	1451	-0.8	-0.2		1417	0.0	0.0
	2054	6.5	2.0		2017	6.0	1.8
2 F	0302	-0.4	-0.1	17 Sa	0225	0.2	0.1
	0913	7.5	2.3		0836	7.0	2.1
	1540	-1.0	-0.3		1503	-0.3	-0.1
	2145	6.5	2.0		2107	6.2	1.9
3 Sa	0350	-0.5	-0.2	18 Su	0311	0.0	0.0
	1000	7.5	2.3		0921	7.3	2.2
	1627	-1.1	-0.3		1550	-0.6	-0.2
	2233	6.5	2.0		2153	6.3	1.9
4 Su	0435	-0.5	-0.2	19 M	0355	-0.2	-0.1
	1047	7.5	2.3		1007	7.5	2.3
	1714	-1.1	-0.3		1635	-0.9	-0.3
	2317	6.4	2.0		2240	6.4	2.0
5 M	0519	-0.3	-0.1	20 Tu	0444	-0.3	-0.1
	1129	7.4	2.3		1054	7.6	2.3
	1756	-0.9	-0.3		1723	-1.0	-0.3
					2328	6.5	2.0
6 Tu	0000	6.3	1.9	21 W	0531	-0.3	-0.1
	0603	-0.1	0.0		1142	7.6	2.3
	1212	7.2	2.2		1812	-1.0	-0.3
	1839	-0.6	-0.2				
7 W	0042	6.2	1.9	22 Th	0017	6.6	2.0
	0646	0.1	0.0		0622	-0.3	-0.1
	1255	7.0	2.1		1233	7.5	2.3
	1920	-0.3	-0.1		1902	-0.8	-0.2
8 Th	0126	6.1	1.9	23 F	0110	6.6	2.0
	0731	0.4	0.1		0716	-0.3	-0.1
	1338	6.8	2.1		1326	7.3	2.2
	2003	0.0	0.0		1954	-0.8	-0.2
9 F	0210	6.1	1.9	24 Sa	0203	6.6	2.0
	0816	0.7	0.2		0816	-0.2	-0.1
	1421	6.5	2.0		1424	7.0	2.1
	2047	0.3	0.1		2050	-0.6	-0.2
10 Sa	0256	6.0	1.8	25 Su	0301	6.6	2.0
	0904	0.9	0.3		0917	-0.1	0.0
	1509	6.3	1.9		1525	6.6	2.0
	2133	0.5	0.2		2149	-0.4	-0.1
11 Su	0343	6.0	1.8	26 M	0404	6.5	2.0
	0956	1.0	0.3		1023	0.0	0.0
	1558	6.1	1.9		1630	6.3	1.9
	2221	0.6	0.2		2250	-0.2	-0.1
12 M	0433	6.1	1.9	27 Tu	0507	6.6	2.0
	1049	1.0	0.3		1130	-0.1	0.0
	1651	5.9	1.8		1735	6.1	1.9
	2310	0.7	0.2		2352	-0.2	-0.1
13 Tu	0523	6.2	1.9	28 W	0608	6.7	2.0
	1143	0.9	0.3		1235	-0.3	-0.1
	1744	5.9	1.8		1842	6.0	1.8
14 W	0001	0.7	0.2	29 Th	0053	-0.2	-0.1
	0613	6.3	1.9		0708	6.8	2.1
	1236	0.7	0.2		1337	-0.5	-0.2
	1836	5.9	1.8		1943	6.0	1.8
15 Th	0050	0.5	0.2	30 F	0149	-0.2	-0.1
	0703	6.5	2.0		0804	7.0	2.1
	1327	0.4	0.1		1433	-0.7	-0.2
	1927	5.9	1.8		2039	6.0	1.8
				31 Sa	0244	-0.3	-0.1
					0857	7.1	2.2
					1524	-0.9	-0.3
					2131	6.1	1.9

Time meridian 75° W.   0000 is midnight.   1200 is noon.
Heights are referred to mean low water which is the chart datum of soundings.

WILLETS POINT, N.Y., 1983

Times and Heights of High and Low Waters

JANUARY

Day	Time (h m)	ft	m	Day	Time (h m)	ft	m
1 Sa	0016	7.2	2.2	16 Su	0021	6.5	2.0
	0644	-0.8	-0.2		0626	0.2	0.1
	1224	8.1	2.5		1212	7.0	2.1
	1935	-1.6	-0.5		1901	-0.2	-0.1
2 Su	0113	7.2	2.2	17 M	0042	6.6	2.0
	0746	-0.7	-0.2		0656	0.2	0.1
	1322	7.8	2.4		1247	7.1	2.2
	2031	-1.4	-0.4		1921	-0.1	0.0
3 M	0215	7.2	2.2	18 Tu	0113	6.8	2.1
	0849	-0.6	-0.2		0731	0.2	0.1
	1427	7.4	2.3		1324	7.0	2.1
	2128	-1.1	-0.3		1954	-0.1	0.0
4 Tu	0318	7.1	2.2	19 W	0153	6.9	2.1
	0955	-0.5	-0.2		0812	0.2	0.1
	1541	7.0	2.1		1407	6.9	2.1
	2227	-0.7	-0.2		2033	-0.1	0.0
5 W	0427	7.0	2.1	20 Th	0235	7.0	2.1
	1100	-0.4	-0.1		0857	0.2	0.1
	1654	6.6	2.0		1456	6.7	2.0
	2327	-0.5	-0.2		2116	0.0	0.0
6 Th	0531	7.0	2.1	21 F	0324	7.0	2.1
	1205	-0.4	-0.1		0949	0.3	0.1
	1802	6.4	2.0		1547	6.5	2.0
					2206	0.1	0.0
7 F	0027	-0.3	-0.1	22 Sa	0416	7.1	2.2
	0633	7.0	2.1		1047	0.3	0.1
	1305	-0.4	-0.1		1644	6.2	1.9
	1905	6.3	1.9		2259	0.2	0.1
8 Sa	0123	-0.1	0.0	23 Su	0512	7.1	2.2
	0731	7.1	2.2		1153	0.2	0.1
	1403	-0.5	-0.2		1747	6.1	1.9
	2001	6.3	1.9				
9 Su	0216	-0.1	0.0	24 M	0001	0.3	0.1
	0824	7.1	2.2		0614	7.2	2.2
	1455	-0.6	-0.2		1325	0.0	0.0
	2055	6.3	1.9		1855	6.1	1.9
10 M	0307	-0.1	0.0	25 Tu	0107	0.2	0.1
	0914	7.2	2.2		0717	7.3	2.2
	1543	-0.7	-0.2		1450	-0.4	-0.1
	2143	6.4	2.0		2005	6.3	1.9
11 Tu	0352	0.0	0.0	26 W	0227	0.0	0.0
	1000	7.2	2.2		0824	7.6	2.3
	1629	-0.7	-0.2		1551	-0.9	-0.3
	2228	6.4	2.0		2117	6.6	2.0
12 W	0433	0.0	0.0	27 Th	0346	-0.3	-0.1
	1041	7.2	2.2		0927	7.8	2.4
	1710	-0.7	-0.2		1649	-1.3	-0.4
	2309	6.5	2.0		2220	6.9	2.1
13 Th	0513	0.1	0.0	28 F	0449	-0.7	-0.2
	1116	7.1	2.2		1030	8.0	2.4
	1747	-0.6	-0.2		1740	-1.6	-0.5
	2345	6.5	2.0		2316	7.3	2.2
14 F	0545	0.2	0.1	29 Sa	0547	-1.0	-0.3
	1141	7.0	2.1		1129	8.1	2.5
	1822	-0.4	-0.1		1830	-1.8	-0.5
15 Sa	0012	6.5	2.0	30 Su	0010	7.5	2.3
	0608	0.2	0.1		0643	-1.2	-0.4
	1149	7.0	2.1		1224	8.0	2.4
	1845	-0.3	-0.1		1919	-1.7	-0.5
				31 M	0102	7.6	2.3
					0738	-1.2	-0.4
					1320	7.8	2.4
					2007	-1.5	-0.5

FEBRUARY

Day	Time (h m)	ft	m	Day	Time (h m)	ft	m
1 Tu	0156	7.5	2.3	16 W	0045	7.2	2.2
	0831	-1.1	-0.3		0709	-0.2	-0.1
	1415	7.4	2.3		1300	7.2	2.2
	2100	-1.1	-0.3		1924	-0.3	-0.1
2 W	0252	7.3	2.2	17 Th	0122	7.4	2.3
	0929	-0.8	-0.2		0748	-0.2	-0.1
	1516	6.9	2.1		1345	7.1	2.2
	2153	-0.7	-0.2		2003	-0.3	-0.1
3 Th	0350	7.1	2.2	18 F	0206	7.4	2.3
	1030	-0.5	-0.2		0831	-0.2	-0.1
	1624	6.5	2.0		1431	6.9	2.1
	2248	-0.3	-0.1		2046	-0.1	0.0
4 F	0453	6.9	2.1	19 Sa	0254	7.4	2.3
	1131	-0.3	-0.1		0922	0.0	0.0
	1728	6.2	1.9		1523	6.6	2.0
	2349	0.1	0.0		2134	0.1	0.0
5 Sa	0556	6.8	2.1	20 Su	0345	7.3	2.2
	1233	-0.1	0.0		1018	0.2	0.1
	1831	6.0	1.8		1619	6.3	1.9
					2230	0.3	0.1
6 Su	0048	0.3	0.1	21 M	0443	7.2	2.2
	0659	6.7	2.0		1127	0.3	0.1
	1331	-0.1	0.0		1724	6.1	1.9
	1931	6.0	1.8		2333	0.5	0.2
7 M	0144	0.4	0.1	22 Tu	0548	7.1	2.2
	0756	6.8	2.1		1323	0.2	0.1
	1427	-0.1	0.0		1838	6.0	1.8
	2027	6.1	1.9				
8 Tu	0237	0.4	0.1	23 W	0057	0.5	0.2
	0847	6.9	2.1		0700	7.1	2.2
	1517	-0.2	-0.1		1442	-0.2	-0.1
	2117	6.2	1.9		2002	6.3	1.9
9 W	0327	0.4	0.1	24 Th	0242	0.2	0.1
	0936	7.0	2.1		0821	7.3	2.2
	1603	-0.3	-0.1		1541	-0.7	-0.2
	2204	6.4	2.0		2117	6.7	2.0
10 Th	0410	0.3	0.1	25 F	0351	-0.3	-0.1
	1018	7.0	2.1		0932	7.6	2.3
	1644	-0.3	-0.1		1635	-1.2	-0.4
	2245	6.5	2.0		2217	7.2	2.2
11 F	0450	0.2	0.1	26 Sa	0449	-0.9	-0.3
	1055	7.1	2.2		1034	7.9	2.4
	1722	-0.3	-0.1		1725	-1.5	-0.5
	2320	6.6	2.0		2308	7.6	2.3
12 Sa	0525	0.1	0.0	27 Su	0540	-1.2	-0.4
	1121	7.0	2.1		1127	8.0	2.4
	1754	-0.3	-0.1		1811	-1.6	-0.5
	2342	6.7	2.0		2357	7.8	2.4
13 Su	0550	0.1	0.0	28 M	0631	-1.4	-0.4
	1130	7.1	2.2		1218	8.0	2.4
	1816	-0.3	-0.1		1858	-1.6	-0.5
	2350	6.8	2.1				
14 M	0610	0.0	0.0				
	1150	7.1	2.2				
	1832	-0.3	-0.1				
15 Tu	0013	7.0	2.1				
	0636	-0.1	0.0				
	1222	7.2	2.2				
	1854	-0.3	-0.1				

MARCH

Day	Time (h m)	ft	m	Day	Time (h m)	ft	m
1 Tu	0042	7.9	2.4	16 W	0616	-0.4	-0.1
	0719	-1.4	-0.4		1201	7.3	2.2
	1305	7.7	2.3		1824	-0.3	-0.1
	1942	-1.3	-0.4				
2 W	0130	7.8	2.4	17 Th	0015	7.7	2.3
	0810	-1.2	-0.4		0648	-0.5	-0.2
	1356	7.3	2.2		1239	7.3	2.2
	2027	-0.9	-0.3		1857	-0.3	-0.1
3 Th	0217	7.5	2.3	18 F	0057	7.8	2.4
	0900	-0.9	-0.3		0729	-0.5	-0.2
	1449	6.9	2.1		1322	7.2	2.2
	2113	-0.4	-0.1		1938	-0.2	-0.1
4 F	0309	7.2	2.2	19 Sa	0140	7.8	2.4
	0955	-0.4	-0.1		0811	-0.3	-0.1
	1547	6.5	2.0		1409	6.9	2.1
	2203	0.1	0.0		2022	0.0	0.0
5 Sa	0409	6.8	2.1	20 Su	0227	7.7	2.3
	1054	0.0	0.0		0902	-0.1	0.0
	1651	6.1	1.9		1502	6.6	2.0
	2301	0.5	0.2		2113	0.3	0.1
6 Su	0515	6.6	2.0	21 M	0322	7.4	2.3
	1156	0.3	0.1		1003	0.2	0.1
	1756	5.9	1.8		1601	6.3	1.9
					2211	0.7	0.2
7 M	0006	0.9	0.3	22 Tu	0424	7.1	2.2
	0619	6.4	2.0		1130	0.5	0.2
	1256	0.5	0.2		1712	6.2	1.9
	1857	5.9	1.8		2327	0.9	0.3
8 Tu	0106	1.0	0.3	23 W	0533	7.0	2.1
	0723	6.5	2.0		1320	0.3	0.1
	1352	0.5	0.2		1840	6.2	1.9
	1956	6.1	1.9				
9 W	0205	0.9	0.3	24 Th	0131	0.7	0.2
	0818	6.6	2.0		0702	7.0	2.1
	1443	0.4	0.1		1429	-0.1	0.0
	2047	6.3	1.9		2010	6.6	2.0
10 Th	0255	0.8	0.2	25 F	0247	0.2	0.1
	0906	6.8	2.1		0832	7.2	2.2
	1529	0.3	0.1		1527	-0.6	-0.2
	2133	6.5	2.0		2111	7.1	2.2
11 F	0340	0.6	0.2	26 Sa	0346	-0.5	-0.2
	0951	6.9	2.1		0935	7.6	2.3
	1610	0.1	0.0		1617	-1.1	-0.4
	2212	6.7	2.0		2204	7.6	2.3
12 Sa	0420	0.3	0.1	27 Su	0439	-1.0	-0.3
	1026	7.0	2.1		1029	7.8	2.4
	1648	0.0	0.0		1705	-1.2	-0.4
	2244	6.9	2.1		2253	7.9	2.4
13 Su	0456	0.1	0.0	28 M	0527	-1.4	-0.4
	1049	7.1	2.2		1118	7.9	2.4
	1721	-0.1	0.0		1750	-1.3	-0.4
	2302	7.0	2.1		2338	8.1	2.5
14 M	0525	-0.1	0.0	29 Tu	0614	-1.5	-0.5
	1102	7.2	2.2		1204	7.8	2.4
	1740	-0.2	-0.1		1833	-1.2	-0.4
	2313	7.2	2.2				
15 Tu	0548	-0.3	-0.1	30 W	0021	8.0	2.4
	1126	7.3	2.2		0701	-1.4	-0.4
	1757	-0.3	-0.1		1249	7.5	2.3
	2340	7.5	2.3		1912	-0.9	-0.3
				31 Th	0103	7.9	2.4
					0745	-1.1	-0.3
					1332	7.2	2.2
					1954	-0.5	-0.2

Time meridian 75° W. 0000 is midnight. 1200 is noon.
Heights are referred to mean low water which is the chart datum of soundings.

WILLETS POINT, N.Y., 1983

Times and Heights of High and Low Waters

APRIL

Day	Time h m	Height ft	Height m	Day	Time h m	Height ft	Height m
1 F	0143	7.6	2.3	16 Sa	0033	8.2	2.5
	0830	-0.7	-0.2		0714	-0.6	-0.2
	1420	6.8	2.1		1305	7.2	2.2
	2031	0.0	0.0		1916	0.0	0.0
2 Sa	0223	7.2	2.2	17 Su	0119	8.0	2.4
	0917	-0.2	-0.1		0801	-0.4	-0.1
	1508	6.4	2.0		1354	7.0	2.1
	2107	0.5	0.2		2004	0.2	0.1
3 Su	0310	6.8	2.1	18 M	0211	7.8	2.4
	1013	0.3	0.1		0855	-0.1	0.0
	1608	6.1	1.9		1451	6.7	2.0
	2153	0.9	0.3		2100	0.6	0.2
4 M	0409	6.5	2.0	19 Tu	0308	7.4	2.3
	1110	0.7	0.2		1006	0.3	0.1
	1712	6.0	1.8		1555	6.5	2.0
	2307	1.3	0.4		2209	0.9	0.3
5 Tu	0531	6.3	1.9	20 W	0413	7.1	2.2
	1212	0.9	0.3		1153	0.4	0.1
	1818	6.0	1.8		1715	6.4	2.0
6 W	0021	1.4	0.4	21 Th	0010	0.9	0.3
	0640	6.3	1.9		0537	6.8	2.1
	1309	1.0	0.3		1308	0.2	0.1
	1917	6.2	1.9		1854	6.7	2.0
7 Th	0125	1.4	0.4	22 F	0134	0.5	0.2
	0740	6.4	2.0		0720	6.9	2.1
	1402	0.9	0.3		1410	-0.1	0.0
	2008	6.4	2.0		2003	7.1	2.2
8 F	0218	1.1	0.3	23 Sa	0237	-0.1	0.0
	0829	6.6	2.0		0829	7.2	2.2
	1447	0.7	0.2		1506	-0.5	-0.2
	2053	6.7	2.0		2058	7.5	2.3
9 Sa	0304	0.8	0.2	24 Su	0332	-0.6	-0.2
	0911	6.7	2.0		0927	7.5	2.3
	1529	0.5	0.2		1556	-0.7	-0.2
	2130	6.9	2.1		2148	7.9	2.4
10 Su	0346	0.4	0.1	25 M	0423	-1.1	-0.3
	0943	6.9	2.1		1017	7.6	2.3
	1605	0.3	0.1		1642	-0.9	-0.3
	2154	7.1	2.2		2236	8.1	2.5
11 M	0423	0.1	0.0	26 Tu	0511	-1.3	-0.4
	1005	7.0	2.1		1104	7.6	2.3
	1633	0.1	0.0		1726	-0.8	-0.2
	2209	7.4	2.3		2318	8.1	2.5
12 Tu	0456	-0.2	-0.1	27 W	0557	-1.4	-0.4
	1025	7.2	2.2		1147	7.5	2.3
	1657	-0.1	0.0		1807	-0.7	-0.2
	2236	7.7	2.3		2359	8.0	2.4
13 W	0524	-0.5	-0.2	28 Th	0641	-1.2	-0.4
	1100	7.3	2.2		1229	7.2	2.2
	1723	-0.2	-0.1		1845	-0.4	-0.1
	2310	7.9	2.4				
14 Th	0555	-0.6	-0.2	29 F	0037	7.8	2.4
	1136	7.3	2.2		0722	-0.9	-0.3
	1755	-0.3	-0.1		1311	7.0	2.1
	2350	8.1	2.5		1919	0.0	0.0
15 F	0630	-0.7	-0.2	30 Sa	0110	7.5	2.3
	1219	7.3	2.2		0804	-0.5	-0.2
	1834	-0.2	-0.1		1351	6.7	2.0
					1946	0.4	0.1

MAY

Day	Time h m	Height ft	Height m	Day	Time h m	Height ft	Height m
1 Su	0142	7.2	2.2	16 M	0104	8.1	2.5
	0843	0.0	0.0		0804	-0.5	-0.2
	1431	6.5	2.0		1346	7.0	2.1
	2015	0.8	0.2		2001	0.3	0.1
2 M	0217	6.9	2.1	17 Tu	0159	7.8	2.4
	0924	0.5	0.2		0910	-0.2	-0.1
	1515	6.3	1.9		1446	6.8	2.1
	2054	1.1	0.3		2109	0.6	0.2
3 Tu	0259	6.6	2.0	18 W	0300	7.4	2.3
	1014	0.8	0.2		1027	0.0	0.0
	1609	6.1	1.9		1600	6.7	2.0
	2145	1.4	0.4		2246	0.7	0.2
4 W	0349	6.4	2.0	19 Th	0416	7.0	2.1
	1109	1.1	0.3		1143	0.1	0.0
	1719	6.1	1.9		1730	6.8	2.1
	2253	1.6	0.5				
5 Th	0448	6.3	1.9	20 F	0012	0.5	0.2
	1207	1.2	0.4		0556	6.9	2.1
	1820	6.3	1.9		1248	0.0	0.0
					1846	7.1	2.2
6 F	0022	1.5	0.5	21 Sa	0122	0.1	0.0
	0611	6.2	1.9		0715	6.9	2.1
	1302	1.2	0.4		1348	-0.2	-0.1
	1910	6.5	2.0		1947	7.4	2.3
7 Sa	0125	1.3	0.4	22 Su	0221	-0.3	-0.1
	0718	6.3	1.9		0816	7.1	2.2
	1349	1.0	0.3		1442	-0.3	-0.1
	1950	6.7	2.0		2040	7.7	2.3
8 Su	0218	0.9	0.3	23 M	0314	-0.7	-0.2
	0802	6.5	2.0		0911	7.2	2.2
	1430	0.8	0.2		1532	-0.5	-0.2
	2018	7.0	2.1		2130	7.9	2.4
9 M	0303	0.5	0.2	24 Tu	0405	-1.0	-0.3
	0835	6.7	2.0		0959	7.2	2.2
	1506	0.5	0.2		1618	-0.5	-0.2
	2048	7.3	2.2		2215	8.0	2.4
10 Tu	0344	0.1	0.0	25 W	0453	-1.1	-0.3
	0911	6.9	2.1		1047	7.2	2.2
	1540	0.3	0.1		1703	-0.4	-0.1
	2121	7.7	2.3		2259	8.0	2.4
11 W	0423	-0.3	-0.1	26 Th	0538	-1.1	-0.3
	0950	7.1	2.2		1131	7.1	2.2
	1612	0.0	0.0		1744	-0.2	-0.1
	2159	8.0	2.4		2339	7.8	2.4
12 Th	0459	-0.6	-0.2	27 F	0621	-0.9	-0.3
	1031	7.2	2.2		1213	6.9	2.1
	1649	-0.1	0.0		1821	0.0	0.0
	2241	8.2	2.5				
13 F	0538	-0.8	-0.2	28 Sa	0013	7.6	2.3
	1116	7.3	2.2		0700	-0.6	-0.2
	1730	-0.2	-0.1		1252	6.8	2.0
	2327	8.3	2.5		1853	0.3	0.1
14 Sa	0621	-0.8	-0.2	29 Su	0044	7.4	2.3
	1203	7.3	2.2		0736	-0.2	-0.1
	1815	-0.1	0.0		1327	6.6	2.0
					1915	0.6	0.2
15 Su	0013	8.3	2.5	30 M	0108	7.2	2.2
	0709	-0.7	-0.2		0812	0.2	0.1
	1253	7.2	2.2		1354	6.5	2.0
	1905	0.1	0.0		1943	0.9	0.3
				31 Tu	0139	7.0	2.1
					0836	0.5	0.2
					1425	6.5	2.0
					2020	1.1	0.3

JUNE

Day	Time h m	Height ft	Height m	Day	Time h m	Height ft	Height m
1 W	0217	6.8	2.1	16 Th	0300	7.4	2.3
	0902	0.7	0.2		1018	-0.4	-0.1
	1500	6.4	2.0		1605	7.1	2.2
	2104	1.3	0.4		2246	0.2	0.1
2 Th	0300	6.7	2.0	17 F	0424	7.1	2.2
	0942	0.9	0.3		1121	-0.2	-0.1
	1545	6.5	2.0		1719	7.2	2.2
	2155	1.4	0.4		2355	0.1	0.0
3 F	0350	6.5	2.0	18 Sa	0548	6.9	2.1
	1027	1.0	0.3		1224	-0.1	0.0
	1632	6.5	2.0		1824	7.4	2.3
	2255	1.4	0.4				
4 Sa	0444	6.4	2.0	19 Su	0100	-0.1	0.0
	1118	1.0	0.3		0656	6.9	2.1
	1723	6.7	2.0		1322	-0.1	0.0
					1925	7.5	2.3
5 Su	0000	1.2	0.4	20 M	0159	-0.4	-0.1
	0541	6.4	2.0		0757	6.9	2.1
	1209	1.0	0.3		1418	-0.1	0.0
	1814	6.9	2.1		2019	7.7	2.3
6 M	0105	0.9	0.3	21 Tu	0255	-0.6	-0.2
	0638	6.4	2.0		0851	6.9	2.1
	1305	0.8	0.2		1509	-0.1	0.0
	1904	7.2	2.2		2111	7.8	2.4
7 Tu	0206	0.5	0.2	22 W	0346	-0.8	-0.2
	0733	6.6	2.0		0941	6.9	2.1
	1355	0.6	0.2		1556	-0.1	0.0
	1952	7.5	2.3		2157	7.8	2.4
8 W	0303	0.1	0.0	23 Th	0434	-0.8	-0.2
	0826	6.7	2.0		1030	6.9	2.1
	1447	0.3	0.1		1641	0.0	0.0
	2042	7.8	2.4		2241	7.8	2.4
9 Th	0351	-0.3	-0.1	24 F	0518	-0.8	-0.2
	0919	6.9	2.1		1113	6.9	2.1
	1535	0.1	0.0		1723	0.1	0.0
	2130	8.1	2.5		2323	7.6	2.3
10 F	0440	-0.6	-0.2	25 Sa	0600	-0.6	-0.2
	1007	7.1	2.2		1153	6.8	2.1
	1623	-0.1	0.0		1801	0.3	0.1
	2219	8.3	2.5		2357	7.5	2.3
11 Sa	0529	-0.9	-0.3	26 Su	0638	-0.3	-0.1
	1100	7.2	2.2		1231	6.7	2.0
	1714	-0.2	-0.1		1831	0.5	0.2
	2309	8.4	2.6				
12 Su	0620	-1.0	-0.3	27 M	0023	7.3	2.2
	1151	7.3	2.2		0711	0.0	0.0
	1808	-0.1	0.0		1301	6.7	2.0
					1852	0.7	0.2
13 M	0001	8.4	2.6	28 Tu	0041	7.2	2.2
	0711	-0.9	-0.3		0738	0.2	0.1
	1245	7.3	2.2		1319	6.7	2.0
	1905	0.0	0.0		1914	0.8	0.2
14 Tu	0054	8.1	2.5	29 W	0106	7.1	2.2
	0810	-0.8	-0.2		0754	0.4	0.1
	1343	7.2	2.2		1343	6.7	2.0
	2012	0.1	0.0		1948	0.9	0.3
15 W	0154	7.8	2.4	30 Th	0143	7.0	2.1
	0912	-0.6	-0.2		0820	0.5	0.2
	1449	7.2	2.2		1417	6.8	2.1
	2129	0.2	0.1		2031	0.9	0.3

Time meridian 75° W. 0000 is midnight. 1200 is noon.
Heights are referred to mean low water which is the chart datum of soundings.

WILLETS POINT, N.Y., 1983

Times and Heights of High and Low Waters

JULY

Day	h m	ft	m	Day	h m	ft	m
1 F	0225	6.9	2.1	16 Sa	0414	7.1	2.2
	0857	0.6	0.2		1053	-0.3	-0.1
	1457	6.9	2.1		1653	7.4	2.3
	2116	1.0	0.3		2332	-0.2	-0.1
2 Sa	0311	6.8	2.1	17 Su	0527	6.9	2.1
	0937	0.7	0.2		1154	0.0	0.0
	1542	7.0	2.1		1759	7.4	2.3
	2207	1.0	0.3				
3 Su	0402	6.6	2.0	18 M	0036	-0.2	-0.1
	1025	0.7	0.2		0634	6.7	2.0
	1630	7.1	2.2		1254	0.1	0.0
	2302	0.9	0.3		1859	7.5	2.3
4 M	0454	6.5	2.0	19 Tu	0136	-0.3	-0.1
	1114	0.7	0.2		0734	6.7	2.0
	1725	7.2	2.2		1350	0.2	0.1
					1957	7.5	2.3
5 Tu	0002	0.8	0.2	20 W	0232	-0.3	-0.1
	0553	6.5	2.0		0830	6.7	2.0
	1209	0.7	0.2		1445	0.2	0.1
	1818	7.4	2.3		2050	7.6	2.3
6 W	0112	0.5	0.2	21 Th	0323	-0.4	-0.1
	0653	6.5	2.0		0920	6.8	2.1
	1307	0.6	0.2		1533	0.3	0.1
	1913	7.6	2.3		2138	7.6	2.3
7 Th	0222	0.2	0.1	22 F	0412	-0.4	-0.1
	0753	6.6	2.0		1009	6.8	2.1
	1405	0.4	0.1		1618	0.3	0.1
	2010	7.9	2.4		2226	7.6	2.3
8 F	0327	-0.2	-0.1	23 Sa	0455	-0.4	-0.1
	0851	6.8	2.1		1051	6.9	2.1
	1507	0.2	0.1		1700	0.4	0.1
	2106	8.2	2.5		2304	7.6	2.3
9 Sa	0425	-0.6	-0.2	24 Su	0537	-0.3	-0.1
	0951	7.1	2.2		1132	6.9	2.1
	1610	0.0	0.0		1737	0.4	0.1
	2202	8.3	2.5		2341	7.5	2.3
10 Su	0519	-0.9	-0.3	25 M	0613	-0.1	0.0
	1047	7.3	2.2		1208	6.9	2.1
	1710	-0.2	-0.1		1809	0.5	0.2
	2257	8.4	2.6				
11 M	0613	-1.1	-0.3	26 Tu	0003	7.4	2.3
	1142	7.5	2.3		0644	0.1	0.0
	1811	-0.3	-0.1		1230	6.9	2.1
	2353	8.4	2.6		1831	0.6	0.2
12 Tu	0706	-1.1	-0.3	27 W	0014	7.3	2.2
	1239	7.6	2.3		0703	0.2	0.1
	1913	-0.4	-0.1		1242	7.0	2.1
					1852	0.6	0.2
13 W	0050	8.2	2.5	28 Th	0039	7.3	2.2
	0759	-1.0	-0.3		0716	0.3	0.1
	1338	7.6	2.3		1305	7.1	2.2
	2015	-0.4	-0.1		1922	0.6	0.2
14 Th	0151	7.9	2.4	29 F	0114	7.3	2.2
	0857	-0.8	-0.2		0742	0.3	0.1
	1439	7.6	2.3		1338	7.2	2.2
	2122	-0.3	-0.1		2000	0.6	0.2
15 F	0300	7.5	2.3	30 Sa	0154	7.2	2.2
	0953	-0.6	-0.2		0818	0.4	0.1
	1545	7.5	2.3		1418	7.3	2.2
	2227	-0.2	-0.1		2041	0.6	0.2
				31 Su	0237	7.0	2.1
					0900	0.4	0.1
					1502	7.4	2.3
					2129	0.7	0.2

AUGUST

Day	h m	ft	m	Day	h m	ft	m
1 M	0327	6.9	2.1	16 Tu	0007	0.0	0.0
	0944	0.5	0.2		0607	6.6	2.0
	1551	7.4	2.3		1221	0.5	0.2
	2223	0.7	0.2		1833	7.2	2.2
2 Tu	0419	6.7	2.0	17 W	0107	0.1	0.0
	1034	0.7	0.2		0707	6.5	2.0
	1645	7.5	2.3		1323	0.7	0.2
	2320	0.7	0.2		1933	7.3	2.2
3 W	0519	6.5	2.0	18 Th	0205	0.1	0.0
	1130	0.7	0.2		0805	6.6	2.0
	1742	7.5	2.3		1418	0.7	0.2
					2028	7.4	2.3
4 Th	0030	0.6	0.2	19 F	0258	0.1	0.0
	0620	6.5	2.0		0858	6.8	2.1
	1233	0.7	0.2		1509	0.6	0.2
	1843	7.6	2.3		2116	7.5	2.3
5 F	0201	0.3	0.1	20 Sa	0346	0.0	0.0
	0728	6.6	2.0		0944	6.9	2.1
	1342	0.6	0.2		1556	0.5	0.2
	1947	7.8	2.4		2203	7.5	2.3
6 Sa	0315	-0.1	0.0	21 Su	0429	0.0	0.0
	0834	6.9	2.1		1028	7.1	2.2
	1459	0.3	0.1		1637	0.5	0.2
	2051	8.1	2.5		2244	7.6	2.3
7 Su	0413	-0.5	-0.2	22 M	0507	0.0	0.0
	0940	7.2	2.2		1107	7.2	2.2
	1612	-0.1	0.0		1715	0.4	0.1
	2154	8.3	2.5		2316	7.5	2.3
8 M	0508	-0.9	-0.3	23 Tu	0542	0.1	0.0
	1039	7.6	2.3		1138	7.2	2.2
	1713	-0.4	-0.1		1746	0.4	0.1
	2252	8.4	2.6		2337	7.4	2.3
9 Tu	0558	-1.1	-0.3	24 W	0610	0.1	0.0
	1134	7.9	2.4		1153	7.2	2.2
	1809	-0.7	-0.2		1808	0.4	0.1
	2349	8.4	2.6		2349	7.4	2.3
10 W	0650	-1.2	-0.4	25 Th	0626	0.2	0.1
	1228	8.0	2.4		1200	7.3	2.2
	1906	-0.8	-0.2		1827	0.3	0.1
11 Th	0046	8.2	2.5	26 F	0012	7.4	2.3
	0738	-1.1	-0.3		0640	0.2	0.1
	1322	8.0	2.4		1230	7.5	2.3
	2003	-0.8	-0.2		1855	0.2	0.1
12 F	0143	7.9	2.4	27 Sa	0045	7.4	2.3
	0831	-0.9	-0.3		0708	0.2	0.1
	1415	7.9	2.4		1303	7.6	2.3
	2100	-0.6	-0.2		1929	0.2	0.1
13 Sa	0244	7.5	2.3	28 Su	0125	7.3	2.2
	0924	-0.5	-0.2		0744	0.3	0.1
	1515	7.7	2.3		1345	7.7	2.3
	2201	-0.4	-0.1		2012	0.3	0.1
14 Su	0352	7.1	2.2	29 M	0209	7.2	2.2
	1020	-0.1	0.0		0825	0.4	0.1
	1622	7.5	2.3		1430	7.7	2.3
	2306	-0.1	0.0		2059	0.4	0.1
15 M	0501	6.7	2.0	30 Tu	0257	7.0	2.1
	1122	0.3	0.1		0910	0.6	0.2
	1730	7.3	2.2		1518	7.7	2.3
					2150	0.6	0.2
				31 W	0353	6.7	2.0
					1001	0.8	0.2
					1614	7.6	2.3
					2251	0.7	0.2

SEPTEMBER

Day	h m	ft	m	Day	h m	ft	m
1 Th	0451	6.5	2.0	16 F	0133	0.6	0.2
	1103	0.9	0.3		0736	6.6	2.0
	1715	7.5	2.3		1349	1.1	0.3
					2000	7.1	2.2
2 F	0009	0.8	0.2	17 Sa	0226	0.5	0.2
	0558	6.5	2.0		0828	6.8	2.1
	1212	1.0	0.3		1442	0.9	0.3
	1822	7.5	2.3		2050	7.2	2.2
3 Sa	0157	0.5	0.2	18 Su	0314	0.4	0.1
	0713	6.7	2.0		0917	7.1	2.2
	1341	0.8	0.2		1527	0.7	0.2
	1933	7.6	2.3		2136	7.4	2.3
4 Su	0304	0.0	0.0	19 M	0356	0.3	0.1
	0829	7.1	2.2		0959	7.2	2.2
	1509	0.3	0.1		1608	0.5	0.2
	2047	7.9	2.4		2218	7.4	2.3
5 M	0400	-0.5	-0.2	20 Tu	0433	0.3	0.1
	0935	7.5	2.3		1033	7.4	2.3
	1612	-0.3	-0.1		1646	0.3	0.1
	2151	8.2	2.5		2248	7.4	2.3
6 Tu	0452	-0.9	-0.3	21 W	0505	0.2	0.1
	1029	7.9	2.4		1100	7.4	2.3
	1709	-0.8	-0.2		1718	0.2	0.1
	2250	8.3	2.5		2305	7.4	2.3
7 W	0540	-1.1	-0.3	22 Th	0531	0.2	0.1
	1121	8.2	2.5		1108	7.5	2.3
	1801	-1.1	-0.3		1741	0.1	0.0
	2343	8.3	2.5		2316	7.4	2.3
8 Th	0628	-1.2	-0.4	23 F	0544	0.2	0.1
	1209	8.3	2.5		1126	7.7	2.3
	1852	-1.2	-0.4		1801	0.0	0.0
					2343	7.4	2.3
9 F	0036	8.1	2.5	24 Sa	0605	0.1	0.0
	0714	-1.0	-0.3		1156	7.9	2.4
	1258	8.3	2.5		1829	-0.1	0.0
	1943	-1.1	-0.3				
10 Sa	0127	7.8	2.4	25 Su	0019	7.4	2.3
	0759	-0.7	-0.2		0637	0.1	0.0
	1348	8.1	2.5		1234	8.0	2.4
	2036	-0.8	-0.2		1906	-0.1	0.0
11 Su	0222	7.4	2.3	26 M	0100	7.4	2.3
	0849	-0.2	-0.1		0714	0.2	0.1
	1441	7.7	2.3		1315	8.0	2.4
	2132	-0.4	-0.1		1947	0.0	0.0
12 M	0322	7.0	2.1	27 Tu	0144	7.2	2.2
	0945	0.2	0.1		0756	0.4	0.1
	1545	7.4	2.3		1401	7.9	2.4
	2234	0.0	0.0		2033	0.2	0.1
13 Tu	0430	6.6	2.0	28 W	0234	7.0	2.1
	1045	0.7	0.2		0844	0.7	0.2
	1654	7.1	2.2		1452	7.7	2.3
	2336	0.4	0.1		2128	0.5	0.2
14 W	0537	6.4	2.0	29 Th	0330	6.7	2.0
	1149	1.0	0.3		0941	0.9	0.3
	1802	6.9	2.1		1550	7.5	2.3
					2235	0.7	0.2
15 Th	0037	0.6	0.2	30 F	0433	6.5	2.0
	0640	6.4	2.0		1046	1.2	0.4
	1251	1.1	0.3		1656	7.3	2.2
	1904	7.0	2.1				

Time meridian 75° W. 0000 is midnight. 1200 is noon.
Heights are referred to mean low water which is the chart datum of soundings.

Times and Heights of High and Low Waters

OCTOBER

Day	Time (h m)	ft	m	Day	Time (h m)	ft	m
1 Sa	0020	0.8	0.2	16 Su	0147	0.9	0.3
	0548	6.5	2.0		0753	6.8	2.1
	1218	1.1	0.3		1406	1.1	0.3
	1811	7.2	2.2		2016	6.9	2.1
2 Su	0149	0.4	0.1	17 M	0234	0.8	0.2
	0715	6.8	2.1		0840	7.0	2.1
	1405	0.7	0.2		1453	0.8	0.2
	1936	7.4	2.3		2101	7.0	2.1
3 M	0250	0.0	0.0	18 Tu	0317	0.6	0.2
	0830	7.3	2.2		0920	7.2	2.2
	1511	0.0	0.0		1535	0.5	0.2
	2053	7.7	2.3		2139	7.1	2.2
4 Tu	0344	-0.5	-0.2	19 W	0351	0.4	0.1
	0927	7.8	2.4		0951	7.3	2.2
	1607	-0.6	-0.2		1612	0.2	0.1
	2152	7.9	2.4		2207	7.1	2.2
5 W	0433	-0.8	-0.2	20 Th	0423	0.3	0.1
	1018	8.2	2.5		1008	7.5	2.3
	1658	-1.1	-0.3		1646	0.0	0.0
	2244	8.1	2.5		2225	7.2	2.2
6 Th	0519	-1.0	-0.3	21 F	0445	0.2	0.1
	1105	8.4	2.6		1023	7.7	2.3
	1747	-1.4	-0.4		1713	-0.2	-0.1
	2333	8.0	2.4		2245	7.2	2.2
7 F	0603	-1.0	-0.3	22 Sa	0504	0.1	0.0
	1148	8.4	2.6		1051	7.9	2.4
	1837	-1.4	-0.4		1737	-0.4	-0.1
					2318	7.3	2.2
8 Sa	0020	7.8	2.4	23 Su	0536	0.0	0.0
	0647	-0.8	-0.2		1127	8.1	2.5
	1234	8.3	2.5		1809	-0.4	-0.1
	1922	-1.2	-0.4		2356	7.3	2.2
9 Su	0108	7.5	2.3	24 M	0610	0.0	0.0
	0730	-0.4	-0.1		1208	8.2	2.5
	1319	8.0	2.4		1847	-0.4	-0.1
	2012	-0.8	-0.2				
10 M	0159	7.1	2.2	25 Tu	0040	7.2	2.2
	0815	0.0	0.0		0650	0.2	0.1
	1406	7.6	2.3		1252	8.1	2.5
	2102	-0.3	-0.1		1931	-0.2	-0.1
11 Tu	0252	6.8	2.1	26 W	0126	7.1	2.2
	0902	0.5	0.2		0735	0.4	0.1
	1500	7.2	2.2		1340	7.9	2.4
	2158	0.2	0.1		2020	0.0	0.0
12 W	0353	6.5	2.0	27 Th	0217	6.9	2.1
	1001	1.0	0.3		0828	0.7	0.2
	1606	6.8	2.1		1433	7.6	2.3
	2258	0.6	0.2		2118	0.3	0.1
13 Th	0502	6.3	1.9	28 F	0316	6.7	2.0
	1107	1.3	0.4		0929	1.0	0.3
	1721	6.6	2.0		1534	7.3	2.2
	2358	0.9	0.3		2239	0.6	0.2
14 F	0605	6.3	1.9	29 Sa	0424	6.5	2.0
	1212	1.4	0.4		1051	1.1	0.3
	1827	6.6	2.0		1645	7.0	2.1
15 Sa	0054	0.9	0.3	30 Su	0024	0.5	0.2
	0703	6.5	2.0		0551	6.6	2.0
	1312	1.3	0.4		1251	0.8	0.2
	1926	6.7	2.0		1816	6.9	2.1
				31 M	0133	0.2	0.1
					0720	7.0	2.1
					1402	0.2	0.1
					1949	7.1	2.2

NOVEMBER

Day	Time (h m)	ft	m	Day	Time (h m)	ft	m
1 Tu	0232	-0.2	-0.1	16 W	0224	0.7	0.2
	0822	7.5	2.3		0829	6.9	2.1
	1501	-0.4	-0.1		1455	0.5	0.2
	2051	7.3	2.2		2048	6.5	2.0
2 W	0324	-0.5	-0.2	17 Th	0302	0.5	0.2
	0915	7.9	2.4		0850	7.2	2.2
	1554	-0.9	-0.3		1535	0.1	0.0
	2146	7.5	2.3		2115	6.6	2.0
3 Th	0412	-0.8	-0.2	18 F	0330	0.3	0.1
	1004	8.2	2.5		0911	7.4	2.3
	1645	-1.3	-0.4		1612	-0.2	-0.1
	2234	7.6	2.3		2140	6.8	2.1
4 F	0459	-0.9	-0.3	19 Sa	0357	0.1	0.0
	1049	8.3	2.5		0943	7.7	2.3
	1732	-1.5	-0.5		1645	-0.5	-0.2
	2321	7.5	2.3		2215	6.9	2.1
5 Sa	0541	-0.9	-0.3	20 Su	0431	0.0	0.0
	1131	8.2	2.5		1021	8.0	2.4
	1817	-1.4	-0.4		1721	-0.7	-0.2
					2254	7.1	2.2
6 Su	0006	7.4	2.3	21 M	0506	-0.1	0.0
	0623	-0.6	-0.2		1103	8.1	2.5
	1213	8.0	2.4		1757	-0.8	-0.2
	1903	-1.2	-0.4		2338	7.1	2.2
7 M	0050	7.1	2.2	22 Tu	0549	-0.1	0.0
	0705	-0.2	-0.1		1148	8.2	2.5
	1254	7.7	2.3		1838	-0.7	-0.2
	1946	-0.8	-0.2				
8 Tu	0137	6.8	2.1	23 W	0024	7.1	2.2
	0740	0.2	0.1		0634	0.0	0.0
	1332	7.4	2.3		1234	8.1	2.5
	2033	-0.3	-0.1		1926	-0.6	-0.2
9 W	0223	6.6	2.0	24 Th	0113	7.0	2.1
	0820	0.6	0.2		0727	0.2	0.1
	1412	7.0	2.1		1326	7.8	2.4
	2121	0.2	0.1		2020	-0.3	-0.1
10 Th	0316	6.3	1.9	25 F	0208	6.8	2.1
	0902	1.0	0.3		0823	0.4	0.1
	1500	6.7	2.0		1421	7.4	2.3
	2213	0.6	0.2		2126	-0.1	0.0
11 F	0416	6.2	1.9	26 Sa	0310	6.7	2.0
	1005	1.3	0.4		0937	0.6	0.2
	1605	6.4	2.0		1526	7.0	2.1
	2305	0.9	0.3		2253	0.1	0.0
12 Sa	0519	6.2	1.9	27 Su	0424	6.7	2.0
	1120	1.5	0.5		1125	0.6	0.2
	1731	6.2	1.9		1645	6.7	2.0
13 Su	0001	1.0	0.3	28 M	0008	0.1	0.0
	0615	6.3	1.9		0555	6.8	2.1
	1223	1.4	0.4		1243	0.3	0.1
	1835	6.2	1.9		1825	6.6	2.0
14 M	0054	1.0	0.3	29 Tu	0112	-0.1	0.0
	0707	6.5	2.0		0709	7.1	2.2
	1320	1.2	0.4		1349	-0.2	-0.1
	1928	6.3	1.9		1941	6.7	2.0
15 Tu	0142	0.9	0.3	30 W	0210	-0.3	-0.1
	0752	6.7	2.0		0808	7.4	2.3
	1410	0.9	0.3		1447	-0.7	-0.2
	2014	6.4	2.0		2040	6.9	2.1

DECEMBER

Day	Time (h m)	ft	m	Day	Time (h m)	ft	m
1 Th	0303	-0.5	-0.2	16 F	0141	0.5	0.2
	0901	7.7	2.3		0739	7.0	2.1
	1540	-1.2	-0.4		1453	0.1	0.0
	2133	7.0	2.1		2015	6.2	1.9
2 F	0356	-0.7	-0.2	17 Sa	0232	0.3	0.1
	0948	7.9	2.4		0824	7.3	2.2
	1629	-1.4	-0.4		1541	-0.3	-0.1
	2221	7.0	2.1		2103	6.4	2.0
3 Sa	0440	-0.7	-0.2	18 Su	0315	0.1	0.0
	1035	7.9	2.4		0911	7.6	2.3
	1716	-1.5	-0.5		1623	-0.6	-0.2
	2309	7.0	2.1		2148	6.7	2.0
4 Su	0524	-0.6	-0.2	19 M	0402	-0.1	0.0
	1119	7.9	2.4		0956	7.9	2.4
	1802	-1.4	-0.4		1706	-0.9	-0.3
	2352	6.9	2.1		2236	6.9	2.1
5 M	0604	-0.4	-0.1	20 Tu	0450	-0.3	-0.1
	1158	7.7	2.3		1045	8.1	2.5
	1844	-1.1	-0.3		1751	-1.1	-0.3
					2324	7.0	2.1
6 Tu	0034	6.8	2.1	21 W	0538	-0.4	-0.1
	0642	-0.1	0.0		1132	8.1	2.5
	1234	7.4	2.3		1837	-1.1	-0.3
	1926	-0.7	-0.2				
7 W	0114	6.6	2.0	22 Th	0013	7.1	2.2
	0716	0.2	0.1		0631	-0.3	-0.1
	1306	7.2	2.2		1223	8.0	2.4
	2003	-0.3	-0.1		1929	-1.0	-0.3
8 Th	0153	6.5	2.0	23 F	0106	7.1	2.2
	0746	0.5	0.2		0727	-0.2	-0.1
	1338	6.9	2.1		1319	7.7	2.3
	2039	0.1	0.0		2023	-0.8	-0.2
9 F	0228	6.3	1.9	24 Sa	0203	7.0	2.1
	0815	0.8	0.2		0833	-0.1	0.0
	1411	6.6	2.0		1417	7.3	2.2
	2108	0.4	0.1		2126	-0.6	-0.2
10 Sa	0302	6.3	1.9	25 Su	0305	6.9	2.1
	0857	1.0	0.3		0955	0.0	0.0
	1452	6.4	2.0		1524	6.9	2.1
	2139	0.6	0.2		2235	-0.4	-0.1
11 Su	0342	6.2	1.9	26 M	0421	6.9	2.1
	0947	1.1	0.3		1115	0.0	0.0
	1541	6.2	1.9		1650	6.5	2.0
	2218	0.8	0.2		2343	-0.3	-0.1
12 M	0427	6.2	1.9	27 Tu	0540	6.9	2.1
	1046	1.2	0.4		1225	-0.2	-0.1
	1635	6.0	1.8		1817	6.4	2.0
	2309	0.9	0.3				
13 Tu	0517	6.3	1.9	28 W	0048	-0.3	-0.1
	1159	1.1	0.3		0649	7.1	2.2
	1731	5.9	1.8		1331	-0.5	-0.2
	2359	0.9	0.3		1925	6.4	2.0
14 W	0606	6.5	2.0	29 Th	0147	-0.3	-0.1
	1308	0.8	0.2		0749	7.3	2.2
	1831	6.0	1.8		1428	-0.9	-0.3
					2024	6.5	2.0
15 Th	0051	0.7	0.2	30 F	0242	-0.4	-0.1
	0654	6.7	2.0		0845	7.4	2.3
	1404	0.5	0.2		1522	-1.1	-0.3
	1923	6.1	1.9		2119	6.4	2.0
				31 Sa	0335	-0.5	-0.2
					0936	7.5	2.3
					1613	-1.3	-0.4
					2208	6.6	2.0

Time meridian 75° W.   0000 is midnight.   1200 is noon.
Heights are referred to mean low water which is the chart datum of soundings.

NEW YORK (The Battery), N.Y., 1983

Times and Heights of High and Low Waters

JANUARY

Day	Time h m	Height ft	Height m	Day	Time h m	Height ft	Height m
1 Sa	0321	-0.9	-0.3	16 Su	0332	-0.1	0.0
	0940	5.5	1.7		0941	4.4	1.3
	1607	-1.3	-0.4		1608	-0.4	-0.1
	2219	4.4	1.3		2215	3.6	1.1
2 Su	0414	-0.8	-0.2	17 M	0403	0.1	0.0
	1037	5.3	1.6		1016	4.3	1.3
	1656	-1.1	-0.3		1640	-0.4	-0.1
	2317	4.4	1.3		2253	3.6	1.1
3 M	0507	-0.6	-0.2	18 Tu	0432	0.2	0.1
	1136	5.0	1.5		1049	4.1	1.2
	1749	-0.9	-0.3		1707	-0.1	0.0
					2328	3.6	1.1
4 Tu	0015	4.4	1.3	19 W	0502	0.3	0.1
	0607	-0.3	-0.1		1124	4.0	1.2
	1231	4.7	1.4		1736	0.0	0.0
	1847	-0.6	-0.2				
5 W	0109	4.3	1.3	20 Th	0007	3.7	1.1
	0714	0.0	0.0		0536	0.4	0.1
	1324	4.4	1.3		1203	3.9	1.2
	1948	-0.4	-0.1		1807	0.1	0.0
6 Th	0204	4.3	1.3	21 F	0044	3.8	1.2
	0823	0.1	0.0		0631	0.5	0.2
	1420	4.0	1.2		1249	3.7	1.1
	2047	-0.3	-0.1		1855	0.2	0.1
7 F	0258	4.3	1.3	22 Sa	0131	3.9	1.2
	0925	0.1	0.0		0804	0.5	0.2
	1518	3.8	1.2		1340	3.6	1.1
	2143	-0.2	-0.1		2012	0.2	0.1
8 Sa	0356	4.3	1.3	23 Su	0227	4.1	1.2
	1023	0.1	0.0		0927	0.4	0.1
	1617	3.6	1.1		1444	3.5	1.1
	2233	-0.2	-0.1		2126	0.1	0.0
9 Su	0453	4.3	1.3	24 M	0336	4.3	1.3
	1115	0.0	0.0		1031	0.1	0.0
	1715	3.5	1.1		1603	3.5	1.1
	2320	-0.2	-0.1		2231	0.0	0.0
10 M	0543	4.5	1.4	25 Tu	0446	4.6	1.4
	1202	-0.1	0.0		1128	-0.3	-0.1
	1806	3.6	1.1		1718	3.7	1.1
					2331	-0.4	-0.1
11 Tu	0006	-0.2	-0.1	26 W	0550	5.0	1.5
	0631	4.6	1.4		1224	-0.6	-0.2
	1248	-0.2	-0.1		1822	3.9	1.2
	1853	3.6	1.1				
12 W	0052	-0.2	-0.1	27 Th	0027	-0.6	-0.2
	0711	4.6	1.4		0646	5.3	1.6
	1335	-0.3	-0.1		1319	-0.9	-0.3
	1934	3.7	1.1		1918	4.2	1.3
13 Th	0136	-0.2	-0.1	28 F	0125	-0.9	-0.3
	0751	4.7	1.4		0740	5.5	1.7
	1416	-0.4	-0.1		1411	-1.2	-0.4
	2016	3.7	1.1		2010	4.5	1.4
14 F	0218	-0.2	-0.1	29 Sa	0219	-1.1	-0.3
	0829	4.6	1.4		0832	5.6	1.7
	1457	-0.5	-0.2		1500	-1.4	-0.4
	2057	3.7	1.1		2105	4.6	1.4
15 Sa	0256	-0.1	0.0	30 Su	0310	-1.1	-0.3
	0906	4.6	1.4		0925	5.5	1.7
	1534	-0.5	-0.2		1547	-1.4	-0.4
	2136	3.6	1.1		2158	4.7	1.4
				31 M	0400	-1.0	-0.3
					1019	5.3	1.6
					1634	-1.2	-0.4
					2253	4.7	1.4

FEBRUARY

Day	Time h m	Height ft	Height m	Day	Time h m	Height ft	Height m
1 Tu	0450	-0.8	-0.2	16 W	0416	-0.1	0.0
	1112	5.0	1.5		1024	4.2	1.3
	1720	-1.0	-0.3		1635	-0.2	-0.1
	2346	4.6	1.4		2248	4.0	1.2
2 W	0544	-0.5	-0.2	17 Th	0445	0.0	0.0
	1204	4.6	1.4		1056	4.1	1.2
	1810	-0.6	-0.2		1701	-0.1	0.0
					2325	4.1	1.2
3 Th	0039	4.5	1.4	18 F	0520	0.1	0.0
	0641	-0.1	0.0		1133	3.9	1.2
	1255	4.2	1.3		1728	0.0	0.0
	1906	-0.3	-0.1				
4 F	0129	4.4	1.3	19 Sa	0007	4.2	1.3
	0746	0.2	0.1		0605	0.3	0.1
	1349	3.8	1.2		1221	3.7	1.1
	2008	0.0	0.0		1812	0.1	0.0
5 Sa	0222	4.2	1.3	20 Su	0058	4.2	1.3
	0851	0.3	0.1		0724	0.4	0.1
	1441	3.5	1.1		1316	3.6	1.1
	2108	0.2	0.1		1916	0.3	0.1
6 Su	0318	4.1	1.2	21 M	0157	4.3	1.3
	0951	0.5	0.2		0858	0.4	0.1
	1541	3.3	1.0		1424	3.5	1.1
	2202	0.2	0.1		2057	0.3	0.1
7 M	0417	4.0	1.2	22 Tu	0308	4.4	1.3
	1046	0.2	0.1		1009	0.1	0.0
	1645	3.3	1.0		1548	3.5	1.1
	2254	0.2	0.1		2215	0.1	0.0
8 Tu	0513	4.1	1.2	23 W	0427	4.6	1.4
	1137	0.1	0.0		1111	-0.2	-0.1
	1742	3.4	1.0		1707	3.7	1.1
	2342	0.1	0.0		2318	-0.2	-0.1
9 W	0603	4.3	1.3	24 Th	0534	4.9	1.5
	1224	0.0	0.0		1208	-0.5	-0.2
	1832	3.5	1.1		1811	4.1	1.2
10 Th	0030	0.0	0.0	25 F	0017	-0.5	-0.2
	0648	4.4	1.3		0635	5.2	1.6
	1309	-0.2	-0.1		1301	-0.9	-0.3
	1914	3.7	1.1		1904	4.5	1.4
11 F	0115	-0.1	0.0	26 Sa	0112	-0.8	-0.2
	0728	4.6	1.4		0726	5.4	1.6
	1351	-0.4	-0.1		1351	-1.1	-0.3
	1955	3.8	1.2		1955	4.8	1.5
12 Sa	0158	-0.2	-0.1	27 Su	0206	-1.1	-0.3
	0808	4.6	1.4		0817	5.5	1.7
	1432	-0.5	-0.2		1438	-1.3	-0.4
	2032	3.9	1.2		2045	5.0	1.5
13 Su	0237	-0.2	-0.1	28 M	0256	-1.2	-0.4
	0844	4.6	1.4		0906	5.4	1.6
	1508	-0.5	-0.2		1523	-1.3	-0.4
	2107	4.0	1.2		2134	5.1	1.6
14 M	0313	-0.2	-0.1				
	0919	4.5	1.4				
	1542	-0.5	-0.2				
	2142	4.0	1.2				
15 Tu	0347	-0.2	-0.1				
	0947	4.4	1.3				
	1611	-0.4	-0.1				
	2216	4.0	1.2				

MARCH

Day	Time h m	Height ft	Height m	Day	Time h m	Height ft	Height m
1 Tu	0343	-1.1	-0.3	16 W	0326	-0.4	-0.1
	0957	5.1	1.6		0922	4.5	1.4
	1606	-1.1	-0.3		1540	-0.3	-0.1
	2224	5.0	1.5		2140	4.6	1.4
2 W	0429	-0.9	-0.3	17 Th	0359	-0.3	-0.1
	1047	4.8	1.5		0955	4.3	1.3
	1651	-0.8	-0.2		1608	-0.2	-0.1
	2315	4.9	1.5		2214	4.6	1.4
3 Th	0517	-0.5	-0.2	18 F	0432	-0.2	-0.1
	1136	4.5	1.4		1036	4.2	1.3
	1733	-0.4	-0.1		1635	-0.1	0.0
					2256	4.6	1.4
4 F	0005	4.7	1.4	19 Sa	0509	-0.1	0.0
	0607	-0.1	0.0		1117	4.0	1.2
	1225	4.1	1.2		1706	0.1	0.0
	1823	0.0	0.0		2344	4.6	1.4
5 Sa	0053	4.4	1.3	20 Su	0557	0.2	0.1
	0706	0.3	0.1		1213	3.8	1.2
	1316	3.7	1.1		1749	0.3	0.1
	1920	0.4	0.1				
6 Su	0143	4.2	1.3	21 M	0039	4.5	1.4
	0814	0.5	0.2		0713	0.4	0.1
	1407	3.4	1.0		1314	3.6	1.1
	2028	0.6	0.2		1859	0.5	0.2
7 M	0237	4.0	1.2	22 Tu	0143	4.5	1.4
	0918	0.6	0.2		0842	0.4	0.1
	1507	3.2	1.0		1424	3.6	1.1
	2130	0.7	0.2		2051	0.5	0.2
8 Tu	0335	3.9	1.2	23 W	0256	4.5	1.4
	1015	0.5	0.2		0953	0.2	0.1
	1612	3.2	1.0		1543	3.7	1.1
	2225	0.6	0.2		2205	0.3	0.1
9 W	0438	3.9	1.2	24 Th	0412	4.6	1.4
	1106	0.4	0.1		1052	-0.1	0.0
	1711	3.4	1.0		1655	4.0	1.2
	2319	0.5	0.2		2309	0.0	0.0
10 Th	0532	4.1	1.2	25 F	0521	4.8	1.5
	1154	0.2	0.1		1147	-0.5	-0.2
	1803	3.6	1.1		1755	4.5	1.4
11 F	0006	0.3	0.1	26 Sa	0006	-0.4	-0.1
	0623	4.3	1.3		0619	5.1	1.6
	1239	0.0	0.0		1238	-0.7	-0.2
	1848	3.9	1.2		1848	4.9	1.5
12 Sa	0051	0.1	0.0	27 Su	0059	-0.7	-0.2
	0701	4.5	1.4		0709	5.2	1.6
	1321	-0.2	-0.1		1327	-0.9	-0.3
	1927	4.1	1.2		1938	5.2	1.6
13 Su	0133	-0.1	0.0	28 M	0150	-0.9	-0.3
	0741	4.6	1.4		0758	5.3	1.6
	1400	-0.4	-0.1		1413	-1.0	-0.3
	2003	4.3	1.3		2023	5.4	1.6
14 M	0213	-0.3	-0.1	29 Tu	0237	-1.0	-0.3
	0815	4.6	1.4		0844	5.2	1.6
	1437	-0.4	-0.1		1457	-1.0	-0.3
	2036	4.4	1.3		2107	5.4	1.6
15 Tu	0251	-0.4	-0.1	30 W	0323	-0.9	-0.3
	0850	4.6	1.4		0932	4.9	1.5
	1510	-0.4	-0.1		1538	-0.8	-0.2
	2108	4.5	1.4		2155	5.2	1.6
				31 Th	0408	-0.7	-0.2
					1019	4.6	1.4
					1618	-0.5	-0.2
					2241	5.0	1.5

Time meridian 75° W. 0000 is midnight. 1200 is noon.
Heights are referred to mean low water which is the chart datum of soundings.

Times and Heights of High and Low Waters

APRIL

Day	Time h m	Height ft	Height m	Day	Time h m	Height ft	Height m
1 F	0450	-0.4	-0.1	16 Sa	0421	-0.4	-0.1
	1108	4.3	1.3		1022	4.2	1.3
	1658	-0.1	0.0		1615	0.0	0.0
	2327	4.7	1.4		2237	5.0	1.5
2 Sa	0536	0.0	0.0	17 Su	0503	-0.2	-0.1
	1157	3.9	1.2		1117	4.0	1.2
	1738	0.3	0.1		1654	0.2	0.1
					2333	4.9	1.5
3 Su	0015	4.5	1.4	18 M	0557	0.0	0.0
	0628	0.4	0.1		1218	3.9	1.2
	1246	3.7	1.1		1746	0.4	0.1
	1832	0.7	0.2				
4 M	0103	4.2	1.3	19 Tu	0034	4.8	1.5
	0732	0.7	0.2		0711	0.2	0.1
	1337	3.4	1.0		1321	3.8	1.2
	1942	1.0	0.3		1913	0.7	0.2
5 Tu	0154	4.0	1.2	20 W	0139	4.6	1.4
	0839	0.8	0.2		0830	0.2	0.1
	1434	3.3	1.0		1427	3.9	1.2
	2054	1.1	0.3		2046	0.6	0.2
6 W	0250	3.8	1.2	21 Th	0248	4.6	1.4
	0938	0.7	0.2		0935	0.1	0.0
	1533	3.4	1.0		1535	4.1	1.2
	2156	1.0	0.3		2156	0.4	0.1
7 Th	0353	3.8	1.2	22 F	0357	4.6	1.4
	1030	0.5	0.2		1033	-0.2	-0.1
	1635	3.5	1.1		1641	4.4	1.3
	2247	0.8	0.2		2257	0.0	0.0
8 F	0452	4.0	1.2	23 Sa	0503	4.7	1.4
	1118	0.3	0.1		1124	-0.4	-0.1
	1729	3.8	1.2		1739	4.8	1.5
	2335	0.5	0.2		2351	-0.3	-0.1
9 Sa	0543	4.2	1.3	24 Su	0600	4.9	1.5
	1201	0.1	0.0		1214	-0.6	-0.2
	1813	4.1	1.2		1828	5.2	1.6
10 Su	0022	0.3	0.1	25 M	0043	-0.5	-0.2
	0628	4.4	1.3		0651	5.0	1.5
	1243	0.0	0.0		1301	-0.7	-0.2
	1853	4.4	1.3		1915	5.4	1.6
11 M	0104	0.0	0.0	26 Tu	0133	-0.7	-0.2
	0707	4.5	1.4		0738	4.9	1.5
	1323	-0.2	-0.1		1346	-0.7	-0.2
	1927	4.7	1.4		1958	5.5	1.7
12 Tu	0146	-0.1	-0.1	27 W	0218	-0.7	-0.2
	0744	4.6	1.4		0821	4.8	1.5
	1402	-0.3	-0.1		1430	-0.6	-0.2
	2002	4.9	1.5		2041	5.5	1.7
13 W	0225	-0.4	-0.1	28 Th	0303	-0.7	-0.2
	0821	4.6	1.4		0906	4.6	1.4
	1437	-0.3	-0.1		1510	-0.4	-0.1
	2034	5.0	1.5		2124	5.3	1.6
14 Th	0306	-0.5	-0.2	29 F	0345	-0.5	-0.2
	0857	4.5	1.4		0952	4.3	1.3
	1509	-0.3	-0.1		1548	-0.1	0.0
	2108	5.1	1.6		2207	5.1	1.6
15 F	0342	-0.5	-0.2	30 Sa	0427	-0.2	-0.1
	0934	4.4	1.3		1039	4.1	1.2
	1541	-0.2	-0.1		1627	0.2	0.1
	2147	5.1	1.6		2253	4.8	1.5

MAY

Day	Time h m	Height ft	Height m	Day	Time h m	Height ft	Height m
1 Su	0509	0.1	0.0	16 M	0501	-0.4	-0.1
	1130	3.8	1.2		1117	4.2	1.3
	1704	0.6	0.2		1653	0.2	0.1
	2338	4.5	1.4		2328	5.2	1.6
2 M	0554	0.4	0.1	17 Tu	0553	-0.2	-0.1
	1221	3.6	1.1		1219	4.1	1.2
	1746	1.0	0.3		1754	0.5	0.2
3 Tu	0026	4.3	1.3	18 W	0031	5.0	1.5
	0649	0.7	0.2		0700	0.0	0.0
	1309	3.5	1.1		1319	4.2	1.3
	1847	1.2	0.4		1916	0.6	0.2
4 W	0112	4.1	1.2	19 Th	0132	4.8	1.5
	0756	0.8	0.2		0810	0.0	0.0
	1401	3.5	1.1		1419	4.3	1.3
	2012	1.3	0.4		2035	0.6	0.2
5 Th	0204	3.9	1.2	20 F	0235	4.7	1.4
	0857	0.8	0.2		0912	-0.1	0.0
	1454	3.6	1.1		1519	4.5	1.4
	2116	1.2	0.4		2142	0.4	0.1
6 F	0301	3.9	1.2	21 Sa	0338	4.6	1.4
	0949	0.6	0.2		1009	-0.2	-0.1
	1550	3.7	1.1		1620	4.8	1.5
	2211	1.0	0.3		2239	0.1	0.0
7 Sa	0401	3.9	1.2	22 Su	0441	4.6	1.4
	1036	0.5	0.2		1100	-0.3	-0.1
	1644	4.1	1.2		1716	5.1	1.6
	2300	0.7	0.2		2333	-0.1	0.0
8 Su	0457	4.0	1.2	23 M	0537	4.6	1.4
	1119	0.3	0.1		1147	-0.3	-0.1
	1731	4.3	1.3		1808	5.3	1.6
	2347	0.4	0.1				
9 M	0546	4.2	1.3	24 Tu	0024	-0.3	-0.1
	1201	0.1	0.0		0628	4.6	1.4
	1812	4.7	1.4		1233	-0.4	-0.1
					1851	5.5	1.7
10 Tu	0032	0.1	0.0	25 W	0113	-0.4	-0.1
	0628	4.4	1.3		0717	4.6	1.4
	1241	0.0	0.0		1319	-0.3	-0.1
	1851	5.0	1.5		1935	5.5	1.7
11 W	0117	-0.2	-0.1	26 Th	0159	-0.4	-0.1
	0710	4.5	1.4		0800	4.5	1.4
	1323	-0.1	0.0		1402	-0.2	-0.1
	1927	5.3	1.6		2017	5.5	1.7
12 Th	0200	-0.4	-0.1	27 F	0244	-0.4	-0.1
	0750	4.5	1.4		0845	4.3	1.3
	1401	-0.2	-0.1		1444	0.0	0.0
	2004	5.5	1.7		2058	5.3	1.6
13 F	0244	-0.5	-0.2	28 Sa	0326	-0.3	-0.1
	0832	4.5	1.4		0928	4.1	1.2
	1441	-0.2	-0.1		1523	0.2	0.1
	2046	5.5	1.7		2139	5.1	1.6
14 Sa	0327	-0.6	-0.2	29 Su	0405	-0.1	0.0
	0919	4.4	1.3		1016	3.9	1.2
	1522	-0.1	0.0		1600	0.5	0.2
	2133	5.5	1.7		2222	4.8	1.5
15 Su	0411	-0.5	-0.2	30 M	0445	0.1	0.0
	1016	4.2	1.3		1104	3.8	1.2
	1605	0.0	0.0		1637	0.7	0.2
	2227	5.3	1.6				
				31 Tu	0525	0.3	0.1
					1152	3.7	1.1
					1714	1.0	0.3
					2351	4.4	1.3

JUNE

Day	Time h m	Height ft	Height m	Day	Time h m	Height ft	Height m
1 W	0610	0.5	0.2	16 Th	0021	5.2	1.6
	1241	3.7	1.1		0641	-0.3	-0.1
	1757	1.2	0.4		1305	4.6	1.4
					1903	0.5	0.2
2 Th	0034	4.2	1.3	17 F	0118	5.0	1.5
	0703	0.7	0.2		0744	-0.1	0.0
	1326	3.7	1.1		1401	4.7	1.4
	1914	1.4	0.4		2016	0.5	0.2
3 F	0116	4.1	1.2	18 Sa	0214	4.7	1.4
	0806	0.7	0.2		0846	-0.1	0.0
	1411	3.8	1.2		1457	4.9	1.5
	2028	1.3	0.4		2122	0.4	0.1
4 Sa	0206	4.0	1.2	19 Su	0314	4.5	1.4
	0858	0.7	0.2		0941	-0.1	0.0
	1457	3.9	1.2		1556	5.0	1.5
	2130	1.2	0.4		2220	0.3	0.1
5 Su	0258	3.9	1.2	20 M	0415	4.3	1.3
	0948	0.6	0.2		1033	-0.1	0.0
	1548	4.2	1.3		1653	5.1	1.6
	2221	0.9	0.3		2313	0.1	0.0
6 M	0357	3.9	1.2	21 Tu	0515	4.3	1.3
	1031	0.4	0.1		1121	-0.1	0.0
	1641	4.5	1.4		1743	5.3	1.6
	2310	0.6	0.2				
7 Tu	0454	4.0	1.2	22 W	0003	0.0	0.0
	1116	0.3	0.1		0606	4.2	1.3
	1727	4.9	1.5		1208	0.0	0.0
	2358	0.2	0.1		1830	5.4	1.6
8 W	0548	4.2	1.3	23 Th	0052	-0.1	0.0
	1158	0.1	0.0		0654	4.2	1.3
	1811	5.2	1.6		1254	0.1	0.0
					1912	5.4	1.6
9 Th	0045	-0.1	0.0	24 F	0139	-0.1	0.0
	0636	4.3	1.3		0740	4.2	1.3
	1245	0.0	0.0		1339	0.2	0.1
	1857	5.5	1.7		1954	5.3	1.6
10 F	0136	-0.3	-0.1	25 Sa	0222	-0.1	0.0
	0725	4.4	1.3		0824	4.1	1.2
	1330	-0.1	0.0		1421	0.3	0.1
	1941	5.7	1.7		2035	5.2	1.6
11 Sa	0224	-0.5	-0.2	26 Su	0304	-0.1	0.0
	0813	4.4	1.3		0907	4.1	1.2
	1421	-0.2	-0.1		1503	0.4	0.1
	2029	5.8	1.8		2115	5.1	1.6
12 Su	0312	-0.7	-0.2	27 M	0344	0.0	0.0
	0907	4.4	1.3		0952	4.0	1.2
	1508	-0.2	-0.1		1541	0.6	0.2
	2121	5.8	1.8		2155	4.9	1.5
13 M	0400	-0.7	-0.2	28 Tu	0422	0.1	0.0
	1007	4.4	1.3		1039	3.9	1.2
	1558	-0.1	0.0		1617	0.7	0.2
	2221	5.6	1.7		2235	4.7	1.4
14 Tu	0448	-0.6	-0.2	29 W	0459	0.2	0.1
	1107	4.5	1.4		1122	3.9	1.2
	1651	0.1	0.0		1651	0.9	0.3
	2320	5.4	1.6		2316	4.5	1.4
15 W	0541	-0.4	-0.1	30 Th	0536	0.4	0.1
	1207	4.6	1.4		1205	3.9	1.2
	1752	0.3	0.1		1725	1.1	0.3
					2352	4.3	1.3

Time meridian 75° W. 0000 is midnight. 1200 is noon.
Heights are referred to mean low water which is the chart datum of soundings.

NEW YORK (The Battery), N.Y., 1983

Times and Heights of High and Low Waters

JULY

Day	Time (h m)	ft	m	Day	Time (h m)	ft	m
1 F	0610	0.6	0.2	16 Sa	0057	5.0	1.5
	1244	3.9	1.2		0714	-0.1	0.0
	1805	1.2	0.4		1336	5.1	1.6
					1951	0.5	0.2
2 Sa	0032	4.2	1.3	17 Su	0151	4.7	1.4
	0655	0.7	0.2		0813	0.1	0.0
	1322	4.0	1.2		1428	5.0	1.5
	1919	1.3	0.4		2057	0.5	0.2
3 Su	0110	4.1	1.2	18 M	0247	4.3	1.3
	0750	0.7	0.2		0912	0.2	0.1
	1404	4.2	1.3		1527	5.0	1.5
	2037	1.2	0.4		2156	0.5	0.2
4 M	0159	4.0	1.2	19 Tu	0347	4.1	1.2
	0847	0.7	0.2		1005	0.3	0.1
	1450	4.4	1.3		1623	5.0	1.5
	2140	1.0	0.3		2252	0.4	0.1
5 Tu	0255	3.9	1.2	20 W	0449	4.0	1.2
	0941	0.6	0.2		1056	0.3	0.1
	1546	4.7	1.4		1718	5.1	1.6
	2234	0.7	0.2		2342	0.3	0.1
6 W	0401	3.9	1.2	21 Th	0545	4.0	1.2
	1030	0.4	0.1		1145	0.4	0.1
	1644	5.0	1.5		1808	5.2	1.6
	2329	0.4	0.1				
7 Th	0509	4.0	1.2	22 F	0032	0.2	0.1
	1123	0.3	0.1		0635	4.1	1.2
	1742	5.3	1.6		1232	0.4	0.1
					1853	5.2	1.6
8 F	0019	0.1	0.0	23 Sa	0117	0.1	0.0
	0609	4.2	1.3		0720	4.1	1.2
	1214	0.1	0.0		1318	0.4	0.1
	1832	5.7	1.7		1933	5.2	1.6
9 Sa	0115	-0.3	-0.1	24 Su	0201	0.0	0.0
	0705	4.4	1.3		0805	4.2	1.3
	1309	-0.1	0.0		1402	0.4	0.1
	1923	5.9	1.8		2014	5.2	1.6
10 Su	0205	-0.5	-0.2	25 M	0242	0.0	0.0
	0757	4.6	1.4		0844	4.2	1.3
	1405	-0.2	-0.1		1443	0.5	0.2
	2015	6.0	1.8		2052	5.1	1.6
11 M	0254	-0.7	-0.2	26 Tu	0320	0.0	0.0
	0854	4.7	1.4		0926	4.2	1.3
	1457	-0.3	-0.1		1521	0.5	0.2
	2110	5.9	1.8		2129	5.0	1.5
12 Tu	0343	-0.8	-0.2	27 W	0356	0.0	0.0
	0952	4.8	1.5		1008	4.2	1.3
	1550	-0.3	-0.1		1555	0.6	0.2
	2206	5.8	1.8		2206	4.8	1.5
13 W	0431	-0.8	-0.2	28 Th	0429	0.2	0.1
	1050	4.9	1.5		1047	4.2	1.3
	1643	-0.1	0.0		1629	0.7	0.2
	2304	5.6	1.7		2240	4.6	1.4
14 Th	0520	-0.6	-0.2	29 F	0458	0.3	0.1
	1148	5.0	1.5		1125	4.2	1.3
	1738	0.1	0.0		1659	0.9	0.3
					2311	4.5	1.4
15 F	0002	5.3	1.6	30 Sa	0525	0.5	0.2
	0615	-0.4	-0.1		1157	4.3	1.3
	1242	5.1	1.6		1730	1.0	0.3
	1842	0.3	0.1		2346	4.3	1.3
				31 Su	0549	0.6	0.2
					1234	4.4	1.3
					1812	1.1	0.3

AUGUST

Day	Time (h m)	ft	m	Day	Time (h m)	ft	m
1 M	0029	4.2	1.3	16 Tu	0221	4.2	1.3
	0626	0.7	0.2		0840	0.6	0.2
	1311	4.5	1.4		1454	4.9	1.5
	1931	1.2	0.4		2130	0.7	0.2
2 Tu	0115	4.0	1.2	17 W	0320	3.9	1.2
	0722	0.8	0.2		0939	0.7	0.2
	1402	4.6	1.4		1553	4.8	1.5
	2059	1.1	0.3		2226	0.7	0.2
3 W	0211	3.9	1.2	18 Th	0422	3.8	1.2
	0841	0.8	0.2		1031	0.7	0.2
	1458	4.8	1.5		1652	4.8	1.5
	2205	1.0	0.3		2318	0.6	0.2
4 Th	0321	3.9	1.2	19 F	0522	3.9	1.2
	0953	0.6	0.2		1122	0.7	0.2
	1609	5.0	1.5		1745	4.9	1.5
	2303	0.5	0.2				
5 F	0441	4.0	1.2	20 Sa	0006	0.4	0.1
	1056	0.4	0.1		0614	4.0	1.2
	1715	5.4	1.6		1211	0.6	0.2
	2358	0.1	0.0		1830	5.0	1.5
6 Sa	0550	4.2	1.3	21 Su	0053	0.3	0.1
	1155	0.2	0.1		0659	4.2	1.3
	1816	5.7	1.7		1257	0.5	0.2
					1912	5.1	1.6
7 Su	0053	-0.2	-0.1	22 M	0135	0.1	0.0
	0649	4.6	1.4		0740	4.4	1.3
	1254	-0.1	0.0		1340	0.4	0.1
	1910	5.9	1.8		1950	5.2	1.6
8 M	0145	-0.5	-0.2	23 Tu	0215	0.0	0.0
	0743	4.9	1.5		0818	4.5	1.4
	1351	-0.3	-0.1		1422	0.4	0.1
	2002	6.1	1.9		2027	5.1	1.6
9 Tu	0234	-0.8	-0.2	24 W	0252	0.0	0.0
	0836	5.1	1.6		0854	4.5	1.4
	1445	-0.5	-0.2		1459	0.4	0.1
	2054	6.0	1.8		2102	5.0	1.5
10 W	0322	-0.9	-0.3	25 Th	0326	0.0	0.0
	0931	5.3	1.6		0929	4.6	1.4
	1536	-0.5	-0.2		1534	0.4	0.1
	2150	5.9	1.8		2134	4.9	1.5
11 Th	0408	-0.8	-0.2	26 F	0357	0.1	0.0
	1026	5.4	1.6		1005	4.6	1.4
	1626	-0.3	-0.1		1606	0.5	0.2
	2245	5.6	1.7		2204	4.7	1.4
12 F	0455	-0.6	-0.2	27 Sa	0423	0.3	0.1
	1120	5.4	1.6		1035	4.6	1.4
	1717	-0.1	0.0		1635	0.6	0.2
	2338	5.3	1.6		2235	4.5	1.4
13 Sa	0543	-0.3	-0.1	28 Su	0443	0.4	0.1
	1215	5.3	1.6		1109	4.6	1.4
	1817	0.2	0.1		1704	0.7	0.2
					2309	4.3	1.3
14 Su	0031	4.9	1.5	29 M	0509	0.5	0.2
	0637	0.0	0.0		1146	4.7	1.4
	1307	5.2	1.6		1744	0.9	0.3
	1921	0.5	0.2		2352	4.1	1.2
15 M	0126	4.5	1.4	30 Tu	0544	0.7	0.2
	0738	0.4	0.1		1233	4.7	1.4
	1358	5.0	1.5		1844	1.0	0.3
	2028	0.7	0.2				
				31 W	0044	4.0	1.2
					0633	0.8	0.2
					1327	4.8	1.5
					2027	1.1	0.3

SEPTEMBER

Day	Time (h m)	ft	m	Day	Time (h m)	ft	m
1 Th	0147	3.9	1.2	16 F	0354	3.7	1.1
	0757	0.9	0.3		1009	1.0	0.3
	1432	4.9	1.5		1618	4.5	1.4
	2142	0.8	0.2		2249	0.7	0.2
2 F	0306	3.8	1.2	17 Sa	0455	3.8	1.2
	0935	0.8	0.2		1100	0.9	0.3
	1547	5.0	1.5		1715	4.6	1.4
	2243	0.5	0.2		2337	0.5	0.2
3 Sa	0430	4.0	1.2	18 Su	0547	4.1	1.2
	1044	0.5	0.2		1147	0.7	0.2
	1700	5.3	1.6		1802	4.8	1.5
	2338	0.1	0.0				
4 Su	0539	4.4	1.3	19 M	0022	0.3	0.1
	1145	0.2	0.1		0632	4.3	1.3
	1801	5.6	1.7		1232	0.6	0.2
					1845	4.9	1.5
5 M	0032	-0.3	-0.1	20 Tu	0104	0.1	0.0
	0635	4.9	1.5		0711	4.6	1.4
	1243	-0.2	-0.1		1315	0.4	0.1
	1856	5.8	1.8		1923	5.0	1.5
6 Tu	0123	-0.6	-0.2	21 W	0143	0.0	0.0
	0748	5.2	1.6		0748	4.7	1.4
	1338	-0.4	-0.1		1357	0.2	0.1
	1947	6.0	1.8		1958	5.0	1.5
7 W	0211	-0.8	-0.2	22 Th	0219	0.0	0.0
	0816	5.5	1.7		0822	4.8	1.5
	1429	-0.6	-0.2		1435	0.2	0.1
	2036	5.9	1.8		2030	5.0	1.5
8 Th	0257	-0.9	-0.3	23 F	0254	0.0	0.0
	0906	5.7	1.7		0853	4.9	1.5
	1518	-0.6	-0.2		1510	0.1	0.0
	2126	5.7	1.7		2102	4.8	1.5
9 F	0342	-0.8	-0.2	24 Sa	0323	0.1	0.0
	0958	5.7	1.7		0925	4.9	1.5
	1606	-0.5	-0.2		1544	0.2	0.1
	2219	5.4	1.6		2131	4.6	1.4
10 Sa	0426	-0.6	-0.2	25 Su	0350	0.2	0.1
	1050	5.6	1.7		0953	4.9	1.5
	1655	-0.2	-0.1		1616	0.3	0.1
	2312	5.0	1.5		2203	4.4	1.3
11 Su	0511	-0.2	-0.1	26 M	0411	0.3	0.1
	1141	5.4	1.6		1027	4.9	1.5
	1746	0.2	0.1		1648	0.5	0.2
					2245	4.2	1.3
12 M	0005	4.6	1.4	27 Tu	0440	0.4	0.1
	0559	0.2	0.1		1114	4.9	1.5
	1233	5.1	1.6		1730	0.6	0.2
	1847	0.6	0.2		2336	4.0	1.2
13 Tu	0058	4.3	1.3	28 W	0516	0.6	0.2
	0658	0.7	0.2		1207	4.8	1.5
	1327	4.9	1.5		1833	0.8	0.2
	1955	0.8	0.2				
14 W	0152	4.0	1.2	29 Th	0036	3.9	1.2
	0804	1.0	0.3		0609	0.8	0.2
	1420	4.7	1.4		1308	4.8	1.5
	2100	0.9	0.3		2008	0.9	0.3
15 Th	0252	3.8	1.2	30 F	0146	3.8	1.2
	0910	1.1	0.3		0747	1.0	0.3
	1519	4.5	1.4		1418	4.8	1.5
	2157	0.8	0.2		2124	0.7	0.2

Time meridian 75° W. 0000 is midnight. 1200 is noon.
Heights are referred to mean low water which is the chart datum of soundings.

NEW YORK (The Battery), N.Y., 1983

Times and Heights of High and Low Waters

OCTOBER

Day	Time (h m)	Height (ft)	Height (m)	Day	Time (h m)	Height (ft)	Height (m)
1 Sa	0303	3.9	1.2	16 Su	0421	3.8	1.2
	0930	0.8	0.2		1032	1.0	0.3
	1535	4.9	1.5		1637	4.3	1.3
	2224	0.3	0.1		2302	0.5	0.2
2 Su	0420	4.2	1.3	17 M	0514	4.0	1.2
	1036	0.5	0.2		1118	0.7	0.2
	1645	5.1	1.6		1726	4.4	1.3
	2318	0.0	0.0		2347	0.3	0.1
3 M	0524	4.6	1.4	18 Tu	0600	4.3	1.3
	1134	0.1	0.0		1204	0.5	0.2
	1745	5.3	1.6		1809	4.6	1.4
4 Tu	0009	-0.4	-0.1	19 W	0027	0.1	0.0
	0619	5.1	1.6		0638	4.6	1.4
	1230	-0.3	-0.1		1248	0.3	0.1
	1839	5.5	1.7		1851	4.7	1.4
5 W	0100	-0.7	-0.2	20 Th	0107	0.0	0.0
	0709	5.5	1.7		0715	4.8	1.5
	1321	-0.6	-0.2		1328	0.1	0.0
	1928	5.6	1.7		1928	4.7	1.4
6 Th	0146	-0.8	-0.2	21 F	0143	-0.1	0.0
	0755	5.7	1.7		0747	5.0	1.5
	1411	-0.7	-0.2		1408	-0.1	0.0
	2016	5.5	1.7		2001	4.7	1.4
7 F	0231	-0.8	-0.2	22 Sa	0219	-0.1	0.0
	0842	5.8	1.8		0819	5.1	1.6
	1459	-0.7	-0.2		1447	-0.2	-0.1
	2103	5.3	1.6		2033	4.6	1.4
8 Sa	0314	-0.7	-0.2	23 Su	0251	-0.1	0.0
	0929	5.7	1.7		0849	5.2	1.6
	1545	-0.6	-0.2		1524	-0.1	0.0
	2152	5.0	1.5		2105	4.4	1.3
9 Su	0356	-0.4	-0.1	24 M	0321	0.0	0.0
	1019	5.5	1.7		0923	5.1	1.6
	1631	-0.3	-0.1		1601	-0.1	0.0
	2245	4.6	1.4		2144	4.2	1.3
10 M	0438	-0.1	0.0	25 Tu	0351	0.1	0.0
	1107	5.2	1.6		1006	5.1	1.6
	1719	0.1	0.0		1640	0.1	0.0
	2336	4.3	1.3		2235	4.0	1.2
11 Tu	0522	0.4	0.1	26 W	0424	0.3	0.1
	1159	4.9	1.5		1058	5.0	1.5
	1813	0.5	0.2		1725	0.3	0.1
					2338	3.8	1.2
12 W	0031	4.0	1.2	27 Th	0507	0.5	0.2
	0613	0.8	0.2		1157	4.8	1.5
	1252	4.6	1.4		1829	0.4	0.1
	1916	0.8	0.2				
13 Th	0124	3.7	1.1	28 F	0042	3.8	1.2
	0722	1.1	0.3		0610	0.7	0.2
	1344	4.4	1.3		1303	4.7	1.4
	2023	0.9	0.3		1953	0.5	0.2
14 F	0221	3.6	1.1	29 Sa	0151	3.8	1.2
	0835	1.3	0.4		0759	0.8	0.2
	1438	4.2	1.3		1410	4.7	1.4
	2125	0.8	0.2		2103	0.3	0.1
15 Sa	0320	3.6	1.1	30 Su	0301	4.0	1.2
	0938	1.2	0.4		0921	0.6	0.2
	1539	4.2	1.3		1520	4.7	1.4
	2217	0.7	0.2		2203	0.0	0.0
				31 M	0407	4.3	1.3
					1025	0.3	0.1
					1628	4.8	1.5
					2257	-0.3	-0.1

NOVEMBER

Day	Time (h m)	Height (ft)	Height (m)	Day	Time (h m)	Height (ft)	Height (m)
1 Tu	0508	4.8	1.5	16 W	0518	4.2	1.3
	1121	-0.1	0.0		1131	0.4	0.1
	1728	4.9	1.5		1729	4.1	1.2
	2347	-0.5	-0.2		2347	0.0	0.0
2 W	0600	5.2	1.6	17 Th	0600	4.5	1.4
	1214	-0.4	-0.1		1216	0.2	0.1
	1821	5.0	1.5		1812	4.2	1.3
3 Th	0033	-0.7	-0.2	18 F	0027	-0.1	0.0
	0649	5.5	1.7		0638	4.8	1.5
	1305	-0.6	-0.2		1259	-0.1	0.0
	1909	5.1	1.6		1854	4.3	1.3
4 F	0120	-0.8	-0.2	19 Sa	0105	-0.2	-0.1
	0734	5.7	1.7		0713	5.0	1.5
	1354	-0.8	-0.2		1342	-0.3	-0.1
	1956	5.0	1.5		1931	4.3	1.3
5 Sa	0205	-0.7	-0.2	20 Su	0144	-0.3	-0.1
	0818	5.7	1.7		0749	5.2	1.6
	1440	-0.7	-0.2		1425	-0.4	-0.1
	2042	4.8	1.5		2008	4.3	1.3
6 Su	0249	-0.6	-0.2	21 M	0223	-0.3	-0.1
	0903	5.6	1.7		0826	5.3	1.6
	1526	-0.6	-0.2		1506	-0.5	-0.2
	2129	4.5	1.4		2049	4.1	1.2
7 M	0329	-0.3	-0.1	22 Tu	0259	-0.3	-0.1
	0950	5.3	1.6		0905	5.3	1.6
	1608	-0.4	-0.1		1550	-0.5	-0.2
	2219	4.2	1.3		2137	4.0	1.2
8 Tu	0410	0.0	0.0	23 W	0337	-0.2	-0.1
	1037	5.0	1.5		0955	5.2	1.6
	1653	0.0	0.0		1632	-0.4	-0.1
	2309	3.9	1.2		2237	3.9	1.2
9 W	0451	0.4	0.1	24 Th	0422	0.0	0.0
	1127	4.7	1.4		1053	5.0	1.5
	1741	0.3	0.1		1722	-0.2	-0.1
					2341	3.8	1.2
10 Th	0002	3.7	1.1	25 F	0512	0.2	0.1
	0536	0.7	0.2		1157	4.8	1.5
	1215	4.4	1.3		1822	-0.1	0.0
	1834	0.5	0.2				
11 F	0055	3.5	1.1	26 Sa	0042	3.9	1.2
	0634	1.1	0.3		0623	0.4	0.1
	1306	4.2	1.3		1258	4.7	1.4
	1939	0.7	0.2		1932	0.0	0.0
12 Sa	0148	3.5	1.1	27 Su	0143	4.0	1.2
	0751	1.2	0.4		0751	0.5	0.2
	1356	4.0	1.2		1359	4.5	1.4
	2042	0.7	0.2		2040	-0.1	0.0
13 Su	0241	3.5	1.1	28 M	0245	4.2	1.3
	0901	1.2	0.4		0907	0.3	0.1
	1450	3.9	1.2		1503	4.4	1.3
	2135	0.6	0.2		2139	-0.3	-0.1
14 M	0336	3.6	1.1	29 Tu	0345	4.4	1.3
	0956	1.0	0.3		1009	0.0	0.0
	1545	3.9	1.2		1607	4.4	1.3
	2223	0.4	0.1		2233	-0.5	-0.2
15 Tu	0430	3.9	1.2	30 W	0446	4.7	1.4
	1045	0.7	0.2		1105	-0.2	-0.1
	1641	4.0	1.2		1708	4.4	1.3
	2305	0.2	0.1		2321	-0.6	-0.2

DECEMBER

Day	Time (h m)	Height (ft)	Height (m)	Day	Time (h m)	Height (ft)	Height (m)
1 Th	0539	5.0	1.5	16 F	0515	4.3	1.3
	1158	-0.5	-0.2		1142	0.1	0.0
	1801	4.4	1.3		1732	3.7	1.1
					2347	-0.1	0.0
2 F	0011	-0.7	-0.2	17 Sa	0601	4.6	1.4
	0630	5.3	1.6		1230	-0.2	-0.1
	1248	-0.6	-0.2		1820	3.8	1.2
	1851	4.4	1.3				
3 Sa	0056	-0.7	-0.2	18 Su	0030	-0.3	-0.1
	0714	5.4	1.6		0643	4.9	1.5
	1336	-0.7	-0.2		1316	-0.4	-0.1
	1936	4.4	1.3		1904	4.0	1.2
4 Su	0141	-0.6	-0.2	19 M	0115	-0.4	-0.1
	0758	5.4	1.6		0724	5.2	1.6
	1423	-0.7	-0.2		1403	-0.7	-0.2
	2022	4.2	1.3		1949	4.0	1.2
5 M	0226	-0.5	-0.2	20 Tu	0201	-0.5	-0.2
	0841	5.2	1.6		0808	5.3	1.6
	1507	-0.6	-0.2		1449	-0.8	-0.2
	2107	4.0	1.2		2038	4.0	1.2
6 Tu	0307	-0.3	-0.1	21 W	0247	-0.6	-0.2
	0925	5.0	1.5		0855	5.3	1.6
	1549	-0.5	-0.2		1534	-0.9	-0.3
	2155	3.8	1.2		2131	4.0	1.2
7 W	0347	-0.1	0.0	22 Th	0332	-0.5	-0.2
	1008	4.7	1.4		0947	5.2	1.6
	1631	-0.3	-0.1		1622	-0.9	-0.3
	2245	3.6	1.1		2231	4.1	1.2
8 Th	0427	0.2	0.1	23 F	0421	-0.4	-0.1
	1055	4.5	1.4		1048	5.1	1.6
	1712	0.0	0.0		1711	-0.8	-0.2
	2335	3.5	1.1		2330	4.1	1.2
9 F	0504	0.5	0.2	24 Sa	0514	-0.3	-0.1
	1141	4.2	1.3		1146	4.9	1.5
	1757	0.2	0.1		1805	-0.6	-0.2
10 Sa	0023	3.4	1.0	25 Su	0029	4.2	1.3
	0549	0.8	0.2		0620	0.0	0.0
	1226	4.0	1.2		1244	4.6	1.4
	1847	0.4	0.1		1906	-0.5	-0.2
11 Su	0109	3.4	1.0	26 M	0127	4.3	1.3
	0652	1.0	0.3		0734	0.1	0.0
	1311	3.8	1.2		1343	4.4	1.3
	1946	0.5	0.2		2011	-0.4	-0.1
12 M	0155	3.4	1.0	27 Tu	0222	4.3	1.3
	0807	1.0	0.3		0846	0.1	0.0
	1355	3.7	1.1		1440	4.2	1.3
	2045	0.4	0.1		2111	-0.4	-0.1
13 Tu	0244	3.5	1.1	28 W	0322	4.5	1.4
	0911	0.9	0.3		0948	-0.1	0.0
	1446	3.6	1.1		1543	4.0	1.2
	2135	0.4	0.1		2207	-0.4	-0.1
14 W	0335	3.7	1.1	29 Th	0422	4.6	1.4
	1004	0.7	0.2		1046	-0.2	-0.1
	1542	3.6	1.1		1644	3.9	1.2
	2220	0.2	0.1		2257	-0.5	-0.2
15 Th	0425	4.0	1.2	30 F	0519	4.8	1.5
	1054	0.4	0.1		1139	-0.4	-0.1
	1638	3.6	1.1		1742	3.9	1.2
	2303	0.1	0.0		2348	-0.5	-0.2
				31 Sa	0611	4.9	1.5
					1230	-0.5	-0.2
					1834	3.9	1.2

Time meridian 75° W. 0000 is midnight. 1200 is noon.
Heights are referred to mean low water which is the chart datum of soundings.

SANDY HOOK, N.J., 1983

Times and Heights of High and Low Waters

JANUARY

Day	Time h m	Height ft	Height m	Day	Time h m	Height ft	Height m
1 Sa	0249	-1.0	-0.3	16 Su	0256	0.0	0.0
	0900	5.7	1.7		0901	4.6	1.4
	1537	-1.3	-0.4		1531	-0.4	-0.1
	2136	4.6	1.4		2122	3.7	1.1
2 Su	0341	-0.9	-0.3	17 M	0331	0.1	0.0
	0955	5.5	1.7		0936	4.4	1.3
	1626	-1.2	-0.4		1605	-0.3	-0.1
	2233	4.5	1.4		2200	3.7	1.1
3 M	0435	-0.7	-0.2	18 Tu	0403	0.2	0.1
	1050	5.1	1.6		1016	4.3	1.3
	1717	-1.0	-0.3		1639	-0.2	-0.1
	2330	4.4	1.3		2240	3.7	1.1
4 Tu	0532	-0.4	-0.1	19 W	0440	0.3	0.1
	1146	4.8	1.5		1055	4.1	1.2
	1812	-0.7	-0.2		1711	-0.1	0.0
					2322	3.7	1.1
5 W	0026	4.4	1.3	20 Th	0521	0.4	0.1
	0633	-0.1	0.0		1140	3.9	1.2
	1239	4.4	1.3		1754	0.0	0.0
	1910	-0.5	-0.2				
6 Th	0121	4.3	1.3	21 F	0009	3.9	1.2
	0739	0.0	0.0		0618	0.4	0.1
	1336	4.1	1.2		1228	3.8	1.2
	2006	-0.3	-0.1		1846	0.0	0.0
7 F	0218	4.3	1.3	22 Sa	0102	4.0	1.2
	0840	0.1	0.0		0732	0.4	0.1
	1433	3.8	1.2		1324	3.7	1.1
	2101	-0.2	-0.1		1949	0.0	0.0
8 Sa	0315	4.3	1.3	23 Su	0202	4.2	1.3
	0937	0.1	0.0		0845	0.3	0.1
	1533	3.6	1.1		1430	3.6	1.1
	2152	-0.2	-0.1		2052	-0.1	0.0
9 Su	0411	4.4	1.3	24 M	0308	4.4	1.3
	1030	0.0	0.0		0949	0.0	0.0
	1633	3.6	1.1		1540	3.7	1.1
	2241	-0.2	-0.1		2151	-0.3	-0.1
10 M	0502	4.5	1.4	25 Tu	0414	4.8	1.5
	1120	-0.1	0.0		1049	-0.3	-0.1
	1724	3.6	1.1		1649	3.9	1.2
	2326	-0.2	-0.1		2250	-0.6	-0.2
11 Tu	0548	4.7	1.4	26 W	0518	5.1	1.6
	1208	-0.2	-0.1		1147	-0.7	-0.2
	1808	3.7	1.1		1750	4.2	1.3
					2350	-0.8	-0.2
12 W	0011	-0.2	-0.1	27 Th	0613	5.5	1.7
	0629	4.8	1.5		1245	-1.0	-0.3
	1254	-0.3	-0.1		1845	4.5	1.4
	1850	3.7	1.1				
13 Th	0056	-0.2	-0.1	28 F	0048	-1.0	-0.3
	0709	4.8	1.5		0704	5.7	1.7
	1337	-0.4	-0.1		1338	-1.3	-0.4
	1930	3.8	1.2		1936	4.7	1.4
14 F	0139	-0.1	0.0	29 Sa	0143	-1.2	-0.4
	0747	4.8	1.5		0755	5.8	1.8
	1418	-0.4	-0.1		1428	-1.4	-0.1
	2007	3.8	1.2		2026	4.9	1.5
15 Sa	0219	-0.1	0.0	30 Su	0237	-1.2	-0.4
	0824	4.7	1.4		0845	5.7	1.7
	1456	-0.4	-0.1		1518	-1.4	-0.4
	2046	3.7	1.1		2118	4.9	1.5
				31 M	0328	-1.1	-0.3
					0936	5.4	1.6
					1603	-1.3	-0.4
					2210	4.8	1.5

FEBRUARY

Day	Time h m	Height ft	Height m	Day	Time h m	Height ft	Height m
1 Tu	0417	-0.9	-0.3	16 W	0347	-0.1	0.0
	1026	5.1	1.6		0951	4.4	1.3
	1649	-1.1	-0.3		1608	-0.3	-0.1
	2303	4.7	1.4		2209	4.2	1.3
2 W	0508	-0.6	-0.2	17 Th	0421	0.0	0.0
	1117	4.7	1.4		1029	4.2	1.3
	1738	-0.7	-0.2		1640	-0.2	-0.1
	2354	4.6	1.4		2251	4.2	1.3
3 Th	0602	-0.3	-0.1	18 F	0501	0.1	0.0
	1207	4.3	1.3		1114	4.0	1.2
	1830	-0.4	-0.1		1716	-0.1	0.0
					2337	4.3	1.3
4 F	0045	4.4	1.3	19 Sa	0554	0.2	0.1
	0702	0.0	0.0		1202	3.8	1.2
	1259	3.9	1.2		1804	0.0	0.0
	1925	-0.1	0.0				
5 Sa	0136	4.3	1.3	20 Su	0028	4.3	1.3
	0804	0.2	0.1		0702	0.3	0.1
	1354	3.6	1.1		1257	3.7	1.1
	2022	0.1	0.0		1910	0.1	0.0
6 Su	0231	4.1	1.2	21 M	0129	4.4	1.3
	0903	0.3	0.1		0819	0.3	0.1
	1452	3.3	1.0		1405	3.6	1.1
	2116	0.2	0.1		2024	0.1	0.0
7 M	0330	4.1	1.2	22 Tu	0239	4.5	1.4
	0959	0.2	0.1		0929	0.1	0.0
	1555	3.3	1.0		1521	3.6	1.1
	2208	0.2	0.1		2133	-0.1	0.0
8 Tu	0427	4.2	1.3	23 W	0353	4.7	1.4
	1051	0.1	0.0		1032	-0.3	-0.1
	1655	3.4	1.0		1634	3.9	1.2
	2259	0.1	0.0		2236	-0.3	-0.1
9 W	0520	4.4	1.3	24 Th	0500	5.0	1.5
	1140	0.0	0.0		1131	-0.6	-0.2
	1745	3.5	1.1		1736	4.3	1.3
	2347	0.1	0.0		2337	-0.6	-0.2
10 Th	0605	4.6	1.4	25 F	0557	5.4	1.6
	1227	-0.2	-0.1		1226	-0.9	-0.3
	1829	3.7	1.1		1829	4.7	1.4
11 F	0034	0.0	0.0	26 Sa	0035	-0.9	-0.3
	0646	4.7	1.4		0651	5.6	1.7
	1312	-0.3	-0.1		1318	-1.2	-0.4
	1909	3.9	1.2		1920	5.0	1.5
12 Sa	0119	-0.1	0.0	27 Su	0130	-1.1	-0.3
	0725	4.8	1.5		0740	5.7	1.7
	1352	-0.4	-0.1		1407	-1.3	-0.4
	1946	4.0	1.2		2007	5.2	1.6
13 Su	0200	-0.2	-0.1	28 M	0221	-1.2	-0.4
	0802	4.8	1.5		0827	5.6	1.7
	1430	-0.5	-0.2		1453	-1.3	-0.4
	2023	4.1	1.2		2056	5.3	1.6
14 M	0237	-0.2	-0.1				
	0839	4.7	1.4				
	1505	-0.4	-0.1				
	2056	4.1	1.2				
15 Tu	0312	-0.2	-0.1				
	0914	4.6	1.4				
	1537	-0.4	-0.1				
	2133	4.1	1.2				

MARCH

Day	Time h m	Height ft	Height m	Day	Time h m	Height ft	Height m
1 Tu	0310	-1.1	-0.3	16 W	0252	-0.3	-0.1
	0914	5.3	1.6		0849	4.7	1.4
	1536	-1.2	-0.4		1505	-0.4	-0.1
	2143	5.2	1.6		2104	4.7	1.4
2 W	0356	-0.9	-0.3	17 Th	0328	-0.3	-0.1
	1000	5.0	1.5		0927	4.5	1.4
	1619	-0.9	-0.3		1539	-0.3	-0.1
	2229	5.0	1.5		2141	4.8	1.5
3 Th	0442	-0.6	-0.2	18 F	0407	-0.2	-0.1
	1047	4.6	1.4		1007	4.3	1.3
	1701	-0.5	-0.2		1612	-0.2	-0.1
	2317	4.8	1.5		2224	4.8	1.5
4 F	0529	-0.2	-0.1	19 Sa	0448	-0.1	0.0
	1135	4.2	1.3		1055	4.1	1.2
	1746	-0.1	0.0		1650	0.0	0.0
					2314	4.7	1.4
5 Sa	0006	4.5	1.4	20 Su	0540	0.1	0.0
	0623	0.1	0.0		1146	3.9	1.2
	1223	3.8	1.2		1741	0.2	0.1
	1838	0.3	0.1				
6 Su	0055	4.3	1.3	21 M	0007	4.6	1.4
	0722	0.4	0.1		0647	0.3	0.1
	1315	3.5	1.1		1246	3.7	1.1
	1937	0.5	0.2		1849	0.4	0.1
7 M	0148	4.1	1.2	22 Tu	0111	4.6	1.4
	0824	0.5	0.2		0804	0.3	0.1
	1411	3.3	1.0		1354	3.7	1.1
	2038	0.6	0.2		2009	0.4	0.1
8 Tu	0247	4.0	1.2	23 W	0222	4.6	1.4
	0923	0.5	0.2		0913	0.1	0.0
	1516	3.2	1.0		1509	3.8	1.2
	2139	0.6	0.2		2122	0.2	0.1
9 W	0348	4.0	1.2	24 Th	0335	4.7	1.4
	1016	0.4	0.1		1014	-0.2	-0.1
	1622	3.4	1.0		1620	4.1	1.2
	2230	0.5	0.2		2227	-0.1	0.0
10 Th	0446	4.2	1.3	25 F	0444	4.9	1.5
	1107	0.2	0.1		1112	-0.5	-0.2
	1716	3.6	1.1		1721	4.6	1.4
	2320	0.3	0.1		2326	-0.4	-0.1
11 F	0536	4.4	1.3	26 Sa	0543	5.2	1.6
	1155	0.0	0.0		1205	-0.8	-0.2
	1803	3.9	1.2		1814	5.0	1.5
12 Sa	0008	0.1	0.0	27 Su	0022	-0.7	-0.2
	0621	4.6	1.4		0633	5.4	1.6
	1238	-0.2	-0.1		1254	-0.9	-0.3
	1841	4.2	1.3		1902	5.4	1.6
13 Su	0054	0.0	0.0	28 M	0114	-0.9	-0.3
	0659	4.8	1.5		0721	5.4	1.6
	1320	-0.3	-0.1		1341	-1.0	-0.3
	1919	4.4	1.3		1945	5.6	1.7
14 M	0135	-0.2	-0.1	29 Tu	0204	-1.0	-0.3
	0738	4.8	1.5		0807	5.3	1.6
	1358	-0.4	-0.1		1426	-1.0	-0.3
	1954	4.6	1.4		2030	5.6	1.7
15 Tu	0214	-0.3	-0.1	30 W	0249	-1.0	-0.3
	0813	4.8	1.5		0849	5.1	1.6
	1433	-0.4	-0.1		1508	-0.8	-0.2
	2027	4.7	1.4		2113	5.5	1.7
				31 Th	0334	-0.8	-0.2
					0933	4.8	1.5
					1547	-0.5	-0.2
					2157	5.2	1.6

Time meridian 75° W. 0000 is midnight. 1200 is noon.
Heights are referred to mean low water which is the chart datum of soundings.

Times and Heights of High and Low Waters

APRIL

Day	Time h m	Height ft	Height m	Day	Time h m	Height ft	Height m
1 F	0416	-0.5	-0.2	16 Sa	0352	-0.4	-0.1
	1016	4.4	1.3		0951	4.4	1.3
	1626	-0.2	-0.1		1552	-0.1	0.0
	2240	4.9	1.5		2205	5.2	1.6
2 Sa	0458	-0.1	0.0	17 Su	0439	-0.2	-0.1
	1102	4.1	1.2		1043	4.2	1.3
	1707	0.2	0.1		1635	0.1	0.0
	2327	4.6	1.4		2258	5.1	1.6
3 Su	0546	0.2	0.1	18 M	0532	0.0	0.0
	1149	3.8	1.2		1141	4.0	1.2
	1753	0.6	0.2		1730	0.3	0.1
					2356	4.9	1.5
4 M	0012	4.4	1.3	19 Tu	0638	0.2	0.1
	0641	0.5	0.2		1243	3.9	1.2
	1239	3.5	1.1		1843	0.5	0.2
	1851	0.9	0.3				
5 Tu	0104	4.1	1.2	20 W	0100	4.8	1.5
	0742	0.7	0.2		0750	0.2	0.1
	1336	3.4	1.0		1349	4.0	1.2
	1958	1.0	0.3		2002	0.5	0.2
6 W	0201	4.0	1.2	21 Th	0209	4.7	1.4
	0844	0.7	0.2		0857	0.0	0.0
	1436	3.4	1.0		1458	4.2	1.3
	2103	1.0	0.3		2113	0.3	0.1
7 Th	0303	4.0	1.2	22 F	0320	4.7	1.4
	0940	0.5	0.2		0956	-0.2	-0.1
	1542	3.5	1.1		1606	4.5	1.4
	2158	0.8	0.2		2214	0.0	0.0
8 F	0404	4.1	1.2	23 Sa	0426	4.8	1.5
	1028	0.3	0.1		1049	-0.4	-0.1
	1641	3.8	1.2		1705	4.9	1.5
	2249	0.6	0.2		2312	-0.3	-0.1
9 Sa	0459	4.3	1.3	24 Su	0523	5.0	1.5
	1115	0.1	0.0		1140	-0.6	-0.2
	1729	4.2	1.3		1755	5.3	1.6
	2339	0.3	0.1				
10 Su	0548	4.6	1.4	25 M	0005	-0.5	-0.2
	1158	0.0	0.0		0614	5.1	1.6
	1811	4.5	1.4		1227	-0.7	-0.2
					1840	5.6	1.7
11 M	0024	0.0	0.0	26 Tu	0056	-0.7	-0.2
	0629	4.7	1.4		0700	5.1	1.6
	1240	-0.2	-0.1		1314	-0.7	-0.2
	1847	4.8	1.5		1922	5.7	1.7
12 Tu	0106	-0.2	-0.1	27 W	0143	-0.7	-0.2
	0706	4.8	1.5		0743	5.0	1.5
	1320	-0.3	-0.1		1357	-0.6	-0.2
	1924	5.1	1.6		2004	5.7	1.7
13 W	0149	-0.3	-0.1	28 Th	0229	-0.7	-0.2
	0747	4.8	1.5		0824	4.8	1.5
	1359	-0.3	-0.1		1439	-0.4	-0.1
	2001	5.2	1.6		2043	5.6	1.7
14 Th	0230	-0.4	-0.1	29 F	0311	-0.5	-0.2
	0824	4.8	1.5		0904	4.5	1.4
	1435	-0.3	-0.1		1515	-0.1	0.0
	2038	5.3	1.6		2125	5.3	1.6
15 F	0312	-0.4	-0.1	30 Sa	0351	-0.3	-0.1
	0906	4.6	1.4		0947	4.2	1.3
	1512	-0.3	-0.1		1555	0.2	0.1
	2118	5.3	1.6		2205	5.0	1.5

MAY

Day	Time h m	Height ft	Height m	Day	Time h m	Height ft	Height m
1 Su	0432	0.0	0.0	16 M	0431	-0.4	-0.1
	1032	4.0	1.2		1034	4.3	1.3
	1632	0.5	0.2		1629	0.1	0.0
	2248	4.7	1.4		2248	5.4	1.6
2 M	0515	0.3	0.1	17 Tu	0525	-0.2	-0.1
	1135	3.7	1.1		1135	4.3	1.3
	1714	0.8	0.2		1727	0.3	0.1
	2335	4.5	1.4		2348	5.1	1.6
3 Tu	0604	0.5	0.2	18 W	0626	-0.1	0.0
	1209	3.6	1.1		1236	4.3	1.3
	1807	1.1	0.3		1838	0.5	0.2
4 W	0025	4.2	1.3	19 Th	0049	4.9	1.5
	0700	0.7	0.2		0733	0.0	0.0
	1300	3.5	1.1		1339	4.4	1.3
	1915	1.2	0.4		1951	0.5	0.2
5 Th	0117	4.1	1.2	20 F	0154	4.7	1.4
	0801	0.7	0.2		0836	-0.1	0.0
	1357	3.6	1.1		1442	4.5	1.4
	2022	1.2	0.4		2059	0.4	0.1
6 F	0214	4.0	1.2	21 Sa	0258	4.6	1.4
	0856	0.6	0.2		0932	-0.2	-0.1
	1459	3.8	1.2		1545	4.8	1.5
	2121	1.0	0.3		2159	0.1	0.0
7 Sa	0316	4.1	1.2	22 Su	0404	4.6	1.4
	0945	0.4	0.1		1022	-0.3	-0.1
	1554	4.0	1.2		1641	5.1	1.6
	2214	0.7	0.2		2254	-0.1	0.0
8 Su	0414	4.2	1.3	23 M	0502	4.7	1.4
	1031	0.2	0.1		1112	-0.3	-0.1
	1646	4.4	1.3		1732	5.4	1.6
	2302	0.4	0.1		2345	-0.3	-0.1
9 M	0507	4.4	1.3	24 Tu	0552	4.7	1.4
	1115	0.0	0.0		1200	-0.3	-0.1
	1731	4.8	1.5		1817	5.6	1.7
	2350	0.1	0.0				
10 Tu	0552	4.6	1.4	25 W	0036	-0.4	-0.1
	1157	-0.1	0.0		0637	4.7	1.4
	1813	5.2	1.6		1245	-0.3	-0.1
					1858	5.7	1.7
11 W	0037	-0.1	0.0	26 Th	0122	-0.4	-0.1
	0637	4.7	1.4		0718	4.6	1.4
	1242	-0.2	-0.1		1327	-0.2	-0.1
	1853	5.5	1.7		1937	5.7	1.7
12 Th	0122	-0.4	-0.1	27 F	0208	-0.4	-0.1
	0718	4.8	1.5		0800	4.5	1.4
	1324	-0.3	-0.1		1409	0.0	0.0
	1933	5.7	1.7		2017	5.5	1.7
13 F	0208	-0.5	-0.2	28 Sa	0249	-0.3	-0.1
	0801	4.7	1.4		0840	4.3	1.3
	1408	-0.3	-0.1		1449	0.2	0.1
	2015	5.8	1.8		2055	5.3	1.6
14 Sa	0255	-0.6	-0.2	29 Su	0328	-0.1	0.0
	0847	4.6	1.4		0921	4.1	1.2
	1452	-0.2	-0.1		1527	0.4	0.1
	2101	5.7	1.7		2136	5.0	1.5
15 Su	0341	-0.5	-0.2	30 M	0408	0.1	0.0
	0938	4.5	1.4		1003	3.9	1.2
	1538	-0.1	0.0		1605	0.7	0.2
	2152	5.6	1.7		2218	4.8	1.5
				31 Tu	0448	0.3	0.1
					1050	3.8	1.2
					1644	0.9	0.3
					2301	4.6	1.4

JUNE

Day	Time h m	Height ft	Height m	Day	Time h m	Height ft	Height m
1 W	0530	0.5	0.2	16 Th	0609	-0.3	-0.1
	1137	3.7	1.1		1222	4.7	1.4
	1730	1.1	0.3		1825	0.3	0.1
	2349	4.4	1.3				
2 Th	0618	0.6	0.2	17 F	0034	5.0	1.5
	1226	3.7	1.1		0708	-0.2	-0.1
	1828	1.3	0.4		1320	4.8	1.5
					1934	0.4	0.1
3 F	0034	4.2	1.3	18 Sa	0133	4.8	1.5
	0712	0.6	0.2		0809	-0.1	0.0
	1317	3.8	1.2		1420	4.9	1.5
	1934	1.3	0.4		2039	0.4	0.1
4 Sa	0128	4.1	1.2	19 Su	0234	4.5	1.4
	0807	0.6	0.2		0903	-0.1	0.0
	1409	4.0	1.2		1518	5.0	1.5
	2039	1.1	0.3		2138	0.2	0.1
5 Su	0225	4.1	1.2	20 M	0334	4.4	1.3
	0857	0.5	0.2		0956	-0.1	0.0
	1506	4.3	1.3		1614	5.2	1.6
	2135	0.8	0.2		2233	0.1	0.0
6 M	0324	4.1	1.2	21 Tu	0435	4.3	1.3
	0945	0.3	0.1		1043	-0.1	0.0
	1601	4.6	1.4		1707	5.3	1.6
	2225	0.5	0.2		2323	0.0	0.0
7 Tu	0422	4.2	1.3	22 W	0528	4.3	1.3
	1030	0.1	0.0		1129	0.0	0.0
	1652	5.0	1.5		1753	5.5	1.7
	2315	0.2	0.1				
8 W	0515	4.4	1.3	23 Th	0013	0.0	0.0
	1118	-0.1	0.0		0615	4.3	1.3
	1739	5.4	1.6		1216	0.1	0.0
					1835	5.5	1.7
9 Th	0006	-0.1	0.0	24 F	0100	-0.1	0.0
	0606	4.6	1.4		0658	4.3	1.3
	1206	-0.2	-0.1		1302	0.2	0.1
	1825	5.7	1.7		1915	5.5	1.7
10 F	0057	-0.4	-0.1	25 Sa	0146	0.0	0.0
	0653	4.7	1.4		0738	4.2	1.3
	1253	-0.3	-0.1		1347	0.3	0.1
	1911	6.0	1.8		1954	5.4	1.6
11 Sa	0149	-0.6	-0.2	26 Su	0228	-0.1	0.0
	0743	4.7	1.4		0818	4.2	1.3
	1344	-0.3	-0.1		1426	0.4	0.1
	1957	6.1	1.9		2033	5.3	1.6
12 Su	0238	-0.7	-0.2	27 M	0306	0.0	0.0
	0832	4.7	1.4		0858	4.1	1.2
	1436	-0.3	-0.1		1506	0.5	0.2
	2046	6.0	1.8		2110	5.1	1.6
13 M	0327	-0.7	-0.2	28 Tu	0344	0.1	0.0
	0925	4.7	1.4		0939	4.0	1.2
	1528	-0.2	-0.1		1543	0.7	0.2
	2139	5.8	1.8		2149	4.9	1.5
14 Tu	0419	-0.6	-0.2	29 W	0421	0.2	0.1
	1024	4.6	1.4		1022	3.9	1.2
	1621	0.0	0.0		1619	0.9	0.3
	2237	5.6	1.7		2231	4.7	1.4
15 W	0511	-0.5	-0.2	30 Th	0458	0.3	0.1
	1124	4.6	1.4		1104	3.9	1.2
	1719	0.2	0.1		1658	1.0	0.3
	2335	5.3	1.6		2313	4.5	1.4

Time meridian 75° W. 0000 is midnight. 1200 is noon.
Heights are referred to mean low water which is the chart datum of soundings.

SANDY HOOK, N.J., 1983

Times and Heights of High and Low Waters

JULY

Day	Time h m	Height ft	m	Day	Time h m	Height ft	m
1 F	0537	0.5	0.2	16 Sa	0012	5.0	1.5
	1149	4.0	1.2		0639	-0.2	-0.1
	1746	1.1	0.3		1255	5.1	1.6
	2356	4.3	1.3		1908	0.3	0.1
2 Sa	0620	0.5	0.2	17 Su	0108	4.7	1.4
	1234	4.1	1.2		0735	0.0	0.0
	1846	1.2	0.4		1348	5.0	1.5
					2013	0.4	0.1
3 Su	0044	4.2	1.3	18 M	0203	4.4	1.3
	0713	0.6	0.2		0832	0.1	0.0
	1322	4.3	1.3		1445	5.0	1.5
	1951	1.1	0.3		2113	0.4	0.1
4 M	0136	4.1	1.2	19 Tu	0305	4.1	1.2
	0803	0.5	0.2		0925	0.2	0.1
	1415	4.5	1.4		1542	5.0	1.5
	2052	0.9	0.3		2208	0.4	0.1
5 Tu	0236	4.0	1.2	20 W	0405	4.0	1.2
	0859	0.4	0.1		1017	0.3	0.1
	1513	4.7	1.4		1638	5.1	1.6
	2150	0.6	0.2		2300	0.3	0.1
6 W	0341	4.1	1.2	21 Th	0502	4.0	1.2
	0950	0.2	0.1		1105	0.3	0.1
	1613	5.1	1.6		1728	5.2	1.6
	2243	0.3	0.1		2350	0.2	0.1
7 Th	0443	4.2	1.3	22 F	0551	4.1	1.2
	1043	0.0	0.0		1151	0.4	0.1
	1709	5.5	1.7		1813	5.3	1.6
	2339	0.0	0.0				
8 F	0539	4.4	1.3	23 Sa	0038	0.2	0.1
	1136	-0.1	0.0		0637	4.2	1.3
	1801	5.8	1.8		1237	0.4	0.1
					1853	5.4	1.6
9 Sa	0035	-0.3	-0.1	24 Su	0122	0.1	0.0
	0633	4.7	1.4		0718	4.2	1.3
	1232	-0.3	-0.1		1323	0.4	0.1
	1851	6.1	1.9		1932	5.3	1.6
10 Su	0129	-0.6	-0.2	25 M	0205	0.0	0.0
	0725	4.8	1.5		0756	4.3	1.3
	1327	-0.4	-0.1		1405	0.4	0.1
	1941	6.2	1.9		2010	5.3	1.6
11 M	0222	-0.8	-0.2	26 Tu	0242	0.0	0.0
	0817	5.0	1.5		0835	4.3	1.3
	1423	-0.4	-0.1		1446	0.5	0.2
	2033	6.2	1.9		2046	5.1	1.6
12 Tu	0312	-0.9	-0.3	27 W	0319	0.1	0.0
	0910	5.0	1.5		0914	4.2	1.3
	1517	-0.4	-0.1		1522	0.6	0.2
	2126	6.0	1.8		2123	4.9	1.5
13 W	0400	-0.8	-0.2	28 Th	0352	0.1	0.0
	1008	5.1	1.6		0951	4.2	1.3
	1610	-0.3	-0.1		1557	0.7	0.2
	2221	5.7	1.7		2202	4.8	1.5
14 Th	0450	-0.7	-0.2	29 F	0424	0.3	0.1
	1104	5.1	1.6		1029	4.3	1.3
	1704	-0.1	0.0		1632	0.8	0.2
	2317	5.4	1.6		2239	4.6	1.4
15 F	0543	-0.5	-0.2	30 Sa	0458	0.4	0.1
	1159	5.1	1.6		1110	4.3	1.3
	1804	0.2	0.1		1711	0.9	0.3
					2321	4.4	1.3
				31 Su	0533	0.5	0.2
					1153	4.4	1.3
					1801	1.0	0.3

AUGUST

Day	Time h m	Height ft	m	Day	Time h m	Height ft	m
1 M	0006	4.2	1.3	16 Tu	0133	4.2	1.3
	0615	0.6	0.2		0757	0.5	0.2
	1238	4.5	1.4		1411	4.9	1.5
	1906	1.0	0.3		2044	0.7	0.2
2 Tu	0057	4.1	1.2	17 W	0230	3.9	1.2
	0713	0.6	0.2		0853	0.6	0.2
	1331	4.7	1.4		1507	4.8	1.5
	2016	0.9	0.3		2140	0.6	0.2
3 W	0157	4.0	1.2	18 Th	0335	3.8	1.2
	0815	0.5	0.2		0948	0.7	0.2
	1434	4.9	1.5		1607	4.8	1.5
	2121	0.7	0.2		2235	0.6	0.2
4 Th	0303	4.0	1.2	19 F	0435	3.8	1.2
	0917	0.4	0.1		1040	0.6	0.2
	1540	5.1	1.6		1702	5.0	1.5
	2221	0.4	0.1		2323	0.4	0.1
5 F	0417	4.1	1.2	20 Sa	0531	4.0	1.2
	1017	0.2	0.1		1129	0.6	0.2
	1644	5.5	1.7		1748	5.1	1.6
	2318	0.0	0.0				
6 Sa	0521	4.4	1.3	21 Su	0009	0.3	0.1
	1116	-0.1	0.0		0614	4.2	1.3
	1744	5.8	1.8		1216	0.5	0.2
					1830	5.2	1.6
7 Su	0014	-0.3	-0.1	22 M	0054	0.1	0.0
	0616	4.8	1.5		0656	4.4	1.3
	1216	-0.3	-0.1		1301	0.4	0.1
	1837	6.1	1.9		1909	5.3	1.6
8 M	0109	-0.6	-0.2	23 Tu	0135	0.0	0.0
	0709	5.1	1.6		0733	4.5	1.4
	1314	-0.5	-0.2		1345	0.4	0.1
	1927	6.3	1.9		1947	5.2	1.6
9 Tu	0202	-0.9	-0.3	24 W	0213	0.0	0.0
	0800	5.3	1.6		0809	4.6	1.4
	1409	-0.6	-0.2		1423	0.4	0.1
	2017	6.2	1.9		2022	5.2	1.6
10 W	0250	-1.0	-0.3	25 Th	0249	0.0	0.0
	0851	5.5	1.7		0845	4.6	1.4
	1502	-0.6	-0.2		1459	0.4	0.1
	2108	6.0	1.8		2056	5.0	1.5
11 Th	0338	-0.9	-0.3	26 F	0322	0.1	0.0
	0944	5.5	1.7		0918	4.6	1.4
	1553	-0.5	-0.2		1534	0.5	0.2
	2200	5.7	1.7		2131	4.8	1.5
12 F	0425	-0.7	-0.2	27 Sa	0351	0.2	0.1
	1037	5.5	1.7		0954	4.6	1.4
	1644	-0.3	-0.1		1608	0.6	0.2
	2253	5.3	1.6		2208	4.6	1.4
13 Sa	0513	-0.5	-0.2	28 Su	0419	0.3	0.1
	1130	5.4	1.6		1032	4.7	1.4
	1739	0.0	0.0		1645	0.7	0.2
	2346	4.9	1.5		2250	4.4	1.3
14 Su	0604	-0.1	0.0	29 M	0452	0.4	0.1
	1223	5.2	1.6		1114	4.7	1.4
	1839	0.4	0.1		1727	0.8	0.2
					2333	4.2	1.3
15 M	0039	4.5	1.4	30 Tu	0531	0.5	0.2
	0658	0.2	0.1		1204	4.8	1.5
	1316	5.0	1.5		1832	0.9	0.3
	1941	0.6	0.2				
				31 W	0028	4.0	1.2
					0628	0.7	0.2
					1300	4.8	1.5
					1947	0.9	0.3

SEPTEMBER

Day	Time h m	Height ft	m	Day	Time h m	Height ft	m
1 Th	0130	3.9	1.2	16 F	0301	3.7	1.1
	0743	0.7	0.2		0919	1.0	0.3
	1404	4.9	1.5		1529	4.5	1.4
	2057	0.7	0.2		2204	0.7	0.2
2 F	0242	3.9	1.2	17 Sa	0406	3.8	1.2
	0858	0.6	0.2		1014	0.9	0.3
	1515	5.1	1.6		1627	4.7	1.4
	2201	0.4	0.1		2252	0.5	0.2
3 Sa	0358	4.1	1.2	18 Su	0503	4.0	1.2
	1004	0.3	0.1		1103	0.7	0.2
	1625	5.4	1.6		1720	4.8	1.5
	2259	0.0	0.0		2338	0.3	0.1
4 Su	0505	4.5	1.4	19 M	0547	4.3	1.3
	1105	0.0	0.0		1150	0.5	0.2
	1726	5.7	1.7		1804	5.0	1.5
	2355	-0.4	-0.1				
5 M	0601	5.0	1.5	20 Tu	0020	0.1	0.0
	1203	-0.3	-0.1		0627	4.6	1.4
	1821	6.0	1.8		1235	0.4	0.1
					1843	5.1	1.6
6 Tu	0048	-0.7	-0.2	21 W	0101	0.0	0.0
	0653	5.4	1.6		0705	4.8	1.5
	1301	-0.6	-0.2		1318	0.2	0.1
	1910	6.1	1.9		1920	5.2	1.6
7 W	0139	-0.9	-0.3	22 Th	0139	-0.1	0.0
	0743	5.7	1.7		0739	4.9	1.5
	1354	-0.7	-0.2		1358	0.2	0.1
	1959	6.1	1.9		1954	5.1	1.6
8 Th	0226	-1.0	-0.3	23 F	0216	-0.1	0.0
	0829	5.8	1.8		0813	5.0	1.5
	1444	-0.8	-0.2		1435	0.1	0.0
	2046	5.9	1.8		2030	5.0	1.5
9 F	0312	-0.9	-0.3	24 Sa	0248	0.0	0.0
	0918	5.8	1.8		0846	5.0	1.5
	1533	-0.6	-0.2		1511	0.2	0.1
	2136	5.5	1.7		2104	4.8	1.5
10 Sa	0355	-0.7	-0.2	25 Su	0320	0.1	0.0
	1007	5.7	1.7		0921	5.0	1.5
	1621	-0.4	-0.1		1548	0.3	0.1
	2225	5.1	1.6		2143	4.5	1.4
11 Su	0440	-0.3	-0.1	26 M	0349	0.2	0.1
	1057	5.5	1.7		0959	5.0	1.5
	1711	0.0	0.0		1625	0.4	0.1
	2317	4.7	1.4		2225	4.3	1.3
12 M	0527	0.1	0.0	27 Tu	0421	0.3	0.1
	1146	5.2	1.6		1045	5.0	1.5
	1805	0.4	0.1		1711	0.6	0.2
					2314	4.1	1.2
13 Tu	0007	4.3	1.3	28 W	0504	0.5	0.2
	0618	0.5	0.2		1137	4.9	1.5
	1239	4.9	1.5		1812	0.7	0.2
	1905	0.7	0.2				
14 W	0100	3.9	1.2	29 Th	0012	3.9	1.2
	0718	0.8	0.2		0604	0.7	0.2
	1333	4.7	1.4		1239	4.9	1.5
	2010	0.8	0.2		1929	0.7	0.2
15 Th	0158	3.7	1.1	30 F	0119	3.8	1.2
	0821	1.0	0.3		0727	0.8	0.2
	1431	4.6	1.4		1345	4.8	1.5
	2109	0.8	0.2		2041	0.5	0.2

Time meridian 75° W. 0000 is midnight. 1200 is noon.
Heights are referred to mean low water which is the chart datum of soundings.

Times and Heights of High and Low Waters

OCTOBER

Day	Time h m	Height ft	Height m	Day	Time h m	Height ft	Height m
1 Sa	0233	3.9	1.2	16 Su	0327	3.7	1.1
	0845	0.6	0.2		0945	1.0	0.3
	1458	4.9	1.5		1548	4.3	1.3
	2145	0.2	0.1		2215	0.4	0.1
2 Su	0346	4.2	1.3	17 M	0427	4.0	1.2
	0954	0.3	0.1		1035	0.7	0.2
	1609	5.1	1.6		1643	4.5	1.4
	2241	-0.1	0.0		2259	0.2	0.1
3 M	0451	4.7	1.4	18 Tu	0513	4.3	1.3
	1054	-0.1	0.0		1120	0.5	0.2
	1710	5.4	1.6		1728	4.7	1.4
	2334	-0.5	-0.2		2342	0.0	0.0
4 Tu	0547	5.2	1.6	19 W	0555	4.6	1.4
	1150	-0.4	-0.1		1205	0.3	0.1
	1804	5.7	1.7		1811	4.8	1.5
5 W	0024	-0.7	-0.2	20 Th	0023	-0.1	0.0
	0635	5.6	1.7		0632	4.9	1.5
	1245	-0.7	-0.2		1248	0.1	0.0
	1853	5.8	1.8		1850	4.9	1.5
6 Th	0112	-0.9	-0.3	21 F	0101	-0.2	-0.1
	0721	5.9	1.8		0709	5.1	1.6
	1337	-0.8	-0.2		1332	-0.1	0.0
	1939	5.7	1.7		1926	4.9	1.5
7 F	0159	-0.9	-0.3	22 Sa	0139	-0.2	-0.1
	0806	6.0	1.8		0743	5.3	1.6
	1426	-0.8	-0.2		1410	-0.1	-0.1
	2025	5.5	1.7		2002	4.8	1.5
8 Sa	0243	-0.8	-0.2	23 Su	0215	-0.2	-0.1
	0849	5.9	1.8		0818	5.3	1.6
	1512	-0.7	-0.2		1451	-0.2	-0.1
	2109	5.1	1.6		2041	4.6	1.4
9 Su	0326	-0.5	-0.2	24 M	0251	-0.1	0.0
	0936	5.7	1.7		0855	5.3	1.6
	1557	-0.4	-0.1		1531	-0.1	0.0
	2155	4.7	1.4		2123	4.4	1.3
10 M	0407	-0.2	-0.1	25 Tu	0325	0.0	0.0
	1023	5.4	1.6		0937	5.2	1.6
	1642	0.1	0.0		1613	0.0	0.0
	2244	4.3	1.3		2209	4.1	1.2
11 Tu	0448	0.2	0.1	26 W	0405	0.2	0.1
	1111	5.1	1.6		1026	5.1	1.6
	1733	0.3	0.1		1701	0.2	0.1
	2335	4.0	1.2		2305	3.9	1.2
12 W	0538	0.6	0.2	27 Th	0453	0.4	0.1
	1202	4.7	1.4		1122	4.9	1.5
	1828	0.6	0.2		1804	0.3	0.1
13 Th	0028	3.7	1.1	28 F	0007	3.8	1.2
	0635	1.0	0.3		0559	0.6	0.2
	1254	4.5	1.4		1226	4.8	1.5
	1931	0.8	0.2		1915	0.4	0.1
14 F	0124	3.6	1.1	29 Sa	0115	3.9	1.2
	0742	1.1	0.3		0719	0.7	0.2
	1349	4.3	1.3		1332	4.7	1.4
	2031	0.8	0.2		2024	0.2	0.1
15 Sa	0226	3.5	1.1	30 Su	0222	4.0	1.2
	0848	1.1	0.3		0838	0.5	0.2
	1448	4.2	1.3		1443	4.7	1.4
	2127	0.6	0.2		2126	0.0	0.0
				31 M	0330	4.4	1.3
					0942	0.2	0.1
					1550	4.8	1.5
					2220	-0.3	-0.1

NOVEMBER

Day	Time h m	Height ft	Height m	Day	Time h m	Height ft	Height m
1 Tu	0433	4.8	1.5	16 W	0431	4.2	1.3
	1041	-0.2	-0.1		1046	0.4	0.1
	1651	5.0	1.5		1649	4.2	1.3
	2310	-0.6	-0.2		2300	-0.1	0.0
2 W	0526	5.3	1.6	17 Th	0518	4.5	1.4
	1136	-0.5	-0.2		1132	0.1	0.0
	1747	5.1	1.6		1736	4.4	1.3
					2342	-0.2	-0.1
3 Th	0000	-0.8	-0.2	18 F	0558	4.9	1.5
	0614	5.6	1.7		1217	-0.1	0.0
	1229	-0.7	-0.2		1818	4.5	1.4
	1833	5.2	1.6				
4 F	0046	-0.8	-0.2	19 Sa	0022	-0.3	-0.1
	0659	5.9	1.8		0637	5.2	1.6
	1318	-0.8	-0.2		1303	-0.3	-0.1
	1918	5.1	1.6		1858	4.5	1.4
5 Sa	0133	-0.7	-0.2	20 Su	0104	-0.4	-0.1
	0741	5.9	1.8		0716	5.4	1.6
	1405	-0.8	-0.2		1349	-0.5	-0.2
	2001	4.9	1.5		1939	4.5	1.4
6 Su	0216	-0.7	-0.2	21 M	0146	-0.4	-0.1
	0823	5.8	1.8		0754	5.5	1.7
	1451	-0.7	-0.2		1432	-0.5	-0.2
	2044	4.6	1.4		2021	4.4	1.3
7 M	0258	-0.4	-0.1	22 Tu	0228	-0.4	-0.1
	0907	5.5	1.7		0836	5.5	1.7
	1533	-0.4	-0.1		1517	-0.5	-0.2
	2128	4.3	1.3		2107	4.2	1.3
8 Tu	0338	-0.1	0.0	23 W	0311	-0.3	-0.1
	0951	5.2	1.6		0923	5.4	1.6
	1618	-0.2	-0.1		1603	-0.4	-0.1
	2213	4.0	1.2		2200	4.1	1.2
9 W	0419	0.3	0.1	24 Th	0357	-0.1	0.0
	1037	4.9	1.5		1016	5.2	1.6
	1701	0.1	0.0		1653	-0.3	-0.1
	2301	3.7	1.1		2258	4.0	1.2
10 Th	0501	0.6	0.2	25 F	0450	0.1	0.0
	1124	4.5	1.4		1114	5.0	1.5
	1751	0.4	0.1		1751	-0.2	-0.1
	2356	3.5	1.1				
11 F	0554	0.9	0.3	26 Sa	0001	3.9	1.2
	1215	4.3	1.3		0554	0.3	0.1
	1847	0.6	0.2		1215	4.7	1.4
					1857	-0.1	0.0
12 Sa	0047	3.4	1.0	27 Su	0103	4.0	1.2
	0658	1.1	0.3		0711	0.3	0.1
	1305	4.1	1.2		1319	4.6	1.4
	1947	0.6	0.2		2003	-0.2	-0.1
13 Su	0144	3.5	1.1	28 M	0206	4.2	1.3
	0805	1.1	0.3		0824	0.2	0.1
	1401	4.0	1.2		1424	4.5	1.4
	2043	0.5	0.2		2102	-0.3	-0.1
14 M	0243	3.6	1.1	29 Tu	0311	4.5	1.4
	0905	0.9	0.3		0927	0.0	0.0
	1500	4.0	1.2		1530	4.4	1.3
	2132	0.3	0.1		2156	-0.5	-0.2
15 Tu	0339	3.8	1.2	30 W	0410	4.8	1.5
	0958	0.7	0.2		1025	-0.3	-0.1
	1557	4.1	1.2		1630	4.5	1.4
	2217	0.1	0.0		2247	-0.6	-0.2

DECEMBER

Day	Time h m	Height ft	Height m	Day	Time h m	Height ft	Height m
1 Th	0505	5.1	1.6	16 F	0433	4.4	1.3
	1120	-0.5	-0.2		1057	0.1	0.0
	1726	4.5	1.4		1657	3.9	1.2
	2334	-0.7	-0.2		2300	-0.3	-0.1
2 F	0555	5.4	1.6	17 Sa	0524	4.8	1.5
	1211	-0.7	-0.2		1147	-0.2	-0.1
	1813	4.5	1.4		1747	4.1	1.2
					2347	-0.4	-0.1
3 Sa	0022	-0.7	-0.2	18 Su	0608	5.1	1.6
	0638	5.6	1.7		1237	-0.5	-0.2
	1259	-0.7	-0.2		1833	4.2	1.3
	1858	4.5	1.4				
4 Su	0108	-0.7	-0.2	19 M	0033	-0.6	-0.2
	0721	5.6	1.7		0651	5.4	1.6
	1348	-0.7	-0.2		1326	-0.7	-0.2
	1940	4.3	1.3		1920	4.3	1.3
5 M	0151	-0.5	-0.2	20 Tu	0122	-0.7	-0.2
	0802	5.4	1.6		0736	5.5	1.7
	1430	-0.7	-0.2		1415	-0.9	-0.3
	2022	4.2	1.3		2006	4.3	1.3
6 Tu	0233	-0.3	-0.1	21 W	0211	-0.7	-0.2
	0842	5.2	1.6		0822	5.6	1.7
	1512	-0.5	-0.2		1503	-0.9	-0.3
	2103	3.9	1.2		2056	4.3	1.3
7 W	0312	-0.1	0.0	22 Th	0259	-0.7	-0.2
	0922	4.9	1.5		0912	5.4	1.6
	1554	-0.3	-0.1		1551	-0.9	-0.3
	2147	3.7	1.1		2151	4.2	1.3
8 Th	0352	0.2	0.1	23 F	0351	-0.6	-0.2
	1005	4.7	1.4		1006	5.3	1.6
	1634	-0.1	0.0		1640	-0.8	-0.2
	2234	3.6	1.1		2248	4.2	1.3
9 F	0431	0.4	0.1	24 Sa	0445	-0.4	-0.1
	1050	4.4	1.3		1103	5.0	1.5
	1717	0.1	0.0		1733	-0.7	-0.2
	2322	3.5	1.1		2346	4.2	1.3
10 Sa	0517	0.7	0.2	25 Su	0546	-0.2	-0.1
	1135	4.1	1.2		1201	4.7	1.4
	1802	0.2	0.1		1833	-0.5	-0.2
11 Su	0009	3.4	1.0	26 M	0045	4.3	1.3
	0610	0.8	0.2		0654	0.0	0.0
	1223	4.0	1.2		1300	4.4	1.3
	1855	0.3	0.1		1934	-0.5	-0.2
12 M	0100	3.5	1.1	27 Tu	0144	4.4	1.3
	0716	0.9	0.3		0803	0.0	0.0
	1313	3.8	1.2		1400	4.2	1.3
	1951	0.3	0.1		2035	-0.4	-0.1
13 Tu	0151	3.6	1.1	28 W	0244	4.5	1.4
	0819	0.8	0.2		0908	-0.1	0.0
	1406	3.7	1.1		1503	4.0	1.2
	2043	0.2	0.1		2129	-0.5	-0.2
14 W	0246	3.7	1.1	29 Th	0345	4.7	1.4
	0916	0.6	0.2		1006	-0.3	-0.1
	1505	3.7	1.1		1606	3.9	1.2
	2130	0.1	0.0		2220	-0.4	-0.1
15 Th	0342	4.0	1.2	30 F	0443	4.8	1.5
	1007	0.4	0.1		1059	-0.4	-0.1
	1601	3.8	1.2		1705	3.9	1.2
	2215	-0.1	0.0		2310	-0.5	-0.2
				31 Sa	0534	5.0	1.5
					1152	-0.4	-0.1
					1755	4.0	1.2
					2357	-0.5	-0.2

Time meridian 75° W. 0000 is midnight. 1200 is noon.
Heights are referred to mean low water which is the chart datum of soundings.

76

PHILADELPHIA, PA., 1983

Times and Heights of High and Low Waters

JANUARY

Day	Time h m	Height ft	m	Day	Time h m	Height ft	m
1 Sa	0249	5.6	1.7	16 Su	0306	4.9	1.5
	0954	-0.6	-0.2		0949	-0.2	-0.1
	1510	6.9	2.1		1515	5.9	1.8
	2237	-0.8	-0.2		2230	-0.2	-0.1
2 Su	0343	5.6	1.7	17 M	0342	4.9	1.5
	1045	-0.6	-0.2		1033	-0.2	-0.1
	1605	6.7	2.0		1551	5.8	1.8
	2327	-0.8	-0.2		2311	-0.2	-0.1
3 M	0440	5.6	1.7	18 Tu	0418	4.9	1.5
	1137	-0.5	-0.2		1117	-0.2	-0.1
	1700	6.5	2.0		1623	5.7	1.7
					2352	-0.2	-0.1
4 Tu	0017	-0.7	-0.2	19 W	0451	4.9	1.5
	0537	5.6	1.7		1202	-0.1	0.0
	1231	-0.4	-0.1		1701	5.5	1.7
	1757	6.3	1.9				
5 W	0106	-0.7	-0.2	20 Th	0034	-0.2	-0.1
	0636	5.6	1.7		0532	5.0	1.5
	1324	-0.3	-0.1		1252	-0.1	0.0
	1855	6.0	1.8		1746	5.3	1.6
6 Th	0156	-0.6	-0.2	21 F	0117	-0.2	-0.1
	0735	5.7	1.7		0621	5.1	1.6
	1420	-0.2	-0.1		1347	0.0	0.0
	1954	5.7	1.7		1841	5.1	1.6
7 F	0248	-0.5	-0.2	22 Sa	0206	-0.2	-0.1
	0831	5.7	1.7		0718	5.2	1.6
	1517	-0.1	0.0		1445	0.0	0.0
	2050	5.5	1.7		1947	4.9	1.5
8 Sa	0339	-0.4	-0.1	23 Su	0258	-0.2	-0.1
	0927	5.8	1.8		0821	5.4	1.6
	1613	-0.1	0.0		1547	0.0	0.0
	2145	5.4	1.6		2051	4.8	1.5
9 Su	0430	-0.3	-0.1	24 M	0356	-0.2	-0.1
	1018	5.9	1.8		0923	5.6	1.7
	1708	-0.1	0.0		1649	0.0	0.0
	2238	5.2	1.6		2152	4.9	1.5
10 M	0520	-0.3	-0.1	25 Tu	0457	-0.3	-0.1
	1108	5.9	1.8		1021	5.9	1.8
	1800	-0.2	-0.1		1748	-0.2	-0.1
	2329	5.2	1.6		2252	5.0	1.5
11 Tu	0609	-0.2	-0.1	26 W	0556	-0.3	-0.1
	1155	6.0	1.8		1119	6.3	1.9
	1851	-0.2	-0.1		1848	-0.3	-0.1
					2350	5.2	1.6
12 W	0016	5.1	1.6	27 Th	0653	-0.5	-0.2
	0656	-0.2	-0.1		1214	6.6	2.0
	1240	6.0	1.8		1942	-0.5	-0.2
	1939	-0.3	-0.1				
13 Th	0103	5.1	1.6	28 F	0045	5.5	1.7
	0741	-0.2	-0.1		0749	-0.6	-0.2
	1321	6.0	1.8		1309	6.8	2.1
	2024	-0.3	-0.1		2035	-0.6	-0.2
14 F	0146	5.0	1.5	29 Sa	0138	5.7	1.7
	0825	-0.2	-0.1		0842	-0.6	-0.2
	1401	6.0	1.8		1401	6.9	2.1
	2108	-0.3	-0.1		2127	-0.7	-0.2
15 Sa	0227	4.9	1.5	30 Su	0232	5.9	1.8
	0908	-0.2	-0.1		0935	-0.6	-0.2
	1439	5.9	1.8		1452	6.9	2.1
	2150	-0.2	-0.1		2214	-0.7	-0.2
				31 M	0324	6.0	1.8
					1026	-0.6	-0.2
					1545	6.8	2.1
					2302	-0.7	-0.2

FEBRUARY

Day	Time h m	Height ft	m	Day	Time h m	Height ft	m
1 Tu	0419	6.1	1.9	16 W	0346	5.4	1.6
	1117	-0.5	-0.2		1058	-0.1	0.0
	1638	6.5	2.0		1559	5.8	1.8
	2348	-0.6	-0.2		2322	-0.1	0.0
2 W	0512	6.0	1.8	17 Th	0416	5.5	1.7
	1207	-0.4	-0.1		1145	-0.1	0.0
	1732	6.2	1.9		1635	5.6	1.7
3 Th	0034	-0.5	-0.2	18 F	0004	-0.1	0.0
	0607	5.9	1.8		0456	5.5	1.7
	1259	-0.3	-0.1		1233	-0.1	0.0
	1827	5.8	1.8		1720	5.4	1.6
4 F	0122	-0.4	-0.1	19 Sa	0047	-0.1	0.0
	0703	5.8	1.8		0540	5.6	1.7
	1352	-0.2	-0.1		1324	0.0	0.0
	1924	5.5	1.7		1812	5.1	1.6
5 Sa	0211	-0.3	-0.1	20 Su	0133	-0.1	0.0
	0757	5.7	1.7		0642	5.6	1.7
	1446	-0.1	0.0		1422	0.1	0.0
	2020	5.2	1.6		1916	4.9	1.5
6 Su	0301	-0.3	-0.1	21 M	0228	-0.1	0.0
	0852	5.6	1.7		0748	5.6	1.7
	1542	-0.1	0.0		1524	0.1	0.0
	2117	5.0	1.5		2024	4.8	1.5
7 M	0353	-0.2	-0.1	22 Tu	0330	-0.1	0.0
	0946	5.6	1.7		0854	5.8	1.8
	1636	-0.1	0.0		1627	0.1	0.0
	2211	4.9	1.5		2131	4.9	1.5
8 Tu	0444	-0.2	-0.1	23 W	0433	-0.1	0.0
	1038	5.6	1.7		0959	6.0	1.8
	1730	-0.1	0.0		1727	0.0	0.0
	2303	4.9	1.5		2233	5.2	1.6
9 W	0537	-0.2	-0.1	24 Th	0535	-0.2	-0.1
	1127	5.7	1.7		1059	6.3	1.9
	1822	-0.2	-0.1		1824	-0.1	0.0
	2353	5.0	1.5		2332	5.5	1.7
10 Th	0626	-0.2	-0.1	25 F	0634	-0.2	-0.1
	1214	5.9	1.8		1156	6.7	2.0
	1909	-0.2	-0.1		1920	-0.2	-0.1
11 F	0040	5.1	1.6	26 Sa	0027	5.9	1.8
	0714	-0.2	-0.1		0731	-0.3	-0.1
	1257	6.0	1.8		1251	6.9	2.1
	1957	-0.2	-0.1		2011	-0.3	-0.1
12 Sa	0123	5.2	1.6	27 Su	0121	6.2	1.9
	0801	-0.2	-0.1		0824	-0.4	-0.1
	1338	6.0	1.8		1343	7.0	2.1
	2040	-0.2	-0.1		2100	-0.4	-0.1
13 Su	0203	5.2	1.6	28 M	0212	6.5	2.0
	0846	-0.2	-0.1		0915	-0.4	-0.1
	1417	6.1	1.9		1433	7.0	2.1
	2122	-0.1	0.0		2148	-0.4	-0.1
14 M	0240	5.3	1.6				
	0931	-0.2	-0.1				
	1452	6.1	1.9				
	2204	-0.1	0.0				
15 Tu	0314	5.3	1.6				
	1014	-0.2	-0.1				
	1526	5.9	1.8				
	2243	-0.1	0.0				

MARCH

Day	Time h m	Height ft	m	Day	Time h m	Height ft	m
1 Tu	0303	6.6	2.0	16 W	0245	6.0	1.8
	1005	-0.3	-0.1		0955	0.0	0.0
	1524	6.9	2.1		1502	6.1	1.9
	2232	-0.3	-0.1		2215	0.2	0.1
2 W	0353	6.6	2.0	17 Th	0315	6.1	1.9
	1054	-0.3	-0.1		1040	0.0	0.0
	1613	6.6	2.0		1537	5.9	1.8
	2317	-0.2	-0.1		2257	0.2	0.1
3 Th	0442	6.4	2.0	18 F	0349	6.1	1.9
	1141	-0.2	-0.1		1127	0.0	0.0
	1704	6.2	1.9		1615	5.7	1.7
					2338	0.1	0.0
4 F	0002	-0.2	-0.1	19 Sa	0429	6.1	1.9
	0533	6.2	1.9		1215	0.0	0.0
	1231	-0.1	0.0		1701	5.4	1.6
	1757	5.7	1.7				
5 Sa	0046	-0.1	0.0	20 Su	0022	0.1	0.0
	0626	5.9	1.8		0517	6.1	1.9
	1321	0.0	0.0		1308	0.1	0.0
	1852	5.4	1.6		1757	5.2	1.6
6 Su	0132	0.0	0.0	21 M	0111	0.1	0.0
	0719	5.7	1.7		0619	6.0	1.8
	1412	0.1	0.0		1404	0.2	0.1
	1948	5.1	1.6		1903	5.0	1.5
7 M	0222	0.0	0.0	22 Tu	0209	0.2	0.1
	0815	5.6	1.7		0727	5.9	1.8
	1505	0.1	0.0		1504	0.2	0.1
	2045	4.9	1.5		2010	5.0	1.5
8 Tu	0313	0.1	0.0	23 W	0311	0.2	0.1
	0910	5.5	1.7		0836	6.0	1.8
	1600	0.1	0.0		1605	0.2	0.1
	2141	4.9	1.5		2116	5.2	1.6
9 W	0409	0.1	0.0	24 Th	0415	0.2	0.1
	1004	5.6	1.7		0942	6.2	1.9
	1656	0.1	0.0		1704	0.2	0.1
	2234	5.0	1.5		2217	5.6	1.7
10 Th	0502	0.0	0.0	25 F	0516	0.2	0.1
	1057	5.8	1.8		1042	6.5	2.0
	1747	0.1	0.0		1803	0.1	0.0
	2325	5.2	1.6		2316	6.0	1.8
11 F	0556	0.0	0.0	26 Sa	0616	0.1	0.0
	1145	5.9	1.8		1139	6.8	2.1
	1838	0.1	0.0		1855	0.1	0.0
12 Sa	0012	5.4	1.6	27 Su	0011	6.5	2.0
	0648	0.0	0.0		0713	0.0	0.0
	1230	6.1	1.9		1233	7.0	2.1
	1926	0.1	0.0		1946	0.0	0.0
13 Su	0055	5.6	1.7	28 M	0102	6.8	2.1
	0736	0.0	0.0		0806	0.0	0.0
	1312	6.2	1.9		1324	7.1	2.2
	2010	0.1	0.0		2033	0.0	0.0
14 M	0134	5.7	1.7	29 Tu	0152	7.0	2.1
	0824	0.0	0.0		0856	0.0	0.0
	1350	6.2	1.9		1413	7.0	2.1
	2053	0.1	0.0		2119	0.1	0.0
15 Tu	0210	5.9	1.8	30 W	0239	7.1	2.2
	0909	0.0	0.0		0944	0.0	0.0
	1426	6.2	1.9		1500	6.8	2.1
	2135	0.2	0.1		2202	0.2	0.1
				31 Th	0325	7.0	2.1
					1030	0.0	0.0
					1547	6.5	2.0
					2244	0.2	0.1

Time meridian 75° W. 0000 is midnight. 1200 is noon.
Heights are referred to mean low water which is the chart datum of soundings.

Times and Heights of High and Low Waters

APRIL

Day	Time h m	ft	m	Day	Time h m	ft	m
1 F	0411	6.8	2.1	16 Sa	0327	6.7	2.0
	1116	0.1	0.0		1109	0.0	0.0
	1636	6.1	1.9		1600	5.7	1.7
	2327	0.3	0.1		2315	0.3	0.1
2 Sa	0457	6.4	2.0	17 Su	0412	6.6	2.0
	1202	0.1	0.0		1200	0.1	0.0
	1725	5.7	1.7		1649	5.5	1.7
3 Su	0010	0.3	0.1	18 M	0002	0.3	0.1
	0546	6.1	1.9		0503	6.5	2.0
	1248	0.2	0.1		1252	0.1	0.0
	1819	5.3	1.6		1746	5.3	1.6
4 M	0053	0.3	0.1	19 Tu	0055	0.3	0.1
	0639	5.8	1.8		0605	6.3	1.9
	1338	0.2	0.1		1347	0.2	0.1
	1914	5.1	1.6		1851	5.3	1.6
5 Tu	0142	0.4	0.1	20 W	0154	0.4	0.1
	0734	5.7	1.7		0711	6.3	1.9
	1430	0.3	0.1		1444	0.3	0.1
	2011	5.0	1.5		1958	5.4	1.6
6 W	0235	0.4	0.1	21 Th	0256	0.5	0.2
	0831	5.6	1.7		0820	6.3	1.9
	1523	0.3	0.1		1543	0.3	0.1
	2108	5.1	1.6		2103	5.7	1.7
7 Th	0331	0.4	0.1	22 F	0358	0.5	0.2
	0927	5.7	1.7		0925	6.4	2.0
	1617	0.4	0.1		1641	0.3	0.1
	2202	5.3	1.6		2204	6.1	1.9
8 F	0428	0.4	0.1	23 Sa	0500	0.4	0.1
	1021	5.9	1.8		1025	6.6	2.0
	1711	0.4	0.1		1736	0.3	0.1
	2254	5.5	1.7		2300	6.6	2.0
9 Sa	0525	0.3	0.1	24 Su	0558	0.4	0.1
	1110	6.1	1.9		1121	6.8	2.1
	1803	0.4	0.1		1829	0.3	0.1
	2340	5.8	1.8		2353	7.0	2.1
10 Su	0619	0.3	0.1	25 M	0653	0.3	0.1
	1158	6.2	1.9		1214	6.9	2.1
	1851	0.4	0.1		1918	0.3	0.1
11 M	0024	6.1	1.9	26 Tu	0043	7.3	2.2
	0710	0.2	0.1		0746	0.3	0.1
	1240	6.3	1.9		1304	6.9	2.1
	1937	0.4	0.1		2005	0.4	0.1
12 Tu	0103	6.3	1.9	27 W	0129	7.4	2.3
	0800	0.2	0.1		0834	0.2	0.1
	1320	6.3	1.9		1350	6.7	2.0
	2022	0.4	0.1		2050	0.4	0.1
13 W	0139	6.5	2.0	28 Th	0213	7.3	2.2
	0847	0.1	0.0		0921	0.2	0.1
	1359	6.2	1.9		1436	6.5	2.0
	2105	0.4	0.1		2132	0.5	0.2
14 Th	0214	6.6	2.0	29 F	0257	7.2	2.2
	0934	0.1	0.0		1006	0.3	0.1
	1436	6.1	1.9		1522	6.2	1.9
	2147	0.4	0.1		2213	0.6	0.2
15 F	0249	6.7	2.0	30 Sa	0339	6.9	2.1
	1022	0.0	0.0		1051	0.3	0.1
	1515	5.9	1.8		1608	5.9	1.8
	2230	0.3	0.1		2253	0.6	0.2

MAY

Day	Time h m	ft	m	Day	Time h m	ft	m
1 Su	0423	6.6	2.0	16 M	0358	7.0	2.1
	1133	0.3	0.1		1142	0.0	0.0
	1656	5.6	1.7		1638	5.6	1.7
	2335	0.6	0.2		2347	0.4	0.1
2 M	0507	6.3	1.9	17 Tu	0453	6.8	2.1
	1218	0.3	0.1		1234	0.0	0.0
	1746	5.3	1.6		1738	5.6	1.7
3 Tu	0018	0.6	0.2	18 W	0042	0.4	0.1
	0557	6.0	1.8		0554	6.6	2.0
	1304	0.4	0.1		1328	0.1	0.0
	1839	5.2	1.6		1841	5.6	1.7
4 W	0106	0.6	0.2	19 Th	0138	0.5	0.2
	0650	5.8	1.8		0700	6.5	2.0
	1353	0.4	0.1		1423	0.2	0.1
	1935	5.1	1.6		1946	5.8	1.8
5 Th	0159	0.6	0.2	20 F	0239	0.5	0.2
	0748	5.7	1.7		0805	6.4	2.0
	1445	0.5	0.2		1519	0.2	0.1
	2031	5.2	1.6		2048	6.1	1.9
6 F	0256	0.6	0.2	21 Sa	0340	0.6	0.2
	0846	5.8	1.8		0907	6.4	2.0
	1538	0.5	0.2		1615	0.2	0.1
	2126	5.5	1.7		2148	6.5	2.0
7 Sa	0355	0.6	0.2	22 Su	0441	0.5	0.2
	0941	5.9	1.8		1006	6.5	2.0
	1633	0.5	0.2		1709	0.3	0.1
	2217	5.8	1.8		2243	6.9	2.1
8 Su	0452	0.6	0.2	23 M	0539	0.5	0.2
	1031	6.0	1.8		1102	6.6	2.0
	1724	0.5	0.2		1800	0.3	0.1
	2304	6.1	1.9		2334	7.2	2.2
9 M	0550	0.5	0.2	24 Tu	0632	0.4	0.1
	1120	6.1	1.9		1153	6.6	2.0
	1814	0.5	0.2		1849	0.4	0.1
	2346	6.4	2.0				
10 Tu	0643	0.4	0.1	25 W	0021	7.3	2.2
	1206	6.1	1.9		0724	0.3	0.1
	1902	0.5	0.2		1241	6.5	2.0
					1935	0.5	0.2
11 W	0028	6.7	2.0	26 Th	0106	7.3	2.2
	0734	0.3	0.1		0812	0.3	0.1
	1248	6.1	1.9		1329	6.3	1.9
	1949	0.5	0.2		2019	0.6	0.2
12 Th	0106	6.9	2.1	27 F	0148	7.2	2.2
	0825	0.1	0.0		0858	0.3	0.1
	1330	6.1	1.9		1413	6.1	1.9
	2035	0.4	0.1		2101	0.6	0.2
13 F	0146	7.0	2.1	28 Sa	0230	7.1	2.2
	0915	0.1	0.0		0940	0.3	0.1
	1411	6.0	1.8		1457	5.9	1.8
	2121	0.4	0.1		2142	0.7	0.2
14 Sa	0226	7.1	2.2	29 Su	0310	6.8	2.1
	1003	0.0	0.0		1024	0.3	0.1
	1457	5.9	1.8		1542	5.6	1.7
	2208	0.3	0.1		2221	0.7	0.2
15 Su	0310	7.1	2.2	30 M	0351	6.6	2.0
	1053	0.0	0.0		1106	0.4	0.1
	1544	5.7	1.7		1626	5.4	1.6
	2255	0.3	0.1		2303	0.7	0.2
				31 Tu	0433	6.3	1.9
					1149	0.4	0.1
					1712	5.3	1.6
					2347	0.7	0.2

JUNE

Day	Time h m	ft	m	Day	Time h m	ft	m
1 W	0517	6.1	1.9	16 Th	0025	0.3	0.1
	1231	0.4	0.1		0541	6.8	2.1
	1802	5.2	1.6		1306	-0.1	0.0
					1827	5.9	1.8
2 Th	0034	0.7	0.2	17 F	0122	0.4	0.1
	0607	5.9	1.8		0644	6.5	2.0
	1319	0.4	0.1		1359	0.0	0.0
	1856	5.2	1.6		1930	6.1	1.9
3 F	0127	0.7	0.2	18 Sa	0220	0.5	0.2
	0701	5.8	1.8		0746	6.4	2.0
	1407	0.4	0.1		1453	0.0	0.0
	1950	5.3	1.6		2030	6.3	1.9
4 Sa	0222	0.7	0.2	19 Su	0319	0.5	0.2
	0800	5.7	1.7		0847	6.3	1.9
	1459	0.5	0.2		1546	0.1	0.0
	2043	5.5	1.7		2128	6.6	2.0
5 Su	0322	0.7	0.2	20 M	0418	0.5	0.2
	0856	5.7	1.7		0945	6.2	1.9
	1551	0.5	0.2		1639	0.2	0.1
	2134	5.8	1.8		2221	6.8	2.1
6 M	0421	0.7	0.2	21 Tu	0516	0.4	0.1
	0950	5.7	1.7		1040	6.1	1.9
	1644	0.5	0.2		1731	0.2	0.1
	2222	6.2	1.9		2311	7.0	2.1
7 Tu	0520	0.5	0.2	22 W	0609	0.3	0.1
	1041	5.8	1.8		1131	6.1	1.9
	1737	0.4	0.1		1819	0.3	0.1
	2309	6.5	2.0		2358	7.1	2.2
8 W	0616	0.4	0.1	23 Th	0701	0.2	0.1
	1129	5.8	1.8		1219	6.0	1.8
	1828	0.4	0.1		1905	0.4	0.1
	2351	6.8	2.1				
9 Th	0709	0.2	0.1	24 F	0042	7.1	2.2
	1216	5.8	1.8		0747	0.2	0.1
	1917	0.4	0.1		1305	5.9	1.8
					1950	0.5	0.2
10 F	0036	7.1	2.2	25 Sa	0125	7.0	2.1
	0802	0.1	0.0		0832	0.2	0.1
	1303	5.9	1.8		1351	5.7	1.7
	2006	0.3	0.1		2033	0.5	0.2
11 Sa	0119	7.2	2.2	26 Su	0205	6.9	2.1
	0852	0.0	0.0		0915	0.3	0.1
	1349	5.9	1.8		1433	5.6	1.7
	2056	0.2	0.1		2113	0.6	0.2
12 Su	0206	7.3	2.2	27 M	0244	6.7	2.0
	0942	-0.1	0.0		0957	0.3	0.1
	1439	5.9	1.8		1515	5.5	1.7
	2147	0.2	0.1		2155	0.6	0.2
13 M	0254	7.3	2.2	28 Tu	0323	6.5	2.0
	1033	-0.1	0.0		1039	0.3	0.1
	1530	5.8	1.8		1557	5.4	1.6
	2237	0.2	0.1		2237	0.6	0.2
14 Tu	0345	7.2	2.2	29 W	0401	6.4	2.0
	1123	-0.1	0.0		1120	0.4	0.1
	1626	5.8	1.8		1639	5.3	1.6
	2330	0.3	0.1		2320	0.6	0.2
15 W	0440	7.0	2.1	30 Th	0440	6.2	1.9
	1215	-0.1	0.0		1202	0.4	0.1
	1725	5.8	1.8		1723	5.2	1.6

Time meridian 75° W.   0000 is midnight.   1200 is noon.
Heights are referred to mean low water which is the chart datum of soundings.

HAMPTON ROADS (Sewells Pt.), VA., 1983

Times and Heights of High and Low Waters

JANUARY

Day	Time h m	Height ft	Height m
1 Sa	0406	-0.6	-0.2
	1031	3.0	0.9
	1656	-0.6	-0.2
	2300	2.5	0.8
2 Su	0502	-0.5	-0.2
	1124	2.9	0.9
	1746	-0.5	-0.2
	2354	2.5	0.8
3 M	0559	-0.3	-0.1
	1218	2.8	0.9
	1839	-0.3	-0.1
4 Tu	0052	2.5	0.8
	0658	-0.1	0.0
	1313	2.6	0.8
	1933	-0.2	-0.1
5 W	0150	2.5	0.8
	0801	0.0	0.0
	1412	2.4	0.7
	2029	-0.1	0.0
6 Th	0251	2.4	0.7
	0907	0.1	0.0
	1510	2.2	0.7
	2125	0.0	0.0
7 F	0352	2.4	0.7
	1012	0.2	0.1
	1612	2.0	0.6
	2221	0.0	0.0
8 Sa	0449	2.4	0.7
	1115	0.1	0.0
	1709	1.8	0.5
	2313	0.0	0.0
9 Su	0544	2.3	0.7
	1214	0.0	0.0
	1804	1.7	0.5
10 M	0003	-0.1	0.0
	0635	2.3	0.7
	1304	-0.1	0.0
	1855	1.7	0.5
11 Tu	0053	-0.2	-0.1
	0718	2.3	0.7
	1348	-0.3	-0.1
	1941	1.6	0.5
12 W	0136	-0.3	-0.1
	0800	2.3	0.7
	1430	-0.4	-0.1
	2023	1.6	0.5
13 Th	0218	-0.4	-0.1
	0841	2.3	0.7
	1509	-0.5	-0.2
	2104	1.6	0.5
14 F	0257	-0.4	-0.1
	0919	2.2	0.7
	1545	-0.5	-0.2
	2142	1.6	0.5
15 Sa	0336	-0.4	-0.1
	0956	2.2	0.7
	1619	-0.5	-0.2
	2221	1.7	0.5
16 Su	0414	-0.4	-0.1
	1033	2.1	0.6
	1654	-0.5	-0.2
	2256	1.7	0.5
17 M	0452	-0.3	-0.1
	1108	2.1	0.6
	1728	-0.4	-0.1
	2333	1.7	0.5
18 Tu	0530	-0.2	-0.1
	1144	2.0	0.6
	1801	-0.3	-0.1
19 W	0010	1.8	0.5
	0610	-0.2	-0.1
	1223	1.9	0.6
	1837	-0.3	-0.1
20 Th	0052	1.9	0.6
	0657	-0.1	0.0
	1302	1.8	0.5
	1916	-0.2	-0.1
21 F	0137	2.0	0.6
	0750	0.0	0.0
	1351	1.8	0.5
	2003	-0.2	-0.1
22 Sa	0233	2.1	0.6
	0849	0.0	0.0
	1445	1.7	0.5
	2056	-0.2	-0.1
23 Su	0332	2.2	0.7
	0956	0.0	0.0
	1551	1.7	0.5
	2157	-0.2	-0.1
24 M	0434	2.3	0.7
	1102	-0.1	0.0
	1657	1.8	0.5
	2302	-0.3	-0.1
25 Tu	0539	2.5	0.8
	1208	-0.2	-0.1
	1803	1.9	0.6
26 W	0006	-0.4	-0.1
	0640	2.6	0.8
	1307	-0.4	-0.1
	1906	2.0	0.6
27 Th	0107	-0.6	-0.2
	0738	2.8	0.9
	1403	-0.5	-0.2
	2003	2.2	0.7
28 F	0207	-0.7	-0.2
	0832	2.9	0.9
	1456	-0.6	-0.2
	2058	2.4	0.7
29 Sa	0302	-0.7	-0.2
	0925	3.0	0.9
	1547	-0.7	-0.2
	2151	2.5	0.8
30 Su	0357	-0.7	-0.2
	1016	3.0	0.9
	1637	-0.7	-0.2
	2243	2.6	0.8
31 M	0450	-0.6	-0.2
	1106	2.9	0.9
	1724	-0.6	-0.2
	2335	2.6	0.8

FEBRUARY

Day	Time h m	Height ft	Height m
1 Tu	0543	-0.4	-0.1
	1157	2.7	0.8
	1813	-0.4	-0.1
2 W	0028	2.6	0.8
	0638	-0.2	-0.1
	1247	2.5	0.8
	1901	-0.3	-0.1
3 Th	0121	2.5	0.8
	0735	0.0	0.0
	1340	2.3	0.7
	1951	-0.1	0.0
4 F	0217	2.4	0.7
	0834	0.1	0.0
	1434	2.0	0.6
	2043	0.0	0.0
5 Sa	0314	2.3	0.7
	0939	0.2	0.1
	1534	1.8	0.5
	2139	0.1	0.0
6 Su	0411	2.2	0.7
	1044	0.2	0.1
	1634	1.7	0.5
	2237	0.1	0.0
7 M	0511	2.2	0.7
	1143	0.1	0.0
	1733	1.6	0.5
	2330	0.0	0.0
8 Tu	0604	2.2	0.7
	1235	0.0	0.0
	1829	1.6	0.5
9 W	0025	-0.1	0.0
	0651	2.2	0.7
	1322	-0.2	-0.1
	1917	1.6	0.5
10 Th	0112	-0.2	-0.1
	0736	2.2	0.7
	1403	-0.3	-0.1
	1959	1.6	0.5
11 F	0154	-0.3	-0.1
	0816	2.2	0.7
	1440	-0.4	-0.1
	2040	1.7	0.5
12 Sa	0236	-0.4	-0.1
	0855	2.2	0.7
	1516	-0.5	-0.2
	2116	1.8	0.5
13 Su	0315	-0.4	-0.1
	0932	2.2	0.7
	1550	-0.5	-0.2
	2152	1.9	0.6
14 M	0352	-0.4	-0.1
	1008	2.2	0.7
	1622	-0.5	-0.2
	2227	1.9	0.6
15 Tu	0429	-0.4	-0.1
	1040	2.1	0.6
	1652	-0.4	-0.1
	2303	2.0	0.6
16 W	0506	-0.3	-0.1
	1114	2.1	0.6
	1724	-0.3	-0.1
	2338	2.1	0.6
17 Th	0546	-0.2	-0.1
	1151	2.0	0.6
	1759	-0.3	-0.1
18 F	0017	2.2	0.7
	0631	-0.1	0.0
	1231	2.0	0.6
	1835	-0.2	-0.1
19 Sa	0105	2.3	0.7
	0721	0.0	0.0
	1321	1.9	0.6
	1927	-0.1	0.0
20 Su	0158	2.3	0.7
	0817	0.1	0.0
	1417	1.9	0.6
	2023	-0.1	0.0
21 M	0302	2.4	0.7
	0929	0.2	0.1
	1522	1.8	0.5
	2131	0.0	0.0
22 Tu	0410	2.5	0.8
	1041	0.1	0.0
	1636	1.9	0.6
	2241	-0.1	0.0
23 W	0519	2.6	0.8
	1150	0.0	0.0
	1747	2.0	0.6
	2352	-0.2	-0.1
24 Th	0624	2.7	0.8
	1251	-0.2	-0.1
	1853	2.2	0.7
25 F	0058	-0.4	-0.1
	0724	2.9	0.9
	1346	-0.4	-0.1
	1951	2.5	0.8
26 Sa	0157	-0.5	-0.2
	0818	3.0	0.9
	1437	-0.5	-0.2
	2044	2.7	0.8
27 Su	0252	-0.6	-0.2
	0910	3.0	0.9
	1526	-0.5	-0.2
	2135	2.8	0.9
28 M	0344	-0.6	-0.2
	0959	3.0	0.9
	1613	-0.5	-0.2
	2224	2.9	0.9

MARCH

Day	Time h m	Height ft	Height m
1 Tu	0435	-0.5	-0.2
	1046	2.8	0.9
	1658	-0.4	-0.1
	2313	2.9	0.9
2 W	0525	-0.3	-0.1
	1132	2.7	0.8
	1741	-0.3	-0.1
	2359	2.8	0.9
3 Th	0613	-0.1	0.0
	1218	2.5	0.8
	1826	-0.1	0.0
4 F	0049	2.7	0.8
	0707	0.1	0.0
	1308	2.2	0.7
	1913	0.0	0.0
5 Sa	0139	2.5	0.8
	0800	0.2	0.1
	1358	2.0	0.6
	2003	0.2	0.1
6 Su	0232	2.4	0.7
	0900	0.4	0.1
	1453	1.8	0.5
	2057	0.3	0.1
7 M	0331	2.3	0.7
	1003	0.4	0.1
	1555	1.7	0.5
	2155	0.3	0.1
8 Tu	0430	2.2	0.7
	1105	0.3	0.1
	1659	1.7	0.5
	2257	0.3	0.1
9 W	0526	2.1	0.6
	1200	0.2	0.1
	1758	1.7	0.5
	2353	0.1	0.0
10 Th	0619	2.2	0.7
	1245	0.0	0.0
	1845	1.7	0.5
11 F	0045	0.0	0.0
	0704	2.2	0.7
	1328	-0.1	0.0
	1930	1.8	0.5
12 Sa	0130	-0.2	-0.1
	0746	2.2	0.7
	1405	-0.3	-0.1
	2009	2.0	0.6
13 Su	0210	-0.3	-0.1
	0826	2.2	0.7
	1440	-0.4	-0.1
	2045	2.1	0.6
14 M	0250	-0.4	-0.1
	0903	2.3	0.7
	1515	-0.4	-0.1
	2121	2.2	0.7
15 Tu	0329	-0.4	-0.1
	0938	2.3	0.7
	1547	-0.4	-0.1
	2156	2.3	0.7
16 W	0406	-0.3	-0.1
	1013	2.2	0.7
	1619	-0.3	-0.1
	2233	2.4	0.7
17 Th	0444	-0.3	-0.1
	1048	2.2	0.7
	1652	-0.2	-0.1
	2311	2.5	0.8
18 F	0524	-0.1	0.0
	1125	2.2	0.7
	1728	-0.1	0.0
	2353	2.6	0.8
19 Sa	0610	0.0	0.0
	1210	2.2	0.7
	1812	0.0	0.0
20 Su	0041	2.6	0.8
	0703	0.2	0.1
	1258	2.1	0.6
	1903	0.1	0.0
21 M	0137	2.6	0.8
	0804	0.3	0.1
	1401	2.1	0.6
	2006	0.2	0.1
22 Tu	0241	2.6	0.8
	0913	0.4	0.1
	1511	2.1	0.6
	2117	0.2	0.1
23 W	0353	2.6	0.8
	1025	0.3	0.1
	1625	2.2	0.7
	2233	0.2	0.1
24 Th	0505	2.7	0.8
	1131	0.2	0.1
	1736	2.4	0.7
	2345	0.1	0.0
25 F	0611	2.8	0.9
	1232	0.0	0.0
	1839	2.6	0.8
26 Sa	0049	-0.1	0.0
	0709	2.9	0.9
	1326	-0.1	0.0
	1936	2.8	0.9
27 Su	0146	-0.3	-0.1
	0803	2.9	0.9
	1415	-0.3	-0.1
	2027	2.9	0.9
28 M	0239	-0.3	-0.1
	0852	2.9	0.9
	1502	-0.3	-0.1
	2116	3.0	0.9
29 Tu	0329	-0.4	-0.1
	0939	2.9	0.9
	1546	-0.3	-0.1
	2201	3.1	0.9
30 W	0416	-0.3	-0.1
	1024	2.8	0.9
	1629	-0.2	-0.1
	2246	3.0	0.9
31 Th	0503	-0.2	-0.1
	1106	2.6	0.8
	1711	-0.1	0.0
	2329	2.9	0.9

Time meridian 75° W.   0000 is midnight.   1200 is noon.
Heights are referred to mean low water which is the chart datum of soundings.

Times and Heights of High and Low Waters

APRIL

Day	Time h m	ft	m	Day	Time h m	ft	m
1 F	0548	0.0	0.0	16 Sa	0509	-0.1	0.0
	1150	2.4	0.7		1108	2.3	0.7
	1753	0.0	0.0		1706	-0.1	0.0
					2333	2.9	0.9
2 Sa	0015	2.8	0.9	17 Su	0557	0.1	0.0
	0636	0.2	0.1		1157	2.3	0.7
	1234	2.2	0.7		1754	0.1	0.0
	1836	0.2	0.1				
3 Su	0102	2.6	0.8	18 M	0025	2.9	0.9
	0727	0.3	0.1		0652	0.2	0.1
	1324	2.1	0.6		1250	2.3	0.7
	1924	0.4	0.1		1852	0.2	0.1
4 M	0150	2.4	0.7	19 Tu	0124	2.8	0.9
	0821	0.4	0.1		0753	0.3	0.1
	1416	1.9	0.6		1355	2.3	0.7
	2015	0.5	0.2		1958	0.4	0.1
5 Tu	0246	2.3	0.7	20 W	0230	2.8	0.9
	0920	0.5	0.2		0900	0.4	0.1
	1520	1.8	0.5		1505	2.3	0.7
	2116	0.5	0.2		2112	0.4	0.1
6 W	0344	2.2	0.7	21 Th	0340	2.7	0.8
	1017	0.4	0.1		1009	0.4	0.1
	1621	1.8	0.5		1618	2.4	0.7
	2218	0.4	0.1		2228	0.4	0.1
7 Th	0444	2.2	0.7	22 F	0449	2.8	0.9
	1113	0.3	0.1		1114	0.3	0.1
	1717	1.8	0.5		1725	2.6	0.8
	2318	0.3	0.1		2336	0.2	0.1
8 F	0536	2.2	0.7	23 Sa	0554	2.8	0.9
	1201	0.2	0.1		1211	0.1	0.0
	1806	1.9	0.6		1824	2.8	0.9
9 Sa	0011	0.2	0.1	24 Su	0038	0.1	0.0
	0625	2.2	0.7		0651	2.8	0.9
	1243	0.0	0.0		1302	0.0	0.0
	1851	2.1	0.6		1917	2.9	0.9
10 Su	0059	0.0	0.0	25 M	0134	-0.1	0.0
	0709	2.2	0.7		0741	2.8	0.9
	1322	-0.1	0.0		1351	-0.1	0.0
	1933	2.2	0.7		2007	3.1	0.9
11 M	0141	-0.2	-0.1	26 Tu	0224	-0.2	-0.1
	0750	2.2	0.7		0831	2.7	0.8
	1359	-0.2	-0.1		1436	-0.2	-0.1
	2010	2.4	0.7		2054	3.1	0.9
12 Tu	0223	-0.3	-0.1	27 W	0312	-0.2	-0.1
	0828	2.3	0.7		0916	2.7	0.8
	1434	-0.3	-0.1		1518	-0.2	-0.1
	2047	2.5	0.8		2137	3.1	0.9
13 W	0303	-0.3	-0.1	28 Th	0358	-0.2	-0.1
	0908	2.3	0.7		0958	2.5	0.8
	1509	-0.3	-0.1		1558	-0.1	0.0
	2127	2.7	0.8		2218	3.0	0.9
14 Th	0342	-0.3	-0.1	29 F	0442	-0.1	0.0
	0945	2.3	0.7		1040	2.4	0.7
	1545	-0.3	-0.1		1639	0.0	0.0
	2205	2.8	0.9		2300	2.9	0.9
15 F	0424	-0.2	-0.1	30 Sa	0525	0.0	0.0
	1024	2.3	0.7		1122	2.3	0.7
	1624	-0.2	-0.1		1719	0.1	0.0
	2247	2.9	0.9		2343	2.7	0.8

MAY

Day	Time h m	ft	m	Day	Time h m	ft	m
1 Su	0609	0.2	0.1	16 M	0546	0.0	0.0
	1207	2.1	0.6		1148	2.4	0.7
	1802	0.3	0.1		1746	0.1	0.0
2 M	0027	2.6	0.8	17 Tu	0015	3.0	0.9
	0655	0.3	0.1		0642	0.1	0.0
	1255	2.0	0.6		1246	2.4	0.7
	1849	0.4	0.1		1847	0.2	0.1
3 Tu	0112	2.4	0.7	18 W	0113	2.9	0.9
	0742	0.3	0.1		0742	0.2	0.1
	1345	1.9	0.6		1349	2.5	0.8
	1939	0.5	0.2		1953	0.3	0.1
4 W	0203	2.3	0.7	19 Th	0219	2.8	0.9
	0835	0.4	0.1		0845	0.3	0.1
	1440	1.9	0.6		1458	2.5	0.8
	2036	0.5	0.2		2105	0.4	0.1
5 Th	0257	2.2	0.7	20 F	0326	2.7	0.8
	0929	0.4	0.1		0948	0.3	0.1
	1539	1.9	0.6		1606	2.6	0.8
	2136	0.5	0.2		2218	0.4	0.1
6 F	0353	2.1	0.6	21 Sa	0430	2.7	0.8
	1021	0.3	0.1		1049	0.2	0.1
	1633	1.9	0.6		1707	2.7	0.8
	2236	0.4	0.1		2324	0.3	0.1
7 Sa	0449	2.1	0.6	22 Su	0532	2.6	0.8
	1108	0.2	0.1		1144	0.1	0.0
	1723	2.1	0.6		1806	2.8	0.9
	2331	0.2	0.1				
8 Su	0539	2.1	0.6	23 M	0024	0.1	0.0
	1152	0.0	0.0		0629	2.6	0.8
	1808	2.2	0.7		1236	0.0	0.0
					1857	2.9	0.9
9 M	0021	0.0	0.0	24 Tu	0117	0.0	0.0
	0625	2.1	0.6		0720	2.5	0.8
	1234	-0.1	0.0		1323	-0.1	0.0
	1853	2.4	0.7		1946	3.0	0.9
10 Tu	0107	-0.1	0.0	25 W	0207	-0.1	0.0
	0711	2.1	0.6		0807	2.4	0.7
	1315	-0.2	-0.1		1407	-0.1	0.0
	1934	2.5	0.8		2030	3.0	0.9
11 W	0154	-0.2	-0.1	26 Th	0254	-0.1	0.0
	0753	2.2	0.7		0852	2.3	0.7
	1353	-0.3	-0.1		1449	-0.1	0.0
	2016	2.7	0.8		2111	2.9	0.9
12 Th	0236	-0.3	-0.1	27 F	0339	-0.1	0.0
	0837	2.3	0.7		0935	2.2	0.7
	1436	-0.3	-0.1		1530	-0.1	0.0
	2059	2.9	0.9		2155	2.8	0.9
13 F	0322	-0.3	-0.1	28 Sa	0421	-0.1	0.0
	0920	2.3	0.7		1016	2.1	0.6
	1518	-0.3	-0.1		1612	0.0	0.0
	2143	3.0	0.9		2235	2.7	0.8
14 Sa	0407	-0.3	-0.1	29 Su	0501	-0.1	0.0
	1006	2.3	0.7		1058	2.1	0.6
	1603	-0.2	-0.1		1652	0.1	0.0
	2229	3.0	0.9		2314	2.6	0.8
15 Su	0457	-0.2	-0.1	30 M	0543	0.0	0.0
	1056	2.4	0.7		1140	2.0	0.6
	1653	-0.1	0.0		1734	0.2	0.1
	2320	3.0	0.9		2357	2.5	0.8
				31 Tu	0626	0.1	0.0
					1226	1.9	0.6
					1818	0.3	0.1

JUNE

Day	Time h m	ft	m	Day	Time h m	ft	m
1 W	0039	2.3	0.7	16 Th	0102	2.9	0.9
	0708	0.2	0.1		0726	0.1	0.0
	1311	1.9	0.6		1339	2.6	0.8
	1905	0.4	0.1		1945	0.2	0.1
2 Th	0123	2.2	0.7	17 F	0203	2.8	0.9
	0752	0.2	0.1		0825	0.2	0.1
	1401	1.9	0.6		1441	2.7	0.8
	1958	0.4	0.1		2054	0.3	0.1
3 F	0213	2.1	0.6	18 Sa	0305	2.6	0.8
	0838	0.2	0.1		0923	0.2	0.1
	1453	1.9	0.6		1545	2.7	0.8
	2055	0.4	0.1		2201	0.3	0.1
4 Sa	0304	2.0	0.6	19 Su	0407	2.5	0.8
	0924	0.2	0.1		1021	0.2	0.1
	1545	2.0	0.6		1647	2.8	0.9
	2153	0.3	0.1		2307	0.3	0.1
5 Su	0357	2.0	0.6	20 M	0507	2.4	0.7
	1013	0.1	0.0		1115	0.1	0.0
	1634	2.1	0.6		1745	2.8	0.9
	2250	0.2	0.1				
6 M	0450	1.9	0.6	21 Tu	0008	0.2	0.1
	1059	0.0	0.0		0603	2.3	0.7
	1723	2.3	0.7		1208	0.1	0.0
	2342	0.1	0.0		1835	2.8	0.9
7 Tu	0542	2.0	0.6	22 W	0101	0.1	0.0
	1146	-0.1	0.0		0656	2.2	0.7
	1811	2.5	0.8		1256	0.0	0.0
					1923	2.8	0.9
8 W	0033	-0.1	0.0	23 Th	0151	0.0	0.0
	0632	2.0	0.6		0744	2.1	0.6
	1233	-0.2	-0.1		1342	0.0	0.0
	1901	2.6	0.8		2008	2.8	0.9
9 Th	0125	-0.2	-0.1	24 F	0236	-0.1	0.0
	0721	2.1	0.6		0830	2.1	0.6
	1318	-0.3	-0.1		1424	-0.1	0.0
	1947	2.8	0.9		2051	2.7	0.8
10 F	0214	-0.3	-0.1	25 Sa	0318	-0.1	0.0
	0810	2.2	0.7		0914	2.0	0.6
	1407	-0.4	-0.1		1506	-0.1	0.0
	2037	3.0	0.9		2131	2.6	0.8
11 Sa	0301	-0.4	-0.1	26 Su	0358	-0.2	-0.1
	0900	2.3	0.7		0955	2.0	0.6
	1457	-0.4	-0.1		1547	-0.1	0.0
	2126	3.1	0.9		2210	2.6	0.8
12 Su	0352	-0.3	-0.1	27 M	0437	-0.1	0.0
	0951	2.4	0.7		1035	2.0	0.6
	1549	-0.3	-0.1		1627	0.0	0.0
	2217	3.1	0.9		2247	2.5	0.8
13 M	0442	-0.3	-0.1	28 Tu	0514	-0.1	0.0
	1044	2.5	0.8		1114	1.9	0.6
	1643	-0.2	-0.1		1709	0.1	0.0
	2309	3.1	0.9		2325	2.4	0.7
14 Tu	0535	-0.2	-0.1	29 W	0551	-0.1	0.0
	1140	2.5	0.8		1154	1.9	0.6
	1741	-0.1	0.0		1749	0.1	0.0
15 W	0005	3.0	0.9	30 Th	0005	2.3	0.7
	0630	-0.1	0.0		0631	0.0	0.0
	1238	2.6	0.8		1236	1.9	0.6
	1842	0.1	0.0		1833	0.2	0.1

Time meridian 75° W. 0000 is midnight. 1200 is noon.
Heights are referred to mean low water which is the chart datum of soundings.

HAMPTON ROADS (Sewells Pt.), VA., 1983
Times and Heights of High and Low Waters

JULY

Day	Time h m	ft	m	Day	Time h m	ft	m
1 F	0045	2.2	0.7	16 Sa	0142	2.8	0.9
	0708	0.1	0.0		0758	0.1	0.0
	1320	2.0	0.6		1420	2.8	0.9
	1920	0.3	0.1		2035	0.3	0.1
2 Sa	0127	2.1	0.6	17 Su	0241	2.6	0.8
	0748	0.1	0.0		0853	0.2	0.1
	1406	2.0	0.6		1520	2.8	0.9
	2011	0.3	0.1		2140	0.4	0.1
3 Su	0212	2.0	0.6	18 M	0340	2.4	0.7
	0830	0.1	0.0		0949	0.3	0.1
	1454	2.1	0.6		1619	2.8	0.9
	2106	0.3	0.1		2245	0.4	0.1
4 M	0306	1.9	0.6	19 Tu	0440	2.2	0.7
	0918	0.1	0.0		1046	0.3	0.1
	1548	2.2	0.7		1717	2.7	0.8
	2204	0.2	0.1		2347	0.4	0.1
5 Tu	0402	1.9	0.6	20 W	0539	2.1	0.6
	1009	0.0	0.0		1140	0.2	0.1
	1641	2.4	0.7		1812	2.7	0.8
	2304	0.1	0.0				
6 W	0457	1.9	0.6	21 Th	0040	0.3	0.1
	1101	-0.1	0.0		0635	2.1	0.6
	1736	2.5	0.8		1231	0.2	0.1
					1859	2.7	0.8
7 Th	0002	0.0	0.0	22 F	0130	0.1	0.0
	0556	2.0	0.6		0722	2.0	0.6
	1158	-0.2	-0.1		1320	0.1	0.0
	1832	2.7	0.8		1945	2.7	0.8
8 F	0058	-0.1	0.0	23 Sa	0213	0.0	0.0
	0653	2.1	0.6		0807	2.0	0.6
	1253	-0.3	-0.1		1403	0.0	0.0
	1925	2.9	0.9		2028	2.6	0.8
9 Sa	0153	-0.3	-0.1	24 Su	0254	-0.1	0.0
	0749	2.2	0.7		0851	2.0	0.6
	1349	-0.4	-0.1		1444	0.0	0.0
	2018	3.1	0.9		2108	2.6	0.8
10 Su	0244	-0.3	-0.1	25 M	0331	-0.1	0.0
	0842	2.4	0.7		0931	2.0	0.6
	1444	-0.4	-0.1		1526	-0.1	0.0
	2112	3.2	1.0		2145	2.5	0.8
11 M	0335	-0.4	-0.1	26 Tu	0408	-0.2	-0.1
	0938	2.5	0.8		1008	2.1	0.6
	1539	-0.4	-0.1		1605	0.0	0.0
	2203	3.2	1.0		2221	2.5	0.8
12 Tu	0426	-0.3	-0.1	27 W	0443	-0.1	0.0
	1032	2.7	0.8		1047	2.1	0.6
	1635	-0.3	-0.1		1642	0.0	0.0
	2256	3.2	1.0		2257	2.4	0.7
13 W	0518	-0.3	-0.1	28 Th	0517	-0.1	0.0
	1127	2.8	0.9		1122	2.1	0.6
	1732	-0.1	0.0		1721	0.1	0.0
	2349	3.1	0.9		2332	2.3	0.7
14 Th	0610	-0.1	0.0	29 F	0549	0.0	0.0
	1223	2.8	0.9		1159	2.2	0.7
	1830	0.0	0.0		1801	0.2	0.1
15 F	0044	2.9	0.9	30 Sa	0009	2.2	0.7
	0702	0.0	0.0		0623	0.1	0.0
	1319	2.8	0.9		1238	2.2	0.7
	1930	0.2	0.1		1844	0.3	0.1
				31 Su	0047	2.2	0.7
					0700	0.1	0.0
					1321	2.3	0.7
					1932	0.3	0.1

AUGUST

Day	Time h m	ft	m	Day	Time h m	ft	m
1 M	0132	2.1	0.6	16 Tu	0310	2.4	0.7
	0742	0.2	0.1		0915	0.5	0.2
	1409	2.4	0.7		1550	2.8	0.9
	2027	0.4	0.1		2219	0.6	0.2
2 Tu	0222	2.0	0.6	17 W	0414	2.2	0.7
	0831	0.2	0.1		1015	0.5	0.2
	1505	2.5	0.8		1649	2.7	0.8
	2126	0.4	0.1		2320	0.6	0.2
3 W	0321	2.0	0.6	18 Th	0513	2.1	0.6
	0927	0.2	0.1		1113	0.5	0.2
	1604	2.6	0.8		1744	2.7	0.8
	2231	0.3	0.1				
4 Th	0423	2.0	0.6	19 F	0017	0.5	0.2
	1029	0.1	0.0		0611	2.1	0.6
	1706	2.7	0.8		1206	0.4	0.1
	2336	0.2	0.1		1834	2.7	0.8
5 F	0529	2.1	0.6	20 Sa	0106	0.3	0.1
	1132	0.0	0.0		0701	2.1	0.6
	1807	2.9	0.9		1257	0.3	0.1
					1920	2.6	0.8
6 Sa	0037	0.1	0.0	21 Su	0147	0.2	0.1
	0633	2.3	0.7		0746	2.2	0.7
	1237	-0.1	0.0		1341	0.2	0.1
	1906	3.1	0.9		2002	2.6	0.8
7 Su	0133	-0.1	0.0	22 M	0224	0.1	0.0
	0733	2.5	0.8		0825	2.2	0.7
	1333	-0.2	-0.1		1423	0.1	0.0
	2002	3.2	1.0		2040	2.6	0.8
8 M	0226	-0.2	-0.1	23 Tu	0301	0.0	0.0
	0828	2.7	0.8		0904	2.3	0.7
	1432	-0.3	-0.1		1503	0.0	0.0
	2056	3.3	1.0		2119	2.6	0.8
9 Tu	0316	-0.3	-0.1	24 W	0334	-0.1	0.0
	0921	2.9	0.9		0939	2.3	0.7
	1527	-0.3	-0.1		1540	0.0	0.0
	2149	3.3	1.0		2152	2.6	0.8
10 W	0407	-0.3	-0.1	25 Th	0407	0.0	0.0
	1015	3.0	0.9		1013	2.4	0.7
	1623	-0.2	-0.1		1616	0.0	0.0
	2239	3.3	1.0		2227	2.5	0.8
11 Th	0455	-0.2	-0.1	26 F	0439	0.0	0.0
	1108	3.1	0.9		1048	2.5	0.8
	1717	-0.1	0.0		1654	0.1	0.0
	2330	3.2	1.0		2259	2.4	0.7
12 F	0545	-0.1	0.0	27 Sa	0509	0.1	0.0
	1200	3.1	0.9		1125	2.5	0.8
	1813	0.1	0.0		1730	0.2	0.1
					2335	2.4	0.7
13 Sa	0023	3.0	0.9	28 Su	0542	0.2	0.1
	0634	0.1	0.0		1202	2.6	0.8
	1255	3.1	0.9		1813	0.3	0.1
	1909	0.3	0.1				
14 Su	0115	2.8	0.9	29 M	0013	2.3	0.7
	0727	0.3	0.1		0618	0.3	0.1
	1350	3.0	0.9		1243	2.6	0.8
	2009	0.5	0.2		1858	0.5	0.2
15 M	0212	2.6	0.8	30 Tu	0057	2.3	0.7
	0819	0.4	0.1		0700	0.3	0.1
	1447	2.9	0.9		1332	2.7	0.8
	2113	0.6	0.2		1953	0.6	0.2
				31 W	0148	2.2	0.7
					0753	0.4	0.1
					1430	2.7	0.8
					2058	0.6	0.2

SEPTEMBER

Day	Time h m	ft	m	Day	Time h m	ft	m
1 Th	0250	2.2	0.7	16 F	0445	2.2	0.7
	0857	0.4	0.1		1045	0.7	0.2
	1536	2.8	0.9		1711	2.6	0.8
	2205	0.6	0.2		2341	0.6	0.2
2 F	0401	2.3	0.7	17 Sa	0542	2.2	0.7
	1006	0.4	0.1		1139	0.6	0.2
	1644	2.9	0.9		1803	2.6	0.8
	2314	0.5	0.2				
3 Sa	0513	2.4	0.7	18 Su	0029	0.5	0.2
	1118	0.3	0.1		0632	2.3	0.7
	1750	3.0	0.9		1232	0.5	0.2
					1848	2.6	0.8
4 Su	0016	0.3	0.1	19 M	0112	0.3	0.1
	0617	2.6	0.8		0714	2.3	0.7
	1224	0.1	0.0		1317	0.3	0.1
	1851	3.2	1.0		1930	2.6	0.8
5 M	0113	0.1	0.0	20 Tu	0149	0.2	0.1
	0717	2.9	0.9		0754	2.4	0.7
	1325	0.0	0.0		1359	0.2	0.1
	1946	3.3	1.0		2010	2.6	0.8
6 Tu	0205	0.0	0.0	21 W	0224	0.1	0.0
	0813	3.1	0.9		0831	2.5	0.8
	1421	-0.1	0.0		1436	0.1	0.0
	2039	3.4	1.0		2047	2.6	0.8
7 W	0255	-0.1	0.0	22 Th	0256	0.0	0.0
	0905	3.3	1.0		0906	2.6	0.8
	1516	-0.2	-0.1		1514	0.0	0.0
	2131	3.4	1.0		2122	2.6	0.8
8 Th	0343	-0.1	0.0	23 F	0329	0.0	0.0
	0955	3.4	1.0		0939	2.7	0.8
	1608	-0.1	0.0		1551	0.1	0.0
	2220	3.3	1.0		2156	2.6	0.8
9 F	0429	-0.1	0.0	24 Sa	0359	0.1	0.0
	1043	3.4	1.0		1014	2.8	0.9
	1658	0.0	0.0		1628	0.1	0.0
	2307	3.2	1.0		2230	2.5	0.8
10 Sa	0517	0.1	0.0	25 Su	0432	0.2	0.1
	1135	3.4	1.0		1051	2.8	0.9
	1751	0.2	0.1		1705	0.2	0.1
	2357	3.0	0.9		2304	2.5	0.8
11 Su	0603	0.3	0.1	26 M	0506	0.2	0.1
	1226	3.3	1.0		1128	2.9	0.9
	1845	0.4	0.1		1749	0.4	0.1
					2346	2.4	0.7
12 M	0047	2.8	0.9	27 Tu	0546	0.4	0.1
	0652	0.4	0.1		1214	2.9	0.9
	1319	3.1	0.9		1836	0.5	0.2
	1940	0.6	0.2				
13 Tu	0140	2.6	0.8	28 W	0033	2.4	0.7
	0745	0.6	0.2		0634	0.5	0.2
	1412	2.9	0.9		1307	2.9	0.9
	2040	0.7	0.2		1933	0.6	0.2
14 W	0238	2.4	0.7	29 Th	0129	2.4	0.7
	0843	0.7	0.2		0731	0.6	0.2
	1513	2.8	0.9		1406	2.9	0.9
	2145	0.8	0.2		2037	0.7	0.2
15 Th	0343	2.3	0.7	30 F	0235	2.4	0.7
	0945	0.8	0.2		0840	0.6	0.2
	1613	2.7	0.8		1516	2.9	0.9
	2249	0.7	0.2		2147	0.7	0.2

Time meridian 75° W. 0000 is midnight. 1200 is noon.
Heights are referred to mean low water which is the chart datum of soundings.

HAMPTON ROADS (Sewells Pt.), VA., 1983
Times and Heights of High and Low Waters

OCTOBER

Day	Time (h m)	Height (ft)	Height (m)
1 Sa	0348	2.5	0.8
	0956	0.6	0.2
	1629	3.0	0.9
	2255	0.6	0.2
2 Su	0502	2.7	0.8
	1110	0.5	0.2
	1736	3.1	0.9
	2357	0.4	0.1
3 M	0604	2.9	0.9
	1216	0.3	0.1
	1835	3.2	1.0
4 Tu	0053	0.2	0.1
	0702	3.1	0.9
	1315	0.1	0.0
	1931	3.3	1.0
5 W	0142	0.1	0.0
	0755	3.3	1.0
	1410	0.0	0.0
	2023	3.3	1.0
6 Th	0231	0.0	0.0
	0846	3.5	1.1
	1501	-0.1	0.0
	2110	3.3	1.0
7 F	0318	0.0	0.0
	0933	3.5	1.1
	1551	0.0	0.0
	2157	3.2	1.0
8 Sa	0403	0.0	0.0
	1021	3.5	1.1
	1640	0.1	0.0
	2243	3.0	0.9
9 Su	0447	0.1	0.0
	1109	3.4	1.0
	1729	0.2	0.1
	2330	2.8	0.9
10 M	0532	0.3	0.1
	1155	3.2	1.0
	1818	0.4	0.1
11 Tu	0019	2.6	0.8
	0619	0.5	0.2
	1243	3.0	0.9
	1910	0.6	0.2
12 W	0109	2.4	0.7
	0708	0.7	0.2
	1337	2.9	0.9
	2008	0.7	0.2
13 Th	0206	2.3	0.7
	0805	0.8	0.2
	1433	2.7	0.8
	2106	0.7	0.2
14 F	0309	2.2	0.7
	0906	0.8	0.2
	1532	2.6	0.8
	2206	0.7	0.2
15 Sa	0411	2.2	0.7
	1008	0.8	0.2
	1629	2.5	0.8
	2300	0.6	0.2
16 Su	0507	2.2	0.7
	1108	0.6	0.2
	1723	2.5	0.8
	2347	0.4	0.1
17 M	0556	2.3	0.7
	1201	0.5	0.2
	1811	2.4	0.7
18 Tu	0029	0.3	0.1
	0639	2.4	0.7
	1245	0.3	0.1
	1854	2.5	0.8
19 W	0106	0.1	0.0
	0717	2.5	0.8
	1330	0.1	0.0
	1936	2.5	0.8
20 Th	0141	0.0	0.0
	0756	2.6	0.8
	1408	0.0	0.0
	2014	2.5	0.8
21 F	0217	0.0	0.0
	0831	2.7	0.8
	1447	-0.1	0.0
	2050	2.4	0.7
22 Sa	0252	0.0	0.0
	0908	2.8	0.9
	1526	-0.1	0.0
	2127	2.4	0.7
23 Su	0327	0.0	0.0
	0946	2.9	0.9
	1607	0.0	0.0
	2203	2.4	0.7
24 M	0402	0.0	0.0
	1024	3.0	0.9
	1645	0.1	0.0
	2245	2.4	0.7
25 Tu	0440	0.1	0.0
	1107	3.0	0.9
	1731	0.2	0.1
	2328	2.4	0.7
26 W	0526	0.3	0.1
	1154	3.0	0.9
	1823	0.4	0.1
27 Th	0019	2.4	0.7
	0618	0.4	0.1
	1249	3.0	0.9
	1919	0.5	0.2
28 F	0119	2.4	0.7
	0721	0.5	0.2
	1353	2.9	0.9
	2022	0.6	0.2
29 Sa	0227	2.5	0.8
	0833	0.6	0.2
	1502	2.9	0.9
	2129	0.6	0.2
30 Su	0340	2.6	0.8
	0949	0.6	0.2
	1612	2.9	0.9
	2235	0.5	0.2
31 M	0449	2.7	0.8
	1100	0.4	0.1
	1718	2.9	0.9
	2335	0.3	0.1

NOVEMBER

Day	Time (h m)	Height (ft)	Height (m)
1 Tu	0550	2.9	0.9
	1206	0.3	0.1
	1816	2.9	0.9
2 W	0029	0.2	0.1
	0647	3.1	0.9
	1304	0.1	0.0
	1912	2.9	0.9
3 Th	0120	0.0	0.0
	0738	3.3	1.0
	1357	0.0	0.0
	2002	2.9	0.9
4 F	0207	-0.1	0.0
	0827	3.3	1.0
	1447	-0.1	0.0
	2050	2.9	0.9
5 Sa	0252	-0.1	0.0
	0912	3.3	1.0
	1535	-0.1	0.0
	2136	2.8	0.9
6 Su	0337	0.0	0.0
	0958	3.3	1.0
	1621	0.0	0.0
	2220	2.6	0.8
7 M	0419	0.1	0.0
	1040	3.1	0.9
	1706	0.1	0.0
	2306	2.5	0.8
8 Tu	0502	0.2	0.1
	1127	3.0	0.9
	1754	0.2	0.1
	2354	2.3	0.7
9 W	0548	0.3	0.1
	1212	2.8	0.9
	1841	0.3	0.1
10 Th	0041	2.2	0.7
	0636	0.5	0.2
	1258	2.6	0.8
	1931	0.4	0.1
11 F	0135	2.1	0.6
	0727	0.6	0.2
	1350	2.4	0.7
	2022	0.5	0.2
12 Sa	0228	2.0	0.6
	0827	0.6	0.2
	1443	2.3	0.7
	2117	0.4	0.1
13 Su	0325	2.0	0.6
	0927	0.6	0.2
	1541	2.2	0.7
	2206	0.4	0.1
14 M	0421	2.1	0.6
	1028	0.5	0.2
	1634	2.1	0.6
	2254	0.3	0.1
15 Tu	0510	2.1	0.6
	1121	0.3	0.1
	1726	2.1	0.6
	2339	0.1	0.0
16 W	0556	2.3	0.7
	1211	0.1	0.0
	1811	2.1	0.6
17 Th	0019	0.0	0.0
	0638	2.4	0.7
	1256	0.0	0.0
	1857	2.1	0.6
18 F	0059	-0.1	0.0
	0719	2.5	0.8
	1339	-0.2	-0.1
	1938	2.1	0.6
19 Sa	0138	-0.2	-0.1
	0759	2.7	0.8
	1421	-0.2	-0.1
	2019	2.1	0.6
20 Su	0216	-0.3	-0.1
	0840	2.8	0.9
	1503	-0.3	-0.1
	2101	2.2	0.7
21 M	0256	-0.3	-0.1
	0921	2.9	0.9
	1547	-0.3	-0.1
	2143	2.2	0.7
22 Tu	0337	-0.2	-0.1
	1005	2.9	0.9
	1631	-0.2	-0.1
	2228	2.3	0.7
23 W	0424	-0.1	0.0
	1052	2.9	0.9
	1719	-0.1	0.0
	2317	2.3	0.7
24 Th	0514	0.0	0.0
	1143	2.9	0.9
	1810	0.1	0.0
25 F	0010	2.3	0.7
	0610	0.1	0.0
	1239	2.8	0.9
	1907	0.2	0.1
26 Sa	0111	2.4	0.7
	0713	0.3	0.1
	1340	2.7	0.8
	2006	0.2	0.1
27 Su	0218	2.4	0.7
	0825	0.4	0.1
	1445	2.7	0.8
	2109	0.3	0.1
28 M	0327	2.5	0.8
	0939	0.3	0.1
	1553	2.6	0.8
	2212	0.2	0.1
29 Tu	0433	2.7	0.8
	1049	0.3	0.1
	1659	2.5	0.8
	2310	0.1	0.0
30 W	0534	2.8	0.9
	1153	0.1	0.0
	1758	2.5	0.8

DECEMBER

Day	Time (h m)	Height (ft)	Height (m)
1 Th	0006	0.0	0.0
	0628	2.9	0.9
	1251	0.0	0.0
	1853	2.5	0.8
2 F	0056	-0.1	0.0
	0720	3.0	0.9
	1344	-0.1	0.0
	1943	2.4	0.7
3 Sa	0145	-0.2	-0.1
	0808	3.0	0.9
	1433	-0.2	-0.1
	2031	2.3	0.7
4 Su	0229	-0.2	-0.1
	0852	3.0	0.9
	1519	-0.3	-0.1
	2116	2.3	0.7
5 M	0314	-0.2	-0.1
	0936	2.9	0.9
	1602	-0.2	-0.1
	2200	2.2	0.7
6 Tu	0355	-0.2	-0.1
	1018	2.8	0.9
	1647	-0.2	-0.1
	2243	2.1	0.6
7 W	0437	-0.1	0.0
	1100	2.6	0.8
	1728	-0.1	0.0
	2325	2.0	0.6
8 Th	0520	0.0	0.0
	1141	2.5	0.8
	1809	0.0	0.0
9 F	0012	1.9	0.6
	0605	0.1	0.0
	1223	2.3	0.7
	1852	0.0	0.0
10 Sa	0058	1.9	0.6
	0652	0.2	0.1
	1308	2.1	0.6
	1935	0.1	0.0
11 Su	0147	1.8	0.5
	0743	0.3	0.1
	1354	2.0	0.6
	2022	0.1	0.0
12 M	0237	1.8	0.5
	0840	0.3	0.1
	1445	1.9	0.6
	2109	0.1	0.0
13 Tu	0329	1.9	0.6
	0936	0.2	0.1
	1538	1.8	0.5
	2156	0.0	0.0
14 W	0419	1.9	0.6
	1036	0.1	0.0
	1633	1.7	0.5
	2242	-0.1	0.0
15 Th	0509	2.1	0.6
	1129	0.0	0.0
	1723	1.7	0.5
	2331	-0.2	-0.1
16 F	0555	2.2	0.7
	1221	-0.2	-0.1
	1814	1.7	0.5
17 Sa	0015	-0.3	-0.1
	0645	2.3	0.7
	1309	-0.3	-0.1
	1903	1.8	0.5
18 Su	0101	-0.4	-0.1
	0730	2.5	0.8
	1354	-0.4	-0.1
	1949	1.9	0.6
19 M	0147	-0.5	-0.2
	0815	2.7	0.8
	1440	-0.5	-0.2
	2037	2.0	0.6
20 Tu	0236	-0.6	-0.2
	0903	2.8	0.9
	1527	-0.5	-0.2
	2127	2.1	0.6
21 W	0323	-0.5	-0.2
	0950	2.8	0.9
	1615	-0.5	-0.2
	2217	2.2	0.7
22 Th	0413	-0.5	-0.2
	1039	2.8	0.9
	1704	-0.4	-0.1
	2308	2.3	0.7
23 F	0509	-0.3	-0.1
	1132	2.8	0.9
	1756	-0.3	-0.1
24 Sa	0002	2.3	0.7
	0605	-0.2	-0.1
	1226	2.7	0.8
	1848	-0.2	-0.1
25 Su	0100	2.4	0.7
	0708	0.0	0.0
	1324	2.6	0.8
	1945	-0.1	0.0
26 M	0203	2.5	0.8
	0814	0.1	0.0
	1425	2.4	0.7
	2043	0.0	0.0
27 Tu	0307	2.5	0.8
	0924	0.1	0.0
	1531	2.3	0.7
	2144	0.0	0.0
28 W	0410	2.5	0.8
	1033	0.1	0.0
	1634	2.2	0.7
	2244	0.0	0.0
29 Th	0513	2.6	0.8
	1139	0.0	0.0
	1736	2.1	0.6
	2340	-0.1	0.0
30 F	0612	2.6	0.8
	1237	-0.1	0.0
	1835	2.0	0.6
31 Sa	0033	-0.2	-0.1
	0702	2.7	0.8
	1331	-0.2	-0.1
	1926	2.0	0.6

Time meridian 75° W. 0000 is midnight. 1200 is noon.
Heights are referred to mean low water which is the chart datum of soundings.

SAVANNAH RIVER ENTRANCE, GA., 1983

Times and Heights of High and Low Waters

JANUARY

Day	Time (h m)	Height (ft)	Height (m)
1 Sa	0312	-1.5	-0.5
	0921	8.4	2.6
	1552	-1.1	-0.3
	2149	6.9	2.1
2 Su	0405	-1.3	-0.4
	1016	8.1	2.5
	1643	-0.9	-0.3
	2248	6.8	2.1
3 M	0459	-1.0	-0.3
	1111	7.7	2.3
	1736	-0.7	-0.2
	2348	6.7	2.0
4 Tu	0557	-0.7	-0.2
	1207	7.3	2.2
	1829	-0.5	-0.2
5 W	0047	6.6	2.0
	0657	-0.3	-0.1
	1303	6.8	2.1
	1927	-0.3	-0.1
6 Th	0147	6.5	2.0
	0758	0.0	0.0
	1358	6.4	2.0
	2025	-0.2	-0.1
7 F	0248	6.5	2.0
	0901	0.1	0.0
	1457	6.1	1.9
	2120	-0.1	0.0
8 Sa	0348	6.6	2.0
	0957	0.2	0.1
	1554	5.9	1.8
	2212	-0.1	0.0
9 Su	0442	6.7	2.0
	1046	0.1	0.0
	1645	5.8	1.8
	2256	-0.2	-0.1
10 M	0534	6.8	2.1
	1140	0.1	0.0
	1740	5.8	1.8
	2346	-0.2	-0.1
11 Tu	0621	6.9	2.1
	1226	0.0	0.0
	1824	5.9	1.8
12 W	0030	-0.3	-0.1
	0701	7.0	2.1
	1312	0.0	0.0
	1903	5.9	1.8
13 Th	0112	-0.3	-0.1
	0738	7.0	2.1
	1354	-0.1	0.0
	1940	6.0	1.8
14 F	0154	-0.3	-0.1
	0812	7.0	2.1
	1435	-0.1	0.0
	2015	6.0	1.8
15 Sa	0234	-0.3	-0.1
	0845	6.9	2.1
	1513	-0.1	0.0
	2050	6.0	1.8
16 Su	0310	-0.2	-0.1
	0918	6.8	2.1
	1550	0.0	0.0
	2126	6.0	1.8
17 M	0347	-0.1	0.0
	0951	6.7	2.0
	1627	0.0	0.0
	2203	6.0	1.8
18 Tu	0427	0.0	0.0
	1027	6.5	2.0
	1701	0.1	0.0
	2245	6.0	1.8
19 W	0506	0.2	0.1
	1108	6.3	1.9
	1741	0.1	0.0
	2331	6.1	1.9
20 Th	0551	0.3	0.1
	1151	6.2	1.9
	1827	0.2	0.1
21 F	0021	6.2	1.9
	0645	0.5	0.2
	1242	6.0	1.8
	1918	0.1	0.0
22 Sa	0115	6.4	2.0
	0746	0.5	0.2
	1334	5.8	1.8
	2015	0.0	0.0
23 Su	0214	6.6	2.0
	0852	0.4	0.1
	1433	5.8	1.8
	2116	-0.2	-0.1
24 M	0319	6.8	2.1
	0957	0.2	0.1
	1543	5.8	1.8
	2215	-0.6	-0.2
25 Tu	0426	7.2	2.2
	1100	-0.1	0.0
	1652	6.0	1.8
	2315	-0.9	-0.3
26 W	0531	7.6	2.3
	1200	-0.5	-0.2
	1758	6.4	2.0
27 Th	0011	-1.3	-0.4
	0631	8.0	2.4
	1256	-0.9	-0.3
	1856	6.7	2.0
28 F	0109	-1.6	-0.5
	0725	8.3	2.5
	1352	-1.2	-0.4
	1951	7.0	2.1
29 Sa	0205	-1.8	-0.5
	0817	8.4	2.6
	1443	-1.4	-0.4
	2043	7.2	2.2
30 Su	0259	-1.8	-0.5
	0908	8.3	2.5
	1533	-1.4	-0.4
	2136	7.2	2.2
31 M	0350	-1.7	-0.5
	0958	8.0	2.4
	1621	-1.3	-0.4
	2229	7.2	2.2

FEBRUARY

Day	Time (h m)	Height (ft)	Height (m)
1 Tu	0442	-1.4	-0.4
	1049	7.6	2.3
	1709	-1.1	-0.3
	2323	7.0	2.1
2 W	0534	-0.9	-0.3
	1141	7.0	2.1
	1759	-0.8	-0.2
3 Th	0018	6.8	2.1
	0628	-0.5	-0.2
	1231	6.5	2.0
	1849	-0.4	-0.1
4 F	0110	6.6	2.0
	0724	0.0	0.0
	1323	6.0	1.8
	1942	-0.1	0.0
5 Sa	0205	6.3	1.9
	0824	0.3	0.1
	1414	5.7	1.7
	2041	0.1	0.0
6 Su	0304	6.2	1.9
	0924	0.5	0.2
	1510	5.4	1.6
	2135	0.2	0.1
7 M	0406	6.2	1.9
	1018	0.5	0.2
	1610	5.3	1.6
	2227	0.2	0.1
8 Tu	0503	6.2	1.9
	1110	0.4	0.1
	1709	5.4	1.6
	2315	0.1	0.0
9 W	0555	6.4	2.0
	1158	0.3	0.1
	1758	5.6	1.7
10 Th	0003	-0.1	0.0
	0637	6.6	2.0
	1243	0.1	0.0
	1841	5.8	1.8
11 F	0048	-0.2	-0.1
	0715	6.8	2.1
	1328	0.0	0.0
	1918	6.0	1.8
12 Sa	0131	-0.3	-0.1
	0749	6.9	2.1
	1408	-0.2	-0.1
	1954	6.1	1.9
13 Su	0212	-0.4	-0.1
	0823	6.9	2.1
	1445	-0.2	-0.1
	2028	6.3	1.9
14 M	0249	-0.4	-0.1
	0854	6.8	2.1
	1521	-0.3	-0.1
	2102	6.4	2.0
15 Tu	0326	-0.4	-0.1
	0926	6.7	2.0
	1557	-0.3	-0.1
	2139	6.5	2.0
16 W	0403	-0.3	-0.1
	1000	6.6	2.0
	1631	-0.2	-0.1
	2218	6.6	2.0
17 Th	0443	-0.1	0.0
	1039	6.4	2.0
	1706	-0.2	-0.1
	2302	6.7	2.0
18 F	0525	0.0	0.0
	1121	6.2	1.9
	1749	-0.1	0.0
	2349	6.7	2.0
19 Sa	0616	0.3	0.1
	1210	6.0	1.8
	1839	0.0	0.0
20 Su	0043	6.7	2.0
	0716	0.5	0.2
	1306	5.8	1.8
	1941	0.0	0.0
21 M	0145	6.7	2.0
	0825	0.5	0.2
	1409	5.7	1.7
	2049	-0.1	0.0
22 Tu	0254	6.8	2.1
	0936	0.4	0.1
	1522	5.7	1.7
	2155	-0.4	-0.1
23 W	0407	7.0	2.1
	1041	0.0	0.0
	1638	6.0	1.8
	2258	-0.8	-0.2
24 Th	0518	7.4	2.3
	1142	-0.4	-0.1
	1747	6.4	2.0
25 F	0000	-1.2	-0.4
	0619	7.8	2.4
	1240	-0.8	-0.2
	1847	7.0	2.1
26 Sa	0056	-1.5	-0.5
	0712	8.1	2.5
	1333	-1.2	-0.4
	1941	7.4	2.3
27 Su	0152	-1.7	-0.5
	0803	8.2	2.5
	1423	-1.4	-0.4
	2029	7.7	2.3
28 M	0245	-1.8	-0.5
	0849	8.1	2.5
	1510	-1.5	-0.5
	2116	7.7	2.3

MARCH

Day	Time (h m)	Height (ft)	Height (m)
1 Tu	0333	-1.7	-0.5
	0935	7.8	2.4
	1555	-1.3	-0.4
	2205	7.6	2.3
2 W	0421	-1.3	-0.4
	1021	7.4	2.3
	1640	-1.1	-0.3
	2253	7.4	2.3
3 Th	0509	-0.9	-0.3
	1107	6.9	2.1
	1724	-0.6	-0.2
	2340	7.0	2.1
4 F	0557	-0.3	-0.1
	1153	6.4	2.0
	1810	-0.2	-0.1
5 Sa	0031	6.7	2.0
	0649	0.2	0.1
	1240	5.9	1.8
	1900	0.3	0.1
6 Su	0121	6.3	1.9
	0745	0.6	0.2
	1331	5.5	1.7
	1956	0.6	0.2
7 M	0216	6.1	1.9
	0845	0.8	0.2
	1426	5.3	1.6
	2054	0.7	0.2
8 Tu	0317	5.9	1.8
	0943	0.8	0.2
	1530	5.2	1.6
	2153	0.7	0.2
9 W	0422	6.0	1.8
	1036	0.7	0.2
	1631	5.4	1.6
	2246	0.5	0.2
10 Th	0518	6.2	1.9
	1126	0.5	0.2
	1726	5.6	1.7
	2335	0.3	0.1
11 F	0608	6.5	2.0
	1211	0.3	0.1
	1812	6.0	1.8
12 Sa	0022	0.0	0.0
	0648	6.7	2.0
	1256	0.1	0.0
	1853	6.3	1.9
13 Su	0105	-0.2	-0.1
	0723	6.9	2.1
	1336	-0.1	0.0
	1928	6.6	2.0
14 M	0147	-0.3	-0.1
	0755	6.9	2.1
	1414	-0.3	-0.1
	2002	6.9	2.1
15 Tu	0226	-0.4	-0.1
	0827	6.9	2.1
	1451	-0.3	-0.1
	2037	7.1	2.2
16 W	0305	-0.4	-0.1
	0900	6.9	2.1
	1524	-0.4	-0.1
	2113	7.2	2.2
17 Th	0342	-0.4	-0.1
	0934	6.7	2.0
	1600	-0.3	-0.1
	2152	7.3	2.2
18 F	0423	-0.2	-0.1
	1013	6.5	2.0
	1639	-0.3	-0.1
	2237	7.3	2.2
19 Sa	0506	0.0	0.0
	1059	6.3	1.9
	1722	-0.1	0.0
	2327	7.2	2.2
20 Su	0556	0.3	0.1
	1148	6.1	1.9
	1815	0.1	0.0
21 M	0023	7.1	2.2
	0657	0.5	0.2
	1247	5.9	1.8
	1919	0.2	0.1
22 Tu	0127	6.9	2.1
	0809	0.6	0.2
	1356	5.8	1.8
	2031	0.2	0.1
23 W	0237	6.9	2.1
	0919	0.5	0.2
	1512	5.9	1.8
	2143	-0.1	0.0
24 Th	0353	7.0	2.1
	1026	0.1	0.0
	1630	6.3	1.9
	2246	-0.5	-0.2
25 F	0505	7.3	2.2
	1126	-0.3	-0.1
	1739	6.8	2.1
	2347	-0.9	-0.3
26 Sa	0604	7.7	2.3
	1219	-0.7	-0.2
	1835	7.4	2.3
27 Su	0044	-1.2	-0.4
	0657	7.9	2.4
	1310	-1.1	-0.3
	1925	7.9	2.4
28 M	0136	-1.4	-0.4
	0744	8.0	2.4
	1358	-1.2	-0.4
	2010	8.1	2.5
29 Tu	0226	-1.5	-0.5
	0828	7.9	2.4
	1443	-1.2	-0.4
	2054	8.2	2.5
30 W	0313	-1.3	-0.4
	0910	7.6	2.3
	1526	-1.0	-0.3
	2138	8.0	2.4
31 Th	0358	-1.0	-0.3
	0952	7.2	2.2
	1608	-0.7	-0.2
	2219	7.6	2.3

Time meridian 75° W. 0000 is midnight. 1200 is noon.
Heights are referred to mean low water which is the chart datum of soundings.

SAVANNAH RIVER ENTRANCE, GA., 1983

Times and Heights of High and Low Waters

APRIL

Day	h m	ft	m	Day	h m	ft	m
1 F	0442	-0.6	-0.2	16 Sa	0407	-0.3	-0.1
	1033	6.7	2.0		0954	6.6	2.0
	1647	-0.3	-0.1		1616	-0.3	-0.1
	2304	7.2	2.2		2218	7.8	2.4
2 Sa	0525	-0.1	0.0	17 Su	0453	0.0	0.0
	1117	6.3	1.9		1043	6.3	1.9
	1732	0.2	0.1		1704	-0.1	0.0
	2349	6.8	2.1		2312	7.6	2.3
3 Su	0613	0.4	0.1	18 M	0546	0.2	0.1
	1201	5.9	1.8		1138	6.1	1.9
	1818	0.6	0.2		1802	0.2	0.1
4 M	0036	6.4	2.0	19 Tu	0010	7.3	2.2
	0706	0.8	0.2		0647	0.5	0.2
	1251	5.6	1.7		1242	6.0	1.8
	1912	1.0	0.3		1908	0.3	0.1
5 Tu	0129	6.1	1.9	20 W	0116	7.1	2.2
	0803	1.0	0.3		0757	0.5	0.2
	1346	5.4	1.6		1353	6.0	1.8
	2015	1.0	0.3		2020	0.3	0.1
6 W	0228	5.9	1.8	21 Th	0226	7.0	2.1
	0903	1.1	0.3		0906	0.4	0.1
	1446	5.4	1.6		1509	6.2	1.9
	2115	1.1	0.3		2132	0.1	0.0
7 Th	0331	5.9	1.8	22 F	0337	7.0	2.1
	0959	0.9	0.3		1009	0.0	0.0
	1548	5.5	1.7		1623	6.7	2.0
	2211	0.9	0.3		2234	-0.2	-0.1
8 F	0433	6.1	1.9	23 Sa	0446	7.2	2.2
	1049	0.7	0.2		1105	-0.4	-0.1
	1646	5.9	1.8		1726	7.2	2.2
	2303	0.6	0.2		2331	-0.6	-0.2
9 Sa	0524	6.3	1.9	24 Su	0545	7.4	2.3
	1134	0.4	0.1		1156	-0.7	-0.2
	1737	6.3	1.9		1819	7.8	2.4
	2350	0.3	0.1				
10 Su	0608	6.6	2.0	25 M	0026	-0.9	-0.3
	1217	0.1	0.0		0636	7.5	2.3
	1819	6.7	2.0		1245	-0.9	-0.3
					1908	8.1	2.5
11 M	0035	0.0	0.0	26 Tu	0117	-1.0	-0.3
	0645	6.8	2.1		0722	7.5	2.3
	1259	-0.1	0.0		1330	-0.9	-0.3
	1858	7.2	2.2		1950	8.3	2.5
12 Tu	0118	-0.2	-0.1	27 W	0205	-1.0	-0.3
	0721	6.9	2.1		0803	7.4	2.3
	1338	-0.3	-0.1		1415	-0.9	-0.3
	1935	7.5	2.3		2031	8.3	2.5
13 W	0200	-0.4	-0.1	28 Th	0250	-0.9	-0.3
	0758	7.0	2.1		0844	7.1	2.2
	1416	-0.4	-0.1		1456	-0.7	-0.2
	2012	7.8	2.4		2110	8.0	2.4
14 Th	0241	-0.4	-0.1	29 F	0333	-0.6	-0.2
	0832	6.9	2.1		0922	6.8	2.1
	1453	-0.4	-0.1		1536	-0.4	-0.1
	2050	7.9	2.4		2149	7.7	2.3
15 F	0323	-0.4	-0.1	30 Sa	0415	-0.3	-0.1
	0912	6.8	2.1		1002	6.4	2.0
	1535	-0.4	-0.1		1616	0.0	0.0
	2131	7.9	2.4		2229	7.3	2.2

MAY

Day	h m	ft	m	Day	h m	ft	m
1 Su	0457	0.1	0.0	16 M	0443	-0.2	-0.1
	1043	6.1	1.9		1035	6.4	2.0
	1656	0.4	0.1		1654	-0.2	-0.1
	2312	6.8	2.1		2301	7.8	2.4
2 M	0540	0.5	0.2	17 Tu	0538	0.0	0.0
	1126	5.8	1.8		1136	6.2	1.9
	1741	0.8	0.2		1753	0.0	0.0
	2357	6.5	2.0				
3 Tu	0629	0.8	0.2	18 W	0002	7.5	2.3
	1215	5.6	1.7		0639	0.1	0.0
	1831	1.1	0.3		1242	6.2	1.9
					1858	0.2	0.1
4 W	0046	6.2	1.9	19 Th	0106	7.2	2.2
	0724	1.0	0.3		0743	0.2	0.1
	1308	5.5	1.7		1351	6.3	1.9
	1930	1.3	0.4		2009	0.3	0.1
5 Th	0139	6.0	1.8	20 F	0213	7.0	2.1
	0820	1.0	0.3		0848	0.0	0.0
	1404	5.6	1.7		1502	6.6	2.0
	2033	1.3	0.4		2117	0.1	0.0
6 F	0236	6.0	1.8	21 Sa	0319	6.9	2.1
	0916	0.9	0.3		0946	-0.2	-0.1
	1503	5.8	1.8		1609	7.0	2.1
	2132	1.1	0.3		2218	-0.1	0.0
7 Sa	0333	6.0	1.8	22 Su	0424	6.9	2.1
	1005	0.6	0.2		1041	-0.4	-0.1
	1601	6.1	1.9		1708	7.4	2.3
	2225	0.8	0.2		2315	-0.4	-0.1
8 Su	0430	6.2	1.9	23 M	0523	6.9	2.1
	1052	0.3	0.1		1129	-0.6	-0.2
	1654	6.6	2.0		1800	7.8	2.4
	2315	0.5	0.2				
9 M	0521	6.4	2.0	24 Tu	0006	-0.5	-0.2
	1134	0.0	0.0		0611	6.9	2.1
	1742	7.1	2.2		1216	-0.7	-0.2
					1845	8.0	2.4
10 Tu	0001	0.1	0.0	25 W	0056	-0.6	-0.2
	0605	6.6	2.0		0657	6.9	2.1
	1219	-0.2	-0.1		1301	-0.7	-0.2
	1824	7.5	2.3		1928	8.1	2.5
11 W	0048	-0.1	0.0	26 Th	0143	-0.6	-0.2
	0647	6.7	2.0		0738	6.8	2.1
	1300	-0.4	-0.1		1345	-0.6	-0.2
	1905	7.9	2.4		2006	8.0	2.4
12 Th	0133	-0.3	-0.1	27 F	0227	-0.5	-0.2
	0728	6.8	2.1		0818	6.6	2.0
	1343	-0.6	-0.2		1427	-0.4	-0.1
	1947	8.2	2.5		2043	7.8	2.4
13 F	0219	-0.5	-0.2	28 Sa	0310	-0.3	-0.1
	0808	6.8	2.1		0808	6.4	2.0
	1428	-0.6	-0.2		1509	-0.1	0.0
	2030	8.3	2.5		2120	7.5	2.3
14 Sa	0305	-0.5	-0.2	29 Su	0350	-0.1	0.0
	0851	6.7	2.0		0933	6.1	1.9
	1514	-0.6	-0.2		1547	0.2	0.1
	2115	8.3	2.5		2157	7.2	2.2
15 Su	0352	-0.4	-0.1	30 M	0432	0.2	0.1
	0939	6.6	2.0		1011	5.9	1.8
	1601	-0.5	-0.2		1627	0.5	0.2
	2206	8.1	2.5		2237	6.8	2.1
				31 Tu	0512	0.4	0.1
					1055	5.8	1.8
					1709	0.7	0.2
					2320	6.6	2.0

JUNE

Day	h m	ft	m	Day	h m	ft	m
1 W	0556	0.6	0.2	16 Th	0623	-0.3	-0.1
	1141	5.7	1.7		1236	6.6	2.0
	1754	1.0	0.3		1846	0.0	0.0
2 Th	0005	6.3	1.9	17 F	0052	7.2	2.2
	0644	0.8	0.2		0723	-0.3	-0.1
	1230	5.7	1.7		1340	6.7	2.0
	1850	1.2	0.4		1952	0.2	0.1
3 F	0055	6.2	1.9	18 Sa	0153	6.9	2.1
	0737	0.8	0.2		0822	-0.3	-0.1
	1324	5.8	1.8		1444	6.9	2.1
	1947	1.2	0.4		2058	0.1	0.0
4 Sa	0144	6.0	1.8	19 Su	0255	6.6	2.0
	0830	0.7	0.2		0920	-0.3	-0.1
	1416	6.0	1.8		1545	7.1	2.2
	2049	1.1	0.3		2159	0.0	0.0
5 Su	0239	6.0	1.8	20 M	0356	6.5	2.0
	0919	0.5	0.2		1012	-0.4	-0.1
	1512	6.3	1.9		1644	7.3	2.2
	2144	0.9	0.3		2254	-0.1	0.0
6 M	0333	6.0	1.8	21 Tu	0454	6.4	2.0
	1008	0.2	0.1		1102	-0.4	-0.1
	1607	6.7	2.0		1738	7.6	2.3
	2236	0.5	0.2		2345	-0.1	0.0
7 Tu	0430	6.1	1.9	22 W	0545	6.3	1.9
	1054	-0.1	0.0		1150	-0.4	-0.1
	1700	7.2	2.2		1824	7.7	2.3
	2327	0.2	0.1				
8 W	0523	6.3	1.9	23 Th	0034	-0.2	-0.1
	1140	-0.4	-0.1		0632	6.3	1.9
	1750	7.7	2.3		1235	-0.4	-0.1
					1907	7.7	2.3
9 Th	0017	-0.1	0.0	24 F	0120	-0.2	-0.1
	0612	6.5	2.0		0713	6.3	1.9
	1226	-0.6	-0.2		1317	-0.3	-0.1
	1838	8.1	2.5		1946	7.7	2.3
10 F	0108	-0.3	-0.1	25 Sa	0204	-0.1	0.0
	0701	6.6	2.0		0753	6.2	1.9
	1315	-0.8	-0.2		1402	-0.1	0.0
	1926	8.4	2.6		2023	7.5	2.3
11 Sa	0159	-0.5	-0.2	26 Su	0246	-0.1	0.0
	0749	6.7	2.0		0830	6.1	1.9
	1405	-0.9	-0.3		1442	0.0	0.0
	2013	8.5	2.6		2057	7.3	2.2
12 Su	0250	-0.6	-0.2	27 M	0327	0.0	0.0
	0838	6.7	2.0		0906	6.0	1.8
	1457	-0.9	-0.3		1522	0.2	0.1
	2103	8.4	2.6		2133	7.1	2.2
13 M	0341	-0.6	-0.2	28 Tu	0406	0.2	0.1
	0931	6.6	2.0		0944	5.9	1.8
	1550	-0.8	-0.2		1602	0.4	0.1
	2157	8.2	2.5		2208	6.9	2.1
14 Tu	0432	-0.6	-0.2	29 W	0445	0.3	0.1
	1029	6.6	2.0		1024	5.9	1.8
	1645	-0.6	-0.2		1640	0.6	0.2
	2253	7.9	2.4		2248	6.7	2.0
15 W	0527	-0.5	-0.2	30 Th	0524	0.4	0.1
	1133	6.5	2.0		1109	5.9	1.8
	1744	-0.3	-0.1		1723	0.8	0.2
	2353	7.6	2.3		2328	6.5	2.0

Time meridian 75° W. 0000 is midnight. 1200 is noon.
Heights are referred to mean low water which is the chart datum of soundings.

SAVANNAH, GA., 1983

Times and Heights of High and Low Waters

JANUARY

Day	h m	ft	m	Day	h m	ft	m
1 Sa	0411	-1.5	-0.5	16 Su	0405	-0.2	-0.1
	1013	8.9	2.7		0956	7.5	2.3
	1650	-0.9	-0.3		1640	0.0	0.0
	2240	7.4	2.3		2158	6.8	2.1
2 Su	0503	-1.3	-0.4	17 M	0442	0.0	0.0
	1103	8.6	2.6		1027	7.4	2.3
	1740	-0.8	-0.2		1717	0.1	0.0
	2333	7.3	2.2		2235	6.8	2.1
3 M	0554	-1.0	-0.3	18 Tu	0517	0.1	0.0
	1154	8.2	2.5		1100	7.3	2.2
	1829	-0.6	-0.2		1754	0.1	0.0
					2314	6.9	2.1
4 Tu	0031	7.2	2.2	19 W	0556	0.2	0.1
	0648	-0.7	-0.2		1139	7.2	2.2
	1247	7.8	2.4		1833	0.2	0.1
	1919	-0.4	-0.1				
5 W	0127	7.1	2.2	20 Th	0001	7.1	2.2
	0743	-0.3	-0.1		0638	0.3	0.1
	1340	7.4	2.3		1223	7.1	2.2
	2012	-0.2	-0.1		1916	0.2	0.1
6 Th	0222	7.1	2.2	21 F	0052	7.2	2.2
	0840	0.0	0.0		0733	0.5	0.2
	1431	7.0	2.1		1315	6.9	2.1
	2106	-0.1	0.0		2010	0.2	0.1
7 F	0317	7.1	2.2	22 Sa	0149	7.3	2.2
	0938	0.1	0.0		0839	0.6	0.2
	1524	6.7	2.0		1411	6.7	2.0
	2159	-0.1	0.0		2110	0.0	0.0
8 Sa	0413	7.1	2.2	23 Su	0251	7.5	2.3
	1034	0.2	0.1		0950	0.5	0.2
	1618	6.5	2.0		1516	6.6	2.0
	2251	-0.2	-0.1		2214	-0.2	-0.1
9 Su	0509	7.2	2.2	24 M	0357	7.6	2.3
	1127	0.1	0.0		1057	0.2	0.1
	1713	6.4	2.0		1627	6.5	2.0
	2341	-0.3	-0.1		2315	-0.5	-0.2
10 M	0604	7.4	2.3	25 Tu	0510	7.9	2.4
	1217	0.0	0.0		1158	-0.1	0.0
	1808	6.5	2.0		1742	6.7	2.0
11 Tu	0029	-0.4	-0.1	26 W	0014	-0.9	-0.3
	0654	7.5	2.3		0621	8.3	2.5
	1306	-0.1	0.0		1257	-0.5	-0.2
	1856	6.5	2.0		1851	7.0	2.1
12 W	0116	-0.4	-0.1	27 Th	0112	-1.3	-0.4
	0738	7.6	2.3		0722	8.7	2.7
	1351	-0.1	0.0		1354	-0.8	-0.2
	1941	6.6	2.0		1951	7.3	2.2
13 Th	0200	-0.4	-0.1	28 F	0208	-1.6	-0.5
	0818	7.7	2.3		0817	8.9	2.7
	1437	-0.1	0.0		1448	-1.1	-0.3
	2018	6.7	2.0		2044	7.6	2.3
14 F	0245	-0.4	-0.1	29 Sa	0302	-1.8	-0.5
	0854	7.7	2.3		0908	9.0	2.7
	1521	-0.1	0.0		1540	-1.2	-0.4
	2052	6.7	2.0		2136	7.8	2.4
15 Sa	0326	-0.3	-0.1	30 Su	0355	-1.8	-0.5
	0926	7.6	2.3		0958	8.9	2.7
	1603	-0.1	0.0		1629	-1.3	-0.4
	2126	6.7	2.0		2224	7.8	2.4
				31 M	0445	-1.6	-0.5
					1045	8.5	2.6
					1716	-1.1	-0.3
					2314	7.7	2.3

FEBRUARY

Day	h m	ft	m	Day	h m	ft	m
1 Tu	0535	-1.3	-0.4	16 W	0455	0.0	0.0
	1133	8.1	2.5		1033	7.3	2.2
	1801	-0.9	-0.3		1722	0.0	0.0
					2248	7.5	2.3
2 W	0006	7.6	2.3	17 Th	0533	0.1	0.0
	0625	-0.9	-0.3		1109	7.2	2.2
	1220	7.6	2.3		1759	0.0	0.0
	1847	-0.6	-0.2		2333	7.6	2.3
3 Th	0055	7.4	2.3	18 F	0615	0.2	0.1
	0715	-0.4	-0.1		1154	7.1	2.2
	1308	7.1	2.2		1841	0.1	0.0
	1935	-0.3	-0.1				
4 F	0147	7.2	2.2	19 Sa	0023	7.6	2.3
	0809	0.0	0.0		0708	0.4	0.1
	1356	6.7	2.0		1244	6.9	2.1
	2028	0.0	0.0		1932	0.1	0.0
5 Sa	0239	7.0	2.1	20 Su	0121	7.7	2.3
	0905	0.3	0.1		0812	0.6	0.2
	1443	6.4	2.0		1345	6.6	2.0
	2122	0.2	0.1		2038	0.1	0.0
6 Su	0332	6.9	2.1	21 M	0224	7.7	2.3
	1001	0.4	0.1		0924	0.6	0.2
	1537	6.2	1.9		1452	6.5	2.0
	2216	0.2	0.1		2148	0.0	0.0
7 M	0430	6.9	2.1	22 Tu	0336	7.7	2.3
	1055	0.4	0.1		1036	0.3	0.1
	1633	6.1	1.9		1608	6.5	2.0
	2310	0.1	0.0		2254	-0.4	-0.1
8 Tu	0529	7.0	2.1	23 W	0451	7.9	2.4
	1148	0.3	0.1		1139	0.0	0.0
	1732	6.2	1.9		1727	6.8	2.1
					2355	-0.8	-0.2
9 W	0000	0.0	0.0	24 Th	0603	8.2	2.5
	0621	7.1	2.2		1237	-0.5	-0.2
	1237	0.2	0.1		1837	7.2	2.2
	1827	6.4	2.0				
10 Th	0049	-0.2	-0.1	25 F	0055	-1.3	-0.4
	0712	7.3	2.2		0706	8.6	2.6
	1323	0.0	0.0		1333	-0.9	-0.3
	1914	6.6	2.0		1936	7.7	2.3
11 F	0135	-0.3	-0.1	26 Sa	0151	-1.6	-0.5
	0752	7.5	2.3		0802	8.9	2.7
	1410	-0.1	0.0		1425	-1.2	-0.4
	1955	6.8	2.1		2029	8.1	2.5
12 Sa	0221	-0.3	-0.1	27 Su	0245	-1.8	-0.5
	0831	7.5	2.3		0852	8.9	2.7
	1453	-0.1	0.0		1515	-1.3	-0.4
	2031	6.9	2.1		2118	8.4	2.6
13 Su	0303	-0.3	-0.1	28 M	0336	-1.8	-0.5
	0903	7.5	2.3		0936	8.7	2.7
	1534	-0.2	-0.1		1603	-1.3	-0.4
	2104	7.0	2.1		2204	8.4	2.6
14 M	0341	-0.2	-0.1				
	0937	7.5	2.3				
	1611	-0.1	0.0				
	2136	7.2	2.2				
15 Tu	0419	-0.1	0.0				
	1000	7.4	2.3				
	1648	-0.1	0.0				
	2210	7.3	2.2				

MARCH

Day	h m	ft	m	Day	h m	ft	m
1 Tu	0426	-1.6	-0.5	16 W	0358	-0.1	0.0
	1022	8.4	2.6		0935	7.4	2.3
	1648	-1.1	-0.3		1617	-0.1	0.0
	2250	8.3	2.5		2149	7.9	2.4
2 W	0513	-1.2	-0.4	17 Th	0435	0.0	0.0
	1104	7.9	2.4		1008	7.3	2.2
	1732	-0.8	-0.2		1653	0.0	0.0
	2335	8.0	2.4		2227	8.1	2.5
3 Th	0559	-0.8	-0.2	18 F	0516	0.1	0.0
	1149	7.4	2.3		1047	7.2	2.2
	1813	-0.4	-0.1		1733	0.0	0.0
					2312	8.1	2.5
4 F	0020	7.7	2.3	19 Sa	0602	0.3	0.1
	0646	-0.3	-0.1		1133	7.0	2.1
	1231	6.9	2.1		1815	0.2	0.1
	1859	0.0	0.0				
5 Sa	0108	7.4	2.3	20 Su	0002	8.1	2.5
	0737	0.2	0.1		0652	0.5	0.2
	1313	6.6	2.0		1225	6.8	2.1
	1949	0.3	0.1		1911	0.3	0.1
6 Su	0155	7.1	2.2	21 M	0100	7.9	2.4
	0830	0.6	0.2		0757	0.6	0.2
	1403	6.3	1.9		1329	6.6	2.0
	2041	0.6	0.2		2017	0.3	0.1
7 M	0249	6.9	2.1	22 Tu	0206	7.8	2.4
	0925	0.8	0.2		0907	0.6	0.2
	1454	6.2	1.9		1441	6.6	2.0
	2140	0.7	0.2		2130	0.2	0.1
8 Tu	0345	6.8	2.1	23 W	0318	7.8	2.4
	1021	0.8	0.2		1016	0.4	0.1
	1553	6.1	1.9		1558	6.7	2.0
	2236	0.6	0.2		2238	-0.1	0.0
9 W	0445	6.8	2.1	24 Th	0433	7.9	2.4
	1113	0.6	0.2		1118	0.0	0.0
	1654	6.3	1.9		1715	7.1	2.2
	2331	0.4	0.1		2339	-0.6	-0.2
10 Th	0544	7.0	2.1	25 F	0544	8.2	2.5
	1205	0.4	0.1		1216	-0.4	-0.1
	1752	6.5	2.0		1822	7.6	2.3
11 F	0021	0.2	0.1	26 Sa	0037	-1.0	-0.3
	0637	7.2	2.2		0646	8.5	2.6
	1253	0.2	0.1		1309	-0.8	-0.2
	1843	6.8	2.1		1920	8.2	2.5
12 Sa	0109	0.0	0.0	27 Su	0133	-1.3	-0.4
	0720	7.4	2.3		0741	8.7	2.7
	1338	0.0	0.0		1359	-1.1	-0.3
	1928	7.1	2.2		2011	8.6	2.6
13 Su	0154	-0.1	0.0	28 M	0225	-1.5	-0.5
	0759	7.5	2.3		0829	8.7	2.7
	1421	-0.1	0.0		1448	-1.2	-0.4
	2006	7.3	2.2		2057	8.8	2.7
14 M	0237	-0.1	0.0	29 Tu	0316	-1.5	-0.5
	0834	7.5	2.3		0914	8.4	2.6
	1502	-0.1	0.0		1534	-1.1	-0.3
	2039	7.6	2.3		2141	8.8	2.7
15 Tu	0318	-0.1	0.0	30 W	0403	-1.3	-0.4
	0906	7.5	2.3		0954	8.1	2.5
	1540	-0.1	0.0		1618	-0.9	-0.3
	2115	7.8	2.4		2223	8.7	2.7
				31 Th	0448	-0.9	-0.3
					1034	7.7	2.3
					1701	-0.5	-0.2
					2304	8.3	2.5

Time meridian 75° W.   0000 is midnight. 1200 is noon.
Heights are referred to mean low water which is the chart datum of soundings.

Times and Heights of High and Low Waters

APRIL

Day	h m	ft	m	Day	h m	ft	m
1 F	0533	-0.5	-0.2	16 Sa	0504	0.1	0.0
	1114	7.2	2.2		1031	7.1	2.2
	1742	-0.1	0.0		1714	0.0	0.0
	2343	8.0	2.4		2256	8.5	2.6
2 Sa	0618	0.0	0.0	17 Su	0551	0.3	0.1
	1152	6.9	2.1		1120	6.9	2.1
	1825	0.3	0.1		1802	0.2	0.1
					2349	8.3	2.5
3 Su	0028	7.6	2.3	18 M	0645	0.4	0.1
	0704	0.4	0.1		1217	6.7	2.0
	1236	6.6	2.0		1858	0.3	0.1
	1911	0.6	0.2				
4 M	0113	7.3	2.2	19 Tu	0050	8.1	2.5
	0753	0.7	0.2		0745	0.5	0.2
	1324	6.4	2.0		1324	6.6	2.0
	2004	0.9	0.3		2004	0.4	0.1
5 Tu	0203	7.0	2.1	20 W	0156	7.9	2.4
	0849	0.9	0.3		0852	0.5	0.2
	1416	6.3	1.9		1438	6.7	2.0
	2101	1.0	0.3		2114	0.4	0.1
6 W	0257	6.9	2.1	21 Th	0306	7.8	2.4
	0944	0.9	0.3		0956	0.3	0.1
	1511	6.3	1.9		1551	7.0	2.1
	2201	1.0	0.3		2220	0.0	0.0
7 Th	0356	6.9	2.1	22 F	0414	7.9	2.4
	1039	0.8	0.2		1057	-0.1	0.0
	1612	6.5	2.0		1659	7.4	2.3
	2256	0.8	0.2		2321	-0.4	-0.1
8 F	0454	6.9	2.1	23 Sa	0523	8.0	2.4
	1129	0.5	0.2		1150	-0.5	-0.2
	1711	6.7	2.0		1803	8.0	2.4
	2347	0.5	0.2				
9 Sa	0550	7.1	2.2	24 Su	0017	-0.7	-0.2
	1218	0.3	0.1		0622	8.1	2.5
	1806	7.1	2.2		1243	-0.8	-0.2
					1859	8.5	2.6
10 Su	0037	0.3	0.1	25 M	0112	-1.0	-0.3
	0639	7.3	2.2		0715	8.2	2.5
	1303	0.1	0.0		1331	-1.0	-0.3
	1854	7.5	2.3		1950	8.8	2.7
11 M	0124	0.1	0.0	26 Tu	0203	-1.1	-0.3
	0724	7.4	2.3		0803	8.1	2.5
	1346	-0.1	0.0		1418	-1.0	-0.3
	1936	7.8	2.4		2034	9.0	2.7
12 Tu	0209	0.0	0.0	27 W	0252	-1.1	-0.3
	0802	7.4	2.3		0846	7.9	2.4
	1428	-0.1	0.0		1504	-0.8	-0.2
	2013	8.1	2.5		2115	8.9	2.7
13 W	0255	0.0	0.0	28 Th	0340	-0.9	-0.3
	0837	7.4	2.3		0927	7.6	2.3
	1509	-0.2	-0.1		1549	-0.6	-0.2
	2051	8.3	2.5		2155	8.7	2.7
14 Th	0337	0.0	0.0	29 F	0423	-0.6	-0.2
	0913	7.3	2.2		1004	7.3	2.2
	1550	-0.1	0.0		1631	-0.3	-0.1
	2129	8.5	2.6		2232	8.4	2.6
15 F	0420	0.0	0.0	30 Sa	0508	-0.3	-0.1
	0950	7.2	2.2		1040	7.0	2.1
	1629	-0.1	0.0		1712	0.1	0.0
	2211	8.5	2.6		2311	8.0	2.4

MAY

Day	h m	ft	m	Day	h m	ft	m
1 Su	0550	0.1	0.0	16 M	0544	0.0	0.0
	1120	6.7	2.0		1117	6.8	2.1
	1751	0.4	0.1		1754	-0.1	0.0
	2349	7.7	2.3		2343	8.4	2.6
2 M	0634	0.4	0.1	17 Tu	0636	0.1	0.0
	1201	6.6	2.0		1218	6.7	2.0
	1836	0.7	0.2		1850	0.1	0.0
3 Tu	0033	7.4	2.3	18 W	0044	8.1	2.5
	0721	0.7	0.2		0735	0.2	0.1
	1247	6.5	2.0		1325	6.7	2.0
	1926	1.0	0.3		1952	0.2	0.1
4 W	0119	7.2	2.2	19 Th	0148	7.9	2.4
	0812	0.8	0.2		0835	0.1	0.0
	1337	6.4	2.0		1433	6.9	2.1
	2020	1.1	0.3		2057	0.2	0.1
5 Th	0211	7.0	2.1	20 F	0249	7.7	2.3
	0905	0.8	0.2		0934	-0.1	0.0
	1433	6.5	2.0		1538	7.2	2.2
	2120	1.1	0.3		2202	0.0	0.0
6 F	0304	6.9	2.1	21 Sa	0353	7.6	2.3
	0958	0.7	0.2		1030	-0.3	-0.1
	1530	6.7	2.0		1641	7.6	2.3
	2217	1.0	0.3		2300	-0.2	-0.1
7 Sa	0402	6.9	2.1	22 Su	0455	7.5	2.3
	1049	0.4	0.1		1124	-0.6	-0.2
	1628	7.0	2.1		1741	8.0	2.4
	2313	0.7	0.2		2356	-0.5	-0.2
8 Su	0457	7.0	2.1	23 M	0553	7.5	2.3
	1139	0.2	0.1		1214	-0.8	-0.2
	1723	7.3	2.2		1837	8.4	2.6
9 M	0003	0.5	0.2	24 Tu	0048	-0.6	-0.2
	0553	7.0	2.1		0648	7.5	2.3
	1225	0.0	0.0		1302	-0.8	-0.2
	1816	7.7	2.3		1925	8.7	2.7
10 Tu	0053	0.2	0.1	25 W	0140	-0.7	-0.2
	0643	7.1	2.2		0735	7.4	2.3
	1311	-0.2	-0.1		1349	-0.8	-0.2
	1904	8.1	2.5		2010	8.8	2.7
11 W	0141	0.0	0.0	26 Th	0229	-0.7	-0.2
	0729	7.2	2.2		0819	7.3	2.2
	1354	-0.3	-0.1		1435	-0.6	-0.2
	1949	8.5	2.6		2049	8.7	2.7
12 Th	0230	0.0	0.0	27 F	0315	-0.6	-0.2
	0811	7.2	2.2		0858	7.1	2.2
	1439	-0.3	-0.1		1520	-0.4	-0.1
	2031	8.7	2.7		2129	8.5	2.6
13 F	0317	-0.1	0.0	28 Sa	0358	-0.4	-0.1
	0853	7.1	2.2		0935	6.9	2.1
	1525	-0.3	-0.1		1602	-0.2	-0.1
	2115	8.8	2.7		2205	8.2	2.5
14 Sa	0407	-0.1	0.0	29 Su	0442	-0.2	-0.1
	0936	7.0	2.1		1011	6.7	2.0
	1613	-0.3	-0.1		1643	0.1	0.0
	2200	8.8	2.7		2240	7.9	2.4
15 Su	0453	-0.1	0.0	30 M	0524	0.1	0.0
	1024	6.9	2.1		1048	6.6	2.0
	1701	-0.2	-0.1		1724	0.4	0.1
	2248	8.6	2.6		2317	7.6	2.3
				31 Tu	0605	0.3	0.1
					1128	6.5	2.0
					1805	0.6	0.2
					2354	7.4	2.3

JUNE

Day	h m	ft	m	Day	h m	ft	m
1 W	0647	0.4	0.1	16 Th	0034	8.1	2.5
	1213	6.5	2.0		0716	-0.3	-0.1
	1847	0.9	0.3		1318	7.0	2.1
					1937	-0.1	0.0
2 Th	0038	7.2	2.2	17 F	0132	7.8	2.4
	0734	0.5	0.2		0812	-0.3	-0.1
	1259	6.5	2.0		1418	7.2	2.2
	1939	1.0	0.3		2038	0.1	0.0
3 F	0126	7.1	2.2	18 Sa	0230	7.5	2.3
	0822	0.5	0.2		0907	-0.3	-0.1
	1353	6.7	2.0		1519	7.4	2.3
	2036	1.1	0.3		2140	0.1	0.0
4 Sa	0214	7.0	2.1	19 Su	0326	7.2	2.2
	0915	0.4	0.1		1002	-0.4	-0.1
	1447	6.9	2.1		1617	7.7	2.3
	2136	1.0	0.3		2237	0.0	0.0
5 Su	0306	6.9	2.1	20 M	0423	7.0	2.1
	1006	0.3	0.1		1055	-0.5	-0.2
	1541	7.2	2.2		1715	7.9	2.4
	2233	0.8	0.2		2332	-0.1	0.0
6 M	0404	6.8	2.1	21 Tu	0521	6.9	2.1
	1057	0.0	0.0		1145	-0.6	-0.2
	1641	7.5	2.3		1810	8.1	2.5
	2329	0.5	0.2				
7 Tu	0502	6.8	2.1	22 W	0024	-0.3	-0.1
	1147	-0.2	-0.1		0617	6.8	2.1
	1736	7.9	2.4		1233	-0.6	-0.2
					1901	8.3	2.5
8 W	0023	0.3	0.1	23 Th	0114	-0.3	-0.1
	0600	6.8	2.1		0706	6.8	2.1
	1235	-0.4	-0.1		1322	-0.6	-0.2
	1833	8.3	2.5		1946	8.4	2.6
9 Th	0114	0.0	0.0	24 F	0202	-0.3	-0.1
	0658	6.8	2.1		0751	6.8	2.1
	1325	-0.5	-0.2		1407	-0.5	-0.2
	1925	8.6	2.6		2027	8.3	2.5
10 F	0207	-0.2	-0.1	25 Sa	0248	-0.3	-0.1
	0751	6.9	2.1		0832	6.8	2.1
	1414	-0.6	-0.2		1451	-0.3	-0.1
	2014	8.9	2.7		2105	8.2	2.5
11 Sa	0300	-0.3	-0.1	26 Su	0333	-0.2	-0.1
	0839	7.0	2.1		0910	6.7	2.0
	1506	-0.7	-0.2		1535	-0.1	0.0
	2102	8.9	2.7		2139	8.0	2.4
12 Su	0351	-0.4	-0.1	27 M	0416	-0.1	0.0
	0928	7.0	2.1		0945	6.7	2.0
	1558	-0.7	-0.2		1616	0.1	0.0
	2152	8.9	2.7		2213	7.8	2.4
13 M	0442	-0.4	-0.1	28 Tu	0456	0.0	0.0
	1020	6.9	2.1		1020	6.6	2.0
	1650	-0.6	-0.2		1655	0.3	0.1
	2243	8.7	2.7		2245	7.6	2.3
14 Tu	0533	-0.4	-0.1	29 W	0535	0.1	0.0
	1117	6.9	2.1		1056	6.6	2.0
	1743	-0.5	-0.2		1735	0.5	0.2
	2337	8.4	2.6		2320	7.5	2.3
15 W	0623	-0.4	-0.1	30 Th	0615	0.2	0.1
	1217	6.9	2.1		1138	6.7	2.0
	1839	-0.3	-0.1		1815	0.7	0.2
					2357	7.3	2.2

Time meridian 75° W. 0000 is midnight. 1200 is noon.
Heights are referred to mean low water which is the chart datum of soundings.

SAVANNAH, GA., 1983

Times and Heights of High and Low Waters

JULY

Day	Time h m	Height ft	Height m	Day	Time h m	Height ft	Height m
1 F	0655	0.3	0.1	16 Sa	0110	7.7	2.3
	1223	6.8	2.1		0744	-0.4	-0.1
	1858	0.8	0.2		1358	7.5	2.3
					2014	0.1	0.0
2 Sa	0039	7.2	2.2	17 Su	0201	7.3	2.2
	0739	0.3	0.1		0837	-0.3	-0.1
	1312	7.0	2.1		1452	7.6	2.3
	1952	1.0	0.3		2114	0.3	0.1
3 Su	0129	7.0	2.1	18 M	0257	6.9	2.1
	0830	0.3	0.1		0931	-0.2	-0.1
	1406	7.2	2.2		1549	7.6	2.3
	2053	1.0	0.3		2212	0.4	0.1
4 M	0220	6.9	2.1	19 Tu	0351	6.6	2.0
	0922	0.2	0.1		1025	-0.2	-0.1
	1500	7.4	2.3		1646	7.7	2.3
	2157	0.9	0.3		2307	0.3	0.1
5 Tu	0316	6.7	2.0	20 W	0449	6.5	2.0
	1016	0.0	0.0		1117	-0.2	-0.1
	1602	7.7	2.3		1742	7.8	2.4
	2257	0.6	0.2		2358	0.2	0.1
6 W	0420	6.6	2.0	21 Th	0545	6.5	2.0
	1111	-0.2	-0.1		1206	-0.2	-0.1
	1702	8.0	2.4		1835	8.0	2.4
	2354	0.3	0.1				
7 Th	0527	6.6	2.0	22 F	0048	0.1	0.0
	1206	-0.5	-0.2		0639	6.6	2.0
	1807	8.4	2.6		1254	-0.2	-0.1
					1922	8.1	2.5
8 F	0050	0.0	0.0	23 Sa	0136	0.0	0.0
	0632	6.7	2.0		0726	6.7	2.0
	1259	-0.7	-0.2		1341	-0.2	-0.1
	1906	8.7	2.7		2003	8.1	2.5
9 Sa	0146	-0.3	-0.1	24 Su	0222	0.0	0.0
	0733	6.9	2.1		0807	6.8	2.1
	1354	-0.9	-0.3		1426	-0.1	0.0
	2000	9.0	2.7		2040	8.1	2.5
10 Su	0241	-0.5	-0.2	25 M	0306	-0.1	0.0
	0828	7.1	2.2		0845	6.8	2.1
	1449	-1.0	-0.3		1511	0.0	0.0
	2053	9.1	2.8		2114	8.0	2.4
11 M	0335	-0.7	-0.2	26 Tu	0348	-0.1	0.0
	0921	7.3	2.2		0920	6.9	2.1
	1544	-1.1	-0.3		1550	0.2	0.1
	2143	9.1	2.8		2145	7.9	2.4
12 Tu	0425	-0.8	-0.2	27 W	0427	0.0	0.0
	1014	7.4	2.3		0952	6.9	2.1
	1637	-1.0	-0.3		1629	0.3	0.1
	2233	8.9	2.7		2214	7.8	2.4
13 W	0514	-0.8	-0.2	28 Th	0504	0.1	0.0
	1108	7.4	2.3		1027	7.0	2.1
	1730	-0.8	-0.2		1706	0.5	0.2
	2325	8.5	2.6		2245	7.6	2.3
14 Th	0603	-0.8	-0.2	29 F	0541	0.2	0.1
	1205	7.4	2.3		1104	7.1	2.2
	1822	-0.5	-0.2		1743	0.7	0.2
					2318	7.5	2.3
15 F	0018	8.1	2.5	30 Sa	0618	0.2	0.1
	0652	-0.6	-0.2		1146	7.3	2.2
	1300	7.5	2.3		1823	0.8	0.2
	1916	-0.2	-0.1				
				31 Su	0000	7.3	2.2
					0655	0.3	0.1
					1236	7.4	2.3
					1913	1.0	0.3

AUGUST

Day	Time h m	Height ft	Height m	Day	Time h m	Height ft	Height m
1 M	0047	7.2	2.2	16 Tu	0222	6.8	2.1
	0742	0.3	0.1		0859	0.3	0.1
	1326	7.6	2.3		1515	7.6	2.3
	2012	1.1	0.3		2143	0.9	0.3
2 Tu	0141	7.0	2.1	17 W	0317	6.5	2.0
	0838	0.3	0.1		0953	0.4	0.1
	1424	7.8	2.4		1614	7.6	2.3
	2120	1.1	0.3		2238	0.8	0.2
3 W	0241	6.8	2.1	18 Th	0414	6.4	2.0
	0940	0.2	0.1		1047	0.4	0.1
	1527	8.0	2.4		1710	7.7	2.3
	2228	0.9	0.3		2329	0.7	0.2
4 Th	0346	6.6	2.0	19 F	0513	6.5	2.0
	1042	0.0	0.0		1139	0.3	0.1
	1634	8.2	2.5		1806	7.8	2.4
	2329	0.5	0.2				
5 F	0501	6.7	2.0	20 Sa	0020	0.6	0.2
	1142	-0.4	-0.1		0609	6.6	2.0
	1744	8.5	2.6		1229	0.2	0.1
					1853	8.0	2.4
6 Sa	0029	0.1	0.0	21 Su	0106	0.4	0.1
	0614	6.9	2.1		0659	6.9	2.1
	1240	-0.7	-0.2		1315	0.2	0.1
	1848	8.9	2.7		1938	8.1	2.5
7 Su	0126	-0.3	-0.1	22 M	0152	0.2	0.1
	0719	7.3	2.2		0742	7.1	2.2
	1338	-1.0	-0.3		1401	0.2	0.1
	1946	9.2	2.8		2015	8.2	2.5
8 M	0221	-0.6	-0.2	23 Tu	0237	0.1	0.0
	0815	7.7	2.3		0821	7.3	2.2
	1433	-1.2	-0.4		1443	0.2	0.1
	2039	9.4	2.9		2048	8.1	2.5
9 Tu	0314	-0.9	-0.3	24 W	0317	0.1	0.0
	0908	8.0	2.4		0853	7.4	2.3
	1527	-1.2	-0.4		1525	0.3	0.1
	2129	9.3	2.8		2117	8.1	2.5
10 W	0403	-1.0	-0.3	25 Th	0356	0.1	0.0
	0959	8.1	2.5		0926	7.5	2.3
	1619	-1.1	-0.3		1603	0.5	0.2
	2218	9.1	2.8		2145	7.9	2.4
11 Th	0451	-1.0	-0.3	26 F	0432	0.2	0.1
	1050	8.2	2.5		0958	7.6	2.3
	1711	-0.9	-0.3		1639	0.6	0.2
	2304	8.6	2.6		2213	7.8	2.4
12 F	0538	-0.8	-0.2	27 Sa	0507	0.3	0.1
	1142	8.1	2.5		1034	7.8	2.4
	1802	-0.5	-0.2		1716	0.8	0.2
	2354	8.1	2.5		2248	7.7	2.3
13 Sa	0625	-0.6	-0.2	28 Su	0541	0.4	0.1
	1236	8.0	2.4		1114	7.9	2.4
	1854	-0.1	0.0		1753	1.0	0.3
					2327	7.5	2.3
14 Su	0042	7.6	2.3	29 M	0618	0.5	0.2
	0713	-0.3	-0.1		1202	8.0	2.4
	1327	7.9	2.4		1844	1.1	0.3
	1947	0.4	0.1				
15 M	0132	7.1	2.2	30 Tu	0015	7.3	2.2
	0804	0.1	0.0		0703	0.5	0.2
	1422	7.8	2.4		1255	8.1	2.5
	2045	0.7	0.2		1942	1.3	0.4
				31 W	0111	7.0	2.1
					0802	0.6	0.2
					1356	8.1	2.5
					2053	1.3	0.4

SEPTEMBER

Day	Time h m	Height ft	Height m	Day	Time h m	Height ft	Height m
1 Th	0214	6.9	2.1	16 F	0339	6.6	2.0
	0912	0.5	0.2		1017	0.9	0.3
	1502	8.2	2.5		1633	7.6	2.3
	2204	1.1	0.3		2259	1.1	0.3
2 F	0325	6.8	2.1	17 Sa	0436	6.7	2.0
	1021	0.3	0.1		1111	0.8	0.2
	1613	8.4	2.6		1729	7.7	2.3
	2310	0.7	0.2		2349	0.9	0.3
3 Sa	0444	7.0	2.1	18 Su	0536	6.9	2.1
	1123	-0.1	0.0		1200	0.6	0.2
	1726	8.7	2.7		1819	7.9	2.4
4 Su	0008	0.2	0.1	19 M	0035	0.6	0.2
	0600	7.4	2.3		0629	7.2	2.2
	1224	-0.6	-0.2		1248	0.5	0.2
	1832	9.1	2.8		1904	8.1	2.5
5 M	0104	-0.2	-0.1	20 Tu	0121	0.4	0.1
	0705	7.9	2.4		0714	7.5	2.3
	1320	-0.9	-0.3		1333	0.4	0.1
	1930	9.4	2.9		1943	8.2	2.5
6 Tu	0157	-0.6	-0.2	21 W	0203	0.3	0.1
	0802	8.4	2.6		0752	7.7	2.3
	1415	-1.1	-0.3		1417	0.4	0.1
	2021	9.5	2.9		2016	8.2	2.5
7 W	0249	-0.9	-0.3	22 Th	0245	0.2	0.1
	0851	8.8	2.7		0826	8.0	2.4
	1509	-1.2	-0.4		1459	0.5	0.2
	2109	9.4	2.9		2047	8.1	2.5
8 Th	0338	-1.0	-0.3	23 F	0323	0.2	0.1
	0940	8.9	2.7		0900	8.1	2.5
	1600	-1.0	-0.3		1538	0.6	0.2
	2155	9.1	2.8		2116	8.0	2.4
9 F	0424	-0.9	-0.3	24 Sa	0400	0.3	0.1
	1029	8.9	2.7		0932	8.3	2.5
	1650	-0.7	-0.2		1615	0.8	0.2
	2240	8.6	2.6		2146	7.8	2.4
10 Sa	0509	-0.7	-0.2	25 Su	0434	0.4	0.1
	1116	8.7	2.7		1008	8.4	2.6
	1739	-0.3	-0.1		1656	0.9	0.3
	2324	8.1	2.5		2219	7.7	2.3
11 Su	0554	-0.3	-0.1	26 M	0510	0.5	0.2
	1205	8.4	2.6		1048	8.4	2.6
	1828	0.2	0.1		1735	1.1	0.3
					2300	7.5	2.3
12 M	0010	7.5	2.3	27 Tu	0549	0.6	0.2
	0640	0.1	0.0		1137	8.4	2.6
	1254	8.1	2.5		1823	1.3	0.4
	1919	0.7	0.2		2349	7.3	2.2
13 Tu	0057	7.1	2.2	28 W	0639	0.7	0.2
	0729	0.5	0.2		1231	8.4	2.6
	1347	7.9	2.4		1924	1.4	0.4
	2012	1.1	0.3				
14 W	0148	6.8	2.1	29 Th	0049	7.0	2.1
	0822	0.8	0.2		0742	0.8	0.2
	1440	7.7	2.3		1335	8.3	2.5
	2109	1.3	0.4		2033	1.4	0.4
15 Th	0240	6.6	2.0	30 F	0158	6.9	2.1
	0921	1.0	0.3		0851	0.7	0.2
	1536	7.6	2.3		1443	8.4	2.6
	2204	1.3	0.4		2145	1.2	0.4

Time meridian 75° W.   0000 is midnight.   1200 is noon.
Heights are referred to mean low water which is the chart datum of soundings.

Times and Heights of High and Low Waters

OCTOBER

Day	Time (h m)	Height (ft)	Height (m)	Day	Time (h m)	Height (ft)	Height (m)
1 Sa	0314	7.0	2.1	16 Su	0357	6.8	2.1
	1001	0.5	0.2		1038	1.1	0.3
	1556	8.5	2.6		1641	7.5	2.3
	2249	0.7	0.2		2313	0.9	0.3
2 Su	0433	7.3	2.2	17 M	0454	7.0	2.1
	1107	0.0	0.0		1129	0.9	0.3
	1707	8.7	2.7		1736	7.7	2.3
	2347	0.2	0.1				
3 M	0545	7.8	2.4	18 Tu	0001	0.6	0.2
	1206	-0.4	-0.1		0550	7.4	2.3
	1812	9.0	2.7		1216	0.7	0.2
					1822	7.8	2.4
4 Tu	0041	-0.3	-0.1	19 W	0045	0.4	0.1
	0648	8.4	2.6		0637	7.7	2.3
	1301	-0.8	-0.2		1304	0.6	0.2
	1909	9.3	2.8		1905	7.9	2.4
5 W	0133	-0.7	-0.2	20 Th	0128	0.2	0.1
	0743	9.0	2.7		0721	8.0	2.4
	1356	-0.9	-0.3		1349	0.5	0.2
	1959	9.3	2.8		1944	7.9	2.4
6 Th	0223	-0.9	-0.3	21 F	0210	0.2	0.1
	0832	9.3	2.8		0759	8.3	2.5
	1448	-1.0	-0.3		1432	0.5	0.2
	2047	9.2	2.8		2018	7.9	2.4
7 F	0310	-0.9	-0.3	22 Sa	0250	0.2	0.1
	0919	9.4	2.9		0835	8.5	2.6
	1539	-0.8	-0.2		1514	0.6	0.2
	2131	8.8	2.7		2050	7.8	2.4
8 Sa	0356	-0.7	-0.2	23 Su	0329	0.2	0.1
	1003	9.3	2.8		0909	8.6	2.6
	1627	-0.5	-0.2		1556	0.7	0.2
	2213	8.4	2.6		2122	7.6	2.3
9 Su	0441	-0.4	-0.1	24 M	0408	0.3	0.1
	1048	9.0	2.7		0949	8.7	2.7
	1714	-0.1	0.0		1640	0.8	0.2
	2255	7.9	2.4		2202	7.5	2.3
10 M	0524	-0.1	0.0	25 Tu	0450	0.4	0.1
	1133	8.6	2.6		1030	8.7	2.7
	1801	0.4	0.1		1724	1.0	0.3
	2337	7.4	2.3		2244	7.3	2.2
11 Tu	0609	0.4	0.1	26 W	0533	0.5	0.2
	1220	8.2	2.5		1120	8.6	2.6
	1850	0.9	0.3		1813	1.1	0.3
					2335	7.1	2.2
12 W	0019	7.0	2.1	27 Th	0626	0.6	0.2
	0655	0.8	0.2		1218	8.4	2.6
	1308	7.9	2.4		1912	1.2	0.4
	1940	1.2	0.4				
13 Th	0110	6.8	2.1	28 F	0039	6.9	2.1
	0747	1.1	0.3		0727	0.7	0.2
	1400	7.6	2.3		1321	8.3	2.5
	2033	1.4	0.4		2017	1.2	0.4
14 F	0201	6.7	2.0	29 Sa	0152	6.9	2.1
	0843	1.3	0.4		0837	0.7	0.2
	1452	7.5	2.3		1428	8.3	2.5
	2129	1.4	0.4		2125	0.9	0.3
15 Sa	0258	6.7	2.0	30 Su	0307	7.1	2.2
	0941	1.3	0.4		0945	0.4	0.1
	1548	7.5	2.3		1538	8.3	2.5
	2224	1.2	0.4		2227	0.5	0.2
				31 M	0422	7.5	2.3
					1049	0.1	0.0
					1646	8.4	2.6
					2323	0.0	0.0

NOVEMBER

Day	Time (h m)	Height (ft)	Height (m)	Day	Time (h m)	Height (ft)	Height (m)
1 Tu	0530	8.0	2.4	16 W	0506	7.3	2.2
	1147	-0.3	-0.1		1144	0.7	0.2
	1750	8.6	2.6		1736	7.3	2.2
2 W	0016	-0.5	-0.2	17 Th	0008	0.2	0.1
	0629	8.6	2.6		0558	7.7	2.3
	1243	-0.6	-0.2		1233	0.6	0.2
	1845	8.7	2.7		1825	7.4	2.3
3 Th	0106	-0.8	-0.2	18 F	0053	0.0	0.0
	0724	9.1	2.8		0645	8.0	2.4
	1336	-0.8	-0.2		1320	0.4	0.1
	1936	8.7	2.7		1910	7.4	2.3
4 F	0155	-0.9	-0.3	19 Sa	0138	-0.1	0.0
	0813	9.3	2.8		0730	8.3	2.5
	1427	-0.8	-0.2		1407	0.3	0.1
	2022	8.5	2.6		1951	7.4	2.3
5 Sa	0242	-0.9	-0.3	20 Su	0219	-0.1	0.0
	0857	9.4	2.9		0812	8.6	2.6
	1517	-0.6	-0.2		1453	0.3	0.1
	2106	8.2	2.5		2029	7.4	2.3
6 Su	0328	-0.7	-0.2	21 M	0304	-0.2	-0.1
	0940	9.2	2.8		0852	8.7	2.7
	1604	-0.4	-0.1		1539	0.3	0.1
	2145	7.9	2.4		2108	7.3	2.2
7 M	0413	-0.4	-0.1	22 Tu	0347	-0.1	0.0
	1021	8.8	2.7		0935	8.7	2.7
	1649	0.0	0.0		1626	0.4	0.1
	2226	7.5	2.3		2151	7.2	2.2
8 Tu	0456	0.0	0.0	23 W	0435	-0.1	0.0
	1103	8.4	2.6		1020	8.6	2.6
	1734	0.4	0.1		1715	0.5	0.2
	2304	7.2	2.2		2237	7.0	2.1
9 W	0538	0.3	0.1	24 Th	0524	0.0	0.0
	1145	8.0	2.4		1112	8.5	2.6
	1818	0.7	0.2		1805	0.6	0.2
	2346	6.9	2.1		2333	6.9	2.1
10 Th	0622	0.7	0.2	25 F	0618	0.1	0.0
	1227	7.7	2.3		1210	8.3	2.5
	1905	1.0	0.3		1900	0.6	0.2
11 F	0031	6.7	2.0	26 Sa	0039	6.8	2.1
	0710	1.0	0.3		0716	0.2	0.1
	1315	7.5	2.3		1311	8.1	2.5
	1956	1.2	0.4		2000	0.5	0.2
12 Sa	0122	6.6	2.0	27 Su	0147	6.9	2.1
	0804	1.2	0.4		0821	0.3	0.1
	1404	7.3	2.2		1414	7.9	2.4
	2049	1.2	0.4		2102	0.4	0.1
13 Su	0213	6.6	2.0	28 M	0257	7.2	2.2
	0901	1.2	0.4		0927	0.2	0.1
	1455	7.2	2.2		1518	7.8	2.4
	2143	1.0	0.3		2201	0.0	0.0
14 M	0312	6.8	2.1	29 Tu	0404	7.5	2.3
	0959	1.2	0.4		1012	-0.1	0.0
	1549	7.2	2.2		1622	7.8	2.4
	2233	0.8	0.2		2257	-0.3	-0.1
15 Tu	0410	7.0	2.1	30 W	0508	7.9	2.4
	1051	1.0	0.3		1127	-0.3	-0.1
	1644	7.3	2.2		1724	7.8	2.4
	2321	0.5	0.2		2350	-0.6	-0.2

DECEMBER

Day	Time (h m)	Height (ft)	Height (m)	Day	Time (h m)	Height (ft)	Height (m)
1 Th	0608	8.4	2.6	16 F	0515	7.5	2.3
	1222	-0.5	-0.2		1200	0.5	0.2
	1821	7.8	2.4		1740	6.8	2.1
2 F	0040	-0.8	-0.2	17 Sa	0017	-0.2	-0.1
	0702	8.7	2.7		0612	7.8	2.4
	1314	-0.7	-0.2		1251	0.2	0.1
	1914	7.8	2.4		1836	6.8	2.1
3 Sa	0129	-0.9	-0.3	18 Su	0106	-0.4	-0.1
	0751	8.9	2.7		0704	8.2	2.5
	1405	-0.7	-0.2		1343	0.1	0.0
	2000	7.7	2.3		1926	6.9	2.1
4 Su	0215	-0.9	-0.3	19 M	0154	-0.6	-0.2
	0836	8.9	2.7		0754	8.4	2.6
	1453	-0.6	-0.2		1433	-0.1	0.0
	2042	7.5	2.3		2013	7.0	2.1
5 M	0302	-0.7	-0.2	20 Tu	0245	-0.7	-0.2
	0916	8.7	2.7		0840	8.6	2.6
	1541	-0.4	-0.1		1524	-0.1	0.0
	2122	7.3	2.2		2100	7.1	2.2
6 Tu	0347	-0.5	-0.2	21 W	0334	-0.8	-0.2
	0957	8.4	2.6		0927	8.7	2.7
	1624	-0.2	-0.1		1613	-0.2	-0.1
	2157	7.1	2.2		2147	7.0	2.1
7 W	0429	-0.2	-0.1	22 Th	0423	-0.8	-0.2
	1034	8.1	2.5		1015	8.6	2.6
	1706	0.1	0.0		1703	-0.1	0.0
	2234	6.9	2.1		2237	7.0	2.1
8 Th	0511	0.1	0.0	23 F	0514	-0.7	-0.2
	1112	7.8	2.4		1106	8.4	2.6
	1749	0.3	0.1		1752	-0.2	-0.1
	2314	6.7	2.0		2333	7.0	2.1
9 F	0552	0.3	0.1	24 Sa	0607	-0.5	-0.2
	1149	7.5	2.3		1201	8.1	2.5
	1831	0.5	0.2		1844	-0.2	-0.1
	2354	6.6	2.0				
10 Sa	0634	0.6	0.2	25 Su	0034	7.0	2.1
	1231	7.3	2.2		0703	-0.3	-0.1
	1916	0.7	0.2		1258	7.8	2.4
					1938	-0.1	0.0
11 Su	0042	6.6	2.0	26 M	0136	7.1	2.2
	0723	0.8	0.2		0804	-0.2	-0.1
	1315	7.1	2.2		1354	7.5	2.3
	2005	0.7	0.2		2036	-0.2	-0.1
12 M	0132	6.6	2.0	27 Tu	0240	7.2	2.2
	0815	1.0	0.3		0906	-0.1	0.0
	1401	7.0	2.1		1454	7.3	2.2
	2057	0.7	0.2		2134	-0.3	-0.1
13 Tu	0224	6.8	2.1	28 W	0343	7.4	2.3
	0913	1.0	0.3		1008	-0.1	0.0
	1453	6.9	2.1		1553	7.1	2.2
	2149	0.5	0.2		2230	-0.4	-0.1
14 W	0319	6.9	2.1	29 Th	0445	7.6	2.3
	1012	0.9	0.3		1106	-0.2	-0.1
	1545	6.8	2.1		1655	6.9	2.1
	2240	0.3	0.1		2323	-0.6	-0.2
15 Th	0417	7.2	2.2	30 F	0545	7.9	2.4
	1108	0.7	0.2		1200	-0.4	-0.1
	1644	6.8	2.1		1755	6.9	2.1
	2331	0.0	0.0				
				31 Sa	0014	-0.7	-0.2
					0640	8.1	2.5
					1252	-0.5	-0.2
					1849	7.0	2.1

Time meridian 75° W.   0000 is midnight.   1200 is noon.
Heights are referred to mean low water which is the chart datum of soundings.

MAYPORT, FLA., 1983

Times and Heights of High and Low Waters

JANUARY

Day	h m	ft	m
1 Sa	0315	-1.2	-0.4
	1006	5.3	1.6
	1609	-1.0	-0.3
	2227	4.3	1.3
2 Su	0413	-1.0	-0.3
	1059	5.1	1.6
	1703	-0.9	-0.3
	2324	4.3	1.3
3 M	0512	-0.7	-0.2
	1152	4.9	1.5
	1800	-0.7	-0.2
4 Tu	0020	4.3	1.3
	0615	-0.4	-0.1
	1246	4.6	1.4
	1855	-0.6	-0.2
5 W	0119	4.3	1.3
	0719	-0.2	-0.1
	1345	4.4	1.3
	1952	-0.4	-0.1
6 Th	0219	4.3	1.3
	0825	0.0	0.0
	1441	4.1	1.2
	2047	-0.3	-0.1
7 F	0317	4.3	1.3
	0928	0.1	0.0
	1538	3.9	1.2
	2141	-0.2	-0.1
8 Sa	0415	4.4	1.3
	1026	0.2	0.1
	1634	3.8	1.2
	2231	-0.2	-0.1
9 Su	0510	4.4	1.3
	1121	0.1	0.0
	1726	3.7	1.1
	2320	-0.2	-0.1
10 M	0558	4.5	1.4
	1209	0.0	0.0
	1815	3.6	1.1
11 Tu	0005	-0.3	-0.1
	0646	4.5	1.4
	1252	-0.1	0.0
	1902	3.6	1.1
12 W	0047	-0.3	-0.1
	0730	4.5	1.4
	1334	-0.1	0.0
	1943	3.6	1.1
13 Th	0125	-0.4	-0.1
	0810	4.5	1.4
	1413	-0.2	-0.1
	2024	3.6	1.1
14 F	0202	-0.4	-0.1
	0849	4.4	1.3
	1448	-0.2	-0.1
	2101	3.6	1.1
15 Sa	0236	-0.3	-0.1
	0926	4.4	1.3
	1523	-0.2	-0.1
	2138	3.6	1.1
16 Su	0310	-0.3	-0.1
	1002	4.3	1.3
	1555	-0.1	0.0
	2214	3.6	1.1
17 M	0347	-0.1	0.0
	1037	4.2	1.3
	1627	-0.1	0.0
	2249	3.7	1.1
18 Tu	0422	0.0	0.0
	1109	4.1	1.2
	1703	0.0	0.0
	2327	3.7	1.1
19 W	0507	0.1	0.0
	1145	4.0	1.2
	1741	0.0	0.0
20 Th	0004	3.8	1.2
	0554	0.3	0.1
	1222	3.9	1.2
	1826	0.0	0.0
21 F	0049	3.9	1.2
	0649	0.4	0.1
	1308	3.8	1.2
	1917	0.0	0.0
22 Sa	0143	4.0	1.2
	0751	0.4	0.1
	1403	3.6	1.1
	2013	-0.1	0.0
23 Su	0245	4.1	1.2
	0902	0.3	0.1
	1504	3.5	1.1
	2113	-0.3	-0.1
24 M	0352	4.3	1.3
	1010	0.1	0.0
	1618	3.5	1.1
	2215	-0.5	-0.2
25 Tu	0502	4.5	1.4
	1115	-0.3	-0.1
	1726	3.6	1.1
	2318	-0.8	-0.2
26 W	0609	4.7	1.4
	1215	-0.6	-0.2
	1832	3.7	1.1
27 Th	0015	-1.1	-0.3
	0709	4.9	1.5
	1312	-0.9	-0.3
	1928	3.9	1.2
28 F	0114	-1.4	-0.4
	0805	5.1	1.6
	1405	-1.2	-0.4
	2025	4.1	1.2
29 Sa	0209	-1.5	-0.5
	0857	5.1	1.6
	1457	-1.3	-0.4
	2118	4.3	1.3
30 Su	0305	-1.5	-0.5
	0949	5.1	1.6
	1547	-1.3	-0.4
	2209	4.3	1.3
31 M	0400	-1.3	-0.4
	1038	4.9	1.5
	1638	-1.2	-0.4
	2300	4.4	1.3

FEBRUARY

Day	h m	ft	m
1 Tu	0455	-1.1	-0.3
	1128	4.6	1.4
	1730	-1.1	-0.3
	2354	4.4	1.3
2 W	0554	-0.7	-0.2
	1218	4.3	1.3
	1821	-0.8	-0.2
3 Th	0046	4.3	1.3
	0653	-0.3	-0.1
	1309	4.0	1.2
	1914	-0.5	-0.2
4 F	0142	4.2	1.3
	0755	0.0	0.0
	1404	3.8	1.2
	2007	-0.3	-0.1
5 Sa	0239	4.1	1.3
	0856	0.2	0.1
	1500	3.5	1.1
	2103	-0.1	0.0
6 Su	0339	4.1	1.2
	0956	0.3	0.1
	1559	3.4	1.0
	2159	0.0	0.0
7 M	0437	4.1	1.2
	1049	0.3	0.1
	1655	3.4	1.0
	2249	0.0	0.0
8 Tu	0532	4.1	1.2
	1142	0.2	0.1
	1747	3.4	1.0
	2337	-0.1	0.0
9 W	0624	4.2	1.3
	1227	0.1	0.0
	1833	3.5	1.1
10 Th	0022	-0.2	-0.1
	0705	4.3	1.3
	1308	-0.1	0.0
	1919	3.6	1.1
11 F	0104	-0.3	-0.1
	0747	4.3	1.3
	1346	-0.2	-0.1
	1959	3.6	1.1
12 Sa	0142	-0.4	-0.1
	0826	4.3	1.3
	1421	-0.3	-0.1
	2037	3.7	1.1
13 Su	0217	-0.4	-0.1
	0903	4.3	1.3
	1453	-0.4	-0.1
	2114	3.8	1.2
14 M	0252	-0.4	-0.1
	0936	4.3	1.3
	1524	-0.4	-0.1
	2149	3.8	1.2
15 Tu	0326	-0.4	-0.1
	1011	4.2	1.3
	1556	-0.4	-0.1
	2222	3.9	1.2
16 W	0403	-0.3	-0.1
	1043	4.1	1.2
	1630	-0.3	-0.1
	2257	4.0	1.2
17 Th	0443	-0.2	-0.1
	1115	4.0	1.2
	1707	-0.3	-0.1
	2336	4.1	1.2
18 F	0531	0.0	0.0
	1154	3.8	1.2
	1752	-0.2	-0.1
19 Sa	0020	4.1	1.2
	0625	0.1	0.0
	1239	3.7	1.1
	1842	-0.2	-0.1
20 Su	0111	4.1	1.2
	0729	0.3	0.1
	1335	3.5	1.1
	1940	-0.1	0.0
21 M	0218	4.2	1.3
	0840	0.2	0.1
	1444	3.4	1.0
	2049	-0.2	-0.1
22 Tu	0334	4.2	1.3
	0953	0.1	0.0
	1557	3.4	1.0
	2157	-0.4	-0.1
23 W	0449	4.4	1.3
	1100	-0.2	-0.1
	1713	3.6	1.1
	2305	-0.7	-0.2
24 Th	0556	4.6	1.4
	1201	-0.6	-0.2
	1819	3.8	1.2
25 F	0006	-1.0	-0.3
	0656	4.8	1.5
	1254	-0.9	-0.3
	1915	4.1	1.2
26 Sa	0104	-1.3	-0.4
	0749	5.0	1.5
	1347	-1.2	-0.4
	2008	4.4	1.3
27 Su	0158	-1.4	-0.4
	0840	5.0	1.5
	1435	-1.3	-0.4
	2100	4.5	1.4
28 M	0251	-1.4	-0.4
	0929	4.9	1.5
	1523	-1.4	-0.4
	2147	4.6	1.4

MARCH

Day	h m	ft	m
1 Tu	0343	-1.3	-0.4
	1014	4.7	1.4
	1609	-1.2	-0.4
	2235	4.7	1.4
2 W	0434	-1.0	-0.3
	1101	4.5	1.4
	1654	-1.0	-0.3
	2323	4.6	1.4
3 Th	0528	-0.6	-0.2
	1146	4.2	1.3
	1741	-0.6	-0.2
4 F	0012	4.4	1.3
	0621	-0.2	-0.1
	1234	3.9	1.2
	1830	-0.3	-0.1
5 Sa	0104	4.3	1.3
	0719	0.1	0.0
	1326	3.7	1.1
	1925	0.0	0.0
6 Su	0158	4.1	1.2
	0817	0.4	0.1
	1420	3.5	1.1
	2021	0.3	0.1
7 M	0257	4.0	1.2
	0921	0.6	0.2
	1520	3.4	1.0
	2120	0.4	0.1
8 Tu	0358	4.0	1.2
	1017	0.6	0.2
	1617	3.4	1.0
	2217	0.4	0.1
9 W	0457	4.0	1.2
	1108	0.5	0.2
	1713	3.5	1.1
	2308	0.3	0.1
10 Th	0550	4.1	1.2
	1153	0.3	0.1
	1803	3.6	1.1
	2356	0.1	0.0
11 F	0635	4.2	1.3
	1235	0.1	0.0
	1848	3.8	1.2
12 Sa	0038	-0.1	0.0
	0717	4.3	1.3
	1312	0.0	0.0
	1929	3.9	1.2
13 Su	0116	-0.2	-0.1
	0756	4.4	1.3
	1345	-0.2	-0.1
	2009	4.1	1.2
14 M	0153	-0.4	-0.1
	0834	4.4	1.3
	1418	-0.4	-0.1
	2046	4.2	1.3
15 Tu	0229	-0.4	-0.1
	0908	4.3	1.3
	1450	-0.4	-0.1
	2120	4.3	1.3
16 W	0306	-0.4	-0.1
	0941	4.2	1.3
	1523	-0.5	-0.2
	2155	4.4	1.3
17 Th	0345	-0.4	-0.1
	1018	4.1	1.2
	1559	-0.4	-0.1
	2232	4.4	1.3
18 F	0429	-0.2	-0.1
	1054	4.0	1.2
	1640	-0.4	-0.1
	2312	4.5	1.4
19 Sa	0515	-0.1	0.0
	1136	3.9	1.2
	1725	-0.2	-0.1
20 Su	0000	4.5	1.4
	0613	0.1	0.0
	1224	3.7	1.1
	1818	-0.1	0.0
21 M	0057	4.4	1.3
	0716	0.3	0.1
	1324	3.6	1.1
	1922	0.0	0.0
22 Tu	0206	4.3	1.3
	0828	0.3	0.1
	1437	3.6	1.1
	2034	0.0	0.0
23 W	0325	4.4	1.3
	0941	0.2	0.1
	1554	3.7	1.1
	2149	-0.1	0.0
24 Th	0439	4.5	1.4
	1047	-0.1	0.0
	1705	3.9	1.2
	2256	-0.4	-0.1
25 F	0542	4.7	1.4
	1142	-0.4	-0.1
	1806	4.2	1.3
	2358	-0.7	-0.2
26 Sa	0640	4.8	1.5
	1235	-0.8	-0.2
	1902	4.5	1.4
27 Su	0055	-1.0	-0.3
	0730	4.9	1.5
	1323	-1.0	-0.3
	1951	4.7	1.4
28 M	0146	-1.1	-0.3
	0819	4.9	1.5
	1409	-1.1	-0.3
	2037	4.9	1.5
29 Tu	0236	-1.1	-0.3
	0905	4.8	1.5
	1454	-1.1	-0.3
	2123	5.0	1.5
30 W	0323	-1.0	-0.3
	0949	4.6	1.4
	1537	-1.0	-0.3
	2208	4.9	1.5
31 Th	0412	-0.7	-0.2
	1031	4.3	1.3
	1618	-0.7	-0.2
	2251	4.8	1.5

Time meridian 75° W. 0000 is midnight. 1200 is noon.
Heights are referred to mean low water which is the chart datum of soundings.

Times and Heights of High and Low Waters

APRIL

Day	Time h m	Height ft	m	Day	Time h m	Height ft	m
1 F	0459	-0.4	-0.1	16 Sa	0416	-0.3	-0.1
	1114	4.1	1.2		1039	4.1	1.2
	1703	-0.3	-0.1		1618	-0.4	-0.1
	2336	4.6	1.4		2259	4.8	1.5
2 Sa	0551	0.0	0.0	17 Su	0506	-0.1	0.0
	1200	3.9	1.2		1126	3.9	1.2
	1746	0.0	0.0		1708	-0.2	-0.1
					2352	4.7	1.4
3 Su	0023	4.4	1.3	18 M	0605	0.1	0.0
	0642	0.3	0.1		1221	3.8	1.2
	1247	3.7	1.1		1807	0.0	0.0
	1837	0.4	0.1				
4 M	0116	4.2	1.3	19 Tu	0053	4.6	1.4
	0738	0.6	0.2		0712	0.2	0.1
	1340	3.6	1.1		1327	3.8	1.2
	1934	0.6	0.2		1915	0.2	0.1
5 Tu	0214	4.1	1.2	20 W	0203	4.5	1.4
	0838	0.8	0.2		0822	0.2	0.1
	1438	3.5	1.1		1437	3.8	1.2
	2037	0.8	0.2		2031	0.2	0.1
6 W	0314	4.0	1.2	21 Th	0317	4.5	1.4
	0933	0.8	0.2		0928	0.1	0.0
	1538	3.6	1.1		1548	4.0	1.2
	2137	0.8	0.2		2144	0.1	0.0
7 Th	0415	4.0	1.2	22 F	0423	4.5	1.4
	1025	0.7	0.2		1028	-0.1	0.0
	1635	3.7	1.1		1652	4.3	1.3
	2231	0.6	0.2		2249	-0.2	-0.1
8 F	0508	4.1	1.2	23 Sa	0525	4.6	1.4
	1111	0.6	0.2		1122	-0.4	-0.1
	1727	3.9	1.2		1751	4.6	1.4
	2321	0.4	0.1		2348	-0.4	-0.1
9 Sa	0556	4.2	1.3	24 Su	0619	4.7	1.4
	1153	0.3	0.1		1211	-0.7	-0.2
	1814	4.1	1.2		1843	4.8	1.5
10 Su	0006	0.2	0.1	25 M	0042	-0.6	-0.2
	0641	4.3	1.3		0709	4.6	1.4
	1230	0.1	0.0		1258	-0.8	-0.2
	1855	4.3	1.3		1931	5.0	1.5
11 M	0048	0.0	0.0	26 Tu	0131	-0.8	-0.2
	0721	4.3	1.3		0755	4.6	1.4
	1304	-0.2	-0.1		1341	-0.9	-0.3
	1936	4.5	1.4		2017	5.1	1.6
12 Tu	0125	-0.2	-0.1	27 W	0219	-0.8	-0.2
	0800	4.3	1.3		0839	4.4	1.3
	1339	-0.4	-0.1		1423	-0.8	-0.2
	2014	4.6	1.4		2059	5.1	1.6
13 W	0206	-0.4	-0.1	28 Th	0303	-0.7	-0.2
	0837	4.3	1.3		0923	4.3	1.3
	1414	-0.5	-0.2		1505	-0.7	-0.2
	2053	4.7	1.4		2142	5.0	1.5
14 Th	0246	-0.4	-0.1	29 F	0348	-0.5	-0.2
	0916	4.2	1.3		1005	4.1	1.2
	1452	-0.5	-0.2		1544	-0.4	-0.1
	2131	4.8	1.5		2224	4.8	1.5
15 F	0330	-0.4	-0.1	30 Sa	0432	-0.2	-0.1
	0955	4.2	1.3		1046	3.9	1.2
	1534	-0.5	-0.2		1626	-0.1	0.0
	2211	4.9	1.5		2307	4.6	1.4

MAY

Day	Time h m	Height ft	m	Day	Time h m	Height ft	m
1 Su	0517	0.1	0.0	16 M	0500	-0.3	-0.1
	1128	3.8	1.2		1120	4.0	1.2
	1707	0.2	0.1		1659	-0.3	-0.1
	2349	4.5	1.4		2349	4.9	1.5
2 M	0605	0.4	0.1	17 Tu	0600	-0.2	-0.1
	1215	3.7	1.1		1221	3.9	1.2
	1753	0.5	0.2		1802	-0.1	0.0
3 Tu	0037	4.3	1.3	18 W	0050	4.7	1.4
	0657	0.7	0.2		0705	-0.1	0.0
	1303	3.6	1.1		1324	4.0	1.2
	1845	0.8	0.2		1912	0.1	0.0
4 W	0130	4.1	1.2	19 Th	0156	4.6	1.4
	0749	0.8	0.2		0808	-0.1	0.0
	1357	3.6	1.1		1430	4.1	1.2
	1945	0.9	0.3		2026	0.1	0.0
5 Th	0225	4.0	1.2	20 F	0300	4.5	1.4
	0844	0.8	0.2		0910	-0.2	-0.1
	1454	3.7	1.1		1535	4.3	1.3
	2048	1.0	0.3		2135	0.1	0.0
6 F	0322	4.0	1.2	21 Sa	0404	4.4	1.3
	0933	0.8	0.2		1007	-0.3	-0.1
	1549	3.8	1.2		1637	4.5	1.4
	2146	0.9	0.3		2239	-0.1	0.0
7 Sa	0418	4.0	1.2	22 Su	0502	4.4	1.3
	1018	0.6	0.2		1058	-0.5	-0.2
	1641	4.0	1.2		1733	4.7	1.4
	2239	0.7	0.2		2334	-0.3	-0.1
8 Su	0508	4.1	1.2	23 M	0555	4.3	1.3
	1100	0.3	0.0		1147	-0.6	-0.2
	1730	4.2	1.3		1822	4.9	1.5
	2328	0.4	0.1				
9 M	0555	4.1	1.2	24 Tu	0027	-0.4	-0.1
	1142	0.0	0.0		0644	4.2	1.3
	1815	4.5	1.4		1232	-0.7	-0.2
					1910	5.0	1.5
10 Tu	0014	0.1	0.0	25 W	0115	-0.5	-0.2
	0640	4.1	1.2		0731	4.2	1.3
	1219	-0.3	-0.1		1315	-0.7	-0.2
	1900	4.7	1.4		1955	5.0	1.5
11 W	0057	-0.2	-0.1	26 Th	0201	-0.5	-0.2
	0723	4.1	1.2		0815	4.0	1.2
	1301	-0.5	-0.2		1356	-0.6	-0.2
	1943	4.9	1.5		2038	4.9	1.5
12 Th	0141	-0.4	-0.1	27 F	0244	-0.5	-0.2
	0806	4.1	1.2		0856	3.9	1.2
	1343	-0.6	-0.2		1436	-0.5	-0.2
	2026	5.0	1.5		2117	4.8	1.5
13 F	0228	-0.5	-0.2	28 Sa	0326	-0.3	-0.1
	0851	4.1	1.2		0937	3.8	1.2
	1427	-0.7	-0.2		1514	-0.3	-0.1
	2112	5.1	1.6		2200	4.7	1.4
14 Sa	0315	-0.6	-0.2	29 Su	0408	-0.1	0.0
	0937	4.1	1.2		1019	3.7	1.1
	1514	-0.7	-0.2		1553	-0.1	0.0
	2201	5.1	1.6		2238	4.6	1.4
15 Su	0405	-0.5	-0.2	30 M	0447	0.1	0.0
	1028	4.0	1.2		1059	3.7	1.1
	1604	-0.5	-0.2		1632	0.2	0.1
	2252	5.0	1.5		2320	4.4	1.3
				31 Tu	0531	0.3	0.1
					1141	3.6	1.1
					1715	0.5	0.2

JUNE

Day	Time h m	Height ft	m	Day	Time h m	Height ft	m
1 W	0002	4.3	1.3	16 Th	0038	4.8	1.5
	0613	0.5	0.2		0648	-0.5	-0.2
	1226	3.6	1.1		1311	4.2	1.3
	1802	0.7	0.2		1905	-0.1	0.0
2 Th	0049	4.1	1.2	17 F	0138	4.6	1.4
	0659	0.6	0.2		0748	-0.4	-0.1
	1316	3.6	1.1		1414	4.3	1.3
	1853	0.9	0.3		2014	0.0	0.0
3 F	0134	4.0	1.2	18 Sa	0238	4.4	1.3
	0745	0.6	0.2		0845	-0.4	-0.1
	1407	3.7	1.1		1516	4.4	1.3
	1953	0.9	0.3		2120	0.0	0.0
4 Sa	0226	3.9	1.2	19 Su	0338	4.2	1.3
	0834	0.6	0.2		0940	-0.4	-0.1
	1458	3.9	1.2		1615	4.6	1.4
	2054	0.9	0.3		2221	0.0	0.0
5 Su	0317	3.9	1.2	20 M	0435	4.1	1.2
	0921	0.4	0.1		1031	-0.4	-0.1
	1551	4.0	1.2		1710	4.7	1.4
	2153	0.7	0.2		2318	-0.1	0.0
6 M	0412	3.8	1.2	21 Tu	0530	4.0	1.2
	1007	0.2	0.1		1121	-0.5	-0.2
	1644	4.3	1.3		1803	4.8	1.5
	2248	0.4	0.1				
7 Tu	0503	3.8	1.2	22 W	0009	-0.2	-0.1
	1055	-0.1	0.0		0619	3.9	1.2
	1735	4.5	1.4		1206	-0.5	-0.2
	2339	0.1	0.0		1849	4.8	1.5
8 W	0555	3.9	1.2	23 Th	0056	-0.3	-0.1
	1142	-0.4	-0.1		0707	3.8	1.2
	1825	4.7	1.4		1249	-0.5	-0.2
					1934	4.8	1.5
9 Th	0030	-0.2	-0.1	24 F	0141	-0.3	-0.1
	0646	3.9	1.2		0752	3.8	1.2
	1230	-0.7	-0.2		1331	-0.5	-0.2
	1914	4.9	1.5		2016	4.8	1.5
10 F	0119	-0.5	-0.2	25 Sa	0222	-0.3	-0.1
	0739	3.9	1.2		0834	3.7	1.1
	1316	-0.9	-0.3		1411	-0.4	-0.1
	2005	5.1	1.6		2057	4.7	1.4
11 Sa	0210	-0.7	-0.2	26 Su	0304	-0.2	-0.1
	0829	4.0	1.2		0913	3.7	1.1
	1405	-0.9	-0.3		1449	-0.3	-0.1
	2057	5.2	1.6		2136	4.6	1.4
12 Su	0303	-0.8	-0.2	27 M	0342	-0.1	0.0
	0922	4.0	1.2		0953	3.7	1.1
	1459	-0.9	-0.3		1527	-0.1	0.0
	2149	5.2	1.6		2213	4.5	1.4
13 M	0355	-0.8	-0.2	28 Tu	0418	0.0	0.0
	1015	4.0	1.2		1033	3.6	1.1
	1552	-0.8	-0.2		1603	0.0	0.0
	2245	5.1	1.6		2252	4.4	1.3
14 Tu	0451	-0.7	-0.2	29 W	0456	0.2	0.1
	1112	4.1	1.2		1112	3.7	1.1
	1651	-0.6	-0.2		1641	0.3	0.1
	2339	5.0	1.5		2331	4.3	1.3
15 W	0549	-0.6	-0.2	30 Th	0531	0.3	0.1
	1210	4.1	1.2		1152	3.7	1.1
	1757	-0.3	-0.1		1723	0.5	0.2

Time meridian 75° W. 0000 is midnight. 1200 is noon.
Heights are referred to mean low water which is the chart datum of soundings.

MAYPORT, FLA., 1983

Times and Heights of High and Low Waters

JULY

Day	Time h m	ft	m	Day	Time h m	ft	m
1 F	0007	4.1	1.2	16 Sa	0113	4.6	1.4
	0610	0.4	0.1		0719	-0.5	-0.2
	1234	3.8	1.2		1349	4.5	1.4
	1810	0.7	0.2		1954	0.0	0.0
2 Sa	0046	4.0	1.2	17 Su	0211	4.3	1.3
	0650	0.4	0.1		0815	-0.4	-0.1
	1318	3.9	1.2		1447	4.6	1.4
	1905	0.8	0.2		2100	0.2	0.1
3 Su	0132	3.9	1.2	18 M	0308	4.1	1.2
	0737	0.4	0.1		0910	-0.2	-0.1
	1407	4.0	1.2		1548	4.6	1.4
	2004	0.8	0.2		2200	0.2	0.1
4 M	0219	3.8	1.2	19 Tu	0406	3.9	1.2
	0827	0.2	0.1		1004	-0.2	-0.1
	1500	4.1	1.2		1646	4.7	1.4
	2109	0.7	0.2		2257	0.2	0.1
5 Tu	0315	3.7	1.1	20 W	0501	3.8	1.2
	0919	0.1	0.0		1056	-0.1	0.0
	1558	4.3	1.3		1738	4.7	1.4
	2210	0.4	0.1		2350	0.2	0.1
6 W	0414	3.7	1.1	21 Th	0555	3.8	1.2
	1014	-0.2	-0.1		1142	-0.1	0.0
	1657	4.6	1.4		1827	4.7	1.4
	2308	0.1	0.0				
7 Th	0516	3.7	1.1	22 F	0035	0.1	0.0
	1108	-0.5	-0.2		0643	3.8	1.2
	1756	4.8	1.5		1228	-0.2	-0.1
					1913	4.8	1.5
8 F	0005	-0.2	-0.1	23 Sa	0120	0.0	0.0
	0617	3.8	1.2		0728	3.8	1.2
	1203	-0.7	-0.2		1310	-0.2	-0.1
	1852	5.0	1.5		1955	4.8	1.5
9 Sa	0101	-0.5	-0.2	24 Su	0200	0.0	0.0
	0715	3.9	1.2		0810	3.8	1.2
	1256	-0.9	-0.3		1350	-0.2	-0.1
	1949	5.2	1.6		2034	4.7	1.4
10 Su	0153	-0.7	-0.2	25 M	0238	0.0	0.0
	0811	4.0	1.2		0850	3.8	1.2
	1351	-1.1	-0.3		1426	-0.1	0.0
	2043	5.3	1.6		2113	4.7	1.4
11 M	0247	-0.9	-0.3	26 Tu	0314	0.0	0.0
	0906	4.2	1.3		0928	3.9	1.2
	1447	-1.1	-0.3		1502	0.0	0.0
	2136	5.3	1.6		2149	4.6	1.4
12 Tu	0340	-1.0	-0.3	27 W	0345	0.0	0.0
	1001	4.3	1.3		1006	3.9	1.2
	1542	-1.0	-0.3		1536	0.2	0.1
	2230	5.2	1.6		2224	4.5	1.4
13 W	0433	-0.9	-0.3	28 Th	0417	0.1	0.0
	1056	4.4	1.3		1043	4.0	1.2
	1642	-0.8	-0.2		1613	0.3	0.1
	2323	5.1	1.6		2259	4.4	1.3
14 Th	0528	-0.8	-0.2	29 F	0451	0.2	0.1
	1153	4.5	1.4		1117	4.0	1.2
	1744	-0.5	-0.2		1653	0.5	0.2
					2331	4.3	1.3
15 F	0018	4.8	1.5	30 Sa	0525	0.3	0.1
	0623	-0.7	-0.2		1154	4.1	1.2
	1250	4.5	1.4		1736	0.7	0.2
	1847	-0.2	-0.1				
				31 Su	0007	4.2	1.3
					0604	0.3	0.1
					1235	4.2	1.3
					1826	0.8	0.2

AUGUST

Day	Time h m	ft	m	Day	Time h m	ft	m
1 M	0045	4.1	1.2	16 Tu	0236	4.1	1.2
	0650	0.3	0.1		0839	0.3	0.1
	1321	4.3	1.3		1518	4.8	1.5
	1925	0.8	0.2		2135	0.7	0.2
2 Tu	0134	3.9	1.2	17 W	0336	4.0	1.2
	0742	0.3	0.1		0936	0.4	0.1
	1417	4.4	1.3		1617	4.8	1.5
	2031	0.8	0.2		2232	0.7	0.2
3 W	0231	3.8	1.2	18 Th	0434	3.9	1.2
	0839	0.2	0.1		1031	0.4	0.1
	1521	4.6	1.4		1713	4.8	1.5
	2140	0.7	0.2		2324	0.7	0.2
4 Th	0338	3.8	1.2	19 F	0527	4.0	1.2
	0940	0.0	0.0		1121	0.4	0.1
	1628	4.7	1.4		1803	4.9	1.5
	2245	0.4	0.1				
5 F	0449	3.8	1.2	20 Sa	0009	0.6	0.2
	1044	-0.2	-0.1		0617	4.0	1.2
	1736	5.0	1.5		1208	0.3	0.1
	2345	0.0	0.0		1851	4.9	1.5
6 Sa	0555	4.0	1.2	21 Su	0054	0.4	0.1
	1145	-0.5	-0.2		0703	4.1	1.2
	1837	5.2	1.6		1250	0.2	0.1
					1931	5.0	1.5
7 Su	0042	-0.3	-0.1	22 M	0132	0.3	0.1
	0657	4.2	1.3		0745	4.2	1.3
	1241	-0.8	-0.2		1329	0.2	0.1
	1933	5.4	1.6		2010	5.0	1.5
8 M	0136	-0.6	-0.2	23 Tu	0208	0.3	0.1
	0755	4.4	1.3		0825	4.3	1.3
	1339	-1.0	-0.3		1405	0.2	0.1
	2028	5.5	1.7		2047	4.9	1.5
9 Tu	0227	-0.8	-0.2	24 W	0240	0.2	0.1
	0849	4.6	1.4		0900	4.4	1.3
	1435	-1.0	-0.3		1439	0.2	0.1
	2119	5.5	1.7		2122	4.9	1.5
10 W	0318	-0.9	-0.3	25 Th	0310	0.2	0.1
	0943	4.8	1.5		0937	4.5	1.4
	1530	-0.9	-0.3		1514	0.3	0.1
	2211	5.4	1.6		2154	4.8	1.5
11 Th	0410	-0.9	-0.3	26 F	0342	0.3	0.1
	1035	4.9	1.5		1009	4.5	1.4
	1627	-0.7	-0.2		1547	0.5	0.2
	2301	5.2	1.6		2226	4.7	1.4
12 F	0459	-0.8	-0.2	27 Sa	0411	0.3	0.1
	1128	5.0	1.5		1043	4.6	1.4
	1725	-0.4	-0.1		1625	0.6	0.2
	2352	4.9	1.5		2258	4.6	1.4
13 Sa	0552	-0.5	-0.2	28 Su	0446	0.4	0.1
	1223	4.9	1.5		1119	4.7	1.4
	1826	0.0	0.0		1709	0.8	0.2
					2333	4.4	1.3
14 Su	0045	4.6	1.4	29 M	0525	0.5	0.2
	0645	-0.2	-0.1		1200	4.7	1.4
	1319	4.9	1.5		1800	0.9	0.3
	1930	0.3	0.1				
15 M	0140	4.4	1.3	30 Tu	0012	4.3	1.3
	0740	0.0	0.0		0613	0.6	0.2
	1418	4.8	1.5		1247	4.8	1.5
	2034	0.6	0.2		1858	1.1	0.3
				31 W	0101	4.2	1.3
					0709	0.6	0.2
					1348	4.8	1.5
					2007	1.1	0.3

SEPTEMBER

Day	Time h m	ft	m	Day	Time h m	ft	m
1 Th	0206	4.1	1.2	16 F	0402	4.2	1.3
	0812	0.6	0.2		1002	1.1	0.3
	1457	4.9	1.5		1641	4.9	1.5
	2119	1.0	0.3		2253	1.2	0.4
2 F	0319	4.1	1.2	17 Sa	0457	4.3	1.3
	0919	0.4	0.1		1057	1.0	0.3
	1612	5.0	1.5		1733	5.0	1.5
	2225	0.7	0.2		2342	1.0	0.3
3 Sa	0433	4.2	1.3	18 Su	0547	4.4	1.3
	1029	0.2	0.1		1143	0.9	0.3
	1721	5.3	1.6		1819	5.1	1.6
	2327	0.3	0.1				
4 Su	0543	4.4	1.3	19 M	0020	0.9	0.3
	1132	-0.1	0.0		0632	4.6	1.4
	1823	5.5	1.7		1225	0.7	0.2
					1900	5.2	1.6
5 M	0025	-0.1	0.0	20 Tu	0058	0.7	0.2
	0643	4.7	1.4		0715	4.7	1.4
	1232	-0.4	-0.1		1304	0.6	0.2
	1918	5.6	1.7		1939	5.2	1.6
6 Tu	0115	-0.4	-0.1	21 W	0132	0.5	0.2
	0738	5.0	1.5		0754	4.9	1.5
	1328	-0.6	-0.2		1340	0.5	0.2
	2010	5.7	1.7		2015	5.1	1.6
7 W	0205	-0.6	-0.2	22 Th	0203	0.4	0.1
	0830	5.3	1.6		0831	5.0	1.5
	1421	-0.7	-0.2		1414	0.5	0.2
	2059	5.7	1.7		2050	5.1	1.6
8 Th	0253	-0.7	-0.2	23 F	0233	0.4	0.1
	0921	5.4	1.6		0905	5.0	1.5
	1515	-0.6	-0.2		1449	0.5	0.2
	2147	5.5	1.7		2123	5.0	1.5
9 F	0341	-0.7	-0.2	24 Sa	0304	0.4	0.1
	1011	5.5	1.7		0937	5.1	1.6
	1609	-0.4	-0.1		1526	0.6	0.2
	2236	5.3	1.6		2157	4.9	1.5
10 Sa	0429	-0.4	-0.1	25 Su	0337	0.4	0.1
	1101	5.5	1.7		1013	5.1	1.6
	1704	0.0	0.0		1604	0.7	0.2
	2323	5.0	1.5		2230	4.7	1.4
11 Su	0517	-0.1	0.0	26 M	0414	0.5	0.2
	1152	5.4	1.6		1050	5.2	1.6
	1800	0.4	0.1		1650	0.9	0.3
					2307	4.6	1.4
12 M	0013	4.7	1.4	27 Tu	0457	0.6	0.2
	0608	0.2	0.1		1135	5.2	1.6
	1246	5.2	1.6		1740	1.1	0.3
	1901	0.7	0.2		2354	4.5	1.4
13 Tu	0106	4.5	1.4	28 W	0546	0.8	0.2
	0705	0.6	0.2		1226	5.1	1.6
	1343	5.0	1.5		1842	1.2	0.4
	2002	1.0	0.3				
14 W	0203	4.3	1.3	29 Th	0049	4.4	1.3
	0804	0.9	0.3		0645	0.9	0.3
	1443	4.9	1.5		1331	5.1	1.6
	2104	1.2	0.4		1951	1.3	0.4
15 Th	0302	4.2	1.3	30 F	0156	4.3	1.3
	0904	1.0	0.3		0754	0.9	0.3
	1544	4.9	1.5		1446	5.1	1.6
	2202	1.2	0.4		2104	1.1	0.3

Time meridian 75° W. 0000 is midnight. 1200 is noon.
Heights are referred to mean low water which is the chart datum of soundings.

Times and Heights of High and Low Waters

OCTOBER

Day	Time h m	Height ft	Height m	Day	Time h m	Height ft	Height m
1 Sa	0313	4.4	1.3	16 Su	0421	4.5	1.4
	0909	0.8	0.2		1023	1.4	0.4
	1559	5.3	1.6		1653	5.0	1.5
	2212	0.9	0.3		2300	1.2	0.4
2 Su	0427	4.6	1.4	17 M	0513	4.7	1.4
	1020	0.5	0.2		1111	1.2	0.4
	1708	5.4	1.6		1740	5.0	1.5
	2310	0.5	0.2		2340	1.0	0.3
3 M	0532	4.9	1.5	18 Tu	0558	4.8	1.5
	1124	0.2	0.1		1155	1.0	0.3
	1806	5.6	1.7		1822	5.1	1.6
4 Tu	0004	0.1	0.0	19 W	0017	0.8	0.2
	0627	5.3	1.6		0640	5.0	1.5
	1222	-0.1	0.0		1235	0.8	0.2
	1859	5.7	1.7		1904	5.1	1.6
5 W	0054	-0.2	-0.1	20 Th	0050	0.6	0.2
	0722	5.6	1.7		0720	5.2	1.6
	1317	-0.3	-0.1		1312	0.6	0.2
	1949	5.7	1.7		1942	5.1	1.6
6 Th	0140	-0.4	-0.1	21 F	0124	0.4	0.1
	0811	5.8	1.8		0758	5.3	1.6
	1408	-0.4	-0.1		1349	0.5	0.2
	2036	5.6	1.7		2018	5.0	1.5
7 F	0226	-0.5	-0.2	22 Sa	0156	0.3	0.1
	0859	5.9	1.8		0834	5.4	1.6
	1458	-0.3	-0.1		1426	0.5	0.2
	2122	5.4	1.6		2054	4.9	1.5
8 Sa	0311	-0.4	-0.1	23 Su	0231	0.3	0.1
	0945	5.8	1.8		0911	5.4	1.6
	1548	-0.1	0.0		1505	0.5	0.2
	2208	5.2	1.6		2131	4.8	1.5
9 Su	0357	-0.1	0.0	24 M	0310	0.3	0.1
	1032	5.7	1.7		0950	5.4	1.6
	1638	0.2	0.1		1550	0.6	0.2
	2255	4.9	1.5		2210	4.7	1.4
10 M	0441	0.2	0.1	25 Tu	0349	0.4	0.1
	1120	5.5	1.7		1033	5.4	1.6
	1731	0.6	0.2		1638	0.7	0.2
	2341	4.7	1.4		2253	4.6	1.4
11 Tu	0531	0.6	0.2	26 W	0438	0.5	0.2
	1210	5.3	1.6		1122	5.4	1.6
	1827	1.0	0.3		1731	0.9	0.3
					2345	4.5	1.4
12 W	0032	4.5	1.4	27 Th	0531	0.7	0.2
	0624	1.0	0.3		1220	5.3	1.6
	1304	5.1	1.6		1834	1.0	0.3
	1926	1.3	0.4				
13 Th	0127	4.4	1.3	28 F	0047	4.4	1.3
	0722	1.3	0.4		0634	0.9	0.3
	1403	5.0	1.5		1325	5.2	1.6
	2027	1.5	0.5		1943	1.0	0.3
14 F	0226	4.3	1.3	29 Sa	0157	4.4	1.3
	0827	1.4	0.4		0748	0.9	0.3
	1503	4.9	1.5		1437	5.2	1.6
	2123	1.5	0.5		2052	0.9	0.3
15 Sa	0325	4.3	1.3	30 Su	0309	4.6	1.4
	0927	1.4	0.4		0904	0.8	0.2
	1600	4.9	1.5		1546	5.2	1.6
	2215	1.4	0.4		2154	0.7	0.2
				31 M	0417	4.8	1.5
					1013	0.6	0.2
					1649	5.3	1.6
					2250	0.3	0.1

NOVEMBER

Day	Time h m	Height ft	Height m	Day	Time h m	Height ft	Height m
1 Tu	0518	5.1	1.6	16 W	0518	4.7	1.4
	1116	0.3	0.1		1116	1.0	0.3
	1748	5.3	1.6		1740	4.6	1.4
	2342	0.0	0.0		2329	0.6	0.2
2 W	0614	5.4	1.6	17 Th	0602	4.9	1.5
	1211	0.0	0.0		1159	0.7	0.2
	1838	5.3	1.6		1822	4.6	1.4
3 Th	0030	-0.2	-0.1	18 F	0006	0.4	0.1
	0703	5.7	1.7		0645	5.1	1.6
	1304	-0.2	-0.1		1240	0.5	0.2
	1928	5.3	1.6		1904	4.6	1.4
4 F	0115	-0.4	-0.1	19 Sa	0045	0.1	0.0
	0752	5.8	1.8		0727	5.2	1.6
	1352	-0.2	-0.1		1323	0.3	0.1
	2014	5.2	1.6		1945	4.6	1.4
5 Sa	0200	-0.3	-0.1	20 Su	0123	0.0	0.0
	0837	5.8	1.8		0808	5.3	1.6
	1441	-0.2	-0.1		1405	0.1	0.0
	2059	5.0	1.5		2027	4.5	1.4
6 Su	0243	-0.3	-0.1	21 M	0204	-0.1	0.0
	0923	5.7	1.7		0850	5.4	1.6
	1528	0.0	0.0		1450	0.1	0.0
	2143	4.8	1.5		2110	4.5	1.4
7 M	0327	-0.1	0.0	22 Tu	0248	-0.2	-0.1
	1007	5.6	1.7		0936	5.4	1.6
	1614	0.2	0.1		1537	0.1	0.0
	2227	4.6	1.4		2155	4.4	1.3
8 Tu	0409	0.2	0.1	23 W	0334	-0.1	0.0
	1053	5.4	1.6		1023	5.4	1.6
	1702	0.6	0.2		1630	0.2	0.1
	2311	4.4	1.3		2246	4.3	1.3
9 W	0454	0.6	0.2	24 Th	0425	0.1	0.0
	1139	5.1	1.6		1115	5.3	1.6
	1752	0.9	0.3		1723	0.3	0.1
					2341	4.3	1.3
10 Th	0000	4.3	1.3	25 F	0524	0.3	0.1
	0543	0.9	0.3		1215	5.1	1.6
	1229	4.9	1.5		1824	0.4	0.1
	1845	1.1	0.3				
11 F	0050	4.2	1.3	26 Sa	0044	4.3	1.3
	0639	1.2	0.4		0630	0.5	0.2
	1319	4.8	1.5		1319	5.0	1.5
	1942	1.3	0.4		1930	0.4	0.1
12 Sa	0144	4.2	1.3	27 Su	0150	4.4	1.3
	0738	1.4	0.4		0743	0.6	0.2
	1415	4.7	1.4		1423	4.9	1.5
	2035	1.3	0.4		2033	0.3	0.1
13 Su	0240	4.2	1.3	28 M	0258	4.5	1.4
	0839	1.5	0.5		0857	0.5	0.2
	1510	4.6	1.4		1528	4.8	1.5
	2124	1.3	0.4		2133	0.2	0.1
14 M	0336	4.3	1.3	29 Tu	0402	4.8	1.5
	0939	1.4	0.4		1004	0.4	0.1
	1605	4.6	1.4		1628	4.8	1.5
	2211	1.1	0.3		2228	0.0	0.0
15 Tu	0428	4.5	1.4	30 W	0502	5.0	1.5
	1031	1.2	0.4		1105	0.2	0.1
	1655	4.6	1.4		1726	4.7	1.4
	2250	0.9	0.3		2318	-0.2	-0.1

DECEMBER

Day	Time h m	Height ft	Height m	Day	Time h m	Height ft	Height m
1 Th	0555	5.2	1.6	16 F	0520	4.5	1.4
	1158	0.0	0.0		1121	0.5	0.2
	1818	4.7	1.4		1738	4.0	1.2
					2324	0.0	0.0
2 F	0007	-0.4	-0.1	17 Sa	0609	4.7	1.4
	0646	5.4	1.6		1211	0.2	0.1
	1251	-0.2	-0.1		1827	4.0	1.2
	1907	4.6	1.4				
3 Sa	0052	-0.5	-0.2	18 Su	0009	-0.3	-0.1
	0733	5.4	1.6		0657	4.9	1.5
	1337	-0.3	-0.1		1258	-0.1	0.0
	1953	4.5	1.4		1917	4.0	1.2
4 Su	0137	-0.5	-0.2	19 M	0055	-0.5	-0.2
	0818	5.4	1.6		0744	5.1	1.6
	1423	-0.3	-0.1		1345	-0.3	-0.1
	2037	4.4	1.3		2006	4.1	1.2
5 M	0218	-0.4	-0.1	20 Tu	0143	-0.7	-0.2
	0900	5.3	1.6		0834	5.2	1.6
	1508	-0.2	-0.1		1434	-0.5	-0.2
	2120	4.2	1.3		2054	4.1	1.2
6 Tu	0300	-0.2	-0.1	21 W	0233	-0.8	-0.2
	0945	5.1	1.6		0925	5.2	1.6
	1552	0.0	0.0		1526	-0.5	-0.2
	2203	4.1	1.2		2144	4.1	1.2
7 W	0341	0.0	0.0	22 Th	0324	-0.7	-0.2
	1027	4.9	1.5		1016	5.2	1.6
	1635	0.2	0.1		1618	-0.5	-0.2
	2245	4.0	1.2		2237	4.2	1.3
8 Th	0422	0.3	0.1	23 F	0418	-0.6	-0.2
	1109	4.8	1.5		1109	5.1	1.6
	1717	0.5	0.2		1712	-0.4	-0.1
	2327	3.9	1.2		2333	4.2	1.3
9 F	0507	0.5	0.2	24 Sa	0517	-0.4	-0.1
	1152	4.6	1.4		1204	4.9	1.5
	1800	0.7	0.2		1809	-0.4	-0.1
10 Sa	0013	3.9	1.2	25 Su	0034	4.2	1.3
	0552	0.8	0.2		0623	-0.1	0.0
	1237	4.4	1.3		1301	4.7	1.4
	1849	0.8	0.2		1909	-0.3	-0.1
11 Su	0101	3.9	1.2	26 M	0135	4.3	1.3
	0645	1.0	0.3		0733	0.0	0.0
	1324	4.3	1.3		1403	4.5	1.4
	1935	0.9	0.3		2009	-0.3	-0.1
12 M	0151	3.9	1.2	27 Tu	0239	4.4	1.3
	0743	1.1	0.3		0843	0.1	0.0
	1413	4.2	1.3		1505	4.3	1.3
	2022	0.8	0.2		2106	-0.3	-0.1
13 Tu	0245	4.0	1.2	28 W	0342	4.5	1.4
	0841	1.1	0.3		0948	0.1	0.0
	1506	4.1	1.2		1604	4.1	1.2
	2108	0.7	0.2		2202	-0.4	-0.1
14 W	0335	4.2	1.3	29 Th	0441	4.7	1.4
	0938	1.0	0.3		1049	0.0	0.0
	1557	4.0	1.2		1702	4.0	1.2
	2154	0.5	0.2		2256	-0.4	-0.1
15 Th	0428	4.3	1.3	30 F	0537	4.8	1.5
	1031	0.8	0.2		1145	-0.2	-0.1
	1649	4.0	1.2		1757	4.0	1.2
	2239	0.3	0.1		2345	-0.5	-0.1
				31 Sa	0628	4.8	1.5
					1234	-0.3	-0.1
					1848	3.9	1.2

Time meridian 75° W. 0000 is midnight. 1200 is noon.
Heights are referred to mean low water which is the chart datum of soundings.

PUNTA GORDA, VENEZUELA, 1983
Times and Heights of High and Low Waters

JANUARY

Day	h m	ft	m		Day	h m	ft	m
1 Sa	0045	-1.6	-0.5		16 Su	0052	-0.7	-0.2
	0642	6.6	2.0			0634	5.6	1.7
	1300	0.0	0.0			1301	0.5	0.2
	1839	7.3	2.2			1834	6.3	1.9
2 Su	0132	-1.4	-0.4		17 M	0127	-0.5	-0.2
	0730	6.5	2.0			0705	5.7	1.7
	1350	0.0	0.0			1333	0.5	0.2
	1928	7.1	2.2			1909	6.2	1.9
3 M	0221	-1.2	-0.4		18 Tu	0202	-0.3	-0.1
	0818	6.3	1.9			0738	5.7	1.7
	1444	0.2	0.1			1409	0.6	0.2
	2020	6.6	2.0			1945	6.1	1.9
4 Tu	0313	-0.7	-0.2		19 W	0236	-0.1	0.0
	0908	6.1	1.9			0815	5.7	1.7
	1539	0.3	0.1			1447	0.7	0.2
	2113	6.1	1.9			2025	5.8	1.8
5 W	0406	-0.3	-0.1		20 Th	0313	0.2	0.1
	1003	5.9	1.8			0855	5.7	1.7
	1639	0.5	0.2			1534	0.7	0.2
	2213	5.6	1.7			2113	5.5	1.7
6 Th	0504	0.2	0.1		21 F	0401	0.6	0.2
	1059	5.7	1.7			0942	5.6	1.7
	1741	0.5	0.2			1633	0.8	0.2
	2320	5.2	1.6			2209	5.1	1.6
7 F	0604	0.5	0.2		22 Sa	0457	0.9	0.3
	1202	5.6	1.7			1037	5.5	1.7
	1844	0.4	0.1			1747	0.7	0.2
						2316	4.8	1.5
8 Sa	0034	4.9	1.5		23 Su	0609	1.1	0.3
	0706	0.7	0.2			1138	5.5	1.7
	1304	5.6	1.7			1859	0.4	0.1
	1945	0.2	0.1					
9 Su	0145	4.9	1.5		24 M	0036	4.7	1.4
	0805	0.8	0.2			0720	1.1	0.3
	1403	5.6	1.7			1248	5.5	1.7
	2042	0.0	0.0			2008	0.0	0.0
10 M	0250	5.0	1.5		25 Tu	0157	4.9	1.5
	0858	0.8	0.2			0826	0.9	0.3
	1455	5.8	1.8			1401	5.8	1.8
	2131	-0.3	-0.1			2109	-0.6	-0.2
11 Tu	0338	5.1	1.6		26 W	0307	5.2	1.6
	0946	0.7	0.2			0927	0.5	0.2
	1541	5.9	1.8			1506	6.2	1.9
	2218	-0.5	-0.2			2204	-1.1	-0.3
12 W	0423	5.3	1.6		27 Th	0407	5.6	1.7
	1031	0.6	0.2			1020	0.1	0.0
	1620	6.1	1.9			1602	6.6	2.0
	2300	-0.7	-0.2			2255	-1.6	-0.5
13 Th	0500	5.4	1.6		28 F	0458	6.0	1.8
	1111	0.5	0.2			1111	-0.3	-0.1
	1655	6.2	1.9			1656	6.9	2.1
	2339	-0.8	-0.2			2343	-1.9	-0.6
14 F	0532	5.5	1.7		29 Sa	0545	6.3	1.9
	1149	0.4	0.1			1159	-0.6	-0.2
	1730	6.3	1.9			1745	7.1	2.2
15 Sa	0016	-0.8	-0.2		30 Su	0029	-1.9	-0.6
	0603	5.6	1.7			0629	6.5	2.0
	1226	0.4	0.1			1246	-0.8	-0.2
	1802	6.3	1.9			1831	7.1	2.2
					31 M	0114	-1.8	-0.5
						0714	6.5	2.0
						1333	-0.8	-0.2
						1917	6.9	2.1

FEBRUARY

Day	h m	ft	m		Day	h m	ft	m
1 Tu	0159	-1.5	-0.5		16 W	0133	-0.6	-0.2
	0754	6.4	2.0			0710	5.9	1.8
	1422	-0.7	-0.2			1345	-0.1	0.0
	2004	6.5	2.0			1926	6.1	1.9
2 W	0247	-1.0	-0.3		17 Th	0204	-0.3	-0.1
	0838	6.2	1.9			0745	6.0	1.8
	1510	-0.5	-0.2			1418	-0.1	0.0
	2050	6.0	1.8			2004	5.9	1.8
3 Th	0334	-0.4	-0.1		18 F	0239	0.0	0.0
	0924	5.9	1.8			0821	6.0	1.8
	1606	-0.2	-0.1			1500	0.0	0.0
	2142	5.4	1.6			2049	5.5	1.7
4 F	0425	0.1	0.0		19 Sa	0318	0.4	0.1
	1011	5.5	1.7			0905	5.8	1.8
	1702	0.1	0.0			1555	0.2	0.1
	2238	4.9	1.5			2140	5.1	1.6
5 Sa	0524	0.6	0.2		20 Su	0414	0.8	0.2
	1106	5.2	1.6			0957	5.6	1.7
	1804	0.2	0.1			1707	0.3	0.1
	2345	4.5	1.4			2246	4.7	1.4
6 Su	0625	1.0	0.3		21 M	0531	1.2	0.4
	1209	5.0	1.5			1100	5.4	1.6
	1907	0.2	0.1			1828	0.3	0.1
7 M	0102	4.3	1.3		22 Tu	0009	4.5	1.4
	0729	1.1	0.3			0656	1.2	0.4
	1316	5.0	1.5			1219	5.3	1.6
	2009	0.1	0.0			1944	-0.1	0.0
8 Tu	0216	4.4	1.3		23 W	0137	4.6	1.4
	0829	1.0	0.3			0808	0.9	0.3
	1421	5.1	1.6			1341	5.5	1.7
	2104	-0.1	0.0			2050	-0.6	-0.2
9 W	0314	4.6	1.4		24 Th	0253	5.1	1.6
	0922	0.8	0.2			0911	0.4	0.1
	1515	5.3	1.6			1453	5.9	1.8
	2154	-0.4	-0.1			2147	-1.1	-0.3
10 Th	0402	4.8	1.5		25 F	0354	5.6	1.7
	1010	0.5	0.2			1007	-0.2	-0.1
	1602	5.6	1.7			1555	6.3	1.9
	2237	-0.6	-0.2			2239	-1.5	-0.5
11 F	0439	5.1	1.6		26 Sa	0444	6.1	1.9
	1052	0.3	0.1			1057	-0.7	-0.2
	1639	5.8	1.8			1648	6.7	2.0
	2319	-0.8	-0.2			2326	-1.8	-0.5
12 Sa	0513	5.3	1.6		27 Su	0528	6.5	2.0
	1130	0.1	0.0			1143	-1.1	-0.3
	1713	6.0	1.8			1734	6.9	2.1
	2354	-0.9	-0.3					
13 Su	0542	5.5	1.7		28 M	0009	-1.9	-0.6
	1206	0.0	0.0			0609	6.7	2.0
	1747	6.1	1.9			1229	-1.3	-0.4
						1818	7.0	2.1
14 M	0029	-0.9	-0.3					
	0610	5.7	1.7					
	1239	-0.1	0.0					
	1818	6.2	1.9					
15 Tu	0102	-0.8	-0.2					
	0640	5.8	1.8					
	1313	-0.1	0.0					
	1850	6.2	1.9					

MARCH

Day	h m	ft	m		Day	h m	ft	m
1 Tu	0053	-1.7	-0.5		16 W	0034	-0.6	-0.2
	0648	6.7	2.0			0610	6.2	1.9
	1314	-1.3	-0.4			1249	-0.6	-0.2
	1901	6.8	2.1			1832	6.3	1.9
2 W	0135	-1.3	-0.4		17 Th	0106	-0.4	-0.1
	0725	6.6	2.0			0641	6.4	2.0
	1356	-1.2	-0.4			1321	-0.6	-0.2
	1943	6.4	2.0			1907	6.2	1.9
3 Th	0218	-0.8	-0.2		18 F	0138	-0.1	0.0
	0802	6.3	1.9			0714	6.4	2.0
	1441	-0.9	-0.3			1356	-0.6	-0.2
	2025	5.9	1.8			1946	6.0	1.8
4 F	0300	-0.2	-0.1		19 Sa	0212	0.2	0.1
	0841	6.0	1.8			0753	6.3	1.9
	1529	-0.5	-0.2			1438	-0.4	-0.1
	2108	5.4	1.6			2029	5.7	1.7
5 Sa	0348	0.4	0.1		20 Su	0255	0.6	0.2
	0922	5.6	1.7			0838	6.1	1.9
	1622	-0.1	0.0			1532	-0.1	0.0
	2158	4.9	1.5			2124	5.3	1.6
6 Su	0440	0.9	0.3		21 M	0352	1.0	0.3
	1011	5.2	1.6			0929	5.7	1.7
	1722	0.3	0.1			1643	0.1	0.0
	2254	4.4	1.3			2230	4.9	1.5
7 M	0545	1.3	0.4		22 Tu	0515	1.3	0.4
	1112	4.8	1.5			1036	5.4	1.6
	1828	0.5	0.2			1807	0.2	0.1
						2354	4.7	1.4
8 Tu	0009	4.2	1.3		23 W	0639	1.3	0.4
	0654	1.4	0.4			1200	5.2	1.6
	1225	4.6	1.4			1923	0.0	0.0
	1932	0.4	0.1					
9 W	0131	4.2	1.3		24 Th	0126	4.8	1.5
	0800	1.2	0.4			0754	0.9	0.3
	1342	4.7	1.4			1328	5.3	1.6
	2032	0.2	0.1			2029	-0.4	-0.1
10 Th	0242	4.4	1.3		25 F	0240	5.3	1.6
	0856	0.9	0.3			0856	0.3	0.1
	1446	5.0	1.5			1445	5.8	1.8
	2125	-0.1	0.0			2127	-0.8	-0.2
11 F	0330	4.8	1.5		26 Sa	0338	5.9	1.8
	0944	0.6	0.2			0951	-0.3	-0.1
	1535	5.4	1.6			1544	6.2	1.9
	2210	-0.4	-0.1			2218	-1.2	-0.4
12 Sa	0410	5.1	1.6		27 Su	0423	6.4	2.0
	1028	0.2	0.1			1041	-0.9	-0.3
	1617	5.7	1.7			1636	6.6	2.0
	2250	-0.6	-0.2			2305	-1.4	-0.4
13 Su	0444	5.5	1.7		28 M	0505	6.7	2.0
	1106	-0.1	0.0			1125	-1.3	-0.4
	1653	6.0	1.8			1721	6.8	2.1
	2327	-0.7	-0.2			2347	-1.3	-0.4
14 M	0513	5.7	1.7		29 Tu	0544	6.9	2.1
	1142	-0.4	-0.1			1207	-1.5	-0.5
	1726	6.1	1.9			1802	6.8	2.1
15 Tu	0002	-0.7	-0.2		30 W	0029	-1.1	-0.3
	0541	6.0	1.8			0620	6.9	2.1
	1216	-0.5	-0.2			1249	-1.5	-0.5
	1759	6.3	1.9			1842	6.6	2.0
					31 Th	0107	-0.7	-0.2
						0653	6.7	2.0
						1330	-1.3	-0.4
						1919	6.3	1.9

Time meridian 60° W. 0000 is midnight. 1200 is noon.
Heights are referred to the chart datum of soundings.

PUNTA GORDA, VENEZUELA, 1983

Times and Heights of High and Low Waters

APRIL

Day	Time (h m)	Height ft	Height m
1 F	0147	-0.3	-0.1
	0727	6.5	2.0
	1412	-1.0	-0.3
	1957	5.9	1.8
2 Sa	0228	0.3	0.1
	0802	6.1	1.9
	1455	-0.5	-0.2
	2036	5.5	1.7
3 Su	0310	0.8	0.2
	0839	5.7	1.7
	1544	-0.1	0.0
	2121	5.1	1.6
4 M	0402	1.3	0.4
	0924	5.3	1.6
	1642	0.4	0.1
	2214	4.7	1.4
5 Tu	0507	1.6	0.5
	1022	4.9	1.5
	1745	0.7	0.2
	2320	4.4	1.3
6 W	0616	1.7	0.5
	1135	4.7	1.4
	1852	0.7	0.2
7 Th	0039	4.4	1.3
	0723	1.5	0.5
	1256	4.7	1.4
	1955	0.6	0.2
8 F	0149	4.6	1.4
	0821	1.1	0.3
	1408	4.9	1.5
	2048	0.3	0.1
9 Sa	0245	5.0	1.5
	0914	0.7	0.2
	1501	5.3	1.6
	2135	0.1	0.0
10 Su	0327	5.4	1.6
	0959	0.2	0.1
	1546	5.6	1.7
	2218	-0.1	0.0
11 M	0404	5.8	1.8
	1037	-0.2	-0.1
	1627	5.9	1.8
	2256	-0.2	-0.1
12 Tu	0436	6.1	1.9
	1116	-0.5	-0.2
	1703	6.2	1.9
	2332	-0.3	-0.1
13 W	0509	6.4	2.0
	1150	-0.8	-0.2
	1737	6.3	1.9
14 Th	0005	-0.2	-0.1
	0541	6.6	2.0
	1227	-0.9	-0.3
	1814	6.4	2.0
15 F	0041	0.0	0.0
	0614	6.8	2.1
	1302	-0.9	-0.3
	1851	6.3	1.9
16 Sa	0117	0.2	0.1
	0650	6.8	2.1
	1341	-0.8	-0.2
	1933	6.1	1.9
17 Su	0156	0.6	0.2
	0732	6.6	2.0
	1427	-0.6	-0.2
	2018	5.8	1.8
18 M	0246	0.9	0.3
	0818	6.3	1.9
	1524	-0.3	-0.1
	2116	5.5	1.7
19 Tu	0348	1.2	0.4
	0915	5.9	1.8
	1633	0.1	0.0
	2225	5.2	1.6
20 W	0506	1.4	0.4
	1025	5.5	1.7
	1748	0.2	0.1
	2345	5.1	1.6
21 Th	0627	1.3	0.4
	1150	5.3	1.6
	1902	0.1	0.0
22 F	0108	5.3	1.6
	0737	0.8	0.2
	1317	5.4	1.6
	2006	-0.1	0.0
23 Sa	0216	5.7	1.7
	0837	0.2	0.1
	1430	5.7	1.7
	2104	-0.4	-0.1
24 Su	0311	6.2	1.9
	0933	-0.4	-0.1
	1530	6.1	1.9
	2154	-0.6	-0.2
25 M	0357	6.6	2.0
	1020	-0.9	-0.3
	1620	6.4	2.0
	2239	-0.7	-0.2
26 Tu	0439	6.9	2.1
	1105	-1.3	-0.4
	1705	6.6	2.0
	2322	-0.6	-0.2
27 W	0516	7.0	2.1
	1147	-1.4	-0.4
	1744	6.6	2.0
28 Th	0003	-0.4	-0.1
	0550	6.9	2.1
	1227	-1.4	-0.4
	1822	6.4	2.0
29 F	0042	0.0	0.0
	0623	6.8	2.1
	1305	-1.2	-0.4
	1857	6.2	1.9
30 Sa	0119	0.3	0.1
	0655	6.6	2.0
	1346	-0.8	-0.2
	1932	5.9	1.8

MAY

Day	Time (h m)	Height ft	Height m
1 Su	0159	0.7	0.2
	0730	6.3	1.9
	1427	-0.4	-0.1
	2010	5.6	1.7
2 M	0241	1.1	0.3
	0806	5.9	1.8
	1513	0.0	0.0
	2050	5.3	1.6
3 Tu	0329	1.5	0.5
	0849	5.6	1.7
	1603	0.4	0.1
	2140	5.0	1.5
4 W	0429	1.7	0.5
	0940	5.2	1.6
	1704	0.7	0.2
	2238	4.8	1.5
5 Th	0536	1.8	0.5
	1046	4.9	1.5
	1807	0.9	0.3
	2346	4.8	1.5
6 F	0643	1.6	0.5
	1202	4.8	1.5
	1908	0.8	0.2
7 Sa	0052	4.9	1.5
	0743	1.3	0.4
	1315	4.9	1.5
	2005	0.7	0.2
8 Su	0149	5.3	1.6
	0837	0.8	0.2
	1417	5.2	1.6
	2053	0.5	0.2
9 M	0237	5.6	1.7
	0922	0.3	0.1
	1511	5.5	1.7
	2139	0.4	0.1
10 Tu	0319	6.0	1.8
	1007	-0.2	-0.1
	1556	5.8	1.8
	2220	0.3	0.1
11 W	0357	6.4	2.0
	1047	-0.6	-0.2
	1636	6.1	1.9
	2300	0.3	0.1
12 Th	0434	6.7	2.0
	1126	-0.9	-0.3
	1717	6.3	1.9
	2339	0.3	0.1
13 F	0511	6.9	2.1
	1204	-1.1	-0.3
	1758	6.4	2.0
14 Sa	0018	0.4	0.1
	0548	7.0	2.1
	1246	-1.1	-0.3
	1839	6.3	1.9
15 Su	0101	0.5	0.2
	0633	7.0	2.1
	1330	-1.0	-0.3
	1925	6.2	1.9
16 M	0148	0.7	0.2
	0719	6.8	2.1
	1420	-0.8	-0.2
	2015	6.0	1.8
17 Tu	0241	1.0	0.3
	0809	6.5	2.0
	1516	-0.4	-0.1
	2112	5.8	1.8
18 W	0345	1.2	0.4
	0908	6.0	1.8
	1621	-0.1	0.0
	2217	5.6	1.7
19 Th	0456	1.2	0.4
	1017	5.6	1.7
	1729	0.1	0.0
	2330	5.6	1.7
20 F	0609	1.0	0.3
	1138	5.4	1.6
	1835	0.2	0.1
21 Sa	0042	5.8	1.8
	0715	0.6	0.2
	1259	5.4	1.6
	1937	0.1	0.0
22 Su	0147	6.1	1.9
	0814	0.1	0.0
	1411	5.6	1.7
	2034	0.1	0.0
23 M	0240	6.4	2.0
	0909	-0.4	-0.1
	1511	5.9	1.8
	2126	0.0	0.0
24 Tu	0327	6.6	2.0
	0958	-0.8	-0.2
	1602	6.1	1.9
	2212	0.0	0.0
25 W	0410	6.8	2.1
	1042	-1.1	-0.3
	1645	6.2	1.9
	2257	0.1	0.0
26 Th	0447	6.8	2.1
	1124	-1.2	-0.4
	1726	6.2	1.9
	2338	0.3	0.1
27 F	0521	6.8	2.1
	1203	-1.1	-0.3
	1802	6.1	1.9
28 Sa	0017	0.5	0.2
	0555	6.7	2.0
	1244	-0.9	-0.3
	1835	6.0	1.8
29 Su	0056	0.8	0.2
	0628	6.5	2.0
	1322	-0.7	-0.2
	1909	5.8	1.8
30 M	0135	1.0	0.3
	0703	6.3	1.9
	1402	-0.4	-0.1
	1946	5.7	1.7
31 Tu	0215	1.3	0.4
	0739	6.1	1.9
	1444	0.0	0.0
	2025	5.5	1.7

JUNE

Day	Time (h m)	Height ft	Height m
1 W	0300	1.5	0.5
	0820	5.8	1.8
	1529	0.3	0.1
	2108	5.4	1.6
2 Th	0353	1.6	0.5
	0908	5.5	1.7
	1622	0.6	0.2
	2158	5.3	1.6
3 F	0454	1.7	0.5
	1006	5.2	1.6
	1719	0.9	0.3
	2254	5.2	1.6
4 Sa	0557	1.6	0.5
	1110	5.0	1.5
	1819	1.0	0.3
	2353	5.3	1.6
5 Su	0659	1.3	0.4
	1219	5.0	1.5
	1915	1.0	0.3
6 M	0051	5.5	1.7
	0755	0.8	0.2
	1329	5.1	1.6
	2009	1.0	0.3
7 Tu	0144	5.8	1.8
	0847	0.3	0.1
	1429	5.3	1.6
	2059	0.9	0.3
8 W	0234	6.2	1.9
	0933	-0.2	-0.1
	1523	5.6	1.7
	2146	0.8	0.2
9 Th	0319	6.5	2.0
	1020	-0.6	-0.2
	1612	5.9	1.8
	2231	0.7	0.2
10 F	0404	6.8	2.1
	1103	-1.0	-0.3
	1700	6.2	1.9
	2316	0.6	0.2
11 Sa	0450	7.1	2.2
	1148	-1.2	-0.4
	1744	6.3	1.9
12 Su	0002	0.5	0.2
	0535	7.2	2.2
	1233	-1.3	-0.4
	1830	6.4	2.0
13 M	0048	0.6	0.2
	0621	7.1	2.2
	1321	-1.2	-0.4
	1919	6.4	2.0
14 Tu	0140	0.6	0.2
	0711	7.0	2.1
	1410	-1.0	-0.3
	2010	6.3	1.9
15 W	0236	0.7	0.2
	0803	6.6	2.0
	1503	-0.7	-0.2
	2103	6.2	1.9
16 Th	0334	0.8	0.2
	0902	6.2	1.9
	1601	-0.3	-0.1
	2201	6.1	1.9
17 F	0438	0.8	0.2
	1006	5.8	1.8
	1703	0.0	0.0
	2304	6.0	1.8
18 Sa	0544	0.7	0.2
	1118	5.5	1.7
	1806	0.3	0.1
19 Su	0008	6.0	1.8
	0649	0.4	0.1
	1233	5.3	1.6
	1907	0.5	0.2
20 M	0110	6.1	1.9
	0749	0.1	0.0
	1347	5.3	1.6
	2005	0.6	0.2
21 Tu	0205	6.3	1.9
	0843	-0.3	-0.1
	1450	5.5	1.7
	2059	0.7	0.2
22 W	0256	6.4	2.0
	0933	-0.6	-0.2
	1543	5.6	1.7
	2149	0.7	0.2
23 Th	0341	6.5	2.0
	1020	-0.8	-0.2
	1628	5.8	1.8
	2233	0.7	0.2
24 F	0423	6.6	2.0
	1103	-0.9	-0.3
	1706	5.8	1.8
	2315	0.8	0.2
25 Sa	0458	6.6	2.0
	1143	-0.8	-0.2
	1743	5.9	1.8
	2356	0.8	0.2
26 Su	0534	6.5	2.0
	1223	-0.7	-0.2
	1816	5.9	1.8
27 M	0036	0.9	0.3
	0608	6.5	2.0
	1301	-0.6	-0.2
	1848	5.8	1.8
28 Tu	0114	1.1	0.3
	0640	6.4	2.0
	1338	-0.4	-0.1
	1923	5.8	1.8
29 W	0152	1.2	0.4
	0717	6.2	1.9
	1418	-0.1	0.0
	1959	5.8	1.8
30 Th	0231	1.3	0.4
	0754	6.0	1.8
	1457	0.2	0.1
	2036	5.8	1.8

Time meridian 60° W. 0000 is midnight. 1200 is noon.
Heights are referred to the chart datum of soundings.

PUNTA GORDA, VENEZUELA, 1983

Times and Heights of High and Low Waters

JULY

Day	Time h m	Height ft	m	Day	Time h m	Height ft	m
1 F	0316	1.4	0.4	16 Sa	0414	0.4	0.1
	0839	5.8	1.8		0945	6.0	1.8
	1539	0.5	0.2		1633	0.2	0.1
	2116	5.7	1.7		2229	6.3	1.9
2 Sa	0409	1.4	0.4	17 Su	0515	0.4	0.1
	0929	5.5	1.7		1051	5.5	1.7
	1627	0.8	0.2		1731	0.7	0.2
	2206	5.7	1.7		2328	6.2	1.9
3 Su	0507	1.4	0.4	18 M	0617	0.4	0.1
	1025	5.2	1.6		1203	5.2	1.6
	1723	1.1	0.3		1833	1.0	0.3
	2258	5.7	1.7				
4 M	0609	1.2	0.4	19 Tu	0028	6.1	1.9
	1130	5.1	1.6		0718	0.3	0.1
	1822	1.3	0.4		1315	5.1	1.6
	2355	5.8	1.8		1935	1.2	0.4
5 Tu	0712	0.9	0.3	20 W	0128	6.1	1.9
	1241	5.0	1.5		0816	0.1	0.0
	1923	1.4	0.4		1426	5.2	1.6
					2031	1.2	0.4
6 W	0054	6.0	1.8	21 Th	0226	6.1	1.9
	0811	0.4	0.1		0909	-0.2	-0.1
	1352	5.2	1.6		1525	5.3	1.6
	2021	1.3	0.4		2125	1.2	0.4
7 Th	0152	6.2	1.9	22 F	0317	6.3	1.9
	0904	-0.1	0.0		0959	-0.3	-0.1
	1456	5.5	1.7		1612	5.5	1.7
	2117	1.1	0.3		2212	1.1	0.3
8 F	0250	6.6	2.0	23 Sa	0400	6.4	2.0
	0956	-0.5	-0.2		1041	-0.5	-0.2
	1554	5.8	1.8		1652	5.7	1.7
	2210	0.9	0.3		2255	1.0	0.3
9 Sa	0343	6.9	2.1	24 Su	0439	6.5	2.0
	1045	-0.9	-0.3		1124	-0.5	-0.2
	1645	6.2	1.9		1725	5.8	1.8
	2300	0.7	0.2		2336	1.0	0.3
10 Su	0434	7.1	2.2	25 M	0516	6.5	2.0
	1133	-1.2	-0.4		1202	-0.5	-0.2
	1734	6.4	2.0		1757	6.0	1.8
	2349	0.5	0.2				
11 M	0524	7.3	2.2	26 Tu	0015	0.9	0.3
	1220	-1.4	-0.4		0549	6.6	2.0
	1821	6.6	2.0		1239	-0.4	-0.1
					1826	6.1	1.9
12 Tu	0037	0.3	0.1	27 W	0052	0.9	0.3
	0613	7.3	2.2		0623	6.6	2.0
	1308	-1.3	-0.4		1314	-0.3	-0.1
	1908	6.8	2.1		1858	6.2	1.9
13 W	0127	0.3	0.1	28 Th	0127	1.0	0.3
	0703	7.2	2.2		0656	6.5	2.0
	1356	-1.1	-0.3		1348	0.0	0.0
	1955	6.8	2.1		1929	6.2	1.9
14 Th	0220	0.3	0.1	29 F	0202	1.0	0.3
	0754	6.9	2.1		0732	6.4	2.0
	1446	-0.8	-0.2		1420	0.3	0.1
	2044	6.7	2.0		2002	6.3	1.9
15 F	0315	0.3	0.1	30 Sa	0241	1.1	0.3
	0847	6.4	2.0		0810	6.1	1.9
	1537	-0.3	-0.1		1457	0.6	0.2
	2134	6.5	2.0		2039	6.3	1.9
				31 Su	0324	1.1	0.3
					0855	5.9	1.8
					1537	1.0	0.3
					2121	6.2	1.9

AUGUST

Day	Time h m	Height ft	m	Day	Time h m	Height ft	m
1 M	0417	1.2	0.4	16 Tu	0541	0.6	0.2
	0945	5.6	1.7		1125	5.2	1.6
	1625	1.4	0.4		1800	1.6	0.5
	2209	6.2	1.9		2343	6.0	1.8
2 Tu	0520	1.2	0.4	17 W	0646	0.7	0.2
	1046	5.3	1.6		1242	5.0	1.5
	1728	1.7	0.5		1904	1.8	0.5
	2304	6.1	1.9				
3 W	0630	1.0	0.3	18 Th	0051	5.9	1.8
	1200	5.1	1.6		0747	0.6	0.2
	1842	1.8	0.5		1357	5.1	1.6
					2005	1.8	0.5
4 Th	0011	6.1	1.9	19 F	0157	6.0	1.8
	0739	0.7	0.2		0843	0.4	0.1
	1321	5.2	1.6		1504	5.3	1.6
	1952	1.7	0.5		2101	1.6	0.5
5 F	0120	6.3	1.9	20 Sa	0253	6.1	1.9
	0840	0.2	0.1		0933	0.2	0.1
	1434	5.5	1.7		1551	5.6	1.7
	2056	1.4	0.4		2151	1.4	0.4
6 Sa	0229	6.6	2.0	21 Su	0341	6.4	2.0
	0936	-0.3	-0.1		1020	0.0	0.0
	1538	5.9	1.8		1628	5.9	1.8
	2152	1.1	0.3		2234	1.2	0.4
7 Su	0328	7.0	2.1	22 M	0423	6.6	2.0
	1028	-0.8	-0.2		1100	-0.2	-0.1
	1631	6.4	2.0		1700	6.1	1.9
	2244	0.6	0.2		2315	1.0	0.3
8 M	0424	7.3	2.2	23 Tu	0457	6.7	2.0
	1116	-1.1	-0.3		1137	-0.2	-0.1
	1720	6.8	2.1		1732	6.3	1.9
	2334	0.3	0.1		2352	0.8	0.2
9 Tu	0516	7.5	2.3	24 W	0530	6.8	2.1
	1203	-1.3	-0.4		1213	-0.2	-0.1
	1805	7.1	2.2		1800	6.5	2.0
10 W	0022	0.0	0.0	25 Th	0026	0.8	0.2
	0604	7.6	2.3		0602	6.9	2.1
	1250	-1.3	-0.4		1245	0.0	0.0
	1848	7.3	2.2		1827	6.7	2.0
11 Th	0110	-0.1	0.0	26 F	0100	0.7	0.2
	0653	7.5	2.3		0634	6.8	2.1
	1333	-1.0	-0.3		1317	0.2	0.1
	1933	7.3	2.2		1855	6.8	2.1
12 F	0159	-0.1	0.0	27 Sa	0133	0.8	0.2
	0740	7.2	2.2		0708	6.7	2.0
	1420	-0.5	-0.2		1346	0.5	0.2
	2015	7.2	2.2		1927	6.9	2.1
13 Sa	0249	0.0	0.0	28 Su	0207	0.8	0.2
	0828	6.7	2.0		0743	6.5	2.0
	1508	0.0	0.0		1418	0.9	0.3
	2100	6.9	2.1		2002	6.9	2.1
14 Su	0342	0.2	0.1	29 M	0244	0.9	0.3
	0921	6.2	1.9		0825	6.2	1.9
	1601	0.6	0.2		1452	1.3	0.4
	2148	6.6	2.0		2043	6.8	2.1
15 M	0440	0.5	0.2	30 Tu	0332	1.1	0.3
	1019	5.6	1.7		0913	5.9	1.8
	1656	1.2	0.4		1534	1.7	0.5
	2242	6.3	1.9		2129	6.6	2.0
				31 W	0438	1.2	0.4
					1014	5.5	1.7
					1648	2.1	0.6
					2227	6.4	2.0

SEPTEMBER

Day	Time h m	Height ft	m	Day	Time h m	Height ft	m
1 Th	0557	1.2	0.4	16 F	0008	5.8	1.8
	1131	5.3	1.6		0714	1.1	0.3
	1814	2.3	0.7		1323	5.1	1.6
	2339	6.2	1.9		1937	2.3	0.7
2 F	0713	0.9	0.3	17 Sa	0121	5.9	1.8
	1259	5.3	1.6		0814	1.0	0.3
	1934	2.1	0.6		1432	5.4	1.6
					2037	2.0	0.6
3 Sa	0100	6.3	1.9	18 Su	0226	6.1	1.9
	0819	0.5	0.2		0906	0.7	0.2
	1421	5.7	1.7		1519	5.8	1.8
	2040	1.7	0.5		2127	1.6	0.5
4 Su	0213	6.6	2.0	19 M	0317	6.4	2.0
	0919	-0.1	0.0		0951	0.4	0.1
	1523	6.3	1.9		1559	6.2	1.9
	2138	1.1	0.3		2210	1.3	0.4
5 M	0319	7.1	2.2	20 Tu	0359	6.7	2.0
	1010	-0.5	-0.2		1031	0.2	0.1
	1615	6.9	2.1		1631	6.5	2.0
	2231	0.5	0.2		2249	1.0	0.3
6 Tu	0415	7.5	2.3	21 W	0436	6.9	2.1
	1059	-0.9	-0.3		1109	0.2	0.1
	1701	7.3	2.2		1700	6.8	2.1
	2319	0.0	0.0		2326	0.7	0.2
7 W	0505	7.8	2.4	22 Th	0508	7.0	2.1
	1143	-1.0	-0.3		1142	0.2	0.1
	1743	7.7	2.3		1726	7.0	2.1
8 Th	0005	-0.3	-0.1	23 F	0000	0.6	0.2
	0552	7.8	2.4		0540	7.1	2.2
	1226	-0.9	-0.3		1216	0.4	0.1
	1825	7.8	2.4		1756	7.2	2.2
9 F	0050	-0.4	-0.1	24 Sa	0033	0.5	0.2
	0637	7.7	2.3		0612	7.1	2.2
	1309	-0.5	-0.2		1247	0.6	0.2
	1903	7.8	2.4		1822	7.4	2.3
10 Sa	0135	-0.4	-0.1	25 Su	0106	0.5	0.2
	0719	7.4	2.3		0646	7.0	2.1
	1354	0.0	0.0		1316	0.9	0.3
	1943	7.6	2.3		1855	7.4	2.3
11 Su	0222	-0.1	0.0	26 M	0138	0.6	0.2
	0804	6.9	2.1		0722	6.8	2.1
	1436	0.6	0.2		1346	1.2	0.4
	2023	7.3	2.2		1930	7.4	2.3
12 M	0313	0.2	0.1	27 Tu	0215	0.7	0.2
	0852	6.3	1.9		0804	6.5	2.0
	1526	1.2	0.4		1420	1.6	0.5
	2105	6.8	2.1		2010	7.2	2.2
13 Tu	0406	0.6	0.2	28 W	0305	1.0	0.3
	0940	5.8	1.8		0852	6.1	1.9
	1619	1.8	0.5		1510	2.1	0.6
	2153	6.4	2.0		2100	6.9	2.1
14 W	0504	1.0	0.3	29 Th	0411	1.2	0.4
	1043	5.3	1.6		0953	5.7	1.7
	1722	2.2	0.7		1628	2.4	0.7
	2254	6.0	1.8		2201	6.6	2.0
15 Th	0609	1.2	0.4	30 F	0533	1.3	0.4
	1200	5.1	1.6		1114	5.5	1.7
	1832	2.4	0.7		1801	2.5	0.8
					2319	6.3	1.9

Time meridian 60° W. 0000 is midnight. 1200 is noon.
Heights are referred to the chart datum of soundings.

Times and Heights of High and Low Waters

OCTOBER

Day	Time h m	Height ft	Height m	Day	Time h m	Height ft	Height m
1 Sa	0651	1.1	0.3	16 Su	0039	5.8	1.8
	1246	5.6	1.7		0738	1.3	0.4
	1920	2.2	0.7		1344	5.5	1.7
					2005	2.1	0.6
2 Su	0046	6.3	1.9	17 M	0149	6.0	1.8
	0800	0.7	0.2		0830	1.1	0.3
	1406	6.1	1.9		1437	5.9	1.8
	2026	1.6	0.5		2056	1.7	0.5
3 M	0205	6.7	2.0	18 Tu	0245	6.3	1.9
	0858	0.2	0.1		0917	0.8	0.2
	1506	6.7	2.0		1517	6.3	1.9
	2122	0.9	0.3		2141	1.2	0.4
4 Tu	0311	7.1	2.2	19 W	0330	6.6	2.0
	0949	-0.2	-0.1		0959	0.6	0.2
	1556	7.3	2.2		1551	6.7	2.0
	2213	0.3	0.1		2221	0.8	0.2
5 W	0404	7.5	2.3	20 Th	0408	6.8	2.1
	1037	-0.4	-0.1		1036	0.6	0.2
	1639	7.8	2.4		1623	7.0	2.1
	2301	-0.2	-0.1		2258	0.5	0.2
6 Th	0452	7.8	2.4	21 F	0444	7.0	2.1
	1120	-0.5	-0.2		1113	0.6	0.2
	1719	8.0	2.4		1652	7.3	2.2
	2345	-0.5	-0.2		2334	0.3	0.1
7 F	0537	7.8	2.4	22 Sa	0518	7.1	2.2
	1202	-0.3	-0.1		1145	0.7	0.2
	1757	8.1	2.5		1721	7.5	2.3
8 Sa	0028	-0.6	-0.2	23 Su	0009	0.2	0.1
	0619	7.6	2.3		0551	7.1	2.2
	1244	0.1	0.0		1218	0.9	0.3
	1833	8.0	2.4		1754	7.6	2.3
9 Su	0111	-0.5	-0.2	24 M	0042	0.2	0.1
	0658	7.3	2.2		0626	7.0	2.1
	1324	0.5	0.2		1250	1.1	0.3
	1909	7.8	2.4		1828	7.7	2.3
10 M	0154	-0.2	-0.1	25 Tu	0119	0.3	0.1
	0740	6.9	2.1		0706	6.8	2.1
	1406	1.1	0.3		1322	1.4	0.4
	1946	7.4	2.3		1906	7.6	2.3
11 Tu	0241	0.3	0.1	26 W	0202	0.4	0.1
	0823	6.4	2.0		0750	6.5	2.0
	1452	1.7	0.5		1407	1.8	0.5
	2027	7.0	2.1		1951	7.3	2.2
12 W	0329	0.7	0.2	27 Th	0252	0.7	0.2
	0908	5.9	1.8		0841	6.2	1.9
	1542	2.2	0.7		1503	2.1	0.6
	2110	6.5	2.0		2041	7.0	2.1
13 Th	0429	1.2	0.4	28 F	0358	1.0	0.3
	1005	5.5	1.7		0945	5.9	1.8
	1646	2.5	0.8		1622	2.4	0.7
	2206	6.1	1.9		2145	6.5	2.0
14 F	0532	1.4	0.4	29 Sa	0515	1.1	0.3
	1114	5.2	1.6		1104	5.7	1.7
	1757	2.7	0.8		1746	2.3	0.7
	2319	5.8	1.8		2304	6.2	1.9
15 Sa	0636	1.5	0.5	30 Su	0628	1.0	0.3
	1233	5.3	1.6		1228	5.9	1.8
	1904	2.5	0.8		1902	1.9	0.6
				31 M	0033	6.2	1.9
					0736	0.7	0.2
					1344	6.4	2.0
					2006	1.3	0.4

NOVEMBER

Day	Time h m	Height ft	Height m	Day	Time h m	Height ft	Height m
1 Tu	0152	6.5	2.0	16 W	0200	5.8	1.8
	0834	0.4	0.1		0837	1.1	0.3
	1442	6.9	2.1		1426	6.2	1.9
	2104	0.6	0.2		2106	1.1	0.3
2 W	0256	6.9	2.1	17 Th	0253	6.1	1.9
	0927	0.1	0.0		0922	0.9	0.3
	1531	7.4	2.3		1506	6.5	2.0
	2154	0.0	0.0		2149	0.6	0.2
3 Th	0351	7.2	2.2	18 F	0338	6.3	1.9
	1013	0.0	0.0		1004	0.8	0.2
	1613	7.7	2.3		1544	6.9	2.1
	2241	-0.4	-0.1		2231	0.2	0.1
4 F	0437	7.4	2.3	19 Sa	0418	6.5	2.0
	1058	0.0	0.0		1042	0.8	0.2
	1655	7.9	2.4		1619	7.2	2.2
	2324	-0.7	-0.2		2308	-0.1	0.0
5 Sa	0521	7.4	2.3	20 Su	0457	6.7	2.0
	1140	0.2	0.1		1119	0.8	0.2
	1731	7.9	2.4		1655	7.4	2.3
					2348	-0.2	-0.1
6 Su	0007	-0.7	-0.2	21 M	0534	6.8	2.1
	0559	7.2	2.2		1157	0.9	0.3
	1220	0.5	0.2		1731	7.6	2.3
	1806	7.8	2.4				
7 M	0049	-0.6	-0.2	22 Tu	0026	-0.3	-0.1
	0639	7.0	2.1		0615	6.7	2.0
	1259	0.9	0.3		1235	1.0	0.3
	1840	7.6	2.3		1810	7.6	2.3
8 Tu	0130	-0.3	-0.1	23 W	0106	-0.3	-0.1
	0716	6.6	2.0		0656	6.6	2.0
	1340	1.3	0.4		1317	1.2	0.4
	1917	7.3	2.2		1852	7.5	2.3
9 W	0212	0.2	0.1	24 Th	0153	-0.1	0.0
	0754	6.3	1.9		0743	6.4	2.0
	1423	1.7	0.5		1404	1.4	0.4
	1954	6.9	2.1		1940	7.2	2.2
10 Th	0259	0.6	0.2	25 F	0246	0.1	0.0
	0836	5.9	1.8		0835	6.2	1.9
	1510	2.1	0.6		1503	1.6	0.5
	2036	6.5	2.0		2033	6.8	2.1
11 F	0350	1.0	0.3	26 Sa	0345	0.4	0.1
	0926	5.6	1.7		0937	6.0	1.8
	1609	2.4	0.7		1614	1.8	0.5
	2124	6.1	1.9		2137	6.4	2.0
12 Sa	0451	1.3	0.4	27 Su	0453	0.6	0.2
	1025	5.4	1.6		1046	5.9	1.8
	1714	2.5	0.8		1728	1.7	0.5
	2230	5.7	1.7		2251	6.0	1.8
13 Su	0551	1.4	0.4	28 M	0601	0.7	0.2
	1132	5.3	1.6		1202	6.0	1.8
	1823	2.4	0.7		1839	1.3	0.4
	2342	5.6	1.7				
14 M	0651	1.4	0.4	29 Tu	0015	5.9	1.8
	1241	5.5	1.7		0707	0.6	0.2
	1925	2.0	0.6		1312	6.3	1.9
					1944	0.8	0.2
15 Tu	0057	5.6	1.7	30 W	0134	6.0	1.8
	0749	1.3	0.4		0806	0.5	0.2
	1339	5.8	1.8		1413	6.7	2.0
	2019	1.6	0.5		2042	0.2	0.1

DECEMBER

Day	Time h m	Height ft	Height m	Day	Time h m	Height ft	Height m
1 Th	0240	6.2	1.9	16 F	0208	5.4	1.6
	0901	0.4	0.1		0842	1.1	0.3
	1506	7.0	2.1		1419	6.1	1.9
	2133	-0.3	-0.1		2119	0.4	0.1
2 F	0335	6.5	2.0	17 Sa	0304	5.6	1.7
	0951	0.3	0.1		0931	0.9	0.3
	1549	7.2	2.2		1506	6.4	2.0
	2222	-0.7	-0.2		2202	-0.1	0.0
3 Sa	0423	6.6	2.0	18 Su	0352	5.9	1.8
	1036	0.3	0.1		1015	0.8	0.2
	1631	7.4	2.3		1551	6.7	2.0
	2305	-0.9	-0.3		2247	-0.5	-0.2
4 Su	0505	6.6	2.0	19 M	0436	6.1	1.9
	1119	0.4	0.1		1057	0.7	0.2
	1708	7.4	2.3		1634	7.0	2.1
	2348	-0.9	-0.3		2329	-0.8	-0.2
5 M	0544	6.5	2.0	20 Tu	0522	6.3	1.9
	1200	0.6	0.2		1141	0.6	0.2
	1743	7.3	2.2		1716	7.2	2.2
6 Tu	0029	-0.7	-0.2	21 W	0013	-0.9	-0.3
	0621	6.4	2.0		0604	6.4	2.0
	1239	0.8	0.2		1224	0.5	0.2
	1818	7.1	2.2		1759	7.3	2.2
7 W	0109	-0.5	-0.2	22 Th	0057	-1.0	-0.3
	0657	6.2	1.9		0648	6.4	2.0
	1319	1.1	0.3		1309	0.5	0.2
	1853	6.9	2.1		1845	7.2	2.2
8 Th	0148	-0.2	-0.1	23 F	0143	-0.9	-0.3
	0733	6.0	1.8		0737	6.3	1.9
	1359	1.3	0.4		1401	0.6	0.2
	1929	6.6	2.0		1933	7.0	2.1
9 F	0231	0.1	0.0	24 Sa	0233	-0.6	-0.2
	0810	5.8	1.8		0826	6.2	1.9
	1441	1.6	0.5		1455	0.7	0.2
	2007	6.3	1.9		2028	6.6	2.0
10 Sa	0316	0.5	0.2	25 Su	0329	-0.3	-0.1
	0852	5.6	1.7		0921	6.1	1.9
	1529	1.8	0.5		1558	0.8	0.2
	2052	6.0	1.8		2126	6.2	1.9
11 Su	0406	0.8	0.2	26 M	0427	0.0	0.0
	0940	5.4	1.6		1022	5.9	1.8
	1627	1.9	0.6		1704	0.8	0.2
	2145	5.6	1.7		2235	5.7	1.7
12 M	0502	1.0	0.3	27 Tu	0532	0.3	0.1
	1033	5.3	1.6		1128	5.9	1.8
	1731	1.9	0.6		1811	0.6	0.2
	2246	5.3	1.6		2349	5.4	1.6
13 Tu	0600	1.2	0.4	28 W	0635	0.5	0.2
	1133	5.3	1.6		1235	5.9	1.8
	1836	1.7	0.5		1918	0.3	0.1
	2356	5.2	1.6				
14 W	0658	1.2	0.4	29 Th	0109	5.3	1.6
	1232	5.5	1.7		0737	0.6	0.2
	1934	1.3	0.4		1339	6.1	1.9
					2016	-0.1	0.0
15 Th	0104	5.2	1.6	30 F	0221	5.4	1.6
	0752	1.2	0.4		0837	0.6	0.2
	1328	5.7	1.7		1437	6.2	1.9
	2027	0.8	0.2		2112	-0.5	-0.2
				31 Sa	0319	5.6	1.7
					0928	0.5	0.2
					1527	6.4	2.0
					2202	-0.8	-0.2

Time meridian 60° W. 0000 is midnight. 1200 is noon.
Heights are referred to the chart datum of soundings.

SURINAME RIVIER ENTRANCE, SURINAM, 1983

Times and Heights of High and Low Waters

JANUARY

Day	Time h m	Height ft	Height m	Day	Time h m	Height ft	Height m
1 Sa	0548	7.8	2.4	16 Su	0545	7.2	2.2
	1151	0.8	0.2		1146	1.3	0.4
	1802	8.3	2.5		1755	7.6	2.3
2 Su	0023	0.3	0.1	17 M	0012	1.0	0.3
	0636	7.6	2.3		0620	7.2	2.2
	1239	1.0	0.3		1223	1.3	0.4
	1852	8.0	2.4		1834	7.6	2.3
3 M	0111	0.6	0.2	18 Tu	0049	1.1	0.3
	0726	7.4	2.3		0700	7.2	2.2
	1332	1.3	0.4		1303	1.4	0.4
	1942	7.6	2.3		1913	7.4	2.3
4 Tu	0201	1.0	0.3	19 W	0129	1.2	0.4
	0817	7.1	2.2		0739	7.1	2.2
	1425	1.6	0.5		1345	1.4	0.4
	2038	7.2	2.2		1958	7.3	2.2
5 W	0257	1.4	0.4	20 Th	0214	1.4	0.4
	0910	6.8	2.1		0824	7.0	2.1
	1523	1.8	0.5		1433	1.6	0.5
	2134	6.8	2.1		2046	7.0	2.1
6 Th	0352	1.8	0.5	21 F	0302	1.6	0.5
	1011	6.6	2.0		0915	6.9	2.1
	1625	2.0	0.6		1528	1.7	0.5
	2239	6.5	2.0		2144	6.8	2.1
7 F	0453	2.1	0.6	22 Sa	0357	1.8	0.5
	1111	6.5	2.0		1013	6.8	2.1
	1729	2.1	0.6		1632	1.8	0.5
	2344	6.3	1.9		2248	6.6	2.0
8 Sa	0554	2.2	0.7	23 Su	0501	2.0	0.6
	1211	6.5	2.0		1117	6.8	2.1
	1830	2.0	0.6		1741	1.7	0.5
9 Su	0045	6.3	1.9	24 M	0000	6.6	2.0
	0653	2.2	0.7		0609	2.0	0.6
	1306	6.6	2.0		1227	6.9	2.1
	1928	1.9	0.6		1853	1.5	0.5
10 M	0141	6.4	2.0	25 Tu	0112	6.7	2.0
	0746	2.1	0.6		0717	1.9	0.6
	1359	6.8	2.1		1333	7.2	2.2
	2020	1.7	0.5		1959	1.2	0.4
11 Tu	0231	6.6	2.0	26 W	0215	7.0	2.1
	0831	2.0	0.6		0820	1.6	0.5
	1444	7.0	2.1		1434	7.6	2.3
	2103	1.5	0.5		2058	0.8	0.2
12 W	0314	6.7	2.0	27 Th	0313	7.3	2.2
	0916	1.8	0.5		0919	1.2	0.4
	1524	7.2	2.2		1529	7.9	2.4
	2145	1.3	0.4		2151	0.4	0.1
13 Th	0354	6.9	2.1	28 F	0406	7.7	2.3
	0956	1.6	0.5		1009	0.9	0.3
	1606	7.4	2.3		1621	8.2	2.5
	2222	1.1	0.3		2241	0.2	0.1
14 F	0432	7.0	2.1	29 Sa	0454	7.9	2.4
	1033	1.5	0.5		1058	0.7	0.2
	1642	7.5	2.3		1709	8.4	2.6
	2259	1.0	0.3		2327	0.1	0.0
15 Sa	0508	7.1	2.2	30 Su	0538	8.0	2.4
	1110	1.4	0.4		1143	0.5	0.2
	1720	7.6	2.3		1754	8.4	2.6
	2336	1.0	0.3				
				31 M	0011	0.2	0.1
					0622	8.0	2.4
					1228	0.6	0.2
					1839	8.2	2.5

FEBRUARY

Day	Time h m	Height ft	Height m	Day	Time h m	Height ft	Height m
1 Tu	0055	0.4	0.1	16 W	0028	0.7	0.2
	0703	7.8	2.4		0634	7.7	2.3
	1311	0.7	0.2		1242	0.7	0.2
	1923	7.9	2.4		1854	7.9	2.4
2 W	0137	0.8	0.2	17 Th	0103	0.8	0.2
	0745	7.6	2.3		0711	7.7	2.3
	1356	1.0	0.3		1321	0.8	0.2
	2008	7.5	2.3		1932	7.7	2.3
3 Th	0219	1.2	0.4	18 F	0140	1.0	0.3
	0830	7.2	2.2		0750	7.5	2.3
	1441	1.4	0.4		1403	1.0	0.3
	2054	7.0	2.1		2017	7.4	2.3
4 F	0304	1.7	0.5	19 Sa	0225	1.4	0.4
	0918	6.9	2.1		0835	7.3	2.2
	1531	1.8	0.5		1451	1.2	0.4
	2146	6.5	2.0		2107	7.0	2.1
5 Sa	0355	2.1	0.6	20 Su	0315	1.8	0.5
	1008	6.5	2.0		0928	7.0	2.1
	1630	2.1	0.6		1549	1.6	0.5
	2246	6.2	1.9		2210	6.6	2.0
6 Su	0453	2.5	0.8	21 M	0416	2.1	0.6
	1110	6.3	1.9		1034	6.7	2.0
	1736	2.3	0.7		1704	1.8	0.5
	2353	5.9	1.8		2326	6.3	1.9
7 M	0600	2.7	0.8	22 Tu	0536	2.4	0.7
	1219	6.2	1.9		1155	6.6	2.0
	1845	2.3	0.7		1827	1.8	0.5
8 Tu	0106	5.9	1.8	23 W	0050	6.4	2.0
	0709	2.6	0.8		0658	2.3	0.7
	1325	6.3	1.9		1315	6.8	2.1
	1951	2.2	0.7		1943	1.5	0.5
9 W	0207	6.1	1.9	24 Th	0205	6.7	2.0
	0810	2.4	0.7		0813	1.9	0.6
	1423	6.5	2.0		1426	7.3	2.2
	2047	1.9	0.6		2050	1.1	0.3
10 Th	0300	6.4	2.0	25 F	0305	7.2	2.2
	0903	2.1	0.6		0911	1.3	0.4
	1513	6.9	2.1		1524	7.7	2.3
	2132	1.6	0.5		2143	0.6	0.2
11 F	0343	6.7	2.0	26 Sa	0356	7.7	2.3
	0945	1.8	0.5		1002	0.8	0.2
	1554	7.2	2.2		1612	8.2	2.5
	2210	1.3	0.4		2230	0.3	0.1
12 Sa	0420	7.0	2.1	27 Su	0440	8.1	2.5
	1022	1.5	0.5		1047	0.4	0.1
	1633	7.5	2.3		1658	8.4	2.6
	2246	1.0	0.3		2311	0.1	0.0
13 Su	0455	7.3	2.2	28 M	0520	8.3	2.5
	1059	1.2	0.4		1128	0.2	0.1
	1708	7.7	2.3		1739	8.5	2.6
	2321	0.8	0.2		2349	0.1	0.0
14 M	0528	7.5	2.3				
	1132	1.0	0.3				
	1741	7.9	2.4				
	2354	0.7	0.2				
15 Tu	0602	7.7	2.3				
	1207	0.8	0.2				
	1817	7.9	2.4				

MARCH

Day	Time h m	Height ft	Height m	Day	Time h m	Height ft	Height m
1 Tu	0559	8.3	2.5	16 W	0535	8.1	2.5
	1207	0.2	0.1		1143	0.3	0.1
	1817	8.4	2.6		1755	8.2	2.5
2 W	0027	0.3	0.1	17 Th	0001	0.5	0.2
	0634	8.2	2.5		0607	8.2	2.5
	1244	0.3	0.1		1218	0.3	0.1
	1857	8.1	2.5		1828	8.1	2.5
3 Th	0103	0.7	0.2	18 F	0034	0.6	0.2
	0711	7.9	2.4		0642	8.1	2.5
	1324	0.6	0.2		1255	0.3	0.1
	1934	7.7	2.3		1907	7.9	2.4
4 F	0140	1.1	0.3	19 Sa	0113	0.9	0.3
	0748	7.6	2.3		0721	7.9	2.4
	1401	1.0	0.3		1337	0.6	0.2
	2012	7.1	2.2		1950	7.5	2.3
5 Sa	0217	1.6	0.5	20 Su	0155	1.3	0.4
	0827	7.1	2.2		0804	7.5	2.3
	1443	1.5	0.5		1425	1.0	0.3
	2057	6.6	2.0		2040	7.0	2.1
6 Su	0302	2.2	0.7	21 M	0243	1.8	0.5
	0912	6.6	2.0		0853	7.1	2.2
	1534	2.1	0.6		1523	1.5	0.5
	2151	6.1	1.9		2144	6.4	2.0
7 M	0355	2.6	0.8	22 Tu	0349	2.3	0.7
	1011	6.1	1.9		1005	6.6	2.0
	1640	2.5	0.8		1640	1.9	0.6
	2302	5.7	1.7		2307	6.1	1.9
8 Tu	0508	3.0	0.9	23 W	0516	2.6	0.8
	1128	5.8	1.8		1135	6.4	2.0
	1803	2.7	0.8		1813	2.0	0.6
9 W	0029	5.6	1.7	24 Th	0040	6.2	1.9
	0637	3.0	0.9		0650	2.4	0.7
	1253	5.9	1.8		1306	6.6	2.0
	1925	2.5	0.8		1935	1.7	0.5
10 Th	0146	5.9	1.8	25 F	0157	6.7	2.0
	0754	2.7	0.8		0805	1.9	0.6
	1405	6.2	1.9		1416	7.1	2.2
	2026	2.1	0.6		2036	1.2	0.4
11 F	0242	6.3	1.9	26 Sa	0252	7.3	2.2
	0847	2.2	0.7		0901	1.3	0.4
	1455	6.7	2.0		1511	7.7	2.3
	2113	1.7	0.5		2127	0.7	0.2
12 Sa	0324	6.8	2.1	27 Su	0338	7.8	2.4
	0929	1.7	0.5		0948	0.7	0.2
	1537	7.2	2.2		1558	8.1	2.5
	2151	1.3	0.4		2209	0.4	0.1
13 Su	0401	7.2	2.2	28 M	0418	8.2	2.5
	1006	1.3	0.4		1028	0.3	0.1
	1614	7.6	2.3		1638	8.3	2.5
	2225	0.9	0.3		2247	0.2	0.1
14 M	0433	7.6	2.3	29 Tu	0455	8.4	2.6
	1039	0.9	0.3		1105	0.0	0.0
	1646	7.9	2.4		1715	8.4	2.6
	2257	0.7	0.2		2323	0.3	0.1
15 Tu	0505	7.9	2.4	30 W	0530	8.5	2.6
	1111	0.5	0.2		1141	0.0	0.0
	1721	8.1	2.5		1751	8.3	2.5
	2329	0.5	0.2		2356	0.7	0.2
				31 Th	0602	8.3	2.5
					1215	0.2	0.1
					1826	8.0	2.4

Time meridian 52° 30' W. 0000 is midnight. 1200 is noon.
Heights are referred to the chart datum of soundings.
Seasonal variations in sea level have not been included in these predictions.

SURINAME RIVIER ENTRANCE, SURINAM, 1983

Times and Heights of High and Low Waters

APRIL

Day	Time (h m)	Height (ft)	Height (m)	Day	Time (h m)	Height (ft)	Height (m)
1 F	0028	0.7	0.2	16 Sa	0010	0.6	0.2
	0636	8.1	2.5		0616	8.3	2.5
	1249	0.5	0.2		1234	0.2	0.1
	1900	7.6	2.3		1847	7.8	2.4
2 Sa	0103	1.1	0.3	17 Su	0049	1.0	0.3
	0709	7.7	2.3		0657	8.0	2.4
	1326	0.9	0.3		1317	0.5	0.2
	1937	7.1	2.2		1932	7.4	2.3
3 Su	0137	1.6	0.5	18 M	0133	1.4	0.4
	0745	7.2	2.2		0745	7.6	2.3
	1404	1.4	0.4		1409	1.0	0.3
	2017	6.6	2.0		2024	6.8	2.1
4 M	0217	2.2	0.7	19 Tu	0225	2.0	0.6
	0829	6.7	2.0		0841	7.0	2.1
	1451	2.0	0.6		1510	1.6	0.5
	2107	6.0	1.8		2133	6.3	1.9
5 Tu	0310	2.7	0.8	20 W	0338	2.5	0.8
	0923	6.1	1.9		0955	6.5	2.0
	1555	2.5	0.8		1631	2.0	0.6
	2219	5.6	1.7		2259	6.1	1.9
6 W	0427	3.1	0.9	21 Th	0510	2.6	0.8
	1044	5.8	1.8		1126	6.3	1.9
	1721	2.7	0.8		1801	2.0	0.6
	2352	5.6	1.7				
7 Th	0603	3.1	0.9	22 F	0029	6.3	1.9
	1219	5.8	1.8		0640	2.3	0.7
	1850	2.6	0.8		1253	6.6	2.0
					1917	1.7	0.5
8 F	0114	5.9	1.8	23 Sa	0138	6.8	2.1
	0725	2.7	0.8		0747	1.8	0.5
	1335	6.1	1.9		1359	7.1	2.2
	1954	2.2	0.7		2015	1.3	0.4
9 Sa	0210	6.4	2.0	24 Su	0228	7.3	2.2
	0820	2.2	0.7		0839	1.2	0.4
	1431	6.7	2.0		1450	7.5	2.3
	2042	1.7	0.5		2101	0.9	0.3
10 Su	0252	6.9	2.1	25 M	0313	7.8	2.4
	0900	1.6	0.5		0924	0.7	0.2
	1509	7.2	2.2		1535	7.9	2.4
	2121	1.2	0.4		2140	0.7	0.2
11 M	0329	7.4	2.3	26 Tu	0350	8.1	2.5
	0937	1.1	0.3		1002	0.3	0.1
	1545	7.6	2.3		1612	8.0	2.4
	2154	0.9	0.3		2217	0.6	0.2
12 Tu	0401	7.8	2.4	27 W	0425	8.3	2.5
	1012	0.6	0.2		1038	0.2	0.1
	1621	8.0	2.4		1648	8.1	2.5
	2227	0.6	0.2		2252	0.6	0.2
13 W	0435	8.1	2.5	28 Th	0459	8.3	2.5
	1045	0.3	0.1		1113	0.2	0.1
	1655	8.2	2.5		1722	8.0	2.4
	2300	0.5	0.2		2324	0.7	0.2
14 Th	0507	8.4	2.6	29 F	0531	8.2	2.5
	1119	0.0	0.0		1146	0.3	0.1
	1730	8.2	2.5		1755	7.7	2.3
	2335	0.5	0.2		2357	1.0	0.3
15 F	0541	8.4	2.6	30 Sa	0604	8.0	2.4
	1156	0.0	0.0		1220	0.6	0.2
	1807	8.1	2.5		1830	7.4	2.3

MAY

Day	Time (h m)	Height (ft)	Height (m)	Day	Time (h m)	Height (ft)	Height (m)
1 Su	0030	1.3	0.4	16 M	0034	1.1	0.3
	0638	7.6	2.3		0644	8.0	2.4
	1255	1.0	0.3		1307	0.6	0.2
	1905	7.0	2.1		1921	7.2	2.2
2 M	0105	1.7	0.5	17 Tu	0124	1.5	0.5
	0715	7.2	2.2		0734	7.5	2.3
	1337	1.4	0.4		1401	1.1	0.3
	1948	6.5	2.0		2019	6.8	2.1
3 Tu	0148	2.2	0.7	18 W	0222	2.0	0.6
	0800	6.7	2.0		0835	7.0	2.1
	1424	1.9	0.6		1507	1.5	0.5
	2041	6.1	1.9		2128	6.5	2.0
4 W	0241	2.6	0.8	19 Th	0334	2.3	0.7
	0854	6.2	1.9		0949	6.6	2.0
	1523	2.3	0.7		1621	1.8	0.5
	2147	5.8	1.8		2247	6.3	1.9
5 Th	0355	2.9	0.9	20 F	0458	2.4	0.7
	1010	5.9	1.8		1112	6.5	2.0
	1642	2.6	0.8		1739	1.9	0.6
	2311	5.7	1.7				
6 F	0523	2.9	0.9	21 Sa	0003	6.5	2.0
	1137	5.9	1.8		0616	2.1	0.6
	1803	2.5	0.8		1229	6.7	2.0
					1848	1.7	0.5
7 Sa	0027	6.0	1.8	22 Su	0107	6.9	2.1
	0639	2.6	0.8		0720	1.7	0.5
	1248	6.2	1.9		1330	7.0	2.1
	1907	2.1	0.6		1943	1.5	0.5
8 Su	0125	6.5	2.0	23 M	0157	7.3	2.2
	0735	2.1	0.6		0811	1.2	0.4
	1346	6.7	2.0		1423	7.2	2.2
	1957	1.7	0.5		2028	1.2	0.4
9 M	0210	7.0	2.1	24 Tu	0240	7.6	2.3
	0821	1.5	0.5		0855	0.9	0.3
	1431	7.1	2.2		1505	7.5	2.3
	2039	1.4	0.4		2111	1.1	0.3
10 Tu	0250	7.5	2.3	25 W	0319	7.8	2.4
	0901	1.0	0.3		0935	0.6	0.2
	1511	7.6	2.3		1545	7.6	2.3
	2119	0.9	0.3		2146	1.0	0.3
11 W	0327	7.9	2.4	26 Th	0356	8.0	2.4
	0940	0.5	0.2		1010	0.5	0.2
	1550	7.9	2.4		1620	7.6	2.3
	2156	0.7	0.2		2221	1.0	0.3
12 Th	0404	8.2	2.5	27 F	0428	8.0	2.4
	1017	0.2	0.1		1046	0.5	0.2
	1629	8.1	2.5		1656	7.5	2.3
	2233	0.6	0.2		2256	1.1	0.3
13 F	0440	8.4	2.6	28 Sa	0503	7.9	2.4
	1057	0.0	0.0		1120	0.6	0.2
	1707	8.1	2.5		1731	7.4	2.3
	2310	0.6	0.2		2329	1.3	0.4
14 Sa	0519	8.5	2.6	29 Su	0538	7.8	2.4
	1136	0.0	0.0		1156	0.8	0.2
	1747	7.9	2.4		1807	7.2	2.2
	2350	0.8	0.2				
15 Su	0559	8.3	2.5	30 M	0005	1.5	0.5
	1220	0.2	0.1		0614	7.5	2.3
	1833	7.6	2.3		1234	1.1	0.3
					1844	6.9	2.1
				31 Tu	0044	1.8	0.5
					0655	7.2	2.2
					1316	1.4	0.4
					1927	6.6	2.0

JUNE

Day	Time (h m)	Height (ft)	Height (m)	Day	Time (h m)	Height (ft)	Height (m)
1 W	0129	2.1	0.6	16 Th	0217	1.7	0.5
	0740	6.8	2.1		0830	7.2	2.2
	1404	1.8	0.5		1457	1.3	0.4
	2017	6.3	1.9		2115	6.8	2.1
2 Th	0222	2.4	0.7	17 F	0323	1.9	0.6
	0833	6.5	2.0		0936	6.9	2.1
	1459	2.1	0.6		1600	1.6	0.5
	2118	6.1	1.9		2218	6.7	2.0
3 F	0323	2.6	0.8	18 Sa	0432	2.0	0.6
	0936	6.3	1.9		1045	6.7	2.0
	1603	2.2	0.7		1704	1.8	0.5
	2224	6.1	1.9		2324	6.7	2.0
4 Sa	0434	2.6	0.8	19 Su	0539	1.9	0.6
	1048	6.2	1.9		1153	6.7	2.0
	1710	2.2	0.7		1808	1.8	0.5
	2331	6.3	1.9				
5 Su	0545	2.4	0.7	20 M	0024	6.8	2.1
	1155	6.4	2.0		0641	1.7	0.5
	1813	2.0	0.6		1253	6.7	2.0
					1904	1.8	0.5
6 M	0029	6.6	2.0	21 Tu	0117	7.0	2.1
	0645	2.0	0.6		0735	1.5	0.5
	1256	6.7	2.0		1349	6.8	2.1
	1909	1.8	0.5		1954	1.7	0.5
7 Tu	0122	7.0	2.1	22 W	0205	7.2	2.2
	0736	1.5	0.5		0823	1.3	0.4
	1347	7.0	2.1		1436	6.9	2.1
	1957	1.5	0.5		2036	1.6	0.5
8 W	0208	7.4	2.3	23 Th	0247	7.4	2.3
	0823	1.0	0.3		0908	1.1	0.3
	1436	7.4	2.3		1516	7.0	2.1
	2042	1.2	0.4		2118	1.5	0.5
9 Th	0252	7.8	2.4	24 F	0327	7.5	2.3
	0909	0.6	0.2		0946	1.0	0.3
	1521	7.6	2.3		1556	7.1	2.2
	2124	0.9	0.3		2157	1.5	0.5
10 F	0336	8.1	2.5	25 Sa	0406	7.6	2.3
	0953	0.3	0.1		1025	1.0	0.3
	1606	7.8	2.4		1635	7.1	2.2
	2209	0.8	0.2		2234	1.5	0.5
11 Sa	0418	8.3	2.5	26 Su	0443	7.6	2.3
	1038	0.1	0.0		1102	1.0	0.3
	1651	7.8	2.4		1712	7.1	2.2
	2251	0.8	0.2		2311	1.5	0.5
12 Su	0503	8.3	2.5	27 M	0522	7.5	2.3
	1123	0.2	0.1		1140	1.0	0.3
	1736	7.8	2.4		1749	7.0	2.1
	2338	0.9	0.3		2349	1.5	0.5
13 M	0549	8.2	2.5	28 Tu	0559	7.4	2.3
	1210	0.3	0.1		1218	1.2	0.4
	1826	7.6	2.3		1828	6.9	2.1
14 Tu	0026	1.1	0.3	29 W	0031	1.6	0.5
	0639	8.0	2.4		0639	7.3	2.2
	1302	0.6	0.2		1300	1.3	0.4
	1916	7.3	2.2		1911	6.8	2.1
15 W	0119	1.4	0.4	30 Th	0111	1.8	0.5
	0732	7.6	2.3		0724	7.1	2.2
	1356	1.0	0.3		1342	1.5	0.5
	2012	7.0	2.1		1955	6.7	2.0

Time meridian 52° 30' W. 0000 is midnight. 1200 is noon.
Heights are referred to the chart datum of soundings.
Seasonal variations in sea level have not been included in these predictions.

PUERTO BELGRANO, ARGENTINA, 1983

Times and Heights of High and Low Waters

JANUARY

Day	Time (h m)	Height (ft)	Height (m)
1 Sa	0054	5.2	1.6
	0618	12.8	3.9
	1342	2.0	0.6
	1930	12.2	3.7
2 Su	0148	4.8	1.5
	0712	12.9	3.9
	1430	1.6	0.5
	2018	12.4	3.8
3 M	0242	4.3	1.3
	0806	13.0	4.0
	1518	1.3	0.4
	2106	12.7	3.9
4 Tu	0336	3.7	1.1
	0900	13.0	4.0
	1606	1.1	0.4
	2200	13.0	4.0
5 W	0424	3.0	0.9
	1000	13.0	4.0
	1654	1.1	0.3
	2254	13.3	4.1
6 Th	0518	2.5	0.8
	1106	12.9	3.9
	1742	1.3	0.4
	2348	13.5	4.1
7 F	0612	2.0	0.6
	1212	12.9	3.9
	1830	1.8	0.5
8 Sa	0042	13.6	4.2
	0706	1.9	0.6
	1318	12.8	3.9
	1924	2.4	0.7
9 Su	0136	13.5	4.1
	0806	1.9	0.6
	1418	12.7	3.9
	2024	3.1	1.0
10 M	0236	13.4	4.1
	0912	2.0	0.6
	1530	12.6	3.8
	2130	3.7	1.1
11 Tu	0342	13.3	4.0
	1018	2.1	0.6
	1636	12.7	3.9
	2236	4.1	1.3
12 W	0454	13.3	4.0
	1118	2.0	0.6
	1736	12.8	3.9
	2336	4.3	1.3
13 Th	0554	13.3	4.1
	1212	1.9	0.6
	1836	12.9	3.9
14 F	0030	4.4	1.4
	0648	13.3	4.1
	1306	1.9	0.6
	1930	13.0	4.0
15 Sa	0118	4.5	1.4
	0736	13.2	4.0
	1348	2.0	0.6
	2012	13.0	4.0
16 Su	0206	4.6	1.4
	0824	12.9	3.9
	1436	2.1	0.6
	2100	12.9	3.9
17 M	0248	4.5	1.4
	0900	12.7	3.9
	1512	2.2	0.7
	2136	12.8	3.9
18 Tu	0324	4.3	1.3
	0936	12.5	3.8
	1548	2.2	0.7
	2206	12.8	3.9
19 W	0400	3.9	1.2
	1000	12.4	3.8
	1618	2.2	0.7
	2230	12.8	3.9
20 Th	0436	3.3	1.0
	1024	12.4	3.8
	1654	2.2	0.7
	2248	13.0	4.0
21 F	0512	2.7	0.8
	1100	12.5	3.8
	1724	2.2	0.7
	2318	13.1	4.0
22 Sa	0548	2.2	0.7
	1142	12.6	3.8
	1806	2.5	0.8
	2354	13.2	4.0
23 Su	0636	1.9	0.6
	1230	12.5	3.8
	1848	2.9	0.9
24 M	0036	13.2	4.0
	0718	1.9	0.6
	1318	12.3	3.8
	1930	3.5	1.1
25 Tu	0118	13.1	4.0
	0812	2.2	0.7
	1418	12.1	3.7
	2018	4.3	1.3
26 W	0212	12.9	3.9
	0912	2.4	0.7
	1518	11.9	3.6
	2118	4.9	1.5
27 Th	0306	12.8	3.9
	1018	2.6	0.8
	1624	11.8	3.6
	2224	5.4	1.7
28 F	0400	12.7	3.9
	1118	2.6	0.8
	1724	11.9	3.6
	2324	5.6	1.7
29 Sa	0506	12.8	3.9
	1218	2.5	0.8
	1818	12.2	3.7
30 Su	0030	5.5	1.7
	0600	12.9	3.9
	1312	2.3	0.7
	1912	12.4	3.8
31 M	0130	5.1	1.6
	0700	12.9	3.9
	1406	2.2	0.7
	2000	12.8	3.9

FEBRUARY

Day	Time (h m)	Height (ft)	Height (m)
1 Tu	0224	4.5	1.4
	0754	12.9	3.9
	1500	2.0	0.6
	2054	13.1	4.0
2 W	0318	3.7	1.1
	0854	12.9	3.9
	1548	1.9	0.6
	2142	13.4	4.1
3 Th	0412	2.8	0.9
	1000	12.9	3.9
	1636	1.8	0.5
	2236	13.6	4.2
4 F	0506	2.0	0.6
	1100	13.0	4.0
	1724	1.8	0.5
	2324	13.8	4.2
5 Sa	0554	1.4	0.4
	1200	13.0	4.0
	1812	2.0	0.6
6 Su	0018	13.9	4.2
	0648	1.1	0.4
	1300	12.9	3.9
	1900	2.4	0.7
7 M	0112	13.8	4.2
	0742	1.1	0.4
	1354	12.8	3.9
	1954	2.9	0.9
8 Tu	0212	13.6	4.2
	0842	1.3	0.4
	1500	12.7	3.9
	2054	3.5	1.1
9 W	0312	13.5	4.1
	0942	1.6	0.5
	1600	12.7	3.9
	2154	4.0	1.2
10 Th	0418	13.4	4.1
	1042	1.8	0.5
	1700	12.9	3.9
	2300	4.4	1.3
11 F	0518	13.4	4.1
	1142	1.9	0.6
	1800	13.0	4.0
12 Sa	0000	4.6	1.4
	0612	13.4	4.1
	1230	2.1	0.6
	1854	13.2	4.0
13 Su	0048	4.8	1.5
	0706	13.3	4.0
	1324	2.3	0.7
	1942	13.2	4.0
14 M	0136	4.8	1.5
	0748	13.0	4.0
	1406	2.6	0.8
	2030	13.1	4.0
15 Tu	0224	4.7	1.4
	0830	12.7	3.9
	1442	2.8	0.9
	2106	13.0	4.0
16 W	0306	4.4	1.3
	0906	12.4	3.8
	1518	3.0	0.9
	2130	12.8	3.9
17 Th	0336	3.9	1.2
	0924	12.2	3.7
	1554	3.0	0.9
	2142	12.7	3.9
18 F	0412	3.1	1.0
	0948	12.2	3.7
	1624	2.9	0.9
	2200	12.8	3.9
19 Sa	0448	2.4	0.7
	1024	12.3	3.7
	1700	2.8	0.8
	2230	13.0	4.0
20 Su	0530	1.7	0.5
	1106	12.3	3.8
	1736	2.8	0.8
	2312	13.2	4.0
21 M	0612	1.4	0.4
	1154	12.2	3.7
	1818	3.0	0.9
	2354	13.2	4.0
22 Tu	0654	1.3	0.4
	1248	12.1	3.7
	1900	3.5	1.1
23 W	0042	13.2	4.0
	0748	1.6	0.5
	1342	11.8	3.6
	1954	4.2	1.3
24 Th	0136	13.0	4.0
	0842	2.0	0.6
	1448	11.6	3.5
	2048	4.9	1.5
25 F	0230	12.8	3.9
	0948	2.4	0.7
	1600	11.6	3.6
	2154	5.5	1.7
26 Sa	0336	12.6	3.8
	1054	2.7	0.8
	1706	11.9	3.6
	2306	5.7	1.7
27 Su	0448	12.6	3.8
	1154	2.8	0.9
	1806	12.3	3.8
28 M	0012	5.5	1.7
	0554	12.7	3.9
	1254	2.8	0.9
	1854	12.7	3.9

MARCH

Day	Time (h m)	Height (ft)	Height (m)
1 Tu	0112	5.0	1.5
	0654	12.7	3.9
	1348	2.8	0.9
	1942	13.1	4.0
2 W	0212	4.2	1.3
	0754	12.7	3.9
	1436	2.7	0.8
	2036	13.3	4.1
3 Th	0306	3.3	1.0
	0854	12.7	3.9
	1530	2.6	0.8
	2124	13.5	4.1
4 F	0400	2.3	0.7
	0954	12.8	3.9
	1612	2.3	0.7
	2212	13.7	4.2
5 Sa	0448	1.5	0.5
	1054	12.9	3.9
	1700	2.1	0.7
	2306	13.8	4.2
6 Su	0536	0.9	0.3
	1142	12.9	3.9
	1748	2.1	0.6
	2354	13.8	4.2
7 M	0624	0.6	0.2
	1236	12.9	3.9
	1830	2.3	0.7
8 Tu	0048	13.8	4.2
	0712	0.6	0.2
	1330	12.8	3.9
	1924	2.7	0.8
9 W	0142	13.6	4.2
	0806	0.9	0.3
	1424	12.7	3.9
	2018	3.3	1.0
10 Th	0242	13.5	4.1
	0906	1.2	0.4
	1524	12.8	3.9
	2118	3.9	1.2
11 F	0342	13.4	4.1
	1006	1.7	0.5
	1624	12.9	3.9
	2218	4.4	1.4
12 Sa	0442	13.3	4.1
	1100	2.1	0.6
	1718	13.0	4.0
	2324	4.7	1.4
13 Su	0536	13.3	4.0
	1200	2.4	0.7
	1812	13.4	4.1
14 M	0018	4.8	1.5
	0630	13.2	4.0
	1248	2.8	0.8
	1906	13.4	4.0
15 Tu	0112	4.7	1.4
	0718	12.9	3.9
	1330	3.1	1.0
	1948	13.3	4.1
16 W	0200	4.4	1.4
	0800	12.6	3.9
	1412	3.4	1.0
	2024	13.1	4.0
17 Th	0242	4.0	1.2
	0830	12.3	3.8
	1448	3.6	1.1
	2030	12.7	3.9
18 F	0318	3.4	1.0
	0848	12.1	3.7
	1524	3.5	1.1
	2042	12.7	3.9
19 Sa	0348	2.6	0.8
	0918	12.1	3.7
	1554	3.3	1.0
	2112	12.8	3.9
20 Su	0430	1.8	0.6
	0954	12.0	3.7
	1630	3.1	1.0
	2148	13.0	4.0
21 M	0506	1.2	0.4
	1042	12.0	3.7
	1712	3.0	0.9
	2230	13.2	4.0
22 Tu	0548	0.8	0.3
	1130	11.9	3.6
	1748	3.1	0.9
	2318	13.3	4.0
23 W	0636	0.8	0.2
	1224	11.8	3.6
	1836	3.5	1.1
24 Th	0006	13.1	4.0
	0724	1.1	0.4
	1318	11.6	3.5
	1930	4.1	1.3
25 F	0106	12.9	3.9
	0818	1.7	0.5
	1424	11.5	3.5
	2030	4.9	1.5
26 Sa	0212	12.5	3.8
	0924	2.4	0.7
	1536	11.7	3.6
	2136	5.4	1.6
27 Su	0324	12.3	3.7
	1030	3.0	0.9
	1648	12.0	3.7
	2248	5.5	1.7
28 M	0442	12.2	3.7
	1130	3.3	1.0
	1748	12.5	3.8
29 Tu	0000	5.1	1.6
	0554	12.3	3.8
	1230	3.4	1.0
	1842	13.0	4.0
30 W	0106	4.4	1.3
	0700	12.5	3.8
	1330	3.4	1.1
	1930	13.3	4.0
31 Th	0206	3.5	1.1
	0800	12.5	3.8
	1418	3.3	1.0
	2018	13.4	4.1

Time meridian 45° W. 0000 is midnight. 1200 is noon.
Heights are referred to the chart datum of soundings.

TABLE 2.—TIDAL DIFFERENCES AND OTHER CONSTANTS

EXPLANATION OF TABLE

The publication of full daily predictions is necessarily limited to a comparatively small number of stations. Tide predictions for many other places, however, can be obtained by applying certain differences to the predictions for the reference stations in table 1. The following pages list the places called "subordinate stations" for which such predictions can be made and the differences or ratios to be used. These differences or ratios are to be applied to the predictions for the proper reference station which is listed in table 2 in bold face type above the differences for the subordinate station. The stations in this table are arranged in geographical order. The index at the end of this volume will assist in locating a particular station.

Caution.—The time and height differences listed in table 2 are average differences derived from comparisons of simultaneous tide observations at the subordinate location and its reference station. Because these figures are constant, they cannot provide for the daily variances of the actual tide. Therefore, it must be realized that although the application of the time and height differences will generally provide reasonably accurate approximations, they cannot result in as accurate predictions as those for the reference stations which are based upon much longer periods of analyses and which do provide for daily variances. In addition, at subordinate stations where the tide is chiefly diurnal, the tide correctors are intended primarily to be used to approximate the times and heights of the higher high and the lower low waters. When the lower high water and higher low water at the reference station are nearly the same height, great reliance should not be placed on the calculated corresponding tides at the subordinate station.

Time difference.—To determine the time of high water or low water at any station listed in this table there is given in the columns headed "Differences, Time" the hours and minutes to be added to or subtracted from the time of high or low water at some reference station. A plus (+) sign indicates that the tide at the subordinate station is later than at the reference station and the difference should be added, a minus (—) sign that it is earlier and should be subtracted.

To obtain the tide at a subordinate station on any date apply the difference to the tide at the reference station for that same date. In some cases, however, to obtain an a. m. tide it may be necessary to use the preceding day's p. m. tide at the reference station, or to obtain a p. m. tide it may be necessary to use the following day's a. m. tide. For example, if a high water occurs at a reference station at 2200 on July 2, and the tide at the subordinate station occurs 3 hours later, then high water will occur at 0100 on July 3 at the subordinate station. For the second case, if a high water at a reference station occurs at 0200 on July 17, and the tide at the subordinate station occurs 5 hours earlier, the high water at the subordinate station will occur at 2100 on July 16. The necessary allowance for change in date when the international date line is crossed is included in the time differences. In such cases use the same date at the reference station as desired for the subordinate station as explained above.

The results obtained by the application of the time differences will be in the kind of time indicated by the time meridian shown above the name of the subordinate station. Summer or daylight saving time is not used in the tide tables.

Height differences.—The height of the tide, referred to the datum of charts, is obtained by means of the height differences or ratios. A plus (+) sign indicates that the difference should be added to the height at the reference station and a minus (—) sign that it should be subtracted. All height differences, ranges, and levels in table 2 are in feet but may be converted to meters by the use of table 7.

Ratio.—For some stations height differences would give unsatisfactory predictions. In such cases they have been omitted and one or two ratios are given. Where two ratios are given, one in the "height of high water" column and one in the "height of low water" column, the high waters and low waters at the reference station should be multiplied by these respective ratios. Where only one is given, the omitted ratio is either unreliable or unknown.

For some subordinate stations there is given in parentheses a ratio as well as a correction in feet. In those instances, each predicted high and low water at the reference station should first be multiplied by the ratio and then the correction in feet is to be added to or subtracted from each product as indicated.

As an example, at Port of Spain, Trinidad, the values in the time and height difference columns in Table 2 are given as —0 44, —1 12, and (*0.31+1.4) as referred to the reference station at Punta Gorda, Venezuela. If we assume that the time predictions in column (1) below are those of Punta Gorda on a particular day, application of the time and height corrections in columns (2) and (3) would result in the tide predictions for Port of Spain in column (4).

(1)		(2)	(3)	(4)		
Time h.m.	Height ft	Time Corrections h.m.	Height Corrections	Time h.m.	ft	Height meters
0326	0.6	—1 12	×0.31+1.4	0214	1.6	0.5
0900	5.1	—0 44	×0.31+1.4	0816	3.0	0.9
1608	—0.3	—1 12	×0.31+1.4	1456	1.3	0.4
2148	5.4	—0 44	×0.31+1.4	2104	3.1	0.9

Range.—The *mean range* is the difference in height between mean high water and mean low water. The *spring range* is the average semidiurnal range occurring semimonthly as the result of the Moon being new or full. It is larger than the mean range where the type of tide is either semidiurnal or mixed, and is of no practical significance where the type of tide is diurnal. Where the tide is chiefly of the diurnal type the table gives the *diurnal range*, which is the difference in height between mean higher high water and mean lower low water.

Datum.—The datum of the predictions obtained through the height differences or ratios is also the datum of the largest scale chart for the locality. To obtain the depth at the time of high or low water, the predicted height should be added to the depth on the chart unless such height is negative (—), when it should be subtracted. To find the height at times between high and low water see table 3. On some charts the depths are given in meters and in such cases the heights of the tide can be reduced to meters by the use of table 7. The chart datum for the Atlantic Coast of the United States and for a part of the West Indies is *mean low water*. For the rest of the area covered by these tables the datums generally used are approximately *mean low water, mean low water springs, Gulf Coast Low Water Datum, mean lower low water, Indian spring low water,* or *the lowest possible low water.*

Mean Tide Level (Half Tide Level).—The mean tide level is a plane midway between mean low water and mean high water. Tabular values are reckoned from chart datum.

NOTE.—Dashes are entered in the place of data which are unknown, unreliable, or not applicable.

TABLE 2.—TIDAL DIFFERENCES AND OTHER CONSTANTS   199

Mean Lower Low Water

Effective November 28, 1980, the term Mean Lower Low Water (MLLW) began to replace the term Gulf Coast Low Water Datum (GCLWD) as chart datum on nautical charts, bathymetric maps, and in the Tide Tables and Coast Pilots of the National Ocean Survey covering the Gulf Coast of the United States.

The area affected by this action extends from the International Border between the United States and Mexico, then easterly along the Gulf Coast of the United States to the southeast corner of Florida, including the Florida Keys.

More specifically, the boundary between the datum of Mean Low Water of the Atlantic Coast and the datum of Mean Lower Low Water of the Gulf Coast is defined as extending:

a. from the intersection of the most westerly segment of the southern boundary of the Biscayne National Monument and the land (just south of Mangrove Point);

b. along the southwest segments of the southern boundary of the Monument to Old Rhodes Point on the southeast corner of Old Rhodes Key;

c. then from Old Rhodes Point to the northwest corner of the John Pennekamp Coral Reef State Park;

d. along the land of the northwestern boundary of the Park (with the exception of the coastal indentations of Largo Sound) to the southwest corner (just southwest of Rock Harbor); and

e. then from the southwest corner of the John Pennekamp Coral Reef State Park along its southwestern boundary and continuing straight out to sea just south of and beyond Molasses Reef.

Appropriate content changes have been made in this tide table to conform to the newly defined chart datum.

TABLE 2. — TIDAL DIFFERENCES AND OTHER CONSTANTS, 1983

NO.	PLACE	POSITION Lat.	Long.	DIFFERENCES Time High Water	Low Water	Height High Water	Low Water	RANGES Mean	Spring	Mean Tide Level
		° ' N	° W	h. m.	h. m.	ft	ft	ft	ft	ft
	LABRADOR Time meridian, 52°30'W			on HALIFAX, p.20						
171	Cartwright Harbour..................	53 42	57 02	-0 03	-0 34	-1.3	-0.6	3.7	4.9	3.4
173	Curlew Harbour......................	53 45	56 33	-0 07	-0 38	-1.6	-0.9	3.7	4.9	3.1
175	Comfort Bight.......................	53 09	55 46	-0 32	-1 03	-1.9	-1.0	3.5	4.6	2.9
177	Square Island Harbour..............	52 44	55 49	-0 34	-1 05	-2.0	-1.1	3.5	4.7	2.8
179	Port Marnham.......................	52 23	55 44	-0 43	-1 14	-2.7	-1.0	2.7	3.6	2.5
180	Battle Harbour.....................	52 16	55 36	-1 03	-1 30	-2.1	-0.3	2.6	3.8	3.1
	Strait of Bell Isle			on HARRINGTON HARBOUR, p.12						
181	Chateau Bay.....................	52 00	55 50	-3 08	-3 19	*0.69	*0.81	2.4	3.1	2.5
183	Red Bay.........................	51 43	56 25	-2 00	-1 55	*0.56	*0.56	2.1	2.6	2.0
185	Forteau Bay.....................	51 27	56 53	-0 26	-0 17	*0.78	*0.81	2.9	3.7	2.8
	NEWFOUNDLAND, East Coast			on HALIFAX, p.20						
201	Pistolet Bay.......................	51 30	55 44	-0 14	-0 28	*0.46	*0.29	2.4	3.1	1.8
203	Ariege Bay.........................	51 10	56 00	-0 34	-0 34	-2.6	-1.5	3.3	4.3	2.3
205	Wild Cove..........................	50 42	56 10	-0 49	-1 01	-2.0	-1.1	3.5	4.7	2.8
207	Sops Island, White Bay.............	49 50	56 46	-0 49	-1 24	*0.46	*0.29	2.4	3.4	1.8
209	Exploits Lower Harbour.............	49 32	55 04	-0 34	-1 09	-3.1	-1.3	2.6	3.5	2.1
211	Fogo Harbour.......................	49 43	54 16	-0 34	-0 42	-2.6	-1.3	3.1	4.2	2.4
213	Valleyfield........................	49 10	53 37	-0 46	-1 13	*0.45	*0.33	2.2	2.9	1.8
215	Port Union.........................	48 30	53 05	-0 53	-1 15	*0.49	*0.48	2.2	3.0	2.1
217	Random Head Harbour, Trinity Bay...	48 06	53 34	-0 53	-1 05	*0.48	*0.33	2.4	3.2	1.9
219	Harbour Grace, Conception Bay......	47 41	53 12	-0 28	-0 46	*0.51	*0.33	2.6	3.5	2.0
221	St. John's.........................	47 34	52 42	-0 34	-0 46	*0.52	*0.38	2.6	3.5	2.1
	NEWFOUNDLAND, South Coast			on ARGENTIA, p.4						
223	Trepassey Harbour..................	46 43	53 23	-0 19	-0 11	-1.2	-0.5	4.2	5.6	3.5
225	St. Mary Harbour, St. Mary Bay.....	46 55	53 35	-0 14	-0 06	-1.2	-0.5	4.2	5.6	3.5
	Placentia Bay									
227	ARGENTIA........................	47 18	53 59	Daily predictions				4.9	6.3	4.4
229	Woody Island....................	47 47	54 10	+0 09	+0 09	-0.5	-0.3	4.7	6.0	4.0
231	Mortier Bay.....................	47 10	55 09	+0 15	+0 26	-1.0	-0.8	4.7	6.0	3.5
233	Great St. Lawrence Harbour.........	46 55	55 22	+0 28	+0 55	-0.7	+0.3	3.9	5.0	4.2
	Time meridian, 60°W									
235	St. Pierre Hbr., St. Pierre Island......	46 47	56 10	-0 09	+0 13	-0.8	+0.2	3.9	5.0	4.1
	Time meridian, 52°30'W									
	Fortune Bay									
237	Grande le Pierre Harbour............	47 40	54 47	+1 09	+1 09	-1.0	+0.2	3.7	4.8	4.0
239	Belleoram.......................	47 32	55 25	+0 57	+0 57	(*0.67+0.8)		3.3	4.3	3.8
241	Ship Cove, Bay d'Espoir............	47 52	55 50	+0 45	+0 53	-0.4	0.0	4.5	5.5	4.2
243	Great Jervis Harbour, Bay d'Espoir......	47 39	56 11	+0 38	+1 05	-1.1	+0.1	3.7	4.8	3.9
245	Hare Bay...........................	47 37	56 32	+0 41	+1 08	(*0.67+0.6)		3.3	4.3	3.6
247	Grey River.........................	47 34	57 07	+0 45	+1 12	(*0.63+0.7)		3.1	4.0	3.5
249	Connoire Bay.......................	47 40	57 54	+0 50	+0 50	(*0.59+0.7)		2.9	3.8	3.3
251	La Poile Bay.......................	47 40	58 24	+1 15	+1 15	(*0.63+0.6)		3.1	4.0	3.4
				on HARRINGTON HARBOUR, p.12						
253	Port Aux Basques...................	47 35	59 09	-1 24	-1 28	*0.80	*0.75	3.1	4.0	2.8
255	Codroy Road........................	47 53	59 24	-1 22	-1 27	*0.74	*0.75	2.8	3.7	2.6
	NEWFOUNDLAND, West Coast									
257	St. Georges Harbour................	48 27	58 30	-0 28	-0 38	*0.78	*0.88	2.8	3.5	2.8
259	Port-au-Port.......................	48 33	58 45	+0 05	+0 10	-1.3	-1.0	3.5	4.5	2.4
261	Frenchman's Cove, Bay of Islands........	49 04	58 10	+0 10	+0 10	-0.5	0.0	3.3	4.2	3.3
263	Norris Cove, Bonne Bay.............	49 31	57 52	+0 10	+0 10	-0.7	-0.4	3.5	4.4	3.0
265	Portland Cove.....................	50 11	57 36	+0 19	+0 19	-0.6	-0.4	3.6	4.6	3.0
267	Port Saunders.....................	50 39	57 18	+0 07	+0 03	-0.3	-0.3	3.8	4.9	3.2
269	Castors Harbour, St. John Bay......	50 55	56 59	+0 10	+0 10	*0.78	*0.75	3.0	4.1	2.7
271	St. Barbe Bay......................	51 12	56 46	0 00	0 00	*0.78	*0.56	3.3	4.4	2.6
	QUEBEC, Gulf of St. Lawrence Time meridian, 60°W									
273	Bradore Bay........................	51 28	57 15	-0 35	-0 30	-0.6	-0.1	3.3	4.4	3.1
275	Mistanoque Harbour.................	51 16	58 12	-0 15	-0 15	-0.4	-0.1	3.5	4.6	3.3
277	HARRINGTON HARBOUR.................	50 30	59 28	Daily predictions				3.8	4.9	3.5
279	Wapitagun Harbour..................	50 12	60 01	+0 15	+0 15	-0.3	+0.1	3.4	4.4	3.4
281	Kegaska............................	50 12	61 14	+0 40	+0 40	-0.9	-0.2	3.1	4.0	3.0
283	Natashquan........................	50 12	61 50	+1 00	+1 10	-0.8	-0.1	3.1	4.0	3.1
285	Betchewun Harbour.................	50 14	63 11	+2 09	+2 13	-0.7	-0.4	3.5	4.6	3.0

Endnotes can be found at the end of table 2.

TABLE 2. — TIDAL DIFFERENCES AND OTHER CONSTANTS, 1983   205

NO.	PLACE	Position Lat.	Position Long.	Time High Water	Time Low Water	Height High Water	Height Low Water	Ranges Mean	Ranges Spring	Mean Tide Level
		° ' N	° ' W	h. m.	h. m.	ft	ft	ft	ft	ft
	NOVA SCOTIA, Bay of Fundy Time meridian, 60°W			on ST. JOHN, N. B., p.24						
565	Ile Haute.......................	45 15	65 00	-0 02	-0 02	+7.4	+0.7	27.5	31.5	18.5
567	Spencer Island..................	45 20	64 42	+0 17	+0 21	*1.47	*1.50	30.5	35.0	21.2
	Minas Basin									
569	Parrsboro (Partridge Island) <2>....	45 22	64 20	+0 51	+0 49	+14.7	- -	34.4	39.0	22.3
571	Horton Bluff, Avon River............	45 06	64 13	+0 58	+1 02	*1.76	*1.38	38.1	43.6	24.6
573	Windsor <2>.........................	45 00	64 08	+1 03	- - -	+19.5	- -	- -	- -	- -
575	Burntcoat Head......................	45 18	63 49	+1 06	+1 12	*1.90	*2.18	38.4	43.5	27.9
577	Truro <2>...........................	45 22	63 20	+1 43	- - -	+26.1	- -	- -	- -	- -
579	Spicer Cove, Chignecto Bay..........	45 26	64 54	+0 12	+0 16	+7.0	+0.8	27.0	30.0	18.3
581	Joggins <2>.........................	45 41	64 28	+0 14	+0 26	+14.2	+1.8	33.2	37.0	22.4
583	Amherst Point, Cumberland Basin.....	45 50	64 17	+0 33	+0 45	*1.69	*1.55	35.6	40.5	24.0
	NEW BRUNSWICK, Bay of Fundy									
	Petitcodiac River <3>									
585	Grindstone Island...................	45 43	64 37	+0 21	+0 28	*1.49	*1.45	31.1	35.6	21.4
587	Hopewell Cape.......................	45 52	64 35	+0 14	+0 39	*1.64	*1.85	33.2	38.0	24.0
589	Moncton <2> <3>.....................	46 05	64 46	+0 46	- - -	+17.2	- -	- -	- -	- -
591	Salisbury...........................	46 01	65 03	+1 31	- - -	+18.2	- -	- -	- -	- -
601	Herring Cove........................	45 35	64 58	+0 22	+0 20	+8.4	+0.9	28.3	32.4	19.1
603	Quaco Bay...........................	45 20	65 32	+0 11	+0 12	+2.0	-0.3	23.1	26.3	15.3
605	ST. JOHN <4>........................	45 15	66 04	Daily predictions				20.8	23.7	14.4
607	Indiantown, St. John River..........	45 16	66 05	+1 30	+2 25	- -	- -	1.2	1.4	2.4
609	Lepreau Harbour.....................	45 07	66 29	-0 01	+0 03	-2.3	-0.5	19.0	21.7	13.0
611	L'Etang Harbour.....................	45 02	66 49	+0 01	+0 05	-3.2	-0.8	18.4	21.0	12.4
613	North Head, Grand Manan Island......	44 46	66 45	-0 05	-0 05	-4.5	-0.9	17.2	19.3	11.7
615	Seal Cove, Grand Manan Island.......	44 37	66 51	-0 15	-0 17	*0.68	*0.65	14.3	16.3	9.8
617	Outer Wood Island <5>...............	44 36	66 48	-0 25	-0 27	-7.8	-0.8	13.8	16.2	10.1
619	Machias Seal Island <5>.............	44 30	67 06	-0 01	- - -	-9.6	-1.7	12.9	14.5	8.8
620	Welshpool, Campobello Island <5>....	44 53	66 57	-0 01	+0 06	-3.5	-1.0	18.3	21.2	12.1
621	Wilsons Beach, Campobello Island <5>....	44 56	66 56	0 00	+0 01	-3.7	+0.1	17.0	19.4	12.6
622	Back Bay, Letite Harbour <5>........	45 03	66 52	0 00	-0 03	-3.5	0.0	17.3	20.1	12.6
623	Midjik Bluff, Passamaquoddy Bay <5>....	45 07	66 54	+0 12	+0 17	-2.0	-0.5	19.3	22.0	13.1
624	St. Andrews, Passamaquoddy Bay <5>......	45 04	67 03	+0 14	+0 20	-2.3	0.0	18.5	21.2	13.2
625	The Ledge, St. Croix River <5>......	45 10	67 12	+0 17	+0 30	-0.8	0.0	20.0	22.8	14.0
	MAINE Time meridian, 75°W			on EASTPORT, p.28						
627	EASTPORT............................	44 54	66 59	Daily predictions			0.0	18.2	20.7	9.1
629	Gleason Cove, Western Passage.......	44 58	67 03	+0 08	+0 07	+0.2	0.0	18.4	20.9	9.2
	St. Croix River									
631	Robbinston......................	45 05	67 06	+0 09	+0 09	+1.0	0.0	19.2	21.8	9.6
633	St. Croix Island................	45 08	67 08	+0 10	+0 12	+1.4	0.0	19.6	22.3	9.8
637	Calais..........................	45 11	67 17	+0 31	+0 34	+1.8	0.0	20.0	22.8	10.0
	Cobscook Bay									
639	Deep Cove, Moose Island.........	44 54	67 01	+0 08	+0 09	+0.5	0.0	18.7	21.3	9.3
641	East Bay........................	44 56	67 07	+0 14	+0 16	+0.9	0.0	19.1	21.8	9.5
643	Coffins Point...................	44 52	67 07	+0 33	+0 38	+0.1	0.0	18.3	20.8	9.1
645	Birch Islands...................	44 52	67 09	+1 05	+1 17	-0.6	0.0	17.6	20.0	8.8
647	Horan Head, South Bay...........	44 52	67 04	+0 18	+0 21	+1.0	0.0	19.2	21.9	9.6
649	Lubec...............................	44 52	66 59	-0 03	-0 01	-0.7	0.0	17.5	20.0	8.7
651	West Quoddy Head....................	44 49	66 59	-0 09	-0 15	-2.5	0.0	15.7	17.9	7.8
653	Moose Cove..........................	44 44	67 06	-0 10	-0 16	-3.4	0.0	14.8	16.9	7.4
655	Cutler, Little River................	44 39	67 13	-0 12	-0 17	-4.6	0.0	13.6	15.5	6.8
657	Stone Island, Machias Bay...........	44 36	67 22	-0 12	-0 29	-5.8	0.0	12.4	14.1	6.2
659	Machiasport, Machias River..........	44 42	67 24	0 00	-0 10	-5.6	0.0	12.6	14.4	6.3
661	Shoppee Point, Englishman Bay.......	44 37	67 30	-0 06	-0 14	-6.1	0.0	12.1	13.8	6.1
663	Roque Island Harbor, Englishman Bay.....	44 34	67 31	-0 11	-0 14	-5.9	0.0	12.3	14.0	6.1
				on PORTLAND, p.32						
665	Steele Harbor Island................	44 30	67 33	-0 28	-0 20	+2.5	0.0	11.6	13.3	5.8
667	Jonesport, Moosabec Reach...........	44 32	67 36	-0 23	-0 17	+2.4	0.0	11.5	13.2	5.8
669	Gibbs Island, Pleasant River........	44 33	67 46	-0 20	-0 11	+2.2	0.0	11.3	13.0	5.6
671	Addison, Pleasant River.............	44 37	67 45	0 00	+0 04	+2.7	0.0	11.8	13.6	5.9
673	Trafton Island, Narraguagus Bay.....	44 29	67 50	-0 23	-0 20	+2.0	0.0	11.1	12.8	5.5
675	Milbridge, Narraguagus River........	44 32	67 53	-0 20	-0 05	+2.2	0.0	11.3	13.0	5.6
677	Pigeon Hill Bay.....................	44 27	67 52	-0 21	-0 18	+2.0	0.0	11.1	12.8	5.6
678	Green Island, Petit Manan Bar.......	44 22	67 52	-0 28	-0 24	+1.5	0.0	10.6	12.2	5.3
679	Pinkham Bay, Dyer Bay...............	44 28	67 55	-0 23	-0 18	+1.8	0.0	10.9	12.5	5.4
681	Garden Point, Gouldsboro Bay........	44 28	67 59	-0 23	-0 18	+1.7	0.0	10.8	12.4	5.4
683	Corea Harbor........................	44 24	67 58	-0 25	-0 20	+1.4	0.0	10.5	12.1	5.2
685	Prospect Harbor.....................	44 24	68 01	-0 24	-0 15	+1.4	0.0	10.5	12.1	5.2
	Frenchman Bay									
701	Winter Harbor...................	44 23	68 05	-0 23	-0 09	+1.0	0.0	10.1	11.6	5.0
703	Eastern Point Harbor............	44 28	68 10	-0 20	-0 14	+1.4	0.0	10.5	12.1	5.2
705	Sullivan........................	44 31	68 12	-0 10	-0 05	+1.4	0.0	10.5	12.1	5.2
707	Mount Desert Narrows............	44 26	68 22	-0 08	-0 08	+1.4	0.0	10.5	12.1	5.3

Endnotes can be found at the end of table 2.

NO.	PLACE	POSITION		DIFFERENCES				RANGES		Mean Tide Level
		Lat.	Long.	Time		Height		Mean	Spring	
				High Water	Low Water	High Water	Low Water			
		° ′ N	° ′ W	h. m.	h. m.	ft	ft	ft	ft	ft
	MAINE Time meridian, 75°W				on PORTLAND, p.32					
	Mount Desert Island									
709	Salsbury Cove........................	44 26	68 17	-0 15	-0 12	+1.5	0.0	10.6	12.2	5.3
711	Bar Harbor..........................	44 23	68 12	-0 22	-0 19	+1.4	0.0	10.5	12.1	5.2
713	Southwest Harbor....................	44 16	68 19	-0 22	-0 12	+1.1	0.0	10.2	11.7	5.1
715	Mount Desert.......................	44 22	68 20	-0 16	-0 08	+1.5	0.0	10.6	12.2	5.3
717	Bass Harbor........................	44 14	68 21	-0 18	-0 11	+0.8	0.0	9.9	11.3	5.0
719	Pretty Marsh Harbor................	44 20	68 25	-0 13	-0 13	+1.1	0.0	10.2	11.7	5.1
	Blue Hill Bay									
721	Union River.......................	44 30	68 26	-0 09	-0 08	+1.3	0.0	10.4	11.9	5.2
723	Blue Hill Harbor..................	44 24	68 34	-0 13	-0 08	+1.0	0.0	10.1	11.6	5.0
725	Allen Cove........................	44 18	68 33	-0 12	-0 12	+1.2	0.0	10.3	11.8	5.1
727	Mackerel Cove....................	44 10	68 26	-0 20	-0 13	+0.9	0.0	10.0	11.5	5.0
729	Burnt Coat Harbor, Swans Island........	44 09	68 27	-0 23	-0 13	+0.4	0.0	9.5	10.8	4.7
	MAINE, Penobscot Bay									
	Eggemoggin Reach									
731	Naskeag Harbor....................	44 14	68 33	-0 16	-0 14	+1.1	0.0	10.2	11.6	5.1
733	Center Harbor....................	44 16	68 35	-0 13	-0 07	+1.0	0.0	10.1	11.5	5.0
735	Sedgwick........................	44 18	68 38	-0 11	-0 06	+1.1	0.0	10.2	11.7	5.1
736	Isle Au Haut........................	44 04	68 38	-0 23	-0 19	+0.2	0.0	9.3	10.7	4.7
737	Head Harbor, Isle Au Haut.............	44 01	68 37	-0 20	-0 20	0.0	0.0	9.1	10.4	4.6
739	Kimball Island.....................	44 04	68 39	-0 20	-0 22	+0.5	0.0	9.6	10.9	4.8
741	Oceanville, Deer Isle..............	44 12	68 38	-0 18	-0 17	+1.0	0.0	10.1	11.5	5.0
743	Stonington, Deer Isle..............	44 09	68 40	-0 18	-0 17	+0.6	0.0	9.7	11.0	4.8
745	Northwest Harbor, Deer Isle........	44 14	68 41	-0 12	-0 12	+1.0	0.0	10.1	11.5	5.0
747	Matinicus Harbor...................	43 52	68 53	-0 17	-0 12	-0.1	0.0	9.0	10.4	4.5
749	Vinalhaven, Vinalhaven Island......	44 03	68 50	-0 13	-0 06	+0.2	0.0	9.3	10.7	4.6
751	Iron Point, North Haven Island.....	44 08	68 52	-0 13	-0 13	+0.4	0.0	9.5	10.8	4.8
753	Pulpit Harbor, North Haven Island......	44 09	68 53	-0 13	-0 15	+0.7	0.0	9.8	11.1	4.9
755	Castine.........................	44 23	68 48	-0 04	-0 01	+0.6	0.0	9.7	11.1	4.8
757	Pumpkin Island, South Bay............	44 25	68 44	+0 11	+0 29	+1.2	0.0	10.3	11.7	5.1
	Penobscot River									
759	Fort Point.......................	44 28	68 49	-0 06	-0 05	+1.2	0.0	10.3	11.8	5.1
761	Bucksport.......................	44 34	68 48	-0 02	-0 01	+1.9	0.0	11.0	12.5	5.5
763	South Orrington..................	44 42	68 49	+0 01	+0 04	+3.2	0.0	12.3	14.0	6.1
765	Hampden.........................	44 45	68 50	+0 02	+0 06	+3.7	0.0	12.8	14.6	6.4
767	Bangor..........................	44 48	68 46	+0 04	+0 13	+4.0	0.0	13.1	14.9	6.5
769	Belfast............................	44 26	69 00	-0 08	-0 01	+0.9	0.0	10.0	11.5	5.0
771	Camden...........................	44 12	69 03	-0 12	-0 06	+0.5	0.0	9.6	10.9	4.8
773	Rockland..........................	44 06	69 06	-0 16	-0 13	+0.6	0.0	9.7	11.2	4.8
775	Owls Head........................	44 06	69 03	-0 16	-0 13	+0.3	0.0	9.4	10.7	4.7
777	Dyer Point, Weskeag River.............	44 02	69 07	-0 10	-0 10	+0.5	0.0	9.6	10.9	4.8
	MAINE, Outer Coast									
779	Tenants Harbor.....................	43 58	69 12	-0 11	-0 11	+0.2	0.0	9.3	10.6	4.6
781	Monhegan Island....................	43 46	69 19	-0 13	-0 09	-0.3	0.0	8.8	10.1	4.4
783	Burnt Island, Georges Islands...........	43 52	69 18	-0 13	-0 12	-0.2	0.0	8.9	10.2	4.4
	St. George River									
785	Port Clyde.......................	43 56	69 16	-0 11	-0 07	-0.2	0.0	8.9	10.2	4.4
787	Otis Cove........................	43 59	69 14	-0 15	-0 14	0.0	0.0	9.1	10.5	4.5
789	Thomaston........................	44 04	69 11	-0 04	-0 03	+0.3	0.0	9.4	10.8	4.7
791	New Harbor, Muscongus Bay.............	43 52	69 29	-0 10	-0 05	-0.3	0.0	8.8	10.1	4.4
793	Muscongus Harbor, Muscongus Sound.......	43 58	69 27	-0 09	-0 03	-0.1	0.0	9.0	10.4	4.5
795	Friendship Harbor...................	43 58	69 20	-0 18	-0 11	-0.1	0.0	9.0	10.4	4.5
	Medomak River									
797	Jones Neck........................	44 01	69 23	-0 10	-0 05	0.0	0.0	9.1	10.5	4.5
799	Waldoboro.......................	44 06	69 23	-0 16	-0 04	+0.4	0.0	9.5	10.9	4.8
801	Pemaquid Harbor, Johns Bay.............	43 53	69 32	-0 05	-0 01	-0.3	0.0	8.8	10.1	4.4
	Damariscotta River									
803	East Boothbay.....................	43 52	69 35	-0 02	+0 04	-0.2	0.0	8.9	10.2	4.4
805	Newcastle........................	44 02	69 32	+0 16	+0 28	+0.2	0.0	9.3	10.7	4.6
807	Damariscove Harbor, Damariscove Island..	43 46	69 37	-0 09	-0 10	-0.3	0.0	8.8	10.1	4.4
809	Boothbay Harbor....................	43 51	69 38	-0 06	-0 08	-0.3	0.0	8.8	10.1	4.4
811	Southport, Townsend Gut.............	43 51	69 40	+0 01	+0 01	-0.2	0.0	8.9	10.2	4.4
	Sheepscot River									
813	Isle of Springs..................	43 52	69 41	-0 02	-0 04	-0.2	0.0	8.9	10.3	4.4
815	Cross River entrance..............	43 56	69 40	+0 07	+0 04	0.0	0.0	9.1	10.5	4.5
817	Wiscasset........................	44 00	69 40	+0 16	+0 04	+0.3	0.0	9.4	10.8	4.7
819	Sheepscot (below rapids)..........	44 03	69 37	+0 20	+0 20	+0.5	0.0	9.6	11.0	4.8
821	Back River.......................	43 57	69 41	+0 34	+0 31	0.0	0.0	9.1	10.5	4.5
823	Robinhood, Sasanoa River..........	43 51	69 44	+0 14	+0 14	-0.3	0.0	8.8	10.1	4.4
825	Mill Point, Sasanoa River.........	43 53	69 46	+0 35	+0 43	-0.3	0.0	8.8	10.1	4.4
827	Upper Hell Gate, Sasanoa River......	43 54	69 47	+1 11	+1 31	-2.1	0.0	7.0	8.0	3.5
	MAINE, Kennebec River									
829	Fort Popham........................	43 45	69 47	+0 09	+0 04	-0.7	0.0	8.4	9.7	4.2
831	Phippsburg.........................	43 49	69 49	+0 26	+0 28	-1.1	0.0	8.0	9.2	4.0

Endnotes can be found at the end of table 2.

TABLE 2. — TIDAL DIFFERENCES AND OTHER CONSTANTS, 1983   207

NO.	PLACE	POSITION Lat.	POSITION Long.	DIFFERENCES Time High Water	DIFFERENCES Time Low Water	DIFFERENCES Height High Water	DIFFERENCES Height Low Water	RANGES Mean	RANGES Spring	Mean Tide Level
		° ′ N	° ′ W	h. m.	h. m.	ft	ft	ft	ft	ft
	Maine, Kennebac River Time meridian, 75°W				on PORTLAND, p.32					
833	Bath..........................	43 55	69 49	+1 01	+1 17	-2.7	0.0	6.4	7.4	3.2
835	Sturgeon Island, Merrymeeting Bay.......	43 59	69 50	+2 00	+2 04	*0.58	*0.58	5.3	6.1	2.6
837	Androscoggin River entrance............	43 57	69 53	+2 24	+3 26	*0.52	*0.52	4.7	5.4	2.3
839	Brunswick, Androscoggin River...........	43 55	69 58	+2 35	+4 36	*0.42	*0.42	3.8	4.4	1.9
841	Bowdoinham, Cathance River.............	44 00	69 54	+2 34	+2 42	*0.63	*0.63	5.7	6.6	2.8
843	Richmond......................	44 05	69 48	+2 48	+3 03	*0.58	*0.58	5.3	6.0	2.6
845	Nehumkeag Island................	44 10	69 45	+3 21	+3 46	*0.58	*0.58	5.3	6.0	2.6
847	Gardiner......................	44 14	69 46	+3 43	+4 25	*0.55	*0.55	5.0	5.7	2.5
849	Hallowell.....................	44 17	69 47	+3 54	+5 03	*0.47	*0.47	4.3	4.9	2.1
851	Augusta.......................	44 19	69 46	+4 03	+5 33	*0.45	*0.45	4.1	4.6	2.0
	MAINE, Casco Bay									
853	Small Point Harbor..............	43 44	69 51	-0 12	-0 09	-0.3	0.0	8.8	10.1	4.4
855	Cundy Harbor, New Meadows River........	43 47	69 54	-0 01	-0 02	-0.2	0.0	8.9	10.2	4.4
857	Howard Point, New Meadows River........	43 53	69 53	-0 05	+0 01	-0.1	0.0	9.0	10.3	4.5
859	Lowell Cove, Orrs Island..........	43 45	69 59	-0 07	-0 06	-0.3	0.0	8.8	10.1	4.4
861	Harpswell Harbor................	43 46	70 00	-0 05	-0 05	-0.1	0.0	9.0	10.4	4.5
863	South Harpswell, Potts Harbor...........	43 44	70 01	+0 02	+0 01	-0.2	0.0	8.9	10.2	4.4
865	Wilson Cove, Middle Bay...........	43 49	69 59	+0 02	+0 02	0.0	0.0	9.1	10.5	4.5
867	Little Flying Point, Maquoit Bay.......	43 50	70 03	-0 01	-0 01	-0.1	0.0	9.0	10.3	4.5
869	South Freeport.................	43 49	70 06	+0 12	+0 10	-0.1	0.0	9.0	10.3	4.5
871	Chebeague Point, Great Chebeague Island.	43 46	70 06	-0 04	-0 06	-0.1	0.0	9.0	10.4	4.5
873	Prince Point..................	43 46	70 10	-0 02	-0 04	-0.1	0.0	9.0	10.4	4.5
875	Peaks Island..................	43 39	70 12	-0 04	-0 08	-0.1	0.0	9.0	10.4	4.5
877	PORTLAND......................	43 40	70 15		Daily predictions			9.1	10.4	4.6
	MAINE, Outer Coast-Continued									
879	Richmond Island................	43 33	70 14	-0 03	0 00	-0.2	0.0	8.9	10.1	4.4
881	Old Orchard Beach...............	43 31	70 22	0 00	-0 03	-0.3	0.0	8.8	10.1	4.4
883	Wood Island Harbor..............	43 27	70 21	+0 02	-0 04	-0.4	0.0	8.7	9.9	4.3
885	Cape Porpoise.................	43 22	70 26	+0 12	+0 17	-0.4	0.0	8.7	9.9	4.3
887	Kennebunkport..................	43 21	70 28	+0 16	+0 16	-0.5	0.0	8.6	9.9	4.3
889	York Harbor...................	43 08	70 38	+0 03	+0 13	-0.5	0.0	8.6	9.9	4.3
	MAINE and NEW HAMPSHIRE Portsmouth Harbor									
891	Jaffrey Point..............	43 03	70 43	-0 03	-0 05	-0.4	0.0	8.7	10.0	4.4
893	Gerrish Island.............	43 04	70 42	-0 02	-0 03	-0.4	0.0	8.7	10.0	4.4
895	Fort Point................	43 04	70 43	+0 03	+0 07	-0.5	0.0	8.6	9.9	4.3
897	Kittery Point..............	43 05	70 42	-0 07	+0 01	-0.4	0.0	8.7	10.0	4.4
899	Seavey Island..............	43 05	70 45	+0 23	+0 13	-1.0	0.0	8.1	9.3	4.0
901	Portsmouth.................	43 05	70 45	+0 22	+0 17	-1.3	0.0	7.8	9.0	3.9
	Piscataqua River									
903	Atlantic Heights..............	43 05	70 46	+0 37	+0 28	-1.6	0.0	7.5	8.6	3.7
905	Dover Point................	43 07	70 50	+1 33	+1 27	-2.7	0.0	6.4	7.4	3.2
907	Salmon Falls River entrance.......	43 11	70 50	+1 35	+1 52	-2.3	0.0	6.8	7.8	3.4
909	Squamscott River RR Bridge..........	43 03	70 55	+2 19	+2 41	-2.3	0.0	6.8	7.8	3.4
911	Gosport Harbor, Isles of Shoals.........	42 59	70 37	+0 02	-0 02	-0.6	0.0	8.5	9.8	4.2
913	Hampton Harbor.................	42 54	70 49	+0 14	+0 32	-0.8	0.0	8.3	9.5	4.1
	MASSACHUSETTS, Outer Coast									
915	Merrimack River entrance..............	42 49	70 49	+0 20	+0 24	-0.8	0.0	8.3	9.5	4.1
917	Newburyport, Merrimack River..........	42 49	70 52	+0 31	+1 11	-1.3	0.0	7.8	9.0	3.9
919	Plum Island Sound (south end)............	42 43	70 47	+0 12	+0 37	-0.5	0.0	8.6	9.9	4.3
921	Annisquam......................	42 39	70 41	0 00	-0 07	-0.4	0.0	8.7	10.1	4.4
923	Rockport.......................	42 40	70 37	+0 04	+0 02	-0.5	0.0	8.6	10.0	4.3
					on BOSTON, p.36					
925	Gloucester.....................	42 36	70 40	-0 03	-0 06	-0.8	0.0	8.7	10.1	4.3
927	Manchester Harbor...............	42 34	70 47	-0 02	-0 06	-0.7	0.0	8.8	10.2	4.4
929	Beverly.......................	42 32	70 53	0 00	-0 05	-0.5	0.0	9.0	10.4	4.5
931	Salem.........................	42 31	70 53	+0 02	+0 01	-0.7	0.0	8.8	10.2	4.4
933	Marblehead....................	42 30	70 51	-0 02	-0 06	-0.4	0.0	9.1	10.6	4.5
	Broad Sound									
935	Nahant....................	42 25	70 55	-0 01	-0 02	-0.5	0.0	9.0	10.4	4.5
937	Lynn Harbor...............	42 27	70 58	+0 08	+0 04	-0.3	0.0	9.2	10.7	4.6
	Boston Harbor									
939	Boston Light..................	42 20	70 53	0 00	+0 01	-0.5	0.0	9.0	10.4	4.5
941	Lovell Island, The Narrows...........	42 20	70 56	+0 02	+0 01	-0.4	0.0	9.1	10.6	4.5
943	Deer Island (south end)................	42 21	70 58	-0 01	-0 02	-0.2	0.0	9.3	10.8	4.6
945	Belle Isle Inlet entrance.............	42 23	71 00	+0 18	+0 15	0.0	0.0	9.5	11.0	4.7
947	Castle Island.................	42 20	71 01	-0 02	0 00	-0.1	0.0	9.4	10.9	4.7

Endnotes can be found at the end of table 2.

NO.	PLACE	POSITION		DIFFERENCES				RANGES		Mean Tide Level
		Lat.	Long.	Time		Height		Mean	Spring	
				High Water	Low Water	High Water	Low Water			
		° ' N	° ' W	h. m.	h. m.	ft	ft	ft	ft	ft

Boston Harbor
Time meridian, 75°W

on BOSTON, p.36

NO.	PLACE	Lat.	Long.	High Water	Low Water	High Water	Low Water	Mean	Spring	Mean Tide Level
949	BOSTON..........................	42 21	71 03	Daily predictions				9.5	11.0	4.7
951	Dover St. Bridge, Fort Point Channel....	42 21	71 04	+0 04	+0 06	+0.1	0.0	9.6	11.0	4.8
	Charles River									
953	Charlestown Bridge.................	42 22	71 04	+0 02	+0 02	0.0	0.0	9.5	11.0	4.7
955	Charles River Dam.............	42 22	71 04	+0 05	+0 04	0.0	0.0	9.5	11.0	4.7
957	Charlestown..................	42 22	71 03	-0 02	-0 01	0.0	0.0	9.5	11.0	4.7
959	Chelsea St. Bridge, Chelsea River.......	42 23	71 01	-0 01	+0 04	+0.1	0.0	9.6	11.1	4.8
965	Neponset, Neponset River.................	42 17	71 02	-0 04	+0 01	0.0	0.0	9.5	11.0	4.7
967	Moon Head..........................	42 19	70 59	-0 01	+0 02	-0.1	0.0	9.4	10.9	4.7
969	Rainsford Island, Nantasket Roads.......	42 19	70 57	-0 02	0 00	-0.4	0.0	9.1	10.6	4.5

Hingham Bay

971	Nut Island.........................	42 17	70 57	+0 07	+0 03	-0.3	0.0	9.2	10.7	4.6
973	Sheep Island...........................	42 17	70 55	+0 07	+0 03	0.0	0.0	9.5	11.0	4.7
975	Weymouth Fore River Bridge..............	42 15	70 58	+0 07	+0 04	0.0	0.0	9.5	11.0	4.7
977	Weymouth Back River Bridge..............	42 15	70 56	+0 06	+0 05	0.0	0.0	9.5	11.0	4.7
979	Crow Point, Hingham Harbor entrance.....	42 16	70 54	0 00	+0 03	-0.1	0.0	9.4	10.9	4.7
981	Hingham..............................	42 15	70 53	+0 07	+0 06	0.0	0.0	9.5	11.0	4.7
983	Nantasket Beach, Weir River.............	42 16	70 52	+0 04	+0 05	-0.1	0.0	9.4	10.9	4.7
985	Strawberry Hill.......................	42 17	70 53	+0 05	+0 05	0.0	0.0	9.5	11.0	4.7
987	Hull.................................	42 18	70 55	+0 03	+0 05	-0.2	0.0	9.3	10.8	4.7

Cohasset Harbor to Davis Bank

989	Cohasset Harbor (White Head)............	42 15	70 47	+0 02	-0 04	-0.7	0.0	8.8	10.2	4.4
991	Scituate.............................	42 12	70 43	-0 05	0 00	-0.7	0.0	8.8	10.2	4.4
992	Damons Point, North River...............	42 10	70 44	+0 18	+0 34	-1.0	0.0	8.5	9.9	4.2
	Cape Cod Bay									
993	Gurnet Point.....................	42 00	70 36	+0 02	+0 07	-0.3	0.0	9.2	10.7	4.6
995	Plymouth......................	41 58	70 40	+0 05	+0 20	0.0	0.0	9.5	11.0	4.7
997	Cape Cod Canal, east entrance.......	41 46	70 30	-0 01	-0 02	-0.8	0.0	8.7	10.1	4.3
999	Barnstable Harbor, Beach Point.....	41 43	70 17	+0 09	+0 28	0.0	0.0	9.5	11.0	4.7
1001	Wellfleet....................	41 55	70 02	+0 12	+0 28	+0.5	0.0	10.0	11.6	5.0
1003	Provincetown..................	42 03	70 11	+0 14	+0 16	-0.4	0.0	9.1	10.6	4.5
1005	Race Point....................	42 04	70 15	-0 03	-0 04	-0.5	0.0	9.0	10.4	4.5
	Cape Cod									
1007	Cape Cod Lighthouse, SE of..........	42 00	70 01	+0 10	+0 09	-1.9	0.0	7.6	8.8	3.8
1009	Nauset Harbor....................	41 48	69 56	+0 30	+0 56	*0.63	*0.63	6.0	7.0	3.0
1011	Chatham (outer coast)............	41 40	69 56	+0 30	+0 24	-2.8	0.0	6.7	7.8	3.3
1013	Chatham (inside).................	41 41	69 57	+1 54	+2 24	*0.38	*0.38	3.6	4.2	1.8
1015	Pleasant Bay.....................	41 44	69 59	+2 26	+3 25	*0.34	*0.34	3.2	3.7	1.6
1017	Monomoy Point....................	41 33	70 00	+0 40	+0 32	*0.39	*0.39	3.7	4.3	1.8
1019	Georges Shoal.........................	41 42	67 46	-0 49	-0 45	*0.44	*0.44	4.2	4.8	2.1
1021	Davis Bank, Nantucket Shoals............	41 08	69 39	+0 04	-0 27	*0.14	*0.14	1.3	1.5	0.6

Nantucket Sound, North Side

1023	Stage Harbor...........................	41 40	69 58	+0 55	+0 46	*0.41	*0.41	3.9	4.7	1.9
1025	Wychmere Harbor........................	41 40	70 04	+0 50	+0 23	*0.39	*0.39	3.7	4.3	1.8
1027	Dennis Port............................	41 39	70 07	+1 01	+0 36	*0.36	*0.36	3.4	4.1	1.7
1029	South Yarmouth, Bass River.............	41 40	70 11	+1 46	+1 44	*0.29	*0.29	2.8	3.4	1.4
1031	Hyannis Port...........................	41 38	70 18	+1 01	+0 29	*0.33	*0.33	3.1	3.7	1.5
1033	Cotuit Highlands.......................	41 36	70 25	+1 15	+0 45	*0.26	*0.26	2.5	3.0	1.2
1035	Poponesset Island, Poponesset Bay.......	41 35	70 28	+2 01	+1 50	*0.24	*0.24	2.3	2.8	1.1
1037	Succonnesset Point.....................	41 33	70 29	+0 52	+0 37	*0.20	*0.20	1.9	2.3	0.9
1039	Falmouth Heights.......................	41 33	70 36	-0 18	-0 11	*0.14	*0.14	1.3	1.6	0.6

Nantucket Island

1041	Tom Nevers Head........................	41 14	70 01	-0 57	-1 22	*0.13	*0.13	1.2	1.4	0.6
1043	Siasconset............................	41 16	69 58	+0 15	+0 19	*0.13	*0.13	1.2	1.4	0.6
1045	Wauwinet (outer shore).................	41 20	70 00	+1 06	+0 57	*0.35	*0.35	3.3	4.0	1.6
1047	Great Point...........................	41 23	70 03	+0 41	+0 26	*0.33	*0.33	3.1	3.7	1.5
1049	Nantucket.............................	41 17	70 06	+1 05	+0 50	*0.32	*0.32	3.0	3.6	1.5
1051	Eel Point.............................	41 17	70 12	+0 37	+0 05	*0.24	*0.24	2.3	2.7	1.1
1053	Tuckernuck Island, East Pond...........	41 18	70 15	+0 46	+0 27	*0.27	*0.27	2.6	3.1	1.3
1055	Muskeget Island, north side............	41 20	70 18	+0 23	+0 13	*0.21	*0.21	2.0	2.4	1.0
1057	Smith Point, north side................	41 17	70 14	+0 46	-0 32	*0.16	*0.16	1.5	1.9	0.8

on NEWPORT, p.40

| 1059 | Miacomet Rip.......................... | 41 14 | 70 06 | +0 18 | +0 55 | *0.49 | *0.49 | 1.7 | 2.0 | 0.8 |

Martha's Vineyard

1061	Wasque Point, Chappaquiddick Island.....	41 22	70 27	+2 05	+3 25	*0.31	*0.31	1.1	1.4	0.6
1063	Off Jobs Neck Pond.....................	41 21	70 35	+0 04	+0 27	-0.8	0.0	2.7	3.2	1.3
1065	Off Chilmark Pond......................	41 20	70 43	-0 13	+0 09	-0.6	0.0	2.9	3.5	1.4

Endnotes can be found at the end of table 2.

TABLE 2. — TIDAL DIFFERENCES AND OTHER CONSTANTS, 1983 209

NO.	PLACE	POSITION Lat.	POSITION Long.	DIFFERENCES Time High Water	DIFFERENCES Time Low Water	DIFFERENCES Height High Water	DIFFERENCES Height Low Water	RANGES Mean	RANGES Spring	Mean Tide Level
		° ' N	° ' W	h. m.	h. m.	ft	ft	ft	ft	ft
	Martha's Vineyard Time meridian, 75°W				on NEWPORT, p.40					
1066	Squibnocket Point......................	41 19	70 46	-0 42	+0 03	-0.6	0.0	2.9	3.7	1.5
1067	Nomans Land...........................	41 16	70 49	-0 16	+0 23	-0.5	0.0	3.0	3.6	1.5
1069	Gay Head..............................	41 21	70 50	-0 03	+0 50	-0.6	0.0	2.9	3.5	1.4
1071	Menemsha Bight........................	41 21	70 46	+0 05	+0 42	-0.8	0.0	2.7	3.4	1.3
1073	Cedar Tree Neck.......................	41 26	70 42	+0 13	+1 37	-1.3	0.0	2.2	2.8	1.1
1075	Off Lake Tashmoo......................	41 28	70 38	+1 11	+2 16	*0.60	*0.60	2.1	2.5	1.0
					on BOSTON, p.36					
1077	West Chop.............................	41 29	70 36	+0 16	-0 31	*0.15	*0.15	1.4	1.7	0.7
1079	Vineyard Haven........................	41 27	70 36	+0 25	-0 01	*0.18	*0.18	1.7	2.0	0.8
1081	East Chop.............................	41 28	70 34	+0 27	-0 14	*0.18	*0.18	1.7	2.0	0.8
1083	Oak Bluffs............................	41 27	70 33	+0 30	-0 14	*0.18	*0.18	1.7	2.0	0.8
1085	Edgartown.............................	41 23	70 31	+0 55	+0 16	*0.20	*0.20	1.9	2.3	0.9
1087	Cape Poge, Chappaquiddick Island.......	41 25	70 27	+0 44	+0 02	*0.23	*0.23	2.2	2.6	1.1
	Vineyard Sound				on NEWPORT, p.40					
1089	Nobska Point..........................	41 31	70 39	+0 44	+2 10	*0.43	*0.43	1.5	1.9	0.7
	Woods Hole									
1091	Little Harbor......................	41 31	70 40	+0 35	+2 26	*0.40	*0.40	1.4	1.8	0.7
1093	Oceanographic Institution..........	41 31	70 40	+0 27	+2 04	*0.51	*0.51	1.8	2.2	0.9
1095	Uncatena Island (south side).......	41 31	70 42	+0 15	+0 27	+0.1	0.0	3.6	4.5	1.8
1097	Tarpaulin Cove........................	41 28	70 46	+0 14	+1 28	*0.54	*0.54	1.9	2.4	0.9
	Quicks Hole									
1099	South side.........................	41 26	70 51	-0 07	+0 14	-1.0	0.0	2.5	3.1	1.2
1101	Middle.............................	41 27	70 51	+0 03	+0 15	-0.5	0.0	3.0	3.7	1.5
1103	North side.........................	41 27	70 51	-0 05	-0 03	0.0	0.0	3.5	4.4	1.7
	Buzzards Bay									
1105	Cuttyhunk Pond entrance...............	41 25	70 55	+0 04	+0 06	-0.1	0.0	3.4	4.2	1.7
1107	Penikese Island.......................	41 27	70 55	-0 14	-0 11	-0.1	0.0	3.4	4.2	1.7
1109	Kettle Cove...........................	41 29	70 47	+0 12	+0 07	+0.3	0.0	3.8	4.7	1.9
1111	West Falmouth Harbor..................	41 36	70 39	+0 24	+0 23	+0.5	0.0	4.0	5.0	2.0
1113	Barlows Landing, Pocasset Harbor......	41 41	70 38	+0 27	+0 23	+0.5	0.0	4.0	5.0	2.0
1115	Abiels Ledge..........................	41 42	70 40	+0 14	+0 21	+0.4	0.0	3.9	4.9	2.0
1117	Monument Beach........................	41 43	70 37	+0 26	+0 23	+0.5	0.0	4.0	5.0	2.0
1119	Cape Cod Canal, RR. bridge <6>........	41 44	70 37	+1 18	- - -	0.0	0.0	3.5	4.1	1.8
1121	Great Hill............................	41 43	70 43	+0 20	+0 20	+0.6	0.0	4.1	5.1	2.0
1123	Wareham, Wareham River................	41 45	70 43	+0 25	+0 21	+0.6	0.0	4.1	5.1	2.0
1125	Bird Island...........................	41 40	70 43	+0 08	+0 03	+0.7	0.0	4.2	5.2	2.1
1127	Marion...............................	41 42	70 46	+0 12	+0 15	+0.5	0.0	4.0	5.0	2.0
1129	Mattapoisett..........................	41 39	70 49	+0 13	+0 10	+0.4	0.0	3.9	4.9	2.0
1131	West Island (west side)...............	41 36	70 50	+0 12	+0 13	+0.2	0.0	3.7	4.6	1.8
1133	Clarks Point..........................	41 36	70 54	+0 06	+0 08	+0.2	0.0	3.7	4.6	1.8
1135	New Bedford...........................	41 38	70 55	+0 10	+0 12	+0.2	0.0	3.7	4.6	1.8
1137	Belleville, Acushnet River............	41 40	70 55	+0 10	+0 14	+0.3	0.0	3.8	4.7	1.9
1139	South Dartmouth, Apponagansett Bay....	41 35	70 57	+0 28	+0 38	+0.2	0.0	3.7	4.6	1.8
1141	Dumpling Rocks........................	41 32	70 55	+0 04	+0 03	+0.2	0.0	3.7	4.6	1.8
	Westport River									
1143	Westport Harbor....................	41 30	71 06	+0 12	+0 38	-0.5	0.0	3.0	3.7	1.5
1145	Hix Bridge, East Branch............	41 34	71 04	+1 43	+2 35	-0.8	0.0	2.7	3.4	1.3
	RHODE ISLAND, Narragansett Bay									
1147	Sakonnet..............................	41 28	71 12	-0 10	+0 04	-0.4	0.0	3.1	3.9	1.6
1149	Tiverton (between bridges)............	41 38	71 13	+0 21	+0 21	+0.3	0.0	3.8	4.7	1.9
1151	Beavertail Point......................	41 27	71 24	-0 02	-0 05	0.0	0.0	3.5	4.4	1.8
1153	NEWPORT...............................	41 30	71 20		Daily predictions			3.5	4.4	1.8
1155	Prudence Island, Sandy Point..........	41 36	71 18	+0 10	+0 09	+0.4	0.0	3.9	4.9	2.0
1157	Bristol Point.........................	41 39	71 16	+0 21	+0 12	+0.5	0.0	4.0	5.0	2.0
	RHODE ISLAND and MASSACHUSETTS Narragansett Bay-Continued									
1159	Fall River, Massachusetts.............	41 44	71 08	+0 31	+0 34	+0.9	0.0	4.4	5.5	2.2
1161	Taunton, Taunton River, Mass..........	41 53	71 06	+1 09	+2 26	-0.7	0.0	2.8	3.5	1.4
1163	Bristol...............................	41 40	71 16	+0 10	0 00	+0.6	0.0	4.1	5.1	2.0
1165	Warren................................	41 44	71 17	+0 21	+0 04	+1.1	0.0	4.6	5.7	2.3
1167	Nayatt Point..........................	41 43	71 20	+0 12	+0 03	+1.1	0.0	4.6	5.7	2.3
1169	Providence............................	41 48	71 24	+0 14	+0 05	+1.1	0.0	4.6	5.7	2.3
1171	Pawtucket, Seekonk River..............	41 52	71 23	+0 21	+0 14	+1.1	0.0	4.6	5.8	2.3
1173	East Greenwich........................	41 40	71 27	+0 16	+0 08	+0.5	0.0	4.0	5.0	2.0
1175	Wickford..............................	41 34	71 27	+0 12	+0 07	+0.3	0.0	3.8	4.7	1.9
1177	Narragansett Pier.....................	41 25	71 27	-0 08	+0 16	-0.3	0.0	3.2	4.0	1.6

Endnotes can be found at the end of table 2.

Cape Cod Canal, Railroad Bridge, No. 1119
    Predictions of the times of low water must be used with cau-
tion because of the peculiarities in the behavior of the tide.
Since the tide may be practically at a stand for as much as two
hours before or after the predicted times of low water, the levels
at other than high and low water times cannot be obtained in the
usual way as in Table 3 (Height of Tide at Any Time).   The pecul-
iar behavior of the tide near low water, which is prevalent at
this place, is illustrated by the first three curves; however
there are brief periods each month when the behavior is as depicted
by the fourth curve.

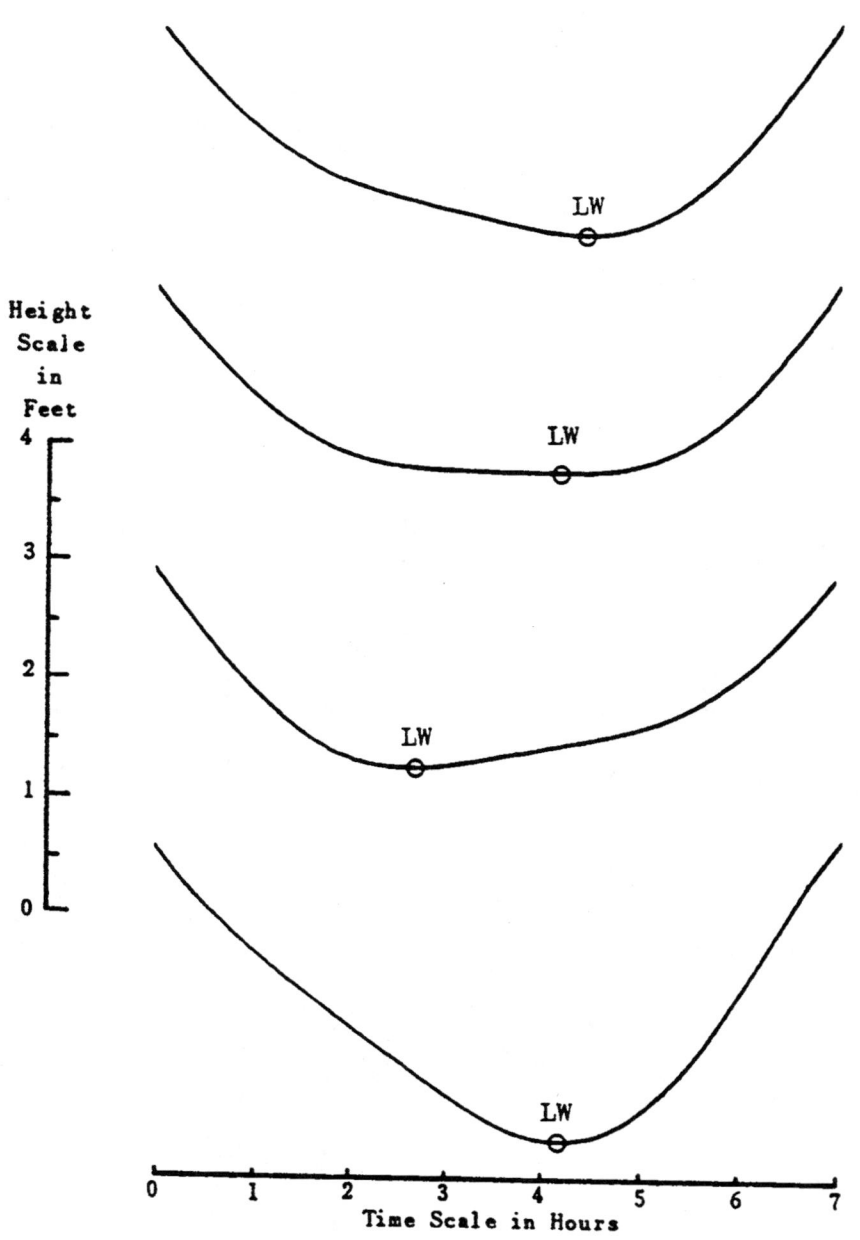

TABLE 2. — TIDAL DIFFERENCES AND OTHER CONSTANTS, 1983   211

NO.	PLACE	POSITION		DIFFERENCES				RANGES		Mean Tide Level
		Lat.	Long.	Time		Height		Mean	Spring	
				High Water	Low Water	High Water	Low Water			
		° ' N	° ' W	h. m.	h. m.	ft	ft	ft	ft	ft
	RHODE ISLAND, Outer Coast Time meridian, 75°W			on NEWPORT, p.40						
1179	Point Judith Harbor of Refuge...........	41 22	71 29	-0 07	+0 22	-0.4	0.0	3.1	3.9	1.5
1181	Block Island (Great Salt Pond)..........	41 11	71 35	+0 05	+0 12	-0.9	0.0	2.6	3.2	1.3
1183	Block Island (Old Harbor)...............	41 10	71 33	-0 14	+0 17	-0.6	0.0	2.9	3.6	1.4
1185	Watch Hill Point........................	41 18	71 52	+0 44	+1 21	-0.9	0.0	2.6	3.2	1.3
				on NEW LONDON, p.44						
1186	Westerly, Pawcatuck River...............	41 23	71 50	-0 27	+0 02	+0.1	0.0	2.7	3.2	1.3
	CONNECTICUT, Long Island Sound									
1187	Stonington, Fishers Island Sound........	41 20	71 54	-0 33	-0 41	+0.1	0.0	2.7	3.2	1.3
1189	Noank, Mystic River entrance............	41 19	71 59	-0 23	-0 08	-0.3	0.0	2.3	2.7	1.2
1191	West Harbor, Fishers Island, N. Y.......	41 16	72 00	-0 01	-0 06	-0.1	0.0	2.5	3.0	1.2
1192	Silver Eel Pond, Fishers Island, N. Y...	41 15	72 02	-0 17	-0 04	-0.3	0.0	2.3	2.7	1.1
	Thames River									
1193	NEW LONDON, State Pier..............	41 22	72 06	Daily predictions				2.6	3.1	1.3
1195	Smith Cove entrance.................	41 24	72 06	-0 01	+0 10	-0.1	0.0	2.5	3.0	1.2
1197	Norwich.............................	41 31	72 05	+0 12	+0 25	+0.4	0.0	3.0	3.6	1.5
1199	Millstone Point....................	41 18	72 10	+0 08	+0 01	+0.1	0.0	2.7	3.2	1.3
	Connecticut River									
1200	Saybrook Jetty......................	41 16	72 21	+1 10	+0 45	+0.9	0.0	3.5	4.2	1.7
1201	Saybrook Point.....................	41 17	72 21	+1 10	+0 53	+0.6	0.0	3.2	3.8	1.6
1202	Lyme, highway bridge...............	41 19	72 21	+1 24	+1 10	+0.5	0.0	3.1	3.7	1.5
1203	Essex..............................	41 21	72 23	+1 38	+1 38	+0.4	0.0	3.0	3.6	1.5
	Connecticut River									
1204	Hadlyme <7>........................	41 25	72 26	+2 18	+2 23	+0.1	0.0	2.7	3.2	1.3
1205	East Haddam........................	41 27	72 28	+2 41	+2 53	+0.3	0.0	2.9	3.5	1.4
1206	Haddam <7>.........................	41 29	72 30	+2 47	+3 08	-0.1	0.0	2.5	3.0	1.2
1207	Higganum Creek.....................	41 30	72 33	+2 54	+3 25	0.0	0.0	2.6	3.1	1.3
1209	Portland <7>.......................	41 34	72 38	+3 50	+4 28	-0.4	0.0	2.2	2.6	1.1
1211	Rocky Hill <7>.....................	41 39	72 38	+4 43	+5 44	-0.6	0.0	2.0	2.4	1.0
1213	Hartford <7>.......................	41 46	72 40	+5 29	+6 52	-0.7	0.0	1.9	2.3	1.0
				on BRIDGEPORT, p.48						
1214	Westbrook, Duck Island Roads............	41 16	72 28	-0 23	-0 34	-2.6	0.0	4.1	4.7	2.0
1215	Duck Island.............................	41 15	72 29	-0 25	-0 37	-2.2	0.0	4.5	5.2	2.2
1217	Madison.................................	41 16	72 36	-0 20	-0 32	-1.8	0.0	4.9	5.6	2.4
1219	Falkner Island.........................	41 13	72 39	-0 13	-0 27	-1.3	0.0	5.4	6.2	2.7
1220	Sachem Head.............................	41 15	72 42	-0 10	-0 17	-1.3	0.0	5.4	6.2	2.7
1221	Money Island...........................	41 15	72 45	-0 11	-0 25	-1.1	0.0	5.6	6.4	2.8
1223	Branford Harbor........................	41 16	72 49	-0 07	-0 20	-0.8	0.0	5.9	6.8	2.9
1225	New Haven Harbor entrance..............	41 14	72 55	-0 08	-0 16	-0.5	0.0	6.2	7.1	3.1
1227	New Haven (city dock)..................	41 18	72 55	+0 02	-0 03	-0.7	0.0	6.0	6.9	3.0
1229	Milford Harbor.........................	41 13	73 03	-0 07	-0 12	-0.1	0.0	6.6	7.6	3.3
1231	Stratford, Housatonic River............	41 11	73 07	+0 27	+0 59	-1.2	0.0	5.5	6.3	2.7
1233	Shelton, Housatonic River..............	41 19	73 05	+1 36	+2 42	-1.7	0.0	5.0	5.8	2.5
1235	BRIDGEPORT..............................	41 10	73 11	Daily predictions				6.7	7.7	3.4
1237	Black Rock Harbor entrance.............	41 09	73 13	-0 03	-0 05	+0.2	0.0	6.9	7.9	3.4
1239	Saugatuck River entrance...............	41 06	73 22	-0 01	-0 01	+0.3	0.0	7.0	8.0	3.5
1241	South Norwalk..........................	41 06	73 25	+0 10	+0 13	+0.4	0.0	7.1	8.2	3.5
1243	Greens Ledge...........................	41 03	73 27	-0 01	-0 03	+0.5	0.0	7.2	8.3	3.6
1245	Stamford...............................	41 02	73 33	+0 04	+0 06	+0.5	0.0	7.2	8.3	3.6
1247	Cos Cob Harbor.........................	41 01	73 36	+0 06	+0 09	+0.5	0.0	7.2	8.3	3.6
1249	Greenwich..............................	41 01	73 37	+0 02	-0 01	+0.7	0.0	7.4	8.5	3.7
1251	Great Captain Island...................	40 59	73 37	+0 01	-0 01	+0.6	0.0	7.3	8.4	3.6
	NEW YORK Long Island Sound, North Side			on WILLETS POINT, p.52						
1253	Port Chester...........................	41 00	73 40	-0 09	-0 12	+0.1	0.0	7.2	8.5	3.6
1254	Rye Beach..............................	40 58	73 40	-0 28	-0 29	+0.1	0.0	7.2	8.4	3.6
1255	Mamaroneck.............................	40 56	73 44	-0 08	-0 11	+0.2	0.0	7.3	8.6	3.6
1257	New Rochelle...........................	40 54	73 47	-0 24	-0 17	+0.1	0.0	7.2	8.6	3.6
1259	Davids Island..........................	40 53	73 46	-0 02	-0 07	+0.1	0.0	7.2	8.5	3.6
1261	City Island............................	40 51	73 47	-0 03	-0 03	+0.1	0.0	7.2	8.5	3.6
1263	Throgs Neck............................	40 48	73 48	+0 02	+0 14	-0.1	0.0	7.0	8.2	3.5
	East River									
1265	Whitestone.............................	40 48	73 49	+0 02	+0 14	0.0	0.0	7.1	8.3	3.5
1267	Old Ferry Point........................	40 48	73 50	+0 04	+0 16	0.0	0.0	7.1	8.3	3.5
1269	College Point, Flushing Bay............	40 47	73 51	+0 20	+0 28	-0.6	0.0	6.5	7.6	3.2
1271	Northern Blvd. Bridge, Flushing Creek...	40 46	73 50	+0 23	+0 37	-0.3	0.0	6.8	8.0	3.4
1273	Westchester, Westchester Creek.........	40 50	73 50	+0 10	+0 16	-0.1	0.0	7.0	8.3	3.5
1275	Hunts Point............................	40 48	73 52	+0 08	+0 15	-0.2	0.0	6.9	8.1	3.4
1277	Westchester Ave. Bridge, Bronx River....	40 50	73 53	+0 10	+0 17	-0.2	0.0	6.9	8.1	3.4
1279	North Brother Island...................	40 48	73 54	+0 09	+0 17	-0.5	0.0	6.6	7.8	3.3
1281	Port Morris (Stony Point)..............	40 48	73 54	+0 13	+0 16	-0.8	0.0	6.3	7.4	3.1

Endnotes can be found at the end of table 2.

TABLE 2. — TIDAL DIFFERENCES AND OTHER CONSTANTS, 1983

NO.	PLACE	POSITION Lat.	POSITION Long.	DIFFERENCES Time High Water	DIFFERENCES Time Low Water	DIFFERENCES Height High Water	DIFFERENCES Height Low Water	RANGES Mean	RANGES Spring	Mean Tide Level
		° ' N	° ' W	h. m.	h. m.	ft	ft	ft	ft	ft
	New York, East River Time meridian, 75°W			on WILLETS POINT, p.52						
1283	Lawrence Point.........................	40 47	73 55	-0 03	+0 13	-0.7	0.0	6.4	7.6	3.2
1285	Wolcott Avenue.........................	40 47	73 55	-0 03	+0 13	-1.0	0.0	6.1	7.2	3.0
				on NEW YORK, p.56						
1287	Pot Cove, Astoria......................	40 47	73 56	+2 20	+2 29	+0.8	0.0	5.3	6.3	2.6
1289	Hell Gate, Hallets Point...............	40 47	73 56	+2 00	+2 04	+0.6	0.0	5.1	6.1	2.5
1291	Horns Hook, East 90th Street...........	40 47	73 57	+1 50	+1 30	+0.3	0.0	4.8	5.8	2.4
1293	Welfare Island, north end..............	40 46	73 56	+1 45	+1 25	+0.3	0.0	4.8	5.8	2.4
1295	37th Avenue, Long Island City..........	40 46	73 57	+1 30	+1 10	0.0	0.0	4.5	5.5	2.2
1297	East 41st Street, New York City........	40 45	73 58	+1 20	+0 56	-0.2	0.0	4.3	5.2	2.1
1299	Hunters Point, Newtown Creek...........	40 44	73 57	+1 18	+0 53	-0.4	0.0	4.1	4.9	2.0
1301	English Kills entrance, Newtown Creek...	40 43	73 55	+1 30	+1 04	-0.3	0.0	4.2	5.0	2.1
1303	East 27th Street, Bellevue Hospital.....	40 44	73 58	+1 08	+1 03	-0.3	0.0	4.2	5.0	2.1
1305	East 19th Street, New York City........	40 44	73 58	+1 02	+0 58	-0.4	0.0	4.1	4.9	2.0
1307	North 3d Street, Brooklyn..............	40 43	73 58	+0 55	+0 42	-0.4	0.0	4.1	4.9	2.0
1309	Williamsburg Bridge....................	40 43	73 58	+0 52	+0 38	-0.4	0.0	4.1	4.9	2.0
1311	Wallabout Bay..........................	40 42	73 59	+0 50	+0 35	-0.4	0.0	4.1	4.9	2.0
1313	Brooklyn Bridge........................	40 42	74 00	+0 13	+0 07	-0.2	0.0	4.3	5.2	2.1
	Harlem River									
1315	East 110th Street, New York City....	40 47	73 56	+1 52	+1 35	+0.6	0.0	5.1	6.1	2.6
1317	Willis Avenue Bridge................	40 48	73 56	+1 47	+1 30	+0.5	0.0	5.0	6.0	2.5
1319	Madison Avenue Bridge...............	40 49	73 56	+1 52	+1 35	+0.4	0.0	4.9	5.9	2.4
1321	Central Bridge.....................	40 50	73 56	+1 52	+1 35	+0.2	0.0	4.7	5.7	2.3
1323	Washington Bridge...................	40 51	73 56	+1 52	+1 35	-0.1	0.0	4.4	5.2	2.2
1325	University Heights Bridge...........	40 52	73 55	+1 40	+1 30	-0.5	0.0	4.0	4.8	2.0
1327	Broadway Bridge.....................	40 52	73 55	+1 20	+1 20	-0.7	0.0	3.8	4.6	1.9
1329	Spuyten Duyvil Bridge...............	40 53	73 56	+1 01	+1 03	-0.9	0.0	3.6	4.3	1.8
	Long Island Sound, South Side			on WILLETS POINT, p.52						
1331	WILLETS POINT..........................	40 48	73 47	Daily predictions				7.1	8.3	3.5
1333	Hewlett Point..........................	40 50	73 45	-0 03	-0 03	0.0	0.0	7.1	8.3	3.5
1335	Port Washington, Manhasset Bay.........	40 50	73 42	-0 01	+0 11	+0.2	0.0	7.3	8.6	3.6
1337	Execution Rocks........................	40 53	73 44	-0 06	-0 08	+0.2	0.0	7.3	8.6	3.6
1339	Glen Cove, Hempstead Harbor............	40 52	73 39	-0 11	-0 06	+0.2	0.0	7.3	8.6	3.6
	Oyster Bay			on BRIDGEPORT, p.48						
1341	Oyster Bay Harbor...................	40 53	73 32	+0 08	+0 11	+0.6	0.0	7.3	8.4	3.6
1343	Bayville Bridge.....................	40 54	73 33	+0 13	+0 18	+0.7	0.0	7.4	8.5	3.7
1345	Cold Spring Harbor..................	40 52	73 28	+0 08	+0 06	+0.7	0.0	7.4	8.5	3.7
1347	Eatons Neck Point......................	40 57	73 24	+0 03	+0 06	+0.4	0.0	7.1	8.2	3.6
1349	Lloyd Harbor entrance, Huntington Bay...	40 55	73 26	+0 03	+0 01	+0.7	0.0	7.4	8.5	3.7
1351	Northport, Northport Bay...............	40 54	73 21	+0 03	+0 06	+0.6	0.0	7.3	8.4	3.6
1353	Nissequogue River entrance.............	40 54	73 14	-0 03	-0 06	+0.3	0.0	7.0	8.0	3.5
1355	Stony Brook, Smithtown Bay.............	40 55	73 09	+0 08	+0 08	-0.6	0.0	6.1	7.0	3.0
1357	Stratford Shoal........................	41 04	73 06	-0 05	-0 09	-0.1	0.0	6.6	7.6	3.3
1359	Port Jefferson Harbor entrance.........	40 58	73 05	+0 03	-0 01	-0.1	0.0	6.6	7.6	3.3
1361	Port Jefferson.........................	40 57	73 05	+0 06	+0 03	-0.1	0.0	6.6	7.6	3.3
1363	Setauket Harbor........................	40 57	73 06	+0 04	+0 09	0.0	0.0	6.7	7.7	3.3
1365	Conscience Bay entrance (Narrows).......	40 58	73 07	+0 02	+0 02	0.0	0.0	6.7	7.7	3.3
1367	Mount Sinai Harbor.....................	40 58	73 02	+0 05	+0 16	-0.7	0.0	6.0	6.9	3.0
1369	Herod Point............................	40 58	72 50	-0 07	-0 16	-0.8	0.0	5.9	6.8	2.9
1370	Northville............................	40 59	72 39	-0 02	-0 05	-1.3	0.0	5.4	6.2	2.7
1371	Mattituck Inlet........................	41 01	72 34	+0 05	-0 06	-1.5	0.0	5.2	6.0	2.6
1373	Horton Point...........................	41 05	72 27	-0 20	-0 35	*0.60	*0.60	4.0	4.6	2.0
1374	Hashamomuck Beach......................	41 06	72 24	+0 04	-0 15	*0.63	*0.63	4.2	4.8	2.1
1375	Truman Beach...........................	41 08	72 19	-0 42	-0 52	*0.51	*0.51	3.4	3.9	1.7
				on NEW LONDON, p.44						
1377	Plum Gut Harbor, Plum Island...........	41 10	72 12	+0 27	+0 16	0.0	0.0	2.6	3.1	1.3
1379	Little Gull Island.....................	41 12	72 06	+0 12	-0 22	-0.4	0.0	2.2	2.6	1.1
	Shelter Island Sound									
1381	Orient..............................	41 08	72 18	+0 36	+0 36	-0.1	0.0	2.5	3.0	1.2
1383	Greenport...........................	41 06	72 22	+1 04	+0 49	-0.2	0.0	2.4	2.9	1.2
1385	Southhold...........................	41 04	72 25	+1 43	+1 33	-0.3	0.0	2.3	2.7	1.1
1387	Noyack Bay..........................	41 00	72 20	+2 05	+1 44	-0.3	0.0	2.3	2.7	1.1
1389	Sag Harbor..........................	41 00	72 18	+0 59	+0 48	-0.1	0.0	2.5	3.0	1.2
1391	Cedar Point.........................	41 02	72 16	+0 44	+0 27	-0.1	0.0	2.5	3.0	1.2
	Peconic Bays									
1393	New Suffolk.........................	41 00	72 28	+2 26	+2 11	0.0	0.0	2.6	3.1	1.3
1395	South Jamesport.....................	40 56	72 35	+2 32	+2 40	+0.1	0.0	2.7	3.2	1.3
1397	Shinnecock Canal....................	40 54	72 30	+2 33	+2 31	-0.2	0.0	2.4	2.9	1.2
1399	Threemile Harbor ent., Gardiners Bay....	41 02	72 11	+0 21	+0 02	-0.2	0.0	2.4	2.9	1.2
1401	Promised Land, Napeague Bay............	41 00	72 05	-0 14	-0 08	-0.3	0.0	2.3	2.7	1.1
1403	Montauk Harbor entrance................	41 04	71 56	-0 25	-0 16	-0.7	0.0	1.9	2.3	0.9
1405	Montauk, Fort Pond Bay.................	41 03	71 58	-0 29	-0 24	-0.5	0.0	2.1	2.5	1.1
1407	Montauk Point, north side..............	41 04	71 52	-1 13	-1 31	-0.6	0.0	2.0	2.4	1.0

Endnotes can be found at the end of table 2.

TABLE 2. — TIDAL DIFFERENCES AND OTHER CONSTANTS, 1983   213

NO.	PLACE	POSITION Lat.	POSITION Long.	DIFFERENCES Time High Water	DIFFERENCES Time Low Water	DIFFERENCES Height High Water	DIFFERENCES Height Low Water	RANGES Mean	RANGES Spring	Mean Tide Level
		° ' N	° ' W	h. m.	h. m.	ft	ft	ft	ft	ft
	Long Island, South Side Time meridian, 75°W				on SANDY HOOK, p.64					
1409	Shinnecock inlet (ocean)...............	40 50	72 28	-0 50	-1 08	*0.63	*0.63	2.9	3.5	1.4
1411	Ponquogue Bridge, Shinnecock Bay........	40 51	72 30	+0 29	+0 14	-2.3	0.0	2.3	2.8	1.2
1413	Potunk Point, Moriches Bay.............	40 48	72 39	+3 35	+3 35	*0.11	*0.11	0.5	0.6	0.2
1415	Moriches Inlet.........................	40 46	72 45	-0 56	-1 11	*0.63	*0.63	2.9	3.5	1.4
1417	Mastic Beach, Moriches Bay.............	40 45	72 50	+3 28	+3 39	*0.11	*0.11	0.5	0.6	0.2
1419	Fire Island Breakwater.................	40 37	73 18	-0 39	-0 51	-0.5	0.0	4.1	5.0	2.0
1421	Democrat Point, Fire Island Inlet.......	40 38	73 18	-0 38	-0 29	*0.57	*0.57	2.6	3.1	1.3
	Great South Bay									
1422	Fire Island Coast Guard Station.....	40 38	73 16	-0 19	-0 17	*0.41	*0.41	1.9	2.3	0.9
1423	Fire Island Radiobeacon..............	40 38	73 13	+0 47	+1 20	*0.15	*0.15	0.7	0.8	0.3
1425	West Fire Island.....................	40 39	73 12	+2 11	+2 16	*0.13	*0.13	0.6	0.7	0.3
1427	Point o' Woods.......................	40 39	73 08	+2 28	+2 33	*0.15	*0.15	0.7	0.8	0.3
1429	Bellport, Bellport Bay...............	40 45	72 56	+3 44	+4 14	*0.17	*0.17	0.8	1.0	0.4
1431	Patchogue...........................	40 45	73 01	+3 23	+3 47	*0.15	*0.15	0.7	0.8	0.3
1433	Sayville (Brown Creek)...............	40 44	73 04	+3 39	+3 44	*0.13	*0.13	0.6	0.7	0.3
1435	Great River, Connetquot River.......	40 43	73 09	+3 20	+3 30	*0.15	*0.15	0.7	0.8	0.3
1437	Bay Shore...........................	40 43	73 14	+2 23	+2 39	*0.13	*0.13	0.6	0.7	0.3
1439	Oakbeach............................	40 38	73 17	+2 24	+2 56	*0.15	*0.15	0.7	0.8	0.3
1441	Babylon.............................	40 41	73 19	+2 12	+2 39	*0.13	*0.13	0.6	0.7	0.3
1443	Gilgo Heading.......................	40 37	73 24	+2 23	+2 56	*0.24	*0.24	1.1	1.3	0.5
1445	Amityville.............................	40 39	73 25	+2 21	+3 03	*0.26	*0.26	1.2	1.4	0.6
1447	Biltmore Shores, South Oyster Bay.......	40 40	73 28	+2 05	+2 30	*0.30	*0.30	1.4	1.7	0.7
1449	Jones Inlet (Point Lookout)............	40 35	73 35	-0 19	-0 27	*0.78	*0.78	3.6	4.3	1.8
	Hempstead Bay									
1451	Deep Creek Meadow....................	40 36	73 32	+1 02	+1 09	*0.52	*0.52	2.4	2.9	1.2
1453	Green Island........................	40 37	73 30	+1 22	+1 29	*0.41	*0.41	1.9	2.3	0.9
1455	Cuba Island.........................	40 37	73 31	+1 08	+1 20	*0.50	*0.50	2.3	2.8	1.1
1457	Bellmore, Bellmore Creek.............	40 40	73 31	+1 29	+1 56	*0.43	*0.43	2.0	2.4	1.0
1459	Neds Creek..........................	40 37	73 33	+0 50	+0 52	-1.9	0.0	2.7	3.3	1.3
1461	Freeport Creek......................	40 38	73 34	+0 34	+0 27	-1.5	0.0	3.1	3.8	1.5
1463	Freeport, Baldwin Bay...............	40 38	73 35	+0 38	+0 53	-1.6	0.0	3.0	3.6	1.5
1465	Long Beach..........................	40 36	73 39	+0 19	0 00	-0.7	0.0	3.9	4.7	1.9
1467	Long Beach (outer coast)...............	40 35	73 39	-0 29	-0 35	-0.1	0.0	4.5	5.4	2.2
	Hempstead Bay-Continued									
1469	East Rockaway.......................	40 38	73 40	+0 42	+0 45	-0.7	0.0	3.9	4.7	1.9
1471	Woodmere, Brosewere Bay.............	40 37	73 42	+0 35	+0 48	-0.7	0.0	3.9	4.7	1.9
1473	East Rockaway Inlet....................	40 36	73 44	-0 06	-0 16	-0.5	0.0	4.1	5.0	2.0
	Jamaica Bay									
1475	Plumb Beach Channel.................	40 35	73 55	+0 03	-0 05	+0.3	0.0	4.9	5.9	2.4
1477	Barren Island, Rockaway Inlet.......	40 35	73 53	0 00	-0 06	+0.4	0.0	5.0	6.0	2.5
1479	Beach Channel (bridge)..............	40 35	73 49	+0 38	+0 22	+0.5	0.0	5.1	6.2	2.5
1481	Motts Basin.........................	40 37	73 46	+0 40	+0 46	+0.8	0.0	5.4	6.5	2.7
1483	Norton Point, Head of Bay...........	40 38	73 45	+0 39	+0 43	+0.8	0.0	5.4	6.5	2.7
1485	J. F. K. International Airport......	40 37	73 47	+0 26	+0 43	+0.7	0.0	5.3	6.4	2.6
1487	Grassy Bay (bridge).................	40 39	73 50	+0 44	+0 45	+0.6	0.0	5.2	6.3	2.6
1489	Canarsie............................	40 38	73 53	+0 28	+0 06	+0.6	0.0	5.2	6.3	2.6
1491	Mill Basin..........................	40 37	73 55	+0 29	+0 02	+0.6	0.0	5.2	6.3	2.6
	NEW YORK and NEW JERSEY New York Harbor									
1493	Coney Island...........................	40 34	73 59	-0 03	-0 19	+0.1	0.0	4.7	5.7	2.3
1495	Norton Point, Gravesend Bay............	40 35	74 00	-0 03	+0 01	+0.1	0.0	4.7	5.7	2.3
1497	Fort Wadsworth, The Narrows............	40 36	74 03	+0 02	+0 12	-0.3	0.0	4.3	5.2	2.1
1499	Fort Hamilton, The Narrows.............	40 37	74 02	+0 03	+0 05	+0.1	0.0	4.7	5.7	2.3
					on NEW YORK, p.56					
1501	Bay Ridge..............................	40 38	74 02	-0 24	-0 24	+0.1	0.0	4.6	5.5	2.3
1503	St. George, Staten Island..............	40 39	74 04	-0 21	-0 18	0.0	0.0	4.5	5.4	2.2
1505	Bayonne, New Jersey....................	40 41	74 06	-0 19	-0 08	0.0	0.0	4.5	5.4	2.2
1507	Gowanus Bay............................	40 40	74 01	-0 19	-0 15	-0.1	0.0	4.4	5.3	2.2
1509	Governors Island......................	40 42	74 01	-0 11	-0 06	-0.1	0.0	4.4	5.3	2.2
1511	NEW YORK (The Battery).................	40 42	74 01		Daily Predictions			4.5	5.4	2.2
	Hudson River <8>									
1513	Jersey City, Con Rail RR. Ferry, N. J...	40 43	74 02	+0 07	+0 07	-0.1	0.0	4.4	5.3	2.2
1515	New York, Desbrosses Street............	40 43	74 01	+0 10	+0 10	-0.1	0.0	4.4	5.3	2.2
1517	New York, Chelsea Docks...............	40 45	74 01	+0 17	+0 16	-0.2	0.0	4.3	5.2	2.1
1519	Hoboken, Castle Point, N. J............	40 45	74 01	+0 17	+0 16	-0.2	0.0	4.3	5.2	2.1
1521	Weehawken, Days Point, N. J............	40 46	74 01	+0 24	+0 23	-0.3	0.0	4.2	5.0	2.1
1523	New York, Union Stock Yards............	40 47	74 00	+0 27	+0 26	-0.3	0.0	4.2	5.0	2.1
1525	New York, 130th Street.................	40 49	73 58	+0 37	+0 35	-0.5	0.0	4.0	4.8	2.0
1527	George Washington Bridge...............	40 51	73 57	+0 46	+0 43	-0.6	0.0	3.9	4.6	1.9
1529	Spuyten Duyvil, west of RR. bridge......	40 53	73 56	+0 58	+0 53	-0.7	0.0	3.8	4.5	1.9
1531	Yonkers................................	40 56	73 54	+1 09	+1 10	-0.8	0.0	3.7	4.4	1.8

Endnotes can be found at the end of table 2.

TABLE 2. — TIDAL DIFFERENCES AND OTHER CONSTANTS, 1983

NO.	PLACE	POSITION		DIFFERENCES				RANGES		Mean Tide Level
		Lat.	Long.	Time		Height		Mean	Spring	
				High Water	Low Water	High Water	Low Water			
		° ' N	° ' W	h. m.	h. m.	ft	ft	ft	ft	ft

	Hudson River <8> Time meridian, 75°W				on NEW YORK, p.56					
1533	Dobbs Ferry.............................	41 01	73 53	+1 29	+1 40	-1.1	0.0	3.4	4.0	1.7
1535	Tarrytown.............................	41 05	73 52	+1 45	+1 54	-1.3	0.0	3.2	3.7	1.6
1537	Ossining.............................	41 10	73 52	+1 53	+2 14	-1.4	0.0	3.1	3.6	1.5
1539	Haverstraw.............................	41 12	73 58	+1 59	+2 25	-1.6	0.0	2.9	3.4	1.4
1541	Peekskill.............................	41 17	73 56	+2 24	+3 00	-1.3	+0.3	2.9	3.4	1.7
1543	West Point.............................	41 24	73 57	+3 16	+3 37	-1.5	+0.3	2.7	3.1	1.6
1545	Newburgh.............................	41 30	74 00	+3 42	+4 00	-1.5	+0.2	2.8	3.2	1.6
1547	New Hamburg.............................	41 35	73 57	+4 00	+4 25	-1.5	+0.1	2.9	3.3	1.5
1549	Poughkeepsie.............................	41 42	73 57	+4 30	+4 43	-1.3	+0.1	3.1	3.5	1.6
1551	Hyde Park.............................	41 47	73 57	+4 56	+5 09	-1.3	0.0	3.2	3.6	1.6
1553	Kingston Point.............................	41 56	73 58	+5 16	+5 31	-0.9	-0.1	3.7	4.2	1.7
1555	Tivoli.............................	42 04	73 56	+5 46	+6 01	-0.8	-0.2	3.9	4.4	1.7
1557	Catskill.............................	42 13	73 51	+6 37	+6 55	-0.7	-0.3	4.1	4.6	1.7
1559	Hudson.............................	42 15	73 48	+6 54	+7 09	-0.9	-0.4	4.0	4.4	1.6
					on ALBANY, p.60					
1561	Coxsackie.............................	42 21	73 48	-1 01	-1 38	-0.5	+0.2	3.9	4.3	2.1
1563	New Baltimore.............................	42 27	73 47	-0 34	-0 56	-0.1	+0.4	4.1	4.5	2.4
1565	Castleton-on-Hudson.............................	42 32	73 46	-0 17	-0 29	-0.2	+0.1	4.3	4.7	·2.2
1567	ALBANY.............................	42 39	73 45		Daily predictions			4.6	5.0	2.5
1569	Troy.............................	42 44	73 42	+0 08	+0 10	+0.1	0.0	4.7	5.1	2.3
	The Kills and Newark Bay				on NEW YORK, p.56					
	Kill Van Kull									
1571	Constable Hook.......................	40 39	74 05	-0 34	-0 21	0.0	0.0	4.5	5.4	2.2
1573	New Brighton.......................	40 39	74 05	-0 12	-0 18	0.0	0.0	4.5	5.4·	2.2
1575	Port Richmond.......................	40 38	74 08	-0 03	+0 05	0.0	0.0	4.5	5.4	2.2
1577	Bergen Point.......................	40 39	74 08	+0 03	+0 03	+0.1	0.0	4.6	5.5	2.3
1579	Shooters Island.......................	40 39	74 10	+0 06	+0 18	+0.1	0.0	4.6	5.5	2.3
1581	Port Newark Terminal.......................	40 41	74 08	-0 01	+0 18	+0.6	0.0	5.1	6.1	2.5
1583	Newark, Passaic River.......................	40 44	74 10	+0 22	+0 52	+0.6	0.0	5.1	6.1	2.5
1585	Passaic, Gregory Ave. bridge...........	40 51	74 07	+0 49	+1 57	+0.6	0.0	5.1	.6.1	2.5
	Hackensack River									
1586	Kearny Point.......................	40 44	74 06	+0 09	+0 33	+0.5	0.0	5.0	6.0	2.5
1587	Secaucus.......................	40 48	74 04	+1 13	+1 09	+0.6	0.0	5.1	6.1	2.6
1588	Little Ferry.......................	40 51	74 02	+1 22	+1 14	+0.8	0.0	5.3	6.4	2.7
1589	Hackensack.......................	40 53	74 02	+1 33	+1 58	+0.8	0.0	5.3	6.4	2.6
					on SANDY HOOK, p.64					
	Arthur Kill									
1591	Elizabethport.......................	40 39	74 11	+0 25	+0 39	+0.3	0.0	4.9	5.9	2.4
1593	Chelsea.......................	40 36	74 12	+0 24	+0 35	+0.4	0.0	5.0	6.0	2.5
1595	Carteret.......................	40 35	74 13	+0 23	+0 31	+0.5	0.0	5.1	6.2	2.6
1597	Rossville.......................	40 33	74 13	+0 17	+0 25	+0.7	0.0	5.3	6.4	2.6
1599	Tottenville.......................	40 31	74 15	+0 03	+0 13	+0.7	0.0	5.3	6.4	2.6
1601	Perth Amboy.......................	40 30	74 16	+0 13	+0 19	+0.6	0.0	5.2	6.3	2.6
	Lower New York Bay, Raritan Bay, etc.									
1603	New Dorp Beach.......................	40 34	74 06	-0 04	+0 04	+0.3	0.0	4.9	5.9	2.4
1605	Great Kills Harbor.......................	40 33	74 08	+0 07	+0 19	+0.1	0.0	4.7	5.7	2.4
1607	Princes Bay.......................	40 31	74 12	+0 01	+0 04	+0.3	0.0	4.9	5.9	2.4
	Raritan River									
1609	South Amboy.......................	40 29	74 17	+0 05	+0 15	+0.4	0.0	5.0	6.0	2.5
1611	Washington Canal.......................	40 28	74 22	+0 34	+0 50	+1.0	0.0	5.6	6.8	2.8
1613	South River highway bridge...........	40 27	74 22	+0 55	+1 02	+0.9	0.0	5.5	6.7	2.8
1615	New Brunswick.......................	40 29	74 26	+0 46	+1 26	+1.2	0.0	5.8	7.0	2.9
1617	Keyport.......................	40 26	74 12	+0 08	+0 19	+0.4	0.0	5.0	6.0	2.5
1619	Keansburg.......................	40 27	74 09	-0 03	-0 01	+0.3	0.0	4.9	5.9	2.4
1621	Port Monmouth.......................	40 26	74 05	-0 02	-0 02	+0.2	0.0	4.8	5.8	2.4
1623	Atlantic Highlands.......................	40 25	74 02	-0 01	0 00	+0.1	0.0	4.7	5.7	2.3
1625	SANDY HOOK.......................	40 28	74 01		Daily predictions			4.6	5.6	2.3
	Sandy Hook Bay									
	Shrewsbury River									
1627	Highlands.......................	40 24	73 59	+0 35	+0 55	-0.8	0.0	3.8	4.6	1.9
1629	Red Bank, Navesink River............	40 21	74 04	+1 48	+2 23	*0.65	*0.65	3.0	3.6	1.5
1631	Normandie.......................	40 23	73 59	+1 09	+1 45	*0.63	*0.63	2.9	3.5	1.4
1633	Sea Bright.......................	40 21	73 59	+2 10	+2 38	*0.37	*0.37	1.7	2.1	0.8
1635	Branchport, Pleasure Bay.......................	40 19	74 00	+3 00	+3 26	*0.37	*0.37	1.7	2.1	0.8
	NEW JERSEY, Outer Coast									
1637	Sea Bright.......................	40 22	73 58	-0 34	-0 45	-0.2	0.0	4.4	5.3	2.2
1639	Long Branch.......................	40 18	73 59	-0 34	-0 45	-0.2	0.0	4.4	5.3	2.2

Endnotes can be found at the end of table 2.

TABLE 2. — TIDAL DIFFERENCES AND OTHER CONSTANTS, 1983   215

NO.	PLACE	POSITION		DIFFERENCES				RANGES		Mean Tide Level
		Lat.	Long.	Time		Height		Mean	Spring	
				High Water	Low Water	High Water	Low Water			
		° ′ N	° ′ W	h. m.	h. m.	ft	ft	ft	ft	ft

	NEW JERSEY, Outer Coast Time meridian, 75°W			on SANDY HOOK, p.64						
1641	Asbury Park......................	40 13	74 00	-0 34	-0 45	-0.3	0.0	4.3	5.2	2.1
1643	Shark River Inlet (entrance).....	40 11	74 01	-0 18	-0 36	-0.6	0.0	4.0	4.8	2.0
1645	Municipal Boat Basin, Shark River.......	40 11	74 02	+0 27	+0 36	-0.9	0.0	3.7	4.4	1.8
1647	Sea Girt........................	40 08	74 02	-0 34	-0 45	-0.3	0.0	4.3	5.2	2.1
1649	Manasquan Inlet.................	40 06	74 02	-0 12	-0 36	-0.6	0.0	4.0	4.8	2.0
	Manasquan River									
1651	Railroad bridge...............	40 06	74 04	+0 20	+0 05	-1.1	0.0	3.5	4.2	1.7
1653	Riviera Beach...............	40 06	74 05	+0 51	+1 25	-1.5	0.0	3.1	3.8	1.5
1655	Seaside Park (ocean).............	39 55	74 05	-0 33	-0 44	-0.4	0.0	4.2	5.1	2.1
	Barnegat Bay									
1657	Mantoloking...................	40 02	74 03	+5 34	+5 34	*0.11	*0.11	0.5	0.6	0.2
1659	Coates Point, highway bridge........	39 57	74 07	+4 19	+4 28	*0.11	*0.11	0.5	0.6	0.2
1661	Toms River (town).............	39 57	74 12	+4 37	+4 47	*0.13	*0.13	0.6	0.7	0.3
1663	Waretown.....................	39 47	74 11	+2 33	+2 49	*0.13	*0.13	0.6	0.7	0.3
1665	Oyster Cr. Chan. (off Sedge Island).	39 47	74 08	+2 16	+2 17	*0.13	*0.13	0.6	0.7	0.3
1667	Barnegat Inlet................	39 46	74 06	-0 20	-0 21	-1.5	0.0	3.1	3.8	1.5
1669	Harvey Cedars.................	39 42	74 08	+3 15	+4 02	*0.17	*0.17	0.8	1.0	0.4
	Little Egg Harbor									
1671	Manahawkin Bridge.............	39 39	74 11	+2 33	+3 20	*0.33	*0.33	1.5	1.8	0.7
1673	Long Point....................	39 36	74 16	+1 48	+1 56	*0.48	*0.48	2.2	2.7	1.1
1675	Tuckerton Creek entrance......	39 35	74 20	+1 40	+1 54	*0.52	*0.52	2.4	2.9	1.2
1677	Beach Haven...................	39 34	74 15	+1 47	+2 01	*0.48	*0.48	2.2	2.7	1.1
1679	Holgate.......................	39 32	74 16	+1 11	+1 07	*0.57	*0.57	2.6	3.1	1.3
	Great Bay									
1681	Little Egg Inlet..............	39 30	74 18	-0 01	-0 03	-0.9	0.0	3.7	4.5	1.8
1683	Seven Islands.................	39 31	74 20	+0 12	+0 16	-1.2	0.0	3.4	4.1	1.7
1685	Graveling Point...............	39 32	74 24	+1 05	+1 18	-1.2	0.0	3.4	4.1	1.7
1687	Mullica River, highway bridge.......	39 33	74 28	+1 55	+2 12	-1.3	0.0	3.3	4.0	1.6
1689	Main Marsh Thorofare..........	39 29	74 23	+1 04	+1 30	-1.3	0.0	3.3	4.0	1.6
1691	Brigantine Channel..............	39 27	74 21	+0 01	+0 03	-1.1	0.0	3.5	4.2	1.7
1693	Grassy Bay......................	39 26	74 24	+1 08	+1 11	-1.2	0.0	3.4	4.1	1.7
1695	Absecon Creek entrance, Absecon Bay.....	39 25	74 29	+1 04	+1 17	-1.0	0.0	3.6	4.4	1.8
1697	Broad Creek, Middle Thorofare.......	39 24	74 26	+0 55	+0 33	-1.2	0.0	3.4	4.1	1.7
1699	Absecon Inlet (Gardner Basin).......	39 23	74 25	+0 14	-0 01	-1.0	0.0	3.6	4.4	1.8
1701	Beach Thorofare (railroad bridges)......	39 22	74 27	+0 52	+0 40	-0.8	0.0	3.8	4.6	1.9
1703	Atlantic City, Steel Pier.............	39 21	74 25	-0 26	-0 35	-0.5	0.0	4.1	5.0	2.0
1705	Chelsea (highway bridge)........	39 21	74 28	+0 49	+0 45	-0.6	0.0	4.0	4.8	2.0
1707	Beach Thorofare (Shelter Island).......	39 21	74 30	+0 39	+0 32	-0.7	0.0	3.9	4.7	1.9
1709	Dock Thorofare (bridge)...........	39 21	74 32	+0 48	+0 32	-0.8	0.0	3.8	4.6	1.9
1711	Longport (inside)..............	39 18	74 32	+0 05	-0 01	-0.7	0.0	3.9	4.7	2.0
1713	Great Egg Harbor Inlet..........	39 18	74 34	+0 12	-0 05	-0.8	0.0	3.8	4.6	1.9
1715	Ocean City (9th Street bridge)..........	39 17	74 35	+0 24	+0 19	-0.9	0.0	3.7	4.5	1.8
1717	Great Egg Harbor Bay............	39 18	74 38	+0 44	+0 57	-1.0	0.0	3.6	4.4	1.8
	Great Egg Harbor River									
1719	Scull Landing.................	39 22	74 43	+1 43	+1 54	-0.9	0.0	3.7	4.5	1.8
1721	Mays Landing..................	39 27	74 44	+2 34	+2 39	-0.6	0.0	4.0	4.8	2.0
1723	Peck Bay (34th Street bridge)...........	39 15	74 38	+0 51	+1 02	-0.9	0.0	3.7	4.5	1.8
1725	Devils Island, Crook Horn Creek.......	39 14	74 39	+0 37	+0 22	-1.0	0.0	3.6	4.4	1.8
1727	Corson Inlet (bridges)...........	39 13	74 39	+0 09	+0 04	-0.7	0.0	3.9	4.7	1.9
1729	Ben Hands Thorofare.............	39 12	74 40	+0 48	+0 32	-0.9	0.0	3.7	4.5	1.8
1731	Sea Isle City (Ludlam Thoro. bridge)....	39 09	74 42	+0 45	+0 49	-0.8	0.0	3.8	4.6	1.9
1733	Sea Isle City (beach)...........	39 09	74 41	-0 19	-0 19	-0.5	0.0	4.1	5.0	2.0
1735	Townsends Inlet.................	39 07	74 43	+0 06	+0 04	-0.8	0.0	3.8	4.6	1.9
1737	Long Reach.....................	39 06	74 45	+0 53	+0 53	-0.8	0.0	3.8	4.6	1.9
1739	Great Sound (ent. to Cresse Thoro.).....	39 05	74 47	+1 03	+1 05	-0.5	0.0	4.1	5.0	2.0
1741	Stone Harbor (Great Chan. bridge)........	39 03	74 46	+0 42	+0 26	-0.5	0.0	4.1	5.0	2.0
1743	Hereford Inlet (North Wildwood).......	39 01	74 48	+0 02	+0 02	-0.5	0.0	4.1	5.0	2.0
1745	Wildwood (beach)...............	38 59	74 48	-0 15	-0 19	-0.5	0.0	4.1	5.0	2.0
1747	Grassy Sound Channel (hwy. bridge)......	39 02	74 49	+0 40	+0 28	-0.5	0.0	4.1	5.0	2.0
1749	West Wildwood (Grassy Sound bridge).....	39 00	74 50	+0 45	+0 29	-0.3	0.0	4.3	5.2	2.1
1751	Swain Channel..................	38 59	74 52	+0 54	+0 27	-0.2	0.0	4.4	5.3	2.2
1753	Cape May Harbor................	38 57	74 53	-0 02	-0 16	-0.2	0.0	4.4	5.3	2.2
1755	Cape May, Municipal Pier.........	38 56	74 55	+0 02	-0 17	-0.3	0.0	4.3	5.2	2.1
	NEW JERSEY and DELAWARE Delaware Bay, Eastern Shore			on BREAKWATER HARBOR, p.68						
1757	Five Fathom Bank................	38 51	74 38	-0 43	-0 38	0.0	0.0	4.1	4.9	2.0
1759	McCrie Shoal...................	38 51	74 51	-0 22	-0 21	+0.2	0.0	4.3	5.2	2.1
1761	Cape May Point.................	38 56	74 58	-0 10	-0 04	+0.6	0.0	4.7	5.6	2.3
1762	Cape May, ferry terminal.........	38 58	74 58	-0 04	-0 01	+0.8	0.0	4.9	5.8	2.4
1763	Bay Shore Channel..............	38 58	74 58	-0 09	-0 03	+0.8	0.0	4.9	5.8	2.4
1765	Miami Beach....................	39 02	74 56	+0 17	+0 26	+1.0	0.0	5.1	6.1	2.5
1767	Dennis Creek entrance..........	39 10	74 54	+0 48	+1 04	+1.5	0.0	5.6	6.6	2.8
1769	East Point, Maurice River Cove....	39 12	75 02	+0 53	+1 12	+1.6	0.0	5.7	6.7	2.8
	Maurice River									
1771	Port Norris...................	39 14	75 02	+1 14	+1 38	+1.6	0.0	5.7	6.7	2.8
1773	Mauricetown..................	39 17	75 02	+1 48	+2 21	+1.7	0.0	5.8	6.8	2.9
1775	Millville....................	39 24	75 02	+2 37	+3 23	+1.9	0.0	6.0	7.0	3.0
1777	Egg Island Point...............	39 11	75 08	+0 33	+1 02	+1.6	0.0	5.7	6.7	2.8

Endnotes can be found at the end of table 2.

NO.	PLACE	POSITION		DIFFERENCES				RANGES		Mean Tide Level
		Lat.	Long.	Time		Height		Mean	Spring	
				High Water	Low Water	High Water	Low Water			
		° ′ N	° ′ W	h. m.	h. m.	ft	ft	ft	ft	ft
	NEW JERSEY and DELAWARE Delaware Bay, Eastern Shore Time meridian, 75°W			on REEDY POINT, p.72						
1779	Fortescue	39 14	75 10	-2 05	-2 19	+0.4	0.0	5.9	7.0	2.9
1781	Ben Davis Point	39 17	75 17	-1 40	-1 49	+0.5	0.0	6.0	6.9	3.0
	Cohansey River									
1783	Entrance	39 21	75 22	-1 30	-1 29	+0.5	0.0	6.0	6.9	3.0
1785	Laning Wharf	39 23	75 20	-1 10	-1 14	+0.5	0.0	6.0	6.8	3.0
1787	Fairton	39 23	75 14	+0 05	-0 24	+0.7	0.0	6.2	7.0	3.1
1789	Bridgeton	39 25	75 14	+0 27	-0 13	+1.0	0.0	6.5	7.3	3.2
1791	Bay Side	39 23	75 24	-1 23	-1 22	+0.6	0.0	6.1	6.9	3.0
	DEL., N.J., and PA. Delaware Bay, Central Lighthouses			on BREAKWATER HARBOR, p.68						
1793	Brandywine Shoal Light	38 59	75 07	+0 09	+0 28	+0.8	0.0	4.9	5.9	2.4
1795	Fourteen Foot Bank Light	39 03	75 11	+0 18	+0 48	+1.1	0.0	5.2	6.2	2.6
1797	Miah Maull Shoal Light	39 08	75 13	+0 28	+1 04	+1.4	0.0	5.5	6.5	2.7
1799	Elbow of Cross Ledge Light	39 11	75 16	+0 40	+1 21	+1.5	0.0	5.6	6.5	2.8
				on REEDY POINT, p.72						
1801	Ship John Shoal Light	39 18	75 23	-1 32	-1 36	+0.2	0.0	5.7	6.6	2.8
	Delaware Bay, Western Shore			on BREAKWATER HARBOR, p.68						
1803	Cape Henlopen	38 48	75 05	-0 05	-0 05	0.0	0.0	4.1	4.9	2.0
1805	BREAKWATER HARBOR	38 47	75 06	Daily predictions				4.1	4.9	2.1
1807	Roosevelt Inlet	38 49	75 12	+0 09	+0 13	+0.3	0.0	4.4	5.2	2.2
1809	Mispillion River entrance	38 57	75 19	+0 33	+1 00	+0.5	0.0	4.6	5.4	2.3
1811	Murderkill River entrance	39 04	75 24	+0 56	+1 32	+0.7	0.0	4.8	5.7	2.4
1813	St. Jones River entrance	39 04	75 24	+0 57	+1 33	+0.7	0.0	4.8	5.7	2.4
1815	Mahon River entrance	39 11	75 24	+1 13	+1 52	+1.3	0.0	5.4	6.3	2.7
1817	Leipsic River entrance	39 15	75 24	+1 18	+1 59	+1.4	0.0	5.5	6.4	2.7
1819	Leipsic, Leipsic River	39 15	75 31	+3 42	+3 50	-0.6	0.0	3.5	4.0	1.7
				on REEDY POINT, p.72						
1821	Woodland Beach	39 20	75 28	-1 15	-1 14	+0.4	0.0	5.9	6.8	2.9
	Delaware River									
1823	Liston Point	39 25	75 32	-0 55	-0 59	+0.2	0.0	5.7	6.4	2.8
1825	Taylors Bridge, Blackbird Creek	39 24	75 36	+1 47	+0 54	-2.6	0.0	2.9	3.3	1.4
1827	Reedy Island	39 31	75 34	-0 16	-0 16	+0.1	0.0	5.6	6.2	2.8
1831	Salem, Salem River	39 35	75 28	+0 19	+0 20	+0.1	0.0	5.6	6.1	2.8
1833	REEDY POINT	39 34	75 34	Daily predictions				5.5	6.0	2.7
	Chesapeake and Delaware Canal									
1835	Biddle Point, Delaware	39 33	75 37	-0 05	+0 01	-0.4	0.0	5.1	5.5	2.5
1837	Summit Bridge, Delaware	39 33	75 44	-0 34	-0 55	*0.64	*0.64	3.5	3.9	1.7
1839	Chesapeake City, Maryland	39 32	75 49	-0 30	-1 06	*0.49	*0.49	2.7	3.0	1.4
1841	Pea Patch Island, Delaware	39 35	75 34	+0 08	+0 12	0.0	0.0	5.5	6.0	2.7
1843	New Castle, Delaware	39 39	75 34	+0 30	+0 49	+0.1	0.0	5.6	6.0	2.8
1845	Deepwater Point, N. J.	39 42	75 31	+0 46	+1 11	+0.1	0.0	5.6	6.0	2.8
1847	Christina River entrance, Del	39 43	75 31	+0 51	+1 16	+0.1	0.0	5.6	5.9	2.8
1849	Wilmington, Christina River, Del	39 44	75 33	+0 56	+1 27	+0.2	0.0	5.7	6.0	2.8
1851	Edgemoor, Del	39 45	75 30	+0 56	+1 27	+0.1	0.0	5.6	5.9	2.8
1853	Oldmans Point, N. J.	39 46	75 28	+1 03	+1 34	+0.1	0.0	5.6	5.9	2.8
				on PHILADELPHIA, p.76						
1855	Marcus Hook, Pa.	39 49	75 25	-1 12	-1 06	-0.6	0.0	5.6	5.9	2.8
1857	Chester, Pa.	39 51	75 21	-0 51	-0 45	-0.5	0.0	5.7	6.0	2.8
1859	Billingsport, N. J.	39 51	75 14	-0 31	-0 25	-0.5	0.0	5.7	6.0	2.8
1861	Fort Mifflin, Pa.	39 52	75 13	-0 21	-0 15	-0.5	0.0	5.7	6.0	2.8
	Schuylkill River									
1863	Girard Point, Pa.	39 54	75 12	-0 17	-0 10	-0.5	0.0	5.7	6.0	2.8
1865	Point Breeze, Pa.	39 55	75 12	-0 13	-0 05	-0.5	0.0	5.7	6.0	2.8
1867	Grays Ferry Bridge, Pa.	39 57	75 12	-0 07	+0 01	-0.4	0.0	5.8	6.1	2.9
1869	Fairmount Bridge, Pa.	39 58	75 11	+0 02	+0 11	-0.4	0.0	5.8	6.1	2.9
1871	Philadelphia, South Broad St., Pa.	39 53	75 11	-0 17	-0 11	-0.4	0.0	5.8	6.1	2.9
1873	Gloucester City, N. J.	39 54	75 08	-0 05	+0 04	-0.4	0.0	5.8	6.1	2.9
1875	Philadelphia, Washington Ave., Pa.	39 56	75 08	+0 04	+0 11	-0.3	0.0	5.9	6.2	3.0
1877	PHILADELPHIA, Pier 11 North, Pa.	39 57	75 08	Daily predictions				6.2	6.6	3.1
1879	Camden, Cooper Point, N. J.	39 57	75 08	+0 12	+0 19	-0.3	0.0	5.9	6.2	3.0
1881	Philadelphia, Pier 80 N (old site), Pa.	39 58	75 07	+0 18	+0 26	-0.3	0.0	5.9	6.2	3.0
1883	Philadelphia, Bridesburg, Pa.	40 00	75 04	+0 34	+0 43	-0.2	0.0	6.0	6.3	3.0
1885	Torresdale, Pa.	40 03	74 59	+1 06	+1 17	0.0	0.0	6.2	6.5	3.1

Endnotes can be found at the end of table 2.

TABLE 2. — TIDAL DIFFERENCES AND OTHER CONSTANTS, 1983   217

NO.	PLACE	POSITION		DIFFERENCES				RANGES		Mean Tide Level
				Time		Height				
		Lat.	Long.	High Water	Low Water	High Water	Low Water	Mean	Spring	
		° ' N	° ' W	h. m.	h. m.	ft	ft	ft	ft	ft
	NEW JERSEY and PENNSYLVANIA **Delaware River-Continued** **Time meridian, 75°W**			on PHILADELPHIA, p.76						
1887	Burlington, N. J........................	40 05	74 52	+1 30	+1 43	+0.2	0.0	6.4	6.7	3.2
1889	Bristol, Pa............................	40 06	74 51	+1 37	+1 51	+0.3	0.0	6.5	6.8	3.3
1891	Florence, N. J.........................	40 07	74 48	+1 47	+2 05	+0.4	0.0	6.6	6.9	3.3
1893	Bordentown, N. J.......................	40 09	74 43	+1 49	+2 15	+0.5	0.0	6.7	7.0	3.3
1895	Trenton, N. J..........................	40 11	74 45	+1 55	+2 40	+0.6	0.0	6.8	7.1	3.4
	DELAWARE, Outer Coast			on SANDY HOOK, p.64						
1897	Rehoboth Beach.........................	38 43	75 05	-0 07	-0 21	-0.7	0.0	3.9	4.7	1.9
	Indian River									
1899	Inlet (bridge).......................	38 37	75 04	+0 34	-0 18	*0.59	*0.59	2.7	3.2	1.3
1900	Inlet (Coast Guard Station)..........	38 37	75 04	+0 41	+0 18	*0.46	*0.46	2.1	2.5	1.1
1901	Oak Orchard..........................	38 36	75 10	+2 44	+3 11	*0.20	*0.20	0.9	1.1	0.5
1903	Possum Point.........................	38 35	75 16	+3 09	+4 00	*0.22	*0.22	1.0	1.2	0.5
1905	Rehoboth Bay...........................	- - -	- - -	- - -	- - -	- -	- -	0.5	0.6	0.2
1907	Fenwick Island Light...................	38 27	75 03	-0 13	-0 19	-0.9	0.0	3.7	4.5	1.8
	MARYLAND, Outer Coast									
1909	Ocean City (outer coast)..............	38 20	75 05	-0 28	-0 30	-1.2	0.0	3.4	4.1	1.7
1910	Ocean City (Isle of Wight Bay)........	38 20	75 05	-0 14	-0 25	-2.4	0.0	2.2	2.7	1.1
1911	North Beach Coast Guard Station........	38 12	75 09	-0 28	-0 29	-1.2	0.0	3.4	4.1	1.7
	MARYLAND and VIRGINIA **Chincoteague Bay**									
1913	Assateague Beach, Toms Cove............	37 52	75 22	+0 06	+0 16	-1.0	0.0	3.6	4.4	1.8
1915	Chincoteague Point.....................	37 54	75 25	+0 05	+0 11	*0.57	*0.57	2.6	3.1	1.3
1917	Bogues Bay, Chincoteague Inlet.........	37 53	75 30	+0 38	+0 57	-1.6	0.0	3.0	3.6	1.5
1918	Wishart Point, Bogues Bay..............	37 53	75 30	+0 20	+0 42	-2.0	0.0	2.6	3.1	1.3
1919	Chincoteague, Chincoteague Channel......	37 56	75 23	+0 40	+0 47	*0.37	*0.37	1.7	2.1	0.9
1921	Piney Island, Assateague Channel.......	37 56	75 21	+1 05	+1 13	*0.46	*0.46	2.1	2.5	1.0
1923	Greenbackville.........................	38 00	75 23	+2 19	+2 48	*0.13	*0.13	0.6	0.7	0.3
1925	George Island Landing..................	38 02	75 22	+2 53	+3 02	*0.13	*0.13	0.6	0.7	0.3
1927	Assacorkin Island......................	38 04	75 19	+3 33	+3 42	*0.09	*0.09	0.4	0.5	0.2
1928	Public Landing.........................	38 09	75 17	+4 58	+5 27	*0.09	*0.09	0.4	0.5	0.2
	VIRGINIA, Outer Coast									
1929	Wallops Island.........................	37 50	75 29	-0 23	-0 32	-1.0	0.0	3.6	4.4	1.8
1930	Gargathy Neck..........................	37 47	75 34	+1 05	+0 56	-1.6	0.0	3.0	3.6	1.5
1931	Metomkin Inlet.........................	37 40	75 36	+0 35	+0 12	-1.0	0.0	3.6	4.4	1.8
1932	Folly Creek, Metomkin Inlet............	37 42	75 38	+0 58	+0 41	-1.3	0.0	3.3	4.0	1.7
1933	Wachapreague Inlet (inside)............	37 35	75 37	+0 09	+0 03	-0.7	0.0	3.9	4.7	1.9
1935	Quinby Inlet entrance..................	37 28	75 40	+0 04	-0 12	-0.6	0.0	4.0	4.8	2.0
1937	The Swash, south end...................	37 30	75 40	+0 19	+0 14	-0.7	0.0	3.9	4.7	1.9
1939	Great Machipongo Inlet (inside)........	37 24	75 43	+0 36	+0 23	-0.7	0.0	3.9	4.7	1.9
1941	Upshur Neck, south end.................	37 28	75 48	+0 50	+0 52	-0.2	0.0	4.4	5.3	2.2
1943	Sand Shoal Inlet (Coast Guard Station)..	37 18	75 47	+0 08	-0 11	-0.5	0.0	4.1	4.9	2.0
1945	Ship Shoal Inlet.......................	37 13	75 48	+0 26	+0 09	-0.6	0.0	4.0	4.8	2.0
1947	Smith Island (Coast Guard Station)......	37 07	75 55	+0 23	+0 59	-1.1	0.0	3.5	4.2	1.7
	Chesapeake Bay, Eastern Shore			on HAMPTON ROADS, p.88						
1949	Fishermans Island......................	37 06	75 59	-0 43	-0 55	+0.5	0.0	3.0	3.6	1.5
1951	Kiptopeke Beach (ferry)................	37 10	75 59	-0 36	-0 30	+0.2	0.0	2.7	3.2	1.4
1953	Old Plantation Flats...................	37 14	76 03	-0 23	-0 10	-0.1	0.0	2.4	2.9	1.2
1955	Cape Charles Harbor....................	37 16	76 01	-0 14	+0 02	-0.1	0.0	2.4	2.9	1.2
1957	Nassawadox Creek.......................	37 28	75 58	+1 00	+0 53	-0.7	0.0	1.8	2.2	0.9
1959	Gaskins Point, Occohannock Creek.......	37 33	75 55	+1 36	+2 08	-0.8	0.0	1.7	2.0	0.9
1961	Pungoteague Creek......................	37 40	75 50	+2 26	+2 42	-0.8	0.0	1.7	2.0	0.8
1963	Onancock, Onancock Creek...............	37 43	75 45	+2 56	+3 14	-0.7	0.0	1.8	2.2	0.9
1965	Watts Island..........................	37 48	75 54	+3 03	+3 07	-0.9	0.0	1.6	1.9	0.8
1967	Tangier Sound Light....................	37 47	75 58	+2 55	+2 53	*0.64	*0.64	1.6	1.9	0.8
1969	Muddy Creek Entrance...................	37 51	75 40	+3 18	+3 48	-0.3	0.0	2.2	2.6	1.1
1970	Guard Shore...........................	37 51	75 42	+3 07	+3 42	-0.2	0.0	2.3	2.7	1.2
	MARYLAND **Chesapeake Bay, Eastern Shore**									
1971	Ape Hole Creek, Pocomoke Sound.........	37 58	75 49	+3 28	+3 53	-0.2	0.0	2.3	2.8	1.1
	Pocomoke River									
1973	Shelltown............................	37 59	75 38	+3 33	+4 11	-0.1	0.0	2.4	2.9	1.2
1975	Pocomoke City........................	38 05	75 34	+5 50	+6 10	-0.9	0.0	1.6	2.0	0.8
1976	Snowhill, city park..................	38 10	75 24	+7 36	+7 48	-0.6	0.0	1.9	2.3	1.0
1977	Janes Island Light....................	37 58	75 55	+3 55	+3 55	-0.7	0.0	1.8	2.2	0.9
1979	Crisfield, Little Annemessex River......	37 59	75 52	+3 51	+4 00	-0.5	0.0	2.0	2.4	1.0

Endnotes can be found at the end of table 2.

NO.	PLACE	POSITION		DIFFERENCES				RANGES		Mean Tide Level
		Lat.	Long.	Time		Height		Mean	Spring	
				High Water	Low Water	High Water	Low Water			
		° ′ N	° ′ W	h. m.	h. m.	ft	ft	ft	ft	ft

	MARYLAND									
	Chesapeake Bay, Eastern Shore									
	Time meridian, 75°W		on HAMPTON ROADS, p.88							
1981	Long Point, Big Annemessex River........	38 03	75 48	+4 20	+4 41	-0.4	0.0	2.1	2.5	1.0
1983	Teague Creek, Manokin River..............	38 06	75 50	+4 39	+5 00	-0.4	0.0	2.1	2.5	1.0
1985	Ewell, Smith Island.....................	38 00	76 02	+4 00	+4 26	*0.64	*0.64	1.6	1.9	0.8
1987	Solomons Lump Light.....................	38 03	76 01	+4 17	+4 20	-0.8	0.0	1.7	2.0	0.8
1989	Holland Island Bar Light................	38 04	76 06	+4 17	+4 25	*0.56	*0.56	1.4	1.7	0.7
1990	Chance...................................	38 10	75 57	+4 41	+4 53	-0.3	0.0	2.2	2.6	1.1
1991	Sharkfin Shoal Light....................	38 12	75 59	+4 47	+5 01	-0.3	0.0	2.2	2.6	1.1
1993	Great Shoals Light, Monie Bay...........	38 13	75 53	+5 01	+5 17	-0.2	0.0	2.3	2.8	1.2
	Wicomico River									
1995	Whitehaven	38 16	75 47	+5 28	+5 42	-0.1	0.0	2.4	2.9	1.2
1997	Salisbury...................	38 22	75 36	+6 22	+6 19	+0.5	0.0	3.0	3.6	1.5
	Nanticoke River									
1999	Roaring Point	38 16	75 55	+5 01	+5 30	-0.2	0.0	2.3	2.8	1.2
2001	Vienna........................	38 29	75 49	+7 42	+7 45	-0.3	0.0	2.2	2.6	1.1
2003	Sharptown.....................	38 32	75 43	+8 20	+8 23	0.0	0.0	2.5	3.0	1.3
2005	Fishing Point, Fishing Bay..............	38 18	76 01	+5 05	+5 29	0.0	0.0	2.5	3.0	1.2
2007	Hooper Strait Light.....................	38 14	76 05	+4 56	+5 02	-0.8	0.0	1.7	2.0	0.8
				on BALTIMORE, p.80						
2009	Hooper Island Light....................	38 15	76 15	-5 07	-5 23	+0.4	0.0	1.5	1.8	0.7
2010	Hooper Island...........................	38 18	76 12	-5 00	-4 51	+0.4	0.0	1.5	1.7	0.8
2011	Barren Island...........................	38 20	76 16	-4 52	-5 07	+0.2	0.0	1.3	1.5	0.6
	Little Choptank River									
2013	Taylors Island, Slaughter Creek.....	38 28	76 18	-3 09	-3 25	+0.1	0.0	1.2	1.4	0.6
2015	Woolford, Church Creek............	38 30	76 10	-3 25	-3 10	+0.3	0.0	1.4	1.6	0.7
2017	Cherry Island, Beckwiths Creek......	38 34	76 13	-3 21	-3 11	+0.2	0.0	1.3	1.5	0.6
2019	Hudson Creek........................	38 35	76 15	-3 49	-3 31	+0.3	0.0	1.4	1.6	0.7
2021	Sharps Island Light.....................	38 38	76 23	-3 51	-4 00	+0.2	0.0	1.3	1.5	0.6
	Choptank River									
2023	Choptank River Light...............	38 39	76 11	-3 17	-3 18	+0.3	0.0	1.4	1.6	0.7
2025	Cambridge..........................	38 34	76 04	-2 44	-2 39	+0.5	0.0	1.6	1.8	0.8
2027	Choptank...........................	38 41	75 57	-2 13	-1 58	+0.5	0.0	1.6	1.8	0.8
2029	Dover Bridge.......................	38 45	76 00	-0 38	-0 53	+0.6	0.0	1.7	1.9	0.9
2031	Denton.............................	38 53	75 50	+0 13	+0 22	+1.1	0.0	2.2	2.5	1.1
2033	Greensboro.........................	38 58	75 49	+1 18	+1 08	+1.4	0.0	2.5	2.9	1.2
2035	Wayman Wharf, Tuckahoe Creek........	38 53	75 57	+0 53	+0 25	+1.3	0.0	2.4	2.8	1.2
	Tred Avon River									
2037	Oxford.............................	38 42	76 10	-3 05	-3 00	+0.3	0.0	1.4	1.6	0.7
2039	Easton Point.......................	38 46	76 06	-2 59	-2 50	+0.5	0.0	1.6	1.8	0.8
2041	Deep Neck Point, Broad Creek............	38 44	76 14	-3 10	-3 01	+0.3	0.0	1.4	1.6	0.7
2043	St. Michaels, San Domingo Creek.........	38 46	76 14	-3 08	-3 06	+0.3	0.0	1.4	1.6	0.7
2045	Avalon, Dogwood Harbor..................	38 42	76 20	-3 08	-3 03	+0.2	0.0	1.3	1.5	0.6
2047	Poplar Island...........................	38 46	76 23	-3 12	-3 18	+0.1	0.0	1.2	1.3	0.6
2049	Ferry Cove, Eastern Bay.................	38 46	76 20	-3 01	-3 04	-0.1	0.0	1.0	1.2	0.5
2051	Claiborne, Eastern Bay..................	38 50	76 17	-2 40	-2 43	0.0	0.0	1.1	1.3	0.5
2053	St. Michaels, Miles River...............	38 47	76 13	-2 18	-2 08	+0.1	0.0	1.2	1.4	0.6
2055	Wye Landing, Wye East River.............	38 54	76 06	-2 05	-1 51	+0.2	0.0	1.3	1.5	0.6
2057	Kent Island Narrows.....................	38 58	76 15	-1 44	-1 38	+0.1	0.0	1.2	1.4	0.6
2058	Matapeake, Kent Island..................	38 58	76 21	-1 24	-1 49	-0.1	0.0	1.0	1.2	0.5
2059	Bloody Point Bar Light..................	38 50	76 24	-2 46	-2 54	0.0	0.0	1.1	1.3	0.5
	Chester River									
2061	Love Point.........................	39 02	76 18	-0 24	-0 46	0.0	0.0	1.1	1.3	0.6
2063	Queenstown.........................	39 00	76 10	-0 08	-0 24	+0.2	0.0	1.3	1.5	0.6
2065	Shipyard Landing, Langford Creek....	39 10	76 11	+0 14	+0 05	+0.4	0.0	1.5	1.7	0.7
2067	Centreville Landing, Corsica River..	39 03	76 04	+0 06	-0 01	+0.5	0.0	1.6	1.8	0.8
2069	Cliffs Point.......................	39 06	76 08	-0 02	-0 17	+0.4	0.0	1.5	1.7	0.7
2070	Cliffs Wharf.......................	39 07	76 08	-0 02	-0 14	+0.4	0.0	1.5	1.7	0.8
2071	Chestertown........................	39 12	76 04	+0 43	+0 24	+0.7	0.0	1.8	2.1	0.9
2073	Crumpton...........................	39 15	75 56	+1 18	+1 13	+1.3	0.0	2.4	2.8	1.2
2075	Millington.........................	39 15	75 50	+2 03	+2 30	+0.9	0.0	2.0	2.3	1.0
2077	Deep Landing, Swan Creek................	39 09	76 16	-0 12	-0 19	0.0	0.0	1.1	1.3	0.5
2079	Tolchester..............................	39 13	76 15	+0 24	+0 13	+0.1	0.0	1.2	1.4	0.6
2081	Worton Creek entrance...................	39 18	76 10	+1 07	+1 03	+0.2	0.0	1.3	1.5	0.6
	Sassafras River									
2083	Betterton..........................	39 22	76 04	+2 27	+2 08	+0.5	0.0	1.6	1.8	0.8
2085	Georgetown.........................	39 22	75 53	+2 01	+1 55	+0.9	0.0	2.0	2.3	1.0
	Elk River									
2087	Town Point Neck....................	39 30	75 55	+3 16	+3 00	+1.0	0.0	2.1	2.4	1.0
2089	Courthouse Point...................	39 31	75 53	+2 49	+2 38	+1.1	0.0	2.2	2.5	1.1
	C & D Canal (See Delaware River)....	- - -	- - -	- - -	- - -	- -	- -	- -	- -	- -
2091	Old Frenchtown Wharf...............	39 34	75 51	+3 00	+2 45	+1.2	0.0	2.3	2.6	1.1
2093	Charlestown, Northeast River............	39 34	75 58	+3 38	+3 48	+0.8	0.0	1.9	2.2	0.9
	Chesapeake Bay, Western Shore									
	Susquehanna River									
2095	Havre de Grace.....................	39 32	76 05	+3 10	+3 30	+0.7	0.0	1.8	2.0	0.9
2097	Port Deposit.......................	39 36	76 07	+4 00	+4 48	+1.0	0.0	2.1	2.4	1.0

Endnotes can be found at the end of table 2.

TABLE 2. — TIDAL DIFFERENCES AND OTHER CONSTANTS, 1983

NO.	PLACE	POSITION		DIFFERENCES				RANGES		Mean Tide Level
		Lat.	Long.	Time		Height		Mean	Spring	
				High Water	Low Water	High Water	Low Water			
		° ' N	° ' W	h. m.	h. m.	ft	ft	ft	ft	ft

on HAMPTON ROADS, p.88

Virginia, York River
Time meridian, 75°W

NO.	PLACE	Lat.	Long.	High Water	Low Water	High Water	Low Water	Mean	Spring	MTL
2321	Mumfort Islands	37 16	76 31	+0 19	+0 12	0.0	0.0	2.5	3.0	1.2
2323	Penniman Spit	37 17	76 35	+0 41	+0 44	0.0	0.0	2.5	3.0	1.2
2324	Cheatham Annex	37 18	76 35	+0 43	+0 35	0.0	0.0	2.5	3.0	1.2
2325	Queen Creek (2 miles upstream)	37 18	76 39	+1 00	+0 59	-0.1	0.0	2.4	2.9	1.2
2327	Clay Bank	37 21	76 37	+0 50	+0 49	+0.3	0.0	2.8	3.4	1.4
2329	Allmondsville	37 23	76 39	+0 59	+1 02	+0.3	0.0	2.8	3.3	1.4
2330	Roane Point	37 27	76 42	+1 42	+1 45	+0.3	0.0	2.8	3.4	1.4
2331	West Point	37 32	76 48	+2 07	+2 33	+0.3	0.0	2.8	3.4	1.4
	Mattaponi River									
2333	Wakema	37 39	76 54	+3 29	+3 52	+0.9	0.0	3.4	3.9	1.7
2335	Walkerton	37 43	77 02	+4 26	+4 54	+1.4	0.0	3.9	4.5	1.9
	Pamunkey River									
2337	Sweet Hall Landing	37 34	76 54	+3 48	+4 06	+0.2	0.0	2.7	3.1	1.3
2339	Lester Manor	37 35	76 59	+4 40	+4 55	+0.3	0.0	2.8	3.2	1.4
2341	White House	37 35	77 01	+5 09	+5 24	+0.5	0.0	3.0	3.4	1.5
2343	Northbury	37 37	77 07	+5 58	+6 13	+0.8	0.0	3.3	3.8	1.6
	Chesapeake Bay, Western Shore-Con.									
2345	York Point, Poquoson River	37 10	76 24	-0 07	+0 01	-0.1	0.0	2.4	2.9	1.2
2347	Messick Point, Back River	37 06	76 19	-0 26	-0 05	-0.2	0.0	2.3	2.8	1.2
	Hampton Roads									
2349	Old Point Comfort	37 00	76 19	-0 04	-0 14	0.0	0.0	2.5	3.0	1.3
2351	Hampton River	37 01	76 20	+0 02	-0 07	+0.1	0.0	2.6	3.1	1.3
2353	HAMPTON ROADS (Sewells Pt.)	36 57	76 20	Daily predictions				2.5	2.9	1.2
2355	Lafayette River	36 54	76 18	+0 11	+0 20	+0.1	0.0	2.6	3.1	1.3
2357	Lafayette River, Granby St. Bridge	36 53	76 17	+0 26	+0 32	+0.2	0.0	2.7	3.2	1.3
	Elizabeth River									
2359	Craney Island	36 54	76 20	+0 13	-0 01	+0.1	0.0	2.6	3.1	1 3
2361	Port Norfolk, Western Branch	36 51	76 20	+0 17	+0 24	+0.1	0.0	2.6	3 1	1.3
2363	Norfolk	36 51	76 18	+0 18	+0 15	+0.3	0.0	2.8	3.4	1.4
2365	Portsmouth, Southern Branch	36 49	76 18	+0 20	+0 20	+0.3	0.0	2.8	3.4	1.4
	Nansemond River									
2367	Pig Point	36 55	76 26	+0 37	+0 35	+0.3	0.0	2.8	3.4	1.4
2369	Town Point	36 53	76 30	+0 33	+0 39	+0.5	0.0	3.0	3.6	1.5
2371	Hollidays Point (bridge)	36 50	76 33	+0 51	+0 58	+0.5	0.0	3.0	3.6	1.5
2373	Suffolk	36 44	76 35	+1 37	+1 30	+1.3	0.0	3.8	4.6	1.9
	James River									
2375	Chuckatuck Creek entrance	36 55	76 30	+0 45	+0 52	+0.3	0.0	2.8	3.4	1.4
2377	Newport News	36 58	76 26	+0 24	+0 23	+0.1	0.0	2.6	3.1	1.3
2378	Huntington Park	37 01	76 28	+0 40	+0 39	+0.1	0.0	2.6	3.1	1.3
2379	Menchville	37 05	76 32	+0 58	+1 14	+0.1	0.0	2.6	3.1	1.3
2381	Smithfield, Pagan River	36 59	76 38	+1 29	+1 23	+0.3	0.0	2.8	3.4	1.4
2383	Burwell Bay	37 03	76 40	+1 20	+1 39	-0.1	0.0	2.4	2.9	1.2
2385	Mulberry Point	37 08	76 38	+2 00	+2 21	-0.1	0.0	2.4	2.9	1.2
2387	Hog Point	37 12	76 41	+2 15	+2 33	-0.4	0.0	2.1	2.5	1.0
2388	Scotland	37 11	76 47	+2 51	+3 20	-0.6	0.0	1.9	2.1	1.0
2389	Jamestown Island	37 12	76 47	+2 58	+3 31	-0.5	0.0	2.0	2.4	1.0
2391	Dillard Wharf	37 12	76 52	+3 33	+4 10	-0.6	0.0	1.9	2.3	0.9
	Chickahominy River									
2393	Ferry Point (bridge)	37 16	76 53	+3 56	+4 21	-0.6	0.0	1.9	2.3	1.0
2395	Wright Island Landing	37 21	76 52	+4 39	+4 58	-0.3	0.0	2.2	2.6	1.1
2397	Mount Airy	37 21	76 55	+5 05	+5 33	-0.3	0.0	2.2	2.6	1.1
2399	Lanexa	37 24	76 54	+5 35	+6 03	+0.1	0.0	2.6	3.1	1.3
2401	Claremont	37 14	76 57	+3 58	+4 30	-0.7	0.0	1.8	2.0	0.9
2403	Sturgeon Point	37 18	77 00	+4 32	+5 04	-0.4	0.0	2.1	2.5	1.0
2405	Windmill Point	37 18	77 06	+5 26	+5 51	-0.2	0.0	2.3	2.7	1.1
2406	Willcox Wharf, Charles City	37 19	77 06	+5 25	+5 45	-0.3	0.0	2.2	2.4	1.1
2407	Westover	37 19	77 09	+5 47	+6 12	-0.1	0.0	2.4	2.8	1.2
2409	Jordon Point	37 19	77 13	+6 11	+6 34	0.0	0.0	2.5	2.9	1.2

on WASHINGTON, p.84

NO.	PLACE	Lat.	Long.	High Water	Low Water	High Water	Low Water	Mean	Spring	MTL
2411	City Point (Hopewell)	37 19	77 16	-4 55	-5 12	-0.3	0.0	2.6	3.0	1.3
2413	Petersburg, Appomattox River	37 14	77 24	-4 25	-4 00	0.0	0.0	2.9	3.3	1.4
2415	Bermuda Hundred	37 20	77 16	-4 50	-5 05	-0.3	0.0	2.6	3.0	1.3
2417	Haxall	37 22	77 15	-4 43	-4 52	-0.2	0.0	2.7	3.1	1.4
2419	Curles, 1 mile north of	37 24	77 18	-4 25	-4 26	-0.1	0.0	2.8	3.2	1.4
2420	Chester	37 23	77 23	-4 12	-3 59	0.0	0.0	2.9	3.2	1.5
2421	Meadowville	37 23	77 19	-4 34	-4 33	0.0	0.0	2.9	3.3	1.4
2423	Kingsland Reach	37 24	77 23	-4 32	-4 28	+0.1	0.0	3.0	3.5	1.5
2425	Falling Creek entrance	37 26	77 26	-4 21	-4 08	+0.3	0.0	3.2	3.7	1.6
2427	Richmond Deepwater Terminal	37 27	77 25	-4 18	-4 01	+0.4	0.0	3.3	3.8	1.6
2429	Lower Rocketts	37 30	77 25	-3 52	-3 32	+0.3	0.0	3.2	3.6	1.6
2431	Richmond (river locks)	37 32	77 25	-3 49	-3 26	+0.3	0.0	3.2	3.6	1.6

Endnotes can be found at the end of table 2.

NO.	PLACE	POSITION		DIFFERENCES				RANGES		Mean Tide Level
		Lat.	Long.	Time		Height		Mean	Spring	
				High Water	Low Water	High Water	Low Water			
		° ' N	° ' W	h. m.	h. m.	ft	ft	ft	ft	ft
	Chesapeake Bay, Southern Shore Time meridian, 75°W			on HAMPTON ROADS, p.88						
2433	Little Creek (RR. Terminal).............	36 55	76 11	-0 48	-0 50	+0.1	0.0	2.6	3.1	1.3
	Lynnhaven Inlet									
2435	Highway bridge, east of.............	36 54	76 05	-0 09	+0 06	-0.5	0.0	2.0	2.4	1.0
	Lynnhaven Bay									
2436	Bayville.......................	36 54	76 06	+0 50	+1 43	-0.8	0.0	1.7	2.0	0.9
2437	Buchanan Creek entrance..............	36 52	76 07	+1 00	+1 51	-0.6	0.0	1.9	2.3	0.9
2438	Long Creek.....................	36 54	76 04	+0 48	+1 19	*0.32	*0.32	0.8	1.0	.0.4
2439	Brown Cove.....................	36 52	76 04	+0 46	+1 43	-0.8	0.0	1.7	2.0	0.8
2440	Cape Henry..........................	36 56	76 00	-0 48	-1 10	+0.3	0.0	2.8	3.4	1.4
	VIRGINIA, Outer Coast									
2441	Virginia Beach......................	36 51	75 58	-1 26	-1 30	+0.9	0.0	3.4	4.1	1.7
2442	False Cape..........................	36 36	75 53	-1 41	-1 40	+1.1	0.0	3.6	4.3	1.8
	NORTH CAROLINA, Outer Coast									
2443	Currituck Beach Light...............	36 23	75 50	-1 46	-1 45	+1.1	0.0	3.6	4.3	1.8
2444	Albemarle and Pamlico Sounds <9>.......	- -	- -	- -	- -	- -	- -	- -	- -	- -
2445	Kitty Hawk (ocean)..................	36 06	75 43	-1 50	-1 49	+0.7	0.0	3.2	3.8	1.6
2446	Jennetts Pier (ocean)...............	35 55	75 36	-1 54	-1 50	+0.8	0.0	3.3	3.9	1.6
2447	Roanoke Sound Channel...............	35 48	75 35	+0 27	+0 37	-2.0	0.0	0.5	0.6	0.3
2448	Oregon Inlet Marina.................	35 48	75 33	-0 38	+0 26	-1.9	0.0	0.6	0.7	0.3
2449	Oregon Inlet........................	35 46	75 31	-1 13	-1 07	-0.5	0.0	2.0	2.4	1.0
2450	Oregon Inlet Bridge.................	35 46	75 32	-1 27	-1 35	-0.6	0.0	1.9	2.3	1.0
2451	Oregon Inlet Channel...............	35 46	75 34	-1 19	-1 14	-1.3	0.0	1.2	1.4	0.6
2452	Old House Channel..................	35 46	75 35	-0 36	-0 12	-1.8	0.0	0.7	0.8	0.4
2453	Oregon Inlet (USCG Station).........	35 46	75 32	-1 40	-1 31	-0.8	0.0	1.7	2.0	0.9
2454	Davis Slough.......................	35 45	75 33	-1 01	-0 41	-1.6	0.0	0.9	1.1	0.5
2455	Cape Hatteras......................	35 14	75 31	-1 54	-2 05	+1.1	0.0	3.6	4.3	1.8
2456	Hatteras (ocean)...................	35 12	75 42	-2 02	-2 05	+0.9	0.0	3.4	4.1	1.7
2457	Hatteras Inlet.....................	35 12	75 44	-1 39	-1 39	-0.5	0.0	2.0	2.4	1.0
2458	Ocracoke Inlet.....................	35 04	76 01	-1 38	-1 41	-0.6	0.0	1.9	2.3	0.9
2459	Ocracoke, Ocracoke Inlet...........	35 07	75 59	-1 23	-1 00	*0.40	*0.40	1.0	1.2	0.5
2461	Cape Lookout.......................	34 37	76 32	-2 04	-2 13	+1.2	0.0	3.7	4.4	1.9
2463	Shell Point, Harkers Island........	34 41	76 32	+0 12	+0 45	-1.2	0.0	1.3	1.6	0.6
2465	Beaufort (Pivers Island)...........	34 43	76 40	-1 01	-1 09	+0.5	0.0	3.0	3.6	1.5
2467	Morehead City......................	34 43	76 42	-0 58	-1 05	+0.4	0.0	2.9	3.5	1.4
2469	Atlantic Beach.....................	34 42	76 43	-2 02	-2 03	+1.1	0.0	3.6	4.3	1.8
2471	Bogue Inlet........................	34 39	77 06	-1 34	-1 37	-0.3	0.0	2.2	2.6	1.1
2473	New River Inlet....................	34 32	77 20	-1 31	-1 35	+0.5	0.0	3.0	3.6	1.5
2475	New Topsail Inlet..................	34 22	77 38	-1 27	-0 52	+0.5	0.0	3.0	3.5	1.5
				on CHARLESTON, p.96						
2477	Masonboro Inlet....................	34 11	77 49	-0 14	+0 05	-1.4	0.0	3.8	4.5	1.9
2479	Wilmington Beach...................	34 02	77 54	-0 48	-0 38	-1.2	0.0	4.0	4.7	2.0
2481	Cape Fear..........................	33 51	77 58	-0 33	-0 28	-0.7	0.0	4.5	5.1	2.2
	Cape Fear River									
2483	Bald Head......................	33 52	78 00	-0 17	-0 11	-0.9	0.0	4.3	4.9	2.2
2485	Fort Caswell...................	33 54	78 01	-0 12	-0 05	-1.0	0.0	4.2	4.8	2.1
2487	Southport......................	33 55	78 01	0 00	+0 11	-1.1	0.0	4.1	4.6	2.0
2489	Reaves Point...................	34 00	77 57	+0 15	+0 45	-1.3	0.0	3.9	4.3	2.0
				on WILMINGTON, p.92						
2491	Campbell Island................	34 07	77 56	-0 49	-0 44	-0.4	0.0	3.8	4.0	1.9
2493	WILMINGTON.....................	34 14	77 57	Daily predictions				4.2	4.5	2.1
2495	Castle Hayne, Northeast River.......	34 21	77 56	+2 40	+2 55	*0.40	*0.40	1.7	1.9	0.8
2497	Bannermans Br., Northeast River.....	34 35	77 46	+5 54	+6 09	*0.31	*0.31	1.3	1.4	0.6
				on CHARLESTON, p.96						
2500	Yaupon Beach.......................	33 54	78 05	-0 39	-0 49	-0.3	0.0	4.9	5.8	2.4
2501	Lockwoods Folly Inlet..............	33 55	78 14	-0 29	-0 12	-1.0	0.0	4.2	4.8	2.1
2503	Shallotte Inlet (Bowen Point).......	33 55	78 22	+0 10	+0 28	-0.6	0.0	4.6	5.4	2.3
2505	Tubbs Inlet........................	33 53	78 29	-0 19	-0 12	-0.7	0.0	4.5	5.1	2.2
	SOUTH CAROLINA, Outer Coast									
2507	Little River, 1 mile above mouth........	33 51	78 34	0 00	+0 03	-0.2	0.0	5.0	5.9	2.5
2509	Little River (town), Little River.......	33 52	78 37	+0 29	+0 02	0.0	0.0	5.2	6.1	2.6
2511	Myrtle Beach.......................	33 41	78 53	-0 27	-0 27	-0.1	0.0	5.1	6.0	2.5
2513	Murrells Inlet.....................	33 32	79 02	-0 09	+0 20	-0.7	0.0	4.5	5.3	2.2
2514	Pawleys Island.....................	33 26	79 07	-0 29	-0 30	-0.4	0.0	4.8	5.6	2.4
2515	North Inlet........................	33 20	79 10	-0 18	0 00	-0.7	0.0	4.5	5.3	2.2
	Winyah Bay									
2517	Entrance (south jetty)..................	33 11	79 09	-0 28	-0 28	-0.6	0.0	4.6	5.4	2.3
2519	Georgetown Lighthouse...................	33 13	79 11	+0 26	+0 25	-1.4	0.0	3.8	4.4	1.9
2521	Estherville-Minim Creek Canal (ferry)...	33 15	79 16	+0 31	+1 04	*0.63	*0.63	3.3	3.9	1.6

Endnotes can be found at the end of table 2.

TABLE 2. — TIDAL DIFFERENCES AND OTHER CONSTANTS, 1983   223

NO.	PLACE	POSITION		DIFFERENCES				RANGES		Mean Tide Level
		Lat.	Long.	Time		Height		Mean	Spring	
				High Water	Low Water	High Water	Low Water			
		° ' N	° ' W	h. m.	h. m.	ft	ft	ft	ft	ft
	South Carolina, Winyah Bay Time meridian, 75°W					on CHARLESTON, p.96				
2523	Frazier Point..................	33 19	79 17	+1 19	+2 03	-1.7	0.0	3.5	4.1	1.7
2525	Georgetown, Sampit River........	33 22	79 17	+1 27	+2 25	*0.63	*0.63	3.3	3.9	1.6
2527	Georgetown, Pee Dee River bridge........	33 22	79 16	+1 34	+2 35	*0.63	*0.63	3.3	3.9	1.6
	Waccamaw River									
2529	Schooner Creek entrance........	33 27	79 10	+2 21	+3 18	*0.62	*0.62	3.2	3.8	1.6
2531	Wachesaw Ldg., 1 mile south of......	33 33	79 06	+3 06	+4 08	*0.56	*0.56	2.9	3.4	1.4
2533	Bull Creek entrance..................	33 36	79 06	+3 38	+4 41	*0.44	*0.44	2.3	2.7	1.1
2535	Enterprise Landing...................	33 40	79 04	+4 54	+5 31	*0.38	*0.38	2.0	2.4	1.0
2537	Toddville...........................	33 45	79 04	+7 10	+7 07	*0.25	*0.25	1.3	1.5	0.6
2539	Conway..............................	33 50	79 02	+7 47	+7 56	*0.23	*0.23	1.2	1.4	0.6
	SOUTH CAROLINA, Outer Coast-Con.									
2541	North Santee River Inlet..............	33 08	79 15	-0 16	0 00	-0.7	0.0	4.5	5.3	2.2
2543	Minim Creek ent., North Santee River....	33 12	79 16	-0 02	+1 02	-1.3	0.0	3.9	4.6	1.9
2544	Cedar Island Point, South Santee River..	33 07	79 16	-0 23	+0 04	-1.1	0.0	4.1	4.8	2.0
2545	Brown Island, South Santee River.......	33 09	79 20	+0 20	+1 27	-1.1	0.0	4.1	4.8	2.0
2547	Cape Romain...........................	33 01	79 21	-0 29	-0 21	-0.5	0.0	4.7	5.5	2.3
2549	Cape Romain, 46 miles east of..........	33 05	78 26	-1 12	-1 17	-1.1	0.0	4.1	4.8	2.0
	Bull Bay									
2551	Five Fathom Creek entrance........	33 00	79 30	-0 13	-0 11	-0.3	0.0	4.9	5.8	2.4
2553	McClellanville, Jeremy Creek......	33 05	79 28	+0 20	+0 21	-0.1	0.0	5.1	6.0	2.5
2555	Harbor River entrance............	33 02	79 32	-0 04	+0 32	-0.3	0.0	4.9	5.8	2.4
2557	Jack Creek entrance...............	32 56	79 35	-0 21	-0 19	-0.2	0.0	5.0	5.9	2.5
2559	Wharf Creek entrance..............	32 55	79 37	+0 05	-0 12	-0.1	0.0	5.1	6.0	2.5
2561	Sewee Bay.........................	32 56	79 39	+0 06	+0 07	-0.2	0.0	5.0	5.9	2.5
2563	Capers Inlet......................	32 51	79 42	-0 16	-0 14	0.0	0.0	5.2	6.1	2.6
2565	Dewees Inlet......................	32 50	79 44	-0 09	-0 16	-0.2	0.0	5.0	5.9	2.5
2567	Isle of Palms (outer coast).......	32 47	79 47	-0 16	-0 17	0.0	0.0	5.2	6.1	2.6
2569	Sullivans Island (outer coast)..........	32 46	79 50	-0 15	-0 16	0.0	0.0	5.2	6.1	2.6
	Charleston Harbor									
2571	Entrance (north jetty)................	32 44	79 48	-0 16	-0 19	0.0	0.0	5.2	6.1	2.6
2573	Fort Sumter...........................	32 45	79 52	-0 09	-0 13	-0.2	0.0	5.0	5.9	2.5
2575	The Cove..............................	32 46	79 52	-0 08	-0 06	-0.1	0.0	5.1	6.0	2.6
2577	CHARLESTON (Customhouse Wharf).........	32 47	79 55		Daily predictions			5.2	6.1	2.6
2579	Shipyard Creek, 0.8 mile above entrance.	32 50	79 57	+0 27	+0 16	+0.1	0.0	5.3	6.3	2.6
	Cooper River									
2581	North Charleston.................	32 52	79 58	+0 40	+0 36	0.0	0.0	5.2	6.1	2.6
2583	Goose Creek entrance.............	32 54	79 57	+0 50	+0 40	0.0	0.0	5.2	6.1	2.6
2585	Yeamans Hall, Goose Creek........	32 56	79 59	+2 36	+2 03	-0.2	0.0	5.0	5.9	2.5
2587	Snow Point, north of.............	32 57	79 56	+1 27	+1 14	-0.3	0.0	4.9	5.8	2.4
2589	Dean Hall........................	33 03	79 56	+2 46	+2 27	-1.1	0.0	4.1	4.8	2.0
2591	Quimby Creek, East Branch........	33 06	79 49	+4 08	+3 47	-0.9	0.0	4.3	5.1	2.1
2593	RR. bridge, West Branch..........	33 06	79 57	+3 18	+3 05	-1.0	0.0	4.2	5.0	2.1
	Wando River									
2597	Cainhoy..........................	32 55	79 50	+0 57	+0 39	+0.8	0.0	6.0	7.1	3.0
2599	Woodville........................	32 55	79 44	+2 07	+1 22	+1.1	0.0	6.3	7.4	3.2
	Ashley River									
2601	Wappoo Creek (highway bridge)........	32 46	79 58	+0 22	+0 22	0.0	0.0	5.2	6.1	2.6
2603	Highway bridge...................	32 47	79 58	+0 22	+0 15	0.0	0.0	5.2	6.1	2.6
2605	Highway bridge (2 miles above)......	32 50	79 58	+0 25	+0 17	+0.3	0.0	5.5	6.5	2.8
2607	Bees Ferry bridge................	32 51	80 03	+1 14	+1 07	+0.3	0.0	5.5	6.4	2.8
2609	Magnolia Gardens.................	32 53	80 05	+1 16	+1 06	+0.4	0.0	5.6	6.6	2.8
2611	Greggs Landing....................	32 56	80 09	+1 47	+1 35	+0.9	0.0	6.1	7.2	3.0
	SOUTH CAROLINA, Outer Coast-Con.									
2613	Folly Island (outer coast)............	32 39	79 56	-0 15	-0 18	0.0	0.0	5.2	6.1	2.6
2615	Folly River (below bridge)............	32 39	79 58	+0 13	-0 09	+0.2	0.0	5.4	6.4	2.7
2617	Legareville, 1 mile above, Stono River..	32 41	80 00	+0 13	+0 06	0.0	0.0	5.2	6.1	2.6
2619	Elliott Cut, Stono River..............	32 46	80 00	+0 48	+0 49	0.0	0.0	5.2	6.1	2.6
2621	Church Flats, RR. bridge, Stono River...	32 45	80 08	+2 06	+1 47	+0.5	0.0	5.7	6.7	2.8
	North Edisto River									
2623	Rockville, Bohicket Creek.........	32 36	80 12	+0 20	+0 05	+0.6	0.0	5.8	6.8	2.9
2624	Point of Pines...................	32 35	80 14	+0 16	+0 11	+0.4	0.0	5.6	6.5	2.8
2625	Dawho River entrance.............	32 38	80 16	+0 46	+0 27	+0.9	0.0	6.1	7.2	3.0
2627	Dawho Ferry, Dawho River.........	32 38	80 20	+1 18	+1 00	+1.3	0.0	6.5	7.7	3.2
2629	Toogoodoo Creek, 2 miles above ent...	32 40	80 18	+1 11	+0 35	+1.2	0.0	6.4	7.6	3.2
2631	Yonges Island, Wadmalaw River....	32 41	80 14	+1 19	+0 34	+1.4	0.0	6.6	7.8	3.3
2633	Ravens Point, Church Creek.......	32 42	80 09	+1 43	+0 49	+1.8	0.0	7.0	8.3	3.5
					on SAVANNAH RIVER ENT., p.100					
2635	Edisto Beach, Edisto Island............	32 30	80 18	-0 35	-0 41	-1.0	0.0	5.9	6.9	2.9
	South Edisto River									
2637	Big Bay Creek entrance............	32 30	80 20	0 00	-0 09	-0.8	0.0	6.1	7.2	3.0
2639	Peters Point, St. Pierre Creek......	32 32	80 21	+0 17	+0 04	-0.7	0.0	6.2	7.3	3.1
2641	Watts Cut ent., 0.8 mile south of...	32 36	80 23	+0 38	+0 55	-0.6	0.0	6.3	7.4	3.1
2643	Dawho River entrance.............	32 39	80 23	+1 28	+1 42	-0.6	0.0	6.3	7.4	3.1
2645	Jacksonboro......................	32 46	80 27	+3 16	+4 21	*0.28	*0.28	1.9	2.2	0.9

Endnotes can be found at the end of table 2.

NO.	PLACE	POSITION Lat.	POSITION Long.	DIFFERENCES Time High Water	DIFFERENCES Time Low Water	DIFFERENCES Height High Water	DIFFERENCES Height Low Water	RANGES Mean	RANGES Spring	Mean Tide Level
		° ' N	° ' W	h. m.	h. m.	ft	ft	ft	ft	ft
	St. Helena Sound Time meridian, 75°W			on SAVANNAH RIVER ENT., p.100						
2647	Harbor River entrance....................	32 24	80 27	-0 01	-0 05	-0.8	0.0	6.1	7.1	3.0
2649	Combahee Bank...........................	32 29	80 26	+0 04	+0 05	-0.7	0.0	6.2	7.3	3.1
2651	Seabrook, Ashepoo River.................	32 31	80 25	+0 13	+0 15	-0.7	0.0	6.2	7.3	3.1
2653	Hutchinson Island, Ashepoo River........	32 33	80 29	+0 41	+0 52	-0.6	0.0	6.3	7.4	3.1
2655	Fields Point, Combahee River............	32 34	80 33	+0 48	+0 58	-0.5	0.0	6.4	7.5	3.2
2657	Highway Bridge, Combahee River..........	32 39	80 41	+2 50	+2 51	*0.64	*0.64	4.4	5.1	2.2
2659	Lucy Point Creek ent., Morgan River.....	32 27	80 37	+0 58	+0 27	-0.1	0.0	6.8	8.0	3.4
2661	Summerhouse Point, Bull River...........	32 32	80 34	+1 03	+0 33	-0.3	0.0	6.6	7.8	3.3
2663	Brickyard Point, Coosaw River...........	32 30	80 40	+1 20	+1 07	+0.4	0.0	7.3	8.5	3.6
2665	Coosaw River............................	32 32	80 41	+1 25	+1 09	+0.3	0.0	7.2	8.4	3.6
2667	Fripp Inlet, Hunting Island.............	32 21	80 28	+0 01	-0 22	-0.7	0.0	6.2	7.3	3.1
	Port Royal Sound									
2669	Martins Industry........................	32 07	80 35	-0 30	-0 41	-0.5	0.0	6.4	7.6	3.2
2671	Hilton Head.............................	32 14	80 40	-0 08	-0 16	-0.3	0.0	6.6	7.8	3.3
2673	Club Bridge Creek entrance..............	32 20	80 33	+0 30	-0 20	-0.1	0.0	6.8	8.0	3.4
2675	Station Creek...........................	32 19	80 36	+0 28	-0 19	0.0	0.0	6.9	8.1	3.4
2677	Chowan Creek, Distant Island............	32 23	80 38	+1 03	+0 30	+0.2	0.0	7.1	8.3	3.5
2679	Parris Island, Beaufort River...........	32 21	80 40	+0 35	+0 17	+0.2	0.0	7.1	8.3	3.5
2681	Port Royal, Battery Creek...............	32 22	80 41	+0 37	+0 24	+0.3	0.0	7.2	8.5	3.6
2683	Beaufort, Beaufort River................	32 26	80 40	+1 13	+0 46	+0.5	0.0	7.4	8.7	3.7
2684	Colleton River Mouth....................	32 19	80 48	+0 46	+0 34	+0.4	0.0	7.3	8.5	3.7
2685	Victoria Bluff, Colleton River..........	32 18	80 48	+1 03	+0 32	+0.6	0.0	7.5	8.7	3.7
2687	Baileys Landing, Okatee River...........	32 21	80 54	+1 33	+0 59	+1.2	0.0	8.1	9.5	4.0
2689	Lemon Island, Chechessee River..........	32 22	80 50	+1 04	+0 45	+0.7	0.0	7.6	8.9	3.8
2691	Archers Creek entrance, Broad River.....	32 21	80 44	+0 41	+0 27	+0.2	0.0	7.1	8.3	3.5
2693	Corning Landing, Whale Branch...........	32 30	80 47	+1 29	+1 13	+1.0	0.0	7.9	9.2	3.9
2695	Skull Creek, north entrance.............	32 16	80 44	+0 26	+0 20	+0.1	0.0	7.0	8.3	3.5
2697	Skull Creek, south entrance.............	32 13	80 47	+0 33	+0 08	+0.7	0.0	7.6	9.0	3.8
2699	Haig Point, Daufuskie Island............	32 09	80 50	+0 09	-0 07	+0.3	0.0	7.2	8.4	3.6
2701	Bluffton, May River.....................	32 14	80 52	+0 54	+0 21	+1.2	0.0	8.1	9.5	4.0
2703	Daufuskie Landing, New River............	32 06	80 54	+0 23	+0 24	+0.3	0.0	7.2	8.5	3.6
2705	Walls Cut, Turtle Island................	32 05	80 55	+0 08	+0 16	+0.2	0.0	7.1	8.3	3.6
	GEORGIA Savannah River									
2707	Tybee Light.............................	32 02	80 51	-0 08	-0 15	-0.1	0.0	6.8	8.0	3.4
2709	SAVANNAH RIVER ENTRANCE.................	32 02	80 54	Daily predictions				6.9	8.1	3.5
				on SAVANNAH, p.104						
2711	Fort Jackson............................	32 05	81 02	-0 07	-0 14	+0.1	0.0	7.5	8.7	3.8
2713	SAVANNAH................................	32 05	81 05	Daily predictions				7.4	8.6	3.7
2715	Port Wentworth..........................	32 09	81 08	+0 33	+0 41	-0.4	0.0	7.0	8.1	3.5
2717	S.C.L. RR. bridge.......................	32 14	81 09	+1 15	+2 12	-1.2	0.0	6.2	7.2	3.1
	Tybee Creek and Wassaw Sound			on SAVANNAH RIVER ENT., p.100						
2719	Tybee Creek entrance....................	31 59	80 51	-0 07	+0 02	-0.1	0.0	6.8	8.0	3.4
2721	Beach Hammock...........................	31 57	80 56	+0 01	-0 10	0.0	0.0	6.9	8.1	3.4
2723	Romerly Marsh Creek.....................	31 56	81 00	+0 10	-0 06	+0.2	0.0	7.1	8.3	3.5
	Wilmington River									
2725	Savannah-Oglethorpe Hotel...........	32 00	81 00	+0 16	+0 03	+0.9	0.0	7.8	9.1	3.9
2727	Thunderbolt.........................	32 02	81 03	+0 34	+0 09	+1.0	0.0	7.9	9.2	3.9
2729	North entrance......................	32 04	81 00	+0 42	+0 41	+0.7	0.0	7.6	8.9	3.8
2731	Isle of Hope, Skidaway River............	31 59	81 03	+0 52	+0 25	+0.9	0.0	7.8	9.1	3.9
	Ossabaw Sound									
2733	Egg Islands.............................	31 50	81 05	+0 06	+0 07	+0.3	0.0	7.2	8.4	3.6
2735	Vernon View, Burnside River.............	31 56	81 06	+0 42	+0 28	+0.6	0.0	7.5	8.8	3.8
2737	Coffee Bluff, Forest River..............	31 56	81 09	+1 07	+0 39	+0.6	0.0	7.5	8.8	3.7
2739	Fort McAllister, Ogeechee River.........	31 53	81 13	+0 50	+1 13	0.0	0.0	6.9	8.1	3.4
2741	Highway bridge, Ogeechee River..........	31 59	81 17	+3 21	+4 22	*0.14	*0.14	1.0	1.2	0.5
2743	Cane Patch Creek entrance...............	31 49	81 09	+0 57	+0 40	+0.3	0.0	7.2	8.4	3.6
	St. Catherines and Sapelo Sounds									
2745	Walburg Creek entrance..................	31 42	81 09	+0 25	+0 20	+0.2	0.0	7.1	8.3	3.6
2747	Kilkenny Club, Kilkenny Creek...........	31 47	81 12	+0 31	+0 13	+1.0	0.0	7.9	9.2	3.9
2749	Sunbury, Medway River...................	31 46	81 17	+0 56	+0 42	+0.6	0.0	7.5	8.8	3.8
2751	Belfast, Belfast River..................	31 49	81 18	+1 25	+1 07	+0.9	0.0	7.8	9.1	3.9

Endnotes can be found at the end of table 2.

TABLE 2. — TIDAL DIFFERENCES AND OTHER CONSTANTS, 1983   225

NO.	PLACE	POSITION		DIFFERENCES				RANGES		Mean Tide Level
		Lat.	Long.	Time		Height		Mean	Spring	
				High Water	Low Water	High Water	Low Water			
		° ' N	° ' W	h. m.	h. m.	ft	ft	ft	ft	ft
	St. Catherines and Sapelo Sounds Time meridian, 75°W			on SAVANNAH RIVER ENT., p.100						
2753	North Newport River.....................	31 40	81 16	+0 58	+0 33	+0.7	0.0	7.6	8.9	3.8
2755	South Newport River.....................	31 38	81 16	+0 39	+0 44	+0.5	0.0	7.4	8.7	3.7
2756	Dallas Bluff, Julienton River...........	31 35	81 19	+0 50	+1 01	+0.7	0.0	7.6	8.9	3.8
2757	Blackbeard Island.......................	31 32	81 12	+0 20	+0 19	0.0	0.0	6.9	8.1	3.4
2758	Dog Hammock, Sapelo River...............	31 32	81 16	+0 31	+0 23	+0.2	0.0	7.1	8.3	3.6
2759	Pine Harbor, Sapelo River...............	31 33	81 22	+1 05	+1 01	+0.3	0.0	7.2	8.4	3.6
2760	Eagle Creek, Mud River..................	31 31	81 17	+0 23	+0 16	+0.3	0.0	7.2	8.4	3.6
2761	Mud River, at Old Teakettle Creek.......	31 29	81 19	+0 47	+0 43	+0.5	0.0	7.4	8.7	3.7
	Doboy and Altamaha Sounds									
2762	Blackbeard Creek, Blackbeard Island.....	31 29	81 13	+0 21	+0 44	-0.4	0.0	6.5	7.6	3.3
2763	Sapelo Island...........................	31 23	81 17	0 00	+0 02	-0.1	0.0	6.8	8.0	3.4
2765	Hudson Creek entrance...................	31 27	81 21	+0 39	+0 28	+0.3	0.0	7.2	8.4	3.6
2767	Threemile Cut entrance, Darien River....	31 21	81 23	+0 46	+0 52	+0.2	0.0	7.1	8.3	3.5
2769	Darien, Darien River....................	31 22	81 26	+1 10	+1 12	+0.4	0.0	7.3	8.5	3.6
2771	Wolf Island.............................	31 20	81 19	+0 06	+0 35	-0.3	0.0	6.6	7.7	3.3
2773	Champney Island, South Altamaha River...	31 20	81 28	+1 12	+2 30	-1.7	0.0	5.2	6.1	2.6
2775	Hampton River entrance..................	31 13	81 19	+0 18	+0 01	-0.3	0.0	6.6	7.8	3.3
2777	Jones Creek entrance, Hampton River.....	31 18	81 20	+1 05	+0 10	+0.3	0.0	7.2	8.5	3.6
	St. Simons Sound									
2779	St. Simons Sound Bar....................	31 06	81 19	+0 01	-0 05	-0.4	0.0	6.5	7.6	3.2
2781	St. Simons Light.......................	31 08	81 24	+0 24	+0 28	-0.3	0.0	6.6	7.7	3.3
2783	Frederica River........................	31 13	81 24	+0 50	+0 53	+0.3	0.0	7.2	8.4	3.6
2785	Troup Creek entrance, Mackay River.....	31 13	81 26	+0 54	+0 49	+0.3	0.0	7.2	8.4	3.6
2787	Brunswick, East River..................	31 09	81 30	+0 55	+0 40	+0.4	0.0	7.3	8.5	3.6
	Turtle River									
2789	Allied Chemical Corp. docks.........	31 11	81 31	+1 05	+0 39	+0.7	0.0	7.6	8.9	3.8
2791	Dillard Creek.......................	31 14	81 34	+1 34	+0 59	+1.1	0.0	8.0	9.4	4.0
2793	Buffalo River entrance..............	31 13	81 35	+1 39	+0 55	+1.1	0.0	8.0	9.4	4.0
2795	Highway bridge, South Brunswick River...	31 09	81 34	+1 09	+0 46	+0.7	0.0	7.6	8.9	3.8
2797	Jekyll Point...........................	31 01	81 26	+0 28	+0 28	-0.3	0.0	6.6	7.7	3.3
2799	Jointer Island, Jointer Creek..........	31 06	81 30	+1 02	+0 49	+0.3	0.0	7.2	8.4	3.6
	Little Satilla River									
2801	2.5 miles above mouth...............	31 04	81 30	+0 47	+0 49	-0.1	0.0	6.8	8.0	3.4
2803	8 miles above mouth.................	31 06	81 34	+1 15	+1 20	+0.4	0.0	7.3	8.5	3.6
2805	Below Spring Bluff..................	31 10	81 37	+2 00	+1 49	+0.6	0.0	7.5	8.8	3.7
2807	Dover Bluff, Dover Creek...............	31 01	81 32	+0 57	+0 49	+0.1	0.0	7.0	8.2	3.5
	Satilla River									
2809	Todd Creek entrance.................	30 58	81 31	+0 43	+0 59	-0.2	0.0	6.7	7.8	3.3
2811	Bailey Cut, 0.8 mile west of........	30 59	81 36	+0 57	+1 20	0.0	0.0	6.9	8.1	3.4
2813	Ceylon..............................	30 58	81 39	+1 25	+1 53	-0.3	0.0	6.6	7.7	3.3
2815	Burnt Fort..........................	30 57	81 54	+4 46	+5 23	*0.46	*0.46	3.2	3.7	1.6
2817	Cumberland Wharf, Cumberland River......	30 56	81 27	+0 40	+0 42	-0.1	0.0	6.8	8.0	3.4
2819	Floyd Creek, 2.8 miles above entrance...	30 56	81 30	+0 59	+0 39	+0.2	0.0	7.1	8.3	3.5
	GEORGIA and FLORIDA Cumberland Sound									
2821	St. Marys Entrance, north jetty.........	30 43	81 26	+0 15	+0 15	-1.1	0.0	5.8	6.8	2.9
2823	Crooked River entrance..................	30 51	81 29	+1 23	+1 12	-0.1	0.0	6.8	8.0	3.4
2825	Harrietts Bluff, Crooked River..........	30 52	81 35	+2 09	+2 12	-0.5	0.0	6.4	7.5	3.2
2827	St. Marys, St. Marys River..............	30 43	81 33	+1 21	+1 13	-0.9	0.0	6.0	7.0	3.0
2829	Crandall, St. Marys River...............	30 43	81 37	+2 10	+1 59	-1.8	0.0	5.1	6.0	2.5
				on MAYPORT, p.108						
2831	Fernandina Beach (outer coast)..........	30 38	81 26	-0 18	-0 01	+1.2	0.0	5.7	6.7	2.8
2833	Fernandina Beach, Amelia River..........	30 40	81 28	+0 32	+0 16	+1.5	0.0	6.0	7.0	3.0
2835	Chester, Bells River....................	30 41	81 32	+0 49	+0 41	+1.9	0.0	6.4	7.5	3.2
2837	S.C.L. RR. bridge, Kingsley Creek.......	30 38	81 29	+0 59	+0 43	+1.5	0.0	6.0	7.0	3.0
	FLORIDA Nassau Sound and Fort George River									
2839	Nassau Sound............................	30 31	81 27	-0 03	+0 06	+0.9	0.0	5.4	6.3	2.7
2841	Amelia City, South Amelia River.........	30 35	81 28	+0 54	+1 03	+1.1	0.0	5.6	6.6	2.8
2843	Nassauville, Nassau River...............	30 34	81 31	+1 04	+1 37	+0.3	0.0	4.8	5.6	2.4
2845	Mink Creek entrance, Nassau River.......	30 32	81 34	+1 58	+2 32	-0.6	0.0	3.9	4.6	1.9
2847	Halfmoon Island, highway bridge.........	30 34	81 36	+3 00	+3 21	-1.0	0.0	3.5	4.1	1.7
2849	Sawpit Creek entrance...................	30 31	81 27	-0 02	+0 30	+0.5	0.0	5.0	5.8	2.5
2851	Fort George Island, Fort George River...	30 26	81 26	+0 29	+0 39	+0.3	0.0	4.8	5.6	2.4
	FLORIDA, St. Johns River									
2853	South Jetty.............................	30 24	81 23	-0 23	-0 17	+0.4	0.0	4.9	5.7	2.4
2855	MAYPORT.................................	30 24	81 26	Daily predictions				4.5	5.3	2.3

Endnotes can be found at the end of table 2.

TABLE 2. — TIDAL DIFFERENCES AND OTHER CONSTANTS, 1983

NO.	PLACE	POSITION Lat.	Long.	DIFFERENCES Time High Water	Low Water	Height High Water	Low Water	RANGES Mean	Spring	Mean Tide Level
		° ' N	° ' W	h. m.	h. m.	ft	ft	ft	ft	ft
	FLORIDA, St. Johns River Time meridian, 75°W			on MAYPORT, p.108						
2857	Pablo Creek bascule bridge..............	30 19	81 26	+1 39	+1 15	*0.64	*0.64	2.9	3.4	1.4
2859	Fulton.................................	30 23	81 30	+0 29	+0 42	-1.1	0.0	3.4	4.0	1.7
2861	Dame Point.............................	30 23	81 33	+0 46	+0 55	*0.67	*0.67	3.0	3.5	1.5
2863	Phoenix Park (Cummers Mill)............	30 23	81 38	+0 58	+1 25	*0.44	*0.44	2.0	2.3	1.0
2865	Jacksonville (Dredge Depot)............	30 21	81 37	+1 24	+1 50	*0.44	*0.44	2.0	2.3	1.0
2867	Jacksonville (RR. bridge)..............	30 19	81 40	+2 06	+2 13	*0.27	*0.27	1.2	1.4	0.6
2869	Ortega River entrance..................	30 17	81 42	+2 27	+2 50	*0.20	*0.20	0.9	1.1	0.5
2871	Orange Park............................	30 10	81 42	+3 49	+4 14	*0.16	*0.16	0.7	0.8	0.3
2873	Green Cove Springs.....................	30 00	81 40	+5 26	+6 13	*0.18	*0.18	0.8	0.9	0.4
2875	East Tocol.............................	29 51	81 34	+6 47	+7 18	*0.22	*0.22	1.0	1.2	0.5
2877	Bridgeport.............................	29 45	81 34	+6 58	+7 32	*0.24	*0.24	1.1	1.3	0.5
2879	Palatka................................	29 39	81 38	+7 26	+8 21	*0.27	*0.27	1.2	1.4	0.6
2881	Welaka.................................	29 29	81 40	+7 46	+8 25	*0.11	*0.11	0.5	0.6	0.2
	FLORIDA, East Coast									
2883	Atlantic Beach.........................	30 20	81 24	-0 25	-0 18	+0.7	0.0	5.2	6.0	2.6
2885	St. Augustine Inlet....................	29 53	81 17	-0 21	-0 01	0.0	0.0	4.5	5.3	2.2
2887	St. Augustine..........................	29 54	81 18	+0 14	+0 43	-0.3	0.0	4.2	5.0	2.1
2889	Daytona Beach (ocean)..................	29 14	81 00	-0 33	-0 32	-0.4	0.0	4.1	4.9	2.0
				on MIAMI HARBOR ENT., p.112						
2891	Ponce de Leon Inlet....................	29 04	80 55	+0 06	+0 20	-0.2	0.0	2.3	2.7	1.2
2893	Cape Canaveral.........................	28 26	80 34	-0 41	-0 41	+1.0	0.0	3.5	4.1	1.8
2894	Oak Hill, Mosquito Lagoon <21>.........	28 52	80 50	- - -	- - -	- -	- -	- -	- -	- -
	Indian River									
2895	Melbourne <22>.....................	28 06	80 37	- - -	- - -	- -	- -	- -	- -	- -
2896	Palm Bay...........................	28 02	80 35	+3 40	+4 19	*0.10	*0.10	0.2	0.2	0.1
2897	Wabasso............................	27 45	80 26	+2 48	+3 19	*0.16	*0.16	0.4	0.5	0.2
2898	Vero Beach.........................	27 38	80 22	+3 21	+3 50	*0.32	*0.32	0.8	1.0	0.4
2900	Fort Pierce........................	27 27	80 19	+1 08	+1 01	*0.48	*0.48	1.2	1.4	0.6
2901	Jensen Beach.......................	27 14	80 13	+2 40	+3 06	*0.40	*0.40	1.0	1.2	0.5
2902	Sebastian Inlet (ocean)................	27 52	80 27	-0 24	-0 20	-0.4	0.0	2.1	2.5	1.0
2903	Vero Beach (ocean).....................	27 40	80 22	-0 31	-0 25	-0.9	0.0	3.4	4.0	1.7
2905	Fort Pierce Inlet, south jetty........	27 28	80 17	-0 09	-0 14	+0.1	0.0	2.6	3.1	1.3
	St. Lucie River									
2907	North Fork.........................	27 15	80 19	+2 50	+3 29	*0.40	*0.40	1.0	1.2	0.5
2908	Stuart.............................	27 12	80 16	+2 37	+3 33	*0.36	*0.36	0.9	1.1	0.4
2909	South Fork.........................	27 10	80 15	+2 54	+3 34	*0.36	*0.36	0.9	1.1	0.4
2911	Sewall Point.......................	27 10	80 11	+1 35	+2 11	*0.36	*0.36	0.9	1.1	0.4
2912	Seminole Shores........................	27 11	80 10	-0 30	-0 14	+0.5	0.0	3.0	3.6	1.5
2913	Great Pocket...........................	27 09	80 10	+1 18	+1 51	*0.44	*0.44	1.1	1.3	0.6
2914	Gomez, South Jupiter Narrows...........	27 06	80 08	+1 56	+2 41	*0.52	*0.52	1.3	1.6	0.6
2916	Hobe Sound - State Park................	27 02	80 06	+1 46	+2 22	-0.9	0.0	1.6	1.9	0.8
2917	Conch Bar, Jupiter Sound...............	26 59	80 06	+1 19	+1 38	-0.8	0.0	1.7	2.0	0.8
2918	Jupiter Sound, south end...............	26 57	80 05	+0 46	+0 49	-0.5	0.0	2.0	2.4	1.0
2919	Jupiter Inlet..........................	26 57	80 04	+0 15	+0 01	0.0	0.0	2.5	3.0	1.2
	Loxahatchee River									
2921	Tequesta...........................	26 57	80 06	+1 18	+2 02	-0.7	0.0	1.8	2.2	0.9
2922	North Fork.........................	26 58	80 07	+1 27	+1 59	-0.6	0.0	1.9	2.3	1.0
2923	Southwest Fork (spillway)..........	26 56	80 09	+1 15	+1 49	-0.5	0.0	2.0	2.4	1.0
2924	Northwest Fork.....................	26 59	80 08	+1 34	+2 10	-0.5	0.0	2.0	2.4	1.0
2926	Southwest Fork.....................	26 57	80 07	+1 15	+1 47	-0.6	0.0	1.9	2.3	1.0
2927	Jupiter, Lake Worth Creek..............	26 56	80 05	+0 57	+1 16	-0.4	0.0	2.1	2.5	1.0
2928	Donald Ross Bridge.....................	26 53	80 04	+0 43	+0 54	-0.2	0.0	2.3	2.8	1.2
2929	North Palm Beach, Lake Worth Creek.....	26 50	80 03	+0 05	+0 17	-0.4	0.0	2.9	3.4	1.3
2931	Port of Palm Beach, Lake Worth.........	26 46	80 03	0 00	+0 12	+0.1	0.0	2.6	3.1	1.3
2932	Palm Beach (ocean).....................	26 43	80 02	-0 21	-0 18	+0.3	0.0	2.8	3.3	1.4
2933	West Palm Beach Canal..................	26 39	80 03	+1 08	+1 36	0.0	0.0	2.5	2.8	1.2
2934	Lake Worth Pier (ocean)................	26 37	80 02	-0 19	-0 17	+0.3	0.0	2.8	3.3	1.4
2936	Boynton Beach..........................	26 33	80 03	+1 26	+2 09	0.0	0.0	2.5	2.8	1.2
2937	Delray Beach...........................	26 28	80 04	+1 45	+2 09	0.0	0.0	2.5	2.9	1.2
2938	Yamato.................................	26 24	80 04	+1 43	+1 59	-0.1	0.0	2.4	2.8	1.2
2939	Boca Raton.............................	26 21	80 05	+0 47	+1 13	-0.3	0.0	2.2	2.5	1.1
2941	Deerfield Beach........................	26 19	80 05	+0 51	+1 07	-0.1	0.0	2.4	2.9	1.2
2942	Hillsboro Beach, Intracoastal waterway.	26 16	80 05	+0 26	+0 38	+0.3	0.0	2.8	3.2	1.4
2943	Hillsboro Inlet (inside)...............	26 16	80 05	+0 08	+0 06	0.0	0.0	2.5	2.9	1.2
2944	Lauderdale-by-the-sea..................	26 11	80 06	-0 08	-0 08	+0.1	0.0	2.6	3.1	1.3
	Fort Lauderdale									
2946	Bahia Mar Yacht Club...............	26 07	80 06	+0 19	+0 38	-0.1	0.0	2.4	2.8	1.2
2947	Andrews Ave. bridge, New River.....	26 07	80 09	+0 39	+0 56	-0.4	0.0	2.1	2.4	1.0
2948	Port Everglades........................	26 06	80 07	-0 06	-0 06	+0.1	0.0	2.6	3.1	1.3
2949	South Port Everglades..................	26 05	80 07	0 00	+0 01	0.0	0.0	2.5	2.9	1.3
2951	Hollywood Beach........................	26 02	80 07	+1 00	+1 08	-0.4	0.0	2.1	2.4	1.0
2952	Golden Beach...........................	25 58	80 08	+1 36	+2 04	-0.4	0.0	2.1	2.4	1.0
2953	Sunny Isles, Biscayne Creek............	25 56	80 08	+2 23	+2 27	-0.7	0.0	1.8	2.2	0.9
2954	North Miami Beach......................	25 56	80 07	-0 04	0 00	0.0	0.0	2.5	3.0	1.2
2956	Bakers Haulover Inlet (inside).........	25 54	80 08	+1 17	+1 35	-0.5	0.0	2.0	2.4	1.0
2957	Indian Creek...........................	25 52	80 09	+1 36	+1 50	-0.4	0.0	2.1	2.5	1.1
2958	Miami Beach............................	25 46	80 08	0 00	0 00	0.0	0.0	2.5	3.0	1.3
2959	MIAMI HARBOR ENTRANCE..................	25 46	80 08	Daily predictions				2.5	3.0	1.3

Endnotes can be found at the end of table 2.

TABLE 2. — TIDAL DIFFERENCES AND OTHER CONSTANTS, 1983   233

NO.	PLACE	POSITION Lat.	Long.	DIFFERENCES Time High Water	Low Water	Height High Water	Low Water	RANGES Mean	Spring	Mean Tide Level
		° ' N	° ' W	h. m.	h. m.	ft	ft	ft	ft	ft
	VENEZUELA Time meridian, 60°W			on ISLA ZAPARA, p.152						
3551	ISLA ZAPARA, Lake Maracaibo.............	11 00	71 35	Daily predictions				2.8	3.0	2.7
3552	Bahia de Tablazos, Lake Maracaibo.......	10 53	71 35	+0 30	+0 11	*0.61	*0.31	2.1	2.3	1.5
3553	Punta de Palmas.........................	10 48	71 37	+0 35	+0 16	*0.49	*0.31	1.6	1.8	1.2
				on AMUAY, p.156				**Mean Diurnal**		
3554	AMUAY...................................	11 45	70 13	Daily predictions				- -	1.2	0.6
3555	La Guaira †.............................	10 36	66 56	-2 29	-1 59	+0.8	+1.0	- -	1.0	1.5
3557	Carenero †..............................	10 32	66 07	-1 51	-1 59	+0.8	+1.0	- -	1.0	1.5
3559	Cumana †................................	10 28	64 11	-2 37	-1 02	-0.1	0.0	- -	1.1	0.5
3561	Porlamar, Isla de Margarita †...........	10 57	63 51	-1 19	-0 59	+0.6	0.0	- -	1.8	0.9
3563	Carupano †..............................	10 40	63 15	-1 17	-0 42	+0.2	0.0	- -	1.4	0.7
	Gulf of Paria			on PUNTA GORDA, p.160				**Mean Spring**		
3565	Macuro..................................	10 39	61 56	-1 15	-2 05	*0.38	*0.38	2.2	2.7	1.4
3567	Puerto de Hierro........................	10 37	62 05	-0 46	-1 19	*0.59	*0.59	3.3	4.2	2.0
3569	Barra de Maturin, channel entrance..	10 18	62 31	-0 22	-0 45	-1.0	+0.2	4.6	5.7	2.8
3571	PUNTA GORDA, Rio San Juan............	10 10	62 38	Daily predictions				5.8	7.1	3.2
3573	Boca Pedernales entrance.............	10 01	62 12	-0 03	-0 34	-1.3	+0.2	4.3	5.4	2.6
3575	Rio Orinoco ent., Isla Ramon Isidro.....	8 39	60 35	+0 07	-0 12	+0.2	+1.0	5.0	6.7	3.8
	TRINIDAD									
3577	Staubles Bay............................	10 41	61 39	-1 07	-2 02	(*0.33+1.7)		1.9	2.5	2.8
3579	Carenage Bay............................	10 41	61 36	-0 58	-1 40	(*0.34+1.6)		2.0	2.6	2.7
3581	Port of Spain...........................	10 39	61 31	-0 44	-1 12	(*0.31+1.4)		1.8	2.3	2.4
3583	Bonasse pier............................	10 05	61 52	-0 43	+1 15	-1.0	+1.4	3.4	4.4	3.4
3585	Erin Bay................................	10 04	61 49	-0 50	-1 41	-0.3	+1.2	4.3	5.6	3.6
3587	Guayaguayare Bay........................	10 09	61 01	-1 32	-2 09	(*0.53+1.3)		3.1	3.8	3.0
3588	Nariva River............................	10 24	61 02	-1 06	-2 16	(*0.41+1.3)		2.4	3.1	2.5
	GUYANA Time meridian, 56°15'W			on SURINAME RIVIER, p.164						
3589	Parika, Essequibo River.................	6 52	58 25	+0 37	+1 01	+1.6	+1.0	6.6	8.3	5.6
3591	Georgetown..............................	6 48	58 10	+0 17	+0 01	+0.9	+1.1	5.8	8.0	5.3
	SURINAM Time meridian, 52°30'W									
3593	Nickerie River..........................	5 57	56 59	+0 09	+0 21	+1.1	0.0	7.1	9.2	4.9
3595	SURINAME RIVIER ENTRANCE................	6 00	55 14	Daily predictions				6.0	7.6	4.3
3597	Paramaribo, Suriname Rivier.............	5 49	55 09	+1 09	+1 42	0.0	0.0	6.0	7.3	4.3
	FRENCH GUIANA Time meridian, 60°W									
3599	Rio Maroni entrance.....................	5 45	53 58	+0 48	+0 54	+0.7	+1.2	5.5	7.2	5.2
3601	Iles du Salut...........................	5 17	52 35	+0 23	+0 23	+1.7	+2.2	5.5	7.2	6.2
3603	Cayenne.................................	4 56	52 20	+0 45	+0 45	+2.4	+1.8	6.6	7.8	6.4
	BRAZIL ⟨16⟩ Time meridian, 45°W.									
3605	Cape Cassipore..........................	3 49	51 01	+1 54	+1 49	+1.5	+0.3	7.2	9.5	5.2
3607	Rio Cunani entrance.....................	2 50	50 53	+2 40	+2 54	(*2.42-0.2)		14.5	19.0	10.1
3609	Ilha de Maraca anchorage................	2 09	50 30	+2 10	+2 22	(*2.42-0.2)		14.5	19.0	10.1
3611	Ilha do Brigue, Amazon River............	0 55	50 05	+7 39	+8 10	+8.3	+1.1	13.2	15.7	9.0
3613	Ponta Pedreira, Amazon River............	0 11	50 43	+7 01	+7 13	*2.08	*2.23	12.3	16.2	9.0
3615	Macapa, Amazon River....................	0 03	51 11	+11 27	+12 43	+2.8	+0.4	8.4	9.5	5.9
		S	W							
3617	Canal de Braganca, Rio Para entrance....	0 23	47 55	+6 39	+6 39	+1.8	-0.1	7.9	10.4	5.1
3619	Salinopolis.............................	0 39	47 23	+3 08	+3 22	*1.99	*1.54	12.5	15.9	8.3
3621	Belem (Para)............................	1 27	48 30	+7 04	+8 07	+2.9	+0.7	8.2	10.1	6.1
3623	Ilhas de Sao Joao.......................	1 17	44 55	+2 01	+2 01	+1.70	*1.31	10.7	14.1	7.0
3625	Sao Luiz................................	2 32	44 18	+2 58	+2 55	(*2.35-0.7)		14.1	17.1	9.3
3627	Santana, Recifes de.....................	2 16	43 36	+1 16	+1 15	*1.58	*1.15	10.0	13.1	6.5
3629	Tutoia, Baia da.........................	2 46	42 14	+0 41	+0 40	+2.4	+0.4	8.0	10.0	5.7
3631	Luis Correia............................	2 53	41 40	+0 31	+0 43	+1.8	+0.4	7.4	9.4	5.4
3633	Camocim.................................	2 53	40 52	+1 37	+1 36	+2.0	+0.4	7.6	9.7	5.5
3635	Rio Ceara (bar).........................	3 41	38 37	+0 17	+0 09	+0.2	-0.1	6.3	8.3	4.3
3637	Fortaleza...............................	3 43	38 29	+0 22	+0 18	+0.2	-0.3	6.5	8.5	4.2
	Time meridian, 30°W			on RECIFE, p.168						
3639	Fernando de Noronha.....................	3 50	32 25	+1 32	+1 33	-1.2	-0.5	4.5	6.0	2.9
3641	Rocas, Atol das.........................	3 51	33 49	+1 43	+1 44	+2.3	0.0	7.5	10.0	4.9

Endnotes can be found at the end of table 2.

NO.	PLACE	POSITION Lat.	POSITION Long.	DIFFERENCES Time High Water	DIFFERENCES Time Low Water	DIFFERENCES Height High Water	DIFFERENCES Height Low Water	RANGES Mean	RANGES Spring	Mean Tide Level
		° ' S	° ' W	h. m.	h. m.	ft	ft	ft	ft	ft
	BRAZIL <16> Time meridian, 45°W				on RECIFE, p.168					
3643	Macau, Rio Acu........................	5 06	36 41	+1 29	+1 58	+0.6	-0.1	5.9	7.6	4.1
3645	Natal................................	5 47	35 12	+0 28	+0 30	+0.1	-0.2	5.5	7.3	3.7
3647	Cabedelo.............................	6 58	34 50	+0 36	+0 37	+0.1	-0.2	5.5	7.2	3.7
3649	Tambau...............................	7 06	34 50	-0 04	-0 03	+0.7	-0.1	6.0	7.6	4.1
3651	RECIFE...............................	8 03	34 52	Daily predictions				5.3	7.1	3.8
3653	Maceio...............................	9 40	35 43	+0 10	+0 14	-0.3	-0.2	5.1	6.8	3.6
3655	Rio Sao Francisco (bar)..............	10 31	36 24	+0 06	+0 14	-0.7	0.0	4.5	6.0	3.5
3657	Aracaju..............................	10 56	37 03	+0 33	+0 48	-0.8	-0.3	4.7	6.1	3.3
3659	Salvador.............................	12 58	38 31	-0 02	-0 08	+0.6	+0.4	5.5	7.4	4.3
3661	Ponta da Areia.......................	12 47	38 30	+0 10	+0 06	+0.6	-0.1	5.9	7.6	4.0
3663	Morro de Sao Paulo...................	13 21	38 54	-0 11	-0 13	-0.6	0.0	4.6	6.0	3.5
3665	Camamu...............................	13 54	38 58	-0 08	-0 04	-0.2	+0.1	4.9	6.5	3.8
3667	Ilheus...............................	14 48	39 02	-0 33	-0 32	-0.1	-0.3	4.6	5.8	3.2
3669	Canavieiras..........................	15 40	38 56	+0 16	+0 22	-1.0	-0.2	4.5	5.8	3.1
3671	Santa Cruz Cabralia..................	16 17	39 02	-0 35	-0 35	-1.2	-0.5	4.5	6.0	2.9
3673	Cumuruxatiba.........................	17 06	39 11	-0 23	-0 09	+0.4	+0.3	5.3	7.2	3.8
3675	Caravelas............................	17 43	39 09	-0 50	-0 49	-0.8	-0.5	4.9	6.4	3.1
3677	Abrolhos Anchorage...................	17 58	38 42	-0 01	+0 04	+0.6	+0.1	5.7	7.6	4.2
3679	Vitoria..............................	20 19	40 19	-0 34	-0 35	*0.66	*0.75	3.3	4.6	2.6
3681	Guarapari............................	20 40	40 30	+0 12	+0 17	*0.62	*0.75	3.1	4.2	2.5
					on RIO DE JANEIRO, p.172					
3683	Sao Joao da Barra....................	21 38	41 03	+0 34	-0 42	-0.1	-0.2	2.6	3.6	2.1
3685	Macae (Imbitiba Bay).................	22 23	41 46	-0 23	-1 08	0.0	-0.2	2.7	3.6	2.1
3687	Armacao dos Buzios...................	22 45	41 53	-0 01	-0 55	-0.1	-0.1	2.5	3.4	2.1
3689	Cabo Frio............................	23 00	42 03	-0 03	-0 05	*0.91	*0.90	2.3	3.2	2.0
3691	RIO DE JANEIRO.......................	22 54	43 10	Daily predictions				2.5	3.5	2.2
3693	Itacurussa...........................	22 56	43 55	+0 50	-0 26	0.0	-0.1	2.6	3.3	2.2
3695	Angra dos Reis.......................	23 01	44 19	-0 35	-0 40	*0.86	*0.86	2.1	3.0	1.9
3697	Parati...............................	23 14	44 43	-0 09	-1 25	-0.1	0.0	2.4	3.4	2.2
3699	Sao Sebastiao........................	23 49	45 24	-0 28	-1 24	*0.94	*1.00	2.3	3.3	2.2
3701	SANTOS...............................	23 56	46 19	Daily predictions				2.6	3.8	2.4
3703	Cananeia.............................	25 01	47 56	+1 09	-1 09	+0.4	+0.2	2.7	4.1	2.6
3705	Paranagua............................	25 31	48 27	+1 51	-1 32	+1.8	+0.2	4.4	6.0	3.2
3707	Sao Francisco do Sul.................	26 15	48 38	+0 38	- - -	+0.8	-0.1	3.4	4.8	2.6
3709	Itajai...............................	26 54	48 39	-0 08	-0 16	(*0.76+0.4)		1.9	2.8	2.1
3711	Porto Belo...........................	27 09	48 33	-0 38	-0 28	*0.74	*0.74	1.8	2.5	1.7
3713	Florianopolis........................	27 36	48 34	-0 14	+0 15	*0.69	*0.70	1.7	2.4	1.6
3715	Imbituba.............................	28 14	48 39	-0 17	-1 10	*0.54	*0.50	1.4	2.0	1.2
3717	Laguna...............................	28 30	48 47	+1 10	-1 31	(*0.32+0.4)		0.8	1.2	1.1
3719	Barra do Rio Grande <18> †...........	32 10	52 05	- - -	- - -	- -	- -	- -	0.8	0.3
	URUGUAY				on BUENOS AIRES, p.180					
3721	Montevideo...........................	34 55	56 13	-5 10	-7 11	(*0.52+1.6)		1.1	1.4	3.0
3723	Colonia, Rio de la Plata.............	34 28	57 51	+0 17	-0 33	(*0.52+1.2)		1.1	1.3	2.6
	ARGENTINA									
	Rio de la Plata									
3725	BUENOS AIRES.........................	34 36	58 22	Daily predictions				2.1	2.5	2.6
3727	La Plata.............................	34 50	57 53	-1 50	-2 04	+0.2	+0.6	1.7	2.0	3.0
3729	Banco Chico..........................	34 50	57 30	-3 00	-3 24	+0.8	+0.8	2.1	2.5	3.4
3731	Banco Cuirassier.....................	35 06	57 08	-5 25	-5 39	+0.8	+0.8	2.1	2.5	3.4
3733	Punta Piedras........................	35 26	57 07	-7 10	-7 23	+2.2	+1.1	3.2	3.8	4.2
3735	Punta Norte del Cabo San Antonio <17>...	36 18	56 47	-8 50	-9 26	+1.2	+0.3	3.0	3.7	3.3
3737	Mar del Plata <17>...................	38 03	57 33	-0 02	+0 14	+0.7	+0.2	2.6	3.0	3.0
3739	Quequen <17>.........................	38 35	58 42	-0 18	-0 22	+1.5	-0.3	3.9	4.2	3.2
					on PUERTO BELGRANO, p.184					
3741	Faro Recalada........................	39 00	61 16	-0 20	-0 15	-4.1	-0.7	6.5	7.1	5.6
3743	Monte Hermoso........................	38 59	61 41	-0 18	-0 27	-2.8	-0.8	7.9	9.1	6.2
	Bahia Blanca									
3745	Punta Ancla..........................	38 57	62 00	-0 15	+0 06	-1.1	-0.3	9.1	9.9	7.2
3747	Puerto Rosales.......................	38 55	62 04	0 00	+0 07	+0.1	-0.1	10.1	11.0	8.0
3749	PUERTO BELGRANO......................	38 53	62 06	Daily predictions				9.9	10.8	8.0
3751	Ingeniero White......................	38 47	62 16	+0 33	+0 18	+0.6	+0.4	10.1	11.0	8.5
3753	General Daniel Cerri.................	38 45	62 23	+0 47	+0 36	*1.19	*1.20	11.8	12.9	9.5
3755	Canal del Sur, Isla Bermejo..........	39 01	61 58	-0 28	-0 12	-1.3	-0.2	8.8	9.6	7.2
3757	Canal Bermejo, Isla Trinidad.........	39 05	61 58	-0 30	-0 14	-1.9	-0.4	8.4	9.2	6.8
3759	Punta Lobos, Isla Trinidad...........	39 14	61 53	-0 48	-0 46	-2.5	-0.6	8.0	8.8	6.4
3761	Punta Laberinto......................	39 26	62 03	-0 49	-0 58	-2.1	-0.9	8.7	9.6	6.5
3763	Bahia Anegada, Islote NW.............	40 01	62 10	-1 39	-1 47	(*0.66-0.5)		6.5	7.2	4.8
3765	Bahia San Blas.......................	40 33	62 14	-3 19	-3 28	*0.53	*0.40	5.6	6.0	4.0
3767	Segunda Barranca.....................	40 47	62 17	-4 49	-4 57	(*0.55-0.4)		5.4	5.9	4.0
3769	Punta Redonda, Rio Negro entrance....	41 02	62 46	-5 48	-5 57	-1.0	-1.0	9.9	11.2	7.0

Endnotes can be found at the end of table 2.

TABLE 2. — TIDAL DIFFERENCES AND OTHER CONSTANTS, 1983   235

NO.	PLACE	POSITION		DIFFERENCES				RANGES		Mean Tide Level
		Lat.	Long.	Time		Height		Mean	Spring	
				High Water	Low Water	High Water	Low Water			
		° ' S	° ' W	h. m.	h. m.	ft	ft	ft	ft	ft
	ARGENTINA Time meridian, 45°W			on COMODORO RIVADAVIA, p.188						
	Golfo San Matias									
3771	Caleta de los Loros...............	41 02	64 06	+7 14	+7 08	*1.45	*1.39	20.3	24.0	14.8
3773	Puerto San Antonio................	40 48	64 52	+7 30	+7 23	(*1.57-1.6)		21.9	25.6	14.6
	Golfo San Jose									
3775	San Roman.........................	42 15	64 14	+7 15	+7 18	(*1.42-1.1)		19.8	23.4	13.5
3777	Pueyrredon (Fondeadero)...........	42 24	64 09	+7 46	+7 40	(*1.52-2.2)		21.2	24.6	13.5
3779	La Argentina (Fondeadero).........	42 23	64 34	+7 04	+6 58	*1.31	*1.36	18.0	23.3	13.5
3781	Punta Norte.......................	42 05	63 46	+6 50	+6 44	-0.8	-1.4	14.5	17.0	9.5
3783	Caleta Valdes.....................	42 31	63 36	+5 04	+4 58	-5.2	-1.9	10.6	12.4	6.7
3785	Punta Delgada.....................	42 46	63 38	+4 08	+4 02	-5.8	-2.0	10.1	11.7	6.4
	Golfo Nuevo									
3787	Punta Ninfas (Fondeadero).........	42 57	64 25	+2 48	+3 31	-2.3	-1.0	12.6	15.4	8.6
3789	Puerto Piramides..................	42 35	64 17	+2 56	+3 33	-2.7	-1.3	12.5	15.0	8.3
3791	Puerto Madryn.....................	42 46	65 02	+3 08	+3 42	-0.8	-0.1	13.2	16.0	9.8
3793	Bahia Engano......................	43 20	65 04	+2 06	+2 00	-2.7	-1.3	12.5	15.2	8.2
3795	Isla Escondida....................	43 43	65 17	+2 10	+2 05	-3.3	-0.3	10.9	13.1	8.5
3797	Bahia Janssen.....................	44 02	65 14	+1 48	+2 03	-4.1	-1.9	11.7	13.9	7.3
3799	Cabo Raso.........................	44 20	65 14	+1 41	+1 26	-4.8	-1.6	10.7	12.4	7.0
3801	Bahia Cruz........................	44 27	65 19	+2 13	+2 07	-6.1	-2.1	9.9	11.5	6.2
3803	Santa Elena, Puerto...............	44 31	65 22	+1 45	+1 40	-3.1	-0.4	11.2	13.6	8.5
3805	Bahia Camarones...................	44 54	65 36	+1 10	+1 14	-2.3	+0.1	11.5	13.7	9.2
	Golfo San Jorge									
3807	Caleta Leones.....................	45 03	65 37	+1 11	+1 05	-0.7	-0.2	13.4	14.7	9.8
3809	Bahia Gil (Caleta Horno)..........	45 02	65 41	+0 42	+0 36	-1.7	+0.3	11.9	14.1	9.6
3811	Puerto Melo.......................	45 01	65 50	+0 27	+0 24	-1.5	+0.1	12.3	14.6	9.6
3813	Isla Tova.........................	45 06	65 59	+0 27	+0 40	-1.5	+0.1	12.3	14.6	9.6
3815	Bahia Bustamante..................	45 07	66 32	+0 28	+0 23	-0.8	+0.7	12.4	14.7	10.2
3817	COMODORO RIVADAVIA................	45 52	67 29	Daily predictions				14.0	16.3	10.3
3819	Cabo Blanco.......................	47 12	65 45	-1 15	-1 20	-2.3	-0.3	11.9	13.2	9.0
3821	Puerto Deseado....................	47 45	65 55	-2 52	-2 44	-0.6	+1.0	12.4	14.5	10.5
3823	Bahia Oso Marino..................	47 56	65 48	-3 35	-3 40	-1.2	+1.2	11.5	14.1	10.3
3825	Bahia de los Nodales..............	48 01	65 57	-3 01	-3 06	-1.2	+0.6	12.6	15.3	9.7
3827	Bahia Laura.......................	48 23	66 29	-5 28	-5 28	+6.7	-1.9	22.5	25.4	12.7
3829	Bahia San Julian (Punta Pena).....	49 15	67 40	-4 58	-5 04	(*1.40-1.4)		19.5	23.6	13.0
				on PUNTA LOYOLA, p.192						
3831	Santa Cruz (Punta Quilla).........	50 07	68 25	+0 43	+0 44	+0.2	+0.1	26.0	32.4	20.4
3833	Ria Coig..........................	50 57	69 10	-0 05	-0 04	0.0	-0.7	26.6	32.2	19.9
3835	PUNTA LOYOLA......................	51 36	69 01	Daily predictions				25.9	32.4	20.3
3837	Rio Gallegos (Reduccion Beacon)...	51 37	69 13	+0 21	+0 30	+4.2	+1.1	29.0	36.2	22.9
3839	Cabo Virgenes.....................	52 21	68 22	-0 36	-0 55	-2.1	0.0	23.8	29.8	19.2
	Tierra del Fuego <19>			on COMODORO RIVADAVIA, p.188						
3841	Bahia San Sebastian...............	53 10	68 30	-7 50	-7 55	*1.69	*1.91	22.8	28.6	17.7
3843	Rio Grande (Muelle)...............	53 48	67 41	-7 50	-7 55	*1.15	*1.18	15.8	19.2	11.8
3845	Cabo San Pablo....................	54 17	66 42	-8 48	-8 53	*1.17	*1.27	16.0	19.3	12.2
				on PUERTO BELGRANO, p.184						
3847	Bahia Thetis......................	54 38	65 15	+1 28	+1 20	-1.4	-0.2	8.7	10.6	7.2
	SOUTH ATLANTIC OCEAN ISLANDS Time meridian, 60°W			on PICTOU, p.8						
	Falkland Islands									
3849	Port Louis (Berkeley Sound).......	51 33	58 09	+7 50	+7 47	-0.9	-1.0	3.3	4.2	3.0
3851	Stanley Harbor....................	51 42	57 51	+7 51	+7 48	-1.0	-1.0	3.2	4.2	2.9
	Time meridian, 31°45'W									
	South Georgia									
3853	Royal Bay (Moltke Harbor).........	54 31	36 01	+9 58	+10 19	*0.36	*0.13	1.7	2.3	1.2
3855	Leith Harbor......................	54 08	36 41	+9 15	+9 35	*0.64	*0.65	2.0	2.7	2.5
	Time meridian, local									
	South Orkneys									
3857	Scotia Bay, Laurie Island.........	60 44	44 39	+8 21	+8 32	-0.3	-0.6	3.5	5.0	3.5
	South Shetlands									
3859	Port Foster, Deception Island.....	62 58	60 34	+8 26	+8 38	0.0	-0.1	3.3	4.3	3.9
	Time meridian, 45°W									
3860	Admiralty Bay.....................	62 03	58 24	+9 49	+10 05	-0.5	-0.4	3.1	4.4	3.5

Endnotes can be found at the end of table 2.

* RATIO. If the ratio is accompanied by a correction factor multiply the heights of the high and low waters at the reference station by the ratio and then apply the correction factor. See note and example on pages 197 and 198.

† The tide at this location is chiefly diurnal. SEE CAUTION NOTE ON PAGE 197.

< 1> Neap low water falls lower than spring low water.

< 2> Wharves are dry at low water.

< 3> There is a bore in the Petitcodiac River. It arrives at Moncton about 2h 30m before high water at St. John; its height is about 3 to 3 1/2 feet on average spring tides, but it sometimes exceeds 5 feet on highest tides. On small tides it is not much more than a large ripple.

< 4> The Reversing Falls at St. John. -- The most turbulence in the gorge occurs on days when the tides are largest. On largest tides the outward fall is between 15 and 16 1/2 feet and is accompanied by a greater turbulence than the inward fall which is between 11 and 12 1/2 feet. The outward fall is at its greatest between 2 hours before and 1 hour after low water at St John: the inward fall is greater just before the time of high water.

< 5> For Eastern Standard time subtract one hour from the predictions obtained using these differences.

< 6> Low water time difference is +2h 47m. SEE CAUTION NOTE ON PAGE 210.

< 7> Tidal information applies only during low river stages.

< 8> Values for the Hudson River above the George Washington Bridge are based upon averages for the six months May to October, when the freshwater discharge is at a minimum.

< 9> In Albermarle and Pamlico Sounds, except near the inlets, the periodic tide has a mean range of less than 0.5 foot.

<10> In the eastern part of Florida Bay the periodic tide has a mean range of less than 0.5 foot.

<11> In Choctawhatchee and Perdido Bays the periodic tide has a mean range of less than 0.5 foot.

<12> At New Orleans the diurnal range of the tide during low river stages averages 0.8 foot. There is no periodic tide at high river stages.

<13> For places on the Pacific coast, see "Tide Tables, West Coast of North and South America."

<14> Inside, in the various bays, except near the inlets, the periodic tide has a mean range of less than 0.5 foot.

<15> Spring range is given instead of diurnal range.

<16> A "Pororoca", a bore, reported to vary from 5 to 15 feet at spring tides, occurs in the Araguary, Guama and Guajara Rivers.

<17> Predictions will be approximate.

<18> Diurnal range is given instead of spring range.

<19> For places in Magellan Strait, on the south coast of Tierra del Fuego and on the Pacific coast, see "Tide Tables, West Coast of North and South America."

<20> The time differences should be applied only to the higher high and the lower low water times of the reference station.

<21> From Oak Hill southward in Mosquito Lagoon the periodic tide is negligible.

<22> In Indian River north of Melbourne, in Banana River and in Banana Creek, the periodic tides are negligible.

<23> Nearby tidal surveys suggest that the tides may actually occur 1/2 to 3/4 of an hour later than these time differences indicate.

TABLE 3.—HEIGHT OF TIDE AT ANY TIME

EXPLANATION OF TABLE

Although the footnote of table 3 may be sufficient explanation, two examples are given here to illustrate its use.

Example 1.—Find the height of the tide at 0755 at New York (The Battery), N.Y., on a day when the predicted tides from table 1 are given as:

Low Water		High Water	
Time	Height	Time	Height
h.m.	ft	h.m.	ft
0522	0.1	1114	4.2
1741	0.6	2310	4.1

An inspection of the above example shows that the desired time falls between the two morning tides.

The duration of rise is $11^h 14^m - 5^h 22^m = 5^h 52^m$.
The time after low water for which the height is required is $7^h 55^m - 5^h 22^m = 2^h 33^m$.
The range of tide is $4.2 - 0.1 = 4.1$ feet.

The duration of rise or fall in table 3 is given in heavy-faced type for each 20 minutes from $4^h 00^m$ to $10^h 40^m$. The nearest tabular value to $5^h 52^m$, the above duration of rise, is $6^h 00^m$; and on the horizontal line of $6^h 00^m$ the nearest tabular time to $2^h 33^m$ after low water for which the height is required is $2^h 36^m$. Following down the column in which this $2^h 36^m$ is found to its intersection with the line of the range 4.0 feet (which is the nearest tabular value to the above range of 4.1 feet) the correction is found to be 1.6 feet, which being reckoned from low water must be added, making $0.1 + 1.6 = 1.7$ feet, or 0.5 meter which is the required height above mean low water, the datum for New York.

Example 2.—Find the height of the tide at 0300 at Portland, Maine, on a day when the predicted tides from table 1 are given as:

High Water		Low Water	
Time	Height	Time	Height
h.m.	ft	h.m.	ft
0012	11.3	0638	—2.0
1251	10.0	1853	—0.8

The duration of fall is $6^h 38^m - 00^h 12^m = 6^h 26^m$.
The time after high water for which the height is required is $3^h 00^m - 00^h 12^m = 2^h 48^m$.
The range of tide is $11.3 - (-2.0) = 13.3$ feet.

Entering table 3 at the duration of fall of $6^h 20^m$, which is the nearest value to $6^h 26^m$, the nearest value on the horizontal line to $2^h 48^m$ is $2^h 45^m$ after high water. Following down this column to its intersection with a range of 13.5 feet which is the nearest tabular value to 13.3 feet, one obtains 5.3 which, being calculated from high water, must be subtracted from it. The approximate height at $03^h 00^m$ is, therefore, $11.3 - 5.3 = 6.0$ feet or 1.8 meters.

When the duration of rise or fall is greater than $10^h 40^m$, enter the table with one-half the given duration and with one-half the time from the nearest high or low water; but if the duration of rise or fall is less than 4 hours, enter the table with double the given duration and with double the time from the nearest high or low water.

Similarly, when the range of tide is greater than 20 feet, enter the table with one-half the given range. The tabular correction should then be doubled before applying it to the given high or low water height. If the range of tide is greater than 40 feet, take one-third of the range and multiply the tabular correction by 3.

If the height at any time is desired for a place listed in table 2, predictions of the high and low waters for the day in question should be obtained by the use of the differences given for the place in that table. Having obtained these predictions, the height for any intermediate time is obtained in the same manner as illustrated in the foregoing examples.

Graphical Method

If the height of the tide is required for a number of times on a certain day the full tide curve for the day may be obtained by the *one-quarter, one-tenth rule*. The procedure is as follows:

1. On cross-section paper plot the high and low water points in the order of their occurrence for the day, measuring time horizontally and height vertically. These are the basic points for the curve.

2. Draw light straight lines connecting the points representing successive high and low waters.

3. Divide each of these straight lines into four equal parts. The halfway point of each line gives another point for the curve.

4. At the quarter point adjacent to high water draw a vertical line above the point and at the quarter point adjacent to low water draw a vertical line below the point, making the length of these lines equal to one-tenth of the range between the high and low waters used. The points marking the ends of these vertical lines give two additional intermediate points for the curve.

5. Draw a smooth curve through the points of high and low waters and the intermediate points, making the curve well rounded near high and low waters. This curve will approximate the actual tide curve and heights for any time of the day may be readily scaled from it.

Caution.—Both methods presented are based on the assumption that the rise and fall conform to simple cosine curves. Therefore the heights obtained will be approximate. The roughness of approximation will vary as the tide curve differs from a cosine curve.

An example of the use of the graphical method is illustrated below. Using the same predicted tides as in example 2, the approximate height at 03ʰ 00ᵐ could be determined as shown below.

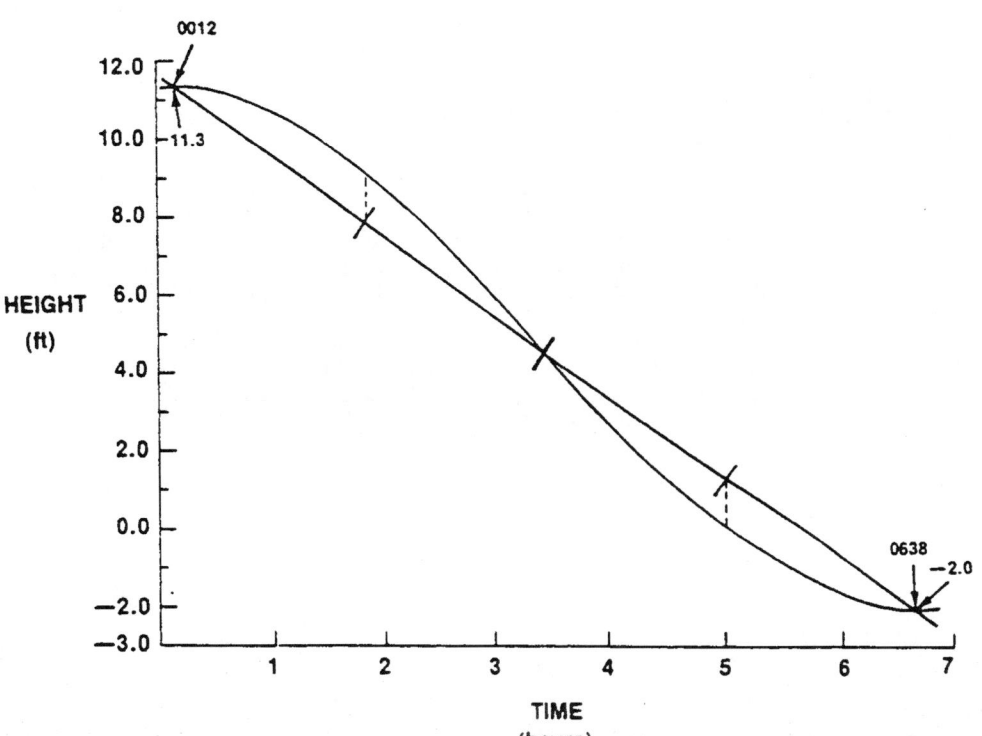

TABLE 3.—HEIGHT OF TIDE AT ANY TIME 239

Time from the nearest high water or low water

Duration of rise or fall (h. m.)	h. m.	h. m.	h. m.	h. m.	h. m.	h. m.	h. m.	h. m.	h. m.	h. m.	h. m.	h. m.	h. m.	h. m.	h. m.
4 00	0 08	0 16	0 24	0 32	0 40	0 48	0 56	1 04	1 12	1 20	1 28	1 36	1 44	1 52	2 00
4 20	0 09	0 17	0 26	0 35	0 43	0 52	1 01	1 09	1 18	1 27	1 35	1 44	1 53	2 01	2 10
4 40	0 09	0 19	0 28	0 37	0 47	0 56	1 05	1 15	1 24	1 33	1 43	1 52	2 01	2 11	2 20
5 00	0 10	0 20	0 30	0 40	0 50	1 00	1 10	1 20	1 30	1 40	1 50	2 00	2 10	2 20	2 30
5 20	0 11	0 21	0 32	0 43	0 53	1 04	1 15	1 25	1 36	1 47	1 57	2 08	2 19	2 29	2 40
5 40	0 11	0 23	0 34	0 45	0 57	1 08	1 19	1 31	1 42	1 53	2 05	2 16	2 27	2 39	2 50
6 00	0 12	0 24	0 36	0 48	1 00	1 12	1 24	1 36	1 48	2 00	2 12	2 24	2 36	2 48	3 00
6 20	0 13	0 25	0 38	0 51	1 03	1 16	1 29	1 41	1 54	2 07	2 19	2 32	2 45	2 57	3 10
6 40	0 13	0 27	0 40	0 53	1 07	1 20	1 33	1 47	2 00	2 13	2 27	2 40	2 53	3 07	3 20
7 00	0 14	0 28	0 42	0 56	1 10	1 24	1 38	1 52	2 06	2 20	2 34	2 48	3 02	3 16	3 30
7 20	0 15	0 29	0 44	0 59	1 13	1 28	1 43	1 57	2 12	2 27	2 41	2 56	3 11	3 25	3 40
7 40	0 15	0 31	0 46	1 01	1 17	1 32	1 47	2 03	2 18	2 33	2 49	3 04	3 19	3 35	3 50
8 00	0 16	0 32	0 48	1 04	1 20	1 36	1 52	2 08	2 24	2 40	2 56	3 12	3 28	3 44	4 00
8 20	0 17	0 33	0 50	1 07	1 23	1 40	1 57	2 13	2 30	2 47	3 03	3 20	3 37	3 53	4 10
8 40	0 17	0 35	0 52	1 09	1 27	1 44	2 01	2 19	2 36	2 53	3 11	3 28	3 45	4 03	4 20
9 00	0 18	0 36	0 54	1 12	1 30	1 48	2 06	2 24	2 42	3 00	3 18	3 36	3 54	4 12	4 30
9 20	0 19	0 37	0 56	1 15	1 33	1 52	2 11	2 29	2 48	3 07	3 25	3 44	4 03	4 21	4 40
9 40	0 19	0 39	0 58	1 17	1 37	1 56	2 15	2 35	2 54	3 13	3 33	3 52	4 11	4 31	4 50
10 00	0 20	0 40	1 00	1 20	1 40	2 00	2 20	2 40	3 00	3 20	3 40	4 00	4 20	4 40	5 00
10 20	0 21	0 41	1 02	1 23	1 43	2 04	2 25	2 45	3 06	3 27	3 47	4 08	4 29	4 49	5 10
10 40	0 21	0 43	1 04	1 25	1 47	2 08	2 29	2 51	3 12	3 33	3 55	4 16	4 37	4 59	5 20

Correction to height

Range of tide (Ft.)	Ft.	Ft.	Ft.	Ft.	Ft.	Ft.	Ft.	Ft.	Ft.	Ft.	Ft.	Ft.	Ft.	Ft.	Ft.
0.5	0.0	0.0	0.0	0.0	0.0	0.0	0.1	0.1	0.1	0.1	0.1	0.2	0.2	0.2	0.2
1.0	0.0	0.0	0.0	0.0	0.1	0.1	0.1	0.2	0.2	0.2	0.3	0.3	0.4	0.4	0.5
1.5	0.0	0.0	0.0	0.1	0.1	0.1	0.2	0.2	0.3	0.4	0.4	0.5	0.6	0.7	0.8
2.0	0.0	0.0	0.0	0.1	0.1	0.2	0.3	0.3	0.4	0.5	0.6	0.7	0.8	0.9	1.0
2.5	0.0	0.0	0.1	0.1	0.2	0.2	0.3	0.4	0.5	0.6	0.7	0.9	1.0	1.1	1.2
3.0	0.0	0.0	0.1	0.1	0.2	0.3	0.4	0.5	0.6	0.8	0.9	1.0	1.2	1.3	1.5
3.5	0.0	0.0	0.1	0.2	0.2	0.3	0.4	0.6	0.7	0.9	1.0	1.2	1.4	1.6	1.8
4.0	0.0	0.0	0.1	0.2	0.3	0.4	0.5	0.7	0.8	1.0	1.2	1.4	1.6	1.8	2.0
4.5	0.0	0.0	0.1	0.2	0.3	0.4	0.6	0.7	0.9	1.1	1.3	1.6	1.8	2.0	2.2
5.0	0.0	0.1	0.1	0.2	0.3	0.5	0.6	0.8	1.0	1.2	1.5	1.7	2.0	2.2	2.5
5.5	0.0	0.1	0.1	0.2	0.4	0.5	0.7	0.9	1.1	1.4	1.6	1.9	2.2	2.5	2.8
6.0	0.0	0.1	0.1	0.3	0.4	0.6	0.8	1.0	1.2	1.5	1.8	2.1	2.4	2.7	3.0
6.5	0.0	0.1	0.2	0.3	0.4	0.6	0.8	1.1	1.3	1.6	1.9	2.2	2.6	2.9	3.2
7.0	0.0	0.1	0.2	0.3	0.5	0.7	0.9	1.2	1.4	1.8	2.1	2.4	2.8	3.1	3.5
7.5	0.0	0.1	0.2	0.3	0.5	0.7	1.0	1.2	1.5	1.9	2.2	2.6	3.0	3.4	3.8
8.0	0.0	0.1	0.2	0.3	0.5	0.8	1.0	1.3	1.6	2.0	2.4	2.8	3.2	3.6	4.0
8.5	0.0	0.1	0.2	0.4	0.6	0.8	1.1	1.4	1.8	2.1	2.5	2.9	3.4	3.8	4.2
9.0	0.0	0.1	0.2	0.4	0.6	0.9	1.2	1.5	1.9	2.2	2.7	3.1	3.6	4.0	4.5
9.5	0.0	0.1	0.2	0.4	0.6	0.9	1.2	1.6	2.0	2.4	2.8	3.3	3.8	4.3	4.8
10.0	0.0	0.1	0.2	0.4	0.7	1.0	1.3	1.7	2.1	2.5	3.0	3.5	4.0	4.5	5.0
10.5	0.0	0.1	0.3	0.5	0.7	1.0	1.3	1.7	2.2	2.6	3.1	3.6	4.2	4.7	5.2
11.0	0.0	0.1	0.3	0.5	0.7	1.1	1.4	1.8	2.3	2.8	3.3	3.8	4.4	4.9	5.5
11.5	0.0	0.1	0.3	0.5	0.8	1.1	1.5	1.9	2.4	2.9	3.4	4.0	4.6	5.1	5.8
12.0	0.0	0.1	0.3	0.5	0.8	1.1	1.5	2.0	2.5	3.0	3.6	4.1	4.8	5.4	6.0
12.5	0.0	0.1	0.3	0.5	0.8	1.2	1.6	2.1	2.6	3.1	3.7	4.3	5.0	5.6	6.2
13.0	0.0	0.1	0.3	0.6	0.9	1.2	1.7	2.2	2.7	3.2	3.9	4.5	5.1	5.8	6.5
13.5	0.0	0.1	0.3	0.6	0.9	1.3	1.7	2.2	2.8	3.4	4.0	4.7	5.3	6.0	6.8
14.0	0.0	0.2	0.3	0.6	0.9	1.3	1.8	2.3	2.9	3.5	4.2	4.8	5.5	6.3	7.0
14.5	0.0	0.2	0.4	0.6	1.0	1.4	1.9	2.4	3.0	3.6	4.3	5.0	5.7	6.5	7.2
15.0	0.0	0.2	0.4	0.6	1.0	1.4	1.9	2.5	3.1	3.8	4.4	5.2	5.9	6.7	7.5
15.5	0.0	0.2	0.4	0.7	1.0	1.5	2.0	2.6	3.2	3.9	4.6	5.4	6.1	6.9	7.8
16.0	0.0	0.2	0.4	0.7	1.1	1.5	2.1	2.6	3.3	4.0	4.7	5.5	6.3	7.2	8.0
16.5	0.0	0.2	0.4	0.7	1.1	1.6	2.1	2.7	3.4	4.1	4.9	5.7	6.5	7.4	8.2
17.0	0.0	0.2	0.4	0.7	1.1	1.6	2.2	2.8	3.5	4.2	5.0	5.9	6.7	7.6	8.5
17.5	0.0	0.2	0.4	0.8	1.2	1.7	2.2	2.9	3.6	4.4	5.2	6.0	6.9	7.8	8.8
18.0	0.0	0.2	0.4	0.8	1.2	1.7	2.3	3.0	3.7	4.5	5.3	6.2	7.1	8.1	9.0
18.5	0.1	0.2	0.5	0.8	1.2	1.8	2.4	3.1	3.8	4.6	5.5	6.4	7.3	8.3	9.2
19.0	0.1	0.2	0.5	0.8	1.3	1.8	2.4	3.1	3.9	4.8	5.6	6.6	7.5	8.5	9.5
19.5	0.1	0.2	0.5	0.8	1.3	1.9	2.5	3.2	4.0	4.9	5.8	6.7	7.7	8.7	9.8
20.0	0.1	0.2	0.5	0.9	1.3	1.9	2.6	3.3	4.1	5.0	5.9	6.9	7.9	9.0	10.0

Obtain from the predictions the high water and low water, one of which is before and the other after the time for which the height is required. The difference between the times of occurrence of these tides is the duration of rise or fall, and the difference between their heights is the range of tide for the above table. Find the difference between the nearest high or low water and the time for which the height is required.

Enter the table with the duration of rise or fall, printed in heavy-faced type, which most nearly agrees with the actual value, and on that horizontal line find the time from the nearest high or low water which agrees most nearly with the corresponding actual difference. The correction sought is in the column directly below, on the line with the range of tide.

When the nearest tide is high water, subtract the correction.

When the nearest tide is low water, add the correction.

TABLE 7.—CONVERSION OF FEET TO METERS   261

Feet	0.0	0.1	0.2	0.3	0.4	0.5	0.6	0.7	0.8	0.9	Feet
					Tenths of a Foot						
0	0.00	0.03	0.06	0.09	0.12	0.15	0.18	0.21	0.24	0.27	0
1	0.30	0.34	0.37	0.40	0.43	0.46	0.49	0.52	0.55	0.58	1
2	0.61	0.64	0.67	0.70	0.73	0.76	0.79	0.82	0.85	0.88	2
3	0.91	0.94	0.98	1.01	1.04	1.07	1.10	1.13	1.16	1.19	3
4	1.22	1.25	1.28	1.31	1.34	1.37	1.40	1.43	1.46	1.49	4
5	1.52	1.55	1.58	1.62	1.65	1.68	1.71	1.74	1.77	1.80	5
6	1.83	1.86	1.89	1.92	1.95	1.98	2.01	2.04	2.07	2.10	6
7	2.13	2.16	2.19	2.23	2.26	2.29	2.32	2.35	2.38	2.41	7
8	2.44	2.47	2.50	2.53	2.56	2.59	2.62	2.65	2.68	2.71	8
9	2.74	2.77	2.80	2.83	2.87	2.90	2.93	2.96	2.99	3.02	9
10	3.05	3.08	3.11	3.14	3.17	3.20	3.23	3.26	3.29	3.32	10
11	3.35	3.38	3.41	3.44	3.47	3.51	3.54	3.57	3.60	3.63	11
12	3.66	3.69	3.72	3.75	3.78	3.81	3.84	3.87	3.90	3.93	12
13	3.96	3.99	4.02	4.05	4.08	4.11	4.15	4.18	4.21	4.24	13
14	4.27	4.30	4.33	4.36	4.39	4.42	4.45	4.48	4.51	4.54	14
15	4.57	4.60	4.63	4.66	4.69	4.72	4.75	4.79	4.82	4.85	15
16	4.88	4.91	4.94	4.97	5.00	5.03	5.06	5.09	5.12	5.15	16
17	5.18	5.21	5.24	5.27	5.30	5.33	5.36	5.39	5.43	5.46	17
18	5.49	5.52	5.55	5.58	5.61	5.64	5.67	5.70	5.73	5.76	18
19	5.79	5.82	5.85	5.88	5.91	5.94	5.97	6.00	6.04	6.07	19
20	6.10	6.13	6.16	6.19	6.22	6.25	6.28	6.31	6.34	6.37	20
21	6.40	6.43	6.46	6.49	6.52	6.55	6.58	6.61	6.64	6.68	21
22	6.71	6.74	6.77	6.80	6.83	6.86	6.89	6.92	6.95	6.98	22
23	7.01	7.04	7.07	7.10	7.13	7.16	7.19	7.22	7.25	7.28	23
24	7.32	7.35	7.38	7.41	7.44	7.47	7.50	7.53	7.56	7.59	24
25	7.62	7.65	7.68	7.71	7.74	7.77	7.80	7.83	7.86	7.89	25
26	7.92	7.96	7.99	8.02	8.05	8.08	8.11	8.14	8.17	8.20	26
27	8.23	8.26	8.29	8.32	8.35	8.38	8.41	8.44	8.47	8.50	27
28	8.53	8.56	8.60	8.63	8.66	8.69	8.72	8.75	8.78	8.81	28
29	8.84	8.87	8.90	8.93	8.96	8.99	9.02	9.05	9.08	9.11	29
30	9.14	9.17	9.20	9.24	9.27	9.30	9.33	9.36	9.39	9.42	30
31	9.45	9.48	9.51	9.54	9.57	9.60	9.63	9.66	9.69	9.72	31
32	9.75	9.78	9.81	9.85	9.88	9.91	9.94	9.97	10.00	10.03	32
33	10.06	10.09	10.12	10.15	10.18	10.21	10.24	10.27	10.30	10.33	33
34	10.36	10.39	10.42	10.45	10.49	10.52	10.55	10.58	10.61	10.64	34
35	10.67	10.70	10.73	10.76	10.79	10.82	10.85	10.88	10.91	10.94	35
36	10.97	11.00	11.03	11.06	11.09	11.13	11.16	11.19	11.22	11.25	36
37	11.28	11.31	11.34	11.37	11.40	11.43	11.46	11.49	11.52	11.55	37
38	11.58	11.61	11.64	11.67	11.70	11.73	11.77	11.80	11.83	11.86	38
39	11.89	11.92	11.95	11.98	12.01	12.04	12.07	12.10	12.13	12.16	39
40	12.19	12.22	12.25	12.28	12.31	12.34	12.37	12.41	12.44	12.47	40
41	12.50	12.53	12.56	12.59	12.62	12.65	12.68	12.71	12.74	12.77	41
42	12.80	12.83	12.86	12.89	12.92	12.95	12.98	13.01	13.05	13.08	42
43	13.11	13.14	13.17	13.20	13.23	13.26	13.29	13.32	13.35	13.38	43
44	13.41	13.44	13.47	13.50	13.53	13.56	13.59	13.62	13.66	13.69	44
45	13.72	13.75	13.78	13.81	13.84	13.87	13.90	13.93	13.96	13.99	45
46	14.02	14.05	14.08	14.11	14.14	14.17	14.20	14.23	14.26	14.30	46
47	14.33	14.36	14.39	14.42	14.45	14.48	14.51	14.54	14.57	14.60	47
48	14.63	14.66	14.69	14.72	14.75	14.78	14.81	14.84	14.87	14.90	48
49	14.94	14.97	15.00	15.03	15.06	15.09	15.12	15.15	15.18	15.21	49
50	15.24	15.27	15.30	15.33	15.36	15.39	15.42	15.45	15.48	15.51	50

TIDE TABLES

Advance information relative to the rise and fall of the tide is given in annual tide tables. These tables include the predicted times and heights of high and low waters for every day in the year for a number of reference stations and differences for obtaining similar predictions for numerous other places.

Tide Tables, Central and Western Pacific Ocean and Indian Ocean.
Tide Tables, East Coast of North and South America (Including Greenland).
Tide Tables, Europe and West Coast of Africa (Including the Mediterranean Sea).
Tide Tables, West Coast of North and South America (Including the Hawaiian Islands).

TIDAL BENCH MARKS

To provide permanent points for the observed heights of the tide and the tidal datum planes determined therefrom, a system of bench marks is established at each tide station. The descriptions and elevations of these bench marks along our coast are compiled, published, and available for distribution. Requests for such bench mark data should specify the coastal locality for which the information is desired.

TIDAL CURRENT TABLES

Accompanying the rise and fall of the tide is a periodic horizontal flow of the water known as the tidal current. Advance information relative to these currents is made available in annual tidal current tables which include daily predictions of the times of slack water and the times and velocities of strength of flood and ebb currents for a number of waterways together with differences for obtaining predictions for numerous other places.

Tidal Current Tables, Atlantic Coast of North America.
Tidal Current Tables, Pacific Coast of North America and Asia.

TIDAL CURRENT CHARTS

Each publication consists of a set of 12 charts which depict, by means of arrows and figures, the direction and speed of the tidal current for each hour of the tidal cycle. The charts, which may be used for any year, present a comprehensive view of the tidal current movement in the respective waterways as a whole and also supply a means for readily determining for any time the direction and speed of the current at various localities throughout the water areas covered. The Narragansett Bay tidal current chart is to be used with the annual tide tables. The other charts require the annual tidal current tables.

Tidal Current Charts, Boston Harbor.
Tidal Current Charts, Charleston Harbor, S.C.
Tidal Current Charts, Delaware Bay and River.
Tidal Current Charts, Long Island Sound and Block Island Sound.
Tidal Current Charts, Narragansett Bay.
Tidal Current Charts, Narragansett Bay to Nantucket Sound.
Tidal Current Charts, New York Harbor.
Tidal Current Charts, Puget Sound, Northern Part.
Tidal Current Charts, Puget Sound, Southern Part.
Tidal Current Charts, San Francisco Bay.
Tidal Current Charts, Upper Chesapeake Bay.
Tidal Current Charts, Tampa Bay.

TIDAL CURRENT DIAGRAMS

The tidal current diagrams are a series of 12 monthly diagrams to be used with the tidal current charts to give the user a convenient method to determine the current flow on a particular day.

Tidal Current Diagrams for Long Island Sound and Block Island Sound.
Tidal Current Diagrams for Boston Harbor.
Tidal Current Diagrams for New York Harbor.
Tidal Current Diagrams for Upper Chesapeake Bay.

[Stations marked with an asterisk (*) are reference stations for which daily predictions are given in table 1. Page numbers of reference stations are given in parentheses.]

	NO.
Catskill, N. Y.	1557
Cawee Islands, Quebec	313
Cayenne, French Guiana	3603
Cayos de Perlas, Nicaragua	3345
Cedar Island Point, S. C.	2544
Cedar Key, Fla.	3119
Cedar Point, Chesapeake Bay, Md.	2165
Cedar Point, Severn River, Md.	2128
Cedar Point, N. Y.	1391
Cedar Tree Neck, Mass.	1073
Center Harbor, Maine	733
Centreville Landing, Md.	2067
Ceylon, Ga.	2813
Chain Bridge, D. C.	2255
one mile below	2253
Chaleur Bay, Canada	377-391
Champlain, Quebec	369
Champney Island, Ga.	2773
Chance, Md.	1990
Chandeleur Light, La.	3217
Channel Key, Fla.	3013
Charles River, Mass.	953-957
Charles River Dam, Mass.	955
Charleston, S. C. * (96)	2577
Charleston Harbor, S. C.	2571-2611
Charleston Harbor entrance, S. C.	2571
Charlestown, Md.	2093
Charlestown, Mass.	957
Charlestown Bridge, Mass.	953
Charlotte Amalie, Virgin Islands	3513
Charlottetown, Prince Edward Island	435
Charlton Island, Hudson Bay	130
Chateau Bay, Labrador	181
Chatham (inside), Mass.	1013
Chatham (outer coast), Mass.	1011
Chatham River, Florida	3033
Cheatham Annex, Va.	2324
Chebeague Point, Maine	871
Chechessee River, S. C.	2689
Chelsea, N. J.	1705
Chelsea, N. Y.	1593
Chelsea River, Mass.	959
Cherry Island, Md.	2017
Cherry Point, Va.	2293
Chesapeake and Delaware Canal	1835-1839
Chesapeake Bay	Pages 217-222
Chesapeake Beach, Md.	2145
Chesapeake City, Md.	1839
Chester, Bells River, Fla.	2835
Chester, Mahone Bay, Nova Scotia	529
Chester, Pa.	1857
Chester River, Md.	2061-2075
Chester, Va.	2420
Chesterfield Inlet, Hudson Bay	125
Chestertown, Md.	2071
Cheticamp, Nova Scotia	461
Chickahominy River, Va.	2393-2399
Chicoutimi, Quebec	333
Chignecto Bay, Nova Scotia	579
Chilmark Pond, Mass.	1065
Chincoteague, Va.	1919
Chincoteague Bay, Md. and Va.	1913-1928
Chincoteague Point, Va.	1915
Choctawhatchee Bay, Fla.	3171
Choptank, Md.	2027
Choptank River, Md.	2023-2035
Choptank River Light, Md.	2023
Chowan Creek, S. C.	2677
Christiansted, Virgin Islands	3515
Christina River, Del.	1849
Christina River entrance, Del.	1847
Christmas Point, Fla.	2977
Christmas Point, Tex.	3289
Chuckatuck Creek entrance, Va.	2375

	NO.
Church Flats, S. C.	2621
Churchill, Hudson Bay	126
Cienfuegos, Cuba	3433
City Island, N. Y.	1261
City Point, Va.	2411
Claiborne, Md.	2051
Clarence Harbor, Bahamas	3387
Claremont, Va.	2401
Clarks Point, Mass.	1133
Clay Bank, Va.	2327
Clear Lake, Tex.	3281
Clearwater Fiord, Canada	111
Clearwater, Fla.	3105
Cliffs Point, Md.	2069
Cliffs Wharf, Md.	2070
Clifton Beach, Md.	2215
Club Bridge Creek, S. C.	2673
Coates Point, N. J.	1659
Coatzcoalcos, Mexico	3315
Cobb Point Bar Light, Md.	2191
Cobscook Bay, Maine	639-647
Coconut Point, Fla.	3049
Codroy Road, Newfoundland	255
Coffee Bluff, Ga.	2737
Coffins Point, Maine	643
Cohansey River, N. J.	1783-1789
Cohansey River entrance, N. J.	1783
Cohasset Harbor, Mass.	989
Cold Spring Harbor, N. Y.	1345
Coles Point, Va.	2183
College Point, N. Y.	1269
Colleton River, S. C.	2684,2685
Colombia	3542-3549
Colonia, Uruguay	3723
Colonial Beach, Va.	2197
Colton's Point, Md.	2189
Combahee Bank, S. C.	2649
Combahee River Highway Bridge, S. C.	2657
Comfort Bight, Labrador	175
Comodoro Rivadavia, Argentina * (188)	3817
Conception Bay, Newfoundland	219
Conch Bar, Jupiter Sound, Fla.	2917
Coney Island, N. Y.	1493
Connecticut	1187-1251
Connecticut River	1200-1213
Connetquot River, N. Y.	1435
Connoire Bay, Newfoundland	249
Conscience Bay entrance, N. Y.	1365
Constable Hook, N. J.	1571
Conway, S. C.	2539
Coon Key, Fla.	3044
Cooper River, S. C.	2581-2593
Cooper River RR. bridge, S. C.	2593
Coosaw River, S. C.	2663-2665
Coral Harbour, Hudson Bay	124
Corbins Neck, Va.	2289
Corea Harbor, Maine	683
Cornfield Harbor, Md.	2170
Corning Landing, S. C.	2693
Corsica River, Md.	2067
Corson Inlet, N. J.	1727
Cortez, Fla.	3073
Cos Cob Harbor, Conn.	1247
Costa Rica	3353
Cote Blanche, La.	3265
Cotuit Highlands, Mass.	1033
Courthouse Point, Md.	2089
Cove Point, Md.	2151
Covenas, Colombia	3544
Coxsackie, N. Y.	1561
Crandall, St. Marys River, Fla.	2829
Craney Island, Va.	2359
Crisfield, Md.	1979
Cristobal, Panama * (144)	3357

	NO.		NO.
Hix Bridge, Mass.......................	1145	Isla Zapara, Venezuela * (152).........	3551
Hobe Sound State Park, Fla............	2916	Isle au Haut, Maine...................	736
Hoboken, N. J.........................	1519	Isle of Hope, Ga......................	2731
Hog Point, Va.........................	2387	Isle of Palms, S. C...................	2567
Holgate, N. J.........................	1679	Isle of Springs, Maine................	813
Holland Island Bar Light, Md..........	1989	Itacurussa, Brazil....................	3693
Hollidays Point, Va...................	2371	Itajai, Brazil........................	3709
Hollywood Beach, Fla..................	2951	Ivigtut, Greenland....................	67
Holsteinsborg, Greenland..............	75		
Honduras...........................	3331-3339	J	
Hooper Island Light, Md...............	2009		
Hooper Island, Md.....................	2010	Jack Bay, La..........................	3221
Hooper Strait Light, Md...............	2007	Jack Creek, S. C......................	2557
Hopedale Harbour, Labrador............	161	Jacksonboro, S. C.....................	2645
Hopes Advance Bay, Ungava Bay..........	140	Jackson Creek, Va.....................	2294
Hopewell Cape, New Brunswick...........	587	Jacksonville Bridge, Fla..............	2867
Hopyard Landing, Va...................	2288	Jacksonville, Fla.....................	2865
Horan Head, Maine.....................	647	Jacmel, Haiti.........................	3481
Horn Island Pass, Miss................	3201	Jaffrey Point, N. H...................	B91
Horns Hook, N. Y......................	1291	Jamaica.............................	3449-3461
Horton Bluff, Nova Scotia.............	571	Jamaica Bay, N. Y.....................	1475-1491
Horton Point, N. Y....................	1373	Jamaica Beach, Tex....................	3287
Housatonic River, Conn............	1231,1233	James Bay, Canada....................	128-130
Howard Point, Maine...................	857	James River, Va......................	2375-2431
Hudson, N. Y..........................	1559	Jamestown Island, Va..................	2389
Hudson Creek entrance, Ga.............	2765	Janes Island Light, Md................	1977
Hudson Creek, Md......................	2019	Jeddore Harbour, Nova Scotia..........	519
Hudson River.......................	1513-1569	Jekyll Point, Ga......................	2797
Hudson Strait and Bay.............	114-147	Jennetts Pier (ocean), N. C...........	2446
Hull, Mass............................	987	Jensen Beach, Fla.....................	2901
Hunters Point, N. Y...................	1299	Jersey City, N. J.....................	1513
Hunting Island, S. C..................	2667	Jobs Neck Pond, Mass..................	1063
Huntington Bay, N. Y..................	1349	Joggins, Nova Scotia..................	581
Huntington Park, Va...................	2378	John F. Kennedy International Airport..	1485
Hunts Point, N. Y.....................	1275	Johns Bay, Maine......................	801
Hutchinson Island, S. C...............	2653	Johns Pass, Fla.......................	3099
Hyannis Port, Mass....................	1031-1033	Jointer Island, Ga....................	2799
Hyde Park, N. Y.......................	1551	Jones Creek, Ga.......................	2777
		Jones Inlet, N. Y.....................	1449
I		Jones Neck, Maine.....................	797
		Jonesport, Moosabec Reach, Maine.......	667
Igloolik, Arctic......................	13	Jordan Point, Va......................	2409
Ile aux Coudres, Quebec...............	341	Joseph Bayou, La......................	3226
Ile Haute, Nova Scotia................	565	Julianehaab..........................	63
Iles du Salut, French Guiana..........	3601	Julienton River, Ga...................	2756
Ilha de Maraca, Brazil................	3609	Jupiter, Lake Worth Creek, Fla.........	2927
Ilha do Brigue, Brazil................	3611	Jupiter Inlet, Fla....................	2919
Ilhas de Sao Joao, Brazil.............	3623	Jupiter Sound, south end, Fla.........	2918
Ilheus, Brazil........................	3667		
Imbituba, Brazil......................	3715	K	
Independence Island, La...............	3241		
Indian Bay, Fla.......................	3113	Kangalaksiorvik Fiord, Labrador........	153
Indian Creek, Fla.....................	2957	Kap Farvel, Greenland.................	57
Indian Harbour, Labrador..............	165	Keansburg, N. J.......................	1619
Indian Head, Md.......................	2225	Kearny Point, N. J....................	1586
Indian Key, Fla.......................	3039	Kegaska, Quebec.......................	281
Indian River, Del.................	1899-1903	Kennebec River, Maine.................	829-851
Indian River, Fla.................	2895-2898	Kennebunkport, Maine..................	887
Indian River Inlet, Del...........	1899,1900	Kent Island Narrows, Md...............	2057
Indian Rocks Beach, Fla...............	3103	Kettle Cove, Mass.....................	1109
Indiantown, New Brunswick.............	607	Key Bridge, D. C......................	2251
Ingeniero White, Argentina............	3751	Key West, Fla. * (116)................	3001
Ingnerit, Greenland...................	85	Keyport, N. J.........................	1617
Ingonish Island, Nova Scotia..........	465	Kilkenny Club, Ga.....................	2747
Iona Shores, Fla......................	3054	Kill Van Kull...................	1571-1577
Ireland Island, Bermuda...............	3361	Kimball Island, Maine.................	739
Iron Point, Maine.....................	751	Kingsland Reach, Va...................	2423
Isaacs Harbour, Nova Scotia...........	509	Kingsley Creek, Fla...................	2837
Isla Bermejo, Argentina...............	3755	Kingston Point, N. Y..................	1553
Isla del Maiz Grande, Nicaragua.......	3347	Kingstown, St. Vincent................	3531
Isla de Providencia, Colombia.........	3542	Kinsale, Va...........................	2175
Isla Escondida, Argentina.............	3795	Kiptopeke Beach (ferry), Va............	1951
Isla Tova, Argentina..................	3813	Kittery Point, Maine..................	897
Isla Trinidad, Argentina.........	3757,3759	Kitts Point, Md.......................	2177

NO.

Mar del Plata, Argentina	3737
Marblehead, Mass.	933
Marco, Big Marco River, Fla	3046
Marcus Hook, Pa.	1855
Marion, Mass.	1127
Marshall Hall, Md.	2231
Martha's Vineyard, Mass.	1061-1087
Martins Industry, S. C.	2669
Maryland	Pages 217-220
Maryland Point Light, Md.	2211
Masonboro Inlet, N. C.	2477
Massachusetts	Pages 207-210
Massacre, Dominican Republic	3465
Massaponax, Va.	2290
Mastic Beach, N. Y.	1417
Matagorda Bay, Tex.	3297,3299
Matamoros, Mexico	3306
Matane, Quebec	321
Matanzas, Cuba	3445
Matanzas Pass, Fla.	3051
Matapeake, Md.	2058
Mathew Town, Bahamas	3393
Mathias Point, Va.	2203
Matinicus Harbor, Maine	747
Matlacha Pass, Fla.	3063
Mattapoisett, Mass.	1129
Mattaponi River, Va.	2333,2335
Mattituck Inlet, N. Y.	1371
Maurice River, Delaware Bay	1771-1775
Mauricetown, N. J.	1773
Mayaguez, P. R.	3507
Mayport, Fla. * (108)	2855
Mays Landing, N. J.	1721
Meadowville, Va.	2421
Medford Bridge, Mass.	963
Medomak River, Maine	797,799
Medway River, Ga.	2749
Melbourne, Fla.	2895
Melville Island	5,7
Memory Rock, Bahamas	3373
Menchville, Va.	2379
Menemsha Bight, Mass.	1071
Mercy Bay, Banks Island	3
Merigomish Harbour, Nova Scotia	449
Mermentau River, La.	3269
Merrimack River, Mass.	915,917
Mesquite Point, Tex.	3274
Messick Point, Va.	2347
Metis-sur-Mer, Quebec	323
Metomkin Inlet, Va.	1931,1932
Mexico	3306-3319
Miacomet Rip, Mass.	1059
Miah Maull Shoal Light, N. J.	1797
Miami Beach, Delaware Bay	1765
Miami Beach, Fla.	2958
Miami, Marina, Fla.	2963
Miami Harbor entrance, Fla. * (112)	2959
Miami (Causeway, east end), Fla.	2964
Miami, 79th St. Causeway, Fla.	2962
Middle Branch, Md.	2121
Middle River, Md.	2107
Midjik Bluff, New Brunswick	623
Milbridge, Maine	675
Miles River, Md.	2053
Milford Harbor, Conn.	1229
Mill Basin, N. Y.	1491
Mill Creek, Va.	2271
Mill Point, Maine	825
Millenbeck, Va.	2275
Millington, Md.	2075
Millstone Point, Conn.	1199
Millville, N. J.	1775
Milton, Fla.	3189
Minas Basin, Nova Scotia	569-577

NO.

Mingan, Quebec	301
	2543
Minim Creek entrance, S. C.	2845
Mink Creek, Fla.	405
Miramichi Bay, New Brunswick	391
Miscou Harbour, New Brunswick	1809
Mispillion River entrance, Del.	3201-3211
Mississippi	3223-3230
Mississippi River	275
Mistanoque Harbour, Quebec	3198
Mobile, Ala * (132)	3193
Mobile Point, Ala.	2301
Mobjack, Va.	2299-2307
Mobjack Bay, Va.	309
Moisie Bay, Quebec	2984
Molasses Reef, Fla.	589
Moncton, New Brunswick	1221
Money Island, Conn.	1993
Monie Bay, Md.	781
Monhegan Island, Maine	1017
Monomoy Point, Mass.	1405
Montauk, N. Y.	1403
Montauk Harbor, N. Y.	1407
Montauk Point, N. Y.	3457
Montego Bay, Jamaica	3743
Monte Hermoso, Argentina	3721
Montevideo, Uruguay	1117
Monument Beach, Mass.	967
Moon Head, Mass.	667
Moosabec Reach, Maine	653
Moose Cove, Maine	129
Moose Factory, Hudson Bay	128
Moosonee, Canada	2467
Morehead City, N. C.	3282
Morgans Point, Tex.	1413,1417
Moriches Bay, N. Y.	1415
Moriches Inlet, N. Y.	3663
Morro de Sao Paulo, Brazil	231
Mortier Bay, Newfoundland	2983
Mosquito Bank, Fla.	1481
Motts Basin, N. Y.	2397
Mount Airy, Va.	715
Mount Desert, Maine	709-719
Mount Desert Island, Maine	707
Mount Desert Narrows, Maine	2188
Mount Holly, Va.	1367
Mount Sinai Harbor, N. Y.	2233
Mount Vernon, Va.	2123
Mountain Point, Md.	1969
Muddy Creek entrance, Va.	2760,2761
Mud River, Ga.	2385
Mulberry Point, Va.	3081
Mullet Key Channel, Fla.	1687
Mullica River, N. J.	2321
Mumfort Islands, Va.	1811
Murderkill River, Del.	337
Murray Bay, Quebec	2513
Murrells Inlet, S. C.	791
Muscongus Bay, Maine	793
Muscongus Harbor, Maine	1055
Muskeget Island, Mass.	47
Myggbukta, Greenland	2511
Myrtle Beach, S. C.	

N

Nachvak Bay, Labrador	155
Nahant, Mass.	935
Nain, Labrador	159
Nanortalik, Greenland	61
Nansemond River, Va.	2367-2373
Nantasket Beach, Mass.	983
Nanticoke River, Md.	1999-2003
Nantucket, Mass.	1049
Nantucket Island, Mass.	1041-1059

	NO.
Richibucto River ent., New Brunswick...	409
Richmond, Maine......................	843
Richmond, Va.........................	2431
Richmond Deepwater Terminal, Va.......	2427
Richmond Island, Maine...............	879
Rigolet, Labrador....................	169
Rio Ceara (bar), Brazil..............	3635
Rio Cunani entrance, Brazil..........	3607
Rio de Janeiro, Brazil * (172).......	3691
Rio de La Plata............... 3723-3733	
Rio Dulce, Guatemala.................	3329
Rio Gallegos, Argentina..............	3837
Rio Grande (Muelle), Argentina.......	3843
Rio Maroni entrance, French Guiana....	3599
Rio Negro ent., Argentina............	3769
Rio Orinoco, Venezuela...............	3575
Rio Sao Francisco, Brazil............	3655
Riohacha, Colombia...................	3549
Riverport, Nova Scotia...............	535
Riverside, Md........................	2209
Riverview, Md........................	2237
Riviera Beach, Baffin Bay, Tex.......	3302
Riviera Beach, N. J..................	1653
Roane Point, Va......................	2330
Roanoke Sound Channel, N. C..........	2447
Roaring Point, Md....................	1999
Robbinston, Maine....................	631
Robinhood, Maine.....................	823
Rocas, Atol das, Brazil..............	3641
Rock Islands, Fla....................	3131
Rock Point, Md.......................	2193
Rockaway Inlet, N. Y.................	1477
Rockland, Maine......................	773
Rockport, Mass.......................	923
Rockville, S. C......................	2623
Rocky Hill, Conn.....................	1211
Rocky Point, Md......................	2109
Romerly Marsh Creek, Ga..............	2723
Roosevelt Inlet, Del.................	1807
Roosevelt Roads, P. R................	3500
Roque Island Harbor, Maine...........	663
Roseau, Dominica.....................	3523
Rose Haven, Md.......................	2144
Rossville, N. Y......................	1597
Round Key, Fla.......................	3041
Round Point, Tex.....................	3283
Royal Bay, South Georgia Island......	3853
Rye Beach, N. Y......................	1254

S

Sabine Bank Lighthouse, Tex..........	3271
Sabine Pass (jetty), Tex.............	3272
Sabine Pass, Tex.....................	3273
Sable Island (north side), Nova Scotia.	523
Sable Island (south side), Nova Scotia.	525
Sachem Head, Conn....................	1220
Safety Harbor, Fla...................	3091
Sag Harbor, N. Y.....................	1389
Sagua de Tanamo, Bahia de, Cuba.......	3415
Saguenay River, Quebec........... 331,333	
Saint Andrew Bay, Fla.......... 3155-3169	
St. Andrew Sound, Ga.......... 2797-2819	
St. Andrews, New Brunswick...........	624
Ste. Anne des Monts, Quebec..........	315
St. Anns Bay, Jamaica................	3459
St. Anns Harbour, Nova Scotia........	467
St. Augustin, Quebec.................	357
St. Augustine, Fla...................	2887
St. Augustine Inlet, Fla.............	2885
St. Barbe Bay, Newfoundland..........	271
St. Barthelemy, Lesser Antilles......	3517
St. Catherines Sound, Ga...... Pages 224,225	
St. Clements Bay, Md.................	2187

	NO.
Ste. Croix, Quebec...................	359
St. Croix Island, Maine..............	633
St. Croix Islands, Virgin Islands....	3515
St. Croix River, Maine.......... 625,631-637	
St. George, N. Y.....................	1503
St. George River, Maine.......... 785-789	
St. George Sound, Fla........... 3141,3143	
St. Georges Harbour, Newfoundland....	257
St. Helena Sound, S. C.......... 2647-2667	
St. James City, Fla..................	3057
St. John, New Brunswick * (24).......	605
St. John's, Newfoundland.............	221
St. Johns River, Fla........... 2853-2881	
St. Jones River entrance, Del........	1813
St. Joseph Bay, Fla..................	3153
St. Joseph Sound, Fla................	3107
St. Laurent d'Orleans, Quebec........	351
St. Lawrence River.............. 315-371	
St. Lucia, Lesser Antilles...... 3527,3529	
St. Lucie River, Fla............ 2907-2911	
St. Margarets Bay, Nova Scotia.......	527
St. Marks, Fla.......................	3137
St. Marks River entrance, Fla. * (124).	3135
St. Mary Bay, Nova Scotia........ 553-557	
St. Mary Harbour, Newfoundland.......	225
St. Mary River, Nova Scotia..........	511
St. Marys, Ga........................	2827
St. Marys City, Md...................	2179
St. Marys Entrance, Ga...............	2821
St. Marys River, Ga. and Fla...... 2827,2829	
St. Marys River, Md............. 2177,2179	
St. Michaels, Md.....................	2043
St. Michaels, Miles River, Md........	2053
St. Nicholaas Bay, Aruba.............	3541
St. Nicolas, Quebec..................	355
St. Paul Island, Nova Scotia.........	439
St. Peter Bay, Cape Breton Island....	477
St. Peters Bay, Prince Edward Island...	425
St. Petersburg Beach Causeway, Fla....	3097
St. Petersburg, Fla. * (120).........	3087
St. Pierre Harbor....................	235
St. Simons Light, Ga.................	2781
St. Simons Sound, Ga............ 2779-2795	
St. Simons Sound Bar, Ga.............	2779
St. Thomas Island, Virgin Islands. 3511,3513	
Sakonnet, R. I.......................	1147
Salem, Mass..........................	931
Salem, N. J..........................	1831
Salinopolis, Brazil..................	3619
Salisbury, Md........................	1997
Salisbury, New Brunswick.............	591
Salmon Falls River, N. H.............	907
Salsbury Cove, Maine.................	709
Salvador, Brazil.....................	3659
San Carlos Bay, Fla............. 3052,3053	
San Juan, P. R. * (148)..............	3505
San Juan del Norte, Nicaragua........	3351
San Luis Pass, Tex...................	3291
San Roman, Argentina.................	3775
San Salvador, Bahamas................	3385
Sanchez, Dominican Republic..........	3471
Sand Key Light, Fla..................	2999
Sand Shoal Inlet, Va.................	1943
Sandy Hook, N. J. * (64).............	1625
Sandy Point, Md......................	2125
Santa Barbara de Samana, Dominican Rep.	3469
Santa Cruz Cabralia, Brazil..........	3671
Santa Cruz (Punta Quilla), Argentina...	3831
Santa Domingo, Dominican Republic....	3477
Santa Elena, Puerto, Argentina.......	3803
Santa Marta, Colombia................	3547
Santa Rosa Sound, Fla................	3175
Santana, Recifes de, Brazil..........	3627
Santos, Brazil * (176)...............	3701

	NO.		NO.
Vermilion Bay, La.	3266,3267	Westover, Va.	2407
Vernon View, Ga.		Westport, Nova Scotia	553
Vero Beach, Fla.	2735	Westport Harbor, Mass.	1143
Vero Beach (ocean), Fla.	2898	Westport River, Mass.	1143,1145
Victoria Bluff, S. C.	2903	Wetappo Creek, Fla.	3165
Vienna, Md.	2685	Weymouth, Nova Scotia	557
Vieux Fort Bay, St. Lucia	2001	Weymouth Back River Bridge	977
Vinalhaven, Maine	3529	Weymouth Fore River Bridge	975
Vineyard Haven, Mass.	749	Wharf Creek, S. C.	2559
Vineyard Sound	1079	White House, Va.	2341
Virgin Islands	1089-1103	Whitehaven, Md.	1995
Virginia	3511-3515	Whitehaven Harbour, Nova Scotia	507
Virginia	Pages 217-222	Whitestone, N. Y.	1265
Virginia Beach, Va.	2441	Whitewater Bay, Fla.	3027
Vitoria, Brazil	3679	Wickford, R. I.	1175
		Wicomico Beach, Md.	2196
W		Wicomico River, Md.	1995,1997
		Wicomico River, Potomac River	2191-2196
Wabasso, Fla.	2897	Wild Cove, Newfoundland	205
Waccamaw River, S. C.	2529-2539	Wildwood Beach, N. J.	1745
Wachapreague Inlet, Va.	1933	Willcox Wharf, Va.	2406
Wachesaw Landing, S. C.	2531	Willets Point, N. Y. * (52)	1331
Wakeham Bay, Hudson Strait	135	Williams Harbour, Labrador	150
Wakema, Va.	2333	Williamsburg Bridge, N. Y.	1309
Walburg Creek, Ga.	2745	Wilmington Beach, N. C.	2479
Waldoboro, Maine	799	Wilmington, Del.	1849
Walkerton, Va.	2335	Wilmington, N. C. * (92)	2493
Wallabout Bay, N. Y.	1311	Wilmington River, Ga.	2725-2729
Wallops Island, Va.	1929	Wilson Cove, Maine	865
Walls Cut, S. C.	2705	Wilsons Beach, New Brunswick	621
Wando River, S. C.	2595-2599	Windmill Point, James River, Va.	2405
Wapitagun Harbour, Quebec	279	Windmill Point, Rappahannock River, Va.	2270
Wappoo Creek, S. C.	2601	Windmill Point Lighthouse, Va.	2267
Wareham, Mass.	1123	Windsor, Nova Scotia	573
Wares Wharf, Va.	2280	Wine Island, La.	3251
Waretown, N. J.	1663	Winter Harbor, Maine	701
Warren, R. I.	1165	Winter Harbour, Melville Island	5
Warrington, Fla.	3179	Winter Island, Fox Channel	123
Washington Canal, N. J.	1611	Winyah Bay, S. C.	2517-2539
Washington, D. C. * (84)	2245	Winyah Bay Entrance, S. C.	2517
Washington National Airport	2243	Wiscasset, Maine	817
Wasque Point, Mass.	1061	Wishart Point, Va.	1918
Wassaw Sound, Ga.	Page 224	Withlacoochee River entrance, Fla.	3117
Watch Hill Point, R. I.	1185	Wolcott Avenue, N. Y.	1285
Watts Cut entrance, S. C.	2641	Wolf Island, Ga.	2771
Watts Island, Va.	1965	Wolf Trap Light, Va.	2297
Wauwinet, Mass.	1045	Wood Island Harbor, Maine	883
Wayman Wharf, Md.	2035	Woodland Beach, Del.	1821
Webeck Harbour, Labrador	163	Woodmere, N. Y.	1471
Weehawken, N. J.	1521	Woods Hole, Mass.	1091-1095
Weeks Bay, La.	3267	Woodville, S. C.	2599
Weir River, Mass.	983	Woody Island, Newfoundland	229
Welaka, Fla.	2881	Woolford, Md.	2015
Welfare Island, N. Y.	1293	Worton Creek, Md.	2081
Wellfleet, Mass.	1001	Wright Island Landing, Va.	2395
Welshpool, New Brunswick	620	Wychmere Harbor, Mass.	1025
Weskeag River, Maine	777	Wye Landing, Md.	205ƒ
West Bay Creek, Fla.	2169		
West Bay, Tex.	3287,3288	**Y**	
West Chop, Mass.	1077		
West Cote Blanche Bay, La.	3265	Yamato, Fla.	2938
West Falmouth Harbor, Mass.	1111	Yarmouth Harbour, Nova Scotia	551
West Fire Island, N. Y.	1425	Yaupon Beach, N. C.	2500
West Harbor, N. Y.	1191	Yeamans Hall, S. C.	2585
West Island, Mass.	1131	Yeocomico River, Va.	2173,2175
West Palm Beach Canal, Fla.	2933	Yonges Island, S. C.	2631
West Point, N. Y.	1543	Yonkers, N. Y.	1531
West Point, Va.	2331	York Harbor, Maine	889
West Quoddy Head, Maine	651	York Point, Va.	2345
West River, Md.	2139,2141	York River, Va.	2311-2343
West Wildwood, N. J.	1749	York Spit Light, Va.	2309
Westbrook, Duck I. Roads, Conn.	1214	Yorktown, Va.	2319
Westchester, N. Y.	1273		
Westerly, Pawcatuck River, R. I.	1186		

MERCHANT MARINE DECK EXAMINATION REFERENCE MATERIAL

PART TWO

1983
TIDAL CURRENT TABLES

ATLANTIC COAST of NORTH AMERICA

CONTENTS

IMPORTANT NOTICES

Daylight saving time is not used in this publication. All daily tidal current predictions and predictions compiled by the use of Table 2 data are based on the standard time meridian indicated for each location. Predicted times may be converted to daylight saving times, where necessary, by adding 1 hour to these data. In converting times from the Astronomical Data page, it should be remembered that daylight saving time is based on a meridian 15° east of the normal standard meridian for a particular place.

Current data have been presented in a different format in Table 2. The new manner of presentation will enable the user to approximate more accurately the times and speeds of the various current phases. Slight changes in terminology also have been made. A full explanation of the proper use of the new table is given on the pages immediately preceding the data.

IV

TIDAL CURRENT TABLES

INTRODUCTION

Current tables for the use of mariners have been published by the National Ocean Survey (formerly the Coast and Geodetic Survey) since 1890. Tables for the Atlantic coast first appeared as a part of the tide tables and consisted of brief directions for obtaining the times of the current for a few locations from the times of high and low waters. Daily predictions of slack water for five stations were given for the year 1916, and by 1923 the tables had so expanded that they were then issued as a separate publication entitled *Current Tables, Atlantic Coast.* A companion volume, *Current Tables, Pacific Coast,* was also issued that year. In 1930 the predictions for the Atlantic coast were extended to include the times and velocities of maximum current.

In the preparation of these tables, all available observations were used. In some cases, however, the observations were insufficient for obtaining final results, and as further information becomes available it will be included in subsequent editions. All persons using these tables are invited to send information or suggestions for increasing their usefulness to the Director, National Ocean Survey, Rockville, Md. 20852, U.S.A. The data for lightship stations are based on observations obtained through the cooperation of the U.S. Coast Guard. By cooperative arrangements, full predictions for Bay of Fundy Entrance (Grand Manan Channel) were furnished by the Canadian Hydrographic Service.

Daily predicted times of slack water and predicted times and velocities of maximum current (flood and ebb) are presented in table 1 for a number of reference stations. Similar predictions for many other locations may be obtained by applying the correction factors listed in table 2 to the predictions of the appropriate reference station. The velocity of a current at times between slack water and maximum current may be approximated by the use of table 3. The duration of weak current near the time of slack water may be computed by the use of table 4.

v

LIST OF REFERENCE STATIONS

TABLE 1.—DAILY CURRENT PREDICTIONS

EXPLANATION OF TABLE

This table gives the predicted times of slack water and the predicted times and velocities of maximum current—flood and ebb—for each day of the year at a number of stations on the Atlantic coast of North America. The times are given in hours and minutes and the velocities in knots.

Time.—The kind of time used for the predictions at each reference station is indicated by the time meridian at the bottom of each page.

Slack water and maximum current.—The columns headed "Slack water" contain the predicted times at which there is no current; or, in other words, the times at which the current has stopped setting in a given direction and is about to begin to set in the opposite direction. Offshore, where the current is rotary, slack water denotes the time of minimum current. Beginning with the slack water before flood the current increases in velocity until the strength or maximum velocity of the flood current is reached; it then decreases until the following slack water or slack before ebb. The ebb current now begins, increases to a maximum velocity, and then decreases to the next slack. The predicted times and velocities of maximum current are given in the columns headed "Maximum Current." Flood velocities are marked with an "F." the ebb velocities with an "E." An entry in the "Slack Water" column will be *slack, flood begins* if the maximum current which follows it is marked "F." Otherwise the entry will be *slack, ebb begins.*

Directions of set.—As the terms flood and ebb do not in all cases clearly indicate the direction of the current, the approximate directions toward which the currents flow are given at the top of each page to distinguish the two streams.

Number of slacks and strengths.—There are usually four slacks and four maximums each day. When a vacancy occurs in any day, the slack or maximum that seems to be missing will be found to occur soon after midnight as the first slack or maximum of the following day. At some stations where the diurnal inequality is large, there may be on certain days a continuous flood or ebb current with varying velocity throughout half the day giving only two slacks and two maximums on that particular day.

Current and tide.—It is important to notice that the predicted slacks and strengths given in this table refer to the horizontal motion of the water and not to the vertical rise and fall of the tide. The relation of current to tide is not constant, but varies from place to place, and the time of slack water does not generally coincide with the time of high or low water, nor does the time of maximum velocity of the current usually coincide with the time of most rapid change in the vertical height of the tide. At stations located on a tidal river or bay the time of slack water may differ from 1 to 3 hours from the time of high or low water. The times of high and low waters are given in the tide tables published by the National Ocean Survey.

Variations from predictions.—In using this table it should be borne in mind that actual times of slack or maximum occasionally differ from the predicted times by as much as half an hour and in rare instances the difference may be as much as an hour. Comparisons of predicted with observed times of slack water indicate that more than 90 percent of the slack waters occurred within half an hour of the predicted times. To make sure, therefore, of getting the full advantage of a favorable current or slack water, the navigator should reach the entrance or strait at least half an hour before the predicted time of the desired condition of current. Currents are frequently disturbed by wind or variations in river discharge. On days when the current is affected by such disturbing influences the times and velocities will differ from those given in the table, but local knowledge will enable one to make proper allowance for these effects.

1

Typical current curves.—The variations in the tidal current from day to day and from place to place are illustrated on the opposite page by the current curves for representative ports along the Atlantic and Gulf Coasts of the United States. Flood current is represented by the solid line curve above the zero velocity (slack water) line and the ebb current by the broken line curve below the slack water line. The curves show clearly that the currents along the Atlantic coast are semi-daily (two floods and two ebbs in a day) in character with their principal variations following changes in the **Moon's** distance and phase. In the Gulf of Mexico, however, the currents are daily in character. As the dominant factor is the change in the **Moon's** declination the currents in the Gulf tend to become semi-daily when the Moon is near the equator. By reference to the curves it will be noted that with this daily type of current there are times when the current may be erratic (marked with an asterisk), or one flood or ebb current of the day may be quite weak. Therefore in using the predictions of the current it is essential to carefully note the velocities as well as the times.

F-Flood, Dir. 032° True   E-Ebb, Dir. 212° True

NOVEMBER

Day	Slack Water Time h.m.	Maximum Current Time h.m.	Vel. knots	Day	Slack Water Time h.m.	Maximum Current Time h.m.	Vel. knots
1 Tu	0225	0535	2.1F	16 W	0225	0535	1.5F
	0855	1205	2.3E		0855	1210	1.6E
	1510	1810	1.9F		1515	1805	1.3F
	2110				2105		
2 W		0025	2.5E	17 Th		0025	1.7E
	0330	0635	2.5F		0315	0625	1.8F
	0950	1300	2.7E		0935	1255	2.1E
	1610	1905	2.4F		1600	1850	1.7F
	2205				2150		
3 Th		0120	2.8E	18 F		0105	2.0E
	0420	0725	2.9F		0400	0705	2.2F
	1035	1350	3.1E		1015	1335	2.5E
	1655	1955	2.7F		1640	1930	2.2F
	2255				2235		
4 F		0205	3.1E	19 Sa		0145	2.4E
	0505	0810	3.1F		0440	0745	2.6F
	1120	1430	3.4E		1050	1410	2.9E
	1740	2035	3.0F		1715	2010	2.6F
	2340				2315		
5 Sa		0250	3.2E	20 Su		0225	2.6E
	0545	0850	3.3F		0520	0820	2.9F
	1155	1510	3.5E		1125	1445	3.2E
	1820	2115	3.1F		1755	2050	2.9F
					2355		
6 Su	0020	0330	3.1E	21 M		0300	2.8E
	0625	0925	3.2F		0600	0900	3.1F
	1230	1550	3.5E		1200	1525	3.4E
	1900	2150	3.0F		1835	2125	3.1F
7 M	0100	0405	3.0E	22 Tu	0035	0340	2.9E
	0705	1000	3.0F		0640	0940	3.2F
	1305	1625	3.3E		1240	1600	3.4E
	1935	2225	2.9F		1915	2210	3.2F
8 Tu	0135	0445	2.7E	23 W	0115	0425	2.9E
	0740	1035	2.8F		0720	1020	3.1F
	1340	1700	3.0E		1320	1645	3.4E
	2010	2300	2.6F		1955	2250	3.1F
9 W	0215	0520	2.3E	24 Th	0200	0505	2.8E
	0815	1110	2.4F		0810	1105	2.9F
	1410	1740	2.6E		1405	1730	3.2E
	2050	2340	2.2F		2040	2335	2.9F
10 Th	0250	0600	1.9E	25 F	0245	0555	2.5E
	0855	1145	2.0F		0900	1150	2.6F
	1440	1915	2.2E		1450	1820	2.9E
	2130				2130		
11 F		0015	1.9F	26 Sa		0030	2.7F
	0330	0645	1.5E		0340	0655	2.3E
	0940	1225	1.5F		0955	1245	2.3F
	1515	1900	1.8E		1545	1920	2.5E
	2215				2230		
12 Sa		0100	1.5F	27 Su		0125	2.4F
	0420	0740	1.1E		0445	0800	2.1E
	1030	1310	1.1F		1100	1350	1.9F
	1600	1955	1.4E		1650	2025	2.3E
	2310				2335		
13 Su		0155	1.2F	28 M		0230	2.2F
	0530	0855	0.9E		0555	0915	2.0E
	1145	1410	0.8F		1215	1500	1.7F
	1705	2110	1.2E		1810	2140	2.1E
14 M	0015	0310	1.1F	29 Tu	0040	0345	2.1F
	0655	1015	1.0E		0710	1025	2.1E
	1310	1535	0.7F		1330	1620	1.7F
	1835	2230	1.2E		1930	2250	2.2E
15 Tu	0125	0430	1.2F	30 W	0150	0455	2.2F
	0805	1120	1.3E		0815	1130	2.4E
	1425	1705	0.9F		1440	1735	1.9F
	2000	2330	1.4E		2040	2355	2.3E

DECEMBER

Day	Slack Water Time h.m.	Maximum Current Time h.m.	Vel. knots	Day	Slack Water Time h.m.	Maximum Current Time h.m.	Vel. knots
1 Th	0250	0600	2.4F	16 F	0220	0525	1.8F
	0915	1230	2.7E		0835	1205	2.1E
	1540	1835	2.2F		1510	1800	1.7F
	2140				2110		
2 F		0050	2.5E	17 Sa		0020	1.8E
	0345	0655	2.6F		0315	0615	2.0F
	1005	1320	2.9E		0925	1250	2.4E
	1630	1925	2.5F		1600	1855	2.1F
	2235				2200		
3 Sa		0140	2.6E	18 Su		0110	2.1E
	0435	0740	2.7F		0405	0705	2.3F
	1050	1405	3.1E		1010	1335	2.7E
	1715	2010	2.6F		1645	1940	2.4F
	2320				2250		
4 Su		0225	2.7E	19 M		0200	2.4E
	0520	0825	2.7F		0455	0755	2.6F
	1130	1450	3.2E		1055	1420	3.0E
	1755	2055	2.7F		1730	2025	2.7F
					2335		
5 M	0005	0310	2.7E	20 Tu		0245	2.6E
	0605	0900	2.7F		0540	0840	2.8F
	1205	1530	3.1E		1140	1505	3.2E
	1835	2130	2.7F		1815	2110	3.0F
6 Tu	0045	0350	2.6E	21 W	0020	0330	2.8E
	0645	0940	2.6F		0630	0925	2.9F
	1240	1605	3.0E		1225	1550	3.3E
	1915	2210	2.6F		1900	2155	3.1F
7 W	0120	0430	2.4E	22 Th	0105	0415	2.9E
	0725	1015	2.4F		0715	1010	3.0F
	1315	1645	2.8E		1310	1635	3.3E
	1950	2245	2.4F		1945	2240	3.2F
8 Th	0200	0510	2.1E	23 F	0155	0505	2.9E
	0800	1050	2.1F		0805	1055	2.9F
	1350	1720	2.5E		1355	1720	3.2E
	2030	2320	2.2F		2030	2330	3.1F
9 F	0235	0545	1.9E	24 Sa	0240	0555	2.8E
	0845	1130	1.9F		0855	1145	2.7F
	1425	1800	2.2E		1445	1810	3.0E
	2110				2120		
10 Sa		0000	2.0F	25 Su		0015	3.0F
	0315	0630	1.7E		0330	0645	2.7E
	0925	1210	1.6F		0950	1235	2.5F
	1500	1840	1.9E		1540	1905	2.8E
	2150				2210		
11 Su		0040	1.8F	26 M		0110	2.7F
	0400	0715	1.5E		0425	0745	2.5E
	1015	1255	1.4F		1045	1335	2.2F
	1545	1925	1.7E		1635	2005	2.5E
	2235				2305		
12 M		0125	1.6F	27 Tu		0205	2.5F
	0445	0810	1.4E		0525	0845	2.4E
	1110	1345	1.2F		1150	1435	2.0F
	1640	2020	1.5E		1740	2105	2.3E
	2325						
13 Tu		0220	1.5F	28 W	0005	0305	2.3F
	0545	0910	1.4E		0625	0945	2.3E
	1215	1445	1.1F		1255	1540	1.8F
	1745	2125	1.4E		1850	2210	2.1E
14 W	0025	0320	1.5F	29 Th	0105	0410	2.1F
	0645	1015	1.5E		0730	1050	2.3E
	1320	1555	1.3F		1400	1655	1.8F
	1900	2230	1.4E		2005	2315	2.0E
15 Th	0125	0425	1.6F	30 F	0210	0515	2.0F
	0740	1110	1.7E		0830	1150	2.4E
	1420	1705	1.4F		1505	1800	1.9F
	2005	2330	1.6E		2110		
				31 Sa		0020	2.0E
					0315	0620	2.1F
					0925	1250	2.5E
					1600	1900	2.1F
					2210		

Time meridian 60° W.   0000 is midnight.   1200 is noon.

PORTSMOUTH HARBOR ENTRANCE (off Wood I.), N.H., 1983

F-Flood, Dir. 355° True   E-Ebb, Dir. 195° True

JANUARY

Day	Slack Water Time h.m.	Max Current Time h.m.	Vel. knots	Day	Slack Water Time h.m.	Max Current Time h.m.	Vel. knots
1 Sa	0139	0424	2.2E	16 Su	0203	0435	1.5E
	0800	1017	1.8F		0822	1023	1.2F
	1352	1654	2.6E		1400	1658	1.9E
	2046	2253	1.6F		2103	2253	1.0F
2 Su	0234	0517	2.1E	17 M	0240	0518	1.5E
	0855	1110	1.7F		0904	1106	1.2F
	1444	1745	2.5E		1430	1741	1.9E
	2138	2346	1.6F		2142	2338	1.1F
3 M	0329	0611	2.1E	18 Tu	0316	0602	1.6E
	0951	1201	1.6F		0948	1149	1.1F
	1538	1838	2.4E		1456	1822	1.9E
	2231				2222		
4 Tu		0039	1.5F	19 W		0021	1.1F
	0426	0706	2.0E		0352	0648	1.6E
	1050	1254	1.4F		1034	1235	1.1F
	1634	1932	2.2E		1523	1908	1.8E
	2326				2303		
5 W		0132	1.4F	20 Th		0106	1.2F
	0523	0803	1.8E		0429	0733	1.6E
	1151	1348	1.2F		1123	1324	1.1F
	1732	2027	2.1E		1558	1955	1.8E
					2346		
6 Th	0022	0227	1.3F	21 F		0153	1.2F
	0621	0902	1.7E		0513	0824	1.6E
	1253	1445	1.0F		1217	1415	1.0F
	1832	2122	1.9E		1644	2044	1.7E
7 F	0118	0319	1.1F	22 Sa	0034	0243	1.2F
	0719	1008	1.7E		0605	0916	1.6E
	1356	1544	0.8F		1315	1508	1.0F
	1932	2221	1.7E		1743	2135	1.7E
8 Sa	0213	0417	1.0F	23 Su	0125	0336	1.2F
	0815	1124	1.7E		0705	1011	1.7E
	1458	1744	0.7F		1414	1603	1.0F
	2032	2323	1.6E		1901	2232	1.7E
9 Su	0308	0612	1.0F	24 M	0219	0431	1.3F
	0908	1246	1.7E		0808	1110	1.8E
	1556	1947	0.7F		1512	1701	1.0F
	2129				2023	2328	1.7E
10 M		0023	1.5E	25 Tu	0315	0528	1.4F
	0359	0657	1.0F		0909	1207	2.0E
	0959	1341	1.7E		1609	1800	1.1F
	1650	2040	0.8F		2134		
	2222						
11 Tu		0115	1.5E	26 W		0027	1.8E
	0448	0758	1.0F		0411	0623	1.5F
	1046	1420	1.8E		1007	1305	2.1E
	1739	2129	0.8F		1703	1859	1.2F
	2312				2238		
12 W		0200	1.4E	27 Th		0124	1.9E
	0534	0734	1.0F		0506	0721	1.6F
	1129	1443	1.8E		1102	1400	2.3E
	1823	2057	0.8F		1755	1956	1.4F
	2359				2336		
13 Th		0236	1.4E	28 F		0220	2.0E
	0617	0816	1.0F		0600	0816	1.7F
	1211	1510	1.9E		1156	1455	2.5E
	1905	2051	0.8F		1846	2052	1.5F
14 F	0042	0314	1.5E	29 Sa	0031	0315	2.1E
	0700	0858	1.1F		0653	0909	1.8F
	1249	1542	1.9E		1248	1546	2.6E
	1945	2131	0.9F		1936	2143	1.6F
15 Sa	0124	0355	1.5E	30 Su	0125	0408	2.2E
	0741	0940	1.1F		0746	1002	1.8F
	1326	1619	1.9E		1339	1637	2.6E
	2025	2212	1.0F		2026	2236	1.6F
				31 M	0217	0501	2.2E
					0839	1052	1.7F
					1429	1727	2.5E
					2115	2325	1.6F

FEBRUARY

Day	Slack Water Time h.m.	Max Current Time h.m.	Vel. knots	Day	Slack Water Time h.m.	Max Current Time h.m.	Vel. knots
1 Tu	0309	0552	2.2E	16 W	0243	0534	1.8E
	0933	1143	1.6F		0921	1127	1.2F
	1520	1815	2.4E		1434	1756	2.0E
	2206				2146	2352	1.3F
2 W		0014	1.6F	17 Th	0314	0619	1.8E
	0401	0643	2.1E		1005	1210	1.2F
	1028	1232	1.4F		1501	1839	1.9E
	1612	1905	2.2E		2225		
	2257						
3 Th		0103	1.4F	18 F		0036	1.3F
	0454	0737	1.9E		0347	0705	1.8E
	1125	1323	1.2F		1052	1257	1.2F
	1706	1957	2.0E		1535	1924	1.8E
	2350				2307		
4 F		0153	1.3F	19 Sa		0123	1.3F
	0548	0830	1.8E		0427	0754	1.8E
	1225	1414	1.0F		1144	1348	1.1F
	1802	2049	1.8E		1620	2015	1.8E
					2356		
5 Sa	0044	0242	1.1F	20 Su		0214	1.3F
	0643	0926	1.7E		0518	0847	1.8E
	1326	1506	0.8F		1242	1440	1.0F
	1901	2144	1.6E		1718	2106	1.7E
6 Su	0140	0335	1.0F	21 M	0051	0305	1.3F
	0739	1031	1.6E		0623	0942	1.8E
	1428	1725	0.6F		1344	1537	1.0F
	2001	2241	1.4E		1839	2206	1.7E
7 M	0236	0427	0.9F	22 Tu	0151	0402	1.3F
	0834	1147	1.5E		0735	1041	1.8E
	1528	1800	0.6F		1446	1636	1.0F
	2100	2339	1.3E		2007	2305	1.7E
8 Tu	0330	0520	0.8F	23 W	0253	0502	1.3F
	0926	1308	1.6E		0844	1143	1.9E
	1623	2019	0.7F		1546	1737	1.1F
	2155				2120		
9 W		0043	1.3E	24 Th		0006	1.7E
	0422	0614	0.8F		0354	0601	1.4F
	1016	1357	1.6E		0948	1242	2.1E
	1713	2105	0.7F		1642	1837	1.2F
	2247				2224		
10 Th		0134	1.3E	25 F		0106	1.9E
	0510	0704	0.9F		0451	0702	1.5F
	1102	1420	1.7E		1046	1341	2.3E
	1757	2150	0.8F		1735	1938	1.3F
	2334				2322		
11 F		0212	1.4E	26 Sa		0206	2.0E
	0555	0751	1.0F		0546	0759	1.6F
	1145	1445	1.8E		1141	1439	2.4E
	1838	2026	0.8F		1826	2035	1.5F
12 Sa	0018	0253	1.5E	27 Su	0016	0300	2.2E
	0638	0834	1.0F		0639	0851	1.6F
	1226	1519	1.9E		1233	1529	2.5E
	1917	2106	0.9F		1915	2127	1.6F
13 Su	0058	0333	1.6E	28 M	0107	0352	2.2E
	0719	0917	1.1F		0731	0944	1.7F
	1303	1556	1.9E		1323	1618	2.5E
	1955	2147	1.1F		2003	2216	1.7F
14 M	0136	0412	1.6E				
	0800	0959	1.2F				
	1337	1634	2.0E				
	2032	2228	1.2F				
15 Tu	0211	0453	1.7E				
	0840	1042	1.2F				
	1407	1713	2.0E				
	2108	2309	1.3F				

Time meridian 75° W.   0000 is midnight.   1200 is noon.

F-Flood, Dir. 355° True   E-Ebb, Dir. 195° True

| MARCH | | | | | | | | | | | | APRIL | | | | | | | | | | | |

Day	Slack Water Time h.m.	Maximum Current Time h.m.	Vel. knots	Day	Slack Water Time h.m.	Maximum Current Time h.m.	Vel. knots	Day	Slack Water Time h.m.	Maximum Current Time h.m.	Vel. knots	Day	Slack Water Time h.m.	Maximum Current Time h.m.	Vel. knots
1 Tu	0156 0822 1411 2050	0442 1033 1705 2302	2.3E 1.6F 2.4E 1.6F	16 W	0138 0815 1343 2033	0427 1017 1646 2239	1.9E 1.3F 2.0E 1.4F	1 F	0301 0942 1524 2155	0550 1139 1808	2.1E 1.3F 1.9E	16 Sa	0214 0918 1435 2123	0528 1123 1746 2344	2.2E 1.4F 1.9E 1.6F
2 W	0244 0913 1500 2138	0531 1120 1751 2346	2.2E 1.5F 2.3E 1.5F	17 Th	0210 0856 1414 2111	0508 1100 1727 2324	2.0E 1.3F 2.0E 1.5F	2 Sa	0346 1032 1612 2244	0000 0634 1226 1854	1.3F 2.0E 1.1F 1.7E	17 Su	0253 1007 1521 2212	0615 1212 1835	2.2E 1.3F 1.9E
3 Th	0332 1005 1548 2227	0617 1207 1838	2.1E 1.4F 2.1E	18 F	0241 0939 1445 2150	0553 1145 1812	2.0E 1.3F 1.9E	3 Su	0431 1125 1702 2336	0041 0720 1311 1940	1.2F 1.8E 0.9F 1.5E	18 M	0339 1100 1619 2308	0032 0705 1303 1930	1.5F 2.1E 1.3F 1.8E
4 F	0420 1058 1638 2317	0031 0705 1254 1923	1.4F 2.0E 1.2F 1.9E	19 Sa	0315 1027 1523 2235	0009 0638 1233 1857	1.5F 2.0E 1.3F 1.9E	4 M	0520 1221 1758	0129 0811 1402 2031	1.0F 1.7E 0.8F 1.4E	19 Tu	0436 1159 1728	0123 0758 1356 2025	1.4F 2.0E 1.2F 1.7E
5 Sa	0510 1155 1731	0116 0755 1342 2014	1.2F 1.8E 1.0F 1.6E	20 Su	0356 1119 1611 2328	0056 0729 1324 1949	1.4F 1.9E 1.2F 1.8E	5 Tu	0031 0613 1319 1857	0218 0903 1451 2125	0.9F 1.6E 0.7F 1.2E	20 W	0011 0544 1300 1842	0218 0857 1456 2127	1.3F 2.0E 1.1F 1.6E
6 Su	0010 0603 1254 1829	0205 0847 1433 2106	1.1F 1.7E 0.8F 1.4E	21 M	0449 1218 1717	0145 0820 1417 2044	1.4F 1.9E 1.1F 1.7E	6 W	0129 0710 1416 1956	0311 0958 1547 2224	0.8F 1.5E 0.6F 1.2E	21 Th	0118 0658 1402 1951	0319 0958 1557 2230	1.2F 1.9E 1.1F 1.6E
7 M	0106 0658 1354 1929	0254 0944 1713 2201	0.9F 1.5E 0.6F 1.3E	22 Tu	0027 0557 1320 1841	0241 0918 1514 2143	1.3F 1.9E 1.1F 1.6E	7 Th	0228 0808 1510 2053	0406 1057 1813 2323	0.7F 1.5E 0.6F 1.2E	22 F	0224 0808 1502 2055	0421 1103 1700 2338	1.1F 1.9E 1.1F 1.7E
8 Tu	0203 0754 1454 2029	0348 1040 1744 2300	0.8F 1.5E 0.5F 1.2E	23 W	0132 0713 1423 2000	0338 1019 1614 2246	1.2F 1.9E 1.0F 1.6E	8 F	0323 0903 1559 2144	0502 1154 1904	0.7F 1.5E 0.7F	23 Sa	0326 0912 1558 2153	0524 1205 1805	1.1F 2.0E 1.2F
9 W	0300 0850 1549 2126	0441 1151 1822	0.7F 1.5E 0.6F	24 Th	0238 0825 1524 2109	0441 1122 1717 2350	1.2F 1.9E 1.1F 1.7E	9 Sa	0415 0955 1644 2231	0021 0557 1243 1832	1.3E 0.8F 1.6E 0.8F	24 Su	0425 1011 1650 2247	0044 0627 1306 1905	1.9E 1.2F 2.1E 1.3F
10 Th	0354 0942 1639 2218	0004 0713 1250 1910	1.2E 0.7F 1.6E 0.7F	25 F	0340 0930 1621 2210	0542 1224 1822	1.2F 2.0E 1.2F	10 Su	0502 1041 1726 2314	0111 0650 1331 1918	1.5E 0.9F 1.7E 1.0F	25 M	0519 1105 1739 2336	0141 0725 1400 1956	2.0E 1.2F 2.1E 1.4F
11 F	0444 1031 1724 2305	0101 0633 1334 2012	1.3E 0.8F 1.6E 0.7F	26 Sa	0439 1029 1714 2306	0053 0643 1325 1922	1.9E 1.3F 2.2E 1.3F	11 M	0546 1125 1805 2353	0154 0737 1410 2003	1.7E 1.0F 1.8E 1.2F	26 Tu	0610 1156 1826	0234 0819 1449 2042	2.1E 1.3F 2.1E 1.5F
12 Sa	0531 1116 1805 2348	0147 0721 1411 1954	1.4E 0.9F 1.7E 0.9F	27 Su	0533 1124 1804 2357	0154 0743 1420 2016	2.0E 1.4F 2.3E 1.5F	12 Tu	0628 1205 1843	0238 0824 1453 2046	1.8E 1.1F 1.9E 1.3F	27 W	0023 0659 1244 1912	0319 0905 1532 2123	2.2E 1.3F 2.1E 1.5F
13 Su	0614 1158 1843	0226 0807 1448 2037	1.6E 1.0F 1.8E 1.0F	28 M	0625 1215 1851	0249 0836 1510 2106	2.2E 1.5F 2.3E 1.6F	13 W	0030 0709 1242 1921	0319 0907 1534 2129	2.0E 1.3F 2.0E 1.5F	28 Th	0107 0746 1330 1956	0400 0946 1615 2203	2.2E 1.3F 2.0E 1.4F
14 M	0028 0655 1236 1921	0307 0853 1525 2116	1.7E 1.1F 1.9E 1.2F	29 Tu	0046 0715 1304 1938	0338 0926 1557 2151	2.2E 1.5F 2.3E 1.6F	14 Th	0105 0751 1318 1959	0400 0951 1617 2212	2.1E 1.3F 2.0E 1.5F	29 F	0150 0833 1415 2040	0441 1031 1656 2245	2.1E 1.2F 1.9E 1.4F
15 Tu	0104 0735 1311 1957	0345 0934 1605 2158	1.8E 1.2F 2.0E 1.3F	30 W	0132 0804 1351 2023	0421 1013 1639 2234	2.3E 1.5F 2.2E 1.6F	15 F	0138 0833 1355 2039	0443 1036 1701 2257	2.1E 1.4F 2.0E 1.6F	30 Sa	0231 0920 1500 2125	0524 1114 1737 2326	2.1E 1.1F 1.7E 1.3F
				31 Th	0217 0853 1437 2109	0507 1056 1723 2317	2.2E 1.4F 2.1E 1.5F								

Time meridian 75° W. 0000 is midnight. 1200 is noon.

BOSTON HARBOR (Deer Island Light), MASSACHUSETTS, 1983

F-Flood, Dir. 254° True   E-Ebb, Dir. 111° True

JANUARY

Day	Slack Water Time h.m.	Max Current Time h.m.	Vel. knots	Day	Slack Water Time h.m.	Max Current Time h.m.	Vel. knots
1 Sa		0309	1.3E	16 Su	0000	0416	1.1E
	0606	0839	1.4E		0628	0927	1.1F
	1153	1536	1.4E		1208	1627	1.2E
	1838	2125	1.4F		1852	2148	1.2F
2 Su	0027	0420	1.3E	17 M	0036	0446	1.0E
	0659	0934	1.3F		0709	0930	1.2F
	1245	1648	1.4E		1247	1606	1.1E
	1930	2228	1.3F		1932	2153	1.2F
3 M	0120	0532	1.2E	18 Tu	0115	0418	1.0E
	0755	1045	1.2F		0751	1005	1.2F
	1340	1800	1.3E		1328	1626	1.1E
	2026	2337	1.2F		2014	2229	1.2F
4 Tu	0216	0637	1.2E	19 W	0156	0447	1.0E
	0852	1205	1.1F		0838	1048	1.2F
	1437	1905	1.2E		1412	1703	1.1E
	2122				2059	2313	1.2F
5 W		0043	1.1F	20 Th	0241	0528	1.1E
	0314	0739	1.2E		0927	1135	1.2F
	0953	1313	1.0F		1500	1747	1.1E
	1537	2007	1.2E		2147		
	2221						
6 Th		0146	1.1F	21 F		0000	1.3F
	0413	0839	1.2E		0329	0618	1.1E
	1056	1417	1.0F		1018	1226	1.2F
	1640	2107	1.2E		1551	1838	1.0E
	2321				2238		
7 F		0247	1.1F	22 Sa		0051	1.3F
	0514	0938	1.3E		0421	0714	1.1E
	1158	1518	1.0F		1111	1320	1.1F
	1743	2205	1.2E		1646	1937	1.0E
					2330		
8 Sa	0020	0344	1.1F	23 Su		0145	1.3F
	0615	1034	1.4E		0515	0818	1.1E
	1258	1615	1.1F		1207	1417	1.1F
	1850	2300	1.3E		1744	2043	1.0E
9 Su	0116	0439	1.1F	24 M	0025	0242	1.3F
	0715	1127	1.4E		0611	0930	1.2E
	1353	1709	1.1F		1301	1519	1.2F
	1956	2352	1.3E		1842	2158	1.1E
10 M	0209	0530	1.2F	25 Tu	0120	0342	1.3F
	0810	1218	1.5E		0707	1052	1.3E
	1444	1759	1.2F		1358	1631	1.2F
	2053				1941	2330	1.2E
11 Tu		0042	1.3E	26 W	0216	0447	1.3F
	0258	0617	1.2F		0804	1204	1.4E
	0857	1306	1.5E		1451	1746	1.3F
	1530	1846	1.2F		2038		
	2136						
12 W		0129	1.3E	27 Th		0036	1.3E
	0341	0703	1.2F		0310	0556	1.4F
	0938	1351	1.5E		0859	1259	1.5E
	1613	1930	1.2F		1544	1846	1.4F
	2212				2133		
13 Th		0214	1.3E	28 F		0130	1.3E
	0425	0745	1.2F		0402	0659	1.4F
	1017	1435	1.4E		0952	1352	1.5E
	1654	2012	1.2F		1636	1941	1.5F
	2248				2227		
14 F		0257	1.2E	29 Sa		0223	1.4E
	0507	0826	1.2F		0456	0756	1.5F
	1054	1516	1.3E		1045	1445	1.5E
	1734	2051	1.2F		1727	2034	1.5F
	2323				2319		
15 Sa		0338	1.1E	30 Su		0316	1.4E
	0547	0902	1.2F		0549	0850	1.5F
	1131	1555	1.2E		1137	1538	1.5E
	1812	2126	1.2F		1818	2126	1.5F
				31 M	0010	0411	1.4E
					0641	0946	1.4F
					1229	1635	1.5E
					1909	2219	1.4F

FEBRUARY

Day	Slack Water Time h.m.	Max Current Time h.m.	Vel. knots	Day	Slack Water Time h.m.	Max Current Time h.m.	Vel. knots
1 Tu	0102	0509	1.4E	16 W	0047	0348	1.1E
	0735	1042	1.3F		0724	0942	1.3F
	1321	1734	1.4E		1302	1556	1.2E
	2000	2315	1.3F		1941	2201	1.4F
2 W	0154	0608	1.3E	17 Th	0126	0417	1.2E
	0830	1142	1.2F		0808	1021	1.3F
	1416	1836	1.3E		1344	1629	1.2E
	2054				2024	2242	1.4F
3 Th		0012	1.2F	18 F	0209	0456	1.2E
	0248	0709	1.3E		0855	1106	1.3F
	0928	1244	1.1F		1429	1712	1.1E
	1513	1937	1.2E		2110	2328	1.4F
	2150						
4 F		0112	1.2F	19 Sa	0255	0542	1.2E
	0343	0809	1.3E		0946	1154	1.2F
	1027	1346	1.0F		1519	1801	1.1E
	1613	2038	1.2E		2202		
	2248						
5 Sa		0212	1.1F	20 Su		0017	1.3F
	0441	0909	1.3E		0345	0633	1.2E
	1127	1446	1.0F		1040	1246	1.2F
	1715	2137	1.1E		1613	1857	1.0E
	2347				2258		
6 Su		0311	1.0F	21 M		0110	1.3F
	0541	1006	1.3E		0440	0737	1.1E
	1228	1545	1.0F		1138	1342	1.1F
	1820	2233	1.2E		1712	2004	1.0E
					2356		
7 M	0044	0408	1.0F	22 Tu		0207	1.2F
	0640	1101	1.3E		0538	0853	1.1E
	1325	1641	1.0F		1236	1445	1.1F
	1932	2327	1.2E		1814	2228	1.0E
8 Tu	0140	0502	1.1F	23 W	0055	0310	1.2F
	0738	1153	1.4E		0639	1100	1.2E
	1419	1734	1.1F		1333	1613	1.1F
	2043				1918	2336	1.1E
9 W		0018	1.2E	24 Th	0153	0430	1.2F
	0231	0552	1.1F		0740	1201	1.3E
	0830	1242	1.4E		1430	1741	1.2F
	1507	1822	1.1F		2018		
	2123						
10 Th		0106	1.2E	25 F		0031	1.3E
	0319	0639	1.1F		0251	0559	1.3F
	0914	1329	1.4E		0839	1255	1.5E
	1550	1907	1.2F		1524	1839	1.3F
	2154				2116		
11 F		0152	1.2E	26 Sa		0124	1.4E
	0402	0723	1.2F		0347	0659	1.4F
	0954	1412	1.4E		0935	1346	1.5E
	1630	1949	1.2F		1617	1932	1.5F
	2227				2210		
12 Sa		0234	1.2E	27 Su		0214	1.5E
	0444	0804	1.2F		0439	0753	1.4F
	1031	1452	1.3E		1029	1435	1.6E
	1709	2028	1.2F		1707	2022	1.5F
	2300				2301		
13 Su		0314	1.2E	28 M		0304	1.5E
	0524	0841	1.2F		0531	0844	1.5F
	1108	1528	1.3E		1120	1525	1.6E
	1746	2102	1.3F		1757	2111	1.5F
	2334				2351		
14 M		0348	1.1E				
	0603	0909	1.2F				
	1144	1550	1.2E				
	1823	2123	1.3F				
15 Tu	0010	0354	1.1E				
	0642	0912	1.2F				
	1222	1533	1.2E				
	1901	2127	1.3F				

Time meridian 75° W.   0000 is midnight.   1200 is noon.
At times of slack water before maximum ebb, the velocity actually averages 0.3 knot in a direction of 184° true.

F-Flood, Dir. 254° True   E-Ebb, Dir. 111° True

MARCH

Day	Slack Water Time h.m.	Max Current Time h.m.	Vel. knots
1 Tu		0354	1.5E
	0622	0933	1.5F
	1211	1615	1.5E
	1845	2159	1.5F
2 W	0040	0445	1.5E
	0713	1024	1.4F
	1301	1709	1.4E
	1934	2248	1.4F
3 Th	0129	0540	1.4E
	0805	1117	1.3F
	1352	1806	1.3E
	2026	2340	1.3F
4 F	0219	0638	1.3E
	0859	1212	1.2F
	1446	1906	1.2E
	2118		
5 Sa		0035	1.2F
	0310	0737	1.3E
	0954	1311	1.1F
	1542	2007	1.1E
	2212		
6 Su		0134	1.1F
	0405	0837	1.2E
	1051	1411	1.0F
	1641	2106	1.1E
	2310		
7 M		0234	1.0F
	0502	0935	1.2E
	1151	1511	0.9F
	1743	2204	1.1E
8 Tu	0009	0333	1.0F
	0600	1031	1.2E
	1250	1609	0.9F
	1847	2259	1.1E
9 W	0107	0430	1.0F
	0658	1125	1.3E
	1344	1703	1.0F
	1951	2351	1.1E
10 Th	0200	0522	1.0F
	0753	1215	1.3E
	1435	1753	1.1F
	2043		
11 F		0040	1.2E
	0250	0611	1.1F
	0842	1301	1.3E
	1520	1838	1.2F
	2122		
12 Sa		0125	1.2E
	0337	0656	1.1F
	0925	1344	1.3E
	1600	1921	1.2F
	2157		
13 Su		0207	1.2E
	0418	0737	1.2F
	1004	1424	1.3E
	1639	1959	1.3F
	2232		
14 M		0245	1.2E
	0458	0814	1.2F
	1042	1458	1.3E
	1717	2033	1.3F
	2306		
15 Tu		0316	1.2E
	0538	0845	1.3F
	1119	1509	1.2E
	1753	2053	1.4F
	2342		
16 W		0313	1.2E
	0617	0853	1.3F
	1157	1506	1.2E
	1831	2101	1.4F
17 Th	0020	0324	1.3E
	0658	0918	1.3F
	1237	1531	1.2E
	1911	2134	1.5F
18 F	0059	0352	1.3E
	0740	0957	1.4F
	1319	1604	1.2E
	1955	2216	1.5F
19 Sa	0141	0430	1.3E
	0828	1040	1.3F
	1403	1645	1.1E
	2042	2300	1.4F
20 Su	0226	0515	1.2E
	0919	1127	1.2F
	1452	1733	1.1E
	2135	2349	1.3F
21 M	0316	0607	1.2E
	1013	1219	1.2F
	1547	1830	1.0E
	2231		
22 Tu		0041	1.2F
	0411	0710	1.1E
	1111	1315	1.1F
	1647	1941	0.9E
	2332		
23 W		0139	1.1F
	0511	0941	1.1E
	1211	1420	1.0F
	1752	2224	1.0E
24 Th	0034	0245	1.0F
	0615	1051	1.2E
	1311	1625	1.0F
	1857	2323	1.1E
25 F	0136	0448	1.1F
	0719	1148	1.3E
	1410	1730	1.2F
	1959		
26 Sa		0017	1.3E
	0234	0553	1.2F
	0820	1241	1.4E
	1505	1826	1.3F
	2057		
27 Su		0109	1.4E
	0330	0648	1.3F
	0918	1332	1.5E
	1557	1917	1.4F
	2151		
28 M		0158	1.5E
	0422	0740	1.4F
	1011	1420	1.6E
	1646	2005	1.5F
	2241		
29 Tu		0247	1.6E
	0512	0828	1.5F
	1102	1508	1.6E
	1734	2052	1.5F
	2329		
30 W		0334	1.6E
	0602	0916	1.5F
	1151	1556	1.5E
	1821	2137	1.5F
31 Th	0016	0423	1.6E
	0650	1003	1.4F
	1240	1645	1.4E
	1909	2222	1.4F

APRIL

Day	Slack Water Time h.m.	Max Current Time h.m.	Vel. knots
1 F	0102	0514	1.5E
	0740	1051	1.3F
	1328	1739	1.3E
	1958	2309	1.3F
2 Sa	0149	0608	1.4E
	0830	1142	1.2F
	1418	1836	1.2E
	2048	2359	1.2F
3 Su	0237	0706	1.3E
	0922	1237	1.1F
	1510	1935	1.1E
	2140		
4 M		0055	1.1F
	0328	0804	1.2E
	1018	1335	1.0F
	1605	2034	1.0E
	2235		
5 Tu		0155	1.0F
	0422	0902	1.1E
	1113	1434	0.9F
	1703	2131	1.0E
	2331		
6 W		0255	0.9F
	0518	0958	1.1E
	1210	1532	0.9F
	1801	2226	1.0E
7 Th	0029	0352	0.9F
	0615	1051	1.2E
	1304	1626	1.0F
	1858	2318	1.1E
8 F	0124	0447	1.0F
	0710	1141	1.2E
	1355	1716	1.0F
	1950		
9 Sa		0007	1.1E
	0216	0536	1.0F
	0801	1228	1.2E
	1441	1803	1.1F
	2036		
10 Su		0052	1.2E
	0302	0622	1.1F
	0848	1311	1.2E
	1524	1845	1.2F
	2118		
11 M		0134	1.2E
	0347	0704	1.2F
	0931	1351	1.2E
	1604	1925	1.3F
	2157		
12 Tu		0211	1.3E
	0428	0742	1.3F
	1012	1422	1.2E
	1644	1957	1.4F
	2235		
13 W		0238	1.3E
	0509	0813	1.3F
	1052	1427	1.2E
	1723	2016	1.4F
	2313		
14 Th		0240	1.3E
	0550	0826	1.4F
	1132	1440	1.2E
	1803	2034	1.5F
	2353		
15 F		0301	1.3E
	0632	0856	1.4F
	1214	1509	1.2E
	1846	2110	1.5F
16 Sa	0034	0333	1.3E
	0718	0934	1.4F
	1257	1546	1.2E
	1930	2152	1.5F
17 Su	0117	0412	1.3E
	0806	1019	1.3F
	1343	1628	1.1E
	2020	2237	1.4F
18 M	0204	0457	1.2E
	0858	1106	1.2F
	1433	1717	1.0E
	2114	2325	1.3F
19 Tu	0255	0551	1.1E
	0952	1158	1.1F
	1529	1817	0.9E
	2212		
20 W		0020	1.1F
	0351	0659	1.1E
	1050	1256	1.0F
	1630	2104	0.9E
	2314		
21 Th		0120	1.0F
	0452	0933	1.1E
	1151	1454	0.9F
	1734	2207	1.0E
22 F	0018	0325	0.9F
	0557	1035	1.2E
	1251	1614	1.0F
	1839	2306	1.2E
23 Sa	0119	0440	1.0F
	0701	1131	1.3E
	1350	1714	1.1F
	1940		
24 Su		0000	1.3E
	0218	0539	1.1F
	0802	1225	1.4E
	1444	1808	1.3F
	2037		
25 M		0051	1.4E
	0313	0633	1.3F
	0900	1314	1.5E
	1536	1858	1.4F
	2130		
26 Tu		0141	1.5E
	0405	0723	1.3F
	0953	1403	1.5E
	1624	1945	1.5F
	2220		
27 W		0228	1.6E
	0453	0811	1.4F
	1043	1450	1.5E
	1711	2031	1.5F
	2306		
28 Th		0315	1.6E
	0541	0857	1.4F
	1131	1537	1.5E
	1758	2115	1.4F
	2351		
29 F		0402	1.5E
	0629	0943	1.4F
	1218	1625	1.4E
	1843	2159	1.4F
30 Sa	0036	0450	1.5E
	0716	1028	1.3F
	1304	1716	1.2E
	1930	2242	1.3F

Time meridian 75° W. 0000 is midnight. 1200 is noon.
At times of slack water before maximum ebb, the velocity actually averages 0.3 knot in a direction of 184° true.

BOSTON HARBOR (Deer Island Light), MASSACHUSETTS, 1983

F-Flood, Dir. 254° True   E-Ebb, Dir. 111° True

MAY

Day	Slack Water Time h.m.	Maximum Current Time h.m.	Vel. knots
1 Su	0120	0541	1.4E
	0803	1116	1.2F
	1350	1808	1.1E
	2019	2326	1.2F
2 M	0206	0634	1.3E
	0852	1205	1.1F
	1439	1904	1.0E
	2109		
3 Tu		0016	1.1F
	0253	0730	1.2E
	0943	1258	1.0F
	1529	2000	1.0E
	2201		
4 W		0113	1.0F
	0344	0826	1.1E
	1037	1354	1.0F
	1622	2055	1.0E
	2256		
5 Th		0212	0.9F
	0437	0920	1.1E
	1129	1449	1.0F
	1716	2148	1.0E
	2350		
6 F		0309	0.9F
	0531	1012	1.1E
	1220	1542	1.0F
	1809	2240	1.0E
7 Sa	0043	0404	1.0F
	0625	1102	1.1E
	1310	1633	1.1F
	1901	2328	1.1E
8 Su	0135	0454	1.0F
	0718	1149	1.1E
	1358	1719	1.2F
	1949		
9 M		0013	1.2E
	0223	0541	1.1F
	0807	1231	1.2E
	1442	1802	1.2F
	2034		
10 Tu		0055	1.2E
	0310	0624	1.2F
	0854	1309	1.2E
	1527	1841	1.3F
	2118		
11 W		0130	1.3E
	0355	0702	1.3F
	0939	1337	1.2E
	1610	1912	1.4F
	2201		
12 Th		0153	1.3E
	0439	0735	1.3F
	1023	1348	1.2E
	1653	1935	1.4F
	2243		
13 F		0209	1.3E
	0523	0800	1.4F
	1107	1416	1.2E
	1738	2008	1.5F
	2326		
14 Sa		0240	1.4E
	0609	0834	1.4F
	1152	1452	1.2E
	1822	2047	1.5F
15 Su	0011	0318	1.4E
	0657	0916	1.4F
	1238	1534	1.2E
	1911	2132	1.4F
16 M	0057	0402	1.3E
	0747	1002	1.3F
	1327	1621	1.1E
	2002	2219	1.3F
17 Tu	0146	0452	1.2E
	0839	1051	1.2F
	1420	1717	1.0E
	2059	2311	1.2F
18 W	0239	0553	1.1E
	0934	1147	1.1F
	1516	1939	1.0E
	2158		
19 Th		0007	1.1F
	0337	0810	1.1E
	1032	1304	1.0F
	1616	2048	1.0E
	2259		
20 F		0157	0.9F
	0438	0917	1.1E
	1132	1453	1.0F
	1718	2149	1.1E
21 Sa	0001	0322	1.0F
	0541	1016	1.2E
	1231	1557	1.1F
	1820	2246	1.2E
22 Su	0102	0425	1.0F
	0644	1112	1.3E
	1329	1654	1.1F
	1919	2341	1.3E
23 M	0200	0521	1.1F
	0745	1205	1.3E
	1422	1747	1.2F
	2016		
24 Tu		0032	1.4E
	0255	0614	1.2F
	0842	1256	1.4E
	1513	1837	1.3F
	2109		
25 W		0122	1.5E
	0346	0704	1.3F
	0935	1345	1.4E
	1602	1924	1.3F
	2157		
26 Th		0210	1.5E
	0434	0752	1.3F
	1025	1433	1.4E
	1649	2010	1.4F
	2243		
27 F		0257	1.5E
	0521	0838	1.3F
	1111	1520	1.4E
	1734	2054	1.3F
	2327		
28 Sa		0343	1.5E
	0607	0923	1.3F
	1156	1607	1.3E
	1820	2137	1.3F
29 Su	0010	0429	1.4E
	0651	1007	1.2F
	1240	1654	1.2E
	1906	2219	1.2F
30 M	0053	0517	1.3E
	0738	1051	1.1F
	1324	1743	1.1E
	1951	2301	1.2F
31 Tu	0136	0605	1.2E
	0823	1136	1.1F
	1409	1833	1.0E
	2040	2340	1.1F

JUNE

Day	Slack Water Time h.m.	Maximum Current Time h.m.	Vel. knots
1 W	0221	0655	1.1E
	0910	1221	1.0F
	1455	1925	1.0E
	2129		
2 Th		0018	1.0F
	0309	0745	1.1E
	0959	1308	1.0F
	1543	2015	1.0E
	2220		
3 F		0109	1.0F
	0358	0836	1.0E
	1048	1357	1.0F
	1632	2105	1.0E
	2311		
4 Sa		0210	1.0F
	0450	0927	1.0E
	1137	1447	1.1F
	1723	2155	1.0E
5 Su	0002	0306	1.0F
	0542	1014	1.0E
	1226	1535	1.1F
	1813	2242	1.1E
6 M	0054	0358	1.1F
	0634	1059	1.0E
	1313	1619	1.2F
	1903	2325	1.1E
7 Tu	0144	0446	1.1F
	0725	1139	1.1E
	1401	1700	1.3F
	1951		
8 W		0005	1.2E
	0233	0530	1.2F
	0816	1210	1.1E
	1449	1738	1.3F
	2039		
9 Th		0036	1.3E
	0321	0612	1.3F
	0905	1235	1.2E
	1537	1816	1.4F
	2126		
10 F		0106	1.3E
	0409	0651	1.3F
	0953	1314	1.2E
	1624	1858	1.4F
	2213		
11 Sa		0142	1.4E
	0458	0733	1.4F
	1042	1357	1.2E
	1712	1942	1.5F
	2301		
12 Su		0224	1.4E
	0547	0816	1.4F
	1131	1444	1.2E
	1802	2029	1.4F
	2350		
13 M		0312	1.4E
	0637	0904	1.3F
	1221	1535	1.2E
	1854	2118	1.4F
14 Tu	0040	0404	1.3E
	0728	0955	1.3F
	1313	1637	1.1E
	1948	2210	1.3F
15 W	0132	0513	1.2E
	0821	1054	1.2F
	1407	1817	1.1E
	2044	2309	1.2F
16 Th	0226	0647	1.2E
	0917	1221	1.1F
	1503	1927	1.1E
	2142		
17 F		0048	1.1F
	0324	0755	1.2E
	1013	1332	1.1F
	1601	2029	1.1E
	2242		
18 Sa		0201	1.0F
	0424	0857	1.2E
	1111	1435	1.1F
	1701	2129	1.2E
	2343		
19 Su		0305	1.0F
	0526	0955	1.2E
	1209	1535	1.2F
	1800	2226	1.3E
20 M	0043	0404	1.0F
	0628	1051	1.2E
	1306	1631	1.1F
	1859	2320	1.4E
21 Tu	0141	0500	1.1F
	0728	1145	1.3E
	1400	1724	1.2F
	1954		
22 W		0012	1.4E
	0235	0553	1.1F
	0826	1237	1.3E
	1451	1814	1.2F
	2047		
23 Th		0102	1.5E
	0327	0643	1.2F
	0919	1326	1.3E
	1540	1903	1.2F
	2135		
24 F		0151	1.5E
	0414	0732	1.2F
	1008	1414	1.3E
	1628	1949	1.2F
	2220		
25 Sa		0238	1.5E
	0500	0818	1.2F
	1052	1501	1.3E
	1712	2034	1.2F
	2303		
26 Su		0324	1.4E
	0544	0902	1.2F
	1134	1547	1.2E
	1758	2117	1.2F
	2345		
27 M		0408	1.4E
	0628	0946	1.2F
	1216	1633	1.2E
	1841	2158	1.1F
28 Tu	0026	0452	1.3E
	0710	1027	1.1F
	1257	1717	1.1E
	1927	2236	1.1F
29 W	0108	0535	1.2E
	0753	1105	1.1F
	1338	1800	1.0E
	2011	2301	1.1F
30 Th	0150	0616	1.1E
	0838	1135	1.1F
	1421	1843	1.0E
	2058	2320	1.1F

Time meridian 75° W.   0000 is midnight.   1200 is noon.
At times of slack water before maximum ebb, the velocity actually averages 0.3 knot in a direction of 184° true.

BOSTON HARBOR (Deer Island Light), MASSACHUSETTS, 1983

F-Flood, Dir. 254° True   E-Ebb, Dir. 111° True

JULY

Day	Slack Water Time (h.m.)	Maximum Current Time (h.m.)	Vel. (knots)
1 F	0235	0650	1.0E
	0921	1149	1.1F
	1505	1921	1.0E
	2145		
2 Sa		0002	1.1F
	0322	0637	1.0E
	1008	1229	1.1F
	1552	1909	1.0E
	2234		
3 Su		0050	1.1F
	0411	0717	1.0E
	1054	1315	1.2F
	1640	1953	1.0E
	2324		
4 M		0140	1.1F
	0502	0806	1.0E
	1142	1405	1.2F
	1730	2045	1.1E
5 Tu	0016	0234	1.1F
	0554	0901	1.0E
	1232	1456	1.3F
	1821	2142	1.1E
6 W	0108	0329	1.2F
	0647	0959	1.1E
	1323	1549	1.3F
	1912	2237	1.2E
7 Th	0159	0424	1.2F
	0740	1056	1.1E
	1415	1642	1.4F
	2003	2335	1.3E
8 F	0250	0520	1.3F
	0833	1154	1.2E
	1507	1735	1.4F
	2055		
9 Sa		0029	1.4E
	0341	0617	1.3F
	0927	1253	1.2E
	1559	1829	1.4F
	2147		
10 Su		0123	1.4E
	0432	0713	1.4F
	1019	1352	1.2E
	1650	1923	1.4F
	2238		
11 M		0218	1.4E
	0523	0808	1.4F
	1111	1453	1.3E
	1742	2018	1.4F
	2330		
12 Tu		0316	1.4E
	0616	0907	1.4F
	1204	1557	1.3E
	1837	2117	1.3F
13 W	0022	0419	1.4E
	0708	1007	1.3F
	1257	1701	1.3E
	1931	2224	1.3F
14 Th	0116	0526	1.3E
	0800	1109	1.3F
	1351	1804	1.2E
	2027	2335	1.2F
15 F	0211	0631	1.3E
	0855	1211	1.2F
	1446	1906	1.2E
	2124		
16 Sa		0040	1.1F
	0309	0733	1.2E
	0950	1312	1.2F
	1542	2006	1.2E
	2223		
17 Su		0143	1.1F
	0408	0834	1.2E
	1048	1412	1.2F
	1640	2106	1.3E
	2322		
18 M		0243	1.1F
	0509	0933	1.2E
	1145	1510	1.1F
	1738	2203	1.3E
19 Tu	0022	0341	1.1F
	0611	1029	1.2E
	1241	1606	1.1F
	1836	2258	1.4E
20 W	0120	0438	1.1F
	0713	1124	1.2E
	1337	1700	1.1F
	1933	2351	1.4E
21 Th	0214	0531	1.1F
	0812	1216	1.2E
	1429	1751	1.1F
	2025		
22 F		0041	1.4E
	0306	0622	1.1F
	0905	1306	1.3E
	1519	1840	1.1F
	2114		
23 Sa		0130	1.4E
	0352	0710	1.1F
	0952	1355	1.3E
	1607	1928	1.1F
	2158		
24 Su		0217	1.4E
	0439	0756	1.2F
	1033	1440	1.2E
	1651	2012	1.1F
	2240		
25 M		0302	1.4E
	0520	0839	1.2F
	1112	1525	1.2E
	1735	2055	1.1F
	2320		
26 Tu		0345	1.3E
	0601	0921	1.2F
	1150	1607	1.2E
	1818	2134	1.1F
27 W	0000	0425	1.2E
	0641	0958	1.1F
	1228	1648	1.1E
	1859	2207	1.1F
28 Th	0039	0502	1.1E
	0721	1029	1.1F
	1306	1724	1.1E
	1941	2212	1.1F
29 F	0119	0503	1.1E
	0802	1030	1.2F
	1347	1710	1.0E
	2026	2242	1.1F
30 Sa	0202	0505	1.1E
	0845	1104	1.2F
	1429	1728	1.1E
	2111	2323	1.2F
31 Su	0247	0540	1.1E
	0929	1146	1.3F
	1514	1808	1.1E
	2159		

AUGUST

Day	Slack Water Time (h.m.)	Maximum Current Time (h.m.)	Vel. (knots)
1 M		0011	1.2F
	0335	0624	1.1E
	1017	1233	1.3F
	1601	1855	1.1E
	2249		
2 Tu		0101	1.2F
	0425	0714	1.1E
	1106	1323	1.3F
	1651	1950	1.2E
	2340		
3 W		0153	1.2F
	0518	0811	1.0E
	1158	1416	1.3F
	1744	2049	1.2E
4 Th	0035	0249	1.2F
	0614	0913	1.1E
	1251	1511	1.3F
	1838	2154	1.2E
5 F	0129	0347	1.2F
	0710	1021	1.1E
	1347	1608	1.3F
	1933	2303	1.3E
6 Sa	0222	0450	1.3F
	0807	1138	1.2E
	1440	1708	1.4F
	2028		
7 Su		0015	1.4E
	0317	0558	1.3F
	0903	1254	1.2E
	1536	1809	1.4F
	2123		
8 M		0118	1.4E
	0409	0703	1.4F
	0958	1355	1.3E
	1630	1915	1.4F
	2217		
9 Tu		0216	1.5E
	0500	0802	1.4F
	1051	1451	1.4E
	1723	2018	1.4F
	2310		
10 W		0311	1.5E
	0552	0858	1.4F
	1144	1546	1.4E
	1818	2118	1.4F
11 Th	0004	0408	1.4E
	0644	0954	1.4F
	1237	1643	1.4E
	1911	2218	1.3F
12 F	0058	0507	1.4E
	0737	1050	1.4F
	1329	1741	1.4E
	2006	2318	1.3F
13 Sa	0152	0607	1.3E
	0830	1147	1.3F
	1423	1841	1.3E
	2102		
14 Su		0018	1.2F
	0248	0708	1.3E
	0924	1246	1.2F
	1518	1941	1.3E
	2200		
15 M		0118	1.1F
	0347	0809	1.2E
	1020	1344	1.2F
	1614	2040	1.3E
	2259		
16 Tu		0218	1.1F
	0447	0908	1.2E
	1119	1443	1.1F
	1712	2138	1.3E
	2358		
17 W		0317	1.0F
	0550	1006	1.2E
	1216	1539	1.1F
	1811	2234	1.3E
18 Th	0056	0414	1.0F
	0654	1101	1.2E
	1311	1635	1.1F
	1909	2327	1.4E
19 F	0150	0508	1.1F
	0801	1154	1.2E
	1407	1727	1.1F
	2003		
20 Sa		0019	1.4E
	0241	0558	1.1F
	0856	1244	1.2E
	1457	1817	1.1F
	2052		
21 Su		0107	1.4E
	0329	0646	1.1F
	0935	1331	1.2E
	1543	1903	1.1F
	2135		
22 M		0153	1.4E
	0412	0731	1.2F
	1011	1416	1.2E
	1628	1947	1.1F
	2215		
23 Tu		0236	1.3E
	0452	0812	1.2F
	1046	1459	1.2E
	1710	2028	1.1F
	2253		
24 W		0317	1.3E
	0531	0851	1.2F
	1121	1539	1.2E
	1750	2105	1.1F
	2331		
25 Th		0354	1.2E
	0610	0925	1.2F
	1157	1614	1.1E
	1830	2132	1.1F
26 F	0009	0418	1.1E
	0648	0936	1.2F
	1233	1624	1.1E
	1911	2134	1.2F
27 Sa	0049	0353	1.1E
	0728	0950	1.3F
	1312	1614	1.1E
	1954	2208	1.2F
28 Su	0130	0421	1.1E
	0809	1027	1.3F
	1354	1646	1.2E
	2039	2250	1.2F
29 M	0214	0459	1.1E
	0853	1111	1.3F
	1438	1728	1.2E
	2128	2337	1.2F
30 Tu	0302	0544	1.1E
	0941	1159	1.3F
	1526	1817	1.2E
	2219		
31 W		0027	1.2F
	0353	0637	1.0E
	1034	1249	1.3F
	1618	1913	1.2E
	2311		

Time meridian 75° W. 0000 is midnight. 1200 is noon.
At times of slack water before maximum ebb, the velocity actually averages 0.3 knot in a direction of 184° true.

BOSTON HARBOR (Deer Island Light), MASSACHUSETTS, 1983

F-Flood, Dir. 254° True   E-Ebb, Dir. 111° True

SEPTEMBER

Day	Slack Water Time h.m.	Maximum Current Time h.m.	Vel. knots
1 Th	0448	0121	1.2F
	1129	0736	1.0E
	1712	1343	1.3F
		2016	1.2E
2 F	0008	0218	1.2F
	0546	0845	1.0E
	1227	1441	1.3F
	1810	2131	1.2E
3 Sa	0103	0321	1.2F
	0646	1016	1.1E
	1323	1543	1.3F
	1908	2306	1.3E
4 Su	0159	0438	1.2F
	0745	1153	1.2E
	1420	1654	1.3F
	2006		
5 M	0253	0015	1.4E
	0843	0556	1.3F
	1516	1248	1.3E
	2102	1812	1.3F
6 Tu	0347	0110	1.5E
	0938	0655	1.4F
	1610	1342	1.4E
	2158	1914	1.4F
7 W	0438	0203	1.5E
	1031	0748	1.5F
	1702	1433	1.5E
	2251	2009	1.4F
8 Th	0529	0254	1.5E
	1122	0839	1.5F
	1756	1525	1.5E
	2343	2104	1.4F
9 F	0619	0347	1.5E
	1213	0930	1.5F
	1849	1619	1.5E
		2157	1.4F
10 Sa	0036	0443	1.4E
	0710	1023	1.4F
	1304	1715	1.4E
	1941	2253	1.3F
11 Su	0129	0541	1.3E
	0801	1118	1.3F
	1355	1813	1.4E
	2037	2351	1.2F
12 M	0224	0642	1.2F
	0857	1215	1.2F
	1448	1913	1.3E
	2132		
13 Tu	0321	0051	1.1F
	0951	0742	1.2E
	1544	1315	1.1F
	2231	2013	1.3E
14 W	0421	0151	1.0F
	1050	0842	1.1E
	1642	1414	1.1F
	2330	2111	1.3E
15 Th	0524	0250	1.0F
	1149	0940	1.1E
	1741	1512	1.0F
		2208	1.3E
16 F	0029	0347	1.0F
	0630	1036	1.2E
	1247	1608	1.0F
	1840	2302	1.3E
17 Sa	0122	0441	1.1F
	0740	1128	1.2E
	1340	1701	1.1F
	1936	2353	1.4E
18 Su	0213	0531	1.1F
	0833	1218	1.2E
	1430	1750	1.1F
	2026		
19 M	0300	0040	1.4E
	0909	0617	1.2F
	1518	1305	1.3E
	2109	1836	1.1F
20 Tu	0341	0125	1.3E
	0942	0701	1.2F
	1600	1349	1.3E
	2148	1918	1.2F
21 W	0421	0207	1.3E
	1015	0741	1.2F
	1641	1429	1.2E
	2225	1958	1.2F
22 Th	0459	0245	1.2E
	1049	0817	1.3F
	1720	1506	1.2E
	2302	2032	1.2F
23 F	0537	0316	1.2E
	1124	0845	1.3F
	1800	1531	1.2E
	2339	2048	1.2F
24 Sa	0614	0302	1.1E
	1201	0845	1.3F
	1840	1514	1.2E
		2101	1.2F
25 Su	0018	0315	1.1E
	0654	0914	1.3F
	1240	1537	1.2E
	1923	2137	1.2F
26 M	0100	0346	1.1E
	0737	0955	1.4F
	1321	1611	1.2E
	2009	2220	1.2F
27 Tu	0144	0426	1.1E
	0822	1039	1.3F
	1406	1655	1.2E
	2059	2307	1.2F
28 W	0232	0513	1.0E
	0913	1128	1.3F
	1455	1745	1.2E
	2150	2358	1.2F
29 Th	0326	0607	1.0E
	1008	1220	1.2F
	1549	1844	1.1E
	2248		
30 F	0423	0053	1.1F
	1107	0712	1.0E
	1646	1316	1.2F
	2344	1955	1.1E

OCTOBER

Day	Slack Water Time h.m.	Maximum Current Time h.m.	Vel. knots
1 Sa	0524	0154	1.1F
	1206	0841	1.0E
	1747	1418	1.1F
		2206	1.2E
2 Su	0041	0313	1.1F
	0627	1046	1.1E
	1305	1535	1.1F
	1848	2311	1.3E
3 M	0139	0449	1.2F
	0727	1142	1.2E
	1402	1710	1.2F
	1948		
4 Tu	0232	0005	1.4E
	0824	0548	1.3F
	1458	1235	1.4E
	2045	1810	1.3F
5 W	0325	0056	1.5E
	0918	0640	1.4F
	1551	1326	1.5E
	2139	1904	1.4F
6 Th	0415	0146	1.5E
	1009	0730	1.5F
	1642	1414	1.5E
	2231	1954	1.4F
7 F	0504	0236	1.5E
	1059	0818	1.5F
	1733	1504	1.6E
	2322	2044	1.4F
8 Sa	0553	0326	1.5E
	1148	0906	1.5F
	1824	1555	1.5E
		2134	1.4F
9 Su	0012	0419	1.4E
	0642	0954	1.4F
	1236	1649	1.5E
	1917	2226	1.3F
10 M	0104	0516	1.3E
	0733	1046	1.3F
	1326	1746	1.4E
	2009	2322	1.2F
11 Tu	0156	0615	1.2E
	0827	1142	1.2F
	1417	1845	1.3E
	2103		
12 W	0252	0020	1.1F
	0921	0715	1.1E
	1511	1242	1.1F
	2200	1944	1.3E
13 Th	0350	0121	1.0F
	1019	0814	1.1E
	1607	1343	1.0F
	2259	2042	1.2E
14 F	0450	0220	1.0F
	1119	0911	1.1E
	1706	1442	1.0F
	2357	2138	1.2E
15 Sa	0551	0317	1.0F
	1216	1007	1.1E
	1804	1538	1.0F
		2232	1.3E
16 Su	0651	0413	1.1F
	1310	1059	1.2E
	1900	1631	1.0F
		2322	1.3E
17 M	0139	0459	1.1F
	0744	1148	1.2E
	1400	1719	1.1F
	1951		
18 Tu	0224	0009	1.3E
	0827	0545	1.2F
	1446	1234	1.3E
	2036	1804	1.2F
19 W	0307	0053	1.3E
	0904	0627	1.3F
	1529	1316	1.3E
	2116	1846	1.2F
20 Th	0346	0133	1.3E
	0940	0706	1.3F
	1609	1355	1.3E
	2154	1924	1.2F
21 F	0424	0209	1.2E
	1016	0739	1.3F
	1649	1426	1.2E
	2232	1955	1.3F
22 Sa	0502	0224	1.1E
	1052	0757	1.4F
	1730	1429	1.2E
	2311	2007	1.3F
23 Su	0541	0220	1.1E
	1130	0811	1.4F
	1811	1439	1.2E
	2350	2032	1.3F
24 M	0623	0245	1.1E
	1210	0845	1.4F
	1856	1508	1.3E
		2110	1.3F
25 Tu	0033	0319	1.1E
	0708	0927	1.4F
	1252	1545	1.2E
	1942	2153	1.3F
26 W	0119	0401	1.1E
	0757	1012	1.3F
	1339	1630	1.2E
	2033	2241	1.2F
27 Th	0208	0450	1.0E
	0850	1101	1.2F
	1429	1723	1.1E
	2128	2333	1.1F
28 F	0303	0548	1.0E
	0948	1154	1.1F
	1525	1826	1.1E
	2225		
29 Sa	0403	0030	1.0F
	1048	0701	0.9E
	1625	1254	1.0F
	2323	2056	1.1E
30 Su	0506	0139	1.0F
	1149	0935	1.0E
	1729	1406	1.0F
		2202	1.2E
31 M	0022	0339	1.1F
	0608	1035	1.2E
	1249	1605	1.1F
	1831	2258	1.3E

Time meridian 75° W. 0000 is midnight. 1200 is noon.
At times of slack water before maximum ebb, the velocity actually averages 0.3 knot in a direction of 184° true.

F-Flood, Dir. 254° True   E-Ebb, Dir. 111° True

NOVEMBER

Day	Slack Water Time h.m.	Maximum Current Time h.m.	Vel. knots
1 Tu	0119	0440	1.2F
	0708	1128	1.3E
	1347	1706	1.2F
	1931	2351	1.4E
2 W	0212	0534	1.3F
	0805	1219	1.4E
	1441	1759	1.3F
	2028		
3 Th		0041	1.5E
	0304	0625	1.4F
	0858	1309	1.5E
	1533	1850	1.4F
	2122		
4 F		0130	1.5E
	0353	0712	1.5F
	0948	1357	1.6E
	1623	1938	1.4F
	2213		
5 Sa		0219	1.5E
	0441	0758	1.5F
	1036	1445	1.6E
	1712	2026	1.4F
	2302		
6 Su		0307	1.4E
	0529	0844	1.5F
	1123	1534	1.5E
	1801	2113	1.4F
	2350		
7 M		0358	1.4E
	0618	0929	1.4F
	1210	1625	1.5E
	1850	2202	1.3F
8 Tu	0039	0452	1.3E
	0708	1017	1.3F
	1257	1719	1.4E
	1941	2254	1.2F
9 W	0129	0548	1.2E
	0759	1109	1.1F
	1346	1815	1.3E
	2033	2349	1.1F
10 Th	0221	0646	1.1E
	0851	1207	1.0F
	1437	1913	1.2E
	2128		
11 F		0047	1.0F
	0315	0742	1.0E
	0948	1307	1.0F
	1531	2009	1.2E
	2222		
12 Sa		0145	1.0F
	0411	0838	1.0E
	1043	1406	0.9F
	1626	2104	1.2E
	2318		
13 Su		0240	1.0F
	0506	0933	1.1E
	1140	1502	0.9F
	1722	2157	1.2E
14 M	0010	0333	1.0F
	0601	1024	1.1E
	1233	1555	1.0F
	1818	2247	1.2E
15 Tu	0059	0421	1.1F
	0653	1113	1.2E
	1323	1643	1.1F
	1909	2335	1.2E
16 W	0144	0507	1.2F
	0739	1158	1.2E
	1410	1728	1.2F
	1956		
17 Th		0017	1.2E
	0228	0549	1.3F
	0822	1239	1.3E
	1454	1810	1.2F
	2040		
18 F		0056	1.2E
	0309	0627	1.3F
	0902	1316	1.3E
	1537	1847	1.3F
	2122		
19 Sa		0126	1.2E
	0350	0658	1.4F
	0941	1341	1.3E
	1619	1918	1.3F
	2203		
20 Su		0131	1.2E
	0431	0716	1.4F
	1021	1347	1.3E
	1701	1937	1.4F
	2244		
21 M		0151	1.2E
	0513	0742	1.5F
	1102	1413	1.3E
	1746	2007	1.4F
	2326		
22 Tu		0224	1.2E
	0558	0821	1.5F
	1144	1448	1.3E
	1830	2048	1.3F
23 W	0011	0302	1.1E
	0645	0903	1.4F
	1229	1528	1.3E
	1919	2132	1.3F
24 Th	0058	0347	1.1E
	0736	0950	1.3F
	1317	1615	1.2E
	2010	2221	1.2F
25 F	0150	0438	1.0E
	0830	1040	1.2F
	1409	1711	1.1E
	2107	2313	1.1F
26 Sa	0245	0541	0.9E
	0929	1135	1.1F
	1506	1823	1.1E
	2203		
27 Su		0013	1.0F
	0345	0817	1.0E
	1030	1239	1.0F
	1608	2045	1.1E
	2302		
28 M		0218	1.0F
	0447	0919	1.1E
	1132	1449	1.0F
	1711	2146	1.2E
29 Tu	0002	0326	1.1F
	0549	1017	1.2E
	1233	1555	1.0F
	1814	2243	1.2E
30 W	0059	0425	1.2F
	0649	1112	1.3E
	1331	1652	1.1F
	1915	2336	1.3E

DECEMBER

Day	Slack Water Time h.m.	Maximum Current Time h.m.	Vel. knots
1 Th	0153	0518	1.3F
	0746	1204	1.4E
	1426	1745	1.2F
	2013		
2 F		0027	1.4E
	0245	0608	1.3F
	0839	1253	1.5E
	1518	1835	1.3F
	2107		
3 Sa		0116	1.4E
	0334	0655	1.4F
	0929	1341	1.6E
	1607	1923	1.3F
	2157		
4 Su		0204	1.4E
	0421	0741	1.4F
	1016	1428	1.6E
	1653	2009	1.3F
	2245		
5 M		0252	1.4E
	0509	0826	1.4F
	1101	1516	1.5E
	1740	2056	1.3F
	2331		
6 Tu		0341	1.3E
	0556	0910	1.3F
	1146	1604	1.4E
	1828	2142	1.2F
7 W	0017	0430	1.2E
	0642	0955	1.2F
	1230	1654	1.4E
	1915	2228	1.2F
8 Th	0103	0521	1.2E
	0731	1040	1.1F
	1316	1745	1.3E
	2003	2317	1.1F
9 F	0150	0614	1.1E
	0821	1129	1.0F
	1403	1838	1.2E
	2052		
10 Sa		0008	1.0F
	0238	0707	1.0E
	0912	1224	1.0F
	1453	1931	1.1E
	2142		
11 Su		0101	1.0F
	0329	0801	1.0E
	1007	1321	0.9F
	1544	2025	1.1E
	2233		
12 M		0154	1.0F
	0420	0853	1.0E
	1059	1417	0.9F
	1638	2117	1.0E
	2323		
13 Tu		0246	1.0F
	0511	0944	1.0E
	1151	1510	1.0F
	1731	2206	1.0E
14 W	0013	0335	1.1F
	0602	1033	1.1E
	1242	1600	1.0F
	1824	2253	1.1E
15 Th	0101	0421	1.2F
	0651	1118	1.2E
	1331	1646	1.1F
	1914	2336	1.1E
16 F	0148	0504	1.3F
	0739	1200	1.2E
	1419	1730	1.2F
	2002		
17 Sa		0015	1.1E
	0232	0542	1.3F
	0824	1234	1.3E
	1504	1809	1.3F
	2049		
18 Su		0041	1.2E
	0318	0613	1.4F
	0908	1258	1.3E
	1550	1843	1.3F
	2134		
19 M		0059	1.2E
	0402	0642	1.5F
	0953	1320	1.4E
	1636	1913	1.4F
	2220		
20 Tu		0132	1.2E
	0449	0720	1.5F
	1037	1356	1.4E
	1721	1950	1.4F
	2306		
21 W		0211	1.2E
	0537	0802	1.5F
	1123	1436	1.4E
	1809	2031	1.4F
	2353		
22 Th		0255	1.2E
	0627	0847	1.4F
	1210	1521	1.3E
	1859	2118	1.3F
23 F	0042	0344	1.1E
	0718	0934	1.3F
	1300	1611	1.2E
	1950	2207	1.2F
24 Sa	0134	0441	1.1E
	0812	1026	1.2F
	1353	1712	1.2E
	2044	2301	1.1F
25 Su	0229	0647	1.0E
	0910	1123	1.1F
	1450	1917	1.1E
	2140		
26 M		0014	1.1F
	0327	0757	1.1E
	1011	1316	1.0F
	1550	2026	1.1E
	2240		
27 Tu		0200	1.0F
	0427	0859	1.1E
	1113	1434	1.0F
	1653	2126	1.1E
	2339		
28 W		0305	1.1F
	0527	0957	1.2E
	1215	1537	1.0F
	1756	2224	1.2E
29 Th	0038	0404	1.1F
	0628	1053	1.3E
	1314	1635	1.1F
	1859	2319	1.3E
30 F	0133	0459	1.2F
	0726	1147	1.4E
	1410	1729	1.2F
	1959		
31 Sa		0011	1.3E
	0227	0550	1.2F
	0821	1237	1.5E
	1502	1820	1.2F
	2054		

Time meridian 75° W.   0000 is midnight.   1200 is noon.
At times of slack water before maximum ebb, the velocity actually averages 0.3 knot in a direction of 184° true.

CAPE COD CANAL (RR. Bridge), MASSACHUSETTS, 1983

F-Flood, Dir. 070° True   E-Ebb, Dir. 250° True

JANUARY

Day	Slack Water Time h.m.	Maximum Current Time h.m.	Vel. knots	Day	Slack Water Time h.m.	Maximum Current Time h.m.	Vel. knots
1 Sa	0419	0118	4.8E	16 Su	0438	0137	4.1E
	1029	0718	4.6F		1049	0733	3.9F
	1646	1337	5.1E		1700	1349	4.5E
	2322	1952	4.9F		2335	1700	4.2F
2 Su	0511	0209	4.7E	17 M	0515	0216	4.1E
	1120	0807	4.5F		1126	0810	3.9F
	1737	1427	5.1E		1737	1431	4.4E
		2045	4.9F			2039	4.1F
3 M	0015	0300	4.7E	18 Tu	0012	0258	4.1E
	0604	0859	4.4F		0553	0847	3.9F
	1214	1519	5.0E		1204	1512	4.4E
	1830	2138	4.7F		1815	2116	4.1F
4 Tu	0109	0354	4.6E	19 W	0050	0341	4.0E
	0659	0956	4.3F		0633	0928	3.8F
	1311	1613	4.8E		1244	1555	4.3E
	1926	2233	4.6F		1856	2158	4.0F
5 W	0205	0449	4.4E	20 Th	0131	0426	4.0E
	0757	1055	4.1F		0717	1013	3.8F
	1411	1709	4.6E		1329	1642	4.1E
	2023	2333	4.3F		1940	2239	3.9F
6 Th	0302	0547	4.3E	21 F	0214	0512	3.9E
	0857	1159	3.9F		0805	1102	3.7F
	1515	1809	4.4E		1421	1733	4.0E
	2123				2029	2330	3.9F
7 F	0400	0035	4.1F	22 Sa	0303	0603	3.9E
	1000	0644	4.2E		0858	1153	3.7F
	1621	1305	3.8F		1521	1828	4.0E
	2224	1909	4.2E		2124		
8 Sa	0457	0140	4.0F	23 Su	0357	0025	3.8F
	1102	0743	4.1E		0957	0658	4.0E
	1725	1418	3.8F		1626	1255	3.7F
	2325	2009	4.0E		2224	1926	3.9E
9 Su	0551	0242	3.9F	24 M	0454	0124	3.8F
	1201	0842	4.1E		1059	0756	4.1E
	1826	1521	3.9F		1734	1400	3.9F
		2108	4.0E		2326	2027	4.0E
10 M	0022	0343	3.8F	25 Tu	0551	0226	3.9F
	0643	0934	4.2E		1201	0855	4.3E
	1254	1619	4.0F		1838	1505	4.1E
	1921	2203	4.0E			2127	4.1E
11 Tu	0115	0432	3.8F	26 W	0028	0327	4.0F
	0730	1023	4.3E		0648	0950	4.5E
	1343	1706	4.1F		1301	1609	4.3F
	2011	2248	4.0E		1938	2222	4.3E
12 W	0202	0513	3.9F	27 Th	0126	0427	4.2F
	0815	1106	4.3E		0742	1047	4.8E
	1427	1747	4.1F		1357	1706	4.6F
	2057	2336	4.0E		2033	2317	4.5E
13 Th	0244	0548	3.9F	28 F	0222	0522	4.4F
	0856	1149	4.4E		0835	1138	5.0E
	1508	1824	4.2F		1450	1800	4.8F
	2139				2125		
14 F	0324	0018	4.1E	29 Sa	0314	0011	4.7E
	0935	0627	3.9F		0926	0613	3.9F
	1546	1231	4.5E		1541	1229	5.1E
	2219	1857	4.2F		2216	1850	4.9F
15 Sa	0402	0058	4.1E	30 Su	0405	0101	4.8E
	1013	0700	3.9F		1016	0704	4.6F
	1623	1310	4.5E		1632	1320	5.0E
	2257	1928	4.2F		2305	1939	5.0F
				31 M	0455	0151	4.8E
					1107	0755	4.7F
					1721	1409	5.2E
					2354	2029	4.9F

FEBRUARY

Day	Slack Water Time h.m.	Maximum Current Time h.m.	Vel. knots	Day	Slack Water Time h.m.	Maximum Current Time h.m.	Vel. knots
1 Tu	0545	0240	4.8E	16 W	0526	0230	4.3E
	1158	0844	4.6F		1140	0822	4.1F
	1811	1459	5.1E		1747	1447	4.5E
		2117	4.8F			2048	4.3F
2 W	0043	0329	4.7E	17 Th	0015	0309	4.3E
	0635	0935	4.4F		0603	0901	4.1F
	1251	1549	4.8E		1218	1528	4.4E
	1901	2207	4.6F		1826	2125	4.2F
3 Th	0133	0420	4.5E	18 F	0051	0352	4.2E
	0727	1029	4.2F		0644	0942	4.1F
	1347	1643	4.6E		1301	1613	4.3E
	1954	2259	4.3F		1908	2208	4.1F
4 F	0225	0511	4.3E	19 Sa	0132	0439	4.1E
	0823	1122	4.0F		0730	1030	4.0F
	1447	1737	4.3E		1351	1703	4.1E
	2049	2353	4.0F		1956	2255	3.9F
5 Sa	0320	0607	4.1E	20 Su	0219	0530	4.1E
	0922	1226	3.8F		0823	1121	3.9F
	1550	1835	4.0E		1451	1758	4.0E
	2148				2051	2350	3.8F
6 Su	0417	0054	3.7F	21 M	0314	0625	4.0E
	1023	0706	4.0E		0923	1226	3.8F
	1655	1335	3.7F		1600	1857	3.9E
	2250	1936	3.8E		2154		
7 M	0515	0201	3.6F	22 Tu	0417	0052	3.7F
	1126	0804	3.9E		1030	0725	4.1E
	1759	1449	3.7F		1713	1335	3.9F
	2351	2035	3.7E		2302	2001	3.9E
8 Tu	0611	0308	3.5F	23 W	0523	0201	3.7F
	1224	0901	4.0E		1138	0828	4.3E
	1857	1552	3.8F		1821	1445	4.1F
		2137	3.7E			2105	4.1E
9 W	0048	0406	3.6F	24 Th	0009	0308	3.9F
	0703	0954	4.1E		0627	0931	4.5E
	1317	1641	3.9F		1242	1553	4.3F
	1949	2227	3.8E		1922	2206	4.3E
10 Th	0138	0451	3.7F	25 F	0112	0412	4.1F
	0750	1043	4.2E		0726	1028	4.7E
	1404	1728	4.0F		1341	1654	4.6F
	2035	2313	3.9E		2018	2301	4.5E
11 F	0223	0532	3.8F	26 Sa	0208	0510	4.4F
	0834	1129	4.3E		0821	1123	5.0E
	1446	1805	4.1F		1435	1746	4.8F
	2116	2354	4.1E		2109	2354	4.7E
12 Sa	0303	0607	3.9F	27 Su	0300	0602	4.6F
	0914	1208	4.4E		0912	1213	5.1E
	1524	1837	4.2F		1526	1836	4.9F
	2155				2157		
13 Su	0340	0033	4.2E	28 M	0349	0042	4.9E
	0952	0640	4.0F		1002	0651	4.7F
	1601	1248	4.5E		1614	1303	5.2E
	2231	1906	4.3F		2243	1922	5.0F
14 M	0415	0112	4.2E				
	1028	0714	4.1F				
	1636	1327	4.6E				
	2306	1939	4.3F				
15 Tu	0450	0150	4.3E				
	1104	0747	4.1F				
	1711	1406	4.6E				
	2340	2011	4.3F				

Time meridian 75° W.   0000 is midnight.   1200 is noon.

CAPE COD CANAL (RR. Bridge), MASSACHUSETTS, 1983

F-Flood, Dir. 070° True   E-Ebb, Dir. 250° True

MARCH

Days 1–15

Day	Slack Water Time (h.m.)	Maximum Current Time (h.m.)	Vel. (knots)
1 Tu		0129	4.9E
	0436	0737	4.7F
	1051	1349	5.1E
	1701	2008	4.9F
	2328		
2 W		0215	4.9E
	0522	0824	4.7F
	1140	1437	5.0E
	1747	2051	4.7F
3 Th	0013	0303	4.8E
	0608	0909	4.5F
	1229	1523	4.8E
	1834	2135	4.5F
4 F	0058	0349	4.6E
	0656	0957	4.3F
	1321	1613	4.5E
	1922	2223	4.1F
5 Sa	0146	0437	4.3E
	0746	1049	4.0F
	1417	1705	4.1E
	2013	2311	3.8F
6 Su	0238	0530	4.1E
	0841	1145	3.8F
	1518	1801	3.8E
	2109		
7 M		0009	3.5F
	0334	0625	3.9E
	0942	1253	3.6F
	1623	1900	3.6E
	2212		
8 Tu		0114	3.3F
	0435	0725	3.8E
	1046	1408	3.5F
	1728	2001	3.5E
	2317		
9 W		0228	3.2F
	0536	0826	3.8E
	1149	1521	3.6F
	1827	2102	3.6E
10 Th	0018	0333	3.4F
	0632	0924	3.9E
	1245	1615	3.8F
	1919	2156	3.7E
11 F	0110	0424	3.6F
	0723	1015	4.1E
	1334	1658	3.9F
	2006	2244	3.9E
12 Sa	0156	0507	3.7F
	0808	1100	4.3E
	1417	1733	4.1F
	2047	2326	4.1E
13 Su	0236	0542	3.9F
	0849	1142	4.4E
	1456	1808	4.2F
	2124		
14 M		0005	4.3E
	0313	0614	4.1F
	0927	1222	4.6E
	1533	1837	4.3F
	2200		
15 Tu		0045	4.4E
	0348	0647	4.2F
	1004	1301	4.6E
	1608	1909	4.4F
	2234		

Days 16–31

Day	Slack Water Time (h.m.)	Maximum Current Time (h.m.)	Vel. (knots)
16 W		0122	4.5E
	0423	0721	4.3F
	1040	1339	4.6E
	1643	1942	4.4F
	2307		
17 Th		0200	4.5E
	0458	0756	4.3F
	1117	1418	4.6E
	1720	2019	4.4F
	2341		
18 F		0240	4.5E
	0535	0835	4.3F
	1156	1500	4.5E
	1759	2056	4.3F
19 Sa	0017	0323	4.4E
	0617	0918	4.3F
	1240	1545	4.4E
	1842	2139	4.1F
20 Su	0057	0410	4.3E
	0703	1005	4.2F
	1332	1636	4.2E
	1931	2227	3.9F
21 M	0146	0500	4.2E
	0757	1100	4.1F
	1434	1735	4.0E
	2028	2324	3.8F
22 Tu	0244	0559	4.1E
	0900	1204	4.0F
	1545	1835	3.9E
	2134		
23 W		0029	3.6F
	0352	0702	4.2E
	1009	1317	4.0F
	1658	1942	3.9E
	2246		
24 Th		0141	3.6F
	0504	0807	4.3E
	1119	1432	4.1F
	1806	2049	4.1E
	2356		
25 F		0255	3.8F
	0611	0911	4.5E
	1226	1543	4.3F
	1906	2149	4.3E
26 Sa	0058	0402	4.1F
	0712	1009	4.7E
	1325	1640	4.6F
	1959	2244	4.5E
27 Su	0153	0457	4.4F
	0807	1104	4.9E
	1418	1733	4.7F
	2048	2336	4.7E
28 M	0243	0549	4.6F
	0858	1155	5.0E
	1508	1818	4.8F
	2134		
29 Tu		0021	4.9E
	0330	0634	4.7F
	0947	1241	5.1E
	1554	1901	4.8F
	2217		
30 W		0107	4.9E
	0415	0719	4.7F
	1034	1327	5.0E
	1638	1941	4.7F
	2259		
31 Th		0150	4.9E
	0458	0802	4.7F
	1121	1413	4.8E
	1722	2022	4.5F
	2341		

APRIL

Days 1–15

Day	Slack Water Time (h.m.)	Maximum Current Time (h.m.)	Vel. (knots)
1 F		0234	4.8E
	0541	0843	4.5F
	1208	1459	4.6E
	1805	2103	4.3F
2 Sa	0023	0317	4.6E
	0625	0929	4.3F
	1257	1544	4.3E
	1850	2145	4.0F
3 Su	0107	0404	4.3E
	0712	1015	4.0F
	1349	1633	4.0E
	1938	2232	3.7F
4 M	0156	0455	4.1E
	0804	1108	3.8F
	1447	1727	3.7E
	2032	2327	3.4F
5 Tu	0252	0550	3.9E
	0901	1209	3.6F
	1549	1826	3.5E
	2133		
6 W		0028	3.2F
	0354	0647	3.7E
	1004	1319	3.5F
	1652	1927	3.4E
	2239		
7 Th		0141	3.1F
	0457	0748	3.7E
	1107	1433	3.5F
	1751	2026	3.5E
	2341		
8 F		0248	3.3F
	0557	0846	3.8E
	1205	1530	3.7F
	1843	2121	3.7E
9 Sa	0035	0345	3.5F
	0649	0940	4.0E
	1256	1615	3.9F
	1929	2210	3.9E
10 Su	0122	0431	3.7F
	0736	1025	4.2E
	1341	1654	4.1F
	2011	2253	4.2E
11 M	0203	0506	4.0F
	0819	1110	4.4E
	1422	1729	4.2F
	2049	2333	4.4E
12 Tu	0241	0543	4.2F
	0859	1152	4.5E
	1500	1803	4.3F
	2124		
13 W		0014	4.5E
	0317	0618	4.3F
	0937	1232	4.6E
	1537	1836	4.4F
	2159		
14 Th		0053	4.6E
	0354	0654	4.4F
	1016	1313	4.7E
	1615	1912	4.4F
	2233		
15 F		0131	4.6E
	0431	0733	4.5F
	1056	1354	4.6E
	1654	1949	4.4F
	2309		

Days 16–30

Day	Slack Water Time (h.m.)	Maximum Current Time (h.m.)	Vel. (knots)
16 Sa		0214	4.6E
	0511	0814	4.5F
	1139	1437	4.5E
	1736	2030	4.3F
	2348		
17 Su		0257	4.6E
	0556	0859	4.5F
	1227	1526	4.4E
	1822	2117	4.1F
18 M	0032	0346	4.5E
	0645	0949	4.3F
	1322	1617	4.2E
	1914	2208	4.0F
19 Tu	0124	0439	4.4E
	0741	1046	4.2F
	1425	1718	4.0E
	2014	2307	3.8F
20 W	0226	0540	4.3E
	0844	1153	4.1F
	1534	1820	4.0E
	2122		
21 Th		0015	3.7F
	0336	0644	4.3E
	0953	1304	4.1F
	1643	1926	4.0E
	2234		
22 F		0130	3.7F
	0448	0749	4.3E
	1102	1419	4.2F
	1747	2032	4.1E
	2342		
23 Sa		0244	3.9F
	0555	0852	4.5E
	1207	1524	4.4F
	1845	2131	4.4E
24 Su	0042	0350	4.1F
	0656	0950	4.6E
	1306	1621	4.5F
	1937	2224	4.6E
25 M	0136	0443	4.4F
	0751	1046	4.8E
	1358	1713	4.7F
	2024	2313	4.7E
26 Tu	0224	0533	4.5F
	0842	1133	4.8E
	1447	1756	4.6F
	2108	2358	4.8E
27 W	0309	0617	4.6F
	0930	1220	4.8E
	1532	1837	4.6F
	2150		
28 Th		0041	4.8E
	0352	0700	4.6F
	1017	1305	4.7E
	1614	1916	4.5F
	2230		
29 F		0124	4.8E
	0434	0741	4.6F
	1102	1347	4.6E
	1656	1953	4.3F
	2310		
30 Sa		0205	4.7E
	0515	0819	4.4F
	1147	1430	4.4E
	1737	2032	4.1F
	2350		

Time meridian 75° W.   0000 is midnight.   1200 is noon.

CAPE COD CANAL (RR. Bridge), MASSACHUSETTS, 1983

F-Flood, Dir. 070° True   E-Ebb, Dir. 250° True

MAY

Day	Slack Water Time (h.m.)	Maximum Current Time (h.m.)	Vel. (knots)
1 Su	0558	0248	4.5E
	1234	0903	4.2F
	1820	1516	4.1E
		2115	3.8F
2 M	0033	0335	4.3E
	0642	0946	4.0F
	1323	1605	3.9E
	1906	2157	3.6F
3 Tu	0119	0423	4.1E
	0730	1033	3.8F
	1417	1656	3.7E
	1957	2249	3.3F
4 W	0212	0514	3.9E
	0823	1130	3.6F
	1514	1750	3.5E
	2055	2348	3.2F
5 Th	0312	0610	3.8E
	0921	1230	3.5F
	1613	1848	3.5E
	2157		
6 F	0415	0051	3.1F
	1021	0708	3.8E
	1709	1334	3.6F
	2258	1947	3.6E
7 Sa	0515	0157	3.3F
	1119	0806	3.8E
	1800	1433	3.7F
	2352	2042	3.8E
8 Su	0609	0255	3.5F
	1211	0858	4.0E
	1847	1524	3.8F
		2131	4.0E
9 M	0041	0343	3.7F
	0659	0950	4.2E
	1259	1609	4.0F
	1930	2216	4.2E
10 Tu	0125	0425	4.0F
	0744	1035	4.3E
	1343	1648	4.2F
	2009	2300	4.4E
11 W	0206	0507	4.2F
	0828	1120	4.5E
	1425	1727	4.3F
	2047	2341	4.6E
12 Th	0246	0546	4.4F
	0910	1203	4.6E
	1506	1804	4.4F
	2124		
13 F	0326	0022	4.7E
	0953	0627	4.5F
	1547	1247	4.6E
	2202	1845	4.4F
14 Sa	0408	0105	4.8E
	1038	0711	4.6F
	1631	1333	4.6E
	2242	1926	4.4F
15 Su	0452	0151	4.8E
	1125	0756	4.6F
	1717	1419	4.5E
	2326	2013	4.3F
16 M	0539	0237	4.8E
	1217	0843	4.6F
	1807	1510	4.4E
		2100	4.2F
17 Tu	0015	0328	4.7E
	0632	0938	4.5F
	1314	1604	4.3E
	1902	2154	4.0F
18 W	0110	0423	4.6E
	0729	1036	4.4F
	1415	1702	4.2E
	2003	2255	3.9F
19 Th	0213	0522	4.5E
	0831	1141	4.3F
	1520	1804	4.1E
	2110		
20 F	0322	0004	3.8F
	0937	0625	4.4E
	1624	1250	4.2F
	2218	1907	4.1E
21 Sa	0431	0116	3.8F
	1043	0728	4.4E
	1724	1400	4.3F
	2322	2009	4.2E
22 Su	0537	0228	4.0F
	1146	0831	4.4E
	1820	1504	4.3F
		2108	4.4E
23 M	0021	0331	4.1F
	0638	0930	4.5E
	1244	1559	4.4F
	1911	2159	4.5E
24 Tu	0115	0426	4.3F
	0734	1022	4.5E
	1336	1648	4.4F
	1958	2248	4.6E
25 W	0203	0516	4.4F
	0826	1112	4.6E
	1424	1733	4.4F
	2042	2334	4.7E
26 Th	0249	0601	4.5F
	0914	1159	4.5E
	1509	1814	4.3F
	2124		
27 F	0331	0017	4.7E
	1000	0642	4.5F
	1551	1243	4.4E
	2204	1851	4.2F
28 Sa	0412	0100	4.7E
	1044	0719	4.4F
	1632	1326	4.3E
	2243	1927	4.1F
29 Su	0453	0141	4.6E
	1128	0800	4.3F
	1712	1409	4.2E
	2322	2008	3.9F
30 M	0533	0222	4.5E
	1212	0837	4.2F
	1753	1453	4.0E
		2046	3.7F
31 Tu	0003	0307	4.3E
	0616	0919	4.0F
	1258	1538	3.9E
	1837	2129	3.6F

JUNE

Day	Slack Water Time (h.m.)	Maximum Current Time (h.m.)	Vel. (knots)
1 W	0048	0354	4.2E
	0700	1002	3.9F
	1346	1627	3.7E
	1925	2216	3.4F
2 Th	0136	0443	4.0E
	0748	1052	3.8F
	1437	1717	3.7E
	2017	2309	3.3F
3 F	0231	0534	3.9E
	0840	1147	3.7F
	1529	1810	3.6E
	2113		
4 Sa	0329	0006	3.3F
	0935	0629	3.8E
	1622	1240	3.7F
	2210	1905	3.7E
5 Su	0428	0104	3.3F
	1030	0725	3.9E
	1713	1335	3.7F
	2305	1957	3.8E
6 M	0525	0201	3.5F
	1123	0818	4.0E
	1800	1429	3.8F
	2356	2049	4.0E
7 Tu	0618	0255	3.7F
	1214	0911	4.1E
	1845	1518	3.9F
		2137	4.2E
8 W	0044	0346	3.9F
	0709	0958	4.2E
	1303	1606	4.1F
	1928	2225	4.4E
9 Th	0130	0432	4.2F
	0757	1048	4.4E
	1350	1648	4.2F
	2010	2309	4.6E
10 F	0216	0520	4.4F
	0845	1135	4.5E
	1437	1736	4.3F
	2053	2355	4.8E
11 Sa	0301	0607	4.6F
	0933	1223	4.6E
	1523	1820	4.4F
	2136		
12 Su	0348	0041	4.9E
	1022	0653	4.7F
	1611	1311	4.6E
	2221	1908	4.4F
13 M	0436	0130	4.9E
	1113	0741	4.7F
	1701	1402	4.6E
	2309	1957	4.4F
14 Tu	0526	0218	4.9E
	1206	0832	4.7F
	1753	1453	4.5E
		2048	4.3F
15 W	0001	0312	4.9E
	0619	0926	4.7F
	1301	1548	4.5E
	1849	2144	4.2F
16 Th	0058	0407	4.8E
	0715	1023	4.6F
	1359	1645	4.4E
	1948	2242	4.1F
17 F	0200	0505	4.6E
	0815	1124	4.4F
	1458	1743	4.3E
	2051	2348	4.0F
18 Sa	0305	0604	4.5E
	0917	1228	4.3F
	1558	1843	4.3E
	2155		
19 Su	0412	0056	3.9F
	1020	0707	4.4E
	1656	1334	4.2F
	2258	1943	4.3E
20 M	0517	0207	4.0F
	1121	0806	4.3E
	1752	1439	4.2F
	2357	2039	4.3E
21 Tu	0619	0311	4.1F
	1220	0905	4.3E
	1844	1534	4.2F
		2133	4.4E
22 W	0052	0406	4.2F
	0716	1001	4.3E
	1313	1627	4.1F
	1932	2224	4.5E
23 Th	0142	0501	4.3F
	0809	1050	4.3E
	1402	1713	4.1F
	2017	2310	4.5E
24 F	0229	0544	4.3F
	0857	1139	4.2E
	1448	1754	4.0F
	2100	2354	4.5E
25 Sa	0312	0625	4.3F
	0943	1221	4.2E
	1530	1833	4.0F
	2141		
26 Su	0353	0037	4.5E
	1026	0705	4.3F
	1610	1305	4.1E
	2220	1909	3.9F
27 M	0432	0118	4.5E
	1108	0742	4.2F
	1649	1346	4.1E
	2259	1944	3.8F
28 Tu	0511	0159	4.4E
	1149	0817	4.2F
	1728	1428	4.0E
	2339	2021	3.8F
29 W	0551	0240	4.4E
	1230	0853	4.1F
	1809	1512	3.9E
		2100	3.7F
30 Th	0020	0325	4.3E
	0631	0936	4.0F
	1312	1555	3.9E
	1852	2145	3.6F

Time meridian 75° W.   0000 is midnight.   1200 is noon.

F-Flood, Dir. 070° True   E-Ebb, Dir. 250° True

JULY

Day	Slack Water Time h.m.	Maximum Current Time h.m.	Vel. knots	Day	Slack Water Time h.m.	Maximum Current Time h.m.	Vel. knots
1 F	0103	0410	4.1E	16 Sa	0142	0442	4.7E
	0715	1017	3.9F		0754	1102	4.5F
	1357	1642	3.8E		1430	1717	4.4E
	1939	2229	3.6F		2026	2325	4.1F
2 Sa	0151	0459	4.0E	17 Su	0244	0540	4.5E
	0801	1104	3.8F		0852	1159	4.3F
	1443	1731	3.8E		1527	1813	4.3E
	2028	2318	3.5F		2127		
3 Su	0244	0550	4.0E	18 M		0030	4.0F
	0850	1153	3.8F		0349	0640	4.3E
	1532	1822	3.8E		0953	1303	4.1F
	2121				1625	1912	4.2E
					2229		
4 M		0015	3.5F	19 Tu		0139	3.9F
	0340	0642	3.9E		0454	0740	4.1E
	0943	1245	3.7F		1054	1408	3.9F
	1622	1913	3.9E		1721	2010	4.2E
	2216				2330		
5 Tu		0110	3.6F	20 W		0248	4.0F
	0440	0737	3.9E		0558	0839	4.0E
	1037	1340	3.8F		1155	1510	3.9F
	1712	2007	4.0E		1816	2108	4.2E
	2311						
6 W		0209	3.7F	21 Th	0028	0349	4.0F
	0539	0833	4.0E		0657	0937	4.0E
	1133	1433	3.8F		1251	1605	3.8F
	1802	2100	4.2E		1907	2200	4.3E
7 Th	0006	0307	3.9F	22 F	0121	0443	4.1F
	0636	0927	4.1E		0751	1031	4.0E
	1227	1528	4.0F		1342	1654	3.8F
	1851	2151	4.4E		1954	2249	4.3E
8 F	0058	0403	4.2F	23 Sa	0209	0532	4.1F
	0731	1019	4.3E		0839	1117	4.0E
	1320	1619	4.1F		1428	1739	3.9F
	1939	2241	4.6E		2039	2333	4.4E
9 Sa	0150	0455	4.4F	24 Su	0252	0609	4.2F
	0824	1110	4.4E		0924	1200	4.1E
	1412	1712	4.3F		1510	1814	3.9F
	2027	2332	4.8E		2120		
10 Su	0240	0546	4.6F	25 M		0015	4.5E
	0916	1202	4.6E		0333	0648	4.2F
	1503	1802	4.4F		1005	1241	4.1E
	2115				1549	1847	3.9F
					2159		
11 M		0023	5.0E	26 Tu		0056	4.5E
	0330	0637	4.8F		0411	0719	4.2F
	1006	1253	4.6E		1044	1322	4.1E
	1554	1851	4.5F		1626	1923	3.9F
	2204				2237		
12 Tu		0112	5.1E	27 W		0136	4.5E
	0421	0727	4.9F		0448	0752	4.2F
	1057	1344	4.7E		1122	1402	4.1E
	1645	1942	4.5F		1703	1959	3.9F
	2255				2315		
13 W		0203	5.1E	28 Th		0215	4.4E
	0512	0818	4.9F		0525	0827	4.2F
	1149	1435	4.7E		1159	1443	4.1E
	1737	2035	4.5F		1740	2034	3.9F
	2348				2353		
14 Th		0254	5.0E	29 F		0257	4.4E
	0604	0911	4.8F		0602	0903	4.1F
	1241	1528	4.6E		1236	1522	4.1E
	1831	2129	4.4F		1819	2115	3.8F
15 F	0043	0348	4.9E	30 Sa	0032	0340	4.3E
	0658	1004	4.7F		0641	0942	4.0F
	1335	1623	4.5E		1315	1607	4.0E
	1927	2226	4.3F		1901	2154	3.8F
				31 Su	0115	0425	4.2E
					0723	1021	3.9F
					1356	1652	3.9E
					1946	2239	3.7F

AUGUST

Day	Slack Water Time h.m.	Maximum Current Time h.m.	Vel. knots	Day	Slack Water Time h.m.	Maximum Current Time h.m.	Vel. knots
1 M	0203	0514	4.0E	16 Tu	0324	0610	4.1E
	0809	1111	3.8F		0923	1229	3.9F
	1441	1740	3.9E		1550	1840	4.1E
	2036	2332	3.7F		2157		
2 Tu	0258	0607	3.9E	17 W		0108	3.8F
	0901	1200	3.7F		0430	0711	3.9E
	1532	1835	3.9E		1025	1338	3.7F
	2132				1649	1939	4.0E
					2300		
3 W		0029	3.7F	18 Th		0222	3.8F
	0401	0700	3.9E		0535	0812	3.8E
	0957	1257	3.7F		1129	1445	3.6F
	1626	1930	4.0E		1747	2038	4.0E
	2231						
4 Th		0131	3.8F	19 F	0001	0327	3.8F
	0506	0800	3.9E		0635	0913	3.8E
	1057	1358	3.7F		1228	1546	3.6F
	1723	2027	4.1E		1842	2134	4.1E
	2332						
5 F		0236	3.9F	20 Sa	0057	0424	3.9F
	0610	0858	4.0E		0729	1007	3.8E
	1158	1458	3.9F		1321	1636	3.7F
	1820	2123	4.4E		1932	2225	4.2E
6 Sa	0032	0337	4.2F	21 Su	0146	0513	4.1F
	0710	0956	4.2E		0817	1056	3.9E
	1258	1557	4.0F		1407	1717	3.8F
	1914	2219	4.6E		2017	2311	4.3E
7 Su	0129	0438	4.4F	22 M	0230	0550	4.1F
	0806	1051	4.4E		0859	1139	4.1E
	1354	1654	4.3F		1448	1754	3.9F
	2007	2313	4.9E		2058	2353	4.4E
8 M	0222	0532	4.7F	23 Tu	0309	0621	4.2F
	0858	1144	4.6E		0939	1217	4.2E
	1447	1745	4.4F		1525	1827	4.0F
	2059				2137		
9 Tu		0004	5.0E	24 W		0031	4.5E
	0314	0621	4.9F		0346	0654	4.2F
	0949	1234	4.8E		1015	1256	4.2E
	1538	1837	4.6F		1601	1900	4.0F
	2150				2214		
10 W		0055	5.2E	25 Th		0110	4.5E
	0405	0713	5.0F		0421	0726	4.3F
	1038	1325	4.8E		1050	1334	4.3E
	1628	1928	4.7F		1635	1932	4.1F
	2240				2250		
11 Th		0144	5.2E	26 F		0149	4.5E
	0455	0802	5.0F		0456	0756	4.3F
	1126	1414	4.9E		1124	1412	4.3E
	1718	2017	4.7F		1710	2007	4.1F
	2332				2326		
12 F		0234	5.1E	27 Sa		0228	4.5E
	0545	0850	4.9F		0531	0831	4.2F
	1215	1503	4.8E		1158	1452	4.2E
	1808	2108	4.6F		1746	2044	4.1F
13 Sa	0025	0325	5.0E	28 Su	0003	0309	4.4E
	0635	0941	4.7F		0609	0906	4.1F
	1305	1554	4.7E		1233	1533	4.2E
	1901	2201	4.4F		1825	2123	4.0F
14 Su	0121	0418	4.7E	29 M	0044	0354	4.2E
	0728	1033	4.4F		0649	0947	4.0F
	1358	1646	4.5E		1311	1618	4.1E
	1956	2258	4.2F		1909	2208	3.9F
15 M	0220	0514	4.4E	30 Tu	0131	0439	4.1E
	0824	1128	4.1F		0734	1030	3.9F
	1452	1743	4.3E		1355	1705	4.0E
	2054	2359	4.0F		1958	2258	3.8F
				31 W	0227	0533	3.9E
					0826	1123	3.7F
					1447	1800	4.0E
					2055	2357	3.8F

Time meridian 75° W.   0000 is midnight.   1200 is noon.

CAPE COD CANAL (RR. Bridge), MASSACHUSETTS, 1983

F-Flood, Dir. 070° True   E-Ebb, Dir. 250° True

SEPTEMBER

Day	Slack Water Time (h.m.)	Max Current Time (h.m.)	Vel. (knots)	Day	Slack Water Time (h.m.)	Max Current Time (h.m.)	Vel. (knots)
1 Th	0332	0632	3.8E	16 F		0151	3.6F
	0925	1222	3.6F		0509	0744	3.6E
	1547	1857	4.0E		1100	1413	3.3F
	2159				1716	2007	3.9E
					2330		
2 F		0106	3.8F	17 Sa		0302	3.7F
	0443	0733	3.8E		0609	0845	3.6E
	1031	1328	3.6F		1202	1518	3.4F
	1652	2001	4.1E		1814	2105	4.0E
	2306						
3 Sa		0212	3.9F	18 Su	0027	0358	3.8F
	0551	0836	4.0E		0702	0940	3.8E
	1138	1435	3.8F		1255	1611	3.6F
	1756	2100	4.4E		1905	2158	4.1E
4 Su	0011	0321	4.2E	19 M	0117	0441	4.0F
	0652	0937	4.2E		0748	1027	3.9E
	1241	1540	4.0F		1340	1654	3.8F
	1856	2158	4.6E		1952	2243	4.3E
5 M	0111	0422	4.5F	20 Tu	0201	0520	4.1F
	0748	1034	4.4E		0829	1110	4.1E
	1338	1640	4.3F		1421	1729	3.9F
	1952	2254	4.9E		2033	2326	4.4E
6 Tu	0206	0516	4.7F	21 W	0240	0553	4.2F
	0839	1126	4.7E		0907	1148	4.3E
	1431	1733	4.5F		1457	1800	4.1F
	2044	2345	5.1E		2112		
7 W	0257	0605	4.9F	22 Th		0005	4.5E
	0928	1215	4.9E		0316	0623	4.3F
	1520	1821	4.7F		0942	1227	4.4E
	2135				1532	1832	4.2F
					2149		
8 Th		0034	5.2E	23 F		0043	4.6E
	0346	0653	5.0F		0351	0653	4.3F
	1014	1303	5.0E		1016	1304	4.4E
	1608	1910	4.8F		1606	1905	4.3F
	2225				2225		
9 F		0123	5.2E	24 Sa		0122	4.6E
	0434	0739	4.9F		0426	0725	4.3F
	1100	1349	5.0E		1048	1342	4.4E
	1656	1958	4.8F		1640	1938	4.3F
	2314				2300		
10 Sa		0212	5.1E	25 Su		0200	4.5E
	0522	0824	4.8F		0501	0758	4.3F
	1146	1437	4.9E		1121	1421	4.4E
	1743	2046	4.7F		1716	2016	4.3F
					2338		
11 Su	0005	0300	4.9E	26 M		0240	4.4E
	0610	0909	4.6F		0539	0835	4.2F
	1233	1526	4.7E		1155	1500	4.3E
	1832	2135	4.5F		1755	2055	4.2F
12 M	0059	0351	4.6E	27 Tu	0020	0326	4.3E
	0659	1000	4.3F		0619	0916	4.0F
	1322	1614	4.5E		1233	1545	4.2E
	1924	2228	4.2F		1839	2140	4.1F
13 Tu	0156	0442	4.3E	28 W	0109	0413	4.1E
	0752	1052	3.9F		0706	1001	3.9F
	1415	1708	4.2E		1318	1636	4.1E
	2020	2327	3.9F		1930	2233	4.0F
14 W	0258	0541	3.9E	29 Th	0207	0508	3.9E
	0851	1150	3.6F		0800	1055	3.7F
	1512	1804	4.0E		1413	1730	4.1E
	2121				2029	2334	3.9F
15 Th		0036	3.7F	30 F	0314	0609	3.8E
	0403	0642	3.7E		0903	1158	3.6F
	0954	1259	3.4F		1519	1833	4.1E
	1614	1905	3.9E		2136		
	2226						

OCTOBER

Day	Slack Water Time (h.m.)	Max Current Time (h.m.)	Vel. (knots)	Day	Slack Water Time (h.m.)	Max Current Time (h.m.)	Vel. (knots)
1 Sa		0042	3.9F	16 Su		0220	3.6F
	0426	0712	3.8E		0535	0810	3.6E
	1013	1309	3.6F		1127	1439	3.3F
	1630	1938	4.2E		1740	2030	3.9E
	2246				2349		
2 Su		0157	4.0F	17 M		0321	3.7F
	0534	0817	4.0E		0627	0905	3.7E
	1123	1421	3.7F		1221	1534	3.5F
	1738	2041	4.4E		1834	2123	4.0E
	2352						
3 M		0305	4.2F	18 Tu	0040	0404	3.9F
	0635	0918	4.2E		0712	0953	4.0E
	1226	1527	4.0F		1307	1616	3.7F
	1841	2140	4.6E		1921	2212	4.2E
4 Tu	0053	0406	4.5F	19 W	0125	0441	4.1F
	0729	1015	4.5E		0754	1038	4.2E
	1323	1624	4.3F		1348	1657	4.0F
	1937	2235	4.9E		2004	2253	4.4E
5 W	0147	0459	4.7F	20 Th	0206	0516	4.2F
	0818	1107	4.8E		0831	1117	4.3E
	1414	1717	4.6F		1426	1729	4.1F
	2029	2326	5.0E		2044	2334	4.5E
6 Th	0238	0546	4.8F	21 F	0243	0549	4.3F
	0905	1154	4.9E		0907	1154	4.5E
	1502	1805	4.8F		1502	1802	4.3F
	2119				2122		
7 F		0016	5.1E	22 Sa		0014	4.5E
	0326	0631	4.9F		0320	0621	4.3F
	0949	1240	5.0E		0941	1234	4.6E
	1548	1853	4.8F		1537	1837	4.4F
	2208				2159		
8 Sa		0102	5.1E	23 Su		0054	4.6E
	0412	0714	4.8F		0356	0654	4.3F
	1032	1325	5.0E		1014	1311	4.6E
	1633	1937	4.8F		1613	1912	4.4F
	2257				2238		
9 Su		0149	4.9E	24 M		0134	4.5E
	0458	0757	4.6F		0433	0729	4.3F
	1116	1411	4.9E		1048	1352	4.6E
	1718	2021	4.7F		1650	1951	4.4F
	2346				2318		
10 M		0234	4.7E	25 Tu		0216	4.4E
	0543	0843	4.4F		0513	0809	4.2F
	1200	1457	4.7E		1124	1435	4.5E
	1804	2109	4.4F		1732	2034	4.4F
11 Tu	0037	0325	4.4E	26 W	0003	0301	4.3E
	0630	0926	4.1F		0556	0852	4.1F
	1246	1544	4.5E		1205	1519	4.4E
	1853	2157	4.2F		1818	2123	4.3F
12 W	0131	0414	4.1E	27 Th	0055	0352	4.1E
	0720	1015	3.7F		0645	0939	3.9F
	1337	1634	4.2E		1253	1610	4.3E
	1946	2253	3.9F		1911	2217	4.2F
13 Th	0230	0510	3.8E	28 F	0154	0449	4.0E
	0817	1111	3.4F		0742	1036	3.7F
	1434	1730	4.0E		1351	1711	4.2E
	2044	2357	3.7F		2011	2318	4.1F
14 F	0333	0608	3.6E	29 Sa	0301	0549	3.9E
	0919	1215	3.2F		0848	1143	3.6F
	1536	1829	3.8E		1459	1812	4.2E
	2148				2118		
15 Sa		0108	3.6F	30 Su		0029	4.0F
	0436	0710	3.5E		0410	0654	3.9E
	1025	1330	3.2F		0958	1253	3.6F
	1640	1931	3.8E		1612	1916	4.3E
	2251				2227		
				31 M		0140	4.1F
					0515	0757	4.1E
					1107	1407	3.8F
					1722	2020	4.4E
					2333		

Time meridian 75° W.   0000 is midnight.   1200 is noon.

CAPE COD CANAL (RR. Bridge), MASSACHUSETTS, 1983

F-Flood, Dir. 070° True   E-Ebb, Dir. 250° True

NOVEMBER

Day	Slack Water Time (h.m.)	Maximum Current Time (h.m.)	Vel. (knots)
1 Tu	0613	0249	4.3F
		0858	4.3E
	1210	1514	4.1F
	1825	2121	4.6E
2 W	0034	0347	4.5F
	0706	0953	4.6E
	1305	1612	4.4F
	1922	2216	4.8E
3 Th	0128	0441	4.6F
	0755	1044	4.8E
	1356	1703	4.6F
	2015	2307	4.9E
4 F	0218	0526	4.7F
	0841	1133	4.9E
	1443	1751	4.7F
	2105	2355	4.9E
5 Sa	0306	0610	4.7F
	0924	1218	5.0E
	1528	1835	4.7F
	2153		
6 Su		0041	4.8E
	0350	0652	4.6F
	1006	1301	4.9E
	1612	1918	4.7F
	2240		
7 M		0127	4.7E
	0434	0733	4.4F
	1048	1345	4.8E
	1655	2001	4.6F
	2328		
8 Tu		0213	4.5E
	0518	0814	4.2F
	1130	1428	4.6E
	1739	2045	4.4F
9 W	0016	0259	4.2E
	0602	0859	3.9F
	1214	1514	4.4E
	1825	2128	4.1F
10 Th	0106	0348	4.0E
	0650	0942	3.7F
	1301	1603	4.2E
	1914	2220	3.9F
11 F	0200	0439	3.7E
	0742	1033	3.4F
	1355	1656	4.0E
	2007	2315	3.7F
12 Sa	0258	0532	3.6E
	0840	1131	3.2F
	1455	1753	3.8E
	2105		
13 Su		0017	3.6F
	0356	0633	3.5E
	0942	1237	3.1F
	1558	1851	3.8E
	2205		
14 M		0123	3.6F
	0452	0730	3.6E
	1043	1346	3.2F
	1659	1948	3.8E
	2303		
15 Tu		0222	3.7F
	0544	0823	3.7E
	1138	1442	3.4F
	1754	2042	3.9E
	2356		
16 W		0311	3.8F
	0631	0914	3.9E
	1227	1531	3.7F
	1845	2131	4.1E
17 Th	0044	0356	3.9F
	0714	0959	4.2E
	1311	1616	3.9F
	1930	2219	4.2E
18 F	0127	0435	4.1F
	0753	1044	4.3E
	1351	1654	4.1F
	2013	2303	4.4E
19 Sa	0209	0510	4.2F
	0831	1123	4.5E
	1430	1733	4.3F
	2055	2346	4.5E
20 Su	0248	0547	4.3F
	0907	1204	4.6E
	1509	1810	4.4F
	2136		
21 M		0027	4.5E
	0328	0626	4.3F
	0943	1245	4.7E
	1548	1851	4.5F
	2218		
22 Tu		0110	4.5E
	0409	0707	4.3F
	1020	1328	4.7E
	1630	1932	4.6F
	2303		
23 W		0155	4.5E
	0452	0746	4.2F
	1101	1413	4.7E
	1714	2018	4.5F
	2351		
24 Th		0243	4.4E
	0539	0835	4.2F
	1146	1500	4.6E
	1803	2109	4.5F
25 F	0044	0336	4.3E
	0631	0924	4.0F
	1237	1555	4.6E
	1857	2202	4.4F
26 Sa	0142	0429	4.1E
	0728	1022	3.9F
	1337	1649	4.5E
	1956	2305	4.3F
27 Su	0245	0530	4.1E
	0832	1127	3.8F
	1444	1753	4.4E
	2100		
28 M		0011	4.2F
	0349	0633	4.1E
	0940	1236	3.8F
	1555	1855	4.4E
	2207		
29 Tu		0119	4.2F
	0451	0736	4.2E
	1047	1348	3.9F
	1703	1959	4.4E
	2312		
30 W		0226	4.3F
	0549	0835	4.4E
	1149	1456	4.1F
	1807	2058	4.5E

DECEMBER

Day	Slack Water Time (h.m.)	Maximum Current Time (h.m.)	Vel. (knots)
1 Th	0012	0326	4.4F
	0642	0930	4.5E
	1246	1555	4.3F
	1906	2156	4.6E
2 F	0108	0419	4.4F
	0731	1022	4.7E
	1337	1648	4.5F
	2000	2248	4.6E
3 Sa	0159	0508	4.4F
	0817	1113	4.8E
	1425	1736	4.6F
	2051	2336	4.6E
4 Su	0247	0553	4.4F
	0901	1155	4.8E
	1510	1821	4.6F
	2139		
5 M		0023	4.5E
	0331	0634	4.3F
	0943	1240	4.8E
	1554	1904	4.5F
	2225		
6 Tu		0108	4.4E
	0414	0712	4.2F
	1024	1321	4.7E
	1636	1945	4.4F
	2311		
7 W		0152	4.3E
	0455	0753	4.0F
	1105	1405	4.6E
	1718	2024	4.3F
	2355		
8 Th		0235	4.1E
	0537	0831	3.9F
	1147	1450	4.4E
	1800	2104	4.1F
9 F	0041	0319	4.0E
	0621	0912	3.7F
	1231	1535	4.3E
	1844	2151	4.0F
10 Sa	0128	0407	3.8E
	0708	1001	3.5F
	1319	1623	4.1E
	1931	2236	3.8F
11 Su	0218	0458	3.7E
	0759	1050	3.4F
	1412	1715	3.9E
	2022	2327	3.7F
12 M	0310	0550	3.6E
	0854	1147	3.3F
	1510	1808	3.8E
	2116		
13 Tu		0023	3.6F
	0403	0644	3.7E
	0951	1245	3.3F
	1610	1905	3.8E
	2211		
14 W		0118	3.6F
	0455	0738	3.7E
	1047	1344	3.4F
	1708	1959	3.8E
	2306		
15 Th		0213	3.7F
	0544	0829	3.9E
	1140	1439	3.6F
	1803	2052	4.0E
	2358		
16 F		0305	3.8F
	0630	0920	4.1E
	1229	1531	3.8F
	1855	2143	4.1E
17 Sa	0047	0350	3.9F
	0713	1006	4.3E
	1316	1619	4.0F
	1943	2231	4.2E
18 Su	0134	0435	4.1F
	0755	1051	4.5E
	1400	1703	4.3F
	2030	2317	4.4E
19 M	0219	0516	4.2F
	0836	1137	4.7E
	1444	1748	4.5F
	2115		
20 Tu		0003	4.5E
	0304	0602	4.3F
	0917	1221	4.8E
	1528	1833	4.6F
	2202		
21 W		0049	4.5E
	0349	0645	4.3F
	0959	1307	4.9E
	1613	1919	4.7F
	2249		
22 Th		0137	4.5E
	0436	0729	4.4F
	1044	1356	4.9E
	1700	2007	4.7F
	2338		
23 F		0226	4.5E
	0525	0819	4.3F
	1132	1444	4.9E
	1750	2056	4.7F
24 Sa	0030	0317	4.5E
	0617	0912	4.2F
	1225	1535	4.8E
	1843	2148	4.6F
25 Su	0125	0413	4.4E
	0713	1007	4.1F
	1323	1632	4.7E
	1940	2247	4.5F
26 M	0222	0508	4.3E
	0813	1108	4.0F
	1427	1730	4.5E
	2040	2348	4.3F
27 Tu	0322	0609	4.3E
	0916	1215	4.0F
	1535	1832	4.4E
	2143		
28 W		0054	4.2F
	0422	0709	4.3E
	1022	1325	4.0F
	1643	1934	4.3E
	2247		
29 Th		0200	4.1F
	0520	0809	4.3E
	1125	1433	4.0F
	1749	2036	4.3E
	2350		
30 F		0301	4.1F
	0616	0908	4.4E
	1224	1539	4.2F
	1850	2134	4.3E
31 Sa	0048	0402	4.1F
	0708	0959	4.5E
	1319	1638	4.3F
	1946	2229	4.3E

Time meridian 75° W.   0000 is midnight.   1200 is noon.

POLLOCK RIP CHANNEL, MASSACHUSETTS, 1983

F-Flood, Dir. 035° True   E-Ebb, Dir. 225° True

JANUARY

Day	Slack Water Time h.m.	Maximum Current Time h.m.	Vel. knots
1 Sa	0402	0053	1.9E
	1021	0712	1.9F
	1618	1307	2.0E
	2308	1944	2.4F
2 Su	0456	0145	1.9E
	1115	0805	1.9F
	1712	1400	2.0E
		2039	2.3F
3 M	0002	0242	1.9E
	0552	0905	1.9F
	1212	1457	1.9E
	1808	2137	2.3F
4 Tu	0057	0337	1.8E
	0650	1007	1.9F
	1311	1557	1.8E
	1907	2241	2.2F
5 W	0155	0438	1.7E
	0750	1113	1.8F
	1413	1659	1.7E
	2008	2344	2.1F
6 Th	0253	0542	1.7E
	0851	1222	1.8F
	1518	1805	1.6E
	2112		
7 F	0352	0051	2.0F
	0953	0646	1.6E
	1622	1327	1.9F
	2216	1914	1.6E
8 Sa	0450	0153	2.0F
	1054	0747	1.6E
	1725	1428	2.0F
	2319	2021	1.5E
9 Su	0546	0254	1.9F
	1151	0851	1.7E
	1824	1528	2.1F
		2122	1.5E
10 M	0017	0349	1.9F
	0639	0942	1.7E
	1243	1617	2.1F
	1918	2215	1.6E
11 Tu	0111	0438	1.9F
	0727	1029	1.7E
	1330	1706	2.2F
	2007	2305	1.6E
12 W	0159	0525	1.9F
	0812	1112	1.7E
	1414	1751	2.2F
	2051	2344	1.6E
13 Th	0242	0607	1.9F
	0854	1150	1.7E
	1453	1830	2.2F
	2133		
14 F	0322	0023	1.6E
	0934	0644	1.8F
	1530	1225	1.8E
	2211	1905	2.2F
15 Sa	0359	0056	1.6E
	1012	0719	1.8F
	1606	1259	1.8E
	2249	1938	2.2F
16 Su	0435	0129	1.7E
	1050	0752	1.8F
	1641	1333	1.8E
	2326	2010	2.2F
17 M	0512	0203	1.7E
	1129	0824	1.8F
	1718	1410	1.8E
		2043	2.1F
18 Tu	0005	0242	1.8E
	0550	0859	1.8F
	1211	1450	1.8E
	1757	2118	2.1F
19 W	0045	0321	1.8E
	0630	0936	1.8F
	1254	1533	1.8E
	1839	2158	2.1F
20 Th	0128	0404	1.8E
	0712	1019	1.8F
	1342	1620	1.7E
	1925	2241	2.0F
21 F	0213	0449	1.7E
	0759	1106	1.8F
	1433	1709	1.7E
	2014	2330	1.9F
22 Sa	0302	0539	1.7E
	0848	1158	1.7F
	1528	1804	1.6E
	2108		
23 Su	0353	0023	1.8F
	0942	0630	1.6E
	1626	1257	1.7F
	2205	1857	1.5E
24 M	0447	0122	1.7F
	1038	0727	1.6E
	1726	1358	1.8F
	2306	1959	1.5E
25 Tu	0542	0222	1.7F
	1136	0824	1.7E
	1826	1503	1.9F
		2100	1.5E
26 W	0008	0325	1.7F
	0638	0922	1.7E
	1233	1603	2.0F
	1923	2201	1.6E
27 Th	0108	0426	1.7F
	0732	1017	1.8E
	1329	1659	2.1F
	2018	2256	1.7E
28 F	0205	0522	1.8F
	0825	1112	1.9E
	1423	1754	2.3F
	2111	2352	1.8E
29 Sa	0259	0616	1.9F
	0918	1205	2.0E
	1516	1845	2.4F
	2202		
30 Su	0352	0045	1.9E
	1010	0708	2.0F
	1608	1259	2.1E
	2253	1938	2.4F
31 M	0443	0135	1.9E
	1102	0800	2.1F
	1700	1350	2.1E
	2343	2029	2.4F

FEBRUARY

Day	Slack Water Time h.m.	Maximum Current Time h.m.	Vel. knots
1 Tu	0534	0225	1.9E
	1155	0852	2.1F
	1752	1443	2.0E
		2121	2.3F
2 W	0034	0317	1.9E
	0627	0946	2.0F
	1251	1537	1.9E
	1846	2216	2.2F
3 Th	0127	0412	1.8E
	0721	1046	2.0F
	1348	1633	1.8E
	1943	2315	2.0F
4 F	0221	0507	1.7E
	0817	1149	1.9F
	1449	1736	1.6E
	2042		
5 Sa	0318	0017	1.9F
	0916	0607	1.6E
	1551	1252	1.9F
	2144	1839	1.5E
6 Su	0415	0120	1.8F
	1017	0711	1.5E
	1654	1354	1.9F
	2247	1946	1.4E
7 M	0513	0221	1.8F
	1116	0812	1.5E
	1755	1457	2.0F
	2348	2052	1.4E
8 Tu	0608	0321	1.8F
	1211	0909	1.6E
	1850	1550	2.0F
		2149	1.5E
9 W	0044	0414	1.8F
	0700	1002	1.6E
	1302	1639	2.1F
	1941	2238	1.5E
10 Th	0133	0459	1.8F
	0747	1050	1.7E
	1347	1722	2.2F
	2025	2319	1.6E
11 F	0217	0542	1.9F
	0830	1127	1.7E
	1428	1804	2.2F
	2106	2356	1.7E
12 Sa	0257	0621	1.9F
	0909	1202	1.8E
	1505	1839	2.2F
	2144		
13 Su	0333	0029	1.7E
	0947	0654	1.9F
	1541	1234	1.8E
	2220	1910	2.2F
14 M	0407	0101	1.8E
	1024	0724	1.9F
	1615	1307	1.9E
	2255	1939	2.2F
15 Tu	0441	0134	1.8E
	1102	0753	1.9F
	1650	1344	1.9E
	2331	2011	2.2F
16 W	0516	0209	1.9E
	1140	0824	2.0F
	1727	1421	1.9E
		2042	2.2F
17 Th	0009	0247	1.9E
	0553	0901	2.0F
	1222	1502	1.9E
	1807	2119	2.1F
18 F	0049	0328	1.9E
	0633	0938	2.0F
	1307	1547	1.8E
	1851	2202	2.0F
19 Sa	0133	0413	1.8E
	0717	1026	1.9F
	1358	1636	1.7E
	1939	2251	1.9F
20 Su	0222	0500	1.7E
	0807	1119	1.8F
	1454	1730	1.6E
	2034	2344	1.7F
21 M	0316	0555	1.6E
	0903	1220	1.8F
	1557	1829	1.5E
	2136		
22 Tu	0416	0048	1.6F
	1006	0652	1.6E
	1702	1329	1.7F
	2244	1934	1.4E
23 W	0518	0157	1.5F
	1111	0758	1.5E
	1807	1444	1.8F
	2352	2044	1.4E
24 Th	0620	0313	1.6F
	1216	0904	1.6E
	1908	1552	2.0F
		2149	1.5E
25 F	0056	0421	1.7F
	0719	1008	1.7E
	1317	1653	2.1F
	2005	2249	1.7E
26 Sa	0155	0518	1.9F
	0814	1104	1.9E
	1413	1748	2.3F
	2057	2342	1.8E
27 Su	0248	0609	2.0F
	0907	1157	2.0E
	1506	1837	2.4F
	2146		
28 M	0338	0032	1.9E
	0957	0700	2.1F
	1556	1248	2.1E
	2234	1925	2.4F

Time meridian 75° W.   0000 is midnight.   1200 is noon.

F-Flood, Dir. 035° True   E-Ebb, Dir. 225° True

MARCH

Day	Slack Water Time h.m.	Maximum Current Time h.m.	Vel. knots
1 Tu	0425	0119	2.0E
	1047	0748	2.2F
	1645	1336	2.1E
	2320	2011	2.4F
2 W	0512	0205	2.0E
	1137	0833	2.2F
	1734	1424	2.0E
		2059	2.3F
3 Th	0007	0252	1.9E
	0600	0924	2.1F
	1229	1515	1.9E
	1823	2147	2.1F
4 F	0056	0341	1.8E
	0649	1015	2.0F
	1322	1606	1.7E
	1915	2241	1.9F
5 Sa	0147	0432	1.7E
	0741	1114	1.9F
	1419	1701	1.6E
	2011	2342	1.8F
6 Su	0242	0527	1.6E
	0837	1216	1.9F
	1520	1804	1.4E
	2111		
7 M	0339	0043	1.7F
	0937	0628	1.5E
	1621	1321	1.8F
	2213	1910	1.3E
8 Tu	0438	0147	1.6F
	1037	0733	1.4E
	1721	1420	1.9F
	2315	2015	1.4E
9 W	0535	0248	1.6F
	1135	0832	1.5E
	1817	1518	2.0F
		2112	1.4E
10 Th	0012	0339	1.7F
	0629	0930	1.5E
	1228	1607	2.0F
	1908	2205	1.5E
11 F	0102	0430	1.8F
	0717	1014	1.6E
	1315	1652	2.1F
	1953	2249	1.6E
12 Sa	0146	0511	1.9F
	0802	1056	1.7E
	1357	1731	2.2F
	2033	2324	1.7E
13 Su	0226	0551	2.0F
	0842	1131	1.8E
	1435	1808	2.2F
	2111	2357	1.8E
14 M	0301	0622	2.0F
	0920	1205	1.9E
	1511	1837	2.2F
	2146		
15 Tu	0335	0029	1.9E
	0957	0652	2.0F
	1546	1238	2.0E
	2221	1905	2.2F
16 W	0408	0100	1.9E
	1033	0719	2.1F
	1621	1315	2.0E
	2257	1936	2.2F
17 Th	0442	0135	2.0E
	1112	0754	2.1F
	1658	1352	2.0E
	2334	2009	2.2F
18 F	0518	0214	2.0E
	1153	0827	2.1F
	1738	1436	2.0E
		2046	2.1F
19 Sa	0014	0255	1.9E
	0558	0908	2.1F
	1239	1517	1.9E
	1823	2131	2.0F
20 Su	0058	0340	1.9E
	0643	0957	2.0F
	1331	1608	1.7E
	1913	2219	1.8F
21 M	0149	0431	1.7E
	0735	1052	1.9F
	1430	1705	1.6E
	2011	2316	1.6F
22 Tu	0248	0529	1.6E
	0836	1156	1.8F
	1536	1808	1.4E
	2118		
23 W	0353	0029	1.5F
	0943	0632	1.5E
	1644	1315	1.8F
	2231	1916	1.4E
24 Th	0501	0153	1.5F
	1055	0743	1.5E
	1751	1435	1.8F
	2342	2031	1.4E
25 F	0607	0310	1.6F
	1203	0853	1.6E
	1852	1545	2.0F
		2139	1.6E
26 Sa	0046	0414	1.8F
	0707	0957	1.7E
	1305	1644	2.2F
	1948	2237	1.7E
27 Su	0143	0510	2.0F
	0803	1056	1.9E
	1402	1735	2.3F
	2039	2330	1.9E
28 M	0233	0559	2.1F
	0854	1147	2.0E
	1453	1824	2.4F
	2126		
29 Tu	0320	0016	2.0E
	0943	0646	2.2F
	1541	1236	2.0E
	2211	1908	2.3F
30 W	0405	0100	2.0E
	1031	0729	2.3F
	1627	1320	2.0E
	2255	1951	2.3F
31 Th	0448	0143	2.0E
	1118	0812	2.2F
	1713	1403	1.9E
	2339	2036	2.1F

APRIL

Day	Slack Water Time h.m.	Maximum Current Time h.m.	Vel. knots
1 F	0532	0226	1.9E
	1207	0858	2.2F
	1759	1449	1.8E
		2121	2.0F
2 Sa	0025	0309	1.8E
	0618	0946	2.1F
	1257	1538	1.7E
	1848	2210	1.8F
3 Su	0114	0356	1.6E
	0706	1040	1.9F
	1351	1631	1.5E
	1940	2303	1.6F
4 M	0206	0447	1.5E
	0759	1139	1.8F
	1447	1727	1.4E
	2038		
5 Tu		0009	1.6F
	0303	0546	1.4E
	0856	1240	1.8F
	1546	1831	1.3E
	2138		
6 W		0112	1.5F
	0401	0649	1.4E
	0955	1340	1.8F
	1644	1932	1.4E
	2238		
7 Th		0209	1.6F
	0459	0750	1.4E
	1053	1437	1.9F
	1739	2034	1.4E
	2334		
8 F		0306	1.7F
	0554	0847	1.5E
	1147	1528	2.0F
	1828	2123	1.6E
9 Sa	0025	0354	1.8F
	0643	0936	1.6E
	1236	1613	2.1F
	1914	2208	1.7E
10 Su	0109	0437	1.9F
	0729	1017	1.7E
	1320	1654	2.1F
	1955	2243	1.8E
11 M	0149	0512	2.0F
	0810	1056	1.8E
	1401	1729	2.2F
	2034	2319	1.9E
12 Tu	0225	0547	2.1F
	0849	1131	1.9E
	1438	1800	2.2F
	2110	2352	1.9E
13 W	0259	0616	2.1F
	0927	1206	1.9E
	1515	1831	2.2F
	2146		
14 Th	0333	0025	2.0E
	1006	0647	2.2F
	1552	1245	2.0E
	2222	1904	2.1F
15 F	0409	0104	2.0E
	1046	0721	2.2F
	1631	1326	2.0E
	2301	1939	2.1F
16 Sa	0447	0141	2.0E
	1130	0800	2.2F
	1714	1409	2.0E
	2343	2020	2.0F
17 Su	0530	0226	2.0E
	1218	0845	2.2F
	1802	1456	1.9E
		2105	1.9F
18 M	0031	0314	1.9E
	0618	0932	2.1F
	1313	1547	1.7E
	1856	2200	1.7F
19 Tu	0126	0409	1.7E
	0714	1034	2.0F
	1414	1647	1.6E
	1958	2307	1.6F
20 W	0229	0508	1.6E
	0818	1145	1.9F
	1520	1752	1.5E
	2108		
21 Th		0023	1.5F
	0338	0617	1.5E
	0929	1307	1.8F
	1628	1905	1.4E
	2221		
22 F		0149	1.5F
	0447	0730	1.5E
	1041	1425	1.9F
	1733	2021	1.5E
	2330		
23 Sa		0259	1.7F
	0553	0843	1.6E
	1149	1532	2.1F
	1833	2127	1.6E
24 Su	0031	0400	1.9F
	0654	0949	1.7E
	1251	1628	2.2F
	1928	2224	1.8E
25 M	0126	0453	2.1F
	0749	1044	1.8E
	1346	1719	2.3F
	2017	2311	1.9E
26 Tu	0215	0544	2.2F
	0840	1135	1.9E
	1437	1806	2.3F
	2103	2357	1.9E
27 W	0300	0629	2.3F
	0928	1220	1.9E
	1524	1851	2.2F
	2147		
28 Th		0038	1.9E
	0342	0711	2.3F
	1014	1304	1.9E
	1608	1931	2.1F
	2229		
29 F		0116	1.9E
	0424	0753	2.2F
	1100	1345	1.8E
	1652	2013	2.0F
	2312		
30 Sa		0157	1.8E
	0505	0837	2.1F
	1146	1428	1.7E
	1736	2055	1.8F
	2356		

Time meridian 75° W.   0000 is midnight.   1200 is noon.

POLLOCK RIP CHANNEL, MASSACHUSETTS, 1983

F-Flood, Dir. 035° True   E-Ebb, Dir. 225° True

MAY

Day	Slack Water Time h.m.	Max Current Time h.m.	Vel. knots	Day	Slack Water Time h.m.	Max Current Time h.m.	Vel. knots
1 Su	0548	0239	1.7E	16 M	0509	0204	2.0E
		0921	2.0F			0827	2.2F
	1233	1511	1.6E		1202	1438	1.8E
	1822	2143	1.7F		1747	2050	1.8F
2 M	0043	0325	1.6E	17 Tu	0011	0255	1.9E
	0634	1009	2.0F		0602	0924	2.1F
	1323	1602	1.5E		1259	1533	1.7E
	1911	2231	1.6F		1845	2150	1.7F
3 Tu	0133	0412	1.5E	18 W	0110	0352	1.8E
	0723	1100	1.9F		0700	1025	2.0F
	1415	1654	1.4E		1400	1636	1.6E
	2005	2330	1.5F		1949	2301	1.6F
4 W	0227	0506	1.5E	19 Th	0214	0454	1.6E
	0817	1158	1.8F		0806	1139	2.0F
	1509	1749	1.4E		1505	1743	1.5E
	2101				2057		
5 Th	0323	0029	1.5F	20 F	0323	0017	1.6F
	0913	0603	1.4E		0915	0605	1.6E
	1603	1255	1.8F		1610	1255	2.0F
	2158	1848	1.4E		2206	1854	1.5E
6 F	0420	0127	1.6F	21 Sa	0431	0137	1.7F
	1009	0703	1.4E		1025	0718	1.6E
	1656	1350	1.9F		1712	1408	2.0F
	2252	1943	1.5E		2312	2005	1.6E
7 Sa	0514	0222	1.7F	22 Su	0536	0244	1.8F
	1103	0759	1.5E		1132	0827	1.6E
	1745	1441	1.9F		1810	1510	2.1F
	2341	2034	1.6E			2106	1.7E
8 Su	0605	0309	1.8F	23 M	0011	0343	2.0F
	1153	0850	1.6E		0637	0934	1.7E
	1831	1528	2.0F		1233	1607	2.1F
		2118	1.7E		1904	2202	1.8E
9 M	0027	0352	1.9F	24 Tu	0105	0437	2.2F
	0652	0936	1.7E		0733	1027	1.8E
	1239	1610	2.0F		1328	1700	2.1F
	1914	2159	1.8E		1953	2253	1.9E
10 Tu	0108	0433	2.0F	25 W	0154	0526	2.2F
	0736	1017	1.7E		0824	1118	1.8E
	1322	1646	2.1F		1419	1747	2.1F
	1954	2237	1.9E		2040	2336	1.9E
11 W	0146	0506	2.1F	26 Th	0239	0611	2.3F
	0817	1058	1.8E		0912	1204	1.8E
	1403	1722	2.1F		1506	1833	2.0F
	2033	2315	1.9E		2123		
12 Th	0224	0542	2.1F	27 F	0321	0017	1.8E
	0859	1137	1.9E		0958	0654	2.2F
	1444	1756	2.0F		1549	1247	1.7E
	2111	2353	2.0E		2205	1914	1.9F
13 F	0301	0617	2.2F	28 Sa	0401	0056	1.8E
	0940	1218	1.9E		1042	0735	2.2F
	1525	1833	2.0F		1631	1328	1.7E
	2151				2247	1953	1.8F
14 Sa	0340	0034	2.0E	29 Su	0441	0134	1.7E
	1024	0656	2.3F		1125	0816	2.1F
	1608	1303	1.9E		1713	1407	1.6E
	2233	1914	2.0F		2329	2034	1.7F
15 Su	0423	0117	2.0E	30 M	0522	0214	1.7E
	1111	0740	2.3F		1209	0855	2.1F
	1655	1348	1.9E		1756	1448	1.6E
	2319	1957	1.9F			2114	1.6F
				31 Tu	0013	0255	1.6E
					0604	0940	2.0F
					1255	1531	1.5E
					1842	2200	1.6F

JUNE

Day	Slack Water Time h.m.	Max Current Time h.m.	Vel. knots	Day	Slack Water Time h.m.	Max Current Time h.m.	Vel. knots
1 W	0101	0340	1.6E	16 Th	0056	0338	1.8E
	0650	1023	1.9F		0649	1019	2.1F
	1342	1619	1.5E		1344	1622	1.7E
	1931	2247	1.6F		1936	2251	1.7F
2 Th	0151	0431	1.5E	17 F	0159	0441	1.7E
	0739	1113	1.9F		0753	1126	2.1F
	1431	1710	1.5E		1445	1727	1.7E
	2022	2342	1.6F		2040		
3 F	0244	0522	1.5E	18 Sa		0005	1.7E
	0830	1205	1.9F		0305	0548	1.6E
	1521	1800	1.5E		0859	1237	2.0F
	2114				1546	1834	1.7E
					2145		
4 Sa		0036	1.6F	19 Su		0114	1.8F
	0338	0617	1.5E		0411	0659	1.6E
	0923	1257	1.9F		1006	1344	2.0F
	1611	1852	1.6E		1647	1943	1.7E
	2205				2248		
5 Su	0431	0127	1.7F	20 M	0516	0220	1.9F
	1016	0709	1.5E		1111	0809	1.6E
	1700	1349	1.9F		1744	1449	2.0F
	2254	1943	1.6E		2347	2044	1.7E
6 M	0523	0220	1.8F	21 Tu	0617	0321	2.1F
	1107	0802	1.6E		1212	0915	1.6E
	1747	1435	1.9F		1839	1544	2.0F
	2341	2031	1.7E			2139	1.8E
7 Tu	0613	0305	1.8F	22 W	0042	0416	2.2F
	1156	0851	1.6E		0714	1011	1.7E
	1832	1520	1.9F		1309	1638	2.0F
		2114	1.8E		1929	2232	1.8E
8 W	0026	0349	1.9F	23 Th	0132	0505	2.2F
	0700	0938	1.7E		0807	1106	1.7E
	1244	1605	1.9F		1400	1727	2.0F
	1915	2158	1.8E		2017	2315	1.8E
9 Th	0108	0430	2.0F	24 F	0218	0554	2.2F
	0746	1023	1.7E		0855	1149	1.6E
	1330	1645	1.9F		1447	1812	1.9F
	1958	2241	1.9E		2101	2357	1.8E
10 F	0150	0510	2.1F	25 Sa	0301	0638	2.2F
	0832	1109	1.8E		0940	1232	1.6E
	1415	1725	2.0F		1531	1853	1.8F
	2041	2324	2.0E		2143		
11 Sa	0233	0552	2.2F	26 Su		0036	1.7E
	0918	1154	1.8E		0340	0719	2.2F
	1502	1812	1.9F		1022	1310	1.6E
	2125				1611	1934	1.8F
					2223		
12 Su	0317	0009	2.0E	27 M	0419	0112	1.7E
	1006	0638	2.3F		1103	0754	2.1F
	1550	1241	1.9E		1650	1346	1.6E
	2211	1854	1.9F		2304	2013	1.7F
13 M	0404	0056	2.0E	28 Tu	0457	0149	1.7E
	1056	0726	2.3F		1143	0833	2.1F
	1641	1332	1.9E		1730	1423	1.6E
	2302	1945	1.9F		2346	2048	1.7F
14 Tu	0455	0147	2.0E	29 W	0536	0230	1.7E
	1149	0816	2.3F		1224	0909	2.1F
	1735	1425	1.8E		1811	1502	1.6E
	2356	2042	1.8F			2124	1.7F
15 W	0550	0239	1.9E	30 Th	0030	0311	1.7E
	1245	0914	2.2F		0618	0947	2.0F
	1834	1522	1.8E		1307	1543	1.6E
		2143	1.8F		1854	2206	1.7F

Time meridian 75° W.   0000 is midnight.   1200 is noon.

F-Flood, Dir. 035° True   E-Ebb, Dir. 225° True

JULY

Day	Slack Water Time h.m.	Maximum Current Time h.m.	Vel. knots
1 F	0116	0356	1.7E
	0702	1029	2.0F
	1352	1628	1.6E
	1940	2251	1.7F
2 Sa	0205	0441	1.6E
	0749	1114	2.0F
	1438	1717	1.7E
	2028	2342	1.7F
3 Su	0256	0533	1.6E
	0838	1200	1.9F
	1526	1804	1.7E
	2116		
4 M		0031	1.7F
	0348	0624	1.6E
	0929	1251	1.8F
	1614	1853	1.7E
	2206		
5 Tu		0122	1.7F
	0442	0715	1.5E
	1022	1343	1.8F
	1703	1943	1.7E
	2256		
6 W		0218	1.8F
	0535	0808	1.5E
	1115	1434	1.8F
	1752	2032	1.7E
	2345		
7 Th		0307	1.9F
	0627	0901	1.6E
	1208	1522	1.8F
	1840	2123	1.8E
8 F	0033	0356	2.0F
	0719	0955	1.6E
	1301	1616	1.8F
	1928	2210	1.8E
9 Sa	0122	0447	2.1F
	0810	1044	1.7E
	1352	1705	1.8F
	2016	2301	1.9E
10 Su	0211	0535	2.2F
	0900	1137	1.8E
	1444	1754	1.9F
	2105	2351	2.0E
11 M	0300	0623	2.3F
	0950	1228	1.8E
	1535	1845	1.9F
	2155		
12 Tu		0042	2.0E
	0351	0715	2.3F
	1041	1319	1.9E
	1628	1938	1.9F
	2247		
13 W		0135	2.0E
	0444	0810	2.3F
	1133	1411	1.9E
	1722	2033	1.9F
	2342		
14 Th		0228	2.0E
	0538	0905	2.3F
	1227	1508	1.9E
	1817	2131	1.9F
15 F	0040	0325	1.9E
	0635	1006	2.2F
	1323	1603	1.8E
	1916	2235	1.9F

Day	Slack Water Time h.m.	Maximum Current Time h.m.	Vel. knots
16 Sa	0140	0425	1.8E
	0735	1107	2.1F
	1420	1704	1.7E
	2016	2342	1.9F
17 Su	0243	0530	1.7E
	0838	1212	2.0F
	1519	1807	1.7E
	2118		
18 M		0048	1.9F
	0348	0636	1.6E
	0943	1321	2.0F
	1618	1914	1.7E
	2220		
19 Tu		0155	2.0F
	0453	0746	1.5E
	1047	1423	1.9F
	1717	2015	1.7E
	2320		
20 W		0256	2.0F
	0556	0851	1.5E
	1150	1522	1.9F
	1813	2115	1.7E
21 Th	0017	0354	2.1F
	0654	0952	1.6E
	1248	1617	1.9F
	1905	2208	1.7E
22 F	0109	0445	2.2F
	0747	1045	1.6E
	1341	1708	1.9F
	1954	2255	1.7E
23 Sa	0156	0534	2.2F
	0835	1131	1.6E
	1428	1751	1.9F
	2039	2338	1.7E
24 Su	0239	0617	2.2F
	0919	1210	1.6E
	1510	1833	1.8F
	2120		
25 M		0016	1.7E
	0318	0656	2.2F
	0959	1247	1.6E
	1548	1910	1.8F
	2200		
26 Tu		0049	1.8E
	0355	0731	2.2F
	1037	1320	1.7E
	1624	1945	1.8F
	2239		
27 W		0124	1.8E
	0431	0803	2.2F
	1114	1354	1.7E
	1701	2016	1.8F
	2318		
28 Th		0201	1.8E
	0508	0836	2.1F
	1151	1429	1.7E
	1737	2050	1.8F
	2358		
29 F		0238	1.8E
	0546	0909	2.1F
	1231	1508	1.8E
	1816	2125	1.8F
30 Sa	0041	0318	1.8E
	0626	0944	2.1F
	1312	1547	1.8E
	1857	2206	1.8F
31 Su	0126	0403	1.7E
	0710	1026	2.0F
	1355	1632	1.7E
	1941	2251	1.8F

AUGUST

Day	Slack Water Time h.m.	Maximum Current Time h.m.	Vel. knots
1 M	0215	0452	1.7E
	0756	1111	1.9F
	1442	1720	1.7E
	2029	2340	1.8F
2 Tu	0307	0543	1.6E
	0847	1202	1.8F
	1531	1809	1.7E
	2119		
3 W		0034	1.8F
	0403	0638	1.5E
	0942	1257	1.7F
	1623	1902	1.6E
	2213		
4 Th		0131	1.8F
	0501	0734	1.5E
	1041	1352	1.6F
	1717	1957	1.6E
	2309		
5 F		0234	1.8F
	0559	0831	1.5E
	1140	1454	1.6F
	1811	2052	1.7E
6 Sa	0005	0332	1.9F
	0656	0931	1.5E
	1239	1555	1.6F
	1905	2148	1.8E
7 Su	0100	0430	2.1F
	0751	1027	1.6E
	1336	1651	1.8F
	1958	2243	1.9E
8 M	0154	0525	2.2F
	0843	1121	1.8E
	1430	1744	1.9F
	2050	2336	2.0E
9 Tu	0247	0615	2.3F
	0934	1214	1.9E
	1522	1836	2.0F
	2141		
10 W		0029	2.1E
	0339	0706	2.4F
	1024	1305	1.9E
	1613	1928	2.1F
	2233		
11 Th		0120	2.1E
	0431	0757	2.4F
	1114	1354	2.0E
	1704	2020	2.1F
	2326		
12 F		0214	2.1E
	0523	0848	2.3F
	1205	1448	1.9E
	1756	2114	2.1F
13 Sa	0021	0305	2.0E
	0617	0943	2.2F
	1257	1540	1.9E
	1850	2212	2.0F
14 Su	0119	0403	1.8E
	0714	1044	2.1F
	1352	1636	1.8E
	1947	2314	2.0F
15 M	0220	0504	1.7E
	0814	1145	1.9F
	1449	1737	1.7E
	2046		

Day	Slack Water Time h.m.	Maximum Current Time h.m.	Vel. knots
16 Tu		0021	1.9F
	0323	0612	1.5E
	0917	1251	1.8F
	1548	1841	1.6E
	2149		
17 W		0128	1.9F
	0428	0721	1.5E
	1022	1356	1.8F
	1648	1949	1.5E
	2251		
18 Th		0230	2.0F
	0531	0828	1.4E
	1126	1457	1.8F
	1746	2048	1.6E
	2349		
19 F		0329	2.1F
	0630	0928	1.5E
	1225	1553	1.8F
	1841	2145	1.6E
20 Sa	0043	0422	2.1F
	0723	1021	1.6E
	1317	1644	1.9F
	1930	2230	1.7E
21 Su	0131	0507	2.2F
	0809	1106	1.6E
	1403	1727	1.9F
	2015	2315	1.7E
22 M	0214	0550	2.2F
	0851	1145	1.7E
	1444	1808	1.9F
	2056	2351	1.8E
23 Tu	0253	0628	2.2F
	0929	1220	1.7E
	1520	1843	1.9F
	2135		
24 W		0025	1.8E
	0329	0701	2.2F
	1005	1251	1.8E
	1554	1915	1.9F
	2212		
25 Th		0056	1.9E
	0403	0730	2.2F
	1041	1321	1.8E
	1628	1944	2.0F
	2249		
26 F		0131	1.9E
	0438	0800	2.2F
	1116	1354	1.9E
	1702	2013	2.0F
	2327		
27 Sa		0208	1.9E
	0514	0829	2.1F
	1153	1429	1.9E
	1737	2048	2.0F
28 Su	0007	0245	1.9E
	0552	0906	2.1F
	1232	1509	1.8E
	1816	2127	1.9F
29 M	0050	0330	1.8E
	0633	0945	2.0F
	1314	1552	1.8E
	1858	2206	1.9F
30 Tu	0139	0415	1.7E
	0720	1028	1.8F
	1400	1639	1.7E
	1945	2258	1.8F
31 W	0232	0508	1.6E
	0812	1121	1.7F
	1452	1732	1.6E
	2038	2355	1.8F

Time meridian 75° W. 0000 is midnight. 1200 is noon.

THE RACE, LONG ISLAND SOUND, 1983

F-Flood, Dir. 295° True   E-Ebb, Dir. 100° True

JANUARY

Day	Slack Water Time (h.m.)	Maximum Current Time (h.m.)	Vel. (knots)
1 Sa	0025	0341	4.1E
	0643	0937	4.1F
	1241	1606	4.7E
	1923	2211	4.0F
2 Su	0119	0435	4.1E
	0741	1029	3.9F
	1336	1702	4.5E
	2017	2304	3.9F
3 M	0214	0533	4.0E
	0841	1128	3.6F
	1432	1759	4.2E
	2113		
4 Tu	0311	0002	3.6F
	0944	0631	3.9E
	1531	1228	3.3F
	2211	1855	3.9E
5 W	0409	0101	3.4F
	1050	0731	3.7E
	1633	1333	3.0F
	2311	1956	3.5E
6 Th	0509	0205	3.2F
	1155	0832	3.6E
	1736	1443	2.7F
		2057	3.3E
7 F	0011	0306	3.0F
	0608	0933	3.5E
	1259	1552	2.6F
	1840	2155	3.1E
8 Sa	0110	0410	2.9F
	0706	1028	3.5E
	1358	1653	2.6F
	1941	2252	3.0E
9 Su	0205	0509	2.8F
	0800	1124	3.6E
	1453	1751	2.6F
	2037	2345	2.9E
10 M	0257	0558	2.8F
	0848	1211	3.6E
	1542	1838	2.6F
	2127		
11 Tu	0345	0032	2.9E
	0933	0643	2.7F
	1627	1258	3.6E
	2211	1921	2.7F
12 W	0428	0118	2.9E
	1013	0724	2.7F
	1708	1341	3.6E
	2251	2000	2.7F
13 Th	0509	0201	2.9E
	1052	0757	2.7F
	1746	1422	3.5E
	2329	2033	2.6F
14 F	0548	0242	2.8E
	1129	0828	2.6F
	1822	1459	3.5E
		2101	2.6F
15 Sa	0005	0321	2.8E
	0625	0904	2.6F
	1205	1538	3.4E
	1856	2134	2.6F
16 Su	0040	0400	2.8E
	0701	0942	2.5F
	1242	1616	3.2E
	1930	2209	2.6F
17 M	0117	0438	2.7E
	0738	1022	2.5F
	1320	1651	3.1E
	2003	2248	2.6F
18 Tu	0154	0514	2.7E
	0818	1104	2.4F
	1400	1727	2.9E
	2039	2331	2.6F
19 W	0234	0552	2.7E
	0903	1149	2.3F
	1444	1802	2.7E
	2119		
20 Th	0317	0015	2.5F
	0952	0637	2.7E
	1532	1240	2.2F
	2203	1849	2.6E
21 F	0405	0102	2.5F
	1048	0729	2.7E
	1627	1331	2.2F
	2254	1942	2.5E
22 Sa	0458	0155	2.6F
	1148	0828	2.9E
	1726	1429	2.2F
	2350	2049	2.5E
23 Su	0555	0250	2.7F
	1250	0929	3.1E
	1829	1528	2.4F
		2152	2.7E
24 M	0050	0349	2.9F
	0654	1031	3.5E
	1350	1627	2.7F
	1932	2254	2.9E
25 Tu	0150	0447	3.2F
	0754	1129	3.8E
	1447	1728	3.0F
	2032	2351	3.3E
26 W	0250	0544	3.5F
	0851	1223	4.2E
	1542	1824	3.4F
	2129		
27 Th	0347	0046	3.7E
	0947	0640	3.8F
	1634	1315	4.6E
	2224	1918	3.8F
28 F	0443	0141	4.0E
	1041	0736	4.1F
	1724	1409	4.8E
	2317	2012	4.0F
29 Sa	0537	0233	4.3E
	1134	0829	4.2F
	1814	1459	4.9E
		2103	4.2F
30 Su	0009	0325	4.4E
	0631	0921	4.2F
	1227	1551	4.8E
	1905	2153	4.2F
31 M	0100	0417	4.4E
	0726	1014	4.0F
	1319	1642	4.6E
	1955	2245	4.0F

FEBRUARY

Day	Slack Water Time (h.m.)	Maximum Current Time (h.m.)	Vel. (knots)
1 Tu	0152	0511	4.3E
	0822	1108	3.7F
	1412	1735	4.2E
	2047	2336	3.7F
2 W	0244	0605	4.0E
	0921	1205	3.3F
	1507	1828	3.8E
	2141		
3 Th	0338	0031	3.4F
	1022	0702	3.8E
	1603	1303	2.9F
	2238	1926	3.4E
4 F	0434	0129	3.0F
	1125	0759	3.5E
	1704	1407	2.5F
	2337	2025	3.0E
5 Sa	0532	0230	2.7F
	1229	0859	3.3E
	1806	1517	2.3F
		2122	2.7E
6 Su	0038	0335	2.5F
	0631	0958	3.2E
	1330	1625	2.2F
	1909	2223	2.6E
7 M	0137	0437	2.4F
	0727	1053	3.2E
	1426	1726	2.3F
	2009	2317	2.6E
8 Tu	0232	0535	2.4F
	0820	1148	3.2E
	1517	1815	2.4F
	2101		
9 W	0322	0008	2.7E
	0907	0623	2.5F
	1602	1233	3.3E
	2146	1900	2.5F
10 Th	0407	0055	2.8E
	0950	0700	2.5F
	1643	1317	3.4E
	2226	1937	2.6F
11 F	0448	0137	2.9E
	1029	0737	2.6F
	1720	1358	3.5E
	2303	2008	2.7F
12 Sa	0526	0217	3.0E
	1107	0808	2.7F
	1755	1435	3.5E
	2338	2035	2.8F
13 Su	0602	0256	3.0E
	1143	0842	2.7F
	1827	1513	3.4E
		2105	2.8F
14 M	0011	0331	3.1E
	0637	0919	2.8F
	1219	1549	3.3E
	1858	2141	2.9F
15 Tu	0046	0407	3.1E
	0712	0956	2.8F
	1256	1622	3.2E
	1929	2216	2.9F
16 W	0121	0443	3.1E
	0749	1037	2.7F
	1334	1651	3.1E
	2003	2257	2.8F
17 Th	0158	0516	3.1E
	0831	1120	2.6F
	1416	1723	2.9E
	2041	2340	2.8F
18 F	0240	0557	3.1E
	0918	1208	2.5F
	1502	1808	2.8E
	2125		
19 Sa	0328	0029	2.7F
	1013	0648	3.0E
	1556	1301	2.4F
	2218	1903	2.6E
20 Su	0423	0122	2.7F
	1115	0751	3.0E
	1657	1358	2.3F
	2318	2015	2.6E
21 M	0525	0221	2.7F
	1221	0901	3.2E
	1804	1501	2.4F
		2126	2.7E
22 Tu	0026	0323	2.8F
	0630	1007	3.4E
	1327	1605	2.6F
	1910	2235	3.0E
23 W	0133	0426	3.1F
	0734	1108	3.8E
	1428	1709	3.0F
	2014	2334	3.4E
24 Th	0238	0529	3.4F
	0836	1207	4.2E
	1524	1809	3.4F
	2113		
25 F	0337	0032	3.8E
	0934	0629	3.8F
	1617	1259	4.5E
	2207	1905	3.8F
26 Sa	0432	0126	4.2E
	1028	0725	4.0F
	1707	1352	4.7E
	2259	1955	4.1F
27 Su	0526	0217	4.5E
	1120	0817	4.2F
	1755	1441	4.8E
	2349	2045	4.2F
28 M	0617	0307	4.6E
	1211	0906	4.2F
	1843	1530	4.7E
		2133	4.2F

Time meridian 75° W.   0000 is midnight.   1200 is noon.

F-Flood, Dir. 295° True   E-Ebb, Dir. 100° True

MARCH

Day	Slack Water Time h.m.	Maximum Current Time h.m.	Vel. knots
1 Tu	0037	0357	4.6E
	0708	0957	4.0F
	1300	1619	4.4E
	1930	2219	4.0F
2 W	0125	0446	4.4E
	0800	1045	3.6F
	1349	1709	4.0E
	2019	2308	3.6F
3 Th	0214	0536	4.0E
	0854	1136	3.2F
	1439	1802	3.6E
	2109	2356	3.2F
4 F	0304	0631	3.7E
	0951	1229	2.8F
	1532	1854	3.1E
	2203		
5 Sa		0047	2.8F
	0356	0727	3.3E
	1051	1326	2.3F
	1629	1950	2.7E
	2302		
6 Su		0146	2.4F
	0451	0823	3.0E
	1153	1435	2.1F
	1730	2051	2.4E
7 M	0004	0250	2.1F
	0550	0921	2.8E
	1255	1548	2.0F
	1833	2151	2.3E
8 Tu	0106	0358	2.0F
	0649	1020	2.8E
	1353	1649	2.0F
	1934	2248	2.4E
9 W	0204	0503	2.1F
	0745	1114	2.9E
	1444	1741	2.2F
	2027	2339	2.5E
10 Th	0255	0554	2.3F
	0836	1203	3.1E
	1530	1826	2.4F
	2113		
11 F		0026	2.8E
	0341	0633	2.4F
	0921	1248	3.3E
	1610	1901	2.6F
	2153		
12 Sa		0109	3.0E
	0422	0710	2.6F
	1002	1327	3.4E
	1647	1934	2.7F
	2230		
13 Su		0149	3.2E
	0500	0742	2.8F
	1041	1406	3.5E
	1721	2003	2.9F
	2305		
14 M		0226	3.3E
	0535	0815	2.9F
	1118	1443	3.5E
	1753	2035	3.0F
	2339		
15 Tu		0303	3.4E
	0610	0854	3.0F
	1155	1518	3.4E
	1824	2112	3.1F

Day	Slack Water Time h.m.	Maximum Current Time h.m.	Vel. knots
16 W	0013	0338	3.5E
	0645	0932	3.0F
	1232	1554	3.3E
	1856	2147	3.1F
17 Th	0049	0412	3.5E
	0723	1013	3.0F
	1311	1627	3.2E
	1931	2228	3.1F
18 F	0128	0445	3.5E
	0805	1056	2.9F
	1353	1703	3.0E
	2011	2311	3.0F
19 Sa	0211	0530	3.4E
	0853	1143	2.7F
	1441	1746	2.9E
	2059		
20 Su		0003	2.9F
	0301	0621	3.3E
	0948	1238	2.6F
	1536	1847	2.7E
	2155		
21 M		0058	2.8F
	0359	0729	3.2E
	1052	1335	2.5F
	1639	1958	2.7E
	2301		
22 Tu		0159	2.7F
	0504	0842	3.2E
	1201	1441	2.5F
	1747	2113	2.8E
23 W	0014	0304	2.8F
	0613	0948	3.4E
	1308	1549	2.7F
	1854	2218	3.1E
24 Th	0125	0412	3.0F
	0720	1052	3.7E
	1410	1654	3.1F
	1958	2319	3.5E
25 F	0229	0519	3.3F
	0823	1151	4.1E
	1506	1755	3.5F
	2056		
26 Sa		0017	4.0E
	0327	0617	3.7F
	0921	1243	4.4E
	1558	1849	3.8F
	2150		
27 Su		0109	4.4E
	0421	0712	3.9F
	1014	1333	4.5E
	1647	1938	4.0F
	2239		
28 M		0159	4.6E
	0512	0804	4.0F
	1104	1422	4.5E
	1733	2024	4.1F
	2327		
29 Tu		0248	4.7E
	0601	0849	4.0F
	1152	1510	4.4E
	1819	2110	4.0F
30 W	0012	0334	4.5E
	0650	0935	3.8F
	1239	1557	4.1E
	1904	2153	3.7F
31 Th	0057	0420	4.3E
	0738	1021	3.4F
	1325	1642	3.7E
	1950	2236	3.4F

APRIL

Day	Slack Water Time h.m.	Maximum Current Time h.m.	Vel. knots
1 F	0142	0508	3.9E
	0827	1107	3.0F
	1412	1731	3.2E
	2038	2323	2.9F
2 Sa	0228	0559	3.5E
	0919	1156	2.6F
	1501	1822	2.8E
	2129		
3 Su		0012	2.5F
	0317	0650	3.1E
	1015	1247	2.2F
	1554	1916	2.4E
	2226		
4 M		0104	2.2F
	0409	0746	2.8E
	1114	1348	2.0F
	1652	2017	2.2E
	2329		
5 Tu		0203	1.9F
	0506	0844	2.6E
	1214	1455	1.9F
	1753	2116	2.2E
6 W	0032	0310	1.8F
	0606	0942	2.6E
	1311	1601	1.9F
	1852	2213	2.3E
7 Th	0131	0418	1.9F
	0705	1037	2.7E
	1403	1656	2.1F
	1946	2305	2.5E
8 F	0223	0509	2.1F
	0758	1126	2.9E
	1449	1739	2.3F
	2032	2351	2.8E
9 Sa	0309	0554	2.4F
	0846	1211	3.1E
	1530	1816	2.6F
	2113		
10 Su		0033	3.1E
	0350	0633	2.6F
	0930	1254	3.2E
	1608	1850	2.8F
	2151		
11 M		0115	3.4E
	0429	0711	2.8F
	1011	1334	3.4E
	1642	1925	3.0F
	2228		
12 Tu		0153	3.6E
	0506	0747	3.0F
	1050	1411	3.4E
	1716	2002	3.2F
	2304		
13 W		0231	3.7E
	0542	0824	3.2F
	1129	1447	3.4E
	1749	2039	3.3F
	2341		
14 Th		0307	3.8E
	0620	0905	3.2F
	1209	1522	3.4E
	1825	2120	3.3F
15 F	0020	0345	3.9E
	0700	0948	3.2F
	1251	1603	3.3E
	1904	2204	3.3F

Day	Slack Water Time h.m.	Maximum Current Time h.m.	Vel. knots
16 Sa	0103	0424	3.8E
	0745	1035	3.1F
	1336	1646	3.2E
	1950	2251	3.2F
17 Su	0150	0514	3.7E
	0835	1124	3.0F
	1427	1737	3.0E
	2043	2344	3.0F
18 M	0243	0611	3.5E
	0932	1220	2.8F
	1524	1841	2.9E
	2144		
19 Tu		0041	2.9F
	0344	0716	3.4E
	1036	1321	2.7F
	1628	1950	2.9E
	2254		
20 W		0145	2.8F
	0450	0826	3.4E
	1143	1426	2.8F
	1734	2059	3.1E
21 Th	0008	0252	2.8F
	0559	0932	3.5E
	1249	1533	2.9F
	1840	2204	3.4E
22 F	0117	0404	3.0F
	0706	1033	3.7E
	1350	1640	3.2F
	1942	2303	3.8E
23 Sa	0219	0510	3.3F
	0809	1132	3.9E
	1446	1739	3.5F
	2038	2358	4.1E
24 Su	0316	0609	3.5F
	0906	1224	4.1E
	1537	1830	3.7F
	2130		
25 M		0051	4.4E
	0408	0702	3.7F
	0958	1315	4.2E
	1625	1920	3.8F
	2218		
26 Tu		0138	4.5E
	0457	0747	3.7F
	1047	1402	4.1E
	1711	2003	3.8F
	2303		
27 W		0224	4.5E
	0545	0834	3.6F
	1133	1447	3.9E
	1755	2046	3.6F
	2347		
28 Th		0310	4.3E
	0631	0916	3.4F
	1218	1530	3.6E
	1839	2124	3.4F
29 F	0029	0356	4.0E
	0716	0957	3.1F
	1301	1616	3.3E
	1922	2205	3.0F
30 Sa	0111	0439	3.7E
	0801	1039	2.8F
	1346	1705	2.9E
	2008	2248	2.7F

Time meridian 75° W.   0000 is midnight.   1200 is noon.

THE RACE, LONG ISLAND SOUND, 1983

F-Flood, Dir. 295° True   E-Ebb, Dir. 100° True

MAY

Day	Slack Water Time h.m.	Maximum Current Time h.m.	Vel. knots
1 Su	0154	0528	3.3E
	0849	1124	2.5F
	1432	1753	2.6E
	2057	2337	2.3F
2 M	0239	0616	3.0E
	0939	1215	2.2F
	1521	1844	2.3E
	2151		
3 Tu	0329	0025	2.0F
	1032	0707	2.7E
	1615	1306	2.0F
	2251	1939	2.2E
4 W	0423	0122	1.8F
	1128	0804	2.5E
	1711	1402	1.9F
	2352	2037	2.2E
5 Th	0521	0221	1.8F
	1223	0901	2.5E
	1806	1501	2.0F
		2133	2.3E
6 F	0051	0322	1.8F
	0619	0956	2.6E
	1314	1555	2.1F
	1858	2224	2.6E
7 Sa	0143	0418	2.0F
	0715	1045	2.7E
	1400	1644	2.3F
	1945	2313	2.9E
8 Su	0231	0508	2.3F
	0805	1132	2.9E
	1443	1725	2.6F
	2029	2358	3.2E
9 M	0314	0551	2.6F
	0852	1217	3.1E
	1522	1807	2.9F
	2110		
10 Tu	0355	0039	3.5E
	0937	0633	2.8F
	1600	1259	3.2E
	2151	1846	3.1F
11 W	0435	0121	3.8E
	1019	0715	3.1F
	1637	1337	3.3E
	2231	1928	3.3F
12 Th	0514	0200	4.0E
	1102	0759	3.3F
	1716	1418	3.4E
	2312	2011	3.5F
13 F	0556	0241	4.1E
	1146	0842	3.4F
	1758	1459	3.4E
	2356	2054	3.5F
14 Sa	0641	0322	4.2E
	1232	0928	3.4F
	1844	1544	3.4E
		2141	3.5F
15 Su	0043	0410	4.1E
	0729	1017	3.4F
	1322	1636	3.4E
	1935	2232	3.4F
16 M	0135	0504	4.0E
	0821	1110	3.3F
	1416	1733	3.3E
	2033	2327	3.2F
17 Tu	0231	0602	3.8E
	0919	1205	3.2F
	1514	1834	3.2E
	2138		
18 W	0332	0029	3.1F
	1021	0706	3.7E
	1616	1306	3.1F
	2248	1939	3.3E
19 Th	0437	0132	2.9F
	1125	0810	3.6E
	1720	1411	3.1F
	2358	2044	3.4E
20 F	0545	0241	2.9F
	1228	0913	3.6E
	1823	1517	3.1F
		2145	3.6E
21 Sa	0104	0352	3.0F
	0650	1013	3.7E
	1328	1621	3.3F
	1923	2244	3.9E
22 Su	0205	0457	3.2F
	0752	1110	3.7E
	1423	1719	3.4F
	2018	2339	4.1E
23 M	0302	0554	3.3F
	0849	1203	3.8E
	1515	1814	3.5F
	2109		
24 Tu	0354	0031	4.3E
	0941	0648	3.4F
	1603	1252	3.7E
	2156	1901	3.5F
25 W	0442	0118	4.3E
	1029	0737	3.3F
	1649	1341	3.6E
	2240	1944	3.4F
26 Th	0528	0205	4.2E
	1114	0818	3.2F
	1733	1426	3.4E
	2322	2022	3.2F
27 F	0612	0249	4.0E
	1157	0858	3.0F
	1816	1509	3.2E
		2100	3.0F
28 Sa	0003	0332	3.8E
	0655	0936	2.8F
	1239	1553	3.0E
	1858	2141	2.8F
29 Su	0042	0416	3.5E
	0737	1014	2.6F
	1321	1639	2.7E
	1941	2220	2.5F
30 M	0123	0459	3.2E
	0820	1055	2.4F
	1404	1723	2.5E
	2027	2305	2.3F
31 Tu	0206	0543	2.9E
	0904	1136	2.3F
	1449	1812	2.3E
	2117	2352	2.0F

JUNE

Day	Slack Water Time h.m.	Maximum Current Time h.m.	Vel. knots
1 W	0252	0633	2.7E
	0950	1226	2.2F
	1537	1904	2.3E
	2211		
2 Th		0043	1.9F
	0342	0722	2.6E
	1039	1317	2.1F
	1627	1957	2.3E
	2308		
3 F	0138	0815	2.5E
	0436	1408	2.1F
	1129	2048	2.4E
	1718		
4 Sa	0004	0232	1.9F
	0532	0908	2.5E
	1219	1459	2.2F
	1809	2141	2.6E
5 Su	0058	0327	2.0F
	0628	0959	2.6E
	1306	1550	2.4F
	1857	2230	2.9E
6 M	0148	0421	2.2F
	0721	1050	2.7E
	1352	1639	2.6F
	1944	2316	3.2E
7 Tu	0235	0509	2.5F
	0813	1134	2.9E
	1435	1725	2.9F
	2030		
8 W		0002	3.6E
	0320	0558	2.8F
	0902	1222	3.1E
	1519	1811	3.2F
	2115		
9 Th		0048	3.9E
	0404	0646	3.1F
	0949	1308	3.3E
	1603	1857	3.4F
	2201		
10 F		0131	4.1E
	0449	0731	3.3F
	1037	1354	3.5E
	1649	1944	3.6F
	2248		
11 Sa		0217	4.3E
	0535	0820	3.5F
	1125	1440	3.6E
	1737	2034	3.7F
	2337		
12 Su		0308	4.4E
	0623	0909	3.6F
	1216	1530	3.7E
	1829	2125	3.7F
13 M	0028	0356	4.4E
	0713	1000	3.7F
	1308	1622	3.7E
	1924	2218	3.7F
14 Tu	0122	0451	4.3E
	0807	1055	3.6F
	1402	1720	3.7E
	2024	2315	3.5F
15 W	0219	0549	4.1E
	0903	1149	3.5F
	1500	1821	3.7E
	2128		
16 Th		0012	3.3F
	0319	0647	3.9E
	1002	1250	3.4F
	1600	1922	3.7E
	2235		
17 F		0118	3.1F
	0422	0748	3.7E
	1103	1353	3.3F
	1701	2025	3.7E
	2342		
18 Sa		0227	3.0F
	0526	0849	3.6E
	1204	1458	3.3F
	1802	2124	3.8E
19 Su	0047	0335	3.0F
	0631	0950	3.5E
	1303	1601	3.3F
	1901	2224	3.9E
20 M	0148	0441	3.0F
	0733	1047	3.4E
	1400	1700	3.3F
	1956	2319	4.0E
21 Tu	0245	0540	3.0F
	0830	1141	3.4E
	1453	1753	3.2F
	2048		
22 W		0010	4.0E
	0337	0631	3.0F
	0923	1230	3.3E
	1543	1842	3.2F
	2135		
23 Th		0059	4.0E
	0426	0720	3.0F
	1012	1321	3.2E
	1630	1925	3.0F
	2219		
24 F		0144	3.9E
	0511	0803	2.9F
	1056	1406	3.1E
	1714	2003	2.9F
	2300		
25 Sa		0228	3.8E
	0554	0842	2.8F
	1138	1449	2.9E
	1756	2039	2.7F
	2339		
26 Su		0309	3.6E
	0634	0917	2.7F
	1217	1531	2.8E
	1837	2116	2.6F
27 M	0017	0350	3.4E
	0712	0951	2.6F
	1256	1613	2.7E
	1917	2153	2.4F
28 Tu	0056	0430	3.2E
	0750	1029	2.5F
	1336	1655	2.6E
	1959	2236	2.3F
29 W	0136	0511	3.0E
	0829	1107	2.4F
	1416	1737	2.5E
	2042	2321	2.2F
30 Th	0219	0554	2.8E
	0908	1149	2.4F
	1459	1825	2.4E
	2130		

Time meridian 75° W.   0000 is midnight.   1200 is noon.

F-Flood, Dir. 295° True   E-Ebb, Dir. 100° True

JULY

Day	Slack Water Time h.m.	Maximum Current Time h.m.	Vel. knots	Day	Slack Water Time h.m.	Maximum Current Time h.m.	Vel. knots
1 F		0008	2.1F	16 Sa		0057	3.2F
	0304	0639	2.6E		0401	0726	3.8E
	0950	1234	2.3F		1037	1327	3.4F
	1543	1913	2.4E		1636	1959	3.8E
	2221				2320		
2 Sa		0056	2.0F	17 Su		0205	3.0F
	0353	0727	2.5E		0504	0824	3.5E
	1035	1323	2.3F		1138	1431	3.2F
	1631	2002	2.5E		1736	2100	3.7E
	2315						
3 Su		0149	2.0F	18 M	0025	0315	2.8F
	0446	0816	2.4E		0607	0923	3.3E
	1122	1412	2.4F		1238	1536	3.0F
	1720	2055	2.7E		1835	2159	3.7E
4 M	0010	0242	2.1F	19 Tu	0127	0418	2.7F
	0542	0913	2.5E		0710	1025	3.1E
	1212	1504	2.5F		1336	1638	2.9F
	1811	2146	2.9E		1932	2256	3.7E
5 Tu	0104	0337	2.2F	20 W	0226	0521	2.7F
	0639	1004	2.6E		0810	1118	3.0E
	1302	1555	2.7F		1432	1735	2.9F
	1902	2237	3.2E		2025	2350	3.7E
6 W	0157	0433	2.5F	21 Th	0319	0617	2.7F
	0735	1057	2.8E		0905	1211	3.0E
	1353	1648	2.9F		1524	1824	2.8F
	1954	2328	3.6E		2114		
7 Th	0248	0526	2.8F	22 F		0037	3.7E
	0829	1151	3.0E		0407	0704	2.7F
	1445	1739	3.2F		0953	1300	2.9E
	2046				1611	1909	2.8F
					2158		
8 F		0019	3.9E	23 Sa		0124	3.6E
	0338	0617	3.1F		0451	0747	2.7F
	0922	1239	3.3E		1036	1346	2.9E
	1536	1832	3.5F		1655	1947	2.7F
	2137				2239		
9 Sa		0109	4.2E	24 Su		0207	3.6E
	0427	0709	3.4F		0532	0824	2.7F
	1015	1330	3.6E		1116	1427	2.9E
	1628	1924	3.8F		1736	2021	2.6F
	2229				2317		
10 Su		0158	4.5E	25 M		0247	3.5E
	0516	0801	3.7F		0609	0851	2.7F
	1106	1424	3.8E		1153	1508	2.9E
	1722	2015	3.9F		1815	2056	2.6F
	2321				2354		
11 M		0249	4.6E	26 Tu		0325	3.4E
	0605	0851	3.9F		0645	0925	2.6F
	1158	1515	4.0E		1228	1547	2.8E
	1816	2108	4.0F		1852	2132	2.5F
12 Tu	0014	0341	4.7E	27 W	0031	0403	3.2E
	0656	0944	4.0F		0719	0958	2.6F
	1251	1607	4.1E		1304	1626	2.8E
	1912	2203	3.9F		1930	2208	2.5F
.13 W	0108	0435	4.6E	28 Th	0109	0440	3.1E
	0748	1035	3.9F		0753	1035	2.6F
	1345	1704	4.1E		1341	1704	2.7E
	2011	2259	3.8F		2009	2249	2.4F
14 Th	0204	0530	4.4E	29 F	0148	0517	2.9E
	0843	1130	3.8F		0827	1114	2.5F
	1440	1802	4.0E		1419	1743	2.7E
	2112	2357	3.5F		2050	2334	2.3F
15 F	0301	0625	4.1E	30 Sa	0229	0553	2.7E
	0939	1228	3.6F		0904	1157	2.5F
	1537	1900	3.9E		1500	1826	2.7E
	2215				2137		
				31 Su		0021	2.2F
					0315	0634	2.6E
					0945	1243	2.5F
					1545	1909	2.7E
					2228		

AUGUST

Day	Slack Water Time h.m.	Maximum Current Time h.m.	Vel. knots	Day	Slack Water Time h.m.	Maximum Current Time h.m.	Vel. knots
1 M		0110	2.1F	16 Tu	0000	0248	2.5F
	0405	0725	2.4E		0540	0857	2.9E
	1032	1332	2.5F		1212	1506	2.7F
	1634	2003	2.8E		1806	2133	3.4E
	2325						
2 Tu		0203	2.1F	17 W	0103	0359	2.4F
	0501	0818	2.4E		0645	0958	2.8E
	1125	1425	2.5F		1313	1615	2.6F
	1729	2104	2.9E		1905	2231	3.3E
3 W	0024	0303	2.2F	18 Th	0202	0503	2.4F
	0602	0924	2.5E		0747	1057	2.7E
	1222	1520	2.7F		1411	1712	2.5F
	1826	2203	3.2E		2001	2325	3.3E
4 Th	0123	0402	2.4F	19 F	0256	0554	2.5F
	0703	1025	2.7E		0842	1151	2.8E
	1321	1617	2.9F		1504	1807	2.6F
	1925	2300	3.5E		2051		
5 F	0220	0457	2.7F	20 Sa		0016	3.4E
	0803	1122	3.0E		0343	0643	2.6F
	1421	1716	3.2F		0930	1236	2.9E
	2022	2355	3.9E		1551	1849	2.6F
					2136		
6 Sa	0314	0554	3.1F	21 Su		0059	3.4E
	0900	1220	3.4E		0426	0724	2.6F
	1518	1812	3.6F		1011	1321	3.0E
	2118				1634	1926	2.6F
					2216		
7 Su		0049	4.3E	22 M		0141	3.5E
	0406	0650	3.5F		0505	0757	2.7F
	0955	1312	3.8E		1048	1402	3.0E
	1614	1907	3.9F		1713	1959	2.7F
	2213				2254		
8 M		0140	4.6E	23 Tu		0220	3.5E
	0456	0741	3.9F		0540	0824	2.7F
	1048	1405	4.2E		1123	1441	3.1E
	1708	2000	4.1F		1750	2031	2.7F
	2306				2330		
9 Tu		0232	4.8E	24 W		0257	3.4E
	0546	0834	4.1F		0613	0853	2.8F
	1139	1458	4.4E		1157	1518	3.1E
	1802	2054	4.2F		1825	2104	2.7F
	2359						
10 W		0324	4.8E	25 Th	0006	0334	3.3E
	0636	0925	4.2F		0645	0925	2.8F
	1231	1550	4.5E		1231	1554	3.1E
	1857	2147	4.1F		1900	2141	2.7F
11 Th	0052	0413	4.7E	26 F	0042	0408	3.1E
	0726	1016	4.1F		0715	1001	2.8F
	1323	1642	4.5E		1305	1629	3.0E
	1953	2239	3.9F		1936	2220	2.6F
12 F	0145	0507	4.4E	27 Sa	0119	0441	3.0E
	0818	1107	3.9F		0748	1042	2.7F
	1415	1736	4.3E		1341	1702	3.0E
	2051	2336	3.6F		2015	2301	2.5F
13 Sa	0240	0602	4.0E	28 Su	0159	0514	2.8E
	0912	1202	3.6F		0823	1123	2.7F
	1510	1834	4.0E		1420	1736	2.9E
	2151				2059	2346	2.4F
14 Su		0035	3.2F	29 M	0242	0549	2.6E
	0337	0657	3.6E		0905	1206	2.6F
	1009	1258	3.3F		1505	1823	2.9E
	1606	1930	3.7E		2150		
	2255						
15 M		0139	2.8F	30 Tu		0038	2.3F
	0437	0758	3.2E		0332	0636	2.5E
	1110	1402	2.9F		0953	1257	2.5F
	1705	2031	3.5E		1556	1924	2.9E
					2248		
				31 W		0133	2.2F
					0430	0742	2.4E
					1050	1352	2.5F
					1655	2027	3.0E
					2352		

Time meridian 75° W.   0000 is midnight. 1200 is noon.

THE RACE, LONG ISLAND SOUND, 1983

F-Flood, Dir. 295° True   E-Ebb, Dir. 100° True

SEPTEMBER

Day	Slack Water Time h.m.	Max Current Time h.m.	Vel. knots	Day	Slack Water Time h.m.	Max Current Time h.m.	Vel. knots
1 Th	0533	0232	2.3F	16 F	0132	0432	2.2F
		0855	2.5E		0718	1031	2.5E
	1155	1454	2.6F		1347	1650	2.2F
	1758	2137	3.2E		1930	2256	3.0E
2 F	0056	0335	2.5F	17 Sa	0225	0525	2.3F
	0639	1002	2.7E		0812	1122	2.7E
	1302	1655	2.9F		1440	1739	2.4F
	1903	2237	3.5E		2022	2345	3.2E
3 Sa	0157	0437	2.8F	18 Su	0312	0611	2.5F
	0742	1106	3.2E		0858	1211	2.9E
	1406	1700	3.2F		1526	1824	2.5F
	2005	2336	3.9E		2108		
4 Su	0253	0538	3.2F	19 M		0031	3.3E
	0841	1201	3.6E		0353	0650	2.6F
	1506	1758	3.6F		0939	1252	3.1E
	2103				1608	1859	2.6F
					2149		
5 M	0346	0030	4.3E	20 Tu		0112	3.4E
	0936	0633	3.7F		0431	0721	2.8F
	1602	1256	4.1E		1015	1333	3.2E
	2158	1852	4.0F		1647	1931	2.8F
					2227		
6 Tu	0436	0123	4.6E	21 W	0506	0149	3.4E
	1028	0725	4.0F		1049	0750	2.9F
	1655	1347	4.5E		1723	1409	3.3E
	2251	1946	4.2F		2304	2003	2.8F
7 W	0525	0212	4.8E	22 Th	0538	0228	3.4E
	1119	0814	4.2F		1123	0818	2.9F
	1748	1439	4.7E		1757	1447	3.4E
	2342	2037	4.3F		2340	2037	2.9F
8 Th	0613	0302	4.8E	23 F	0609	0303	3.3E
	1208	0903	4.3F		1156	0853	3.0F
	1840	1528	4.7E		1831	1521	3.4E
		2128	4.2F			2112	2.9F
9 F	0033	0353	4.6E	24 Sa	0016	0337	3.2E
	0702	0951	4.2F		0639	0930	3.0F
	1258	1619	4.6E		1230	1553	3.4E
	1933	2219	3.9F		1906	2153	2.8F
10 Sa	0124	0443	4.2E	25 Su	0053	0406	3.0E
	0752	1042	3.9F		0712	1007	2.9F
	1348	1712	4.3E		1307	1630	3.3E
	2027	2311	3.5F		1946	2235	2.7F
11 Su	0216	0536	3.8E	26 M	0133	0439	2.9E
	0844	1133	3.5F		0749	1050	2.8F
	1439	1805	3.9E		1347	1705	3.2E
	2125				2030	2320	2.6F
12 M	0310	0005	3.0F	27 Tu	0217	0520	2.7E
	0940	0631	3.3E		0833	1137	2.7F
	1533	1227	3.0F		1433	1754	3.1E
	2226	1901	3.6E		2122		
13 Tu	0409	0106	2.6F	28 W	0309	0011	2.5F
	1040	0729	2.9E		0926	0612	2.6E
	1631	1326	2.6F		1528	1231	2.6F
	2330	2001	3.2E		2221	1853	3.0E
14 W	0511	0217	2.3F	29 Th	0409	0106	2.4F
	1144	0828	2.6E		1029	0723	2.5E
	1731	1432	2.3F		1631	1330	2.5F
		2102	3.0E		2327	2007	3.0E
15 Th	0033	0329	2.2F	30 F		0209	2.4F
	0615	0930	2.5E		0514	0840	2.6E
	1248	1546	2.2F		1140	1433	2.6F
	1833	2201	3.0E		1738	2115	3.2E

OCTOBER

Day	Slack Water Time h.m.	Max Current Time h.m.	Vel. knots	Day	Slack Water Time h.m.	Max Current Time h.m.	Vel. knots
1 Sa	0034	0314	2.6F	16 Su	0146	0447	2.2F
	0621	0949	2.9E		0733	1049	2.6E
	1251	1540	2.9F		1410	1702	2.2F
	1846	2218	3.5E		1946	2311	2.9E
2 Su	0136	0418	2.9F	17 M	0233	0532	2.4F
	0725	1050	3.4E		0819	1139	2.9E
	1356	1644	3.2F		1456	1745	2.4F
	1950	2318	3.9E		2033	2354	3.1E
3 M	0233	0519	3.4F	18 Tu	0315	0607	2.6F
	0823	1145	3.9E		0900	1220	3.2E
	1456	1745	3.6F		1538	1824	2.6F
	2049				2117		
4 Tu		0013	4.2E	19 W		0039	3.2E
	0325	0614	3.8F		0352	0639	2.8F
	0918	1239	4.4E		0937	1259	3.4E
	1550	1840	3.9F		1616	1858	2.8F
	2144				2157		
5 W	0415	0104	4.5E	20 Th		0118	3.3E
	1009	0705	4.1F		0427	0711	2.9F
	1642	1330	4.7E		1013	1338	3.6E
	2235	1931	4.1F		1653	1931	2.9F
					2235		
6 Th	0503	0153	4.6E	21 F	0500	0155	3.3E
	1057	0753	4.2F		1048	0744	3.1F
	1733	1419	4.8E		1728	1414	3.7E
	2325	2021	4.1F		2312	2009	3.0F
7 F	0550	0242	4.5E	22 Sa	0532	0231	3.3E
	1145	0840	4.2F		1123	0820	3.1F
	1822	1508	4.8E		1804	1449	3.7E
		2110	4.0F		2350	2046	3.1F
8 Sa	0013	0331	4.3E	23 Su	0606	0305	3.2E
	0637	0925	4.0F		1159	0859	3.2F
	1232	1554	4.6E		1841	1526	3.7E
	1912	2157	3.7F			2127	3.0F
9 Su	0102	0417	3.9E	24 M	0030	0340	3.1E
	0725	1014	3.6F		0642	0942	3.1F
	1319	1645	4.2E		1239	1603	3.6E
	2004	2245	3.3F		1922	2210	3.0F
10 M	0151	0508	3.5E	25 Tu	0112	0419	3.0E
	0815	1102	3.2F		0724	1026	3.0F
	1407	1736	3.8E		1322	1642	3.5E
	2057	2336	2.9F		2009	2301	2.8F
11 Tu	0243	0602	3.0E	26 W	0200	0504	2.8E
	0910	1153	2.7F		0813	1115	2.9F
	1458	1831	3.3E		1412	1738	3.4E
	2155				2102	2352	2.7F
12 W		0034	2.4F	27 Th	0254	0605	2.7E
	0338	0658	2.6E		0911	1210	2.7F
	1009	1250	2.3F		1510	1841	3.3E
	1553	1929	3.0E		2202		
	2255						
13 Th		0135	2.1F	28 F	0354	0050	2.6F
	0437	0759	2.4E		1018	0715	2.7E
	1113	1353	2.0F		1614	1313	2.7F
	1652	2027	2.8E		2307	1950	3.2E
	2356						
14 F		0248	2.0F	29 Sa	0459	0151	2.7F
	0540	0859	2.3E		1131	0826	2.9E
	1218	1502	1.9F		1723	1417	2.7F
	1753	2127	2.7E			2057	3.3E
15 Sa	0054	0351	2.1F	30 Su	0013	0256	2.8F
	0639	0956	2.4E		0605	0930	3.2E
	1317	1609	2.0F		1242	1526	2.9F
	1852	2220	2.8E		1831	2201	3.5E
				31 M	0115	0402	3.1F
					0707	1031	3.6E
					1346	1633	3.2F
					1935	2259	3.8E

Time meridian 75° W.   0000 is midnight.   1200 is noon.

F-Flood, Dir. 295° True　　E-Ebb, Dir. 100° True

NOVEMBER

Day	Slack Water Time h.m.	Max Current Time h.m.	Vel. knots	Day	Slack Water Time h.m.	Max Current Time h.m.	Vel. knots
1 Tu	0212	0503	3.5F	16 W	0230	0513	2.5F
	0805	1129	4.1E		0816	1143	3.2E
	1444	1735	3.5F		1503	1742	2.5F
	2034	2354	4.1E		2039		
2 W	0305	0557	3.8F	17 Th		0001	3.0E
	0859	1222	4.4E		0309	0554	2.8F
	1538	1829	3.7F		0856	1226	3.4E
	2128				1543	1822	2.7F
					2122		
3 Th		0045	4.2E	18 F		0043	3.1E
	0354	0646	3.9F		0346	0630	3.0F
	0949	1311	4.7E		0935	1304	3.7E
	1629	1918	3.9F		1622	1859	2.9F
	2219				2204		
4 F		0133	4.2E	19 Sa		0124	3.2E
	0442	0735	4.0F		0422	0710	3.1F
	1036	1400	4.7E		1014	1345	3.8E
	1718	2005	3.8F		1700	1941	3.1F
	2308				2245		
5 Sa		0222	4.1E	20 Su		0203	3.2E
	0528	0818	3.9F		0459	0751	3.3F
	1122	1447	4.6E		1053	1421	3.9E
	1806	2052	3.7F		1739	2021	3.2F
	2355				2327		
6 Su		0308	3.9E	21 M		0240	3.2E
	0614	0904	3.6F		0537	0833	3.3F
	1207	1533	4.3E		1134	1504	4.0E
	1853	2137	3.4F		1820	2105	3.2F
7 M	0041	0356	3.5E	22 Tu	0010	0321	3.2E
	0701	0947	3.3F		0620	0918	3.4F
	1251	1619	4.0E		1218	1545	4.0E
	1941	2223	3.1F		1904	2152	3.2F
8 Tu	0127	0445	3.2E	23 W	0056	0408	3.2E
	0749	1033	2.9F		0707	1007	3.3F
	1336	1708	3.6E		1306	1632	3.9E
	2030	2309	2.7F		1952	2239	3.2F
9 W	0216	0533	2.8E	24 Th	0146	0458	3.1E
	0840	1120	2.5F		0801	1058	3.2F
	1424	1759	3.2E		1358	1727	3.7E
	2122	2357	2.4F		2046	2336	3.1F
10 Th	0306	0629	2.5E	25 F	0241	0559	3.1E
	0936	1210	2.1F		0901	1153	3.0F
	1514	1853	2.9E		1457	1828	3.6E
	2216				2145		
11 F		0051	2.1F	26 Sa		0031	3.0F
	0401	0723	2.3E		0341	0704	3.1E
	1037	1306	1.9F		1009	1257	2.9F
	1609	1948	2.6E		1600	1933	3.5E
	2312				2247		
12 Sa		0150	2.0F	27 Su		0134	3.0F
	0457	0822	2.3E		0443	0808	3.3E
	1139	1408	1.8F		1120	1402	2.8F
	1707	2042	2.6E		1707	2038	3.5E
					2351		
13 Su	0007	0251	2.0F	28 M		0238	3.1F
	0553	0916	2.4E		0547	0912	3.5E
	1238	1514	1.8F		1229	1512	2.9F
	1805	2139	2.6E		1814	2139	3.5E
14 M	0059	0346	2.1F	29 Tu	0052	0343	3.2F
	0645	1009	2.6E		0648	1013	3.8E
	1331	1609	2.0F		1332	1620	3.1F
	1901	2228	2.7E		1918	2239	3.7E
15 Tu	0146	0433	2.3F	30 W	0150	0443	3.4F
	0733	1100	2.9E		0746	1110	4.1E
	1419	1659	2.2F		1431	1721	3.3F
	1952	2315	2.8E		2018	2334	3.8E

DECEMBER

Day	Slack Water Time h.m.	Max Current Time h.m.	Vel. knots	Day	Slack Water Time h.m.	Max Current Time h.m.	Vel. knots
1 Th	0244	0539	3.6F	16 F	0223	0510	2.7F
	0840	1203	4.3E		0815	1147	3.4E
	1525	1816	3.4F		1509	1745	2.6F
	2113				2046		
2 F		0027	3.8E	17 Sa		0007	2.9E
	0335	0630	3.7F		0305	0555	2.9F
	0930	1255	4.5E		0859	1233	3.7E
	1616	1909	3.5F		1552	1830	2.8F
	2204				2133		
3 Sa		0116	3.8E	18 Su		0050	3.1E
	0424	0717	3.6F		0348	0640	3.2F
	1017	1340	4.4E		0943	1316	3.9E
	1704	1955	3.4F		1634	1915	3.1F
	2252				2219		
4 Su		0203	3.7E	19 M		0134	3.2E
	0510	0802	3.5F		0431	0725	3.4F
	1102	1427	4.3E		1028	1359	4.1E
	1751	2038	3.3F		1717	2001	3.3F
	2338				2304		
5 M		0249	3.5E	20 Tu		0220	3.4E
	0555	0845	3.3F		0516	0810	3.6F
	1145	1512	4.1E		1114	1443	4.3E
	1835	2121	3.1F		1801	2046	3.5F
					2351		
6 Tu	0022	0335	3.2E	21 W		0305	3.5E
	0640	0926	3.0F		0603	0859	3.6F
	1227	1555	3.8E		1202	1530	4.3E
	1919	2159	2.9F		1847	2135	3.6F
7 W	0105	0419	3.0E	22 Th	0040	0354	3.6E
	0725	1007	2.7F		0655	0949	3.6F
	1309	1642	3.5E		1253	1619	4.3E
	2003	2240	2.6F		1936	2224	3.6F
8 Th	0149	0507	2.7E	23 F	0132	0448	3.6E
	0812	1050	2.4F		0750	1044	3.5F
	1351	1727	3.1E		1346	1715	4.1E
	2047	2323	2.4F		2029	2317	3.5F
9 F	0234	0556	2.5E	24 Sa	0226	0546	3.6E
	0902	1136	2.2F		0851	1139	3.4F
	1437	1816	2.9E		1444	1812	3.9E
	2134				2125		
10 Sa		0012	2.3F	25 Su		0013	3.4F
	0321	0646	2.4E		0323	0647	3.6E
	0956	1226	2.0F		0955	1240	3.2F
	1526	1906	2.6E		1545	1913	3.7E
	2222				2225		
11 Su		0100	2.1F	26 M		0114	3.3F
	0411	0738	2.3E		0423	0748	3.6E
	1053	1319	1.8F		1103	1344	3.0F
	1619	1958	2.5E		1649	2016	3.6E
	2313				2326		
12 M		0151	2.1F	27 Tu		0217	3.3F
	0502	0831	2.4E		0525	0851	3.7E
	1150	1416	1.8F		1211	1454	2.9F
	1715	2052	2.4E		1754	2117	3.5E
13 Tu	0003	0242	2.2F	28 W	0028	0322	3.2F
	0553	0924	2.6E		0626	0952	3.8E
	1245	1512	1.9F		1315	1605	2.9F
	1811	2144	2.5E		1859	2216	3.4E
14 W	0052	0333	2.3F	29 Th	0128	0425	3.3F
	0642	1015	2.8E		0725	1050	4.0E
	1337	1605	2.1F		1416	1709	3.0F
	1906	2233	2.6E		2001	2313	3.4E
15 Th	0139	0424	2.5F	30 F	0225	0526	3.3F
	0729	1103	3.1E		0821	1145	4.1E
	1424	1657	2.3F		1512	1806	3.1F
	1958	2321	2.7E		2058		
				31 Sa		0009	3.4E
					0318	0617	3.3F
					0913	1236	4.1E
					1603	1857	3.1F
					2151		

Time meridian 75° W.　0000 is midnight.　1200 is noon.

HELL GATE (off Mill Rock), EAST RIVER, NEW YORK, 1983

F-Flood, Dir. 050° True   E-Ebb, Dir. 230° True

JANUARY

Day	Slack Water Time (h.m.)	Max Current Time (h.m.)	Vel. (knots)
1 Sa		0141	5.1E
	0509	0806	3.9F
	1112	1411	5.2E
	1747	2039	3.7F
	2341		
2 Su		0235	5.0E
	0605	0903	3.8F
	1207	1506	5.1E
	1842	2135	3.6F
3 M	0036	0330	4.9E
	0703	1001	3.6F
	1304	1601	4.9E
	1939	2233	3.5F
4 Tu	0132	0427	4.8E
	0803	1059	3.4F
	1402	1700	4.7E
	2038	2333	3.3F
5 W	0230	0528	4.6E
	0906	1204	3.3F
	1501	1801	4.5E
	2138		
6 Th		0036	3.2F
	0329	0635	4.5E
	1009	1308	3.1F
	1601	1908	4.4E
	2237		
7 F		0139	3.1F
	0428	0740	4.4E
	1110	1411	3.1F
	1659	2014	4.3E
	2334		
8 Sa		0239	3.1F
	0524	0845	4.4E
	1207	1510	3.1F
	1754	2111	4.3E
9 Su	0027	0330	3.1F
	0617	0941	4.4E
	1300	1559	3.1F
	1845	2200	4.3E
10 M	0116	0419	3.2F
	0706	1026	4.5E
	1347	1645	3.2F
	1933	2245	4.4E
11 Tu	0201	0504	3.2F
	0752	1107	4.6E
	1431	1730	3.2F
	2016	2322	4.5E
12 W	0243	0543	3.3F
	0835	1140	4.7E
	1512	1807	3.3F
	2058	2356	4.5E
13 Th	0323	0620	3.4F
	0916	1217	4.7E
	1551	1844	3.3F
	2138		
14 F		0031	4.6E
	0401	0657	3.4F
	0956	1253	4.8E
	1629	1919	3.3F
	2217		
15 Sa		0107	4.7E
	0439	0733	3.4F
	1035	1328	4.8E
	1707	1956	3.3F
	2255		
16 Su		0144	4.7E
	0516	0809	3.4F
	1114	1405	4.8E
	1744	2032	3.3F
	2333		
17 M		0223	4.7E
	0554	0848	3.4F
	1153	1446	4.8E
	1822	2109	3.2F
18 Tu	0011	0302	4.7E
	0632	0927	3.3F
	1232	1527	4.7E
	1900	2148	3.2F
19 W	0051	0345	4.6E
	0713	1008	3.2F
	1314	1609	4.6E
	1940	2231	3.1F
20 Th	0133	0430	4.6E
	0758	1055	3.1F
	1359	1654	4.5E
	2024	2319	3.0F
21 F	0219	0519	4.5E
	0848	1144	3.1F
	1450	1745	4.5E
	2113		
22 Sa		0008	3.0F
	0312	0613	4.5E
	0945	1239	3.0F
	1545	1838	4.4E
	2208		
23 Su		0105	3.0F
	0410	0708	4.5E
	1048	1339	3.0F
	1646	1937	4.4E
	2309		
24 M		0204	3.1F
	0512	0809	4.6E
	1152	1442	3.1F
	1749	2039	4.5E
25 Tu	0011	0308	3.3F
	0615	0912	4.7E
	1255	1547	3.3F
	1851	2140	4.6E
26 W	0112	0409	3.5F
	0717	1014	4.9E
	1355	1647	3.4F
	1950	2241	4.8E
27 Th	0211	0510	3.7F
	0816	1114	5.1E
	1452	1745	3.6F
	2047	2340	4.9E
28 F	0308	0608	3.8F
	0913	1212	5.2E
	1546	1840	3.8F
	2141		
29 Sa		0036	5.1E
	0402	0703	3.9F
	1008	1307	5.2E
	1639	1934	3.8F
	2234		
30 Su		0130	5.1E
	0456	0757	4.0F
	1101	1400	5.2E
	1730	2025	3.8F
	2327		
31 M		0223	5.1E
	0550	0850	3.9F
	1154	1451	5.1E
	1822	2118	3.8F

FEBRUARY

Day	Slack Water Time (h.m.)	Max Current Time (h.m.)	Vel. (knots)
1 Tu	0018	0314	5.0E
	0644	0942	3.8F
	1247	1542	5.0E
	1915	2211	3.6F
2 W	0111	0408	4.9E
	0739	1037	3.6F
	1340	1636	4.7E
	2008	2305	3.4F
3 Th	0204	0502	4.7E
	0836	1134	3.4F
	1434	1730	4.5E
	2103		
4 F		0001	3.2F
	0259	0558	4.4E
	0934	1233	3.1F
	1530	1826	4.3E
	2159		
5 Sa		0101	3.0F
	0355	0657	4.3E
	1033	1334	3.0F
	1626	1927	4.1E
	2256		
6 Su		0200	2.9F
	0451	0801	4.2E
	1131	1436	2.9F
	1722	2028	4.0E
	2352		
7 M		0259	2.9F
	0546	0902	4.1E
	1226	1531	2.9F
	1815	2125	4.0E
8 Tu	0044	0350	3.0F
	0638	0957	4.2E
	1316	1618	3.0F
	1905	2213	4.1E
9 W	0131	0435	3.1F
	0726	1038	4.3E
	1401	1701	3.1F
	1951	2254	4.3E
10 Th	0214	0517	3.2F
	0811	1117	4.5E
	1443	1742	3.2F
	2033	2330	4.4E
11 F	0255	0556	3.4F
	0853	1152	4.6E
	1523	1819	3.3F
	2114		
12 Sa		0005	4.5E
	0333	0631	3.5F
	0934	1228	4.7E
	1600	1854	3.4F
	2153		
13 Su		0043	4.7E
	0410	0709	3.5F
	1013	1305	4.8E
	1636	1927	3.5F
	2230		
14 M		0119	4.8E
	0447	0743	3.6F
	1051	1339	4.8E
	1712	2002	3.5F
	2307		
15 Tu		0156	4.8E
	0523	0821	3.6F
	1129	1418	4.8E
	1747	2039	3.5F
	2344		
16 W		0235	4.8E
	0600	0858	3.6F
	1207	1457	4.8E
	1822	2116	3.4F
17 Th	0022	0316	4.8E
	0639	0939	3.5F
	1248	1539	4.7E
	1900	2159	3.4F
18 F	0103	0358	4.8E
	0722	1024	3.4F
	1332	1625	4.6E
	1942	2244	3.3F
19 Sa	0149	0447	4.7E
	0811	1112	3.2F
	1421	1712	4.5E
	2031	2335	3.2F
20 Su	0242	0540	4.6E
	0909	1207	3.1F
	1518	1806	4.4E
	2129		
21 M		0034	3.1F
	0344	0639	4.5E
	1015	1312	3.0F
	1622	1909	4.3E
	2236		
22 Tu		0138	3.1F
	0451	0744	4.5E
	1126	1417	3.1F
	1729	2014	4.3E
	2346		
23 W		0249	3.2F
	0600	0852	4.6E
	1234	1531	3.2F
	1836	2121	4.5E
24 Th	0054	0357	3.4F
	0706	1000	4.7E
	1337	1635	3.4F
	1937	2229	4.7E
25 F	0156	0501	3.7F
	0807	1104	4.9E
	1435	1736	3.7F
	2035	2330	4.9E
26 Sa	0254	0600	3.9F
	0903	1202	5.1E
	1528	1828	3.9F
	2128		
27 Su		0026	5.1E
	0348	0653	4.0F
	0957	1256	5.1E
	1619	1919	4.0F
	2219		
28 M		0119	5.2E
	0440	0743	4.1F
	1048	1345	5.2E
	1708	2006	4.0F
	2309		

Time meridian 75° W.   0000 is midnight.   1200 is noon.

HELL GATE (off Mill Rock), EAST RIVER, NEW YORK, 1983

F-Flood, Dir. 050° True   E-Ebb, Dir. 230° True

MARCH

Day	Slack Water Time h.m.	Maximum Current Time h.m.	Vel. knots
1 Tu	0530	0207	5.2E
		0832	4.0F
	1137	1431	5.1E
	1756	2055	3.9F
	2357		
2 W		0254	5.1E
	0620	0921	3.9F
	1226	1519	4.9E
	1844	2143	3.7F
3 Th	0046	0342	4.9E
	0710	1011	3.7F
	1315	1607	4.7E
	1933	2231	3.5F
4 F	0135	0430	4.6E
	0801	1102	3.4F
	1405	1653	4.4E
	2023	2321	3.3F
5 Sa	0226	0516	4.4E
	0855	1154	3.1F
	1457	1742	4.1E
	2117		
6 Su		0016	3.0F
	0320	0610	4.1E
	0951	1252	2.9F
	1552	1835	3.9E
	2213		
7 M		0117	2.9F
	0416	0708	4.0E
	1049	1351	2.8F
	1648	1936	3.8E
	2310		
8 Tu		0216	2.8F
	0513	0811	3.9E
	1146	1452	2.8F
	1743	2039	3.8E
9 W	0005	0312	2.9F
	0608	0912	4.0E
	1238	1543	2.9F
	1835	2134	3.9E
10 Th	0056	0403	3.0F
	0658	1000	4.1E
	1326	1632	3.0F
	1923	2219	4.1E
11 F	0141	0448	3.2F
	0745	1045	4.3E
	1409	1710	3.2F
	2006	2258	4.3E
12 Sa	0223	0527	3.4F
	0828	1122	4.5E
	1449	1749	3.3F
	2047	2336	4.5E
13 Su	0302	0605	3.5F
	0909	1159	4.6E
	1527	1823	3.5F
	2125		
14 M	0339	0014	4.7E
	0948	0640	3.6F
	1602	1237	4.8E
	2203	1858	3.6F
15 Tu	0416	0050	4.8E
	1026	0716	3.7F
	1637	1312	4.8E
	2239	1933	3.6F
16 W	0453	0128	4.9E
	1104	0752	3.8F
	1712	1351	4.9E
	2317	2010	3.7F
17 Th	0530	0209	5.0E
	1143	0832	3.7F
	1748	1432	4.9E
	2356	2047	3.6F
18 F	0611	0250	4.9E
	1224	0913	3.6F
	1827	1513	4.8E
		2132	3.6F
19 Sa	0038	0335	4.9E
	0655	0958	3.5F
	1309	1559	4.6E
	1910	2217	3.4F
20 Su	0127	0424	4.7E
	0746	1049	3.3F
	1400	1646	4.5E
	2002	2309	3.3F
21 M	0222	0517	4.6E
	0845	1146	3.2F
	1500	1745	4.3E
	2104		
22 Tu		0010	3.2F
	0327	0619	4.4E
	0954	1252	3.1F
	1607	1848	4.2E
	2217		
23 W		0121	3.1F
	0438	0726	4.4E
	1108	1405	3.1F
	1716	1958	4.2E
	2332		
24 Th		0237	3.2F
	0549	0839	4.4E
	1217	1518	3.2F
	1824	2111	4.4E
25 F	0041	0349	3.5F
	0655	0952	4.6E
	1320	1623	3.5F
	1925	2219	4.6E
26 Sa	0143	0451	3.7F
	0755	1055	4.8E
	1416	1722	3.7F
	2020	2319	4.9E
27 Su	0239	0547	3.9F
	0850	1149	4.9E
	1508	1811	3.9F
	2111		
28 M	0331	0014	5.1E
	0941	0637	4.0F
	1556	1239	5.0E
	2200	1900	4.0F
29 Tu	0420	0101	5.1E
	1029	0726	4.1F
	1643	1323	5.0E
	2247	1945	4.0F
30 W	0507	0146	5.1E
	1115	0811	4.0F
	1728	1409	5.0E
	2333	2028	3.9F
31 Th	0554	0227	5.0E
	1201	0854	3.9F
	1813	1450	4.8E
		2114	3.7F

APRIL

Day	Slack Water Time h.m.	Maximum Current Time h.m.	Vel. knots
1 F	0018	0310	4.8E
	0640	0940	3.6F
	1247	1532	4.6E
	1858	2158	3.5F
2 Sa	0104	0351	4.6E
	0727	1026	3.4F
	1334	1617	4.3E
	1945	2244	3.2F
3 Su	0152	0437	4.3E
	0817	1114	3.1F
	1423	1703	4.1E
	2036	2335	3.0F
4 M	0243	0528	4.1E
	0910	1206	2.9F
	1515	1754	3.9E
	2130		
5 Tu		0031	2.8F
	0338	0620	3.9E
	1006	1306	2.7F
	1610	1848	3.7E
	2228		
6 W		0132	2.7F
	0434	0719	3.8E
	1103	1405	2.7F
	1706	1947	3.7E
	2325		
7 Th		0229	2.8F
	0530	0819	3.9E
	1158	1501	2.8F
	1759	2045	3.8E
8 F	0017	0324	2.9F
	0623	0915	4.0E
	1247	1550	3.0F
	1847	2137	4.1E
9 Sa	0105	0409	3.1F
	0711	1003	4.2E
	1331	1631	3.2F
	1932	2221	4.3E
10 Su	0148	0451	3.3F
	0755	1044	4.4E
	1412	1710	3.3F
	2013	2302	4.5E
11 M	0229	0530	3.5F
	0837	1124	4.6E
	1451	1749	3.5F
	2053	2341	4.7E
12 Tu	0308	0608	3.7F
	0918	1202	4.8E
	1528	1824	3.6F
	2131		
13 W		0021	4.9E
	0347	0647	3.8F
	0957	1241	4.9E
	1604	1902	3.7F
	2210		
14 Th	0427	0101	5.0E
	1037	0726	3.8F
	1641	1321	4.9E
	2250	1941	3.8F
15 F	0507	0142	5.1E
	1119	0807	3.8F
	1721	1404	4.9E
	2332	2023	3.7F
16 Sa	0551	0225	5.0E
	1203	0850	3.7F
	1804	1449	4.8E
		2108	3.6F
17 Su	0018	0314	4.9E
	0639	0939	3.5F
	1251	1536	4.6E
	1852	2159	3.5F
18 M	0110	0404	4.8E
	0733	1031	3.4F
	1345	1631	4.5E
	1949	2256	3.3F
19 Tu	0209	0501	4.6E
	0835	1132	3.2F
	1447	1728	4.3E
	2056		
20 W		0001	3.2F
	0315	0604	4.4E
	0945	1242	3.1F
	1555	1836	4.2E
	2210		
21 Th	0426	0113	3.2F
	1057	0715	4.3E
	1703	1356	3.1F
	2324	1949	4.2E
22 F	0536	0229	3.2F
	1203	0830	4.4E
	1808	1507	3.3F
		2104	4.4E
23 Sa	0031	0338	3.4F
	0640	0941	4.5E
	1304	1610	3.5F
	1907	2211	4.7E
24 Su	0130	0438	3.7F
	0738	1042	4.7E
	1357	1703	3.7F
	2000	2308	4.9E
25 M	0224	0531	3.8F
	0830	1132	4.8E
	1447	1753	3.8F
	2050	2353	5.0E
26 Tu	0314	0618	3.9F
	0919	1217	4.9E
	1533	1838	3.9F
	2136		
27 W		0040	5.1E
	0400	0703	3.9F
	1004	1300	4.9E
	1618	1921	3.9F
	2221		
28 Th	0445	0122	5.1E
	1049	0747	3.9F
	1701	1341	4.8E
	2304	2002	3.8F
29 F	0529	0203	5.0E
	1132	0828	3.7F
	1744	1421	4.7E
	2348	2043	3.6F
30 Sa	0613	0239	4.8E
	1215	0911	3.5F
	1827	1500	4.5E
		2126	3.4F

Time meridian 75° W.   0000 is midnight.   1200 is noon.

HELL GATE (off Mill Rock), EAST RIVER, NEW YORK, 1983

F-Flood, Dir. 050° True   E-Ebb, Dir. 230° True

MAY

Day	Slack Water Time (h.m.)	Maximum Current Time (h.m.)	Vel. (knots)
1 Su	0032	0322	4.6E
	0657	0952	3.3F
	1300	1543	4.3E
	1912	2210	3.2F
2 M	0117	0404	4.4E
	0744	1036	3.1F
	1346	1627	4.0E
	2000	2256	3.0F
3 Tu	0205	0450	4.2E
	0834	1126	2.9F
	1435	1712	4.0E
	2052	2347	2.8F
4 W	0256	0541	4.0E
	0927	1220	2.7F
	1528	1805	3.9E
	2147		
5 Th		0043	2.7F
	0351	0635	4.0E
	1022	1316	2.7F
	1621	1900	3.9E
	2243		
6 F		0140	2.8F
	0446	0730	4.0E
	1115	1411	2.8F
	1714	1955	4.0E
	2336		
7 Sa		0233	2.9F
	0539	0823	4.1E
	1205	1502	2.9F
	1803	2049	4.1E
8 Su	0026	0325	3.0F
	0629	0915	4.2E
	1251	1547	3.1F
	1849	2138	4.4E
9 M	0112	0410	3.2F
	0715	1000	4.4E
	1333	1629	3.3F
	1933	2223	4.6E
10 Tu	0156	0454	3.4F
	0800	1045	4.6E
	1414	1710	3.5F
	2016	2306	4.8E
11 W	0238	0533	3.6F
	0843	1130	4.8E
	1454	1753	3.6F
	2058	2351	5.0E
12 Th	0321	0616	3.7F
	0926	1213	4.9E
	1535	1834	3.7F
	2141		
13 F		0036	5.1E
	0405	0659	3.8F
	1010	1256	4.9E
	1617	1917	3.8F
	2225		
14 Sa		0120	5.1E
	0450	0746	3.7F
	1056	1343	4.9E
	1702	2004	3.8F
	2312		
15 Su		0209	5.1E
	0539	0834	3.7F
	1144	1430	4.8E
	1751	2053	3.7F
16 M	0003	0258	5.0E
	0631	0927	3.5F
	1236	1522	4.7E
	1845	2148	3.5F
17 Tu	0058	0351	4.8E
	0728	1024	3.4F
	1333	1617	4.5E
	1946	2246	3.4F
18 W	0158	0450	4.6E
	0831	1125	3.2F
	1435	1718	4.4E
	2054	2354	3.2F
19 Th	0304	0554	4.5E
	0938	1233	3.1F
	1540	1829	4.3E
	2205		
20 F		0107	3.2F
	0412	0707	4.4E
	1045	1345	3.2F
	1645	1941	4.4E
	2314		
21 Sa		0217	3.3F
	0518	0817	4.4E
	1148	1452	3.3F
	1747	2053	4.5E
22 Su	0018	0324	3.4F
	0619	0925	4.5E
	1245	1550	3.5F
	1844	2154	4.7E
23 M	0115	0419	3.5F
	0715	1022	4.6E
	1337	1641	3.6F
	1936	2248	4.8E
24 Tu	0207	0510	3.6F
	0806	1111	4.7E
	1425	1730	3.7F
	2025	2335	4.9E
25 W	0255	0558	3.7F
	0853	1156	4.8E
	1510	1815	3.7F
	2110		
26 Th		0018	5.0E
	0340	0641	3.7F
	0937	1233	4.8E
	1554	1857	3.7F
	2154		
27 F		0057	4.9E
	0423	0722	3.6F
	1020	1314	4.7E
	1636	1936	3.6F
	2236		
28 Sa		0134	4.9E
	0505	0801	3.5F
	1102	1350	4.6E
	1717	2015	3.5F
	2318		
29 Su		0213	4.8E
	0548	0842	3.4F
	1144	1428	4.5E
	1759	2057	3.4F
30 M	0000	0251	4.6E
	0630	0922	3.2F
	1226	1509	4.4E
	1842	2136	3.2F
31 Tu	0043	0332	4.5E
	0714	1004	3.1F
	1310	1552	4.3E
	1927	2221	3.1F

JUNE

Day	Slack Water Time (h.m.)	Maximum Current Time (h.m.)	Vel. (knots)
1 W	0128	0416	4.4E
	0800	1049	2.9F
	1356	1637	4.2E
	2015	2306	2.9F
2 Th	0216	0503	4.2E
	0848	1138	2.8F
	1444	1726	4.1E
	2106	2357	2.8F
3 F	0306	0554	4.2E
	0938	1227	2.8F
	1534	1817	4.1E
	2158		
4 Sa		0051	2.8F
	0358	0645	4.1E
	1029	1317	2.8F
	1625	1909	4.1E
	2251		
5 Su		0144	2.9F
	0451	0738	4.2E
	1118	1410	2.9F
	1715	2002	4.3E
	2343		
6 M		0235	3.0F
	0543	0830	4.3E
	1206	1459	3.1F
	1804	2053	4.5E
7 Tu	0033	0327	3.2F
	0633	0921	4.5E
	1252	1547	3.2F
	1852	2146	4.7E
8 W	0122	0415	3.3F
	0722	1010	4.6E
	1338	1635	3.4F
	1940	2234	4.9E
9 Th	0210	0504	3.5F
	0810	1058	4.8E
	1423	1722	3.6F
	2028	2323	5.0E
10 F	0258	0552	3.6F
	0858	1146	4.9E
	1510	1809	3.7F
	2116		
11 Sa		0012	5.1E
	0346	0641	3.7F
	0946	1235	4.9E
	1558	1858	3.8F
	2206		
12 Su		0103	5.2E
	0436	0730	3.7F
	1036	1325	4.9E
	1649	1950	3.8F
	2257		
13 M		0154	5.1E
	0528	0821	3.7F
	1128	1418	4.9E
	1742	2041	3.7F
	2351		
14 Tu		0247	5.1E
	0623	0916	3.6F
	1223	1511	4.8E
	1840	2140	3.6F
15 W	0048	0343	4.9E
	0721	1014	3.4F
	1320	1608	4.7E
	1941	2240	3.5F
16 Th	0148	0440	4.7E
	0821	1115	3.3F
	1420	1710	4.6E
	2047	2345	3.3F
17 F	0251	0544	4.6E
	0924	1221	3.3F
	1522	1816	4.5E
	2153		
18 Sa		0055	3.3F
	0354	0652	4.5E
	1026	1327	3.2F
	1624	1927	4.5E
	2258		
19 Su		0200	3.3F
	0457	0801	4.4E
	1126	1430	3.3F
	1724	2035	4.5E
	2359		
20 M		0306	3.3F
	0556	0904	4.4E
	1222	1527	3.4F
	1820	2136	4.6E
21 Tu	0055	0359	3.4F
	0650	0959	4.5E
	1314	1618	3.4F
	1912	2227	4.7E
22 W	0146	0450	3.4F
	0740	1051	4.5E
	1402	1707	3.5F
	2000	2314	4.7E
23 Th	0234	0535	3.5F
	0827	1130	4.6E
	1447	1751	3.5F
	2045	2355	4.8E
24 F	0318	0618	3.5F
	0911	1209	4.6E
	1530	1831	3.5F
	2128		
25 Sa		0032	4.8E
	0400	0657	3.5F
	0953	1248	4.6E
	1611	1909	3.5F
	2210		
26 Su		0108	4.8E
	0441	0735	3.4F
	1034	1324	4.6E
	1651	1950	3.5F
	2251		
27 M		0146	4.7E
	0521	0813	3.4F
	1114	1402	4.6E
	1731	2029	3.4F
	2332		
28 Tu		0223	4.7E
	0601	0852	3.3F
	1155	1440	4.5E
	1812	2107	3.3F
29 W	0013	0302	4.6E
	0642	0932	3.2F
	1236	1521	4.4E
	1853	2148	3.2F
30 Th	0056	0345	4.5E
	0723	1014	3.1F
	1319	1602	4.4E
	1936	2233	3.1F

Time meridian 75° W.   0000 is midnight.   1200 is noon.

F-Flood, Dir. 050° True   E-Ebb, Dir. 230° True

JULY

Day	Slack Water Time h.m.	Maximum Current Time h.m.	Vel. knots	Day	Slack Water Time h.m.	Maximum Current Time h.m.	Vel. knots
1 F	0140	0428	4.4E	16 Sa	0234	0528	4.6E
	0806	1056	3.0F		0900	1201	3.4F
	1402	1648	4.3E		1502	1757	4.5E
	2021	2315	3.0F		2130		
2 Sa	0226	0515	4.3E	17 Su		0033	3.3F
	0851	1142	2.9F		0334	0629	4.4E
	1449	1737	4.3E		0959	1302	3.3F
	2110				1601	1903	4.4E
					2233		
3 Su		0006	3.0F	18 M		0138	3.2F
	0315	0602	4.3E		0434	0736	4.3E
	0938	1233	2.9F		1058	1405	3.2F
	1538	1826	4.3E		1700	2010	4.4E
	2202				2333		
4 M		0057	3.0F	19 Tu		0239	3.2F
	0406	0652	4.3E		0532	0840	4.2E
	1027	1321	3.0F		1154	1505	3.2F
	1629	1919	4.4E		1756	2113	4.4E
	2257						
5 Tu		0152	3.0F	20 W	0029	0334	3.2F
	0500	0747	4.3E		0626	0937	4.2E
	1118	1414	3.1F		1247	1556	3.3F
	1723	2014	4.5E		1849	2206	4.4E
	2352						
6 W		0245	3.1F	21 Th	0121	0425	3.2F
	0555	0842	4.4E		0717	1024	4.3E
	1210	1509	3.2F		1336	1645	3.4F
	1817	2110	4.6E		1938	2252	4.5E
7 Th	0047	0341	3.3F	22 F	0208	0511	3.3F
	0649	0937	4.5E		0804	1107	4.3E
	1303	1602	3.4F		1421	1730	3.4F
	1911	2206	4.8E		2024	2333	4.5E
8 F	0142	0438	3.4F	23 Sa	0252	0552	3.3F
	0743	1028	4.7E		0848	1146	4.4E
	1356	1655	3.6F		1503	1809	3.5F
	2005	2300	5.0E		2107		
9 Sa	0236	0529	3.6F	24 Su		0009	4.6E
	0836	1124	4.8E		0333	0633	3.4F
	1449	1749	3.8F		0929	1222	4.5E
	2059	2353	5.1E		1544	1846	3.5F
					2148		
10 Su	0329	0622	3.7F	25 M		0044	4.6E
	0929	1217	4.9E		0412	0710	3.4F
	1542	1844	3.9F		1009	1257	4.5E
	2153				1622	1923	3.5F
					2228		
11 M		0047	5.1E	26 Tu		0119	4.7E
	0421	0715	3.8F		0450	0745	3.4F
	1022	1312	5.0E		1048	1333	4.6E
	1636	1939	3.9F		1700	1959	3.5F
	2247				2308		
12 Tu		0142	5.1E	27 W		0156	4.7E
	0515	0809	3.8F		0528	0821	3.4F
	1116	1405	5.0E		1127	1412	4.6E
	1731	2032	3.9F		1738	2037	3.5F
	2342				2347		
13 W		0237	5.1E	28 Th		0233	4.7E
	0609	0903	3.7F		0605	0858	3.4F
	1210	1501	4.9E		1206	1451	4.6E
	1828	2129	3.8F		1816	2116	3.4F
14 Th	0038	0332	4.9E	29 F	0027	0312	4.6E
	0704	1001	3.6F		0642	0935	3.3F
	1306	1556	4.8E		1245	1530	4.5E
	1927	2227	3.6F		1855	2155	3.3F
15 F	0135	0427	4.8E	30 Sa	0108	0355	4.5E
	0801	1059	3.5F		0720	1017	3.2F
	1403	1656	4.7E		1326	1613	4.5E
	2028	2329	3.5F		1936	2236	3.3F
				31 Su	0151	0437	4.4E
					0800	1059	3.1F
					1409	1700	4.4E
					2022	2325	3.2F

AUGUST

Day	Slack Water Time h.m.	Maximum Current Time h.m.	Vel. knots	Day	Slack Water Time h.m.	Maximum Current Time h.m.	Vel. knots
1 M	0238	0522	4.3E	16 Tu		0109	3.2F
	0845	1149	3.1F		0409	0702	4.1E
	1458	1747	4.4E		1024	1335	3.2F
	2113				1635	1937	4.1E
					2301		
2 Tu		0016	3.1F	17 W		0212	3.1F
	0329	0613	4.3E		0508	0809	4.0E
	0935	1240	3.1F		1122	1436	3.1F
	1551	1843	4.4E		1732	2041	4.1E
	2211				2358		
3 W		0113	3.1F	18 Th		0310	3.1F
	0425	0712	4.3E		0603	0912	3.9E
	1031	1337	3.2F		1217	1531	3.2F
	1650	1940	4.4E		1827	2140	4.1E
	2313						
4 Th		0211	3.1F	19 F	0051	0403	3.1F
	0525	0807	4.3E		0655	1003	4.0E
	1131	1436	3.3F		1307	1620	3.2F
	1751	2041	4.5E		1917	2229	4.2E
5 F	0016	0312	3.2F	20 Sa	0138	0448	3.2F
	0625	0909	4.4E		0742	1045	4.1E
	1233	1538	3.4F		1353	1708	3.4F
	1851	2140	4.7E		2003	2308	4.3E
6 Sa	0117	0413	3.4F	21 Su	0222	0529	3.3F
	0724	1008	4.6E		0825	1122	4.3E
	1333	1639	3.6F		1434	1743	3.5F
	1950	2242	4.8E		2045	2343	4.4E
7 Su	0215	0513	3.6F	22 M	0302	0604	3.4F
	0821	1107	4.8E		0905	1155	4.4E
	1431	1736	3.8F		1514	1820	3.6F
	2048	2339	5.0E		2126		
8 M	0310	0609	3.8F	23 Tu		0018	4.5E
	0916	1204	4.9E		0340	0641	3.5F
	1527	1831	4.0F		0944	1231	4.5E
	2143				1551	1856	3.6F
					2205		
9 Tu		0036	5.1E	24 W		0052	4.6E
	0403	0702	3.9F		0416	0715	3.6F
	1009	1300	5.0E		1022	1306	4.6E
	1621	1927	4.0F		1628	1931	3.7F
	2237				2243		
10 W		0129	5.1E	25 Th		0126	4.7E
	0456	0756	3.9F		0452	0750	3.6F
	1102	1353	5.1E		1058	1341	4.6E
	1716	2021	4.0F		1703	2006	3.7F
	2330				2321		
11 Th		0221	5.1E	26 F		0203	4.7E
	0548	0847	3.9F		0526	0825	3.6F
	1155	1447	5.0E		1135	1420	4.7E
	1810	2114	4.0F		1739	2042	3.6F
					2359		
12 F	0024	0313	4.9E	27 Sa		0240	4.6E
	0640	0942	3.8F		0600	0901	3.5F
	1248	1539	4.9E		1212	1501	4.7E
	1905	2209	3.8F		1816	2122	3.6F
13 Sa	0118	0407	4.7E	28 Su	0038	0319	4.6E
	0733	1036	3.7F		0636	0940	3.4F
	1342	1636	4.7E		1252	1542	4.6E
	2002	2306	3.6F		1856	2203	3.5F
14 Su	0214	0502	4.5E	29 M	0120	0404	4.5E
	0828	1132	3.5F		0714	1021	3.4F
	1438	1731	4.5E		1335	1624	4.5E
	2100				1941	2250	3.3F
15 M		0006	3.4F	30 Tu	0206	0451	4.3E
	0311	0603	4.3E		0758	1110	3.3F
	0925	1232	3.3F		1425	1715	4.4E
	1536	1834	4.3E		2033	2342	3.2F
	2201			31 W	0259	0542	4.2E
					0851	1203	3.2F
					1522	1810	4.4E
					2134		

Time meridian 75° W. 0000 is midnight. 1200 is noon.

THE NARROWS, NEW YORK HARBOR, NEW YORK, 1983

F-Flood, Dir. 340° True   E-Ebb, Dir. 160° True

JANUARY

Day	Slack Water Time h.m.	Max Current Time h.m.	Vel. knots	Day	Slack Water Time h.m.	Max Current Time h.m.	Vel. knots
1 Sa	0509	0152	2.3E	16 Su	0528	0206	1.8E
	1112	0754	2.4F		1118	0801	1.8F
	1807	1429	2.6E		1821	1438	2.1E
	2330	2028	1.8F		2336	2032	1.4F
2 Su	0604	0243	2.3E	17 M	0609	0247	1.8E
	1204	0850	2.3F		1159	0846	1.7F
	1859	1519	2.6E		1901	1515	2.0E
		2127	1.8F			2117	1.4F
3 M	0026	0336	2.2E	18 Tu	0019	0326	1.7E
	0703	0945	2.1F		0653	0933	1.6F
	1256	1609	2.4E		1239	1552	2.0E
	1953	2227	1.8F		1942	2201	1.4F
4 Tu	0123	0431	2.1E	19 W	0104	0409	1.7E
	0807	1044	1.9F		0744	1020	1.5F
	1347	1703	2.2E		1320	1633	1.9E
	2049	2325	1.8F		2025	2250	1.5F
5 W	0220	0531	1.9E	20 Th	0151	0457	1.6E
	0911	1144	1.7F		0841	1107	1.4F
	1440	1802	2.1E		1404	1720	1.8E
	2143				2109	2335	1.5F
6 Th	0320	0023	1.8F	21 F	0241	0552	1.6E
	1014	0637	1.9E		0940	1156	1.3F
	1535	1242	1.5F		1451	1813	1.7E
	2237	1900	2.0E		2154		
7 F	0422	0121	1.7F	22 Sa	0337	0024	1.6F
	1115	0742	1.8E		1039	0657	1.6E
	1632	1345	1.4F		1544	1250	1.3F
	2329	1958	1.9E		2242	1911	1.7E
8 Sa	0524	0227	1.7F	23 Su	0436	0117	1.7F
	1214	0839	1.9E		1138	0756	1.8E
	1729	1502	1.3F		1643	1345	1.2F
		2049	1.9E		2333	2008	1.8E
9 Su	0020	0330	1.8F	24 M	0536	0213	1.8F
	0620	0931	1.9E		1238	0854	1.9E
	1312	1606	1.2F		1743	1446	1.2F
	1823	2138	1.8E			2101	1.9E
10 M	0111	0423	1.8F	25 Tu	0028	0314	1.9F
	0710	1020	1.9E		0634	0947	2.1E
	1406	1655	1.3F		1335	1547	1.4F
	1912	2223	1.8E		1841	2154	2.0E
11 Tu	0159	0510	1.9F	26 W	0124	0413	2.1F
	0755	1109	2.0E		0728	1041	2.2E
	1455	1740	1.3F		1430	1648	1.5F
	1958	2310	1.8E		1936	2251	2.1E
12 W	0245	0545	1.9F	27 Th	0220	0508	2.3F
	0837	1156	2.0E		0820	1137	2.4E
	1540	1815	1.3F		1520	1740	1.7F
	2042	2359	1.7E		2030	2347	2.2E
13 Th	0328	0618	1.9F	28 F	0313	0559	2.4F
	0918	1238	2.0E		0912	1229	2.5E
	1622	1846	1.3F		1608	1831	1.9F
	2125				2124		
14 F	0409	0042	1.7E	29 Sa	0406	0043	2.4E
	0958	0646	1.9F		1003	0649	2.5F
	1702	1320	2.1E		1655	1321	2.6E
	2208	1915	1.4F		2218	1918	2.0F
15 Sa	0448	0127	1.8E	30 Su	0457	0137	2.4E
	1038	0722	1.9F		1053	0738	2.4F
	1741	1359	2.1E		1742	1410	2.6E
	2252	1951	1.4F		2313	2010	2.0F
				31 M	0550	0228	2.4E
					1143	0831	2.3F
					1831	1457	2.6E
						2104	2.0F

FEBRUARY

Day	Slack Water Time h.m.	Max Current Time h.m.	Vel. knots	Day	Slack Water Time h.m.	Max Current Time h.m.	Vel. knots
1 Tu	0007	0316	2.4E	16 W	0630	0300	1.9E
	0646	0924	2.1F		1210	0904	1.7F
	1232	1545	2.4E		1858	1521	2.0E
	1922	2201	1.9F			2130	1.6F
2 W	0100	0409	2.2E	17 Th	0035	0339	1.9E
	0745	1020	1.9F		0717	0950	1.6F
	1320	1634	2.2E		1250	1558	1.9E
	2015	2253	1.9F		1937	2217	1.7F
3 Th	0154	0505	2.0E	18 F	0120	0424	1.8E
	0846	1116	1.6F		0811	1039	1.5F
	1409	1725	2.0E		1332	1637	1.8E
	2109	2347	1.8F		2021	2304	1.7F
4 F	0249	0604	1.8E	19 Sa	0210	0519	1.8E
	0947	1210	1.4F		0911	1128	1.4F
	1500	1824	1.8E		1419	1731	1.7E
	2203				2112	2353	1.7F
5 Sa	0348	0043	1.7F	20 Su	0304	0622	1.7E
	1048	0708	1.7E		1012	1221	1.3F
	1555	1309	1.2F		1512	1836	1.7E
	2256	1923	1.7E		2207		
6 Su	0449	0142	1.6F	21 M	0405	0047	1.7F
	1147	0809	1.7E		1113	0728	1.8E
	1654	1424	1.1F		1614	1318	1.2F
	2350	2020	1.7E		2306	1941	1.7E
7 M	0548	0253	1.6F	22 Tu	0509	0146	1.8F
	1245	0904	1.7E		1214	0828	1.9E
	1752	1537	1.1F		1719	1420	1.2F
		2112	1.6E			2040	1.8E
8 Tu	0042	0357	1.6F	23 W	0007	0249	1.9F
	0641	0953	1.8E		0611	0924	2.1E
	1340	1632	1.1F		1312	1528	1.3F
	1846	2157	1.6E		1822	2138	2.0E
9 W	0134	0448	1.7F	24 Th	0108	0357	2.0F
	0728	1042	1.9E		0708	1019	2.2E
	1430	1717	1.2F		1407	1635	1.6F
	1935	2246	1.7E		1921	2235	2.1E
10 Th	0222	0527	1.8F	25 F	0207	0457	2.2F
	0811	1126	1.9E		0802	1116	2.4E
	1514	1759	1.3F		1458	1730	1.8F
	2020	2333	1.7E		2016	2330	2.3E
11 F	0307	0558	1.8F	26 Sa	0302	0548	2.3F
	0852	1211	2.0E		0853	1209	2.5E
	1555	1828	1.4F		1545	1815	2.0F
	2103				2109		
12 Sa	0349	0021	1.8E	27 Su	0354	0027	2.4E
	0932	0628	1.9F		0942	0636	2.4F
	1634	1254	2.1E		1631	1300	2.6E
	2145	1853	1.5F		2201	1901	2.1F
13 Su	0429	0104	1.8E	28 M	0445	0120	2.5E
	1012	0659	1.9F		1031	0723	2.3F
	1710	1333	2.1E		1716	1348	2.6E
	2227	1925	1.5F		2253	1947	2.1F
14 M	0508	0145	1.9E				
	1051	0738	1.8F				
	1746	1410	2.1E				
	2309	2002	1.6F				
15 Tu	0548	0223	1.9E				
	1130	0819	1.8F				
	1822	1446	2.1E				
	2351	2045	1.6F				

Time meridian 75° W.   0000 is midnight.   1200 is noon.

F-Flood, Dir. 340° True   E-Ebb, Dir. 160° True

MARCH

Day	Slack Water Time h.m.	Max Current Time h.m.	Vel. knots	Day	Slack Water Time h.m.	Max Current Time h.m.	Vel. knots
1 Tu	0535	0209	2.5E	16 W		0159	2.1E
	1118	0809	2.2F		0527	0753	1.8F
	1802	1434	2.5E		1101	1416	2.1E
	2344	2036	2.1F		1742	2012	1.8F
					2324		
2 W	0627	0257	2.4E	17 Th		0239	2.1E
	1205	0900	2.0F		0609	0836	1.7F
	1849	1517	2.4E		1141	1453	2.1E
		2129	2.0F		1816	2057	1.8F
3 Th	0035	0345	2.3E	18 F	0008	0318	2.1E
	0722	0951	1.7F		0656	0925	1.6F
	1251	1603	2.2E		1222	1530	2.0E
	1939	2220	1.9F		1855	2145	1.8F
4 F	0125	0434	2.1E	19 Sa	0054	0401	2.0E
	0820	1045	1.5F		0750	1014	1.5F
	1338	1651	1.9E		1307	1609	1.9E
	2033	2311	1.8F		1942	2236	1.8F
5 Sa	0216	0528	1.8E	20 Su	0144	0453	1.9E
	0920	1136	1.3F		0850	1105	1.4F
	1427	1746	1.7E		1355	1702	1.7E
	2128				2040	2329	1.8F
6 Su	0310	0002	1.6F	21 M	0239	0556	1.8E
	1019	0631	1.7E		0952	1159	1.3F
	1520	1232	1.1F		1451	1811	1.7E
	2223	1846	1.5E		2143		
7 M	0409	0055	1.5F	22 Tu		0026	1.8F
	1117	0733	1.6E		0340	0705	1.8E
	1619	1333	1.0F		1052	1256	1.3F
	2318	1947	1.5E		1555	1921	1.7E
					2248		
8 Tu	0509	0201	1.4F	23 W		0123	1.8F
	1214	0831	1.6E		0445	0809	1.9E
	1721	1500	1.0F		1152	1401	1.3F
		2041	1.5E		1703	2024	1.8E
					2353		
9 W	0013	0318	1.4F	24 Th		0229	1.8F
	0605	0921	1.7E		0549	0905	2.1E
	1308	1602	1.1F		1249	1512	1.4F
	1819	2132	1.6E		1808	2125	2.0E
10 Th	0106	0415	1.5F	25 F	0055	0344	1.9F
	0655	1008	1.8E		0648	1000	2.2E
	1357	1651	1.2F		1343	1623	1.7F
	1910	2219	1.6E		1907	2219	2.2E
11 F	0157	0458	1.6F	26 Sa	0155	0448	2.1F
	0740	1055	1.9E		0742	1052	2.3E
	1442	1730	1.4F		1433	1718	1.9F
	1955	2308	1.7E		2001	2316	2.3E
12 Sa	0243	0533	1.7F	27 Su	0250	0538	2.2F
	0822	1138	2.0E		0831	1146	2.4E
	1522	1759	1.5F		1520	1801	2.1F
	2038	2353	1.8E		2053		
13 Su	0327	0605	1.8F	28 M		0009	2.4E
	0902	1221	2.0E		0342	0624	2.2F
	1600	1824	1.6F		0919	1235	2.4E
	2119				1604	1844	2.2F
					2143		
14 M	0408	0036	2.0E	29 Tu	0431	0101	2.5E
	0942	0636	1.8F		1006	0705	2.1F
	1635	1302	2.1E		1648	1321	2.4E
	2200	1857	1.7F		2232	1925	2.2F
15 Tu	0447	0120	2.0E	30 W		0149	2.5E
	1021	0712	1.8F		0519	0748	2.0F
	1709	1339	2.1E		1051	1407	2.4E
	2242	1933	1.8F		1732	2009	2.1F
					2320		
				31 Th		0235	2.4E
					0608	0834	1.8F
					1137	1448	2.2E
					1816	2055	2.0F

APRIL

Day	Slack Water Time h.m.	Max Current Time h.m.	Vel. knots	Day	Slack Water Time h.m.	Max Current Time h.m.	Vel. knots
1 F	0007	0319	2.3E	16 Sa		0300	2.3E
	0700	0923	1.6F		0639	0900	1.6F
	1222	1533	2.0E		1158	1505	2.0E
	1904	2143	1.9F		1824	2120	2.0F
2 Sa	0055	0405	2.1E	17 Su	0033	0345	2.2E
	0755	1014	1.4F		0733	0952	1.5F
	1307	1618	1.8E		1247	1550	1.9E
	1956	2234	1.7F		1916	2215	1.9F
3 Su	0143	0456	1.8E	18 M	0124	0436	2.1E
	0852	1105	1.2F		0832	1047	1.4F
	1355	1709	1.6E		1339	1646	1.8E
	2052	2323	1.6F		2019	2308	1.9F
4 M	0233	0554	1.7E	19 Tu	0219	0537	2.0E
	0949	1158	1.1F		0933	1142	1.4F
	1448	1810	1.4E		1437	1755	1.7E
	2149				2128		
5 Tu	0327	0014	1.4F	20 W		0006	1.8F
	1045	0654	1.6E		0319	0645	1.9E
	1546	1252	1.0F		1032	1241	1.4F
	2246	1912	1.4E		1542	1906	1.7E
					2235		
6 W	0425	0111	1.3F	21 Th		0107	1.7F
	1139	0755	1.6E		0423	0748	2.0E
	1649	1404	1.0F		1128	1345	1.4F
	2342	2010	1.4E		1650	2011	1.9E
					2340		
7 Th	0523	0214	1.3F	22 F		0214	1.7F
	1230	0846	1.7E		0527	0846	2.1E
	1748	1517	1.1F		1223	1501	1.6F
		2101	1.5E		1755	2109	2.0E
8 F	0036	0330	1.4F	23 Sa	0042	0331	1.8F
	0616	0933	1.8E		0625	0938	2.2E
	1318	1612	1.3F		1316	1607	1.8F
	1840	2150	1.7E		1853	2203	2.2E
9 Sa	0128	0422	1.5F	24 Su	0141	0434	1.9F
	0704	1016	1.9E		0718	1029	2.3E
	1403	1655	1.5F		1406	1700	2.0F
	1927	2236	1.8E		1946	2258	2.3E
10 Su	0216	0501	1.6F	25 M	0236	0524	2.0F
	0747	1101	1.9E		0807	1120	2.3E
	1444	1723	1.6F		1453	1745	2.2F
	2009	2323	1.9E		2035	2351	2.4E
11 M	0302	0536	1.7F	26 Tu	0327	0608	2.0F
	0828	1143	2.0E		0853	1209	2.3E
	1522	1752	1.8F		1538	1824	2.2F
	2051				2123		
12 Tu		0009	2.1E	27 W		0040	2.4E
	0345	0609	1.8F		0416	0647	1.9F
	0909	1226	2.1E		0938	1255	2.2E
	1557	1825	1.9F		1621	1901	2.2F
	2132				2209		
13 W		0052	2.2E	28 Th		0128	2.4E
	0426	0647	1.8F		0503	0727	1.7F
	0949	1307	2.1E		1023	1341	2.2E
	1631	1902	2.0F		1703	1940	2.1F
	2214				2255		
14 Th		0133	2.2E	29 F		0212	2.3E
	0507	0726	1.7F		0550	0809	1.6F
	1030	1347	2.1E		1108	1422	2.0E
	1705	1944	2.1F		1746	2023	2.0F
	2258				2340		
15 F	0551	0217	2.3E	30 Sa		0255	2.2E
	1113	0811	1.7F		0638	0854	1.4F
	1742	1426	2.1E		1153	1505	1.9E
	2344	2031	2.0F		1831	2109	1.8F

Time meridian 75° W.   0000 is midnight.   1200 is noon.

THE NARROWS, NEW YORK HARBOR, NEW YORK, 1983

F-Flood, Dir. 340° True   E-Ebb, Dir. 160° True

MAY

Day	Slack Water Time h.m.	Maximum Current Time h.m.	Vel. knots	Day	Slack Water Time h.m.	Maximum Current Time h.m.	Vel. knots
1 Su	0025	0338	2.0E	16 M	0015	0329	2.3E
	0730	0945	1.3F		0716	0933	1.5F
	1239	1546	1.7E		1231	1538	2.0E
	1921	2158	1.7F		1900	2153	2.0F
2 M	0111	0427	1.9E	17 Tu	0107	0420	2.2E
	0824	1036	1.2F		0814	1030	1.5F
	1327	1637	1.5E		1326	1633	1.9E
	2016	2249	1.5F		2006	2252	1.9F
3 Tu	0158	0515	1.7E	18 W	0201	0519	2.1E
	0918	1127	1.1F		0912	1128	1.5F
	1418	1732	1.4E		1426	1740	1.8E
	2114	2339	1.4F		2115	2351	1.8F
4 W	0248	0614	1.6E	19 Th	0259	0623	2.1E
	1011	1219	1.1F		1009	1227	1.6F
	1514	1833	1.3E		1529	1850	1.8E
	2211				2221		
5 Th		0030	1.3F	20 F		0050	1.7F
	0341	0713	1.6E		0400	0726	2.1E
	1101	1312	1.1F		1103	1330	1.6F
	1614	1936	1.4E		1635	1954	1.9E
	2307				2325		
6 F		0123	1.3F	21 Sa		0156	1.7F
	0437	0805	1.7E		0501	0824	2.1E
	1149	1411	1.2F		1156	1440	1.7F
	1712	2030	1.5E		1739	2053	2.1E
7 Sa	0002	0223	1.3F	22 Su	0026	0312	1.6F
	0532	0854	1.8E		0600	0915	2.2E
	1235	1509	1.3F		1248	1550	1.9F
	1806	2118	1.7E		1837	2146	2.2E
8 Su	0055	0325	1.4F	23 M	0125	0419	1.7F
	0622	0938	1.9E		0653	1006	2.2E
	1319	1600	1.5F		1338	1641	2.0F
	1854	2203	1.8E		1929	2239	2.2E
9 M	0146	0416	1.5F	24 Tu	0220	0511	1.7F
	0708	1021	1.9E		0741	1052	2.1E
	1401	1639	1.7F		1426	1726	2.1F
	1938	2251	2.0E		2017	2330	2.3E
10 Tu	0234	0458	1.6F	25 W	0312	0552	1.7F
	0752	1104	2.0E		0827	1140	2.1E
	1441	1716	1.9F		1512	1805	2.2F
	2021	2337	2.1E		2103		
11 W	0320	0539	1.6F	26 Th		0021	2.3E
	0834	1150	2.0E		0400	0633	1.6F
	1518	1755	2.1F		0911	1229	2.0E
	2104				1555	1840	2.1F
					2147		
12 Th		0022	2.2E	27 F		0107	2.2E
	0404	0620	1.7F		0446	0708	1.5F
	0917	1233	2.0E		0956	1315	1.9E
	1555	1836	2.2F		1637	1916	2.0F
	2149				2231		
13 F		0109	2.3E	28 Sa		0151	2.2E
	0448	0702	1.7F		0531	0745	1.4F
	1001	1318	2.1E		1040	1358	1.9E
	1634	1919	2.2F		1719	1954	1.9F
	2235				2314		
14 Sa		0156	2.4E	29 Su		0234	2.1E
	0533	0749	1.6F		0617	0828	1.3F
	1048	1403	2.1E		1126	1439	1.8E
	1716	2006	2.2F		1802	2039	1.8F
	2324				2358		
15 Su		0241	2.4E	30 M		0313	2.0E
	0622	0838	1.6F		0704	0916	1.2F
	1138	1449	2.0E		1213	1521	1.6E
	1804	2057	2.1F		1849	2126	1.6F
				31 Tu	0041	0358	1.9E
					0754	1008	1.2F
					1300	1608	1.5E
					1941	2217	1.5F

JUNE

Day	Slack Water Time h.m.	Maximum Current Time h.m.	Vel. knots	Day	Slack Water Time h.m.	Maximum Current Time h.m.	Vel. knots
1 W	0125	0444	1.8E	16 Th	0143	0458	2.3E
	0844	1055	1.2F		0847	1113	1.7F
	1350	1659	1.4E		1411	1722	1.9E
	2038	2306	1.4F		2059	2333	1.9F
2 Th	0211	0534	1.7E	17 F	0237	0558	2.2E
	0933	1144	1.2F		0942	1212	1.7F
	1441	1755	1.4E		1512	1829	1.9E
	2135	2355	1.4F		2204		
3 F	0300	0630	1.7E	18 Sa		0032	1.7F
	1020	1229	1.3F		0334	0700	2.1E
	1536	1856	1.4E		1036	1311	1.8F
	2231				1616	1935	1.9E
					2306		
4 Sa		0045	1.3F	19 Su		0138	1.6F
	0352	0724	1.7E		0433	0757	2.1E
	1106	1320	1.3F		1129	1418	1.8F
	1633	1951	1.5E		1719	2033	2.0E
	2326						
5 Su		0138	1.3F	20 M	0007	0250	1.5F
	0445	0812	1.8E		0531	0849	2.1E
	1150	1411	1.4F		1220	1525	1.9F
	1728	2043	1.7E		1817	2128	2.1E
6 M	0020	0233	1.3F	21 Tu	0106	0357	1.5F
	0538	0858	1.8E		0625	0941	2.0E
	1234	1505	1.6F		1311	1622	2.0F
	1818	2131	1.8E		1910	2219	2.1E
7 Tu	0113	0330	1.3F	22 W	0202	0452	1.5F
	0628	0941	1.9E		0715	1026	2.0E
	1317	1556	1.8F		1401	1708	2.0F
	1906	2217	2.0E		1957	2308	2.1E
8 W	0205	0424	1.4F	23 Th	0255	0539	1.5F
	0715	1028	1.9E		0802	1114	1.9E
	1400	1642	2.0F		1448	1749	2.0F
	1952	2306	2.1E		2042		
9 Th	0254	0510	1.5F	24 F		0000	2.1E
	0801	1111	2.0E		0342	0618	1.4F
	1442	1728	2.2F		0847	1203	1.9E
	2038	2357	2.3E		1532	1822	2.0F
					2125		
10 F	0342	0556	1.6F	25 Sa		0046	2.1E
	0847	1202	2.0E		0427	0653	1.4F
	1526	1811	2.3F		0931	1249	1.8E
	2126				1615	1855	2.0F
					2207		
11 Sa		0048	2.4E	26 Su		0129	2.1E
	0428	0641	1.7F		0510	0726	1.3F
	0936	1252	2.1E		1016	1334	1.8E
	1610	1857	2.4F		1656	1931	1.9F
	2215				2249		
12 Su		0136	2.5E	27 M		0210	2.1E
	0515	0728	1.7F		0553	0805	1.3F
	1027	1343	2.1E		1101	1418	1.7E
	1658	1946	2.3F		1738	2012	1.8F
	2305				2331		
13 M		0225	2.5E	28 Tu		0250	2.1E
	0604	0819	1.7F		0636	0848	1.3F
	1121	1434	2.2E		1147	1457	1.7E
	1750	2039	2.2F		1822	2057	1.7F
	2357						
14 Tu		0313	2.5E	29 W	0012	0329	2.0E
	0656	0915	1.7F		0721	0935	1.3F
	1216	1525	2.1E		1233	1540	1.6E
	1848	2136	2.1F		1909	2144	1.6F
15 W	0050	0404	2.4E	30 Th	0054	0411	1.9E
	0751	1015	1.7F		0806	1020	1.3F
	1313	1621	2.0E		1320	1625	1.5E
	1953	2233	2.0F		2002	2234	1.5F

Time meridian 75° W.   0000 is midnight.   1200 is noon.

F-Flood, Dir. 340° True   E-Ebb, Dir. 160° True

JULY

Day	Slack Water Time h.m.	Maximum Current Time h.m.	Vel. knots
1 F	0137	0456	1.8E
	0852	1107	1.3F
	1408	1716	1.5E
	2058	2321	1.4F
2 Sa	0222	0544	1.7E
	0937	1152	1.4F
	1458	1813	1.5E
	2155		
3 Su	0309	0010	1.3F
	1021	0637	1.7E
	1552	1240	1.5F
	2250	1913	1.6E
4 M	0401	0059	1.3F
	1104	0730	1.7E
	1648	1327	1.5F
	2346	2006	1.7E
5 Tu	0455	0152	1.2F
	1149	0819	1.8E
	1743	1422	1.7F
		2058	1.8E
6 W	0042	0249	1.2F
	0549	0908	1.8E
	1235	1517	1.8F
	1835	2146	2.0E
7 Th	0136	0347	1.3F
	0641	0954	1.9E
	1323	1610	2.0F
	1926	2239	2.1E
8 F	0229	0442	1.4F
	0732	1045	2.0E
	1413	1702	2.2F
	2015	2331	2.3E
9 Sa	0319	0533	1.6F
	0823	1138	2.1E
	1503	1751	2.4F
	2105		
10 Su	0406	0024	2.4E
	0914	0620	1.7F
	1553	1231	2.2E
	2155	1838	2.4F
11 M	0453	0117	2.5E
	1008	0710	1.8F
	1644	1326	2.3E
	2247	1927	2.4F
12 Tu	0541	0206	2.6E
	1103	0801	1.8F
	1738	1418	2.3E
	2338	2020	2.3F
13 W	0631	0255	2.6E
	1159	0856	1.9F
	1835	1511	2.3E
		2116	2.2F
14 Th	0030	0343	2.5E
	0724	0953	1.9F
	1255	1604	2.2E
	1936	2215	2.0F
15 F	0121	0436	2.3E
	0818	1053	1.9F
	1352	1701	2.1E
	2040	2315	1.8F

Day	Slack Water Time h.m.	Maximum Current Time h.m.	Vel. knots
16 Sa	0213	0531	2.2E
	0913	1150	1.9F
	1450	1803	2.0E
	2144		
17 Su	0306	0011	1.7F
	1007	0630	2.0E
	1551	1246	1.8F
	2245	1909	1.9E
18 M	0403	0112	1.5F
	1100	0730	2.0E
	1653	1348	1.8F
	2346	2012	1.9E
19 Tu	0501	0221	1.3F
	1153	0822	1.9E
	1753	1455	1.8F
		2107	1.9E
20 W	0045	0336	1.3F
	0558	0915	1.9E
	1246	1600	1.8F
	1847	2159	2.0E
21 Th	0142	0434	1.3F
	0651	1003	1.8E
	1337	1649	1.9F
	1936	2248	2.0E
22 F	0234	0523	1.3F
	0739	1051	1.8E
	1426	1732	1.9F
	2020	2335	2.0E
23 Sa	0322	0602	1.3F
	0825	1139	1.8E
	1512	1809	1.9F
	2102		
24 Su	0405	0022	2.0E
	0909	0637	1.4F
	1555	1227	1.8E
	2143	1836	1.9F
25 M	0445	0103	2.0E
	0953	0706	1.4F
	1636	1313	1.8E
	2223	1910	1.8F
26 Tu	0525	0144	2.1E
	1037	0738	1.4F
	1716	1353	1.8E
	2303	1946	1.8F
27 W	0604	0225	2.1E
	1121	0815	1.4F
	1757	1434	1.8E
	2343	2029	1.7F
28 Th	0644	0300	2.0E
	1204	0858	1.4F
	1841	1513	1.8E
		2114	1.6F
29 F	0023	0337	2.0E
	0724	0945	1.4F
	1248	1552	1.7E
	1930	2201	1.5F
30 Sa	0104	0416	1.9E
	0806	1033	1.5F
	1333	1637	1.6E
	2023	2250	1.4F
31 Su	0146	0459	1.8E
	0849	1118	1.5F
	1421	1733	1.6E
	2120	2337	1.3F

AUGUST

Day	Slack Water Time h.m.	Maximum Current Time h.m.	Vel. knots
1 M	0231	0550	1.7E
	0934	1205	1.6F
	1513	1832	1.6E
	2218		
2 Tu	0320	0027	1.2F
	1020	0647	1.7E
	1610	1254	1.6F
	2315	1933	1.7E
3 W	0416	0118	1.2F
	1109	0743	1.7E
	1709	1347	1.7F
		2028	1.8E
4 Th	0013	0217	1.2F
	0515	0836	1.8E
	1201	1445	1.8F
	1807	2122	2.0E
5 F	0109	0318	1.3F
	0614	0931	1.9E
	1257	1546	2.0F
	1902	2213	2.1E
6 Sa	0204	0420	1.4F
	0709	1024	2.0E
	1353	1642	2.2F
	1954	2307	2.3E
7 Su	0255	0513	1.6F
	0803	1117	2.2E
	1447	1734	2.3F
	2045		
8 M	0002	0002	2.4E
	0343	0604	1.8F
	0857	1215	2.3E
	1540	1824	2.4F
	2136		
9 Tu	0429	0054	2.5E
	0951	0653	2.0F
	1632	1309	2.4E
	2226	1913	2.4F
10 W	0516	0144	2.6E
	1045	0742	2.0F
	1725	1403	2.5E
	2317	2002	2.3F
11 Th	0603	0232	2.6E
	1140	0834	2.1F
	1819	1452	2.5E
		2057	2.2F
12 F	0007	0319	2.5E
	0653	0929	2.0F
	1234	1544	2.3E
	1917	2152	2.1F
13 Sa	0056	0409	2.3E
	0746	1027	2.0F
	1328	1637	2.2E
	2018	2249	1.8F
14 Su	0145	0500	2.1E
	0841	1119	1.9F
	1423	1736	2.0E
	2121	2347	1.5F
15 M	0237	0557	1.9E
	0936	1216	1.8F
	1522	1840	1.9E
	2222		

Day	Slack Water Time h.m.	Maximum Current Time h.m.	Vel. knots
16 Tu		0043	1.3F
	0332	0658	1.8E
	1032	1314	1.7F
	1623	1944	1.8E
	2322		
17 W	0431	0152	1.2F
	1126	0757	1.7E
	1724	1426	1.6F
		2043	1.8E
18 Th	0021	0310	1.1F
	0531	0850	1.7E
	1221	1531	1.6F
	1820	2134	1.8E
19 F	0117	0411	1.2F
	0627	0941	1.7E
	1314	1629	1.7F
	1910	2221	1.9E
20 Sa	0208	0500	1.3F
	0718	1029	1.7E
	1404	1714	1.8F
	1954	2308	1.9E
21 Su	0255	0543	1.4F
	0804	1116	1.7E
	1451	1749	1.8F
	2035	2353	2.0E
22 M	0337	0618	1.4F
	0847	1201	1.8E
	1534	1818	1.8F
	2115		
23 Tu	0415	0035	2.0E
	0929	0643	1.5F
	1615	1247	1.8E
	2154	1848	1.8F
24 W	0452	0116	2.1E
	1011	0709	1.5F
	1655	1328	1.9E
	2234	1921	1.8F
25 Th	0528	0154	2.1E
	1052	0746	1.6F
	1735	1409	1.9E
	2313	2000	1.7F
26 F	0604	0231	2.1E
	1134	0826	1.6F
	1816	1447	1.9E
	2352	2045	1.6F
27 Sa	0640	0306	2.0E
	1217	0909	1.6F
	1901	1526	1.9E
		2130	1.5F
28 Su	0032	0339	1.9E
	0717	0956	1.6F
	1301	1605	1.8E
	1953	2218	1.4F
29 M	0113	0418	1.8E
	0800	1043	1.6F
	1348	1656	1.7E
	2050	2307	1.3F
30 Tu	0157	0503	1.7E
	0848	1132	1.7F
	1440	1755	1.7E
	2150	2358	1.2F
31 W	0248	0605	1.6E
	0942	1224	1.7F
	1537	1901	1.7E
	2249		

Time meridian 75° W.   0000 is midnight.   1200 is noon.

DELAWARE BAY ENTRANCE, 1983

F-Flood, Dir. 305° True   E-Ebb, Dir. 140° True

JANUARY

Day	Slack Water Time h.m.	Max Current Time h.m.	Vel. knots	Day	Slack Water Time h.m.	Max Current Time h.m.	Vel. knots
1 Sa	0442	0127	1.8E	16 Su		0137	1.6E
	1056	0746	2.0F		0451	0752	1.7F
	1733	1403	2.0E		1056	1401	1.8E
	2321	2020	1.7F		1731	2018	1.5F
					2315		
2 Su	0539	0222	1.8E	17 M		0215	1.6E
	1151	0841	1.9F		0528	0833	1.7F
	1829	1458	1.9E		1133	1442	1.8E
		2116	1.7F		1807	2101	1.5F
					2355		
3 M	0020	0320	1.7E	18 Tu	0258		1.6E
	0640	0940	1.8F		0610	0915	1.6F
	1249	1557	1.9E		1213	1525	1.8E
	1927	2214	1.6F		1846	2142	1.6F
4 Tu	0122	0423	1.7E	19 W	0040	0343	1.6E
	0745	1039	1.7F		0656	1002	1.6F
	1349	1656	1.8E		1257	1608	1.8E
	2026	2315	1.6F		1930	2233	1.6F
5 W	0226	0527	1.6E	20 Th	0129	0434	1.6E
	0851	1143	1.6F		0748	1053	1.5F
	1451	1759	1.8E		1346	1658	1.7E
	2126				2017	2321	1.6F
6 Th	0330	0018	1.7F	21 F	0222	0527	1.6E
	0957	0635	1.7E		0845	1146	1.5F
	1552	1245	1.6F		1439	1751	1.7E
	2224	1900	1.7E		2109		
7 F	0432	0117	1.7F	22 Sa	0318	0016	1.6F
	1059	0740	1.7E		0947	0624	1.6E
	1652	1345	1.6F		1536	1243	1.5F
	2319	1959	1.8E		2205	1846	1.7E
8 Sa	0529	0216	1.8F	23 Su	0418	0111	1.7F
	1158	0839	1.8E		1050	0724	1.7E
	1748	1444	1.6F		1636	1341	1.5F
		2059	1.8E		2302	1945	1.7E
9 Su	0011	0309	1.9F	24 M	0518	0210	1.7F
	0622	0934	1.9E		1153	0823	1.7E
	1252	1537	1.6F		1736	1442	1.5F
	1839	2146	1.8E			2041	1.7E
10 M	0100	0359	1.9F	25 Tu	0000	0305	1.8F
	0711	1022	1.9E		0617	0924	1.8E
	1341	1626	1.6F		1254	1539	1.5F
	1927	2231	1.7E		1836	2140	1.7E
11 Tu	0145	0444	1.9F	26 W	0058	0403	1.9F
	0755	1105	1.9E		0714	1020	1.9E
	1427	1707	1.6F		1352	1635	1.6F
	2011	2314	1.7E		1934	2237	1.8E
12 W	0226	0523	1.9F	27 Th	0154	0457	2.0F
	0836	1144	1.9E		0810	1116	2.0E
	1508	1750	1.5F		1446	1730	1.7F
	2051	2349	1.7E		2031	2332	1.8E
13 Th	0305	0600	1.8F	28 F	0249	0551	2.0F
	0913	1217	1.8E		0903	1210	2.0E
	1547	1826	1.5F		1539	1823	1.7F
	2128				2126		
14 F	0341	0025	1.6E	29 Sa	0343	0026	1.9E
	0948	0639	1.8F		0955	0644	2.0F
	1623	1251	1.8E		1630	1301	2.1E
	2203	1904	1.5F		2219	1917	1.8F
15 Sa	0416	0100	1.6E	30 Su	0438	0120	1.9E
	1022	0715	1.7F		1047	0737	2.0F
	1657	1326	1.8E		1720	1353	2.1E
	2238	1939	1.5F		2313	2008	1.8F
				31 M	0532	0213	1.9E
					1138	0828	1.9F
					1811	1442	2.0E
						2101	1.8F

FEBRUARY

Day	Slack Water Time h.m.	Max Current Time h.m.	Vel. knots	Day	Slack Water Time h.m.	Max Current Time h.m.	Vel. knots
1 Tu	0007	0306	1.8E	16 W		0231	1.8E
	0628	0922	1.8F		0545	0850	1.7F
	1230	1535	1.9E		1143	1451	1.9E
	1902	2152	1.8F		1809	2112	1.7F
2 W	0102	0401	1.8E	17 Th	0008	0312	1.8E
	0725	1017	1.7F		0628	0931	1.7F
	1323	1630	1.9E		1224	1534	1.8E
	1955	2246	1.8F		1849	2155	1.7F
3 Th	0158	0459	1.7E	18 F	0054	0401	1.8E
	0824	1111	1.6F		0716	1020	1.6F
	1418	1725	1.8E		1310	1623	1.8E
	2049	2343	1.7F		1935	2246	1.7F
4 F	0256	0600	1.7E	19 Sa	0145	0453	1.8E
	0925	1209	1.5F		0812	1113	1.5F
	1515	1821	1.7E		1402	1714	1.7E
	2144				2027	2339	1.7F
5 Sa		0038	1.7F	20 Su	0242	0550	1.7E
	0354	0657	1.7E		0914	1209	1.4F
	1025	1306	1.5F		1500	1813	1.6E
	1612	1919	1.6E		2126		
	2239						
6 Su		0134	1.7F	21 M		0038	1.7F
	0451	0758	1.7E		0344	0651	1.7E
	1124	1407	1.5F		1022	1312	1.4F
	1710	2014	1.6E		1605	1913	1.6E
	2333				2231		
7 M		0229	1.7F	22 Tu		0140	1.7F
	0545	0856	1.7E		0450	0756	1.7E
	1219	1502	1.5F		1131	1417	1.4F
	1805	2111	1.6E		1714	2020	1.6E
					2339		
8 Tu	0025	0324	1.7F	23 W		0245	1.7F
	0637	0947	1.8E		0556	0904	1.7E
	1311	1552	1.5F		1238	1521	1.5F
	1856	2158	1.6E		1822	2124	1.6E
9 W	0114	0412	1.7F	24 Th	0045	0346	1.8F
	0724	1034	1.8E		0700	1006	1.8E
	1359	1641	1.5F		1339	1625	1.6F
	1944	2245	1.6E		1926	2229	1.7E
10 Th	0200	0456	1.8F	25 F	0147	0448	1.9F
	0808	1117	1.8E		0759	1107	1.9E
	1442	1724	1.5F		1435	1720	1.7F
	2027	2325	1.6E		2025	2326	1.8E
11 F	0242	0539	1.7F	26 Sa	0245	0542	2.0F
	0848	1154	1.8E		0854	1201	2.0E
	1521	1802	1.5F		1527	1815	1.8F
	2106				2119		
12 Sa		0003	1.6E	27 Su		0021	1.9E
	0320	0615	1.7F		0339	0636	2.0F
	0924	1228	1.8E		0945	1250	2.1E
	1557	1840	1.6F		1615	1903	1.9F
	2142				2210		
13 Su		0040	1.6E	28 M		0112	2.0E
	0356	0651	1.7F		0430	0726	2.0F
	0958	1301	1.8E		1033	1339	2.1E
	1630	1915	1.6F		1701	1952	1.9F
	2216				2259		
14 M	0430	0115	1.7E				
	1031	0728	1.7F				
	1701	1336	1.8E				
	2251	1953	1.6F				
15 Tu	0506	0152	1.7E				
	1105	0807	1.7F				
	1733	1412	1.9E				
	2328	2032	1.7F				

Time meridian 75° W.   0000 is midnight.   1200 is noon.

F-Flood, Dir. 305° True   E-Ebb, Dir. 140° True

MARCH

Day	Slack Water Time (h.m.)	Max Current Time (h.m.)	Vel. (knots)
1 Tu	0521	0200	2.0E
	1120	0812	1.9F
	1746	1424	2.0E
	2347	2037	1.9F
2 W	0610	0248	2.0E
	1206	0900	1.9F
	1832	1509	1.9E
		2126	1.9F
3 Th	0035	0335	1.9E
	0701	0949	1.7F
	1253	1555	1.8E
	1918	2213	1.8F
4 F	0124	0426	1.8E
	0753	1037	1.6F
	1342	1644	1.7E
	2008	2303	1.7F
5 Sa	0216	0518	1.7E
	0848	1131	1.5F
	1435	1737	1.6E
	2100	2356	1.7F
6 Su	0310	0613	1.6E
	0946	1227	1.4F
	1531	1832	1.5E
	2156		
7 M	0407	0053	1.6F
	1045	0714	1.6E
	1630	1326	1.3F
	2253	1933	1.5E
8 Tu	0504	0150	1.6F
	1143	0813	1.6E
	1729	1424	1.4F
	2350	2033	1.5E
9 W	0559	0245	1.6F
	1237	0910	1.6E
	1824	1521	1.4F
		2124	1.5E
10 Th	0043	0337	1.6F
	0650	0959	1.7E
	1326	1612	1.5F
	1915	2216	1.5E
11 F	0132	0426	1.7F
	0736	1045	1.8E
	1411	1654	1.5F
	2000	2300	1.6E
12 Sa	0217	0509	1.7F
	0818	1126	1.8E
	1450	1736	1.6F
	2040	2339	1.7E
13 Su	0257	0549	1.7F
	0856	1159	1.8E
	1525	1812	1.7F
	2116		
14 M	0334	0015	1.7E
	0931	0626	1.7F
	1557	1233	1.9E
	2150	1848	1.7F
15 Tu	0409	0050	1.8E
	1004	0703	1.8F
	1628	1308	1.9E
	2224	1925	1.8F
16 W	0444	0127	1.9E
	1037	0740	1.8F
	1659	1343	1.9E
	2259	2000	1.8F
17 Th	0521	0205	1.9E
	1114	0821	1.7F
	1733	1422	1.9E
	2339	2041	1.9F
18 F	0603	0248	1.9E
	1155	0902	1.7F
	1813	1503	1.9E
		2125	1.9F
19 Sa	0023	0333	1.9E
	0651	0950	1.6F
	1241	1550	1.8E
	1900	2213	1.8F
20 Su	0114	0424	1.8E
	0746	1043	1.5F
	1334	1644	1.7E
	1954	2310	1.7F
21 M	0212	0523	1.7E
	0850	1144	1.4F
	1436	1745	1.6E
	2059		
22 Tu	0318	0012	1.6F
	1002	0627	1.7E
	1547	1251	1.3F
	2212	1852	1.5E
23 W	0430	0119	1.6F
	1116	0738	1.6E
	1703	1401	1.4F
	2328	2004	1.5E
24 Th	0541	0230	1.6F
	1224	0849	1.7E
	1815	1511	1.5F
		2118	1.6E
25 F	0039	0337	1.7F
	0648	0958	1.8E
	1325	1612	1.6F
	1919	2225	1.7E
26 Sa	0142	0438	1.8F
	0748	1057	1.9E
	1419	1710	1.8F
	2016	2322	1.9E
27 Su	0239	0533	1.9F
	0841	1148	2.0E
	1508	1759	1.9F
	2107		
28 M	0330	0012	2.0E
	0930	0624	2.0F
	1554	1235	2.1E
	2154	1846	2.0F
29 Tu	0418	0059	2.1E
	1014	0707	2.0F
	1636	1316	2.0E
	2239	1929	2.0F
30 W	0504	0142	2.1E
	1057	0753	1.9F
	1717	1357	2.0E
	2321	2012	2.0F
31 Th	0549	0224	2.0E
	1139	0834	1.8F
	1758	1438	1.9E
		2053	1.9F

APRIL

Day	Slack Water Time (h.m.)	Max Current Time (h.m.)	Vel. (knots)
1 F	0004	0306	1.9E
	0634	0919	1.7F
	1221	1521	1.8E
	1840	2138	1.8F
2 Sa	0048	0251	1.8E
	0721	1004	1.5F
	1306	1607	1.6E
	1926	2224	1.7F
3 Su	0134	0438	1.7E
	0812	1055	1.4F
	1356	1657	1.5E
	2016	2316	1.6F
4 M	0225	0532	1.6E
	0906	1148	1.3F
	1451	1750	1.4E
	2112		
5 Tu	0321	0009	1.5F
	1004	0628	1.6E
	1551	1247	1.3F
	2213	1848	1.4E
6 W	0419	0107	1.5F
	1102	0727	1.6E
	1652	1345	1.3F
	2313	1951	1.4E
7 Th	0516	0207	1.5F
	1157	0826	1.6E
	1750	1442	1.4F
		2049	1.4E
8 F	0010	0302	1.5F
	0610	0919	1.7E
	1247	1534	1.5F
	1842	2144	1.5E
9 Sa	0102	0353	1.6F
	0659	1006	1.7E
	1332	1621	1.6F
	1929	2229	1.6E
10 Su	0149	0438	1.6F
	0744	1048	1.8E
	1412	1702	1.7F
	2009	2309	1.7E
11 M	0231	0519	1.7F
	0823	1125	1.8E
	1448	1739	1.8F
	2046	2346	1.8E
12 Tu	0309	0559	1.7F
	0859	1201	1.9E
	1520	1817	1.9F
	2121		
13 W	0345	0022	1.9E
	0934	0637	1.8F
	1552	1237	1.9E
	2155	1854	1.9F
14 Th	0421	0101	2.0E
	1009	0714	1.8F
	1624	1312	1.9E
	2232	1931	2.0F
15 F	0500	0138	2.0E
	1047	0755	1.7F
	1701	1353	1.9E
	2313	2012	2.0F
16 Sa	0543	0221	2.0E
	1130	0840	1.7F
	1744	1437	1.8E
	2359	2059	1.9F
17 Su	0632	0310	2.0E
	1219	0929	1.6F
	1833	1526	1.7E
		2149	1.8F
18 M	0051	0401	1.9E
	0730	1026	1.5F
	1317	1623	1.6E
	1933	2246	1.7F
19 Tu	0151	0503	1.8E
	0836	1128	1.4F
	1424	1728	1.5E
	2045	2353	1.6F
20 W	0300	0612	1.7E
	0949	1238	1.4F
	1540	1842	1.4E
	2204		
21 Th	0415	0105	1.5F
	1101	0725	1.7E
	1658	1349	1.4F
	2322	2000	1.5E
22 F	0527	0217	1.6F
	1207	0838	1.7E
	1807	1459	1.6F
		2111	1.6E
23 Sa	0032	0324	1.7F
	0633	0943	1.8E
	1306	1600	1.8F
	1909	2215	1.8E
24 Su	0133	0422	1.8F
	0731	1040	1.9E
	1357	1651	1.9F
	2002	2310	2.0E
25 M	0227	0517	1.9F
	0823	1130	2.0E
	1444	1740	2.0F
	2050	2359	2.1E
26 Tu	0317	0604	1.9F
	0909	1213	2.0E
	1528	1823	2.1F
	2134		
27 W	0402	0040	2.1E
	0952	0649	1.9F
	1608	1254	1.9E
	2215	1904	2.1F
28 Th	0445	0121	2.1E
	1032	0728	1.8F
	1646	1331	1.9E
	2254	1942	2.0F
29 F	0526	0159	2.0E
	1110	0808	1.7F
	1724	1409	1.7E
	2332	2024	1.9F
30 Sa	0608	0237	1.9E
	1150	0849	1.6F
	1803	1448	1.6E
		2103	1.8F

Time meridian 75° W. 0000 is midnight. 1200 is noon.

60

DELAWARE BAY ENTRANCE, 1983

F-Flood, Dir. 305° True   E-Ebb, Dir. 140° True

MAY

Day	Slack Water Time h.m.	Maximum Current Time h.m.	Vel. knots
1 Su	0012	0316	1.8E
	0651	0932	1.5F
	1233	1529	1.5E
	1846	2148	1.7F
2 M	0055	0403	1.7E
	0737	1020	1.4F
	1321	1618	1.4E
	1935	2236	1.6F
3 Tu	0143	0452	1.7E
	0828	1113	1.3F
	1415	1712	1.4E
	2030	2330	1.5F
4 W	0235	0547	1.6E
	0923	1208	1.3F
	1514	1809	1.3E
	2131		
5 Th		0028	1.4F
	0332	0643	1.6E
	1019	1304	1.4F
	1615	1911	1.4E
	2234		
6 F		0125	1.4F
	0430	0741	1.6E
	1113	1401	1.5F
	1712	2010	1.4E
	2333		
7 Sa		0222	1.5F
	0526	0834	1.7E
	1203	1455	1.6F
	1805	2104	1.6E
8 Su	0027	0315	1.5F
	0617	0922	1.7E
	1248	1542	1.7F
	1852	2153	1.7E
9 M	0115	0402	1.6F
	0703	1008	1.8E
	1329	1625	1.8F
	1934	2234	1.8E
10 Tu	0200	0445	1.6F
	0745	1048	1.8E
	1406	1705	1.8F
	2013	2314	1.9E
11 W	0241	0528	1.7F
	0825	1127	1.9E
	1441	1744	2.0F
	2050	2355	2.0E
12 Th	0321	0608	1.7F
	0903	1205	1.9E
	1516	1823	2.0F
	2128		
13 F		0034	2.1E
	0400	0650	1.7F
	0942	1246	1.9E
	1553	1905	2.0F
	2208		
14 Sa		0117	2.1E
	0443	0734	1.7F
	1025	1329	1.8E
	1635	1950	2.0F
	2252		
15 Su		0203	2.1E
	0529	0821	1.6F
	1112	1416	1.8E
	1722	2037	1.9F
	2340		

Day	Slack Water Time h.m.	Maximum Current Time h.m.	Vel. knots
16 M		0254	2.0E
	0621	0913	1.6F
	1206	1509	1.7E
	1818	2132	1.8F
17 Tu	0035	0348	1.9E
	0721	1010	1.5F
	1309	1611	1.5E
	1923	2233	1.7F
18 W	0138	0450	1.8E
	0827	1115	1.5F
	1420	1720	1.5E
	2039	2341	1.6F
19 Th	0247	0600	1.7E
	0937	1225	1.5F
	1536	1835	1.5E
	2158		
20 F		0052	1.5F
	0400	0712	1.7E
	1044	1335	1.6F
	1649	1950	1.6E
	2313		
21 Sa		0202	1.6F
	0509	0821	1.8E
	1145	1440	1.7F
	1754	2101	1.7E
22 Su	0019	0308	1.7F
	0612	0923	1.9E
	1241	1537	1.9F
	1851	2200	1.9E
23 M	0118	0405	1.7F
	0708	1016	1.9E
	1331	1629	2.0F
	1943	2251	2.0E
24 Tu	0211	0456	1.8F
	0759	1105	1.9E
	1417	1716	2.1F
	2029	2339	2.1E
25 W	0259	0542	1.8F
	0845	1148	1.9E
	1459	1757	2.1F
	2111		
26 Th		0020	2.1E
	0343	0625	1.7F
	0927	1227	1.8E
	1539	1838	2.0F
	2150		
27 F		0057	2.0E
	0425	0703	1.6F
	1006	1302	1.7E
	1616	1914	1.9F
	2227		
28 Sa		0133	1.9E
	0504	0742	1.5F
	1043	1338	1.6E
	1652	1952	1.8F
	2303		
29 Su		0208	1.9E
	0543	0822	1.5F
	1122	1416	1.5E
	1729	2032	1.7F
	2339		
30 M		0247	1.8E
	0623	0903	1.4F
	1203	1457	1.4E
	1811	2114	1.6F
31 Tu	0019	0328	1.8E
	0705	0949	1.4F
	1250	1546	1.4E
	1858	2201	1.5F

JUNE

Day	Slack Water Time h.m.	Maximum Current Time h.m.	Vel. knots
1 W	0104	0415	1.7E
	0752	1038	1.4F
	1342	1637	1.4E
	1951	2252	1.5F
2 Th	0153	0505	1.7E
	0842	1132	1.4F
	1437	1732	1.4E
	2050	2347	1.4F
3 F	0246	0600	1.7E
	0933	1225	1.5F
	1535	1829	1.4E
	2151		
4 Sa		0044	1.4F
	0342	0653	1.7E
	1025	1318	1.6F
	1630	1927	1.5E
	2251		
5 Su		0140	1.4F
	0437	0747	1.7E
	1114	1411	1.7F
	1723	2020	1.6E
	2347		
6 M		0233	1.5F
	0530	0837	1.7E
	1200	1459	1.8F
	1812	2111	1.7E
7 Tu	0039	0323	1.5F
	0619	0923	1.8E
	1244	1546	1.9F
	1857	2159	1.8E
8 W	0127	0411	1.6F
	0706	1010	1.8E
	1325	1629	2.0F
	1940	2245	2.0E
9 Th	0213	0457	1.6F
	0750	1053	1.8E
	1405	1714	2.0F
	2022	2329	2.0E
10 F	0257	0543	1.6F
	0835	1136	1.8E
	1446	1757	2.1F
	2104		
11 Sa		0012	2.1E
	0342	0629	1.6F
	0920	1223	1.8E
	1530	1842	2.1F
	2149		
12 Su		0059	2.1E
	0429	0716	1.6F
	1009	1310	1.8E
	1617	1933	2.0F
	2237		
13 M		0146	2.1E
	0519	0807	1.6F
	1102	1402	1.7E
	1710	2024	1.9F
	2328		
14 Tu		0241	2.0E
	0613	0900	1.6F
	1200	1459	1.6E
	1810	2120	1.8F
15 W	0025	0337	1.9E
	0712	1001	1.6F
	1305	1602	1.6E
	1918	2221	1.7F

Day	Slack Water Time h.m.	Maximum Current Time h.m.	Vel. knots
16 Th	0126	0439	1.9E
	0815	1105	1.6F
	1414	1711	1.5E
	2032	2327	1.6F
17 F	0232	0543	1.8E
	0918	1209	1.7F
	1524	1822	1.6E
	2146		
18 Sa		0037	1.6F
	0340	0651	1.8E
	1019	1314	1.8F
	1631	1935	1.7E
	2255		
19 Su		0140	1.6F
	0445	0757	1.8E
	1117	1416	1.9F
	1732	2042	1.8E
	2359		
20 M		0245	1.6F
	0546	0856	1.9E
	1212	1511	2.0F
	1828	2138	1.9E
21 Tu	0057	0340	1.6F
	0641	0947	1.9E
	1302	1604	2.0F
	1918	2229	2.0E
22 W	0150	0432	1.6F
	0732	1038	1.8E
	1348	1647	2.1F
	2005	2316	2.0E
23 Th	0238	0519	1.6F
	0819	1122	1.8E
	1431	1733	2.0F
	2047	2357	2.0E
24 F	0323	0602	1.6F
	0902	1200	1.7E
	1511	1809	1.9F
	2125		
25 Sa		0034	2.0E
	0404	0641	1.5F
	0942	1238	1.6E
	1549	1850	1.9F
	2201		
26 Su		0107	1.9E
	0442	0718	1.5F
	1020	1314	1.5E
	1625	1926	1.8F
	2236		
27 M		0142	1.8E
	0519	0759	1.4F
	1058	1351	1.5E
	1702	2004	1.7F
	2311		
28 Tu		0218	1.8E
	0556	0837	1.4F
	1138	1432	1.4E
	1741	2045	1.6F
	2348		
29 W		0300	1.8E
	0634	0919	1.4F
	1221	1515	1.4E
	1825	2132	1.6F
30 Th	0029	0341	1.8E
	0716	1006	1.5F
	1308	1604	1.4E
	1915	2217	1.5F

Time meridian 75° W.   0000 is midnight.   1200 is noon.

F-Flood, Dir. 305° True   E-Ebb, Dir. 140° True

JULY

Day	Slack Water Time h.m.	Maximum Current Time h.m.	Vel. knots	Day	Slack Water Time h.m.	Maximum Current Time h.m.	Vel. knots
1 F	0114	0430	1.8E	16 Sa	0212	0521	1.9E
	0800	1055	1.5F		0852	1148	1.8F
	1359	1654	1.4E		1503	1803	1.7E
	2009	2309	1.5F		2125		
2 Sa	0203	0517	1.8E	17 Su		0012	1.6F
	0847	1144	1.6F		0313	0625	1.8E
	1452	1749	1.5E		0950	1248	1.8F
	2107				1605	1909	1.7E
					2231		
3 Su		0002	1.4F	18 M		0113	1.5F
	0255	0610	1.7E		0415	0726	1.8E
	0935	1236	1.7F		1046	1345	1.9F
	1546	1844	1.5E		1704	2014	1.8E
	2207				2334		
4 M		0057	1.4F	19 Tu		0213	1.5F
	0348	0700	1.7E		0515	0823	1.8E
	1024	1329	1.7F		1140	1442	1.9F
	1639	1939	1.6E		1800	2111	1.9E
	2305						
5 Tu		0153	1.4F	20 W	0032	0312	1.5F
	0443	0753	1.7E		0611	0921	1.7E
	1112	1420	1.8F		1231	1533	2.0F
	1731	2032	1.7E		1851	2204	1.9E
6 W	0002	0246	1.4F	21 Th	0126	0403	1.5F
	0536	0844	1.7E		0704	1012	1.7E
	1201	1511	1.9F		1320	1621	2.0F
	1821	2126	1.8E		1938	2250	1.9E
7 Th	0056	0337	1.5F	22 F	0215	0454	1.5F
	0629	0933	1.7E		0753	1053	1.6E
	1248	1558	2.0F		1405	1704	1.9F
	1910	2215	1.9E		2022	2335	1.9E
8 F	0148	0428	1.5F	23 Sa	0300	0539	1.5F
	0721	1024	1.7E		0838	1136	1.6E
	1336	1647	2.0F		1447	1745	1.9F
	1958	2304	2.0E		2101		
9 Sa	0238	0519	1.6F	24 Su		0010	1.9E
	0812	1114	1.8E		0341	0618	1.5F
	1424	1736	2.1F		0919	1215	1.5E
	2046	2353	2.1E		1525	1824	1.8F
					2137		
10 Su	0328	0610	1.6F	25 M		0045	1.9E
	0905	1205	1.8E		0419	0654	1.4F
	1515	1826	2.0F		0957	1251	1.5E
	2135				1602	1902	1.7F
					2211		
11 M		0044	2.1E	26 Tu		0120	1.9E
	0418	0701	1.6F		0454	0733	1.5F
	0959	1258	1.7E		1034	1326	1.5E
	1608	1919	2.0F		1638	1939	1.7F
	2226				2244		
12 Tu		0136	2.1E	27 W		0152	1.9E
	0509	0755	1.7F		0528	0811	1.5F
	1055	1353	1.7E		1112	1405	1.5E
	1705	2012	1.9F		1715	2018	1.7F
	2318				2319		
13 W		0227	2.1E	28 Th		0229	1.9E
	0603	0850	1.7F		0602	0850	1.5F
	1154	1450	1.7E		1151	1447	1.5E
	1805	2107	1.8F		1756	2101	1.6F
					2356		
14 Th	0013	0325	2.0E	29 F		0310	1.9E
	0658	0948	1.7F		0638	0933	1.6F
	1256	1551	1.6E		1233	1530	1.5E
	1910	2207	1.7F		1840	2145	1.6F
15 F	0111	0423	1.9E	30 Sa	0037	0351	1.9E
	0754	1047	1.7F		0717	1018	1.6F
	1359	1656	1.6E		1319	1617	1.6E
	2017	2309	1.6F		1930	2230	1.5F
				31 Su	0121	0436	1.8E
					0800	1103	1.7F
					1409	1708	1.6E
					2024	2321	1.5F

AUGUST

Day	Slack Water Time h.m.	Maximum Current Time h.m.	Vel. knots	Day	Slack Water Time h.m.	Maximum Current Time h.m.	Vel. knots
1 M	0210	0524	1.8E	16 Tu		0043	1.4F
	0846	1155	1.7F		0341	0647	1.7E
	1502	1803	1.6E		1011	1312	1.8F
	2123				1631	1937	1.7E
					2304		
2 Tu		0016	1.4F	17 W		0142	1.4F
	0303	0619	1.7E		0441	0749	1.6E
	0936	1248	1.8F		1107	1408	1.8F
	1557	1859	1.6E		1728	2039	1.7E
	2225						
3 W		0113	1.4F	18 Th	0003	0241	1.4F
	0400	0712	1.7E		0540	0846	1.6E
	1030	1341	1.8F		1201	1503	1.8F
	1654	1958	1.7E		1821	2134	1.8E
	2328						
4 Th		0211	1.4F	19 F	0058	0334	1.4F
	0459	0809	1.7E		0635	0941	1.6E
	1125	1438	1.9F		1252	1552	1.8F
	1750	2057	1.8E		1910	2225	1.8E
5 F	0029	0310	1.4F	20 Sa	0148	0428	1.4F
	0600	0907	1.7E		0727	1029	1.6E
	1221	1533	1.9F		1339	1641	1.8F
	1846	2153	1.9E		1955	2306	1.9E
6 Sa	0127	0405	1.4F	21 Su	0233	0513	1.5F
	0700	1004	1.7E		0813	1114	1.6E
	1317	1629	2.0F		1423	1722	1.8F
	1941	2248	2.0E		2035	2345	1.9E
7 Su	0223	0503	1.5F	22 M	0314	0552	1.5F
	0759	1059	1.7E		0855	1151	1.6E
	1412	1722	2.0F		1503	1801	1.8F
	2033	2341	2.0E		2112		
8 M	0315	0557	1.6F	23 Tu		0020	1.9E
	0856	1156	1.8E		0351	0631	1.5F
	1508	1815	2.0F		0933	1227	1.6E
	2125				1541	1838	1.8F
					2145		
9 Tu		0034	2.1E	24 W		0052	1.9E
	0406	0649	1.7F		0424	0706	1.6F
	0951	1249	1.8E		1009	1302	1.6E
	1603	1907	2.0F		1616	1913	1.7F
	2216				2217		
10 W		0124	2.1E	25 Th		0125	1.9E
	0456	0742	1.8F		0455	0742	1.6F
	1046	1345	1.8E		1043	1339	1.6E
	1659	1958	2.0F		1651	1951	1.7F
	2306				2249		
11 Th		0215	2.1E	26 F		0158	1.9E
	0545	0834	1.8F		0526	0819	1.7F
	1142	1437	1.8E		1119	1416	1.6E
	1756	2053	1.9F		1727	2029	1.7F
	2357				2324		
12 F		0306	2.1E	27 Sa		0236	1.9E
	0636	0927	1.9F		0558	0858	1.7F
	1238	1535	1.8E		1158	1457	1.7E
	1854	2148	1.8F		1808	2112	1.6F
13 Sa	0050	0401	2.0E	28 Su	0001	0313	1.9E
	0727	1023	1.9F		0634	0938	1.8F
	1335	1633	1.7E		1240	1542	1.7E
	1955	2242	1.6F		1854	2157	1.6F
14 Su	0145	0455	1.9E	29 M	0044	0358	1.9E
	0821	1118	1.9F		0715	1027	1.8F
	1434	1733	1.7E		1328	1631	1.7E
	2058	2340	1.5F		1946	2244	1.5F
15 M	0242	0551	1.8E	30 Tu	0131	0449	1.8E
	0916	1215	1.8F		0802	1116	1.8F
	1533	1836	1.7E		1421	1727	1.6E
	2201				2046	2341	1.4F
				31 W	0225	0540	1.7E
					0856	1209	1.7F
					1520	1824	1.6E
					2152		

Time meridian 75° W.   0000 is midnight.   1200 is noon.

DELAWARE BAY ENTRANCE, 1983

F-Flood, Dir. 305° True   E-Ebb, Dir. 140° True

SEPTEMBER

Day	Slack Water Time h.m.	Maximum Current Time h.m.	Vel. knots
1 Th		0041	1.3F
	0326	0641	1.6E
	0955	1310	1.7F
	1622	1929	1.6E
	2301		
2 F		0144	1.3F
	0433	0743	1.6E
	1059	1412	1.8F
	1727	2033	1.7E
3 Sa	0009	0249	1.3F
	0542	0849	1.6E
	1205	1515	1.8F
	1829	2136	1.8E
4 Su	0111	0351	1.4F
	0648	0953	1.6E
	1308	1614	1.9F
	1928	2235	1.9E
5 M	0208	0451	1.6F
	0751	1051	1.7E
	1407	1710	2.0F
	2022	2330	2.1E
6 Tu	0300	0545	1.7F
	0848	1147	1.8E
	1503	1803	2.0F
	2114		
7 W		0022	2.1E
	0349	0637	1.9F
	0941	1240	1.9E
	1557	1855	2.0F
	2202		
8 Th		0110	2.2E
	0436	0724	1.9F
	1033	1331	1.9E
	1649	1944	2.0F
	2250		
9 F		0156	2.1E
	0522	0812	2.0F
	1123	1421	1.9E
	1741	2031	1.9F
	2336		
10 Sa		0243	2.1E
	0608	0903	2.0F
	1213	1512	1.9E
	1833	2122	1.8F
11 Su	0024	0330	2.0E
	0656	0952	1.9F
	1305	1604	1.8E
	1928	2213	1.6F
12 M	0114	0421	1.8E
	0746	1043	1.8F
	1359	1659	1.7E
	2027	2308	1.5F
13 Tu	0207	0512	1.7E
	0839	1136	1.8F
	1456	1758	1.6E
	2128		
14 W		0007	1.3F
	0305	0611	1.6E
	0935	1235	1.7F
	1554	1859	1.6E
	2230		
15 Th		0106	1.3F
	0406	0712	1.6E
	1033	1331	1.7F
	1652	2000	1.6E
	2330		
16 F		0209	1.3F
	0507	0813	1.5E
	1130	1430	1.7F
	1747	2059	1.7E
17 Sa	0025	0304	1.3F
	0606	0909	1.5E
	1224	1521	1.8F
	1838	2150	1.8E
18 Su	0116	0357	1.4F
	0659	1000	1.5E
	1313	1609	1.8F
	1924	2235	1.8E
19 M	0201	0444	1.5F
	0746	1045	1.6E
	1359	1654	1.8F
	2006	2314	1.9E
20 Tu	0241	0523	1.6F
	0828	1126	1.6E
	1440	1733	1.8F
	2043	2349	1.9E
21 W	0317	0600	1.7F
	0905	1202	1.7E
	1517	1811	1.8F
	2117		
22 Th		0021	1.9E
	0349	0636	1.7F
	0939	1235	1.7E
	1552	1847	1.8F
	2148		
23 F		0055	1.9E
	0419	0710	1.8F
	1012	1310	1.8E
	1625	1923	1.8F
	2219		
24 Sa		0126	2.0E
	0448	0747	1.8F
	1046	1347	1.8E
	1701	1958	1.7F
	2253		
25 Su		0203	1.9E
	0519	0824	1.8F
	1123	1424	1.8E
	1739	2041	1.7F
	2329		
26 M		0240	1.9E
	0555	0905	1.8F
	1205	1510	1.8E
	1824	2124	1.6F
27 Tu	0011	0325	1.8E
	0637	0951	1.8F
	1253	1557	1.7E
	1916	2216	1.5F
28 W	0100	0414	1.7E
	0726	1043	1.8F
	1347	1656	1.7E
	2017	2311	1.3F
29 Th	0157	0510	1.6E
	0825	1143	1.7F
	1450	1757	1.6E
	2127		
30 F		0016	1.3F
	0303	0617	1.5E
	0932	1246	1.6F
	1559	1905	1.6E
	2242		

OCTOBER

Day	Slack Water Time h.m.	Maximum Current Time h.m.	Vel. knots
1 Sa		0124	1.3F
	0418	0726	1.5E
	1046	1353	1.7F
	1709	2016	1.7E
	2352		
2 Su		0234	1.4F
	0533	0838	1.6E
	1158	1502	1.8F
	1815	2124	1.8E
3 M	0055	0337	1.5F
	0642	0944	1.7E
	1303	1603	1.9F
	1915	2222	1.9E
4 Tu	0151	0438	1.7F
	0742	1045	1.8E
	1402	1700	2.0F
	2010	2317	2.1E
5 W	0241	0530	1.9F
	0837	1139	2.0E
	1456	1751	2.0F
	2059		
6 Th		0004	2.1E
	0328	0619	2.0F
	0927	1228	2.0E
	1546	1837	2.0F
	2145		
7 F		0051	2.1E
	0412	0704	2.1F
	1014	1315	2.0E
	1634	1923	2.0F
	2229		
8 Sa		0135	2.1E
	0455	0749	2.0F
	1100	1400	2.0E
	1722	2009	1.8F
	2312		
9 Su		0215	2.0E
	0538	0834	2.0F
	1145	1443	1.9E
	1810	2056	1.7F
	2356		
10 M		0301	1.9E
	0622	0920	1.9F
	1232	1532	1.8E
	1900	2141	1.5F
11 Tu	0042	0347	1.7E
	0709	1006	1.8F
	1322	1623	1.7E
	1954	2233	1.4F
12 W	0133	0436	1.6E
	0800	1058	1.7F
	1415	1719	1.6E
	2051	2331	1.3F
13 Th	0229	0532	1.5E
	0856	1156	1.6F
	1512	1816	1.5E
	2152		
14 F		0029	1.2F
	0331	0633	1.4E
	0956	1252	1.5F
	1611	1919	1.5E
	2251		
15 Sa		0130	1.3F
	0433	0735	1.4E
	1056	1353	1.6F
	1707	2018	1.6E
	2347		
16 Su		0229	1.4F
	0533	0836	1.5E
	1152	1447	1.6F
	1800	2110	1.7E
17 M	0037	0320	1.5F
	0626	0927	1.6E
	1244	1536	1.7F
	1848	2159	1.8E
18 Tu	0122	0406	1.6F
	0713	1014	1.7E
	1330	1625	1.7F
	1931	2238	1.9E
19 W	0202	0447	1.7F
	0755	1054	1.7E
	1412	1704	1.8F
	2010	2313	1.9E
20 Th	0238	0528	1.8F
	0833	1130	1.8E
	1450	1742	1.8F
	2045	2349	1.9E
21 F	0311	0603	1.8F
	0907	1206	1.9E
	1526	1817	1.8F
	2117		
22 Sa		0022	1.9E
	0341	0637	1.9F
	0941	1242	1.9E
	1600	1853	1.8F
	2149		
23 Su		0055	1.9E
	0411	0714	1.9F
	1015	1319	1.9E
	1636	1932	1.7F
	2224		
24 M		0130	1.9E
	0444	0755	1.9F
	1053	1358	1.9E
	1716	2013	1.7F
	2302		
25 Tu		0211	1.9E
	0522	0836	1.9F
	1136	1443	1.9E
	1801	2100	1.6F
	2346		
26 W		0257	1.8E
	0607	0925	1.8F
	1225	1534	1.8E
	1855	2151	1.4F
27 Th	0038	0348	1.7E
	0701	1017	1.7F
	1322	1629	1.7E
	1959	2252	1.3F
28 F	0140	0451	1.5E
	0806	1122	1.6F
	1428	1737	1.6E
	2111		
29 Sa		0000	1.3F
	0253	0600	1.5E
	0921	1231	1.6F
	1541	1850	1.6E
	2226		
30 Su		0111	1.3F
	0412	0716	1.5E
	1039	1341	1.6F
	1654	2001	1.7E
	2335		
31 M		0220	1.5F
	0526	0830	1.6E
	1152	1449	1.7F
	1800	2110	1.8E

Time meridian 75° W.   0000 is midnight.   1200 is noon.

F-Flood, Dir. 305° True   E-Ebb, Dir. 140° True

NOVEMBER

Day	Slack Water Time h.m.	Maximum Current Time h.m.	Vel. knots	Day	Slack Water Time h.m.	Maximum Current Time h.m.	Vel. knots
1 Tu	0036	0324	1.7F	16 W	0038	0327	1.7F
	0632	0937	1.8F		0635	0936	1.7E
	1256	1550	1.8F		1257	1546	1.7F
	1900	2209	2.0E		1851	2155	1.8E
2 W	0130	0422	1.9F	17 Th	0119	0412	1.8F
	0730	1035	1.9F		0718	1019	1.8E
	1352	1646	1.9F		1341	1629	1.7F
	1953	2300	2.1E		1932	2235	1.9E
3 Th	0219	0513	2.0F	18 F	0157	0451	1.9F
	0821	1126	2.1E		0758	1057	1.9E
	1444	1735	2.0F		1421	1710	1.7F
	2041	2349	2.1E		2010	2312	1.9E
4 F	0305	0558	2.1F	19 Sa	0231	0529	1.9F
	0909	1213	2.1E		0835	1138	1.9E
	1532	1820	1.9F		1459	1749	1.7F
	2126				2046	2348	1.9E
5 Sa		0031	2.1E	20 Su	0304	0607	2.0F
	0347	0641	2.1F		0911	1213	2.0E
	0953	1256	2.1E		1537	1828	1.7F
	1618	1903	1.9F		2121		
	2207						
6 Su		0110	2.0E	21 M		0025	1.9E
	0428	0725	2.0F		0338	0645	2.0F
	1036	1339	2.0E		0949	1254	2.0E
	1702	1946	1.7F		1616	1909	1.7F
	2248				2159		
7 M		0149	1.9E	22 Tu		0106	1.9E
	0508	0808	1.9F		0415	0725	2.0F
	1117	1417	1.9E		1029	1337	2.0E
	1746	2029	1.6F		1658	1952	1.6F
	2329				2241		
8 Tu		0231	1.7E	23 W		0149	1.8E
	0550	0847	1.8F		0458	0812	1.9F
	1200	1503	1.8E		1115	1423	1.9E
	1832	2112	1.5F		1746	2043	1.6F
					2330		
9 W	0012	0312	1.6E	24 Th		0240	1.7E
	0634	0935	1.7F		0548	0903	1.8F
	1245	1548	1.7E		1207	1516	1.8E
	1921	2203	1.4F		1842	2135	1.5F
10 Th	0100	0401	1.5E	25 F	0027	0335	1.6E
	0723	1024	1.6F		0647	1002	1.7F
	1334	1639	1.6E		1306	1617	1.7E
	2014	2255	1.3F		1947	2238	1.4F
11 F	0154	0455	1.4E	26 Sa	0133	0439	1.5E
	0818	1115	1.5F		0757	1105	1.6F
	1428	1734	1.5E		1413	1722	1.7E
	2110	2350	1.3F		2057	2345	1.4F
12 Sa	0254	0554	1.4E	27 Su	0247	0550	1.5E
	0917	1213	1.5F		0915	1215	1.6F
	1525	1832	1.5E		1525	1834	1.6E
	2207				2207		
13 Su		0049	1.3F	28 M		0055	1.5F
	0355	0654	1.4E		0403	0706	1.5E
	1018	1313	1.5F		1031	1325	1.6F
	1622	1929	1.6E		1636	1944	1.7E
	2302				2313		
14 M		0145	1.4F	29 Tu		0203	1.6F
	0454	0753	1.5E		0513	0820	1.7E
	1115	1408	1.5F		1140	1432	1.7F
	1716	2023	1.7E		1741	2049	1.8E
	2352						
15 Tu		0239	1.5F	30 W	0012	0304	1.8F
	0547	0849	1.6E		0616	0923	1.9E
	1208	1459	1.6F		1243	1534	1.8F
	1806	2112	1.8E		1840	2147	1.9E

DECEMBER

Day	Slack Water Time h.m.	Maximum Current Time h.m.	Vel. knots	Day	Slack Water Time h.m.	Maximum Current Time h.m.	Vel. knots
1 Th	0106	0403	2.0F	16 F	0033	0331	1.8F
	0712	1020	2.0E		0639	0942	1.8E
	1339	1629	1.8F		1306	1554	1.6F
	1933	2240	2.0E		1852	2155	1.8E
2 F	0155	0451	2.0F	17 Sa	0114	0414	1.9F
	0803	1110	2.1E		0722	1025	1.9E
	1430	1716	1.9F		1351	1637	1.6F
	2021	2325	2.0E		1935	2238	1.8E
3 Sa	0240	0538	2.1F	18 Su	0154	0457	1.9F
	0849	1155	2.1E		0804	1107	1.9E
	1517	1803	1.8F		1434	1720	1.7F
	2105				2016	2319	1.8E
4 Su		0006	1.9E	19 M	0233	0538	2.0F
	0323	0619	2.0F		0845	1149	2.0E
	0932	1238	2.0E		1516	1804	1.7F
	1601	1844	1.7F		2058		
	2146						
5 M		0047	1.8E	20 Tu		0002	1.8E
	0403	0700	2.0F		0313	0622	2.0F
	1012	1317	1.9E		0927	1234	2.0E
	1643	1924	1.6F		1600	1849	1.7F
	2226				2142		
6 Tu		0125	1.7E	21 W		0045	1.8E
	0442	0739	1.9F		0357	0708	2.0F
	1051	1355	1.8E		1012	1319	2.0E
	1724	2005	1.5F		1646	1938	1.6F
	2305				2229		
7 W		0204	1.6E	22 Th		0134	1.8E
	0521	0821	1.8F		0445	0757	1.9F
	1130	1434	1.8E		1101	1410	2.0E
	1806	2047	1.4F		1737	2027	1.6F
	2346				2322		
8 Th		0243	1.5E	23 F		0228	1.7E
	0603	0901	1.7F		0540	0850	1.8F
	1211	1516	1.7E		1155	1503	1.9E
	1849	2132	1.4F		1833	2122	1.6F
9 F	0031	0329	1.5E	24 Sa	0021	0325	1.7E
	0648	0948	1.6F		0642	0948	1.7F
	1256	1601	1.6E		1254	1601	1.8E
	1936	2220	1.4F		1934	2224	1.6F
10 Sa	0120	0420	1.4E	25 Su	0127	0430	1.6E
	0739	1039	1.5F		0751	1051	1.7F
	1345	1652	1.6E		1358	1706	1.8E
	2026	2312	1.4F		2038	2329	1.6F
11 Su	0215	0515	1.4E	26 M	0237	0540	1.6E
	0836	1132	1.5F		0904	1157	1.6F
	1437	1747	1.6E		1506	1813	1.7E
	2118				2143		
12 M		0006	1.4F	27 Tu		0035	1.6F
	0312	0612	1.4E		0347	0650	1.7E
	0934	1227	1.5F		1015	1305	1.6F
	1532	1840	1.6E		1613	1921	1.8E
	2211				2246		
13 Tu		0101	1.5F	28 W		0140	1.7F
	0408	0708	1.5E		0453	0801	1.8E
	1032	1323	1.5F		1123	1412	1.6F
	1626	1935	1.7E		1717	2023	1.8E
	2301				2345		
14 W		0154	1.6F	29 Th		0240	1.9F
	0502	0801	1.6E		0555	0904	1.9E
	1127	1417	1.5F		1224	1511	1.7F
	1718	2023	1.7E		1816	2126	1.8E
	2349						
15 Th		0242	1.7F	30 F	0040	0337	1.9F
	0552	0854	1.7E		0651	1000	2.0E
	1219	1507	1.6F		1321	1606	1.7F
	1807	2111	1.7E		1910	2219	1.9E
				31 Sa	0130	0428	2.0F
					0742	1051	2.0E
					1412	1700	1.7F
					2000	2304	1.8E

Time meridian 75° W.   0000 is midnight.   1200 is noon.

CHESAPEAKE BAY ENTRANCE, VIRGINIA, 1983

F-Flood, Dir. 305° True   E-Ebb, Dir. 125° True

JANUARY

Day	Slack Water Time h.m.	Max Current Time h.m.	Vel. knots	Day	Slack Water Time h.m.	Max Current Time h.m.	Vel. knots
1 Sa	0002	0355	2.0E	16 Su		0404	1.4E
	0717	1015	1.7F		0729	1014	1.0F
	1332	1648	1.7E		1320	1646	1.2E
	2006	2227	1.0F		2007	2216	0.6F
2 Su	0056	0449	1.9E	17 M	0033	0438	1.4E
	0811	1107	1.6F		0807	1049.	1.0F
	1422	1741	1.6E		1351	1721	1.2E
	2100	2322	0.9F		2043	2253	0.6F
3 M	0153	0545	1.8E	18 Tu	0113	0515	1.4E
	0907	1200	1.4F		0847	1126	1.0F
	1512	1836	1.5E		1422	1759	1.1E
	2156				2121	2334	0.7F
4 Tu		0019	0.9F	19 W	0158	0559	1.3E
	0254	0645	1.6E		0931	1207	0.9F
	1007	1255	1.2F		1456	1836	1.1E
	1602	1932	1.5E		2204		
	2255						
5 W		0121	0.8F	20 Th		0023	0.7F
	0400	0747	1.5E		0249	0645	1.2E
	1110	1351	1.0F		1020	1251	0.8F
	1652	2029	1.4E		1533	1921	1.1E
	2355				2251		
6 Th		0225	0.8F	21 F		0116	0.7F
	0511	0854	1.3E		0348	0741	1.2E
	1217	1452	0.8F		1115	1340	0.7F
	1742	2127	1.4E		1615	2009	1.2E
					2344		
7 F	0055	0333	0.8F	22 Sa		0213	0.8F
	0626	1002	1.2E		0457	0848	1.1E
	1326	1554	0.7F		1217	1435	0.6F
	1833	2225	1.4E		1704	2108	1.3E
8 Sa	0153	0436	0.8F	23 Su	0042	0317	0.8F
	0737	1105	1.2E		0614	0956	1.1E
	1433	1652	0.6F		1323	1536	0.6F
	1922	2320	1.4E		1759	2209	1.4E
9 Su	0247	0537	0.9F	24 M	0141	0426	1.0F
	0842	1206	1.2E		0732	1105	1.2E
	1533	1746	0.5F		1428	1642	0.6F
	2008				1900	2310	1.5E
10 M		0008	1.4E	25 Tu	0239	0529	1.2F
	0336	0627	0.9F		0844	1209	1.3E
	0938	1257	1.2E		1530	1743	0.7F
	1625	1834	0.5F		2003		
	2052						
11 Tu		0053	1.4E	26 W		0009	1.7E
	0420	0716	1.0F		0335	0631	1.4F
	1026	1345	1.2E		0948	1309	1.4E
	1710	1915	0.5F		1626	1843	0.8F
	2132				2105		
12 W		0138	1.4E	27 Th		0108	1.8E
	0501	0755	1.0F		0429	0729	1.5F
	1108	1424	1.2E		1045	1402	1.6E
	1750	1954	0.5F		1718	1939	0.9F
	2209				2205		
13 Th		0217	1.5E	28 F		0201	2.0E
	0540	0832	1.0F		0522	0820	1.6F
	1145	1503	1.2E		1137	1453	1.7E
	1825	2030	0.5F		1808	2032	1.0F
	2245				2302		
14 F		0253	1.5E	29 Sa		0254	2.1E
	0616	0905	1.1F		0614	0911	1.7F
	1218	1540	1.2E		1226	1542	1.7E
	1859	2105	0.6F		1856	2124	1.1F
	2320				2358		
15 Sa		0329	1.5E	30 Su		0345	2.1E
	0653	0939	1.1F		0706	1001	1.6F
	1250	1615	1.2E		1312	1631	1.7E
	1933	2140	0.6F		1944	2214	1.1F
	2356						
				31 M	0052	0437	2.0E
					0758	1049	1.5F
					1357	1718	1.7E
					2033	2304	1.1F

FEBRUARY

Day	Slack Water Time h.m.	Max Current Time h.m.	Vel. knots	Day	Slack Water Time h.m.	Max Current Time h.m.	Vel. knots
1 Tu	0147	0529	1.9E	16 W	0103	0453	1.5E
	0850	1138	1.3F		0823	1058	1.0F
	1440	1804	1.6E		1345	1719	1.3E
	2124	2355	1.0F		2040	2311	0.9F
2 W	0243	0623	1.7E	17 Th	0146	0532	1.4E
	0945	1226	1.1F		0904	1135	0.9F
	1522	1856	1.5E		1416	1756	1.3E
	2217				2121	2354	0.9F
3 Th		0049	1.0F	18 F	0235	0619	1.3E
	0341	0721	1.4E		0951	1216	0.8F
	1043	1317	0.9F		1450	1837	1.3E
	1604	1949	1.4E		2208		
	2313						
4 F		0150	0.9F	19 Sa		0046	0.9F
	0444	0822	1.3E		0332	0714	1.2E
	1147	1411	0.7F		1046	1305	0.7F
	1648	2045	1.3E		1531	1928	1.3E
					2304		
5 Sa	0013	0252	0.8F	20 Su		0141	0.9F
	0553	0927	1.1E		0438	0818	1.1E
	1256	1507	0.5F		1149	1402	0.6F
	1734	2141	1.2E		1619	2031	1.3E
6 Su	0114	0357	0.7F	21 M	0006	0250	0.9F
	0705	1036	1.0E		0555	0931	1.1E
	1406	1609	0.4F		1300	1506	0.5F
	1825	2242	1.2E		1719	2139	1.4E
7 M	0214	0503	0.7F	22 Tu	0112	0359	1.0F
	0813	1136	1.0E		0715	1048	1.1E
	1512	1714	0.3F		1411	1619	0.5F
	1921	2339	1.3E		1830	2248	1.5E
8 Tu	0309	0602	0.8F	23 W	0218	0511	1.1F
	0912	1231	1.0E		0830	1153	1.2E
	1606	1809	0.4F		1515	1726	0.6F
	2016				1945	2356	1.6E
9 W		0028	1.3E	24 Th	0320	0617	1.3F
	0358	0651	0.9F		0934	1254	1.4E
	1002	1320	1.1E		1612	1830	0.8F
	1650	1851	0.4F		2056		
	2106						
10 Th		0115	1.4E	25 F		0056	1.8E
	0441	0736	0.9F		0418	0715	1.5F
	1043	1403	1.2E		1029	1347	1.6E
	1727	1936	0.5F		1702	1929	1.0F
	2151				2200		
11 F		0157	1.4E	26 Sa		0151	2.0E
	0520	0811	1.0F		0512	0808	1.5F
	1120	1440	1.2E		1118	1436	1.7E
	1800	2011	0.6F		1749	2020	1.1F
	2231				2259		
12 Sa		0234	1.5E	27 Su		0242	2.0E
	0557	0844	1.0F		0603	0855	1.6F
	1152	1515	1.2E		1203	1520	1.8E
	1831	2045	0.6F		1834	2109	1.2F
	2309				2353		
13 Su		0310	1.5E	28 M		0333	2.0E
	0633	0916	1.1F		0653	0942	1.5F
	1222	1545	1.3E		1245	1605	1.8E
	1901	2120	0.7F		1918	2155	1.3F
	2345						
14 M		0343	1.5E				
	0708	0948	1.1F				
	1249	1617	1.3E				
	1932	2152	0.8F				
15 Tu	0023	0418	1.5E				
	0744	1021	1.0F				
	1317	1647	1.3E				
	2005	2230	0.8F				

Time meridian 75° W. 0000 is midnight. 1200 is noon.
* Current weak and variable.

F-Flood, Dir. 305° True   E-Ebb, Dir. 125° True

MARCH

Day	Slack Water Time h.m.	Maximum Current Time h.m.	Vel. knots
1 Tu	0045	0422	2.0E
	0742	1024	1.4F
	1324	1650	1.8E
	2003	2243	1.3F
2 W	0135	0510	1.8E
	0831	1109	1.2F
	1401	1733	1.7E
	2050	2329	1.2F
3 Th	0226	0601	1.6E
	0922	1151	1.0F
	1437	1819	1.5E
	2138		
4 F		0016	1.1F
	0317	0650	1.4E
	1016	1237	0.7F
	1513	1905	1.4E
	2231		
5 Sa		0111	0.9F
	0413	0748	1.2E
	1115	1327	0.5F
	1550	1959	1.2E
	2329		
6 Su		0208	0.8F
	0514	0852	1.0E
	1223	1420	0.4F
	1632	2100	1.1E
7 M	0032	0311	0.7F
	0623	0958	0.9E
	1336	1524	0.3F
	1726	2203	1.1E
8 Tu	0137	0420	0.6F
	0733	1105	0.9E
	1444	1636	0.3F
	1833	2308	1.1E
9 W	0237	0527	0.7F
	0834	1202	1.0E
	1538	1737	0.3F
	1942		
10 Th		0002	1.2E
	0329	0621	0.8F
	0925	1249	1.1E
	1620	1825	0.4F
	2041		
11 F		0049	1.3E
	0415	0704	0.9F
	1008	1331	1.2E
	1655	1907	0.5F
	2131		
12 Sa		0132	1.4E
	0455	0739	0.9F
	1044	1408	1.2E
	1726	1945	0.7F
	2215		
13 Su		0210	1.5E
	0533	0814	1.0F
	1116	1441	1.3E
	1756	2021	0.8F
	2254		
14 M		0246	1.5E
	0609	0849	1.0F
	1144	1512	1.4E
	1826	2055	0.9F
	2333		
15 Tu		0322	1.6E
	0644	0918	1.0F
	1211	1542	1.4E
	1856	2128	1.0F
16 W	0011	0355	1.6E
	0721	0954	1.0F
	1238	1613	1.4E
	1929	2205	1.1F
17 Th	0052	0433	1.5E
	0800	1027	1.0F
	1307	1646	1.4E
	2006	2247	1.1F
18 F	0137	0514	1.5E
	0842	1106	0.9F
	1338	1722	1.4E
	2048	2332	1.1F
19 Sa	0226	0603	1.3E
	0931	1151	0.8F
	1414	1808	1.4E
	2138		
20 Su		0023	1.1F
	0323	0656	1.2E
	1027	1238	0.7F
	1457	1859	1.4E
	2235		
21 M		0122	1.1F
	0428	0803	1.1E
	1133	1338	0.5F
	1549	2003	1.4E
	2341		
22 Tu		0232	1.0F
	0544	0918	1.1E
	1247	1447	0.5F
	1655	2120	1.4E
23 W	0052	0343	1.0F
	0702	1033	1.1E
	1359	1603	0.5F
	1817	2235	1.5E
24 Th	0203	0457	1.1F
	0814	1140	1.3E
	1502	1717	0.6F
	1940	2343	1.6E
25 F	0308	0602	1.2F
	0914	1238	1.5E
	1555	1820	0.8F
	2054		
26 Sa		0044	1.8E
	0406	0700	1.3F
	1006	1327	1.6E
	1642	1917	1.0F
	2158		
27 Su		0140	1.9E
	0500	0749	1.4F
	1052	1414	1.7E
	1727	2007	1.2F
	2254		
28 M		0229	1.9E
	0550	0835	1.4F
	1133	1457	1.8E
	1809	2053	1.3F
	2346		
29 Tu		0317	1.9E
	0638	0918	1.3F
	1211	1538	1.8E
	1851	2136	1.4F
30 W	0034	0404	1.8E
	0724	0959	1.1F
	1245	1619	1.7E
	1934	2220	1.3F
31 Th	0121	0449	1.7E
	0811	1038	1.0F
	1318	1659	1.6E
	2017	2303	1.2F

APRIL

Day	Slack Water Time h.m.	Maximum Current Time h.m.	Vel. knots
1 F	0206	0534	1.5E
	0858	1118	0.8F
	1350	1741	1.5E
	2102	2346	1.1F
2 Sa	0252	0623	1.3E
	0948	1159	0.6F
	1422	1826	1.3E
	2151		
3 Su		0032	0.9F
	0341	0714	1.1E
	1045	1246	0.4F
	1456	1915	1.2E
	2246		
4 M		0126	0.8F
	0435	0814	1.0E
	1149	1337	0.3F
	1538	2015	1.1E
	2348		
5 Tu		0225	0.7F
	0537	0919	0.9E
		1440	*
		2120	1.0E
6 W	0053	0331	0.6F
	0643	1026	0.9E
		1551	*
		2226	1.1E
7 Th	0156	0439	0.6F
	0745	1122	1.0E
	1458	1655	0.3F
	1905	2323	1.1E
8 F	0252	0536	0.7F
	0837	1209	1.1E
	1539	1750	0.5F
	2011		
9 Sa		0018	1.2E
	0340	0621	0.8F
	0920	1254	1.2E
	1614	1834	0.6F
	2105		
10 Su		0059	1.4E
	0423	0700	0.9F
	0957	1329	1.3E
	1646	1912	0.8F
	2152		
11 M		0142	1.5E
	0503	0739	0.9F
	1030	1402	1.4E
	1717	1950	0.9F
	2235		
12 Tu		0220	1.5E
	0541	0811	1.0F
	1100	1435	1.5E
	1749	2026	1.1F
	2317		
13 W		0255	1.6E
	0619	0846	1.0F
	1129	1507	1.5E
	1822	2104	1.2F
	2359		
14 Th		0336	1.6E
	0658	0925	1.0F
	1159	1540	1.6E
	1858	2145	1.3F
15 F	0043	0414	1.6E
	0740	1001	0.9F
	1232	1617	1.6E
	1939	2228	1.3F
16 Sa	0130	0459	1.5E
	0826	1044	0.8F
	1307	1700	1.6E
	2025	2315	1.3F
17 Su	0222	0548	1.4E
	0917	1129	0.7F
	1348	1746	1.5E
	2117		
18 M		0008	1.3F
	0319	0648	1.3E
	1017	1224	0.6F
	1436	1843	1.5E
	2217		
19 Tu		0110	1.2F
	0424	0757	1.2E
	1125	1327	0.5F
	1535	1954	1.4E
	2325		
20 W		0218	1.1F
	0535	0908	1.2E
	1237	1439	0.5F
	1650	2110	1.4E
21 Th	0037	0329	1.1F
	0646	1019	1.2E
	1344	1555	0.6F
	1817	2226	1.4E
22 F	0148	0441	1.1F
	0751	1120	1.4E
	1443	1706	0.7F
	1940	2333	1.6E
23 Sa	0254	0544	1.1F
	0847	1215	1.5E
	1534	1806	0.9F
	2051		
24 Su		0031	1.7E
	0353	0638	1.1F
	0936	1304	1.6E
	1620	1903	1.1F
	2153		
25 M		0126	1.7E
	0447	0729	1.1F
	1019	1347	1.7E
	1703	1948	1.3F
	2247		
26 Tu		0215	1.8E
	0536	0810	1.1F
	1057	1430	1.8E
	1745	2035	1.3F
	2336		
27 W		0302	1.7E
	0622	0850	1.0F
	1132	1511	1.7E
	1825	2116	1.3F
28 Th	0021	0345	1.6E
	0707	0930	0.9F
	1204	1548	1.7E
	1906	2156	1.3F
29 F	0105	0428	1.5E
	0751	1006	0.8F
	1235	1628	1.6E
	1947	2237	1.2F
30 Sa	0146	0512	1.3E
	0835	1045	0.6F
	1305	1706	1.5E
	2030	2318	1.1F

Time meridian 75° W.   0000 is midnight.   1200 is noon.
* Current weak and variable.

CHESAPEAKE BAY ENTRANCE, VIRGINIA, 1983

F-Flood, Dir. 305° True   E-Ebb, Dir. 125° True

MAY

Day	Slack Water Time h.m.	Maximum Current Time h.m.	Vel. knots	Day	Slack Water Time h.m.	Maximum Current Time h.m.	Vel. knots
1 Su	0228 0923 1337 2117	0557 1125 1747	1.2E 0.5F 1.3E	16 M	0219 0907 1333 2104	0541 1118 1735	1.4E 0.7F 1.7E
2 M	0311 1015 1413 2208	0000 0646 1211 1836	0.9F 1.1E 0.4F 1.2E	17 Tu	0316 1007 1429 2205	0000 0642 1214 1836	1.4F 1.3E 0.6F 1.6E
3 Tu	0359 1114 1457 2305	0049 0741 1258 1933	0.8F 1.0E 0.3F 1.1E	18 W	0417 1112 1535 2312	0101 0745 1319 1946	1.3F 1.3E 0.6F 1.5E
4 W	0452 1217 1554	0144 0838 1402 2038	0.7F 0.9E 0.3F 1.0E	19 Th	0520 1219 1653	0203 0851 1430 2100	1.1F 1.3E 0.6F 1.4E
5 Th	0007 0549 1317 1707	0242 0940 1505 2141	0.6F 0.9E 0.3F 1.0E	20 F	0022 0623 1322 1817	0312 0956 1543 2209	1.1F 1.3E 0.7F 1.4E
6 F	0109 0646 1407 1824	0345 1035 1608 2242	0.6F 1.0E 0.4F 1.1E	21 Sa	0132 0721 1419 1936	0418 1055 1652 2317	1.0F 1.4E 0.8F 1.5E
7 Sa	0206 0738 1450 1933	0441 1124 1705 2336	0.7F 1.1E 0.5F 1.2E	22 Su	0238 0814 1510 2045	0520 1150 1753	1.0F 1.5E 1.0F
8 Su	0258 0822 1527 2033	0530 1206 1752	0.7F 1.2E 0.7F	23 M	0338 0900 1557 2144	0018 0613 1238 1844	1.5E 0.9F 1.6E 1.1F
9 M	0345 0902 1603 2125	0021 0615 1244 1835	1.3E 0.8F 1.3E 0.9F	24 Tu	0432 0942 1640 2237	0109 0702 1323 1932	1.6E 0.9F 1.7E 1.2F
10 Tu	0429 0938 1638 2213	0107 0657 1320 1919	1.4E 0.9F 1.4E 1.1F	25 W	0521 1019 1722 2325	0158 0745 1404 2016	1.5E 0.8F 1.7E 1.3F
11 W	0511 1013 1714 2300	0151 0737 1359 2000	1.5E 0.9F 1.6E 1.2F	26 Th	0607 1053 1803	0244 0826 1445 2056	1.5E 0.8F 1.6E 1.3F
12 Th	0553 1048 1752 2347	0232 0818 1433 2041	1.5E 0.9F 1.6E 1.4F	27 F	0008 0650 1125 1843	0328 0902 1523 2135	1.4E 0.7F 1.6E 1.2F
13 F	0637 1124 1833	0313 0855 1514 2126	1.6E 0.9F 1.7E 1.5F	28 Sa	0048 0732 1156 1923	0409 0940 1600 2211	1.3E 0.6F 1.5E 1.1F
14 Sa	0035 0722 1203 1919	0401 0942 1555 2212	1.5E 0.9F 1.7E 1.5F	29 Su	0127 0814 1228 2004	0449 1018 1637 2251	1.2E 0.5F 1.4E 1.1F
15 Su	0125 0812 1245 2009	0450 1025 1644 2303	1.5E 0.8F 1.7E 1.5F	30 M	0205 0858 1303 2048	0532 1056 1718 2331	1.1E 0.5F 1.3E 1.0F
				31 Tu	0243 0945 1342 2135	0616 1141 1802	1.1E 0.4F 1.2E

JUNE

Day	Slack Water Time h.m.	Maximum Current Time h.m.	Vel. knots	Day	Slack Water Time h.m.	Maximum Current Time h.m.	Vel. knots
1 W	0325 1036 1429 2226	0016 0704 1228 1856	0.9F 1.0E 0.4F 1.1E	16 Th	0400 1051 1537 2257	0045 0727 1308 1933	1.3F 1.4E 0.7F 1.5E
2 Th	0409 1129 1524 2322	0106 0756 1321 1953	0.8F 1.0E 0.4F 1.1E	17 F	0455 1152 1652	0147 0826 1415 2044	1.2F 1.4E 0.8F 1.5E
3 F	0456 1222 1629	0157 0849 1420 2054	0.7F 1.0E 0.4F 1.0E	18 Sa	0005 0551 1253 1810	0248 0927 1524 2151	1.0F 1.4E 0.8F 1.4E
4 Sa	0020 0545 1311 1741	0252 0940 1520 2153	0.7F 1.0E 0.5F 1.1E	19 Su	0113 0644 1350 1925	0352 1025 1629 2258	0.9F 1.5E 0.9F 1.4E
5 Su	0118 0634 1356 1852	0349 1031 1615 2251	0.7F 1.1E 0.6F 1.1E	20 M	0220 0735 1444 2033	0453 1120 1729 2358	0.8F 1.5E 1.0F 1.4E
6 M	0213 0720 1439 1957	0440 1114 1708 2342	0.7F 1.2E 0.8F 1.2E	21 Tu	0322 0821 1533 2132	0546 1209 1825	0.7F 1.5E 1.1F
7 Tu	0305 0804 1520 2057	0529 1158 1759	0.7F 1.4E 1.0F	22 W	0418 0904 1619 2225	0051 0635 1254 1915	1.4E 0.7F 1.6E 1.1F
8 W	0354 0847 1601 2152	0034 0615 1241 1848	1.3E 0.8F 1.5E 1.2F	23 Th	0508 0943 1702 2312	0142 0722 1339 1958	1.3E 0.6F 1.6E 1.1F
9 Th	0442 0929 1644 2244	0122 0700 1325 1936	1.4E 0.8F 1.6E 1.3F	24 F	0552 1019 1743 2353	0227 0800 1421 2039	1.3E 0.6F 1.5E 1.1F
10 F	0529 1012 1728 2336	0210 0747 1408 2023	1.5E 0.8F 1.8E 1.5F	25 Sa	0633 1054 1823	0310 0838 1500 2114	1.3E 0.5F 1.5E 1.1F
11 Sa	0617 1057 1815	0256 0835 1451 2112	1.5E 0.9F 1.8E 1.6F	26 Su	0031 0712 1128 1902	0349 0916 1538 2152	1.2E 0.5F 1.5E 1.1F
12 Su	0027 0706 1144 1904	0347 0923 1540 2201	1.6E 0.9F 1.9E 1.6F	27 M	0106 0750 1203 1941	0427 0952 1615 2228	1.2E 0.5F 1.4E 1.0F
13 M	0119 0758 1234 1957	0437 1013 1631 2254	1.5E 0.8F 1.8E 1.6F	28 Tu	0140 0829 1241 2022	0507 1031 1656 2306	1.1E 0.5F 1.3E 1.0F
14 Tu	0211 0852 1329 2053	0531 1106 1729 2347	1.5E 0.8F 1.8E 1.5F	29 W	0214 0909 1321 2105	0544 1112 1735 2346	1.1E 0.5F 1.3E 0.9F
15 W	0305 0950 1429 2153	0629 1203 1829	1.5E 0.8F 1.7E	30 Th	0249 0952 1406 2151	0626 1157 1820	1.1E 0.5F 1.2E

Time meridian 75° W.   0000 is midnight.   1200 is noon.
* Current weak and variable.

F-Flood, Dir. 305° True   E-Ebb, Dir. 125° True

JULY

Day	Slack Water Time h.m.	Max Current Time h.m.	Vel. knots	Day	Slack Water Time h.m.	Max Current Time h.m.	Vel. knots
1 F	0325	0029	0.8F	16 Sa		0121	1.1F
	0708	0708	1.0E		0421	0756	1.5E
	1037	1242	0.5F		1119	1351	0.9F
	1457	1909	1.1E		1640	2021	1.4E
	2241				2344		
2 Sa	0405	0114	0.8F	17 Su		0219	0.9F
	1125	0755	1.1E		0511	0855	1.4E
	1556	1336	0.5F		1219	1457	0.9F
	2334	2005	1.1E		1753	2128	1.3E
3 Su	0446	0201	0.7F	18 M	0052	0319	0.7F
	1214	0842	1.1E		0601	0954	1.4E
	1702	1429	0.6F		1319	1601	0.9F
		2104	1.1E		1907	2236	1.2E
4 M	0032	0256	0.7F	19 Tu	0200	0420	0.6F
	0532	0933	1.2E		0652	1051	1.4E
	1303	1530	0.7F		1417	1708	0.9F
	1813	2205	1.1E		2015	2337	1.2E
5 Tu	0131	0350	0.6F	20 W	0306	0521	0.5F
	0619	1025	1.3E		0741	1142	1.4E
	1352	1627	0.8F		1511	1805	1.0F
	1924	2305	1.2E		2116		
6 W	0228	0444	0.6F	21 Th		0034	1.2E
	0710	1116	1.4E		0403	0612	0.5F
	1441	1727	1.0F		0829	1234	1.4E
	2031				1600	1857	1.0F
					2209		
7 Th		0005	1.2E	22 F		0125	1.2E
	0324	0538	0.7F		0453	0700	0.5F
	0801	1205	1.6E		0914	1319	1.5E
	1531	1821	1.2F		1645	1942	1.0F
	2132				2254		
8 F		0058	1.3E	23 Sa		0208	1.2E
	0417	0631	0.7F		0535	0741	0.5F
	0854	1256	1.7E		0955	1400	1.5E
	1620	1915	1.4F		1726	2019	1.0F
	2230				2333		
9 Sa		0151	1.5E	24 Su		0250	1.2E
	0508	0723	0.8F		0613	0819	0.5F
	0947	1347	1.8E		1034	1443	1.5E
	1710	2008	1.5F		1805	2056	1.0F
	2324						
10 Su		0242	1.5E	25 M	0008	0325	1.2E
	0558	0816	0.9F		0647	0856	0.5F
	1040	1437	1.9E		1111	1518	1.5E
	1800	2057	1.6F		1843	2131	1.0F
11 M	0015	0331	1.6E	26 Tu	0040	0401	1.2E
	0648	0909	0.9F		0721	0929	0.6F
	1134	1530	2.0E		1148	1555	1.4E
	1852	2149	1.7F		1920	2203	1.0F
12 Tu	0105	0421	1.6E	27 W	0110	0435	1.2E
	0739	1001	1.0F		0755	1006	0.6F
	1230	1621	2.0E		1225	1630	1.4E
	1945	2240	1.6F		1957	2236	1.0F
13 W	0155	0514	1.6E	28 Th	0139	0511	1.2E
	0831	1055	1.0F		0830	1044	0.6F
	1327	1718	1.9E		1305	1706	1.4E
	2040	2333	1.5F		2036	2315	0.9F
14 Th	0243	0605	1.6E	29 F	0209	0544	1.2E
	0925	1151	1.0F		0907	1125	0.7F
	1427	1816	1.7E		1347	1748	1.3E
	2138				2118	2350	0.9F
15 F		0026	1.3F	30 Sa	0240	0621	1.1E
	0332	0701	1.6E		0947	1206	0.7F
	1021	1250	0.9F		1434	1829	1.2E
	1531	1917	1.6E		2204		
	2239						
				31 Su		0033	0.8F
					0314	0702	1.1E
					1031	1255	0.7F
					1528	1922	1.1E
					2255		

AUGUST

Day	Slack Water Time h.m.	Max Current Time h.m.	Vel. knots	Day	Slack Water Time h.m.	Max Current Time h.m.	Vel. knots
1 M		0117	0.7F	16 Tu	0029	0244	0.6F
	0352	0749	1.2E		0512	0917	1.3E
	1121	1350	0.7F		1246	1530	0.8F
	1631	2025	1.1E		1842	2211	1.1E
	2353						
2 Tu		0210	0.6F	17 W	0141	0348	0.4F
	0435	0843	1.2E		0605	1017	1.3E
	1215	1449	0.8F		1348	1642	0.8F
	1742	2128	1.1E		1951	2314	1.1E
3 W	0055	0307	0.6F	18 Th	0249	0452	0.4F
	0526	0939	1.3E		0702	1116	1.3E
	1312	1555	0.9F		1447	1743	0.8F
	1857	2235	1.1E		2053		
4 Th	0159	0408	0.6F	19 F		0012	1.1E
	0625	1039	1.4E		0347	0550	0.4F
	1410	1658	1.1F		0759	1211	1.3E
	2010	2340	1.2E		1539	1834	0.9F
					2145		
5 F	0301	0512	0.6F	20 Sa		0103	1.1E
	0728	1140	1.6E		0433	0639	0.4F
	1507	1759	1.2F		0852	1300	1.4E
	2116				1625	1919	0.9F
					2228		
6 Sa		0039	1.3E	21 Su		0144	1.2E
	0357	0609	0.7F		0511	0721	0.5F
	0832	1238	1.7E		0939	1341	1.4E
	1602	1859	1.4F		1707	1956	1.0F
	2214				2305		
7 Su		0135	1.5E	22 M		0223	1.2E
	0449	0709	0.8F		0545	0758	0.6F
	0933	1334	1.9E		1021	1421	1.5E
	1655	1952	1.6F		1745	2031	1.0F
	2308				2338		
8 M		0224	1.6E	23 Tu		0258	1.2E
	0539	0803	1.0F		0616	0833	0.7F
	1033	1426	2.0E		1059	1458	1.5E
	1748	2043	1.6F		1821	2102	1.0F
	2357						
9 Tu		0313	1.7E	24 W	0007	0331	1.3E
	0627	0855	1.1F		0647	0905	0.7F
	1130	1518	2.1E		1135	1533	1.5E
	1839	2133	1.6F		1856	2134	1.0F
10 W	0044	0402	1.8E	25 Th	0034	0401	1.3E
	0715	0947	1.2F		0717	0940	0.8F
	1226	1610	2.0E		1212	1605	1.5E
	1931	2221	1.6F		1932	2207	1.0F
11 Th	0129	0449	1.8E	26 F	0059	0432	1.3E
	0804	1039	1.2F		0749	1015	0.8F
	1322	1703	1.9E		1249	1642	1.4E
	2024	2310	1.4F		2009	2241	0.9F
12 F	0213	0538	1.7E	27 Sa	0126	0501	1.3E
	0853	1130	1.2F		0823	1052	0.9F
	1419	1758	1.8E		1330	1719	1.4E
	2119	2358	1.2F		2048	2316	0.9F
13 Sa	0256	0628	1.6E	28 Su	0154	0536	1.3E
	0947	1224	1.1F		0901	1133	0.9F
	1518	1855	1.6E		1415	1800	1.3E
	2218				2133	2355	0.8F
14 Su		0049	1.0F	29 M	0226	0614	1.2E
	0339	0721	1.5E		0945	1220	0.9F
	1043	1321	1.0F		1507	1849	1.2E
	1621	1957	1.4E		2224		
	2321						
15 M		0143	0.7F	30 Tu		0042	0.7F
	0424	0818	1.4E		0303	0701	1.2E
	1143	1425	0.9F*		1037	1316	0.9F
	1730	2102	1.2E		1608	1946	1.1E
					2323		
				31 W		0133	0.6F
					0348	0758	1.3E
					1136	1419	0.9F
					1720	2100	1.0E

Time meridian 75° W.   0000 is midnight.   1200 is noon.
* Current weak and variable.

SAVANNAH RIVER ENTRANCE (between jetties), GEORGIA, 1983

F-Flood, Dir. 260° True   E-Ebb, Dir. 080° True

JANUARY

Day	Slack Water Time h.m.	Max Current Time h.m.	Vel. knots	Day	Slack Water Time h.m.	Max Current Time h.m.	Vel. knots
1 Sa	0434	0121	2.9E	16 Su	0448	0132	2.2E
	0711	0711	2.4F		1009	0711	1.6F
	1021	1355	3.3E		1732	1359	2.5E
	1723	1943	2.0F		2225	1939	1.3F
	2246						
2 Su	0529	0214	2.9E	17 M	0528	0214	2.2E
	1114	0803	2.3F		1041	0752	1.6F
	1816	1447	3.2E		1810	1438	2.5E
	2342	2037	1.9F		2301	2020	1.4F
3 M	0625	0310	2.8E	18 Tu	0610	0256	2.1E
	1206	0857	2.1F		1115	0837	1.5F
	1909	1541	3.1E		1848	1519	2.4E
		2131	1.8F		2341	2105	1.4F
4 Tu	0039	0403	2.7E	19 W	0656	0341	2.1E
	0724	0949	1.9F		1153	0919	1.5F
	1300	1634	2.9E		1929	1602	2.4E
	2004	2223	1.7F			2148	1.4F
5 W	0138	0502	2.6E	20 Th	0024	0427	2.1E
	0826	1045	1.6F		0745	1006	1.4F
	1355	1730	2.7E		1235	1648	2.3E
	2059	2321	1.6F		2013	2237	1.5F
6 Th	0239	0602	2.5E	21 F	0113	0518	2.1E
	0929	1141	1.4F		0838	1057	1.4F
	1452	1826	2.5E		1323	1738	2.3E
	2155				2101	2327	1.5F
7 F	0339	0015	1.5F	22 Sa	0208	0612	2.2E
	1032	0659	2.4E		0936	1152	1.3F
	1549	1240	1.2F		1416	1833	2.2E
	2250	1922	2.4E		2153		
8 Sa	0438	0111	1.4F	23 Su	0309	0022	1.6F
	1134	0800	2.3E		1037	0709	2.3E
	1647	1337	1.0F		1517	1249	1.3F
	2343	2018	2.3E		2248	1928	2.3E
9 Su	0534	0204	1.3F	24 M	0415	0117	1.7F
	1233	0857	2.3E		1139	0807	2.4E
	1742	1435	0.9F		1624	1349	1.3F
		2111	2.2E		2344	2026	2.4E
10 M	0034	0258	1.3F	25 Tu	0521	0216	1.8F
	0625	0950	2.4E		1239	0908	2.6E
	1326	1527	0.9F		1734	1449	1.4F
	1833	2200	2.2E			2126	2.5E
11 Tu	0121	0344	1.4F	26 W	0041	0314	2.0F
	0711	1036	2.4E		0626	1006	2.8E
	1414	1614	0.9F		1336	1549	1.6F
	1920	2247	2.2E		1842	2222	2.7E
12 W	0206	0428	1.4F	27 Th	0138	0413	2.1F
	0753	1119	2.4E		0726	1059	3.0E
	1458	1700	1.0F		1430	1646	1.7F
	2003	2330	2.2E		1945	2318	2.8E
13 Th	0248	0510	1.5F	28 F	0233	0509	2.3F
	0831	1200	2.5E		0823	1154	3.2E
	1539	1739	1.1F		1522	1742	1.9F
	2041				2044		
14 F	0328	0011	2.2E	29 Sa	0327	0013	3.0E
	0906	0551	1.5F		0917	0601	2.3F
	1617	1241	2.5E		1613	1245	3.3E
	2117	1819	1.1F		2139	1835	2.0F
15 Sa	0408	0051	2.2E	30 Su	0420	0105	3.0E
	0938	0630	1.6F		1008	0654	2.3F
	1655	1320	2.5E		1703	1336	3.3E
	2151	1858	1.2F		2233	1926	2.0F
				31 M	0514	0157	3.0E
					1058	0746	2.3F
					1752	1426	3.3E
					2325	2017	2.0F

FEBRUARY

Day	Slack Water Time h.m.	Max Current Time h.m.	Vel. knots	Day	Slack Water Time h.m.	Max Current Time h.m.	Vel. knots
1 Tu	0608	0248	3.0E	16 W	0546	0230	2.4E
	1147	0837	2.1F		1052	0811	1.6F
	1842	1517	3.1E		1813	1450	2.5E
		2106	1.9F		2316	2036	1.6F
2 W	0017	0342	2.8E	17 Th	0630	0313	2.4E
	0703	0926	1.8F		1129	0854	1.6F
	1235	1608	2.9E		1852	1531	2.5E
	1933	2154	1.8F		2358	2118	1.7F
3 Th	0110	0436	2.6E	18 F	0717	0357	2.4E
	0800	1017	1.6F		1210	0941	1.5F
	1323	1659	2.6E		1936	1616	2.4E
	2025	2245	1.6F			2205	1.7F
4 F	0204	0529	2.5E	19 Sa	0046	0446	2.3E
	0859	1108	1.3F		0810	1030	1.5F
	1414	1752	2.4E		1256	1705	2.3E
	2119	2338	1.4F		2025	2256	1.7F
5 Sa	0300	0628	2.3E	20 Su	0139	0541	2.3E
	1001	1202	1.0F		0908	1124	1.4F
	1507	1846	2.2E		1350	1801	2.2E
	2214				2120	2351	1.7F
6 Su	0358	0029	1.3F	21 M	0240	0642	2.4E
	1104	0725	2.2E		1011	1223	1.3F
	1604	1257	0.9F		1452	1902	2.2E
	2309	1943	2.1E		2220		
7 M	0455	0125	1.2F	22 Tu	0348	0050	1.7F
	1204	0823	2.2E		1116	0744	2.4E
	1703	1356	0.8F		1603	1324	1.3F
		2038	2.0E		2322	2004	2.3E
8 Tu	0003	0219	1.2F	23 W	0500	0152	1.8F
	0549	0916	2.2E		1218	0847	2.6E
	1259	1452	0.8F		1719	1429	1.4F
	1800	2129	2.0E			2105	2.5E
9 W	0054	0311	1.2F	24 Th	0024	0255	1.9F
	0640	1009	2.3E		0609	0946	2.8E
	1348	1546	0.8F		1317	1530	1.5F
	1852	2219	2.0E		1831	2206	2.7E
10 Th	0141	0359	1.3F	25 F	0123	0356	2.0F
	0725	1054	2.3E		0712	1044	3.0E
	1432	1631	0.9F		1411	1628	1.7F
	1939	2306	2.1E		1935	2302	2.9E
11 F	0225	0444	1.4F	26 Sa	0220	0453	2.1F
	0805	1137	2.4E		0809	1136	3.2E
	1512	1713	1.1F		1502	1725	1.9F
	2020	2349	2.2E		2032	2357	3.0E
12 Sa	0307	0526	1.5F	27 Su	0314	0545	2.2F
	0842	1216	2.5E		0901	1227	3.2E
	1549	1755	1.2F		1551	1816	2.0F
	2057				2125		
13 Su	0347	0030	2.2E	28 M	0406	0048	3.1E
	0915	0608	1.5F		0951	0637	2.2F
	1625	1255	2.5E		1639	1316	3.3E
	2130	1833	1.3F		2215	1904	2.1F
14 M	0426	0108	2.3E				
	0946	0649	1.6F				
	1701	1333	2.6E				
	2204	1912	1.5F				
15 Tu	0505	0148	2.3E				
	1018	0728	1.6F				
	1736	1411	2.6E				
	2238	1955	1.6F				

F-Flood, Dir. 260° True   E-Ebb, Dir. 080° True

MARCH

Day	Slack Water Time (h.m.)	Max Current Time (h.m.)	Vel. (knots)	Day	Slack Water Time (h.m.)	Max Current Time (h.m.)	Vel. (knots)
1 Tu	0457	0137	3.1E	16 W	0442	0122	2.5E
	1037	0725	2.1F		0953	0703	1.7F
	1725	1402	3.2E		1701	1340	2.6E
	2303	1951	2.1F		2215	1925	1.8F
2 W	0548	0227	3.0E	17 Th	0523	0203	2.6E
	1122	0813	2.0F		1028	0746	1.7F
	1812	1450	3.0E		1739	1421	2.6E
	2350	2036	2.0F		2253	2008	1.9F
3 Th	0640	0316	2.9E	18 F	0607	0246	2.6E
	1205	0859	1.7F		1107	0829	1.7F
	1900	1536	2.8E		1820	1504	2.5E
		2122	1.8F		2336	2053	1.9F
4 F	0036	0404	2.7E	19 Sa	0656	0332	2.6E
	0733	0945	1.5F		1149	0917	1.6F
	1248	1623	2.5E		1906	1550	2.4E
	1949	2210	1.6F			2140	1.9F
5 Sa	0124	0458	2.4E	20 Su	0024	0423	2.5E
	0829	1036	1.2F		0749	1008	1.5F
	1332	1716	2.3E		1238	1641	2.3E
	2040	2259	1.4F		1958	2231	1.8F
6 Su	0214	0551	2.2E	21 M	0118	0518	2.5E
	0927	1125	1.0F		0848	1103	1.4F
	1421	1809	2.0E		1334	1740	2.3E
	2136	2350	1.2F		2056	2327	1.7F
7 M	0309	0649	2.1E	22 Tu	0220	0618	2.4E
	1029	1218	0.8F		0952	1202	1.3F
	1517	1905	1.9E		1439	1841	2.2E
	2233				2201		
8 Tu	0407	0044	1.1F	23 W	0330	0030	1.7F
	1129	0746	2.0E		1057	0722	2.5E
	1621	1317	0.7F		1556	1306	1.3F
	2330	2004	1.8E		2307	1947	2.3E
9 W	0505	0141	1.0F	24 Th	0444	0133	1.7F
	1225	0842	2.1E		1159	0826	2.6E
	1725	1416	0.7F		1713	1411	1.4F
		2101	1.9E			2051	2.5E
10 Th	0025	0236	1.1F	25 F	0011	0239	1.7F
	0600	0934	2.2E		0554	0927	2.8E
	1315	1511	0.8F		1257	1514	1.5F
	1822	2152	2.0E		1823	2152	2.7E
11 F	0115	0327	1.2F	26 Sa	0112	0340	1.8F
	0649	1022	2.3E		0656	1024	2.9E
	1359	1601	1.0F		1350	1612	1.7F
	1911	2237	2.1E		1923	2247	2.7E
12 Sa	0201	0415	1.3F	27 Su	0208	0438	1.9F
	0733	1107	2.4E		0752	1115	3.0E
	1438	1644	1.2F		1440	1704	1.9F
	1953	2322	2.2E		2018	2339	3.0E
13 Su	0243	0500	1.4F	28 M	0301	0529	2.0F
	0811	1146	2.5E		0842	1204	3.1E
	1515	1726	1.3F		1527	1755	2.0F
	2031				2107		
14 M	0323	0003	2.4E	29 Tu	0351	0030	3.1E
	0846	0541	1.5F		0929	0616	2.0F
	1551	1226	2.6E		1612	1251	3.1E
	2105	1807	1.5F		2153	1839	2.1F
15 Tu	0403	0044	2.5E	30 W	0440	0115	3.1E
	0919	0624	1.6F		1012	0701	1.9F
	1626	1304	2.6E		1656	1335	3.0E
	2139	1846	1.7F		2237	1924	2.0F
				31 Th	0528	0201	3.0E
					1053	0747	1.8F
					1740	1421	2.8E
					2319	2007	1.9F

APRIL

Day	Slack Water Time (h.m.)	Max Current Time (h.m.)	Vel. (knots)	Day	Slack Water Time (h.m.)	Max Current Time (h.m.)	Vel. (knots)
1 F	0616	0249	2.8E	16 Sa	0549	0224	2.8E
	1132	0830	1.6F		1048	0809	1.7F
	1825	1505	2.6E		1753	1440	2.6E
		2048	1.8F		2319	2028	2.0F
2 Sa	0000	0335	2.6E	17 Su	0639	0311	2.8E
	0705	0914	1.4F		1135	0858	1.7F
	1211	1551	2.3E		1843	1529	2.5E
	1912	2134	1.6F			2118	2.0F
3 Su	0042	0424	2.4E	18 M	0009	0405	2.7E
	0758	1000	1.2F		0733	0951	1.6F
	1252	1639	2.1E		1228	1624	2.4E
	2003	2221	1.4F		1939	2213	1.9F
4 M	0126	0515	2.2E	19 Tu	0105	0501	2.6E
	0853	1048	1.0F		0833	1047	1.5F
	1337	1733	1.9E		1328	1724	2.3E
	2057	2310	1.2F		2041	2312	1.7F
5 Tu	0215	0609	2.1E	20 W	0208	0602	2.6E
	0951	1144	0.8F		0935	1146	1.4F
	1433	1830	1.8E		1439	1828	2.3E
	2155				2147		
6 W	0311	0005	1.1F	21 Th	0318	0013	1.6F
	1049	0707	2.0E		1038	0706	2.6E
	1538	1239	0.8F		1555	1251	1.4F
	2255	1927	1.8E		2255	1933	2.4E
7 Th	0412	0100	1.0F	22 F	0429	0117	1.6F
	1144	0803	2.0E		1139	0807	2.6E
	1645	1338	0.8F		1707	1354	1.5F
	2351	2026	1.8E		2359	2036	2.5E
8 F	0511	0158	1.0F	23 Sa	0536	0220	1.6F
	1233	0854	2.1E		1235	0908	2.7E
	1745	1433	0.9F		1812	1455	1.6F
		2117	2.0E			2136	2.7E
9 Sa	0044	0251	1.1F	24 Su	0059	0321	1.6F
	0604	0943	2.2E		0637	1001	2.8E
	1318	1524	1.1F		1327	1552	1.7F
	1835	2206	2.1E		1908	2231	2.8E
10 Su	0131	0342	1.2F	25 M	0155	0418	1.7F
	0651	1028	2.3E		0730	1054	2.9E
	1358	1609	1.3F		1415	1643	1.9F
	1919	2251	2.3E		2000	2320	2.9E
11 M	0215	0427	1.4F	26 Tu	0246	0509	1.7F
	0733	1113	2.5E		0819	1142	2.9E
	1436	1651	1.5F		1501	1729	1.9F
	1958	2335	2.5E		2046		
12 Tu	0257	0513	1.5F	27 W	0335	0009	3.0E
	0812	1152	2.5E		0903	0554	1.7F
	1513	1736	1.7F		1544	1223	2.8E
	2035				2130	1814	1.9F
13 W	0338	0015	2.6E	28 Th	0421	0054	3.0E
	0849	0555	1.6F		0944	0637	1.6F
	1550	1232	2.6E		1627	1309	2.7E
	2113	1817	1.9F		2210	1855	1.9F
14 Th	0419	0056	2.7E	29 F	0507	0137	2.9E
	0926	0639	1.7F		1023	0721	1.5F
	1628	1314	2.6E		1709	1353	2.5E
	2152	1900	2.0F		2248	1936	1.8F
15 F	0503	0139	2.8E	30 Sa	0553	0221	2.7E
	1006	0722	1.8F		1100	0802	1.4F
	1709	1355	2.6E		1753	1436	2.4E
	2234	1943	2.0F		2325	2018	1.7F

Time meridian 75° W.   0000 is midnight.   1200 is noon.

MOBILE BAY ENTRANCE, ALABAMA, 1983

F-Flood, Dir. 025° True   E-Ebb, Dir. 190° True

JANUARY

Day	Slack Water Time h.m.	Maximum Current Time h.m.	Vel. knots	Day	Slack Water Time h.m.	Maximum Current Time h.m.	Vel. knots
1 Sa	1220	0552 / 1845	3.1E / 2.9F	16 Su	0028 / 1230	0616 / 1901	2.1E / 1.9F
2 Su	0051 / 1314	0643 / 1933	2.8E / 2.5F	17 M	0106 / 1308	0657 / 1930	1.9E / 1.7F
3 M	0142 / 1401	0724 / 2017	2.3E / 1.9F	18 Tu	0141 / 1342	0732 / 1950	1.6E / 1.4F
4 Tu	0225 / 1432	0759 / 2046	1.7E / 1.3F	19 W	0211 / 1409	0755 / 2000	1.3E / 1.0F
5 W	0252 / 1417	0808 / 1945	1.0E / 0.6F	20 Th	0233 / 1417	0816 / 1913	0.8E / 0.5F
6 Th	0213 / 1157 / 2109	0654 / 1621	0.5E / 0.4F	21 F	0150	0642 / 1624	0.3E / *
7 F	0840 / 1949	0251 / 1453	0.4E / 0.8F	22 Sa	0602 / 1821	0109 / 1240	0.4E / 0.6F
8 Sa	0744 / 1959	0125 / 1437	1.0E / 1.2F	23 Su	0601 / 1838	0031 / 1236	1.0E / 1.2F
9 Su	0756 / 2028	0138 / 1450	1.5E / 1.6F	24 M	0640 / 1920	0057 / 1311	1.6E / 1.8F
10 M	0825 / 2103	0215 / 1519	1.9E / 1.8F	25 Tu	0730 / 2012	0135 / 1359	2.2E / 2.3F
11 Tu	0900 / 2143	0244 / 1548	2.1E / 2.0F	26 W	0826 / 2109	0221 / 1459	2.6E / 2.6F
12 W	0940 / 2224	0328 / 1631	2.2E / 2.1F	27 Th	0926 / 2207	0313 / 1600	2.9E / 2.8F
13 Th	1023 / 2306	0408 / 1707	2.3E / 2.1F	28 F	1027 / 2305	0405 / 1702	3.0E / 2.9F
14 F	1106 / 2348	0451 / 1749	2.3E / 2.1F	29 Sa	1128	0500 / 1759	2.9E / 2.7F
15 Sa	1149	0533 / 1826	2.2E / 2.0F	30 Su	0002 / 1226	0549 / 1900	2.5E / 2.3F
				31 M	0055 / 1320	0630 / 1945	2.0E / 1.7F

FEBRUARY

Day	Slack Water Time h.m.	Maximum Current Time h.m.	Vel. knots	Day	Slack Water Time h.m.	Maximum Current Time h.m.	Vel. knots
1 Tu	0143 / 1403	0707 / 2031	1.4E / 1.0F	16 W	0151 / 1402	0720 / 2019	0.9E / 0.6F
2 W	0221 / 1401	0700 / 2018	0.8E / 0.3F	17 Th	0246	0733 / 2006	0.4E / *
3 Th	1734	0554 / 1332 / 2314	* / 0.3F / 0.4E	18 F		0308 / 0848 / 2126	* / * / 0.4E
4 F	0545 / 1738	1232 / 2329	0.7F / 1.0E	19 Sa	0258 / 1538	0939 / 2223	0.7F / 1.0E
5 Sa	0547 / 1816	1241	1.2F	20 Su	0406 / 1641	1028 / 2312	1.3F / 1.6E
6 Su	0621 / 1901	0012 / 1310	1.4E / 1.5F	21 M	0505 / 1745	1128	1.8F
7 M	0703 / 1949	0055 / 1348	1.7E / 1.7F	22 Tu	0606 / 1850	0012 / 1228	2.1E / 2.1F
8 Tu	0748 / 2039	0136 / 1442	1.9E / 1.8F	23 W	0709 / 1957	0104 / 1340	2.4E / 2.4F
9 W	0837 / 2129	0227 / 1531	2.0E / 1.9F	24 Th	0815 / 2102	0201 / 1446	2.6E / 2.5F
10 Th	0927 / 2218	0313 / 1623	2.1E / 1.9F	25 F	0921 / 2207	0257 / 1556	2.6E / 2.4F
11 F	1017 / 2304	0358 / 1715	2.1E / 1.8F	26 Sa	1028 / 2309	0355 / 1710	2.4E / 2.2F
12 Sa	1104 / 2348	0439 / 1757	2.0E / 1.8F	27 Su	1137	0448 / 1813	2.1E / 1.8F
13 Su	1149	0522 / 1839	1.9E / 1.6F	28 M	0011 / 1252	0530 / 1935	1.5E / 1.2F
14 M	0029 / 1231	0557 / 1915	1.6E / 1.4F				
15 Tu	0109 / 1314	0640 / 1938	1.3E / 1.1F				

Time meridian 90° W. 0000 is midnight. 1200 IS noon.
If three consecutive entries are marked (F) the middle one is not a true maximum but an intermediate value to show the current pattern.
* Current weak and variable.

F-Flood, Dir. 025° True   E-Ebb, Dir. 190° True

MARCH

Day	Slack Water Time h.m.	Maximum Current Time h.m.	Vel. knots	Day	Slack Water Time h.m.	Maximum Current Time h.m.	Vel. knots
1 Tu	0116 / 1449	0613 / 2112	0.9E / 0.7F	16 W	0223 / 1747	0700 / 2340	0.4E / 0.4F
2 W	0244 / 2045	0600 / 1048 / 1559	0.3E / * / 0.3E	17 Th	2233	1636	0.5E
3 Th	1331	0907 / 1917	0.4F / 0.7E	18 F	1209	0612 / 1839	0.7F / 0.9E
4 F	0151 / 1453	0922 / 2053	0.9F / 1.1E	19 Sa	0049 / 1332	0730 / 2000	1.2F / 1.4E
5 Sa	0314 / 1558	1006 / 2202	1.2F / 1.4E	20 Su	0211 / 1444	0839 / 2111	1.6F / 1.8E
6 Su	0413 / 1659	1054 / 2305	1.4F / 1.6E	21 M	0321 / 1556	0940 / 2224	2.0F / 2.1E
7 M	0509 / 1801	1140	1.5F	22 Tu	0429 / 1710	1044 / 2329	2.2F / 2.3E
8 Tu	0606 / 1905	0001 / 1243	1.7E / 1.6F	23 W	0537 / 1824	1154	2.2F
9 W	0704 / 2009	0059 / 1352	1.8E / 1.6F	24 Th	0646 / 1938	0035 / 1313	2.3E / 2.2F
10 Th	0803 / 2109	0153 / 1505	1.8E / 1.5F	25 F	0755 / 2050	0135 / 1433	2.2E / 1.9F
11 F	0902 / 2205	0243 / 1614	1.8E / 1.5F	26 Sa	0907 / 2202	0232 / 1603	1.9E / 1.6F
12 Sa	1000 / 2258	0339 / 1717	1.7E / 1.4F	27 Su	1030 / 2322	0327 / 1745	1.5E / 1.1F
13 Su	1057 / 2350	0422 / 1812	1.5E / 1.2F	28 M	1315	0415 / 1948	0.9E / 0.7F
14 M	1201	0457 / 1857	1.2E / 1.0F	29 Tu	0123 / 1840	0436 / 0811 / 1407 / 2324	0.3E / * / 0.4E / 0.4F
15 Tu	0050 / 1341	0559 / 2025	0.8E / 0.7F	30 W	1037 / 2214	0236 / 0611 / 1620	0.3F / 0.4F / 0.8E
				31 Th	1200	0637 / 1736	0.9F / 1.2E

APRIL

Day	Slack Water Time h.m.	Maximum Current Time h.m.	Vel. knots	Day	Slack Water Time h.m.	Maximum Current Time h.m.	Vel. knots
1 F	0001 / 1300	0720 / 1851	1.3F / 1.5E	16 Sa	1219	0621 / 1831	1.7F / 2.0E
2 Sa	0111 / 1356	0804 / 1954	1.5F / 1.7E	17 Su	0048 / 1320	0715 / 1936	2.1F / 2.2E
3 Su	0211 / 1454	0839 / 2057	1.6F / 1.8E	18 M	0154 / 1425	0813 / 2043	2.3F / 2.4E
4 M	0309 / 1556	0933 / 2206	1.7F / 1.8E	19 Tu	0259 / 1533	0914 / 2147	2.4F / 2.4E
5 Tu	0408 / 1702	1024 / 2306	1.6F / 1.7E	20 W	0404 / 1643	1017 / 2253	2.3F / 2.2E
6 W	0508 / 1813	1128	1.5F	21 Th	0507 / 1753	1123 / 2353	2.0F / 1.9E
7 Th	0609 / 1923	0013 / 1238	1.6E / 1.3F	22 F	0608 / 1904	1225	1.6F
8 F	0709 / 2031	0110 / 1406	1.5E / 1.2F	23 Sa	0706 / 2020	0044 / 1354	1.5E / 1.0F
9 Sa	0810 / 2138	0204 / 1542	1.3E / 1.0F	24 Su	0802 / 2205	0125 / 1624	0.9E / 0.5F
10 Su	0918 / 2256	0254 / 1719	1.1E / 0.7F	25 M	1801	0112 / 0743 / 1348	0.3E / * / 0.3E
11 M	1139	0348 / 1948	0.7E / 0.5F	26 Tu	0938 / 2055	0536 / 1502	0.4F / 0.9E
12 Tu	0101 / 1749	0437 / 0905 / 1329 / 2312	0.3E / * / 0.3E / 0.4F	27 W	1025 / 2210	0511 / 1600	1.0F / 1.4E
13 W	0833 / 2043	1512	0.7E	28 Th	1108 / 2305	0531 / 1648	1.4F / 1.8E
14 Th	1016 / 2225	0349 / 1622	0.8F / 1.2E	29 F	1152 / 2356	0606 / 1737	1.7F / 2.0E
15 F	1119 / 2340	0520 / 1724	1.3F / 1.6E	30 Sa	1237	0641 / 1826	1.9F / 2.1E

Time meridian 90° W. 0000 is midnight. 1200 is noon.
If three consecutive entries are marked (F) the middle one is not a true maximum but an intermediate value to show the current pattern.
* Current weak and variable.

MOBILE BAY ENTRANCE, ALABAMA, 1983

F-Flood, Dir. 025° True   E-Ebb, Dir. 190° True

MAY

Day	Slack Water Time h.m.	Maximum Current Time h.m.	Vel. knots	Day	Slack Water Time h.m.	Maximum Current Time h.m.	Vel. knots
1 Su	0045 1324	0721 1921	2.0F 2.1E	16 M	0047 1318	0712 1927	2.7F 2.7E
2 M	0136 1415	0758 2016	1.9F 2.0E	17 Tu	0147 1417	0803 2027	2.7F 2.6E
3 Tu	0228 1511	0844 2117	1.8F 1.9E	18 W	0245 1516	0900 2121	2.4F 2.3E
4 W	0322 1610	0930 2217	1.6F 1.7E	19 Th	0340 1613	0949 2212	2.0F 1.9E
5 Th	0414 1711	1016 2306	1.4F 1.5E	20 F	0426 1704	1021 2248	1.5F 1.3E
6 F	0503 1813	1051	1.1F	21 Sa	0452 1739	1025 2249	0.8F 0.7E
7 Sa	0547 1920	0003 1109	1.2E 0.8F	22 Su	0405	0748 2032	0.3F *
8 Su	0623 2100	0052 1039	0.8E 0.4F	23 M	0928 2050	0527 1435	0.5F 0.7E
9 M		0112 0828 1409 2142	0.4E * * *	24 Tu	0925 2110	0429 1456	1.0F 1.3E
10 Tu	1946	0102 0513 1429	* * 0.7E	25 W	0952 2145	0430 1533	1.4F 1.8E
11 W	0913 2056	0314 1518	0.7F 1.2E	26 Th	1026 2223	0445 1608	1.8F 2.1E
12 Th	0951 2154	0351 1553	1.3F 1.7E	27 F	1103 2303	0514 1651	2.1F 2.3E
13 F	1036 2250	0438 1643	1.8F 2.1E	28 Sa	1142 2346	0545 1732	2.2F 2.4E
14 Sa	1126 2348	0526 1733	2.3F 2.5E	29 Su	1224	0621 1815	2.2F 2.3E
15 Su	1221	0615 1827	2.6F 2.7E	30 M	0030 1309	0700 1903	2.1F 2.2E
				31 Tu	0117 1355	0735 1954	2.0F 2.1E

JUNE

Day	Slack Water Time h.m.	Maximum Current Time h.m.	Vel. knots	Day	Slack Water Time h.m.	Maximum Current Time h.m.	Vel. knots
1 W	0203 1441	0819 2043	1.8F 1.9E	16 Th	0233 1459	0846 2048	2.1F 1.8E
2 Th	0246 1526	0848 2126	1.6F 1.6E	17 F	0309 1532	0915 2106	1.4F 1.2E
3 F	0325 1605	0903 2207	1.3F 1.2E	18 Sa	0310 1514	0842 2027	0.8F 0.6E
4 Sa	0353 1634	0910 2236	0.9F 0.8E	19 Su	0125 1028 2144	0541 1554	0.5F 0.4E
5 Su	0400 1542	0812 2212	0.5F 0.3E	20 M	0836 2025	0353 1408	0.8F 1.0E
6 M	0243 1030 1958	0645 1441	0.3F 0.4E	21 Tu	0840 2036	0326 1421	1.3F 1.6E
7 Tu	0847 1952	0413 1423	0.5F 0.9E	22 W	0906 2105	0336 1450	1.7F 2.0E
8 W	0843 2027	0253 1438	1.0F 1.5E	23 Th	0940 2140	0356 1527	2.0F 2.3E
9 Th	0911 2112	0313 1518	1.6F 2.0E	24 F	1018 2218	0428 1602	2.2F 2.4E
10 F	0951 2202	0351 1556	2.1F 2.5E	25 Sa	1057 2259	0500 1643	2.3F 2.4E
11 Sa	1039 2257	0434 1639	2.6F 2.8E	26 Su	1139 2342	0542 1724	2.3F 2.4E
12 Su	1131 2353	0529 1733	2.8F 3.0E	27 M	1221	0620 1808	2.2F 2.3E
13 M	1225	0618 1827	3.0F 3.0E	28 Tu	0025 1302	0655 1853	2.1F 2.2E
14 Tu	0050 1320	0711 1920	2.9F 2.8E	29 W	0106 1342	0730 1937	1.9F 2.0E
15 W	0145 1412	0800 2009	2.6F 2.4E	30 Th	0144 1419	0748 2012	1.7F 1.7E

Time meridian 90° W. 0000 is midnight. 1200 is noon.
If three consecutive entries are marked (F) the middle one is not a true maximum but an intermediate value to show the current pattern.
* Current weak and variable.

F-Flood, Dir. 025° True   E-Ebb, Dir. 190° True

JULY

Day	Slack Water Time (h.m.)	Maximum Current Time (h.m.)	Vel. (knots)
1 F	0217, 1449	0808, 2038	1.4F, 1.3E
2 Sa	0241, 1504	0815, 2048	1.0F, 0.8E
3 Su	0240, 1354	0731, 1939	0.6F, 0.3E
4 M	0100, 0937, 1932	0536, 1409	0.4F, 0.4E
5 Tu	0750, 1905	0253, 1342	0.6F, 1.0E
6 W	0745, 1934	0147, 1349	1.1F, 1.6E
7 Th	0815, 2017	0208, 1418	1.7F, 2.1C
8 F	0857, 2108	0251, 1501	2.2F, 2.6E
9 Sa	0948, 2204	0345, 1550	2.6F, 2.9E
10 Su	1041, 2302	0437, 1642	2.9F, 3.1E
11 M	1137, 2359	0533, 1732	3.0F, 3.0E
12 Tu	1231	0628, 1826	2.8F, 2.7E
13 W	0055, 1323	0719, 1909	2.5F, 2.3E
14 Th	0145, 1408	0800, 1939	2.0F, 1.7E
15 F	0222, 1440	0834, 1951	1.3F, 1.0E
16 Sa	0215, 1408, 2319	0748, 1845	0.6F, 0.4E
17 Su	0807, 1937	0334, 1352	0.4F, 0.4E
18 M	0703, 1905	0157, 1254	0.8F, 1.0E
19 Tu	0725, 1929	0206, 1315	1.3F, 1.6E
20 W	0801, 2004	0222, 1350	1.7F, 2.0E
21 Th	0842, 2045	0251, 1427	1.9F, 2.2E
22 F	0926, 2128	0331, 1508	2.1F, 2.3E
23 Sa	1011, 2212	0417, 1554	2.1F, 2.3E
24 Su	1055, 2257	0458, 1635	2.1F, 2.3E
25 M	1139, 2340	0546, 1716	2.1F, 2.2E
26 Tu	1221	0623, 1759	2.0F, 2.0E
27 W	0022, 1300	0658, 1840	1.8F, 1.8E
28 Th	0059, 1336	0727, 1909	1.5F, 1.5E
29 F	0133, 1408	0748, 1947	1.2F, 1.1E
30 Sa	0201, 1433	0749, 1951	0.8F, 0.7E
31 Su	0208	0642, 1813	0.4F, *

AUGUST

Day	Slack Water Time (h.m.)	Maximum Current Time (h.m.)	Vel. (knots)
1 M	1713	0333, 1221, 2355	*, 0.4E, 0.5F
2 Tu	0547, 1731	1200, 2353	0.9E, 1.1F
3 W	0611, 1813	1229	1.5E
4 Th	0655, 1905	0042, 1312	1.6F, 2.0E
5 F	0748, 2002	0131, 1358	2.1F, 2.4E
6 Sa	0846, 2102	0232, 1447	2.5F, 2.7E
7 Su	0945, 2204	0336, 1540	2.7F, 2.9E
8 M	1045, 2307	0438, 1638	2.7F, 2.8E
9 Tu	1143	0542, 1727	2.6F, 2.5E
10 W	0008, 1239	0636, 1815	2.2F, 2.0E
11 Th	0109, 1333	0739, 1845	1.6F, 1.3E
12 F	0210, 1425	0842, 1857	1.0F, 0.6E
13 Sa		0931, 1703, 2348	*, *, 0.3F
14 Su	0334, 1613	0930, 2321	0.5E, 0.8F
15 M	0437, 1659	1038, 2345	1.1E, 1.3F
16 Tu	0532, 1747	1133	1.5E
17 W	0626, 1836	0036, 1224	1.6F, 1.8E
18 Th	0721, 1926	0120, 1310	1.8F, 2.0E
19 F	0816, 2018	0214, 1359	1.8F, 2.0E
20 Sa	0910, 2111	0314, 1451	1.8F, 2.0E
21 Su	1003, 2203	0411, 1539	1.8F, 2.0E
22 M	1053, 2252	0506, 1622	1.8F, 1.9E
23 Tu	1139, 2340	0554, 1711	1.6F, 1.7E
24 W	1223	0637, 1748	1.5F, 1.5E
25 Th	0026, 1307	0712, 1829	1.2F, 1.1E
26 F	0115, 1358	0800, 1912	0.9F, 0.7E
27 Sa	0224, 1525	0912, 1933	0.5F, 0.3E
28 Su		1838	*
29 M	1406	0824, 2040	0.5E, 0.7F
30 Tu	0251, 1525	0933, 2143	1.0E, 1.2F
31 W	0401, 1629	1036, 2240	1.5E, 1.7F

Time meridian 90° W. 0000 is midnight. 1200 IS noon.
If three consecutive entries are marked (F) the middle one is not a true maximum but an intermediate
value to show the current pattern.
* Current weak and variable.

GALVESTON BAY ENTRANCE (between jetties), TEXAS, 1983

F-Flood, Dir. 300° True   E-Ebb, Dir. 100° True

JANUARY

Days 1–15

Day	Slack Water Time h.m.	Maximum Current Time h.m.	Vel. knots
1 Sa	0239	1013	3.9E
	1456	1827	2.9F
2 Su	0312	1107	3.4E
	1551	1918	2.5F
3 M	0251	1201	2.7E
	1647	2004	2.0F
4 Tu	0145	0455	0.4E
		0705	0.3E
		1317	1.9E
	1744	2045	1.6F
5 W	0119	0455	0.8E
		0845	*
		1445	1.1E
	1843	2125	1.1F
6 Th	0059	0500	1.3E
	0853	1035	0.4F
	1345	1639	0.5E
	1947	2203	0.7F
7 F	0034	0525	1.8E
	0926	1232	1.0F
	1647	1911	0.3E
	2100	2243	0.4F
8 Sa	0021	0552	2.2E
	1003	1346	1.6F
	1838	2053	0.3E
		2324	*
9 Su		0626	2.6E
	1040	1429	2.0F
	1949	2136	0.3E
10 M		0006	*
		0658	2.8E
	1118	1458	2.2F
	2047	2231	0.3E
11 Tu		0041	*
		0735	3.0E
	1156	1527	2.4F
		2327	*
12 W		0120	*
		0807	3.1E
	1234	1558	2.4F
13 Th		0021	*
		0152	*
		0845	3.1E
	1312	1633	2.4F
14 F	0018	0920	3.1E
	1350	1708	2.3F
15 Sa	0149	0949	3.0E
	1428	1743	2.1F

Days 16–31

Day	Slack Water Time h.m.	Maximum Current Time h.m.	Vel. knots
16 Su	0242	1018	2.8E
	1506	1823	1.9F
17 M	0308	1049	2.5E
	1544	1901	1.7F
18 Tu	0310	1118	2.1E
	1623	1941	1.4F
19 W	0125	1144	1.6E
	1707	2018	1.1F
20 Th	0029	0321	0.4E
		0819	*
		1312	0.9E
	1803	2059	0.7F
	2326		
21 F		0336	0.8E
	0821	0950	0.3F
	1132	1537	0.4E
	1941	2135	0.3F
	2303		
22 Sa		0408	1.4E
	0839	1112	0.9F
		1948	*
		2210	*
23 Su		0448	1.9E
	0912	1221	1.6F
	1826	2113	0.4E
		2252	0.3E
24 M		0529	2.6E
	0952	1323	2.3F
	1942	2217	0.4E
		2327	0.4E
25 Tu		0615	3.2E
	1037	1413	2.8F
	2054	2319	0.3E
		2345	0.3E
26 W		0702	3.7E
	1125	1501	3.2F
	2217		
27 Th		0748	4.0E
	1215	1548	3.3F
28 F	0201	0837	4.1E
	1306	1631	3.2F
29 Sa		0100	*
		0217	*
		0928	4.0E
	1356	1715	2.9F
30 Su		0048	*
		0324	0.3F
	0447	1017	3.6E
	1446	1753	2.4F
31 M		0036	*
		0429	0.4F
	0555	1106	2.9E
	1535	1833	1.9F
	2326		

FEBRUARY

Days 1–15

Day	Slack Water Time h.m.	Maximum Current Time h.m.	Vel. knots
1 Tu		0102	0.3E
	0340	0546	0.4F
	0707	1203	2.1E
	1624	1908	1.4F
	2301		
2 W		0139	0.7E
	0525	0704	0.4F
	0838	1312	1.2E
	1718	1946	0.9F
	2228		
3 Th		0225	1.1E
	0644	0833	0.5F
	1143	1449	0.5E
	1828	2025	0.4F
	2208		
4 F		0317	1.5E
	0746	1021	0.8F
		1822	*
		2108	*
5 Sa		0414	1.9E
	0840	1254	1.3F
	1752	1947	0.3E
		2156	*
6 Su		0501	2.2E
	0929	1343	1.8F
	1846	2049	0.4E
		2245	*
7 M		0555	2.4E
	1014	1418	2.1F
	1931	2124	0.4E
		2342	*
8 Tu		0638	2.7E
	1058	1452	2.2F
	2014	2211	0.4E
9 W		0025	*
		0718	2.9E
	1140	1515	2.3F
	2100	2242	0.3E
10 Th		0111	*
		0759	3.0E
	1220	1536	2.2F
		2322	*
11 F		0149	*
		0834	3.0E
	1258	1605	2.2F
		2339	*
12 Sa		0229	0.3F
	0338	0909	3.0E
	1335	1634	2.0F
		2319	*
13 Su		0304	0.3F
	0425	0944	2.8E
	1410	1706	1.8F
		2326	*
14 M		0342	0.3F
	0511	1014	2.5E
	1444	1738	1.6F
		2341	*
15 Tu		0428	0.3F
	0600	1048	2.1E
	1519	1810	1.2F
	2201		

Days 16–28

Day	Slack Water Time h.m.	Maximum Current Time h.m.	Vel. knots
16 W		0010	0.3E
	0213	0529	0.3F
	0700	1123	1.6E
	1558	1842	0.8F
	2115		
17 Th		0031	0.6E
	0341	0639	0.4F
	0820	1218	1.0E
	1649	1911	0.4F
	2053		
18 F		0046	0.9E
	0512	0800	0.6F
	1026	1354	0.4E
		1941	*
19 Sa		0129	1.3E
	0628	0924	1.0F
	1602		
20 Su		0233	1.7E
	0733	1053	1.5F
	1743		
21 M		0346	2.2E
	0832	1209	2.1F
	1839		
22 Tu		0455	2.7E
	0928	1312	2.6F
	1932	2208	0.5E
		2302	0.5E
23 W		0555	3.2E
	1023	1400	2.9F
	2024	2228	0.4E
		2359	0.3E
24 Th		0652	3.6E
	1115	1443	3.0F
		2240	*
25 F		0059	*
		0745	3.7E
	1206	1524	2.9F
		2231	*
26 Sa		0151	0.4F
	0314	0834	3.7E
	1256	1601	2.6F
		2226	*
27 Su		0245	0.7F
	0431	0926	3.3E
	1343	1636	2.1F
	2108	2241	0.4E
28 M	0046	0345	0.9F
	0543	1015	2.7E
	1430	1705	1.6F
	2049	2309	0.7E

Time meridian 90° W. 0000 is midnight. 1200 is noon.
* Current weak and variable.
If three consecutive entries are marked (E) the middle one is not a true maximum but an intermediate value to show the current pattern.

GALVESTON BAY ENTRANCE (between jetties), TEXAS, 1983

F-Flood, Dir. 300° True   E-Ebb, Dir. 100° True

MARCH

Day	Slack Water Time (h.m.)	Max Current Time (h.m.)	Vel. (knots)
1 Tu	0151	0445	1.0F
	0657	1109	2.0E
	1517	1737	1.1F
	2021	2338	1.1E
2 W	0300	0548	1.1F
	0824	1203	1.2E
	1610	1810	0.6F
	2000		
3 Th		0013	1.4E
	0414	0657	1.1F
	1039	1321	0.5E
	1844		
4 F		0053	1.6E
	0529	0815	1.1F
	1423	1737	0.3E
		1914	*
5 Sa		0147	1.7E
	0641	0956	1.3F
	1635	1910	0.5E
		1957	0.4E
6 Su		0256	1.8E
	0748	1220	1.6F
	1726	1959	0.6E
		2111	0.6E
7 M		0415	2.0E
	0848	1309	1.8F
	1807	2035	0.6E
		2226	0.5E
8 Tu		0521	2.2E
	0942	1346	2.0F
	1843	2104	0.6E
	2323		0.3E
9 W		0615	2.4E
	1031	1415	2.0F
	1916	2132	0.5E
10 Th		0014	*
		0703	2.6E
	1116	1436	2.0F
	1942	2154	0.4E
11 F		0100	*
		0745	2.7E
	1157	1459	1.9F
	2000	2157	0.3E
	2358		
12 Sa		0143	0.4F
	0310	0821	2.7E
	1235	1523	1.8F
	2007	2145	0.3E
13 Su	0004	0224	0.6F
	0407	0856	2.6E
	1311	1549	1.6F
	2006	2158	0.4E
14 M	0018	0307	0.8F
	0502	0933	2.3E
	1347	1617	1.3F
	1947	2214	0.6E
15 Tu	0043	0353	0.9F
	0558	1008	1.9E
	1425	1646	1.0F
	1917	2228	0.9E

Day	Slack Water Time (h.m.)	Max Current Time (h.m.)	Vel. (knots)
16 W	0120	0440	1.0F
	0701	1052	1.5E
	1508	1715	0.6F
	1859	2243	1.2E
17 Th	0205	0538	1.2F
	0819	1146	0.9E
		1736	*
		2250	1.5E
18 F	0259	0639	1.3F
	1025	1303	0.4E
		1538	*
		2313	1.8E
19 Sa	0406	0756	1.5F
	1456	2348	2.1E
20 Su	0524	0912	1.7F
	1634		
21 M		0058	2.3E
	0646	1035	2.0F
	1725		
22 Tu		0301	2.4E
	0800	1156	2.4F
	1809		
23 W		0433	2.7E
	0906	1251	2.6F
	1846	2119	0.6E
		2305	0.5E
24 Th		0542	3.0E
	1005	1335	2.6F
	1907	2124	0.5E
25 F		0005	*
		0645	3.1E
	1100	1412	2.5F
	1912	2117	0.5E
	2330		
26 Sa		0108	0.4F
	0231	0742	3.0E
	1150	1444	2.2F
	1908	2111	0.7E
	2345		
27 Su		0205	0.9F
	0403	0836	2.7E
	1239	1516	1.8F
	1856	2126	1.0E
28 M	0017	0257	1.3F
	0526	0926	2.3E
	1326	1545	1.3F
	1835	2146	1.4E
29 Tu	0059	0352	1.5F
	0648	1020	1.7E
	1414	1612	0.8F
	1814	2212	1.7E
30 W	0145	0449	1.7F
	0820	1118	1.1E
	1511	1641	0.4F
	1800	2238	2.0E
31 Th	0236	0545	1.7F
	1014	1226	0.5E
		1709	*
		2306	2.1E

APRIL

Day	Slack Water Time (h.m.)	Max Current Time (h.m.)	Vel. (knots)
1 F	0330	0646	1.7F
	1250	2341	2.1E
2 Sa	0432	0756	1.6F
	1508		
3 Su		0017	2.0E
	0542	0912	1.6F
	1604		
4 M		0142	1.9E
	0654	1107	1.7F
	1645		
5 Tu		0313	1.8E
	0802	1218	1.8F
	1719	2009	0.8E
		2157	0.7E
6 W		0433	1.9E
	0902	1251	1.8F
	1745	2033	0.8E
		2308	0.4E
7 Th		0542	2.1E
	0954	1316	1.8F
	1803	2047	0.7E
8 F	0000		*
		0633	2.2E
	1041	1339	1.7F
	1812	2052	0.7E
	2327		
9 Sa		0054	0.3E
	0211	0720	2.2E
	1123	1406	1.6F
	1814	2044	0.7E
	2335		
10 Su		0135	0.7F
	0331	0802	2.1E
	1204	1432	1.4F
	1805	2044	0.9E
	2350		
11 M		0221	1.0F
	0440	0844	1.9E
	1244	1458	1.1F
	1740	2059	1.2E
12 Tu	0010	0305	1.3F
	0549	0927	1.6E
	1328	1527	0.7F
	1721	2114	1.5E
13 W	0037	0353	1.6F
	0703	1017	1.2E
	1422	1549	0.3F
	1705	2129	1.9E
14 Th	0111	0443	1.8F
	0833	1106	0.7E
	1608		*
		2139	2.2E
15 F	0153	0538	2.0F
	1037	1231	0.3E
		1356	0.3E
		2159	2.5E

Day	Slack Water Time (h.m.)	Max Current Time (h.m.)	Vel. (knots)
16 Sa	0244	0639	2.2F
	1350	2237	2.7E
17 Su	0346	0746	2.2F
	1524	2322	2.8E
18 M	0459	0900	2.3F
	1615		
19 Tu		0033	2.7E
	0618	1015	2.4F
	1654		
20 W		0239	2.5E
	0733	1120	2.4F
	1720	2025	0.8E
		2142	0.8E
21 Th		0415	2.5E
	0841	1215	2.4F
	1729	2021	0.8E
		2307	0.3E
22 F		0530	2.4E
	0941	1252	2.1F
	1727	2015	0.9E
	2306		
23 Sa		0016	0.3F
	0129	0640	2.3E
	1036	1327	1.8F
	1719	2004	1.1E
	2314		
24 Su		0116	0.9F
	0335	0743	2.0E
	1127	1356	1.4F
	1704	2019	1.5E
	2342		
25 M		0210	1.4F
	0518	0837	1.6E
	1217	1423	1.0F
	1643	2037	2.0E
26 Tu	0016	0305	1.8F
	0650	0937	1.1E
	1309	1452	0.6F
	1628	2104	2.3E
27 W	0054	0355	2.1F
	0820	1043	0.7E
	1519		*
		2127	2.5E
28 Th	0133	0449	2.2F
	1000	1203	0.3E
	1541		*
		2156	2.6E
29 F	0216	0539	2.2F
	1208	2217	2.6E
30 Sa	0302	0633	2.1F
	1354	2243	2.5E

Time meridian 90° W. 0000 is midnight. 1200 is noon.
* Current weak and variable.
If three consecutive entries are marked (E) the middle one is not a true maximum but an intermediate
value to show the current pattern.

GALVESTON BAY ENTRANCE (between jetties), TEXAS, 1983

F-Flood, Dir. 300° True   E-Ebb, Dir. 100° True

MAY

Days 1–15

Day	Slack Water Time h.m.	Max Current Time h.m.	Vel. knots
1 Su	0355	0731	2.0F
	1451	2313	2.3E
2 M	0457	0839	1.9F
	1533		
3 Tu	0604	0000	2.0E
	1606	0956	1.8F
4 W	0711	0212	1.8E
	1628	1055	1.8F
		1936	0.9E
		2129	0.8E
5 Th	0811	0340	1.7E
	1640	1136	1.7F
		1952	0.9E
		2240	0.4E
6 F	0906	0456	1.7E
	1643	1211	1.6F
		2002	0.9E
		2340	*
7 Sa	0955	0559	1.6E
	1639	1240	1.4F
	2301	1943	1.0E
8 Su	0226	0037	0.5F
	1042	0654	1.5E
	1622	1309	1.2F
	2311	1938	1.2E
9 M	0409	0129	1.0F
	1129	0744	1.3E
	1556	1336	0.9F
	2329	1950	1.6E
10 Tu	0538	0212	1.4F
	1221	0839	1.1E
	1539	1405	0.5F
	2353	2008	2.0E
11 W	0705	0301	1.9F
		0936	0.8E
		1433	*
		2029	2.4E
12 Th	0024	0350	2.3F
	0838	1042	0.5E
		1448	*
		2045	2.8E
13 F	0102	0441	2.6F
	1031	2113	3.1E
14 Sa	0147	0534	2.8F
	1306	2145	3.3E
15 Su	0240	0635	2.8F
	1426	2228	3.3E

Days 16–31

Day	Slack Water Time h.m.	Max Current Time h.m.	Vel. knots
16 M	0340	0737	2.8F
	1516	2325	3.2E
17 Tu	0447	0841	2.7F
	1552		
18 W	0557	0043	2.8E
	1608	0946	2.5F
19 Th	0706	0226	2.4E
	1604	1041	2.2F
		1915	0.9E
		2150	0.5E
20 F	0810	0357	2.0E
	1554	1124	1.9F
		1913	1.1E
		2310	*
21 Sa	0910	0520	1.6E
	1542	1159	1.5F
	2233	1902	1.4E
22 Su	0306	0027	0.7F
	1006	0643	1.3E
	1523	1228	1.1F
	2259	1917	1.9E
23 M	0511	0130	1.3F
	1101	0757	0.9E
	1503	1303	0.8F
	2331	1934	2.3E
24 Tu	0650	0224	1.8F
	1158	0913	0.6E
	1454	1331	0.4F
		2003	2.7E
25 W	0007	0313	2.2F
	0823	1042	0.4E
		1358	*
		2027	2.9E
26 Th	0044	0402	2.4F
	1001	1224	0.3E
		1421	*
		2056	3.0E
27 F	0122	0445	2.5F
	1142	2125	3.0E
28 Sa	0202	0533	2.4F
	1257	2154	2.9E
29 Su	0245	0619	2.3F
	1352	2221	2.7E
30 M	0333	0711	2.2F
	1436	2259	2.5E
31 Tu	0426	0805	2.0F
	1509	2342	2.2E

JUNE

Days 1–15

Day	Slack Water Time h.m.	Max Current Time h.m.	Vel. knots
1 W	0522	0900	1.9F
	1529		
2 Th	0619	0105	1.9E
	1533	0946	1.7F
	2052	1905	0.8E
		2052	0.7E
3 F	0715	0241	1.6E
	1527	1029	1.5F
		1913	0.9E
		2215	0.4E
4 Sa	0811	0404	1.3E
	1515	1104	1.3F
		1854	1.0E
		2326	*
5 Su	0905	0521	1.0E
	1448	1140	1.0F
	2226	1830	1.3E
6 M	0317	0022	0.7F
	1003	0630	0.8E
	1419	1215	0.7F
	2240	1839	1.7E
7 Tu	0518	0118	1.3F
	1107	0739	0.6E
	1405	1242	0.4F
	2303	1900	2.2E
8 W	0654	0207	1.9F
	2334	0859	0.4E
		1312	*
		1926	2.7E
9 Th	0829	0256	2.4F
		1112	0.3E
		1327	*
		1955	3.2E
10 F	0012	0344	2.8F
	1026	2024	3.5E
11 Sa	0056	0438	3.1F
	1225	2103	3.8E
12 Su	0145	0529	3.2F
	1340	2151	3.8E
13 M	0239	0624	3.1F
	1435	2240	3.6E
14 Tu	0336	0721	2.9F
	1509	2335	3.2E
15 W	0436	0813	2.6F
	1513		

Days 16–30

Day	Slack Water Time h.m.	Max Current Time h.m.	Vel. knots
16 Th	0537	0046	2.6E
	1445	0904	2.2F
		1805	0.7E
		2011	0.5E
17 F	0637	0215	1.9E
	1424	0947	1.8F
		1756	1.0E
		2150	*
18 Sa	0737	0350	1.3E
	1405	1028	1.3F
		1751	1.4E
		2321	0.5F
19 Su	0838	0526	0.8E
	1342	1103	0.9F
	2204	1808	2.0E
20 M	0457	0041	1.1F
	0940	0716	0.4E
	1327	1137	0.6F
	2239	1831	2.5E
21 Tu	0653	0150	1.7F
	1047	0901	0.3E
	1324	1212	0.3F
	2317	1900	2.8E
22 W		0239	2.2F
		1021	*
		1245	*
	2355	1935	3.1E
23 Th		0322	2.4F
		1128	*
		1312	*
		2007	3.2E
24 F	0033	0403	2.5F
		1243	*
		1302	*
		2042	3.2E
25 Sa	0112	0439	2.5F
	1200	2111	3.1E
26 Su	0152	0519	2.4F
	1300	2146	3.0E
27 M	0234	0602	2.3F
	1351	2221	2.8E
28 Tu	0316	0642	2.1F
	1429	2302	2.6E
29 W	0400	0726	1.9F
	1451	2331	2.2E
30 Th	0445	0809	1.7F
	1443		

Time meridian 90° W. 0000 is midnight. 1200 is noon.
* Current weak and variable.
If three consecutive entries are marked (E) the middle one is not a true maximum but an intermediate value to show the current pattern.

GALVESTON BAY ENTRANCE (between jetties), TEXAS, 1983

F-Flood, Dir. 300° True   E-Ebb, Dir. 100° True

JULY

Day	Slack Water Time (h.m.)	Maximum Current — Time (h.m.) Vel. (knots)
1 F	0532, 1416	0012 1.8E; 0852 1.5F; 1820 0.6E; 2021 0.5E
2 Sa	0623, 1350	0142 1.3E; 0930 1.2F; 1806 0.8E; 2144 *
3 Su	0721, 1306, 2129	0320 0.8E; 1012 0.9F; 1712 1.1E; 2301 0.4F
4 M	0131, 0833, 1237, 2140	0457 0.5E; 1047 0.5F; 1730 1.6E
5 Tu	0446, 2205	0009 1.0F; 0656 0.3E; 1121 *; 1748 2.1E
6 W	0637, 2238	0106 1.7F; 0924 0.3E; 1150 *; 1820 2.6E
7 Th	0813, 2318	0201 2.3F; 1053 0.3E; 1211 *; 1852 3.2E
8 F	0950	0250 2.8F; 1935 3.6E
9 Sa	0003, 1129	0339 3.1F; 2016 4.0E
10 Su	0051, 1308	0427 3.3F; 2105 4.1E
11 M	0142, 1434	0518 3.2F; 2154 3.9E
12 Tu	0234, 1534	0604 2.9F; 2248 3.5E
13 W	0327, 1508	0650 2.6F; 2345 2.9E
14 Th	0421, 1311	0733 2.1F; 1557 0.3E; 1837 *
15 F	0515, 1238	0046 2.1E; 0814 1.6F; 1538 0.7E; 2009 *
16 Sa	0611, 1210, 2005	0209 1.2E; 0851 1.1F; 1559 1.3E; 2150 0.5F
17 Su	0058, 0715, 1145, 2049	0352 0.5E; 0932 0.7F; 1642 1.8E; 2341 1.0F
18 M	1137, 2133	0650 *; 1012 0.3F; 1714 2.3E
19 Tu	2216	0117 1.6F; 0820 *; 1054 *; 1758 2.6E
20 W	0745, 2259	0206 2.0F; 0924 0.3E; 1137 *; 1835 2.9E
21 Th	0840, 2340	0249 2.3F; 1021 0.3E; 1218 *; 1915 3.0E
22 F	—	0324 2.4F; 1118 *; 1300 *; 1953 3.1E
23 Sa	0021	0353 2.4F; 1158 *; 1338 *; 2033 3.1E
24 Su	0101	0424 2.4F; 1242 *; 1415 *; 2105 3.1E
25 M	0141	0454 2.2F; 1344 *; 1444 *; 2142 3.0E
26 Tu	0219, 1506	0528 2.1F; 2215 2.7E
27 W	0257, 1505	0603 1.9F; 2250 2.4E
28 Th	0334, 1446	0641 1.6F; 2318 2.0E
29 F	0413	0715 1.3F; 1410 *; 1512 *; 1648 *; 1833 *
30 Sa	0456, 1136	0000 1.5E; 0756 1.0F; 1430 0.4E; 1956 *
31 Su	0551, 1046, 1944, 2312	0109 0.9E; 0836 0.6F; 1459 0.8E; 2118 0.3F

AUGUST

Day	Slack Water Time (h.m.)	Maximum Current — Time (h.m.) Vel. (knots)
1 M	2012	0309 0.4E; 0912 *; 1542 1.3E; 2242 0.8F
2 Tu	2048	0739 *; 0947 *; 1620 1.8E; 2356 1.5F
3 W	0607, 2130	0900 0.4E; 1022 0.3E; 1703 2.3E
4 Th	0721, 2215	0054 2.1F; 1002 0.4E; 1057 0.4E; 1750 2.9E
5 F	0830, 2304	0149 2.6F; 1835 3.4E
6 Sa	0949, 2353	0236 3.0F; 1924 3.8E
7 Su	—	0323 3.1F; 1214 *; 1238 *; 2016 4.0E
8 M	0044, 1521	0407 3.0F; 1226 *; 1400 0.3F; 2105 3.9E
9 Tu	0134, 1636	0447 2.8F; 1144 *; 1503 0.4F; 2154 3.6E
10 W	0224, 1748	0527 2.3F; 1151 *; 1612 0.5F; 2250 2.9E
11 Th	0313, 1041, 1437, 1906	0605 1.8F; 1220 0.3E; 1724 0.6F; 2346 2.1E
12 F	0404, 1009, 1624, 2041	0640 1.3F; 1255 0.8E; 1840 0.6F
13 Sa	0459, 0938, 1749, 2336	0055 1.3E; 0715 0.8F; 1340 1.2E; 2003 0.8F
14 Su	0612, 0922, 1901	0221 0.5E; 0755 0.3F; 1432 1.6E; 2139 1.0F
15 M	2003	0609 *; 0837 *; 1532 2.0E
16 Tu	0530, 2058	0003 1.5F; 0730 0.3E; 0926 *; 1629 2.3E
17 W	0626, 2150	0106 1.9F; 0831 0.4E; 1015 0.3E; 1727 2.5E
18 Th	0711, 2237	0155 2.1F; 0915 0.5E; 1117 0.3E; 1818 2.7E
19 F	0753, 2322	0230 2.2F; 0950 0.4E; 1206 *; 1902 2.8E
20 Sa	0834	0303 2.2F; 1025 0.3E; 1255 *; 1942 2.9E
21 Su	0004, 1054	0324 2.2F; 1338 *; 2023 2.9E
22 M	0044, 1534	0351 2.0F; 1109 *; 1415 0.3F; 2058 2.9E
23 Tu	0122, 1624	0417 1.9F; 1057 *; 1456 0.4F; 2134 2.7E
24 W	0158, 1713	0449 1.7F; 1058 *; 1539 0.5F; 2204 2.4E
25 Th	0234, 1804	0515 1.4F; 1119 *; 1624 0.5F; 2240 2.0E
26 F	0311, 0906, 1405, 1904	0547 1.1F; 1139 0.4E; 1720 0.5F; 2321 1.5E
27 Sa	0353, 0832, 1514, 2020	0619 0.7F; 1157 0.7E; 1826 0.5F
28 Su	0459, 0812, 1632, 2221	0015 0.9E; 0649 0.3F; 1212 1.0E; 1938 0.7F
29 M	0724, 1749	0149 0.4E; 1236 1.3E; 2059 1.0F
30 Tu	0309, 1858	1339 1.6E; 2220 1.4F
31 W	0506, 2001	1507 2.0E; 2339 1.9F

Time meridian 90° W. 0000 is midnight. 1200 is noon.
* Current weak and variable.
If three consecutive entries are marked (E) the middle one is not a true maximum but an intermediate value to show the current pattern.

GALVESTON BAY ENTRANCE (between jetties), TEXAS, 1983

F-Flood, Dir. 300° True   E-Ebb, Dir. 100° True

SEPTEMBER

Day	Slack Water Time (h.m.)	Max Current Time (h.m.)	Vel. (knots)
1 Th	0604, 2059	1624	2.5E
2 F	0658, 2155	0041 / 1724	2.4F / 2.9E
3 Sa	0749, 2249	0132 / 1006 / 1142 / 1827	2.7F / 0.4E / 0.3E / 3.3E
4 Su	2340	0215 / 1017 / 1237 / 1918	2.8F / * / * / 3.5E
5 M	1453	0255 / 0954 / 1332 / 2011	2.7F / * / 0.4F / 3.5E
6 Tu	0030, 1614	0333 / 0954 / 1423 / 2100	2.5F / * / 0.8F / 3.2E
7 W	0119, 0825, 1218, 1731	0408 / 1011 / 1523 / 2155	2.0F / 0.5E / 1.1F / 2.7E
8 Th	0208, 0801, 1319, 1851	0440 / 1037 / 1624 / 2247	1.5F / 0.9E / 1.2F / 2.0E
9 F	0258, 0733, 1426, 2026	0512 / 1106 / 1731 / 2355	1.0F / 1.3E / 1.3F / 1.2E
10 Sa	0357, 0715, 1536, 2248	0541 / 1141 / 1836	0.5F / 1.6E / 1.4F
11 Su	1650	0115 / 0614 / 1224 / 1951	0.5E / * / 1.8E / 1.4F
12 M	0209, 1804	0527 / 0643 / 1314 / 2125	0.3E / 0.3E / 2.0E / 1.5F
13 Tu	0408, 1915	1427 / 2338	2.0E / 1.8F
14 W	0500, 2020	0742 / 0840 / 1544	0.7E / 0.6E / 2.1E
15 Th	0541, 2118	0040 / 0812 / 1003 / 1656	2.0F / 0.7E / 0.6E / 2.2E
16 F	0615, 2209	0123 / 0841 / 1105 / 1756	2.0F / 0.7E / 0.4E / 2.4E
17 Sa	0645, 2256	0152 / 0909 / 1201 / 1847	2.0F / 0.6E / * / 2.5E
18 Su	0706, 2338	0216 / 0928 / 1246 / 1929	2.0F / 0.5E / * / 2.6E
19 M	0720, 1145, 1505	0236 / 0927 / 1332 / 2005	1.8F / 0.4E / 0.5F / 2.5E
20 Tu	0018, 0726, 1158, 1604	0303 / 0922 / 1412 / 2042	1.7F / 0.5E / 0.7F / 2.4E
21 W	0055, 0721, 1215, 1700	0329 / 0930 / 1456 / 2122	1.4F / 0.6E / 0.9F / 2.1E
22 Th	0133, 0659, 1238, 1758	0355 / 0945 / 1542 / 2157	1.2F / 0.8E / 1.0F / 1.7E
23 F	0212, 0634, 1310, 1901	0424 / 1005 / 1630 / 2240	0.8F / 1.0E / 1.1F / 1.3E
24 Sa	0301, 0618, 1349, 2019	0451 / 1012 / 1719 / 2335	0.4F / 1.3E / 1.2F / 0.8E
25 Su	1437, 2231	0509 / 1022 / 1823	* / 1.6E / 1.4F
26 M	1536	0057 / 0256 / 1042 / 1926	0.3E / * / 1.9E / 1.5F
27 Tu	0222, 1648	1114 / 2042	2.1E / 1.7F
28 W	0359, 1809	1212 / 2205	2.2E / 2.0F
29 Th	0451, 1925	1400 / 2320	2.3E / 2.3F
30 F	0535, 2032	1556	2.5E

OCTOBER

Day	Slack Water Time (h.m.)	Max Current Time (h.m.)	Vel. (knots)
1 Sa	0611, 2133	0015 / 0903 / 1040 / 1713	2.5F / 0.7E / 0.6E / 2.8E
2 Su	0632, 2229	0100 / 0904 / 1145 / 1815	2.5F / 0.5E / * / 2.9E
3 M	0635, 2321	0141 / 0846 / 1245 / 1910	2.4F / 0.5E / 0.4F / 2.9E
4 Tu	0630, 1122, 1543	0213 / 0835 / 1342 / 2009	2.1F / 0.7E / 0.9F / 2.6E
5 W	0011, 0614, 1152, 1712	0245 / 0854 / 1439 / 2103	1.7F / 1.1E / 1.4F / 2.2E
6 Th	0100, 0551, 1233, 1841	0317 / 0918 / 1532 / 2158	1.2F / 1.6E / 1.7F / 1.6E
7 F	0151, 0533, 1319, 2020	0343 / 0939 / 1631 / 2301	0.7F / 2.0E / 1.9F / 1.0E
8 Sa	0255, 0517, 1410, 2219	0411 / 1013 / 1728	0.3F / 2.3E / 2.0F
9 Su	1505	0017 / 0432 / 1043 / 1829	0.4E / * / 2.4E / 2.0F
10 M	0105, 1607	1112 / 1937	2.4E / 1.9F
11 Tu	0253, 1716	1157 / 2101	2.3E / 1.9F
12 W	0344, 1828	1306 / 2239	2.1E / 1.9F
13 Th	0423, 1937	1448 / 2353	1.9E / 1.9F
14 F	0453, 2038	0747 / 0940 / 1617	0.9E / 0.7E / 1.9E
15 Sa	0516, 2132	0030 / 0809 / 1051 / 1727	1.9F / 0.9E / 0.4E / 2.0E
16 Su	0531, 2219	0053 / 0825 / 1146 / 1821	1.8F / 0.8E / * / 2.0E
17 M	0537, 2303	0116 / 0825 / 1237 / 1903	1.7F / 0.8E / 0.4F / 2.0E
18 Tu	0537, 1124, 1531, 2344	0143 / 0820 / 1323 / 1947	1.5F / 0.9E / 0.7F / 1.9E
19 W	0525, 1142, 1642	0209 / 0821 / 1409 / 2028	1.3F / 1.1E / 1.1F / 1.7E
20 Th	0025, 0502, 1203, 1752	0236 / 0836 / 1455 / 2114	1.0F / 1.4E / 1.4F / 1.4E
21 F	0109, 0446, 1228, 1906	0302 / 0852 / 1537 / 2200	0.6F / 1.7E / 1.7F / 1.0E
22 Sa	1259, 2036	0323 / 0906 / 1627 / 2257	* / 2.0E / 1.9F / 0.6E
23 Su	1336	0339 / 0922 / 1715	* / 2.3E / 2.0F
24 M	1422	0019 / 0108 / 0934 / 1812	* / * / 2.6E / 2.1F
25 Tu	0145, 1518	1005 / 1921	2.7E / 2.2F
26 W	0302, 1625	1046 / 2029	2.8E / 2.3F
27 Th	0350, 1741	1146 / 2144	2.7E / 2.4F
28 F	0428, 1856	1333 / 2249	2.5E / 2.4F
29 Sa	0454, 2005	0814 / 0914 / 1533 / 2340	0.9E / 0.9E / 2.4E / 2.3F
30 Su	0501, 2107	0804 / 1042 / 1655	0.8E / 0.4E / 2.3E
31 M	0457, 2204	0021 / 0752 / 1150 / 1809	2.1F / 0.9E / * / 2.1E

Time meridian 90° W.   0000 is midnight.   1200 is noon.
* Current weak and variable.
If three consecutive entries are marked (E) the middle one is not a true maximum but an intermediate value to show the current pattern.

F-Flood, Dir. 300° True   E-Ebb, Dir. 100° True

NOVEMBER

Day	Slack Water Time h.m.	Max Current Time h.m.	Vel. knots	Day	Slack Water Time h.m.	Max Current Time h.m.	Vel. knots
1 Tu		0056	1.8F	16 W		0047	1.1F
	0447	0739	1.2E		0352	0721	1.4E
	1054	1253	0.8F		1102	1313	1.0F
	1511	1912	1.9E		1617	1933	1.2E
	2256				2309		
2 W		0125	1.4F	17 Th		0113	0.8F
	0428	0748	1.7E		0328	0736	1.8E
	1118	1353	1.4F		1121	1401	1.5F
	1702	2014	1.5E		1744	2030	0.9E
	2348						
3 Th		0152	1.0F	18 F	0000	0142	0.5F
	0406	0809	2.2E		0314	0752	2.1E
	1152	1448	1.9F		1145	1447	1.9F
	1840	2112	1.0E		1906	2125	0.7E
4 F	0041	0221	0.5F	19 Sa		0209	*
	0354	0838	2.6E			0812	2.5E
	1230	1537	2.3F		1214	1533	2.3F
	2016	2226	0.6E		2035	2228	0.4E
5 Sa		0249	*	20 Su		0225	*
		0904	2.9E			0830	2.8E
	1312	1632	2.5F		1248	1622	2.5F
	2204				2228		
6 Su		0042	0.3F	21 M		0853	3.1E
		0306	*		1329	1715	2.7F
		0936	3.0E				
	1356	1723	2.5F				
7 M	0027	0958	2.9E	22 Tu	0104	0922	3.3E
	1444	1817	2.4F		1417	1806	2.7F
8 Tu	0152	1029	2.8E	23 W	0214	1003	3.4E
	1538	1921	2.2F		1512	1909	2.7F
9 W	0242	1058	2.5E	24 Th	0303	1050	3.2E
	1638	2027	2.1F		1615	2013	2.6F
10 Th	0320	1151	2.2E	25 F	0339	1153	2.9E
	1744	2139	1.9F		1722	2113	2.5F
11 F	0349	1349	1.9E	26 Sa	0356	1329	2.4E
	1849	2236	1.8F		1830	2207	2.2F
12 Sa	0408	0716	0.9E	27 Su	0347	0704	0.8E
		0912	0.8E			0911	0.7E
		1524	1.7E			1515	2.0E
	1950	2321	1.7F		1935	2253	1.9F
13 Su	0416	0731	0.9E	28 M	0332	0651	1.0E
		1026	0.5E			1042	*
		1636	1.6E			1648	1.5E
	2045	2346	1.6F		2037	2328	1.5F
14 M	0416	0742	1.0E	29 Tu	0315	0639	1.4E
		1132	*		1014	1202	0.6F
		1743	1.5E		1435	1806	1.2E
	2135				2136		
15 Tu		0018	1.4F	30 W		0003	1.1F
	0410	0727	1.1E		0252	0648	1.9E
	1051	1224	0.5F		1036	1307	1.3F
	1430	1839	1.3E		1655	1933	0.8E
	2222				2233		

DECEMBER

Day	Slack Water Time h.m.	Max Current Time h.m.	Vel. knots	Day	Slack Water Time h.m.	Max Current Time h.m.	Vel. knots
1 Th		0035	0.7F	16 F		0027	0.3F
	0233	0709	2.5E		0145	0651	2.2E
	1108	1407	1.9F		1056	1355	1.8F
	1839	2051	0.5E		1852	2107	0.4E
	2332						
2 F		0107	0.4F	17 Sa		0054	*
	0226	0738	2.9E			0715	2.7E
	1145	1457	2.4F		1125	1439	2.3F
	2017	2225	0.3E		2020	2303	0.3E
3 Sa		0135	*	18 Su		0116	*
		0807	3.2E			0744	3.1E
	1224	1545	2.6F		1200	1528	2.7F
					2208		
4 Su		0001	*	19 M		0813	3.5E
	0157	0839	3.3E		1240	1617	3.0F
	1304	1629	2.7F				
	2343						
5 M		0914	3.3E	20 Tu	0013	0850	3.7E
	1346	1718	2.7F		1325	1706	3.1F
6 Tu	0056	0945	3.2E	21 W	0135	0929	3.8E
	1430	1804	2.5F		1415	1758	3.0F
7 W	0148	1016	2.9E	22 Th	0232	1013	3.7E
	1518	1855	2.3F		1508	1850	2.8F
8 Th	0230	1052	2.6E	23 F	0312	1106	3.3E
	1609	1948	2.1F		1605	1942	2.5F
9 F	0301	1133	2.3E	24 Sa	0322	1208	2.7E
	1703	2037	1.9F		1703	2028	2.1F
10 Sa	0318	1238	1.9E	25 Su	0238	0556	0.5E
	1800	2123	1.7F			0720	0.5E
						1330	2.0E
					1803	2116	1.7F
11 Su	0317	0647	0.8E	26 M	0201	0537	0.8E
		0832	0.7E			0911	*
		1420	1.5F			1501	1.3E
	1856	2206	1.4F		1905	2154	1.3F
12 M	0307	0654	0.9E	27 Tu	0135	0524	1.3E
		0952	0.4E		0912	1050	0.4F
		1547	1.2E		1338	1652	0.7E
	1953	2248	1.2F		2011	2236	0.8F
13 Tu	0252	0645	1.0E	28 W	0106	0537	1.9E
		1109	*		0939	1224	1.1F
		1710	0.9E		1643	1907	0.4E
	2050	2323	0.9F		2120	2311	0.5F
14 W	0225	0621	1.4E	29 Th	0053	0606	2.5E
	1017	1212	0.6F		1016	1329	1.8F
	1532	1827	0.7E		1844	2046	0.3E
	2148	2353	0.6F			2346	*
15 Th	0157	0628	1.8E	30 F		0638	2.9E
	1032	1306	1.3F		1055	1424	2.3F
	1723	1939	0.5E			2013	0.3E
	2252						
				31 Sa		0022	*
						0715	3.2E
					1135	1506	2.6F
						2307	*

Time meridian 90° W. 0000 is midnight. 1200 is noon.
* Current weak and variable.
If three consecutive entries are marked (E) the middle one is not a true maximum but an intermediate value to show the current pattern.

VIEQUES PASSAGE, PUERTO RICO, 1983

F-Flood, Dir. 250° True   E-Ebb, Dir. 055° True

JANUARY

Day	Slack Water Time h.m.	Max Current Time h.m.	Vel. knots
1 Sa	0329	0036	0.6F
	0843	0610	0.5E
	1526	1214	0.9F
	2241	1859	1.1E
2 Su	0427	0125	0.7F
	0949	0710	0.5E
	1617	1312	0.6F
	2324	1948	1.0E
3 M	0524	0216	0.7F
	1058	0810	0.6E
	1708	1407	0.7F
		2037	1.0E
4 Tu	0007	0307	0.7F
	0620	0910	0.6E
	1209	1508	0.6F
	1800	2130	0.9E
5 W	0049	0359	0.8F
	0717	1013	0.6E
	1324	1612	0.5F
	1853	2217	0.8E
6 Th	0131	0448	0.8F
	0812	1117	0.7E
	1441	1713	0.4F
	1947	2307	0.6E
7 F	0212	0539	0.8F
	0905	1216	0.7E
	1557	1817	0.3F
	2045	2358	0.5E
8 Sa	0254	0630	0.8F
	0957	1317	0.7E
	1709	1923	0.3F
	2145		
9 Su	0335	0051	0.5F
	1045	0718	0.8F
	1813	1414	0.8E
	2247	2025	0.3F
10 M	0416	0140	0.4E
	1130	0804	0.8F
	1908	1502	0.8E
	2350	2120	0.3F
11 Tu	0458	0235	0.3E
	1212	0848	0.8F
	1956	1549	0.8E
		2212	0.3F
12 W	0049	0322	0.3E
	0541	0931	0.7F
	1252	1632	0.9E
	2036	2259	0.3F
13 Th	0144	0411	0.3E
	0626	1013	0.7F
	1330	1711	0.9E
	2113	2342	0.4F
14 F	0234	0457	0.3E
	0712	1054	0.7F
	1407	1748	0.9E
	2146		
15 Sa	0320	0021	0.4F
	0800	0543	0.3E
	1444	1135	0.6F
	2217	1823	0.9E
16 Su	0402	0100	0.5F
	0851	0629	0.3E
	1521	1218	0.6F
	2247	1901	0.8E
17 M	0441	0135	0.5F
	0944	0713	0.3E
	1559	1301	0.6F
	2316	1936	0.8E
18 Tu	0520	0208	0.5F
	1041	0802	0.4E
	1639	1348	0.5F
	2343	2015	0.7E
19 W	0559	0245	0.6F
	1142	0847	0.4E
	1719	1434	0.4F
		2051	0.7E
20 Th	0012	0321	0.6F
	0640	0939	0.5E
	1248	1527	0.4F
	1803	2131	0.6E
21 F	0042	0403	0.7F
	0724	1030	0.6E
	1357	1622	0.3F
	1851	2215	0.6E
22 Sa	0116	0444	0.7F
	0812	1124	0.7E
	1507	1723	0.3F
	1945	2302	0.5E
23 Su	0154	0533	0.8F
	0902	1224	0.7E
	1617	1826	0.3F
	2045	2353	0.5E
24 M	0239	0624	0.8F
	0954	1321	0.8E
	1721	1932	0.3F
	2151		
25 Tu	0330	0054	0.5E
	1048	0719	0.9F
	1819	1418	0.9E
	2259	2034	0.3F
26 W	0427	0156	0.5E
	1142	0815	0.9F
	1911	1513	1.0E
		2132	0.4F
27 Th	0006	0253	0.5E
	0529	0912	0.9F
	1236	1607	1.0E
	1959	2228	0.5F
28 F	0110	0358	0.5E
	0633	1013	0.9F
	1329	1659	1.1E
	2044	2322	0.6F
29 Sa	0211	0459	0.6E
	0739	1108	0.9F
	1421	1748	1.0E
	2127		
30 Su	0308	0011	0.6F
	0844	0559	0.6E
	1512	1204	0.9F
	2209	1838	1.0E
31 M	0404	0100	0.7F
	0950	0659	0.7E
	1602	1300	0.8F
	2250	1925	1.0E

FEBRUARY

Day	Slack Water Time h.m.	Max Current Time h.m.	Vel. knots
1 Tu	0458	0148	0.8F
	1056	0754	0.7E
	1651	1357	0.7F
	2330	2014	0.9E
2 W	0551	0237	0.8F
	1203	0851	0.7E
	1740	1452	0.6F
		2059	0.8E
3 Th	0011	0326	0.8F
	0644	0951	0.7E
	1312	1548	0.5F
	1829	2146	0.7E
4 F	0051	0415	0.8F
	0737	1048	0.7E
	1422	1647	0.4F
	1921	2234	0.6E
5 Sa	0132	0502	0.8F
	0828	1145	0.7E
	1533	1748	0.3F
	2016	2324	0.5E
6 Su	0213	0551	0.8F
	0919	1243	0.7E
	1640	1852	0.3F
	2115		
7 M	0257	0018	0.4E
	1007	0639	0.7F
	1741	1336	0.7E
	2219	1953	0.3F
8 Tu	0343	0111	0.3E
	1054	0730	0.7F
	1833	1429	0.8E
	2323	2050	0.3F
9 W	0431	0203	0.3E
	1139	0819	0.7F
	1918	1516	0.8E
		2139	0.3F
10 Th	0023	0257	0.3E
	0522	0904	0.7F
	1221	1557	0.8E
	1957	2226	0.4F
11 F	0116	0351	0.3E
	0613	0953	0.6F
	1303	1640	0.8E
	2032	2309	0.4F
12 Sa	0202	0437	0.3E
	0706	1035	0.6F
	1343	1720	0.8E
	2104	2345	0.5F
13 Su	0243	0523	0.4E
	0758	1119	0.6F
	1422	1756	0.8E
	2133		
14 M	0321	0020	0.5F
	0850	0606	0.4E
	1502	1202	0.6F
	2201	1832	0.8E
15 Tu	0358	0056	0.5F
	0943	0650	0.5E
	1541	1247	0.5F
	2228	1906	0.7E
16 W	0435	0127	0.6F
	1037	0736	0.5E
	1620	1332	0.5F
	2255	1941	0.7E
17 Th	0514	0202	0.6F
	1134	0819	0.6E
	1701	1417	0.5F
	2324	2017	0.6E
18 F	0557	0241	0.7F
	1234	0908	0.7E
	1744	1508	0.4F
	2357	2059	0.6E
19 Sa	0643	0324	0.7F
	1338	0959	0.7E
	1832	1600	0.4F
		2142	0.5E
20 Su	0035	0409	0.8F
	0734	1052	0.7E
	1443	1701	0.3F
	1926	2231	0.5E
21 M	0120	0502	0.8F
	0828	1153	0.8E
	1548	1800	0.3F
	2027	2333	0.5E
22 Tu	0213	0558	0.8F
	0925	1255	0.8E
	1650	1909	0.3F
	2135		
23 W	0313	0036	0.5E
	1023	0701	0.8F
	1746	1353	0.9E
	2244	2010	0.4F
24 Th	0420	0139	0.5E
	1122	0758	0.8F
	1837	1450	0.9E
	2351	2107	0.5F
25 F	0529	0247	0.5E
	1219	0901	0.8F
	1924	1545	0.9E
		2204	0.5F
26 Sa	0053	0350	0.6E
	0638	1001	0.8F
	1314	1637	0.9E
	2008	2255	0.6F
27 Su	0150	0450	0.7E
	0745	1059	0.9F
	1407	1725	0.9E
	2050	2345	0.7F
28 M	0245	0545	0.7E
	0849	1154	0.8F
	1457	1813	0.9E
	2130		

Time meridian 60° W. 0000 is midnight. 1200 is noon.

TABLE 2.—CURRENT DIFFERENCES AND OTHER CONSTANTS AND ROTARY TIDAL CURRENTS

EXPLANATION OF TABLE

In this publication, reference stations are those for which daily predictions are listed in Table 1. Those stations appearing in Table 2 are called subordinate stations. The principal purpose of Table 2 is to present data that will enable one to determine the approximate times of minimum currents (slack waters) and the times and speeds of maximum currents at numerous subordinate stations on the Atlantic Coast of North America. By applying the specific corrections given in Table 2 to the predicted times and speeds of the current at the appropriate reference station, reasonable approximations of the current at the subordinate station may be compiled.

Locations and Depths

Because the latitude and longitude are listed according to the exactness recorded in the original survey records, the locations of the subordinate stations are presented in varying degrees of accuracy. Since a minute of latitude is nearly equivalent to a mile, a location given to the nearest minute may not indicate the exact position of the station. This should be remembered, especially in the case of a narrow stream, where the nearest minute of latitude or longitude may locate a station inland. In such cases, unless the description locates the station elsewhere, reference is made to the current in the center of the channel. In some instances, the charts may not present a convenient name for locating a station. In those cases, the position may be described by a bearing from some prominent place on the chart.

Although current measurements may have been recorded at various depths in the past, the data listed here for most of the subordinate stations are mean values determined to have been representative of the current at each location. For that reason, no specific current meter depths for those stations are given in Table 2. Beginning with the Boston Harbor tidal current survey in 1971, data for individual meter depths were published and subsequent new data may be presented in a similar manner.

Since most of the current data in Table 2 came from meters suspended from survey vessels or anchored buoys, the listed depths are those measured downward from the surface. Some later data have come from meters anchored at fixed depths from the bottom. Those meter positions were defined as depths below chart datum. Such defined depths in this and subsequent editions will be accompanied by the small letter "d".

Minimum Currents

The reader may note that at many locations the current may not diminish to a true slack water or zero speed stage. For that reason, the phrases, "minimum before flood" and "minimum before ebb" are used in Table 2 rather than "slack water" although either or both minimums may actually reach a zero speed value at some locations. Table 2 lists the average speeds and directions of the minimums.

Maximum Currents

Near the coast and in inland tidal waters, the current increases from minimum current (slack water) for a period of about 3 hours until the maximum speed or the strength of the current is reached. The speed then decreases for another period of about 3 hours when minimum current is again reached and the current begins a similar cycle in the opposite direction. The current that flows toward the coast or up a stream is known as the flood current; the opposite flow is known as the ebb current. Table 2 lists the average speeds and directions of the maximum floods and maximum ebbs. The directions are given in degrees, true, reading clockwise from 000° at north to 359° and are the directions toward which the currents flow.

Time Differences and Speed Ratios

Table 2 contains mean time differences by which the reader can compile approximate times for the minimum and maximum current phases at the subordinate stations. Time differences for those phases should be applied to the corresponding phases at the reference station. It will be seen upon inspection that some subordinate stations exhibit either a double flood or a double ebb stage or both. Explanations of these stages can be found in the glossary located elsewhere in this publication. In those cases, a separate time difference is listed for each of the three flood (or ebb) phases and these should be applied only to the daily maximum flood (or ebb) phase at the reference station. The results obtained by the application of the time differences will be based upon the time meridian shown above the name of the subordinate station. Differences of time meridians between a subordinate station and its reference station have been accounted for and no further adjustment by the reader is needed. Summer or daylight saving time is not used in this publication.

The speed ratios are used to compile approximations of the daily current speeds at the subordinate stations and refer only to the maximum floods and ebbs. No attempt is made to predict the speeds of the minimum currents. Normally, these ratios should be applied to the corresponding maximum current phases at the reference station. As mentioned above, however, some subordinate stations may exhibit either a double flood or a double ebb or both. As with the time differences, separate ratios are listed for each of the three flood (or ebb phases) and should be applied only to the daily maximum flood (or ebb) speed at the reference station. It should be noted that although the speed of a given current phase at a subordinate station is obtained by reference to the corresponding phase at the reference station, the directions of the current at the two places may differ considerably. Table 2 lists the average directions of the various current phases at the subordinate stations.

Rotary Tidal Currents

The last page of Table 2 is a listing of data for those stations which exhibited rotary current patterns. Briefly, a rotary current can be described as one which flows continually with the direction of flow changing through all points of the compass during the tidal period. A more complete description can be found in the glossary located elsewhere in this publication. The average speeds and directions are listed in half-hour increments as referred to the predicted times of "minimum before flood" at the reference station in Table 1. The Moon, at times of new, full, or perigee may increase these speeds 15 to 20 percent above average; or 30 to 40 percent if perigee occurs at or near the time of new or full Moon. Conversely, the Moon at times of quadrature or apogee may decrease the speeds 15 to 20 percent or 30 to 40 percent if they occur together. Near average speeds may be expected when apogee occurs near or at new or full Moon, or when perigee occurs at or near quadrature. The directions of the currents are given in degrees, true reading clockwise from 000° at north to 359° and are the direction toward which the water is flowing.

Example of The Use of Table 2

Suppose we wish to calculate the times of the minimum currents and the times and speeds of the maximum currents on a particular morning at the location listed as Winthrop Head, 1.1 nautical miles east of. From Table 2 we learn that the reference station is Boston

Harbor whose morning currents are listed below. Currents for Winthrop Head can be approximated by using the Table 2 corrections as indicated.

	Minimum before flood h.m.	Maximum flood h.m.	Maximum flood kn	Minimum before ebb h.m.	Maximum ebb h.m.	Maximum ebb kn
Boston Harbor	0052	0419	1.2	0645	1109	1.4
Table 2 corrections	−0112	+0019	×0.4 ratio	+0031	−0146	×0.3 ratio
Winthrop Head	2340*	0438	0.5	0716	0923	0.4

* this minimum current phase is seen to occur just before midnight of the previous day.

Table 2 states that the average speeds and directions of the minimums before flood and ebb are 0.3 knots at 103° and 0.2 knots at 297°; respectively. The average directions of the maximum flood and maximum ebb are 205° and 019°; respectively.

TABLE 2. - CURRENT DIFFERENCES AND OTHER CONSTANTS, 1983

NO.	PLACE	POSITION Lat. N	POSITION Long. W	METER DEPTH (ft)	TIME DIFF. Min. before Flood	TIME DIFF. Flood	TIME DIFF. Min. before Ebb	TIME DIFF. Ebb	SPEED RATIOS Flood	SPEED RATIOS Ebb	AVG SPEED Minimum before Flood (knots deg.)	AVG SPEED Maximum Flood (knots deg.)	AVG SPEED Minimum before Ebb (knots deg.)	AVG SPEED Maximum Ebb (knots deg.)
	BAY OF FUNDY Time meridian, 60°W													
						on BAY OF FUNDY ENTRANCE, p.4									
1	Brazil Rock, 6 miles east of.........	43 22	65 18		-2 02	-2 00	-1 56	-2 00	0.4	0.4	0.0 --	1.0 275	0.0 --	1.0 050
6	Cape Sable, 3 miles south of.........	43 20	65 38		-3 02	-2 10	-1 21	-2 10	1.0	0.8	0.0 --	2.2 275	0.0 --	2.0 095
11	Cape Sable, 12 miles south of........	43 11	65 37		-1 12	-1 00	-0 46	-1 00	0.7	0.7	0.0 --	1.7 285	0.0 --	1.6 090
16	Blonde Rock, 5 miles south of........	43 15	65 59		-1 02	-0 50	-0 36	-0 50	0.9	0.8	0.0 --	2.0 310	0.0 --	2.0 125
21	Seal Island, 13 miles southwest of...	43 16	66 15		-0 17	+0 10	+0 39	+0 10	1.1	0.7	0.0 --	2.6 325	0.0 --	1.6 140
26	Cape Fourchu, 17 miles southwest of..	43 34	66 24		+0 38	+0 45	+0 44	+0 45	0.5	0.5	0.0 --	1.2 355	0.0 --	1.2 145
31	Cape Fourchu, 4 miles west of........	43 47	66 15		-0 12	0 00	+0 09	0 00	0.9	0.7	0.0 --	2.0 000	0.0 --	1.7 175
36	Lurcher Shoal, 6 miles east of.......	43 52	66 21		+0 08	+0 30	+0 39	+0 30	0.9	0.8	0.0 --	1.4 355	0.0 --	1.8 175
41	Lurcher Shoal, 10 miles west of......	43 46	66 42		+0 23	+0 30	-0 34	+0 30	0.6	0.7	0.0 --	1.4 000	0.0 --	1.6 160
46	Lurcher Shoal, 10 miles northwest of.	43 59	66 37		-0 02	+0 30	+0 49	+0 30	0.8	0.5	0.0 --	1.8 005	0.0 --	1.2 175
51	Brier Island, 5 miles west of........	44 13	66 30		+0 43	+0 50	+0 54	+0 50	1.2	1.0	0.0 --	2.7 005	0.0 --	2.5 185
56	Brier Island, 15 miles west of.......	44 17	66 44		-0 42	-0 15	+0 14	-0 15	0.6	0.5	0.0 --	2.6 060	0.0 --	1.2 250
61	Gannet Rock, 5 miles southeast of....	44 29	66 41		+0 38	+0 30	+0 09	+0 30	1.1	1.6	0.0 --	2.6 040	0.0 --	3.9 230
66	Boars Head, 10 miles northwest of....	44 31	66 23		+0 48	+0 55	+0 59	+0 55	0.8	0.8	0.0 --	1.9 020	0.0 --	2.0 205
71	Prim Point, 20 miles west of.........	44 44	66 15		+0 38	+0 45	+0 54	+0 45	0.7	0.6	0.0 --	1.6 040	0.0 --	1.4 235
76	Cape Spencer, 14 miles south of......	44 58	65 52		+0 51	+0 55	+0 57	+0 55	0.7	0.7	0.0 --	1.7 050	0.0 --	1.6 245
81	BAY OF FUNDY ENTRANCE................	44 45.2	66 55.9			Daily predictions						0.0 --	2.3 032	0.0 --	2.4 212
	MAINE COAST Time meridian, 75°W													
						on PORTSMOUTH HARBOR ENTRANCE, p.10									
86	Eastport, Friar Roads................	44 54	66 59		0 00	0 00	0 00	0 00	1.2	1.2	0.0 --	3.0 210	0.0 --	3.0 040
91	Western Passage, off Kendall Head....	44 55.9	67 01.9		+0 27	+0 11	+0 13	+0 40	1.4	1.3	0.0 --	3.2 319	0.0 --	3.1 142
96	Western Passage, off Frost Ledge.....	44 57.9	67 30.2		+0 33	+0 04	-0 16	+0 15	0.9	0.7	0.0 --	2.1 330	0.0 --	1.7 150
101	Pond Point, 7.6 miles SSE of.........	44 20.1	67 34.36		+0 13	-0 20	-1 33	-0 05	0.2	0.5	0.0 --	0.5 015	0.0 --	1.2 215
106	Moosabec Reach, east end.............	44 31.71	67 39.00		-2 45	-3 08	-3 13	-3 39	0.4	0.4	0.0 --	1.0 110	0.0 --	1.0 258
111	Moosabec Reach, west end.............	44 31.25	68 10.0		-1 43	-1 43	-2 00	-1 44	0.4	0.5	0.0 --	1.2 092	0.0 --	1.2 253
116	Bar Harbor, 1.2 miles east of <1>....	44 23.0	68 27.9			+0 30	+0 09	+0 48	0.1	0.3	0.0 --	0.2 328	0.0 --	0.7 148
121	Casco Passage, east end, Blue Hill Bay..	44 11.7	68 27.9		-1 49	-1 44	-1 02	-1 58	0.3	0.3	0.0 --	0.7 086	0.0 --	0.7 284
126	Hat Island, SE of, Jericho Bay.......	44 08.0	68 29.7		-1 02	-0 35	-0 50	-1 20	0.4	0.5	0.0 --	0.9 318	0.0 --	1.3 124
136	Isle Au Haut, 0.8 mi. east of Richs Pt..	44 05.0	68 35.0		-2 13	-1 47	-2 09	-1 47	1.2	0.8	0.0 --	1.4 336	0.0 --	1.5 139
146	West Penobscot Bay, off Monroe Island...	44 04.5	69 00.6		-1 09	-1 24	-2 20	-1 12	0.2	0.3	0.0 --	0.3 006	0.0 --	0.6 159
156	Muscongus Sound.....................	43 56.5	69 26.9			Current weak and variable									
166	Damariscotta River, off Cavis Point..	43 52.5	69 35.0		-0 49	-0 44	-1 24	-1 18	0.5	0.6	0.0 --	0.6 350	0.0 --	1.0 215
176	Sheepscot River, off Barter Island...	43 54.0	69 41.5		-0 48	-1 02	-1 15	-0 33	0.7	0.6	0.0 --	0.8 005	0.0 --	1.1 200
186	Lowe Point, NE of, Sasanoa River.....	43 51.1	69 43.3		-0 48	+0 09	-0 46	-0 27	1.4	1.0	0.0 --	1.7 327	0.0 --	1.8 152
196	Lower Hell Gate, Knubble Bay <2>.....	43 52.6	69 43.8		-0 23	+0 37	-0 46	+0 06	2.5	1.9	0.0 --	3.0 290	0.0 --	3.5 155
206	Upper Hell Gate, Sasanoa River.......	43 53.7	69 46.3		+3 31	+2 48	+1 20	+2 03	0.8	0.5	0.0 --	1.0 307	0.0 --	0.8 142
	KENNEBEC RIVER													
211	Hunniwell Point, northeast of........	43 45.4	69 46.9		+0 05	+0 12	+0 05	+0 24	2.0	1.6	0.0 --	2.4 332	0.0 --	2.9 151
216	Bald Head, 0.3 mile southwest of.....	43 48.1	69 47.6		+0 23	+0 28	-0 04	+0 23	1.3	1.3	0.0 --	1.6 321	0.0 --	2.3 153

Endnotes can be found at the end of Table 2.

TABLE 2. – CURRENT DIFFERENCES AND OTHER CONSTANTS, 1983

NO.	PLACE	METER DEPTH (ft)	POSITION Lat. (° ' N)	POSITION Long. (° ' W)	TIME DIFF. Min. before Flood (h.m.)	TIME DIFF. Flood (h.m.)	TIME DIFF. Min. before Ebb (h.m.)	TIME DIFF. Ebb (h.m.)	SPEED RATIOS Flood	SPEED RATIOS Ebb	Min. before Flood (knots)	(deg.)	Max. Flood (knots)	(deg.)	Min. before Ebb (knots)	(deg.)	Max. Ebb (knots)	(deg.)
	KENNEBEC RIVER Time meridian, 75°W					on PORTSMOUTH HARBOR ENTRANCE, p.10												
221	Bluff Head, west of..........		43 51.3	69 47.8	+0 33	+0 53	+0 26	+0 24	1.9	1.9	0.0	–	2.3	014	0.0	–	3.4	184
226	Fiddler Ledge, north of......		43 52.8	69 47.8	+0 47	+1 12	+0 22	+0 48	1.6	1.4	0.0	–	1.9	267	0.0	–	2.6	113
231	Doubling Point, south of.....		43 52.8	69 48.4	+0 28	+0 49	+0 23	+0 53	2.2	1.7	0.0	–	2.6	300	0.0	–	3.0	127
236	Lincoln Ledge, east of <3>...		43 53.8	69 48.6	+0 32	+0 45	+0 23	+0 34	1.6	1.6	0.0	–	1.9	359	0.0	–	2.8	174
241	Bath, 0.2 mile south of bridge <3>...		43 54.5	69 48.5	+0 29	+1 28	+0 43	+0 23	0.8	0.8	0.0	–	1.0	003	0.0	–	1.5	177
	CASCO BAY																	
251	Broad Sound, west of Eagle Island...		43 42.7	70 03.8	-1 16	-1 05	-1 27	-0 59	0.8	0.7	0.0	–	0.9	010	0.0	–	1.3	168
261	Hussey Sound, SW of Overset Island...	15	43 40.27	70 10.52	-1 28	-1 18	-0 58	-1 30	0.9	0.6	0.0	–	1.1	316	0.3	189	1.2	153
	...do..........	25	43 40.27	70 10.52	-1 39	-1 19	-1 06	-1 32	0.9	0.6	0.0	–	1.1	318	0.3	211	1.1	155
	...do..........	40	43 40.27	70 10.52	-1 58	-1 16	-1 05	-1 32	0.9	0.5	0.1	228	1.1	314	0.3	200	1.0	154
271	Hussey Sound, SE of Pumpkin Nob...	40	43 40.45	70 10.78	-2 21	-1 29	-1 32	-1 14	1.0	0.5	0.1	068	1.2	346	0.1	066	0.9	168
281	Hussey Sound, east of Crow Island...	40	43 41.33	70 10.79	-2 18	-0 42	-0 55	-1 24	0.7	0.4	0.1	114	0.9	016	0.0	–	0.8	197
291	Portland Hbr. ent., SW of Cushing I...		43 37.9	70 12.7	-1 43	-1 11	-1 20	-0 58	0.8	0.6	0.0	–	1.0	322	0.0	–	1.1	154
301	Diamond I. Ledge, midchannel SW. of...		43 39.6	70 13.5	-1 26	-1 12	-1 11	-1 06	0.8	0.5	0.0	–	0.9	300	0.0	–	0.9	150
311	Portland Breakwater Light 0.3 mi. NW of <1> <4>...		43 39.5	70 14.5	- - -	-0 47	- - -	-1 07	0.3	0.3	0.0	–	0.4		0.0	–	0.5	048
321	Grand Trunk Wharves, off ends <1>...		43 39.5	70 14.7	- - -	-1 45	- - -	-1 50	0.5	0.2	0.0	–	0.6	250	0.0	–	0.4	040
331	Portland Bridge, center of draw...		43 38.7	70 15.5	-1 06	-0 17	-0 38	-0 15	0.8	0.6	0.0	–	0.9	225	0.0	–	1.0	050
	MAINE COAST–Continued																	
341	Cape Elizabeth...........		43 34	70 11	-1 35	-1 35	-1 35	-1 35	0.2	0.2	0.0	–	0.3	340	0.0	–	0.3	160
351	Cape Porpoise...........		43 22	70 24	-0 55	-0 55	-0 55	-0 55	0.2	0.2	0.0	–	0.3	035	0.0	–	0.3	215
361	Cape Neddick............		43 10	70 35	-0 20	-0 20	-0 20	-0 20	0.3	0.3	0.0	–	0.4	025	0.0	–	0.4	205
371	York Harbor entrance, 3 miles south of..		43 08	70 33	-0 15	-0 15	-0 15	-0 15	0.3	0.3	0.0	–	0.4	025	0.0	–	0.4	205
	PORTSMOUTH HARBOR																	
381	Kitts Rocks, 0.2 mile west of...		43 03	70 42	0 00	0 00	0 00	0 00	0.7	0.9	0.0	–	0.8	325	0.0	–	1.6	175
391	Little Harbor entrance...		43 03	70 42	-1 00	-1 00	-1 00	-1 00	0.6	0.6	0.0	–	0.7	310	0.0	–	1.1	130
401	PORTSMOUTH HARBOR ENT. (off Wood I.)...		43 03.8	70 42.3	Daily predictions						0.0	–	1.2	355	0.0	–	1.8	195
411	Fort Point...........		43 04	70 42	+0 05	+0 05	+0 05	+0 05	1.2	1.1	0.0	–	1.5	350	0.0	–	2.0	130
421	Salamander Point.........		43 05	70 43	+0 10	+0 10	+0 10	+0 10	1.1	0.7	0.0	–	1.3	260	0.0	–	1.3	085
431	Hick Rocks and Clarks Island, between...		43 05	70 43	-0 35	-0 50	-0 35	-0 50	0.8	0.4	0.0	–	0.9	335	0.0	–	0.8	195
441	Kittery Point Bridge...		43 05	70 43	-1 10	-1 10	-1 10	-1 10	0.7	0.6	0.0	–	0.8	020	0.0	–	1.1	200
451	Jamaica Island, northeast of...		43 05	70 43	-0 25	-0 25	-0 25	-0 25	0.8	0.7	0.0	–	1.0	315	0.0	–	1.0	135
461	Seavey Island, north of...		43 05	70 44	+0 15	+0 15	+0 15	+0 15	1.2	1.0	0.0	–	1.4	260	0.0	–	1.8	080
471	Clarks I. and Seavey I. between <5>...		43 05	70 44					1.5	1.0	0.0	–	1.8	200	0.0	–		
481	Clarks Island, south of...		43 04	70 44	+0 15	+0 15	+0 15	+0 15	1.7	1.7	0.0	–	2.1	260	0.0	–	3.1	080
491	Seavey Island, south of...		43 04	70 44	+0 15	+0 15	+0 15	+0 15	2.5	2.1	0.0	–	3.0	260	0.0	–	3.8	090
501	Marvin Island and Goat Island, between...		43 04	70 44	-1 00	-1 00	-1 00	-1 00	1.0	0.4	0.0	–	1.2	160	0.0	–	1.2	340
511	Henderson Point, west of...		43 05	70 44	+0 30	+0 30	+0 30	+0 30	2.2	1.3	0.0	–	2.6	340	0.0	–	2.3	170
521	Off Gangway Rock...		43 05	70 45	+0 30	+0 30	+0 30	+0 30	1.7	1.7	0.0	–	2.1	280	0.0	–	3.0	110
531	Badgers Island, east of...		43 05	70 45	+0 25	+0 25	+0 25	+0 25	0.9	0.2	0.0	–	1.1	240	0.0	–	0.4	050

Endnotes can be found at the end of Table 2.

TABLE 2. – CURRENT DIFFERENCES AND OTHER CONSTANTS, 1983

NO.	PLACE	METER DEPTH (ft)	POSITION Lat. (°′ N)	POSITION Long. (°′ W)	TIME DIFFERENCES Min. before Flood (h.m.)	Flood (h.m.)	Min. before Ebb (h.m.)	Ebb (h.m.)	SPEED RATIOS Flood	Ebb	AVERAGE SPEEDS — Min. before Flood (knots)	(deg.)	Max. Flood (knots)	(deg.)	Min. before Ebb (knots)	(deg.)	Max. Ebb (knots)	(deg.)
	PORTSMOUTH HARBOR Time meridian, 75°W				*on PORTSMOUTH HARBOR ENTRANCE, p.10*													
541	Badgers Island, southwest of...........		43 05	70 45	+0 30	+0 30	+0 30	+0 30	2.7	2.0	0.0	--	3.3	330	0.0	--	3.7	125
	PISCATAQUA RIVER and TRIBUTARIES																	
546	NW of Nobles Island (RR. bridge).......		43 05	70 46	+0 35	+0 35	+0 35	+0 35	1.3	0.5	0.0	--	1.6	050	0.0	--	0.9	200
551	Nobles Island, north of................		43 06	70 46	+0 30	+0 30	+0 30	+0 30	3.0	2.4	0.0	--	3.6	305	0.0	--	4.4	140
556	Frankfort Island, south of.............		43 07	70 48	+0 30	+0 30	+0 30	+0 30	2.2	1.6	0.0	--	2.6	310	0.0	--	2.9	130
561	Little Bay entrance, Dover Point.......		43 07	70 50	+0 35	+0 35	+0 35	+0 35	3.2	2.3	0.0	--	3.8	270	0.0	--	4.2	095
566	Furber Strait.........................		43 05	70 52	+0 40	+0 40	+0 40	+0 40	1.7	1.2	0.0	--	2.0	185	0.0	--	2.1	010
	MASSACHUSETTS COAST																	
571	Gunboat Shoal.........................		43 01	70 42	+0 05	+0 05	+0 05	+0 05	0.4	0.3	0.0	--	0.5	340	0.0	--	0.5	160
576	Isles of Shoals Light, White Island...		42 58	70 37	0 00	0 00	0 00	0 00	0.2	0.2	0.0	--	0.3	020	0.0	--	0.3	200
					on BOSTON HARBOR, p.16													
581	Merrimack River entrance..............		42 49.1	70 48.6	+1 04	+1 15	+1 13	-0 34	2.0	1.2	0.0	--	2.2	285	0.0	--	1.4	105
586	Newburyport, Merrimack River..........		42 48.8	70 52.1	+1 28	+1 48	+1 47	+0 35	1.4	1.2	0.0	--	1.5	288	0.0	--	1.4	098
591	Plum Island Sound entrance............		42 42.3	70 47.3	+0 36	+0 50	+0 48	-0 07	1.5	1.2	0.0	--	1.6	316	0.0	--	1.5	184
596	Annisquam Harbor Light................		42 40.1	70 41.1	+0 42	+0 49	+0 58	+0 03	0.9	1.1	0.0	--	1.0	200	0.0	--	1.3	013
601	Gloucester Harbor entrance............		42 34.9	70 40.5	-0 28	+0 01	-0 29	-0 36	0.3	0.2	0.0	--	0.3	340	0.0	--	0.3	195
606	Blynman Canal ent., Gloucester Harbor..		42 36.6	70 40.4	-0 06	+1 09	-0 15	-0 39	2.7	2.8	0.0	--	3.0	310	0.0	--	3.3	130
611	Marblehead Channel....................		42 30	70 49	+1 09	+1 09	+1 09	+1 09	0.4	0.3	0.0	--	0.4	285	0.0	--	0.4	105
616	Ram Island, 0.2 n.mi. NNE of..........	10	42 28.75	70 51.68	See Rotary Tidal Currents, p.185													
621	Ram Island, 0.2 n.mi. southeast of....	10	42 28.45	70 51.55	See Rotary Tidal Currents, p.185													
626	Great Pig Rocks, southeast of.........	10	42 27.53	70 50.70	See Rotary Tidal Currents, p.185													
631	Galloupes Point, 0.4 n.mi. south of...	10	42 27.24	70 53.70	See Rotary Tidal Currents, p.185													
636	Little Nahant, 0.9 n.mi. northeast of.	10	42 26.85	70 54.84	See Rotary Tidal Currents, p.185													
641	Egg Rock, 0.2 n.mi. north of..........	10	42 26.25	70 53.93	See Rotary Tidal Currents, p.185													
646	Egg Rock, southwest of................	10	42 25.85	70 54.20	See Rotary Tidal Currents, p.185													
651	Nahant, 1.8 n.mi. NE of East Point....	10	42 26.00	70 52.02	+0 32	+0 49	+0 15	+1 00	0.6	0.6	0.0	--	0.7	252	0.1	291	0.7	144
	.....do...........................	45	42 26.00	70 52.02	-0 21	+1 04	+1 14	-0 31	0.3	0.2	0.0	--	0.3	250	0.0	--	0.2	070
	.....do...........................	80	42 26.00	70 52.02	-0 25	+1 04	+1 15	-0 31	0.2	0.1	0.1	329	0.2	238	0.0	--	0.2	077
656	Nahant, 0.4 n.mi. east of East Point..	15	42 25.23	70 53.63	+0 04	-0 41	+0 15	+0 22	0.4	0.5	0.2	118	0.4	205	0.0	--	0.6	045
	.....do...........................	25	42 25.23	70 53.63	+0 03	-0 26	+0 08	+0 29	0.4	0.4	0.1	102	0.4	198	0.1	282	0.5	027
661	Nahant, 1 n.mi. SE of East Point......	45	42 23.83	70 51.17	+0 04	+1 04	+1 13	+0 14	0.3	0.2	0.0	--	0.3	253	0.0	--	0.3	074
	.....do...........................	70	42 23.83	70 51.17	-0 22	-0 04	+0 19	-1 01	0.5	0.2	0.0	--	0.2	261	0.0	--	0.3	090
666	Pea Island, 0.4 n.mi. southeast of....	15	42 24.63	70 54.13	+0 53	+0 55	+0 42	-0 01	0.5	0.4	0.0	--	0.5	239	0.1	161	0.5	063
	.....do...........................	25	42 24.63	70 54.13	+0 34	+0 34	+0 57	+0 29	0.4	0.3	0.0	--	0.5	224	0.0	--	0.4	048
	.....do...........................	65	42 24.63	70 54.13	-0 37	-0 59	+0 14	-0 31	0.3	0.3	0.1	332	0.4	271	0.0	--	0.4	035
671	Bass Point, 1.2 n.mi. southeast of....	45	42 24.12	70 55.07	-0 22	+1 20	+0 58	-0 14	0.7	0.6	0.1	351	0.7	259	0.0	--	0.7	066
	.....do...........................	10	42 24.12	70 55.07	-0 29	-0 10	+0 52	-0 29	0.3	0.2	0.0	--	0.4	251	0.0	--	0.3	086
676	Bass Point, 0.5 n.mi. SSW of..........	60	42 24.57	70 56.53	-0 29	-0 10	+0 31	-0 59	0.2	0.2	0.0	--	0.3	250	0.0	--	0.2	091
681	Bass Point, 0.7 n.mi. west of.........	15	42 25.13	70 57.25	See Rotary Tidal Currents, p.185													

Endnotes can be found at the end of Table 2.

TABLE 2. - CURRENT DIFFERENCES AND OTHER CONSTANTS, 1983

NO.	PLACE	METER DEPTH (ft)	POSITION Lat. (°N)	POSITION Long. (°W)	TIME DIFF. Min. before Flood (h.m.)	TIME DIFF. Flood (h.m.)	TIME DIFF. Min. before Ebb (h.m.)	TIME DIFF. Ebb (h.m.)	SPEED RATIOS Flood	SPEED RATIOS Ebb	Minimum before Flood (knots)	Minimum before Flood (deg.)	Maximum Flood (knots)	Maximum Flood (deg.)	Minimum before Ebb (knots)	Minimum before Ebb (deg.)	Maximum Ebb (knots)	Maximum Ebb (deg.)
	CAPE COD BAY Time meridian, 75°W				on BOSTON HARBOR, p.16													
1231	Race Point, 7 miles north of.........		42 11	70 16	-0 01	-0 01	-0 01	-0 01	1.4	1.2	0.0	--	1.5	290	0.0	--	1.5	061
1236	Race Point, 1 mile northwest of.....		42 05	70 15	-0 06	-0 06	-0 06	-0 06	0.9	0.8	0.0	--	1.0	226	0.0	--	0.9	061
1241	Provincetown Harbor.............		42 03	70 10	+0 04	+0 04	+0 04	+0 04	0.5	0.3	0.0	--	0.6	315	0.0	--	0.4	135
1246	Wellfleet Harbor.............		41 54	70 03	+0 09	+0 09	+0 09	+0 09	0.6	0.4	0.0	--	0.7	020	0.0	--	0.5	200
1251	Barnstable Harbor.............		41 43.6	70 16.4	+0 19	+0 58	+0 22	+0 29	1.1	1.2	0.0	--	1.2	192	0.0	--	1.4	004
1256	Sandwich Harbor.............		41 46	70 29	Current weak and variable				--	--							--	--
	Cape Cod Canal (see Index)......		-- --	-- --														
1261	Sagamore Beach.............		41 48	70 31	Current weak and variable													
1266	Ellisville Harbor, 1 mile east of.....		41 51	70 30	+0 14	+0 14	+0 14	+0 14	0.3	0.2	0.0	--	0.3	200	0.0	--	0.3	020
1271	Manomet Point.............		41 56	70 32	+0 04	+0 04	+0 04	+0 04	1.0	0.7	0.0	--	1.1	155	0.0	--	0.9	010
1276	Gurnet Point, 1 mile east of.......		42 00	70 35	-0 06	-0 06	-0 06	-0 06	1.3	0.8	0.0	--	1.4	250	0.0	--	1.0	--
1281	Plymouth Harbor.............		41 58	70 39	+0 04	+0 04	+0 04	+0 04	0.5	0.3	0.0	--	0.5	245	0.0	--	0.4	010
1286	Farnham Rock, 1 mile east of......		42 06	70 35	-0 21	-0 21	-0 21	-0 21	1.0	0.8	0.0	--	1.1	180	0.0	--	0.9	010
	MASSACHUSETTS COAST-Continued				on POLLOCK RIP CHANNEL, p.28													
1291	Nauset Beach Light, 5 miles northeast of		41 56	69 54	See table 5.													
1296	Georges Bank and vicinity.............		-- --	-- --	See table 5.													
1301	Davis Bank.............		-- --	-- --	See table 5.													
1306	Monomoy Point, 23 miles east of......		41 35	69 30	See table 5.													
1311	Nantucket Shoals.............		40 37	69 37	See table 5.													
1316	Nantucket Island, 28 miles east of.....		41 20	69 21	See table 5.													
1321	Old Man Shoal, Nantucket Shoals......		41 13.6	69 59.0	+1 23	+1 03	+1 17	+1 14	0.9	0.9	0.0	--	1.9	080	0.0	--	1.6	225
1326	Miacomet Pond, 3.0 miles SSE of.....		41 11.4	70 05.8	+2 19	+2 03	+2 22	+2 16	0.6	0.8	0.0	--	1.3	080	0.0	--	1.4	280
1331	Tuckernuck Island, 4.2 miles SSW of.....		41 13.57	70 16.90	+4 08	+3 13	+2 17	+3 56	0.3	0.6	0.0	--	0.5	090	0.0	--	1.0	280
1336	Martha's Vineyard, 1.4 miles S of <I>.....		41 19.50	70 39.90	-- --	-2 53	-- --	-2 47	0.1	0.1	0.0	--	0.3	230	0.0	--	0.3	095
	NANTUCKET SOUND ENTRANCE																	
1341	Pollock Rip Channel, east end.........		41 33.9	69 55.4	-0 14	-0 39	-0 23	-0 38	1.0	1.1	0.0	--	2.0	053	0.0	--	1.8	212
1346	POLLOCK RIP CHANNEL (Butler Hole)......		41 33	69 59	Daily predictions					1.1	0.0	--	2.0	037	0.0	--	1.8	226
1351	Great Round Shoal Channel.............		-- --	-- --	See table 5.													
	NANTUCKET SOUND																	
1356	Monomoy Pt., channel 0.2 mile west of...		41 33.0	70 01.3	0 00	+0 39	+0 18	-0 23	0.8	1.2	0.0	--	1.7	170	0.0	--	2.0	346
1361	Chatham Roads.............		41 38.6	70 01.7	Current weak and variable													
1366	Stage Harbor, west of Morris Island.....		41 39.4	69 58.5	+3 07	+1 29	+2 24	+4 28	0.3	0.6	0.0	--	0.5	335	0.0	--	1.0	144
1371	Dennis Port, 2.2 miles south of.......		41 37.0	70 06.9	+1 28	+0 52	+0 27	+1 04	0.2	0.3	0.1	138	0.3	077	0.1	052	0.3	269
1376	Monomoy Point, 6 miles west of......		41 33.5	70 09.0	+1 22	+1 52	+1 09	+1 22	0.6	0.8	0.1	194	0.5	090	0.1	256	0.5	275
1381	Handkerchief Lighted Whistle Buoy "H".....		41 29.3	70 04.0	+1 08	+1 10	+0 49	+0 59	0.6	0.8	0.0	--	1.3	080	0.0	--	1.3	251
1386	Halfmoon Shoal, 1.9 miles northeast of...		41 29.05	70 11.55	+1 42	+1 49	+1 24	+1 44	0.4	0.3	0.0	--	0.8	110	0.0	--	0.6	265
1391	Halfmoon Shoal, 3.5 miles east of......		41 28.1	70 09.2	+1 13	+1 23	+1 06	+1 11	0.6	0.6	0.0	--	1.1	088	0.0	--	1.0	295
1396	Great Point, 0.5 mile west of........		41 23.6	70 03.7	+0 25	+1 37	+1 13	+0 33	0.6	0.7	0.0	--	1.1	029	0.0	--	1.2	195
1401	Great Point, 3 miles west of.........		41 23.4	70 06.8	+1 15	+1 23	+0 51	+1 08	0.4	0.5	0.0	--	0.8	066	0.0	--	0.8	248
1406	Tuckernuck Shoal, off east end.........		41 24.3	70 10.4	+1 22	+1 34	+1 09	+1 10	0.5	0.5	0.3	000	0.9	113	0.3	186	0.9	287

Endnotes can be found at the end of Table 2.

TABLE 2. - CURRENT DIFFERENCES AND OTHER CONSTANTS, 1983

NO.	PLACE	METER DEPTH (ft)	POSITION Lat. °′ N	POSITION Long. °′ W	TIME DIFFERENCES Min. before Flood h. m.	Flood h. m.	Min. before Ebb h. m.	Ebb h. m.	SPEED RATIOS Flood	Ebb	Minimum before Flood knots	deg.	Maximum Flood knots	deg.	Minimum before Ebb knots	deg.	Maximum Ebb knots	deg.
	NANTUCKET SOUND Time meridian, 75°W				on POLLOCK RIP CHANNEL, p.28													
1411	Brant Point, 2 miles NNW of (1).........		41 19.25	70 06.30	- - -	+1 43	- - -	+2 36	0.2	0.2	0.0	--	0.3	090	0.0	--	0.3	275
1416	Nantucket Harbor entrance channel.....		41 18.4	70 06.0	+3 22	+1 55	+2 44	+3 58	0.6	0.9	0.0	--	1.2	171	0.0	--	1.5	350
1421	Eel Pt., Nantucket I. 2.5 miles NE of...		41 19.3	70 10.2	+1 13	+1 12	+1 02	+1 15	0.3	0.2	0.0	--	0.6	094	0.0	--	0.4	284
1426	Muskeget I., channel 1 mile northeast of		41 21.0	70 17.1	+1 29	+0 45	+0 57	+0 56	0.6	0.9	0.0	--	1.1	108	0.0	--	1.5	295
1431	Muskeget Rock, 1.3 miles southwest of...		41 19.2	70 23.6	+1 40	+0 23	+0 57	+1 08	0.6	0.6	0.0	--	1.3	021	0.0	--	1.5	192
1436	Muskeget Channel......		41 20.9	70 25.2	+1 40	+0 38	+1 29	+1 02	1.9	1.9	0.0	--	3.8	021	0.0	--	3.3	200
1441	Wasque Point, 2.0 miles southwest of....		41 19.90	70 29.25	+1 30	+1 04	+1 11	+0 32	0.6	0.6	0.0	--	1.3	075	0.0	--	1.2	280
								+1 15		0.5							0.9	280
								+1 53		0.6							1.1	280
1446	Long Shoal-Norton Shoal, between.........		41 24.50	70 20.00	+1 31	+1 12	+1 26	+1 13	0.7	0.6	0.0	--	1.4	100	0.0	--	1.1	260
1451	Cape Page Lt., 1.7 miles SSE of.........		41 24.0	70 25.6	+0 58	-0 07	+0 49	+0 48	0.8	0.7	0.0	--	1.6	025	0.0	--	1.3	215
1456	Cross Rip Channel..................		41 26.9	70 17.5	+1 48	+1 48	+1 55	+1 59	0.6	0.7	0.0	--	1.6	091	0.0	--	0.9	272
1461	Cape Page Lt., 3.2 miles northeast of...		41 27.5	70 24.0	+2 42	+2 03	+2 33	+2 37	0.8	0.7	0.0	--	1.6	095	0.0	--	1.2	300
1466	Broken Ground-Horseshoe Shoal, between..		41 33.0	70 17.1	+1 46	+1 55	+1 15	+1 20	0.5	0.5	0.0	--	1.1	107	0.1	224	0.9	276
1471	Point Gammon, 1.2 miles south of.......		41 35.3	70 15.4	+1 15	+1 03	+1 06	+1 02	0.5	0.6	0.2	000	1.1	105	0.0	--	1.0	260
1476	Hyannis Harbor, entrance off breakwater.		41 37.4	70 17.5	Current weak and variable													
1481	Lewis Bay entrance channel...........		41 37.9	70 16.4	+2 46	+0 53	+2 44	+4 22	0.5	0.8	0.0	--	0.9	004	0.0	--	1.3	184
1486	Cotuit Bay entrance (Bluff Point)......		41 36.6	70 25.8	+2 44	+2 33	+2 51	+3 35	0.3	0.4	0.0	--	0.5	035	0.0	--	0.7	218
1491	Wreck Shoal-Eldridge Shoal, between.....		41 32.0	70 25.7	+1 47	+1 32	+1 44	+1 45	0.8	0.8	0.0	--	1.7	062	0.0	--	1.4	245
1496	Hedge Fence Lighted Gong Buoy 22.......		41 28.3	70 29.00	+2 48	+2 34	+2 38	+2 44	0.7	0.7	0.0	--	1.4	108	0.0	--	1.2	268
1501	Cape Page Light, 1.4 miles west of.....		41 25.45	70 29.00	+2 13	+1 54	+1 26	+1 39	0.2	0.1	0.0	--	0.3	095	0.0	--	0.2	250
1506	Edgartown, Inner Harbor............		41 23.4	70 30.5	+0 25	-1 04	+0 35	-0 20	0.6	0.6	0.0	--	1.1	075	0.0	--	1.1	270
1511	Katama Pt., 0.6 mi. NNW of, Katama B....		41 21.9	70 30.3	+0 12	-0 43	+0 20	-0 31	0.2	0.3	0.0	--	0.4	325	0.0	--	0.5	180
1516	East Chop-Squash Meadow, between........		41 27.9	70 32.2	+2 07	+0 55	+1 43	+2 04	0.7	1.1	0.0	--	1.4	131	0.0	--	1.8	329
1521	East Chop, 1 mile north of............		41 29.1	70 33.5	+2 40	+1 52	+2 17	+2 11	1.1	1.3	0.0	--	2.2	116	0.0	--	2.2	297
1526	Vineyard Haven...................		41 28.1	70 35.2	Current weak and variable													
1531	West Chop, 0.8 mile north of..........		41 29.6	70 35.7	+2 49	+1 58	+2 20	+2 35	1.6	1.8	0.0	--	3.1	096	0.0	--	3.0	282
1536	Hedge Fence-L'Hommedieu Shoal, between..		41 30.3	70 32.2	+2 27	+1 38	+1 38	+1 52	1.0	1.3	0.0	--	2.1	106	0.0	--	2.2	276
1541	Waquoit Bay entrance...............		41 32.9	70 31.8	+3 21	+2 14	+3 40	+4 01	0.8	0.8	0.0	--	1.5	348	0.0	--	1.4	203
1546	L'Hommedieu Shoal, north of west end....		41 31.6	70 34.6	+2 30	+2 03	+2 12	+2 11	1.2	1.4	0.0	--	2.3	080	0.0	--	2.3	268
1551	Nobska Point, 1.8 miles east of........		41 31.1	70 37.1	+2 13	+1 45	+1 55	+1 49	1.2	1.0	0.0	--	2.3	063	0.0	--	1.7	240
	VINEYARD SOUND																	
1556	West Chop, 0.2 mile west of..........		41 29.0	70 36.6	+1 19	+1 34	+1 50	+1 16	1.3	0.8	0.0	--	2.7	059	0.0	--	1.4	241
1561	Nobska Point, 1 mile southeast of......		41 30.1	70 38.6	+2 33	+2 15	+2 25	+2 19	1.3	1.4	0.0	--	2.6	071	0.0	--	2.4	259
1566	Norton Point, 0.5 mile north of.......		41 28.1	70 39.9	+1 55	+1 44	+2 01	+1 12	1.7	1.4	0.0	--	3.4	050	0.0	--	2.4	240
1571	Tarpaulin Cove, 1.5 miles east of......		41 28.3	70 43.5	+2 49	+2 07	+2 11	+2 33	1.0	1.2	0.0	--	1.9	055	0.0	--	2.3	232
1576	Robinsons Hole, 1.2 miles southeast of..		41 26.1	70 46.8	+2 30	+1 51	+2 11	+2 02	1.0	1.2	0.0	--	1.9	060	0.0	--	2.1	240
1581	Gay Head, 3 miles northeast of........		41 23.1	70 47.0	+2 25	+1 50	+1 42	+2 11	0.5	0.8	0.0	--	0.9	081	0.0	--	1.3	238
1586	Menemsha Bight <6>................		41 21.3	70 46.3														
1591	Gay Head, 3 miles north of...........		41 24.1	70 51.2	+2 13	+1 24	+1 55	+1 17	0.6	0.7	0.0	--	1.1	074	0.0	--	1.2	255

Endnotes can be found at the end of Table 2.

TABLE 2. - CURRENT DIFFERENCES AND OTHER CONSTANTS, 1983

NO.	PLACE	METER DEPTH (ft)	Lat. (° ′ N)	Long. (° ′ W)	Min. before Flood (h. m.)	Flood (h. m.)	Min. before Ebb (h. m.)	Ebb (h. m.)	Flood	Ebb	Minimum before Flood (knots deg.)	Maximum Flood (knots deg.)	Minimum before Ebb (knots deg.)	Maximum Ebb (knots deg.)
	VINEYARD SOUND Time meridian, 75°W					on POLLOCK RIP CHANNEL, p.28								
1596	Gay Head, 1.5 miles northwest of...		41 21.8	70 51.8	+1 30	+0 54	+1 42	+1 16	1.0	1.2	0.0 --	2.0 012	0.0 --	2.0 249
1601	Cuttyhunk Island, 3.2 miles southwest of...		41 23	71 00	See table 5.									
1606	Browns Ledge...		41 19.8	71 05.9	See table 5.									
	VINEYARD SOUND-BUZZARDS BAY					on CAPE COD CANAL, p.22								
	Woods Hole													
1611	South end...		41 30.8	70 40.2	+0 29	+1 40	+1 17	+0 08	0.4	0.2	0.0 --	1.5 135	0.0 --	1.1 318
1616	0.1 mile SW of Devils Foot Island...		41 31.2	70 41.1	+0 20	+1 41	+0 55	+0 31	0.9	0.8	0.0 --	3.5 094	0.0 --	3.6 276
1621	North end...		41 31.5	70 41.6	-0 29	+1 25	+1 09	-0 04	0.2	0.2	0.0 --	0.8 160	0.0 --	0.7 007
	Robinsons Hole													
1626	South end...		41 26.7	70 48.2	+1 14	+1 42	+1 20	+1 01	0.7	0.6	0.0 --	0.8 162	0.0 --	1.0 339
1631	Middle...		41 27.0	70 48.4	+1 30	+2 00	+1 02	+1 47	0.7	0.6	0.0 --	2.8 146	0.0 --	2.9 316
1636	North end...		41 27.4	70 48.7	+1 54	+2 00	+0 52	+1 17	0.2	0.3	0.0 --	1.0 161	0.0 --	1.2 338
	Quicks Hole													
1641	South end...		41 26.3	70 50.5	+2 18	+1 42	+1 17	+0 53	0.5	0.4	0.0 --	1.9 140	0.0 --	2.0 300
1646	Middle...		41 26.6	70 50.9	+2 21	+2 00	+1 26	+0 41	0.6	0.5	0.0 --	2.5 167	0.0 --	2.2 339
1651	North end...		41 27.1	70 51.0	+2 42	+2 06	+1 44	+0 23	0.5	0.6	0.0 --	2.0 165	0.0 --	2.6 002
1656	Canapitsit Channel...		41 25.4	70 54.5	+2 03	+2 27	+2 03	+0 26	0.6	0.4	0.0 --	2.6 156	0.0 --	1.7 312
1661	Westport River entrance...		41 30.5	71 05.3	+0 09	-0 05	-0 26	-1 13	1.1	1.5	0.0 --	2.2 290	0.0 --	2.5 108
	BUZZARDS BAY ⟨7⟩					on POLLOCK RIP CHANNEL, p.28								
						See table 5.								
1666	Gooseberry Neck, 2 miles SSE of...		41 27	71 01	-0 19	-1 31	-2 44	-1 54	0.4	0.7	0.0 --	0.8 062	0.0 --	1.2 237
1671	Ribbon Reef-Sow & Pigs Reef, between...		41 25.3	70 58.2	-1 37	-0 25	-0 55	-0 57	0.6	0.6	0.0 --	1.2 050	0.0 --	1.1 254
1676	Penikese Island, 0.8 mile northwest of...		41 27.9	70 56.2	-1 43	-0 15	-1 30	-2 39	0.4	0.5	0.0 --	0.7 093	0.0 --	0.9 287
1681	Penikese Island, 0.2 mile south of...		41 26.6	70 55.5	-2 15	-0 57	-2 01	-2 41	0.5	0.6	0.0 --	0.9 091	0.0 --	1.1 247
1686	Gull I. and Nashawena I., between...		41 26.2	70 54.2	-3 16	-1 07	-1 28	-2 27	0.4	0.4	0.0 --	0.8 069	0.0 --	0.6 255
1691	Weepecket Island, south of...		41 30	70 44.3	Current weak and variable						0.0 --	0.4 --	0.0 --	0.3 --
1696	Quanquisset Harbor entrance...		41 32.4	70 39.8	Current weak and variable									
1701	West Falmouth Harbor entrance...		41 36.5	70 39.3	Current weak and variable									
1706	Megansett Harbor...		41 38.8	70 39.2	Current weak and variable									
1711	Abiels Ledge, 0.4 mile south of...		41 41.1	70 40.4	+0 26	-0 36	-0 06	-0 23	0.4	0.6	0.0 --	0.8 035	0.0 --	1.0 216
1716	Dumpling Rocks, 0.2 mile southeast of...		41 32.0	70 55.1	-1 43	-1 03	-1 32	-2 09	0.4	0.6	0.0 --	0.8 066	0.0 --	1.1 190
1721	Apponagansett Bay...		41 35	70 57	Current weak and variable									
1726	Clarks Cove...		41 36	70 55	Current weak and variable									
1731	New Bedford Harbor and approaches...				Current weak and variable									
1736	West Island and Long Island, between...	6	41 35.6	70 50.4	Current weak and variable						0.0 --	0.3 --	0.0 --	0.4 --
1741	West Island, 1 mile southeast of...		41 34.0	70 48.6	-0 43	-0 43	-1 28	-1 42	0.4	0.5	0.0 --	0.7 079	0.0 --	0.8 203
1746	Nasketucket Bay...		41 37.1	70 50.2	Current weak and variable						0.0 --	0.3 --	0.0 --	0.3 --
1751	Mattapoisett Harbor...		41 40	70 47	Current weak and variable									
1756	Sippican Harbor...		41 41	70 44	Current weak and variable						0.0 --	0.3 --	0.0 --	0.4 --
1761	Wareham River, off Long Beach Point...		41 44.0	70 43.0	-1 41	-0 31	-1 22	-1 23	0.3	0.4	0.0 --	0.6 022	0.0 --	0.6 202

Endnotes can be found at the end of Table 2.

TABLE 2. – CURRENT DIFFERENCES AND OTHER CONSTANTS, 1983

NO.	PLACE	METER DEPTH (ft)	POSITION Lat. (° ' N)	POSITION Long. (° ' W)	TIME DIFF. Min. before Flood (h. m.)	TIME DIFF. Flood (h. m.)	TIME DIFF. Min. before Ebb (h. m.)	TIME DIFF. Ebb (h. m.)	SPEED RATIO Flood	SPEED RATIO Ebb	AVG. Minimum before Flood (knots deg.)	AVG. Maximum Flood (knots deg.)	AVG. Minimum before Ebb (knots deg.)	AVG. Maximum Ebb (knots deg.)
	BUZZARDS BAY <7> Time meridian, 75°W				on POLLOCK RIP CHANNEL, p.28									
1766	Wareham River, off Barneys Point		41 44.7	70 42.4	-1 49	-0 27	-1 22	-1 31	0.4	0.4	0.0 -	0.7 010	0.0 -	0.6 185
					on CAPE COD CANAL, p.22									
1771	Onset Bay, south of Onset Island		41 43.9	70 38.7	Current weak and variable									
1776	Onset Bay, south of Wickets Island		41 44.1	70 39.3	Current weak and variable									
	CAPE COD CANAL				Daily predictions									
1781	CAPE COD CANAL, railroad bridge		41 44.5	70 36.8	-0 03	-0 03	-0 03	-0 04	0.8	0.9	0.0 -	4.0 070	0.0 -	4.5 250
1786	Bourne Highway bridge		41 45	70 35	-0 07	-0 03	-0 09	-0 10	0.8	0.8	0.0 -	3.3 065	0.0 -	4.0 245
1791	Bournedale		41 46	70 34	-0 07	-0 04	-0 11	-0 13	0.7	0.6	0.0 -	3.4 030	0.0 -	3.6 210
1796	Sagamore Bridge		41 46	70 33	-0 09	-0 06	-0 17	-0 13	0.6	0.6	0.0 -	2.8 095	0.0 -	2.5 275
1801	Cape Cod Canal, east end	15	41 46.5	70 30.0	-0 13	-0 06	-0 17	-0 19			0.0 -	2.4 065	0.0 -	2.6 245
	NARRAGANSETT BAY <8>				on POLLOCK RIP CHANNEL, p.28									
1811	Sakonnet River (except Narrows)		41 --.-	-- ---.-	Current weak and variable									
1821	Tiverton, Stone bridge, Sakonnet R. <9>		41 37.5	71 13.0	-2 58	-5 02 -2 54 -0 36	-2 26	-3 06	1.4 0.3 1.3	1.6	0.0 -	2.7 010 0.6 010 2.5 010	0.0 -	2.7 190
1831	Tiverton, RR. bridge, Sakonnet R. <10>		41 38.3	71 12.9	-3 26	-5 06 -3 04 -1 15	-2 48	-3 41	1.2 0.8	1.4	0.0 -	2.3 000 1.5 000	0.0 -	2.4 180
1841	Brenton Point, 1.4 n.mi. southwest of	7	41 25.9	71 22.6	-1 03	-0 38	-1 20	-1 04	0.2	0.4	0.0 -	0.4 347	0.0 -	0.6 170
1851	Castle Hill, west of	7	41 27.8	71 22.2	-1 22	-3 00	-1 31	-1 31	0.5	0.8	0.0 -	1.0 000	0.0 -	1.4 210
1861	Bull Point, east of	10	41 28.8	71 21.0	-1 10	-0 47	-1 10	-1 33	0.6	0.8	0.0 -	1.2 001	0.0 -	1.5 206
1871	Mackerel Cove		41 28.5	71 22.8	Current weak and variable									
1881	Newport Harbor, S and E of Goat Island		41 29	71 20	-1 58	-1 29	-1 24	-1 38	0.4	0.6	0.0 -	0.8 340	0.0 -	1.1 166
1891	Rose Island, northeast of		41 30.2	71 20.0	-0 42	-0 34	-1 20	-1 28	0.4	0.6	0.0 -	0.7 001	0.0 -	1.0 172
1901	Rose Island, west of		41 29.8	71 21.0	-1 40	-1 28	-1 14	-1 16	0.3	0.4	0.0 -	0.5 033	0.0 -	0.7 217
1911	Gould Island, southeast of		41 31.5	71 20.2	-1 56	-1 13	-0 50	-1 37	0.4	0.4	0.0 -	0.8 040	0.0 -	0.6 236
1921	Dyer Island-Carrs Point (between)	7	41 34.5	71 17.8	Current weak and variable									
1931	Dyer Island, west of	7	41 35.2	71 18.5	-1 04	-0 46	-0 53	-1 34	0.4	0.6	0.0 -	0.8 023	0.0 -	1.0 216
1941	Bristol Harbor				Current weak and variable									
1951	Mount Hope Bridge	7	41 38.4	71 15.5	-1 22	-1 34	-1 08	-0 58	0.6	0.8	0.0 -	1.1 047	0.0 -	1.4 230
1961	Mount Hope Bay				Current weak and variable									
1971	Kickamuit R. (Narrows), Mt. Hope Bay	7	41 41.9	71 14.7	-2 04	-3 34 -1 40 -0 54	-1 19	-0 48	0.7 0.5 0.9	1.0	0.0 -	1.4 000 0.9 000 1.7 000	0.0 -	1.7 191
1981	Beavertail Point, 0.8 mile northwest of		41 27.5	71 24.7	-0 11	-0 54	-1 31	-0 19	0.3	0.6	0.0 -	0.5 003	0.0 -	1.0 188
1991	Dutch Island and Beaver Head, between		41 29.8	71 24.2	-1 56	-1 32	-1 58	-1 47	0.5	0.6	0.0 -	1.0 030	0.0 -	1.0 233
2001	Dutch Island, west of	7	41 30.3	71 24.6	-1 33	-1 49	-1 21	-1 16	0.7	0.7	0.0 -	1.3 014	0.0 -	1.2 206
2011	Wickford Harbor		41 34	71 26	Current weak and variable							0.3 -		0.3 -
2021	Prudence Island, west of		41 --.-	-- ---.-	Current weak and variable									
2031	Greenwich Bay entrance		41 40.0	71 23.6	Current weak and variable							0.3 -		0.4 -

Endnotes can be found at the end of Table 2.

151

TABLE 2. – CURRENT DIFFERENCES AND OTHER CONSTANTS, 1983

NO.	PLACE	METER DEPTH (ft)	POSITION Lat. (°′N)	POSITION Long. (°′W)	TIME DIFFERENCES Min. before Flood (h.m.)	Flood (h.m.)	Min. before Ebb (h.m.)	Ebb (h.m.)	SPEED RATIOS Flood	Ebb	AVG Min. before Flood (knots / deg.)	Max. Flood (knots / deg.)	Min. before Ebb (knots / deg.)	Max. Ebb (knots / deg.)
	NARRAGANSETT BAY <8> Time meridian, 75°W				on POLLOCK RIP CHANNEL, p.28									
2041	Patience Island, narrows east of		41 39.5	71 21.2	-2 41	-2 29	-2 44	-2 37	0.4	0.5	0.0 --	0.7 354	0.0 --	0.9 157
2051	Patience I. and Warwick Neck, between		41 39.8	71 22.4	-1 40	-1 21	-1 18	-1 13	0.3	0.5	0.0 --	0.6 040	0.0 --	0.8 224
2061	Warren River entrance		41 42.7	71 17.8	Current weak and variable						0.0 --	0.4 020	0.0 --	0.3 200
2071	Warren River		41 43.7	71 17.3	-0 14	+0 11	-0 22	-1 05	0.5	0.5	0.0 --	1.0 358	0.0 --	0.9 171
2081	Hog Island to Providence		- -	- -	Current weak and variable									
2091	India Point RR. Bridge, Seekonk R. <9>		41 49.0	71 23.3	-1 48	-4 02 / -2 30 / -0 12	-1 31	-1 06	0.5 / 0.2 / 0.7	0.8	0.0 --	1.0 020 / 0.4 020 / 1.3 020	0.0 --	1.4 180
2101	Cold Spring Pt., Seekonk River <10>		41 49.6	71 22.8	-1 48	-4 14 / -2 24 / -0 26	-1 31	-1 02	0.4 / 0.1 / 0.6	0.8	0.0 --	0.8 030 / 0.2 030 / 1.1 030	0.0 --	1.4 210
	BLOCK ISLAND SOUND				on THE RACE, p.34									
2106	Point Judith Harbor of Refuge, south entrance		41 21.48	71 29.75	-2 23	-2 52	-2 26	-3 59 / -2 41 / -1 56	0.2	0.2 / 0.1 / 0.2	0.0 --	0.6 329	0.0 --	0.8 141 / 0.4 141 / 0.7 141
2111	Harbor of Refuge, west entrance		41 22	71 31	See table 5.									
2116	Pond entrance		41 23	71 31	-3 23	-3 01	-3 16	-3 52	0.6	0.4	0.0 --	1.8 351	0.0 --	1.5 186
2121	2.4 miles southwest of		41 19.87	71 30.65	-0 48	-0 01	+0 18	-0 24	0.2	0.2	0.0 --	0.7 258	0.0 --	0.6 090
2126	4.5 miles southwest of		41 18	71 33	See table 5.									
	Block Island													
2131	four miles north of	15	41 18	71 32	-0 30	+0 03	+0 35	+0 21	0.2	0.2	0.0 --	0.8 285	0.0 --	0.8 076
2136	Sandy Point, 2.1 miles NNE of		41 15.85	71 34.00	+0 09	-0 53	-0 30	-0 43	0.4	0.5	0.0 --	1.0 296	0.0 --	1.7 066
2141	Sandy Pt., 1.5 miles north of	7	41 15	71 34	-0 22	-0 30	-1 03	-0 50	0.6	0.5	0.0 --	1.9 315	0.0 --	2.1 063
2146	Clay Head, 1.2 miles ENE of	15	41 13.35	71 31.85	-2 20	-1 32	-0 37	-0 55	0.2	0.1	0.5 220	0.7 298	0.0 --	0.5 164
2151	Old Harbor Pt., 0.5 mile southeast of		41 09	71 32	-0 10	-0 29	-0 34	+0 09	0.1	0.5	0.0 --	0.2 336	0.0 --	0.6 175
2156	Lewis Pt., 1.0 mile southwest of		41 08.20	71 37.30	-1 37	-1 08	-0 34	-1 13	0.7	0.4	0.0 --	1.9 298	0.0 --	1.8 136
2161	Lewis Pt., 1.5 miles west of		41 09	71 38	-1 31	-1 15	-0 44	-0 57	0.4	0.1	0.0 --	1.4 318	0.0 --	1.7 170
2166	Great Salt Pond entrance		41 11.97	71 35.50	-4 18	-3 35	-3 34	-4 22	0.1	0.2	0.0 --	0.3 165	0.0 --	0.3 326
2171	Great Salt Pond ent., 1 mile NW of <11>	7	41 12	71 36	-0 52	-0 58	-1 50	-0 32	0.1	0.1	0.0 --	0.4 158	0.0 --	0.7 035
2176	Sandy Point, 0.4 mile west of <11>		41 13.80	71 35.13		-1 24		-1 35	-	0.2	0.0 --	-	0.0 --	0.7 011
2181	Green Hill Point, 1.1 miles south of		41 20.90	71 35.77	-1 06	-0 47	-0 34	-0 55	0.2	0.1	0.0 --	0.6 258	0.0 --	0.4 070
2186	Sandy Point, 4.1 miles northwest of	15	41 17.10	71 38.00	-0 04	+0 11	+0 22	+0 04	0.2	0.2	0.0 --	0.7 270	0.0 --	0.6 084
2191	Grace Point, 2.0 miles northwest of		41 12	71 38	See table 5.									
2196	Quonochontaug Beach, 1.1 miles S of	15	41 18.80	71 42.82	-0 52	-0 06	+0 37	-0 20	0.4	0.1	0.0 --	1.1 248	0.0 --	0.4 078
2201	Quonochontaug Beach, 3.8 miles S of		41 16.35	71 43.00	-0 05	-0 06	+0 29	+0 08	0.2	0.2	0.0 --	0.7 243	0.0 --	0.6 058
2206	Lewis Point, 6.0 miles WNW of	15	41 11.60	71 44.20	+0 51	+0 40	+0 06	+0 35	0.5	0.3	0.0 --	0.6 286	0.0 --	1.2 097
2211	Southwest Ledge		41 07	71 42	-0 33	-0 33	-0 10	-0 08	0.5	0.5	0.0 --	1.5 321	0.0 --	2.1 141
2216	Southwest Ledge, 2.0 miles west of	15	41 06.80	71 43.00	+0 02	+0 10	+0 01	-0 41	0.5	0.2	0.0 --	1.5 354	0.0 --	1.9 168
2221	Watch Hill Point, 2.2 miles east of		41 18.16	71 48.60	-0 37	-0 08	+0 35	-0 21	0.4	0.2	0.0 --	1.2 260	0.0 --	0.7 086
2226	Watch Hill Point, 5.2 miles SSE of		41 13.20	71 49.00	+0 26	+0 18	+0 29	+0 12	0.4	0.3	0.0 --	1.2 265	0.0 --	1.2 064
2231	Montauk Point, 5.4 miles NNE of	15	41 09.55	71 49.48	+0 25	-0 03	-0 47	+0 12	0.4	0.5	0.0 --	1.1 279	0.0 --	1.6 079
2236	Montauk Point, 1.2 miles east of	15	41 04.50	71 49.80	-1 30	-1 09	-0 48	-1 53	1.0	0.8	0.0 --	2.8 346	0.0 --	2.8 162
2241	Montauk Point, 1 mile northeast of		41 05	71 51	-2 02	-1 29	-1 10	-1 41	0.7	0.4	0.0 --	2.4 356	0.0 --	1.9 145

Endnotes can be found at the end of Table 2.

TABLE 2. - CURRENT DIFFERENCES AND OTHER CONSTANTS, 1903

NO.	PLACE	METER DEPTH (ft)	Lat. (°N)	Long. (°W)	Min. before Flood (h.m)	Flood (h.m)	Min. before Ebb (h.m)	Ebb (h.m)	SR Flood	SR Ebb	Min. before Flood (knots deg.)	Max. Flood (knots deg.)	Min. before Ebb (knots deg.)	Max. Ebb (knots deg.)
	BLOCK ISLAND SOUND Time meridian, 75°W					on THE RACE, p.34								
2246	Wicopesset Island, 1.1 miles SSE of.....		41 16.50	71 54.80	-1 02	-0 10	+0 39	-0 07	0.5	0.2	0.0 --	1.5 250	0.0 --	0.8 073
2251	East Pt., Fishers I., 4.1 miles S of....	15	41 13.40	71 55.50	+0 42	+0 32	+0 11	+0 12	0.3	0.5	0.0 --	0.9 236	0.0 --	1.8 073
2256	Cerberus Shoal, 1.5 miles east of......	15	41 10.45	71 55.17	-0 23	-0 15	-0 33	-0 52	0.4	0.5	0.0 --	1.1 256	0.0 --	1.8 092
2261	Shagwong Reef & Cerberus Shoal, between.		41 07.90	71 55.50	-0 38	-0 47	-0 35	-0 57	0.6	0.5	0.0 --	1.9 241	0.0 --	1.8 056
2266	Montauk Harbor entrance...............	6	41 04.78	71 56.35	-2 25	-2 47	-3 12	-4 49	0.4	0.1	0.0 --	1.2 226	0.0 --	0.6 033
								-2 32		0.2	0.0 --		0.0 --	0.2 024
								-0 44		0.1	0.0 --		0.0 --	0.5 353
2271	Mt. Prospect, 0.6 mile SSE of.........	15	41 14.75	71 59.80	-0 42	-0 06	0 00	-0 59	0.6	0.5	0.0 --	1.7 275	0.0 --	1.6 054
2276	Cerberus Shoal and Fishers I., between.	7	41 13	71 58	0 57	-0 05	+0 11	-0 06	0.4	0.3	0.0 --	1.3 264	0.0 --	1.3 096
2281	Little Gull Island, 3.7 miles ESE of..		41 10.7	72 02.1		See table 5,								
2286	Gardiners Island, 3 miles northeast of..	10	41 07.9	72 02.0	-0 45	-0 56	-0 21	-0 26	0.3	0.2	0.0 --	0.9 305	0.0 --	1.0 138
2291	Eastern Plain Point, 1.2 miles N of...		41 07.12	72 04.85	-2 53	-1 51	-1 18	-2 23	0.3	0.3	0.0 --	1.0 290	0.0 --	0.8 110
2296	Eastern Plain Pt., 3.9 miles ENE of...		41 07.05	71 59.80	-1 09	-1 26	-0 32	-1 01	0.3	0.3	0.0 --	1.0 246	0.0 --	1.0 096
2301	Little Gull Island, 0.8 mile SSE of <5i>		41 11.67	72 06.23	-2 18	-0 50	-0 33	-3 02	0.4	0.2	0.0 --	1.3 331	0.0 --	0.6 105
								-1 54		0.0	0.0 --		0.0 --	0.1 252
								-0 32		0.2	0.0 --		0.0 --	0.6 174
2306	Rocky Point, 2 miles WNW of...........	15	41 03.55	72 01.80	-1 30	-1 01	-0 59	-0 59	0.1	0.1	0.1 192	0.3 255	0.2 340	0.3 065
	GARDINERS BAY, etc.													
2311	Goff Point, 0.4 mile northwest of.....		41 01.49	72 03.75	-1 54	-2 25	-1 35	-2 31	0.4	0.5	0.0 --	1.2 225	0.0 --	1.6 010
2316	Acabonack Hbr. ent., 0.6 mile ESE of..		41 01.30	72 07.40	-1 42	-2 10	-1 15	-2 30	0.5	0.3	0.0 --	1.4 345	0.0 --	1.2 140
2321	Hog Creek Point, north of.............		41 04.10	72 09.70	-1 04	-0 49	-1 31	-1 52	0.1	0.1	0.0 --	0.3 281	0.0 --	0.3 067
2326	Ram Island, 2.2 miles east of.........		41 04.70	72 13.80	-0 27	-0 24	-0 24	-0 12	0.1	0.1	0.0 --	0.2 250	0.0 --	0.3 090
2331	Orient Point, 2.4 miles SSE of........		41 07.50	72 12.30	+0 11	-0 34	+1 01	-0 31	0.1	0.1	0.0 --	0.4 270	0.0 --	0.3 025
2336	Gardiners Pt., Ruins, 1.1 miles N of..	15	41 09.50	72 08.83	-0 20	-0 17	-0 19	+0 04	0.4	0.5	0.0 --	1.2 270	0.0 --	1.8 066
2341	Gardiners Point & Plum Island, between.		41 09.33	72 09.52	-0 26	-0 31	-0 42	-0 30	0.5	0.2	0.0 --	1.4 288	0.0 --	1.6 100
2346	Ram Island, 1.4 miles NNE of..........		41 05.8	72 15.8	-0 07	-0 02	-0 03	+0 17	0.1	0.2	0.0 --	0.4 240	0.0 --	0.6 075
2351	Long Beach Pt., 0.7 mile southwest of..	15	41 06.25	72 18.40	+0 25	-0 11	+0 34	0 00	0.5	0.5	0.0 --	1.3 307	0.0 --	1.8 101
2356	Hay Beach Point, 0.3 mile NW of <52>...		41 06.65	72 70.43	+0 12	+0 20	+0 51	-0 51	0.5	0.3	0.0 --	1.5 210	0.0 --	1.2 025
								+0 38		0.2	0.0 --		0.0 --	0.6 025
								+1 35		0.2	0.0 --		0.0 --	0.8 020
2361	Jennings Point, 0.2 mile NNW of.......	13	41 04.48	72 22.95	+0 24	+0 09	+0 27	+0 03	0.6	0.4	0.0 --	1.6 290	0.0 --	1.5 055
2366	Cedar Point, 0.2 mile west of.........		41 02.38	72 16.07	-0 19	-0 16	+0 19	-0 41	0.8	0.5	0.0 --	1.8 195	0.0 --	1.6 005
2371	North Haven Peninsula, north of.......		41 02.47	72 19.25	+0 04	-0 30	+0 29	-0 34	0.8	0.6	0.0 --	2.4 230	0.0 --	2.1 035
2376	Paradise Point, 0.4 mile east of......	13	41 02.88	72 22.57	+0 18	+0 03	+0 35	+0 06	0.5	0.4	0.0 --	1.5 145	0.0 --	1.5 345
2381	Little Peconic Bay entrance...........	19	41 01.58	72 23.08	+0 27	+0 01	+0 43	+0 21	0.6	0.4	0.0 --	1.6 240	0.0 --	1.5 015
2386	Robins Island, 0.5 mile south of......		40 56.98	72 27.18	+0 24	-0 12	+0 46	+0 35	0.6	0.2	0.0 --	1.7 245	0.0 --	1.6 065
								-1 31		0.1	0.0 --		0.0 --	0.2 243
								-0 07		0.2	0.0 --		0.0 --	0.5 234
	FISHERS ISLAND SOUND													
2391	Edwards Pt. and Sandy Pt., between.....	4	41 19.90	71 53.88	-2 34	-3 17	-2 25	-3 41	0.4	0.3	0.0 --	1.1 035	0.0 --	1.0 227
2396	Napatree Point, 0.7 mile southwest of...		41 17.92	71 54.00	-0 56	-1 07	-0 57	-1 18	0.6	0.6	0.0 --	1.7 284	0.0 --	2.2 113
2401	Little Narragansett Bay entrance.......		41 20	71 53	-1 56	-1 59	-2 09	-2 35	0.4	0.3	0.0 --	1.3 092	0.0 --	1.3 268

Endnotes can be found at the end of Table 2.

TABLE 2. – CURRENT DIFFERENCES AND OTHER CONSTANTS, 1983

NO.	PLACE	METER DEPTH (ft)	POSITION Lat. (° ′ N)	POSITION Long. (° ′ W)	TIME DIFFERENCES Min. before Flood (h.m.)	Flood (h.m.)	Min. before Ebb (h.m.)	Ebb (h.m.)	SPEED RATIOS Flood	SPEED RATIOS Ebb	Minimum before Flood (knots, deg.)	Maximum Flood (knots, deg.)	Minimum before Ebb (knots, deg.)	Maximum Ebb (knots, deg.)
	FISHERS ISLAND SOUND Time meridian, 75°W				*on THE RACE, p.34*									
2406	Avondale, Pawcatuck River <51>	6	41 19.90	71 50.73	-1 56	-2 42	-2 17	-3 40	0.2	0.2	0.0 –	0.6 058	0.0 –	0.5 265
								-1 08		0.0				0.1 243
								+0 04		0.1				0.2 263
2411	Ram Island Reef, south of	7	41 18.1	71 58.5	-0 52	-0 47	-0 41	-0 50	0.4	0.4	0.0 –	1.3 255	0.0 –	1.6 088
2416	Noank <51>	4	41 19.12	71 59.30	-1 36	-3 16	-4 10	-4 30	0.2	0.1	0.0 –	0.5 340	0.0 –	0.3 173
							-1 24			0.0				– –
2421	Mystic, Highway Bridge, Mystic River	6	41 21.25	71 58.18	-2 02	-2 50	-2 07	+0 19	0.2	0.1	0.0 –	0.5 039	0.0 –	0.5 162
								-3 39		0.0				0.4 231
								-1 40						0.2 234
								-0 20						0.3 232
2426	Clay Point, 1.3 miles NNE of	15	41 17.88	71 58.53	-0 42	-0 49	-0 40	-1 15	0.5	0.5	0.0 –	1.4 264	0.0 –	1.9 035
2431	North Hill Point, 1.1 miles NNW of		41 17.57	72 01.68	-1 05	-0 26	-0 18	-1 37	0.5	0.4	0.0 –	1.5 258	0.0 –	1.2 082
	LONG ISLAND SOUND													
	The Race													
2436	Race Point, 0.4 mile southwest of		41 14.70	72 02.60	-0 24	-0 35	-0 43	-0 44	0.9	1.0	0.0 –	2.6 288	0.0 –	3.5 135
2441	THE RACE, near Valiant Rock		41 14.20	72 03.60	Daily predictions						0.0 –	2.9 295	0.0 –	3.5 100
2446	0.5 mile NE of Little Gull Island		41 13	72 06	-0 30	-0 14	-0 11	-0 26	1.0	0.7	0.0 –	3.3 002	0.0 –	3.1 107
2451	Little Gull I., 1.1 miles ENE of		41 13.10	72 05.10	-0 07	-0 11	+0 01	-0 45	1.4	1.3	0.0 –	4.0 301	0.0 –	4.7 130
2456	Great Gull Island, 0.7 mile WSW of		41 11.67	72 08.02	-0 51	-0 33	-0 31	-1 42	0.9	0.9	0.0 –	2.6 299	0.0 –	3.2 133
2461	Plum Gut		41 10.00	72 12.80	-1 22	-1 30	-1 01	-2 05	1.2	1.2	0.0 –	3.5 323	0.0 –	4.3 126
2466	Eastern Point, 1.5 miles south of		41 17.8	72 04.4	-1 57	-1 50	-1 03	-1 50	0.1	0.1	0.0 –	0.4 249	0.0 –	0.4 055
2471	New London Harbor entrance		41 19.08	72 05.02	-1 22	-1 51	-2 12	-1 15	0.1	0.1	0.0 –	0.1 348	0.0 –	0.2 211
	Thames River													
2476	Winthrop Point		41 21.63	72 05.30	-1 17	-1 59	-0 54	-2 35	0.1	0.1	0.0 –	0.4 012	0.0 –	0.4 180
								-1 08		0.0				0.2 186
								+0 04		0.0				0.3 185
2481	Off Smith Cove	5	41 23.98	72 05.18	-1 18	-2 20	-1 29	-1 54	0.2	0.1	0.0 –	0.7 019	0.0 –	0.5 199
								-1 30		0.1				0.2 202
								+0 13		0.2				0.6 198
2486	Off Stoddard Hill	15	41 27.65	72 04.12	-1 17	-2 23	-0 40	-2 29	0.2	0.2	0.0 –	0.7 332	0.0 –	0.4 164
								-1 11		0.0				0.2 165
								+0 26		0.2				0.5 161
2491	Lower Coal Dock	15	41 30.88	72 04.72	Current weak and variable									
2496	Goshen Point, 1.9 miles SSE of	15	41 16.00	72 06.30	-1 05	-1 00	-1 03	-1 49	0.4	0.5	0.0 –	1.2 285	0.0 –	1.6 062
2501	Little Gull Island, 0.8 mile NNW of	15	41 13.10	72 06.93	+0 17	-1 19	-2 29	-0 46	0.7	0.8	0.0 –	1.9 258	0.0 –	2.9 043
2506	Bartlett Reef, 0.2 mile south of		41 16.2	72 07.7	-2 01	-0 50	-1 00	-1 31	0.3	0.3	0.0 –	1.4 255	0.0 –	1.3 090
2511	Twotree Island Channel	11	41 17.87	72 08.47	-1 06	-1 27	-0 43	-1 42	0.4	0.4	0.0 –	1.6 267	0.0 –	1.6 099
2516	Niantic (Railroad Bridge)	5	41 19.40	72 10.62	-0 53	-1 03	-0 53	-0 40	0.6	0.2	0.0 –	1.6 352	0.0 –	0.8 178
2521	Black Point, 0.8 mile south of	15	41 16.40	72 12.50	-0 50	-1 11	-0 25	-1 10	0.4	0.4	0.0 –	1.2 260	0.0 –	1.4 073
2526	Black Point and Plum Island, between	15	41 14.00	72 12.30	+0 25	+0 04	+0 29	+0 26	0.7	0.7	0.0 –	2.1 236	0.0 –	2.4 076
2531	Plum Island, 0.8 mile NNW of	15	41 11.87	72 11.92	+0 04	-0 16	-1 13	-0 41	0.6	0.7	0.0 –	1.7 247	0.0 –	2.4 065
2536	Branford Reef, 1.5 miles southwest of	15	41 12.57	72 49.83	-0 13	-0 14	-0 09	-0 18	0.3	0.2	0.0 –	0.8 272	0.0 –	0.7 068
2541	Branford Reef, 5.0 miles south of	15	41 08.65	72 49.67	-0 01	+0 09	+0 11	+0 03	0.2	0.2	0.0 –	0.7 260	0.0 –	0.8 074
2546	Hatchett Point, 1.1 miles WSW of		41 16.35	72 16.92	-2 37	-1 11	-0 52	-2 37	0.4	0.3	0.0 –	1.3 240	0.0 –	1.2 045

Endnotes can be found at the end of Table 2.

TABLE 2. – CURRENT DIFFERENCES AND OTHER CONSTANTS, 1903

NO.	PLACE	METER DEPTH (ft)	POSITION Lat. (°N)	POSITION Long. (°W)	TIME DIFF. Min. before Flood (h.m.)	TIME DIFF. Flood (h.m.)	TIME DIFF. Min. before Ebb (h.m.)	TIME DIFF. Ebb (h.m.)	SPEED RATIO Flood	SPEED RATIO Ebb	Min. before Flood (knots deg.)	Maximum Flood (knots deg.)	Min. before Ebb (knots deg.)	Maximum Ebb (knots deg.)
	LONG ISLAND SOUND *Time meridian, 75°W*													
	Connecticut River													
2551	Lynde Point, channel east of......		41 16	72 20	+0 42	+0 50	+0 18	+0 29	0.3	0.2	0.0 --	0.9 344	0.0 --	0.7 161
2556	Saybrook Point, 0.2 mile northeast of		41 17.02	72 20.87	+0 35	+0 51	+0 47	+0 30	0.5	0.4	0.0 --	1.5 355	0.0 --	1.5 160
2561	Railroad drawbridge.............	15	41 19.00	72 20.77	+0 27	-0 26	+0 54	+1 06	0.2	0.3	0.0 --	1.0 360	0.0 --	1.0 198
	(on THE RACE, p.34)					+0 35						0.6 359		
	(on THE RACE, p.34)					+1 31						0.9 356		
2566	Eustasia Island, 0.6 mile ESE of.....	15	41 23.30	72 24.23	+1 53	+1 38	+1 23	+1 26	0.4	0.4	0.0 --	1.1 290	0.0 --	1.4 070
2571	Eddy Rock Shoal, west of..........	15	41 26.57	72 27.78	+1 41	+2 16	+2 01	+1 20	0.3	0.2	0.0 --	0.8 350	0.0 --	0.6 155
2576	Higganum Creek, 0.5 mile ESE of.....		41 30.02	72 32.62	+3 06	+2 52	+2 35	+3 01	0.3	0.3	0.0 --	0.8 270	0.0 --	1.0 080
2581	Wilcox Island Park, east of.......		41 34.33	72 38.88	+4 06	+3 36	+3 07	+3 35	0.3	0.3	0.0 --	0.9 355	0.0 --	1.0 160
2586	Rocky Hill.......................	9	41 39.82	72 37.73	+4 41	+3 37	+3 21	+3 30	0.2	0.2	0.0 --	0.6 335	0.0 --	0.8 135
2591	Hartford Jetty <42>.............	9	41 45.07	72 39.02	+5 45	+4 39	+3 22	+4 29	0.2	0.2	0.0 --	0.1 290	0.0 --	0.7 095
2596	Saybrook Breakwater, 1.5 miles SE of.		41 14.78	72 19.05	-1 30	-1 11	-0 55	-1 57	0.7	0.6	0.0 --	1.9 260	0.0 --	2.0 070
2601	Mulford Point, 3.1 miles northwest of		41 12.00	72 19.08	-0 06	-1 05	-0 05	-0 24	0.7	0.6	0.0 --	1.9 269	0.0 --	2.3 066
2606	Orient Point, 1 mile WNW of.........	15	41 10.02	72 15.11	-1 09	-2 02	-0 33	-1 15	0.5	0.9	0.0 --	1.9 245	0.0 --	3.1 055
	(on THE RACE, p.34)					-0 59			0.7			0.8 255		
	(on THE RACE, p.34)					-0 09			0.7			2.1 245		
2611	Rocky Point, 0.3 mile north of......	15	41 08.63	72 21.42	-0 27	-1 02	-1 01	-0 28	0.6	0.6	0.0 --	1.8 279	0.0 --	2.1 041
2616	Cornfield Point, 3 miles south of....	7	41 12.9	72 22.4	-0 56	-0 17	-0 44	-0 20	0.6	0.4	0.0 --	2.0 256	0.0 --	1.7 094
2621	Cornfield Point, 1.1 miles south of..	15	41 14.65	72 23.40	-1 01	-1 34	-1 02	-2 03	0.5	0.5	0.0 --	1.4 293	0.0 --	1.6 108
2626	Kesley Point, 2.1 miles southeast of.		41 14.10	72 27.93	-0 35	-1 02	-0 54	-1 00	0.5	0.5	0.0 --	1.5 260	0.0 --	1.8 070
2631	Six Mile Reef, 1.5 miles north of....		41 12.66	72 26.87	-0 17	-0 12	-0 23	-0 41	0.6	0.4	0.0 --	1.6 290	0.0 --	1.3 095
2636	Six Mile Reef, 2 miles east of......		41 10.83	72 26.90	-0 36	-0 12	-0 07	-0 35	0.6	0.6	0.0 --	1.6 235	0.0 --	2.1 040
2641	Horton Point, 1.4 miles NNW of......		41 06.30	72 27.40	+0 04	+0 08	-0 03	-0 18	0.5	0.6	0.0 --	1.4 260	0.0 --	2.0 040
2646	Kelsey Point, 1 mile south of.......		41 14	72 30	-1 32	-1 00	-1 03	-1 51	0.5	0.3	0.0 --	2.0 249	0.0 --	1.5 118
2651	Hammonasset Point, 1.2 miles SW of..	15	41 14.22	72 34.00	-0 59	-1 15	-0 44	-1 31	0.3	0.4	0.0 --	1.0 287	0.0 --	1.5 106
2656	Hammonasset Point, 5 miles south of.	15	41 09.80	72 34.17	-0 03	-0 03	-0 24	-0 06	0.5	0.4	0.0 --	1.4 284	0.0 --	1.5 090
2661	Mattituck Inlet, 1 mile northwest of.	15	41 01.68	72 34.22	-0 21	-0 15	-0 08	-0 26	0.3	0.3	0.0 --	0.9 241	0.0 --	1.0 053
2666	Sachem Head, 1 mile SSE of.........		41 13.65	72 42.30	-0 38	-0 36	-0 35	-1 02	0.4	0.3	0.0 --	1.1 255	0.0 --	1.0 065
2671	Sachem Head 6.2 miles south of.....	15	41 08.73	72 42.30	+0 29	+0 24	-0 12	-0 04	0.6	0.3	0.0 --	0.6 260	0.0 --	0.9 065
2676	Roanoke Point, 5.6 miles north of...	15	41 04.37	72 42.53	-0 02	-0 02	-0 15	-0 24	0.2	0.3	0.0 --	0.7 255	0.0 --	0.9 050
2681	Roanoke Point, 2.3 miles NNW of....		41 00.92	72 42.97	-1 19	-0 22	-0 10	-0 29	0.3	0.2	0.0 --	0.9 270	0.0 --	0.7 070
2686	Sachem Head, 1 mile south of.......		41 14	72 43	-0 46	+0 03	-0 33	-0 38	0.3	0.3	0.0 --	0.9 278	0.0 --	1.2 004
2691	Herod Point, 2.8 miles north of.....	15	41 00.97	72 49.93	-0 29	-0 17	-0 27	-0 06	0.3	0.2	0.1 020	0.4 290	0.1 020	0.6 090
2696	Herod Point, 6.5 miles north of.....	15	41 04.65	72 49.80	-0 27	+0 06	+0 12	-0 07	0.3	0.2	0.0 --	0.9 254	0.0 --	0.7 070
2701	New Haven Harbor entrance <12>...		41 14	72 55	-1 11	-1 34	-0 37	-1 15	0.4	0.2	0.0 --	1.4 319	0.0 --	0.9 152
2706	City Point, 1.3 miles northeast of...		41 17.83	72 54.42	+0 11	+0 30	+0 33	+0 08	0.1	0.1	0.0 --	0.3 015	0.0 --	0.4 215
2711	Oyster River Pt., 1.3 miles SSE of <1>		41 12.87	72 58.00	-	-0 15	-	-0 47	0.1	0.1	0.0 --	0.3 255	0.0 --	0.3 060
2716	Pond Point, 4.2 miles SSE of.......		41 08.60	72 58.08	-0 20	+0 04	-0 04	-0 14	0.2	0.2	0.0 --	0.6 265	0.0 --	0.6 065
2721	Stratford Shoal, 6 miles east of.....		41 04.52	72 58.43	+0 01	-0 02	-0 07	-0 09	0.3	0.2	0.0 --	0.6 265	0.0 --	0.6 060
2726	Sound Beach, 2.2 miles north of.....		41 00.33	72 58.45	-0 03	-0 06	-0 15	-0 25	0.3	0.2	0.0 --	0.6 265	0.0 --	0.9 075
2731	Charles Island, 0.8 mile SSE of.....		41 10.77	73 02.63	-0 51	-0 36	-0 30	-0 54	0.1	0.1	0.0 --	0.4 250	0.0 --	0.4 070
	Housatonic River													
2736	Milford Point, 0.2 mile west of.....	10	41 10.35	73 06.82	-0 06	+0 01	+0 15	-0 55	0.4	0.3	0.0 --	1.2 330	0.0 --	1.2 135
2741	Railroad drawbridge, above........	5	41 12.53	73 06.67	+0 34	+0 13	+0 29	-0 55	0.4	0.4	0.0 --	1.1 350	0.0 --	1.3 185
2746	Fowler Island, 0.1 mile NNW of.....	5	41 14.40	73 06.23	+0 48	+0 10	+0 30	+0 48	0.4	0.3	0.0 --	1.1 040	0.0 --	1.1 270

Endnotes can be found at the end of Table 2.

TABLE 2. - CURRENT DIFFERENCES AND OTHER CONSTANTS, 1983

NO.	PLACE	METER DEPTH (ft)	POSITION Lat. °′ N	POSITION Long. °′ W	TIME DIFFERENCES Min. before Flood h.m.	Flood h.m.	Min. before Ebb h.m.	Ebb h.m.	SPEED RATIOS Flood	Ebb	AVERAGE SPEEDS AND DIRECTIONS Minimum before Flood knots deg.	Maximum Flood knots deg.	Minimum before Ebb knots deg.	Maximum Ebb knots deg.
	LONG ISLAND SOUND Time meridian, 75°W				on THE RACE, p.34									
	Housatonic River													
2751	Wooster Island, 0.1 mile southwest of <13>	5	41 16.67	73 05.20	+1 19	+0 33	+0 20	+0 22	0.2	0.2	0.0 -	0.6 020	0.0 -	0.7 220
2756	Derby-Shelton Bridge, below <13>		41 18.73	73 04.78	- --	- --	-0 08	-0 06	-	0.1			0.0 -	0.4 095
2761	Point No Point, 2.1 miles south of	15	41 06.75	73 07.13	-0 30	-0 06	-0 08	-0 01	0.4	0.3	0.0 -	1.3 251	0.0 -	1.2 074
2766	Old Field Point, 1 mile east of	15	40 58.47	73 05.80	+3 26	+2 31	+2 25	+1 56	0.1	0.2	0.0 -	0.2 105	0.0 -	0.6 308
	...do	22	40 58.47	73 05.80	+2 30	+1 54	+2 17	+1 44	0.1	0.3	0.0 -	1.0 110	0.0 -	0.5 297
2771	Old Field Point, 2 miles northeast of	15	41 00.23	73 05.70	+0 33	+0 13	+0 11	+0 58	0.2	0.3	0.0 -	1.0 266	0.0 -	1.1 092
	...do	40	41 00.23	73 05.70	+0 22	+0 08	-0 12	+0 41	0.1	0.3	0.0 -	0.5 236	0.0 -	0.6 081
2776	Stratford Point, 4.3 miles south of	15	41 04.77	73 06.67	+0 12	+0 19	+0 05	+0 14	0.2	0.2	0.0 -	1.0 254	0.0 -	1.0 075
	...do	60	41 04.77	73 06.67	-0 36	-0 09	+0 23	+0 15	0.2	0.2	0.0 -	0.6 291	0.0 -	0.8 078
2781	Stratford Point, 6.1 miles south of	15	41 02.97	73 05.80	-0 18	+0 03	+0 16	+0 30	0.3	0.2	0.0 -	1.0 267	0.0 -	0.8 080
	...do	51	41 02.97	73 05.80	-0 43	-0 31	-0 34	-0 12	0.3	0.2	0.0 -	0.9 279	0.0 -	0.9 087
2786	Port Jefferson Harbor entrance		40 58	73 06	+0 11	+0 40	+0 32	+0 14	0.8	0.4	0.0 -	2.6 151	0.0 -	1.9 323
2791	Crane Neck Point, 0.5 mile northwest of		40 58	73 10	-0 45	-1 24	-1 38	-1 34	0.4	0.3	0.0 -	1.3 256	0.0 -	1.5 016
2796	Bridgeport Hbr. ent., btn. jetties <14>	4	41 09	73 11	-0 10	-0 22	+0 05	-0 03	0.2	0.1	0.0 -	0.7 340	0.0 -	0.6 176
2801	Crane Neck Point, 3.4 miles WNW of	15	40 59.00	73 13.87	-0 12	+0 02	-0 25	+0 09	0.1	0.2	0.0 -	0.5 261	0.0 -	0.6 079
2806	Crane Neck Point, 3.7 miles WSW of	15	40 56.30	73 13.87	-1 32	-0 31	-0 24	-0 18	0.1	0.1	0.0 -	0.4 066	0.0 -	0.4 232
2811	Shoal Point, 6 miles south of	15	41 01.70	73 14.03	-0 20	+0 28	+0 42	+0 55	0.2	0.1	0.0 -	0.4 232	0.0 -	0.4 047
2816	Pine Creek Point, 2.3 miles SSE of	15	41 05.05	73 14.40	-0 20	+0 06	+0 21	+0 23	0.2	0.2	0.0 -	0.7 272	0.0 -	0.6 084
2821	Saugatuck River, 0.3 mi. NW of Bluff Pt.	15	41 06.27	73 21.92	-0 12	-0 41	+0 20	+0 10	0.2	0.1	0.0 -	0.5 265	0.0 -	0.4 080
2826	Saugatuck R., 0.5 mile above Bluff Pt.		41 06	73 23	Current weak and variable									
2831	Sheffield l. Tower, 1.1 miles SE of	15	41 01.97	73 24.33	+0 33	+0 39	+0 59	+0 33	0.3	0.2	0.0 -	0.9 283	0.0 -	0.8 081
	...do	60	41 01.97	73 24.33	-0 27	+0 24	+1 00	+0 36	0.1	0.2	0.0 -	0.6 269	0.0 -	0.5 076
2836	Sheffield I. Hbr., 0.5 mile southeast of	12	41 03.32	73 25.25	-2 41	-3 54	-3 36	-2 12	0.1	0.1	0.0 -	0.6 229	0.0 -	0.4 042
2841	Norwalk River, off Gregory Point	15	41 05.20	73 24.22	-0 12	-0 21	+0 29	+0 30	0.5	0.4	0.0 -	1.4 322	0.0 -	0.5 155
2846	Eaton's Neck Pt., 1.3 miles north of	15	40 58.60	73 23.77	+0 31	+0 21	+0 05	+0 21	0.2	0.1	0.0 -	0.5 283	0.0 -	1.4 286
2851	Eaton's Neck Pt., 1.8 miles west of	15	40 57	73 26	-1 09	-1 01	-0 28	+0 29	0.3	0.4	0.0 -	0.7 199	0.0 -	0.6 068
2856	Eaton's Neck Pt., 3 miles north of	170	41 00.38	73 23.80	+0 40	+0 30	+0 36	+0 17	0.2	0.2	0.0 -	0.6 253	0.0 -	0.6 046
	...do	15	41 00.38	73 23.80	+0 17	+0 13	+0 26	+0 28	0.3	0.2	0.0 -	0.6 264	0.0 -	0.6 078
	...do	40	41 00.38	73 23.80	-0 38	-0 22	+1 26	+0 44	0.2	0.2	0.0 -	0.5 188	0.0 -	0.5 054
2861	Huntington Bay, off East Fort Point	15	40 55.60	73 25.05	-0 06	+0 14	+0 14	+0 51	0.2	0.2	0.0 -	0.5 190	0.0 -	0.5 014
	...do	30	40 55.60	73 25.05	-0 54	+0 10	+0 05	+0 16	0.1	0.1	0.0 -	0.4 179	0.0 -	0.3 007
2866	Northport Bay entrance (in channel)	15	40 54.53	73 24.45	-0 11	+0 14	+0 12	+0 30	0.1	0.1	0.0 -	0.4 100	0.0 -	0.4 267
2871	Northport Bay, south of Duck I. Bluff	15	40 55	73 23	+0 31	+0 54	+1 14	-0 05	0.1	0.1	0.0 -	0.4 007	0.0 -	0.3 286
2876	Long Neck Point, 0.6 mile south of	15	41 01.58	73 28.68	-1 20	-0 05	+1 12	+0 11	0.3	0.3	0.0 -	0.8 252	0.0 -	0.5 073
	...do	27	41 01.58	73 28.68	-1 05	-0 08	+1 20	+0 09	0.3	0.3	0.0 -	0.8 257	0.0 -	0.5 080
2881	Lloyd Point, 1.3 miles NNW of	40	40 57.95	73 29.70	+1 16	+0 54	+1 07	+1 05	0.3	0.3	0.0 -	1.0 255	0.0 -	0.9 055
	...do	15	40 57.95	73 29.70	-0 08	+0 13	+0 13	+0 37	0.3	0.3	0.0 -	1.0 269	0.0 -	0.7 053
2886	Shippan Point, 1.3 miles SSE of	40	40 59.90	73 31.00	+0 28	+0 07	+0 07	+0 16	0.3	0.3	0.0 -	0.9 239	0.0 -	0.9 055
	...do	15	40 59.98	73 31.03	+0 10	+0 11	+0 46	-0 10	0.2	0.2	0.0 -	0.7 247	0.0 -	0.8 071
	Oyster Bay													
2891	Rocky Point, 1 mile east of	15	40 55.15	73 30.03	+0 11	+0 20	+0 14	+0 42	0.2	0.2	0.0 -	0.6 117	0.0 -	0.5 306
2896	Harbor ent., south of Plum Point		40 54	73 31	-0 04	+0 07	+0 04	+0 04	0.2	0.2	0.0 -	0.7 244	0.0 -	0.7 054
2901	Harbor, west of Soper Point		40 53	73 32	+0 26	+0 01	+0 01	+0 26	0.2	0.1	0.0 -	0.6 333	0.0 -	0.4 140
2906	Cold Spring Harbor		40 53	73 29	Current weak and variable									
2911	Stamford Harbor entrance	12	41 00.88	73 32.20	-1 30	-1 17	-2 07	-0 22	0.1	0.2	0.0 -	0.4 329	0.0 -	0.8 134

Endnotes can be found at the end of Table 2.

TABLE 2. - CURRENT DIFFERENCES AND OTHER CONSTANTS, 1983

NO.	PLACE	METER DEPTH (ft)	POSITION Lat. (N)	POSITION Long. (W)	TIME DIFF. Min. before Flood (h.m.)	TIME DIFF. Flood (h.m.)	TIME DIFF. Min. before Ebb (h.m.)	TIME DIFF. Ebb (h.m.)	SPEED RATIOS Flood	SPEED RATIOS Ebb	AVG Minimum before Flood (knots deg.)	AVG Maximum Flood (knots deg.)	AVG Minimum before Ebb (knots deg.)	AVG Maximum Ebb (knots deg.)
	LONG ISLAND SOUND Time meridian, 75°W													
						on THE RACE, p.34								
2916	Greenwich Point, 1.1 miles south of.....	15	40 59.02	73 34.02	+1 13	+1 03	+1 39	+1 13	0.2	0.2	0.0 --	0.7 258	0.0 --	0.8 073
	...do.....	55	40 59.02	73 34.02	+1 16	+0 56	+0 41	+1 15	0.2	0.1	0.0 --	0.6 265	0.0 --	0.4 069
2921	Greenwich Point, 2.5 miles south of.....	15	40 57.60	73 33.68	+0 39	+0 15	+0 47	+0 41	0.2	0.2	0.0 --	0.7 242	0.0 --	0.7 052
	...do.....	55	40 57.60	73 33.68	+1 15	+0 01	-0 37	-0 05	0.2	0.2	0.0 --	0.4 256	0.0 --	0.4 079
2926	Oak Neck Point, 0.6 mile north of......	55	40 55.50	73 34.02	+2 43	+2 03	+2 15	+2 23	0.2	0.1	0.0 --	0.5 260	0.0 --	0.6 072
	...do.....	30	40 55.50	73 34.02	+0 46	+1 40	+1 31	+2 03	0.2	0.2	0.0 --	0.5 300	0.0 --	0.5 090
2931	Captain Hbr. Ent., 0.6 mile southwest of	15	40 59.65	73 35.67	+1 24	+1 49	+1 39	+2 12	0.2	0.2	0.0 --	0.6 312	0.0 --	0.7 118
	...do.....	30	40 59.65	73 35.67	+1 14	+1 19	+0 48	+2 10	0.2	0.1	0.0 --	0.5 319	0.0 --	0.7 142
2936	Cos Cob Harbor, off Goose Island......		41 01	73 36	+0 13	-0 07	+0 04	-0 40	0.2	0.2	0.0 --	0.5 013	0.0 --	0.4 188
2941	Peningo Neck, 0.6 mi. off Parsonage Pt..	15	40 56.32	73 40.50	+1 01	+0 28	+1 06	+0 39	0.2	0.2	0.0 --	0.7 226	0.0 --	0.7 035
2946	Matinecock Point, 0.7 mile NNW of......	15	40 54.80	73 38.40	+1 06	+0 32	+1 24	+0 48	0.2	0.2	0.0 --	0.6 233	0.0 --	0.6 046
	...do.....	40	40 54.80	73 38.40	+0 27	+0 12	+1 23	+0 32	0.2	0.1	0.0 --	0.7 262	0.3 --	0.5 053
2951	Matinecock Point, 1.7 miles northwest of	15	40 55.48	73 39.37	+1 12	+1 04	+0 57	+1 14	0.1	0.1	0.0 --	0.4 234	0.0 --	0.4 055
2956	Hempstead Harbor, 0.3 mile north of.....	15	40 51.72	73 40.47	Current weak and variable									
2961	Hempstead Harbor, 0.5 mile east of.....	15	40 51.50	73 39.98	-- --	+0 05	-- --	-0 19	0.1	--	0.0 --	0.3 157	0.0 --	0.1 331
2966	Old Town Wharf, 0.5 mile north of......	5	40 48.78	73 39.08	-- --	-0 22	-- --	-- --	0.1	--	0.0 --	0.4 196	0.0 --	-- --
2971	Hempstead Harbor, off Glenwood Landing..	10	40 49.68	73 39.00	-0 46	-0 05	-0 07	-0 47	0.3	0.2	0.0 --	0.9 138	0.0 --	0.7 320
2976	Delancey Point, 1 mile southeast of.....	15	40 55.00	73 42.73	+0 37	+0 14	+1 04	+0 07	0.2	0.1	0.0 --	0.5 244	0.0 --	0.4 059
	...do.....	33	40 55.00	73 42.73	-- --	+0 11	+0 59	-0 27	0.1	0.1	0.0 --	0.4 239	0.0 --	0.3 069
2981	Mamaroneck Harbor......		40 56	73 43	Current weak and variable									
2986	Echo Bay entrance......		40 54	73 46	Current weak and variable									
						on THROGS NECK, p.40								
2991	Davids Island, channel 0.1 mile east of.		40 53	73 46	Current weak and variable									
2996	Huckleberry Island, 0.2 mile NW of.....	15	40 53.43	73 45.43	-3 15	-4 07	-3 42	-3 53	0.4	0.3	0.0 --	0.2 069	0.0 --	0.2 234
3001	Huckleberry Island, 0.6 mile SE of.....	15	40 52.80	73 44.75	-2 25	-0 24	-3 14	-2 37	0.6	0.4	0.0 --	0.4 025	0.0 --	0.3 226
3006	Execution Rocks, 0.4 mile southwest of.	15	40 52.40	73 44.00	-2 38	-3 03	-2 48	-2 51	1.0	0.5	0.0 --	0.6 058	0.0 --	0.4 246
3011	Manhasset Bay entrance......	15	40 49.75	73 43.78	+2 58	+2 27	+2 27	+2 51	0.6	0.4	0.0 --	0.4 115	0.0 --	0.3 307
3016	Hart Island, 0.2 mile north of.........	15	40 51.82	73 46.27	-2 23	-3 55	-4 17	-3 23	0.3	0.3	0.0 --	0.2 098	0.0 --	0.3 264
3021	Hart Island, southeast of.........	15	40 50.62	73 45.77	-1 44	-0 07	-1 32	-0 18	0.9	0.5	0.0 --	0.6 032	0.0 --	0.2 283
3026	Hart Island and City Island, between.....	15	40 51.37	73 46.73	-1 48	-2 51	-2 19	-2 40	0.4	0.3	0.0 --	0.2 349	0.0 --	0.4 216
3031	City Island Bridge.........	10	40 51.47	73 47.60	-2 59		4 27	-4 26	0.6	0.3	0.0	0.2 352		0.5 198
3036	Eastchester Bay, near Big Tom.........	5	40 50.20	73 47.72	-3 05	-3 51	-4 07	-3 27	0.2	0.2	0.0 --	0.1 327	0.0 --	0.2 196
3041	Hutchinson R., Pelham Highway Bridge....	5	40 51.70	73 49.00	+2 41	+2 37	+1 51	+2 00	1.4	0.6	0.0 --	0.8 097	0.0 --	0.4 294
3046	City Island, 0.6 mile southeast of......	15	40 49.72	73 46.47	-1 17	-0 45	-2 59	-3 40	0.8	0.7	0.0 --	0.5 038	0.0 --	0.4 251

Endnotes can be found at the end of Table 2.

TABLE 2. – CURRENT DIFFERENCES AND OTHER CONSTANTS, 1983

NO.	PLACE	METER DEPTH (ft)	POSITION Lat. ° ′ N	POSITION Long. ° ′ W	TIME DIFF. Min. before Flood h.m.	TIME DIFF. Flood h.m.	TIME DIFF. Min. before Ebb h.m.	TIME DIFF. Ebb h.m.	SPEED RATIOS Flood	SPEED RATIOS Ebb	AVG SPEED Min. before Flood knots deg.	AVG SPEED Maximum Flood knots deg.	AVG SPEED Min. before Ebb knots deg.	AVG SPEED Maximum Ebb knots deg.
	LONG ISLAND SOUND Time meridian, 75°W				*on THROGS NECK, p.40*									
3051	Elm Point, 0.2 mile west of...........	15	40 48.92	73 46.02	-1 33	-3 16 / -2 49 / -0 09	-1 48	-0 26	0.3 / 0.2 / 1.0	0.7	0.0 --	0.2 026 / 0.1 028 / 0.6 024	0.0 --	0.6 213
3056	Throgs Neck, 0.4 mile south of.........	15	40 47.90.	73 47.45	+0 36	+0 18	+0 20	+0 06	1.0		0.0 --	0.8 090	0.0 --	0.6 278
3061	THROGS NECK, 0.2 mile south of........	15	40 48.12	73 47.48	Daily predictions				1.3	0.8	0.0 --	0.6 090	0.0 --	0.8 289
	EAST RIVER				*on HELL GATE, p.46*									
3066	Cryders Point, 0.4 mile NNW of........		40 48.02	73 47.92	-0 29	-0 43	-0 30	-1 00	0.4	0.2	0.0 --	1.3 110	0.0 --	1.1 285
3071	Old Ferry Point.......................		40 48	73 50	-1 23	-0 37	-0 02	-0 38	0.5	0.3	0.0 --	1.7 076	0.0 --	1.5 240
3076	Clason Point, 0.2 mile SSW of.........		40 48.04	73 51.07	-0 22	-0 46	0 00	-0 32	0.5	0.3	0.0 --	1.8 070	0.0 --	1.5 250
3081	Flushing Creek entrance...............		40 45.9	73 50.7	Current weak and variable									
3086	Rikers I. chan., off La Guardia Field.		40 47	73 53	+0 04	-0 04	+0 04	-0 08	0.3	0.3	0.0 --	1.1 088	0.0 --	1.3 261
3091	Bronx River (1 mile north of Hunts Pt.).		40 48.9	73 52.5	Current weak and variable									
3096	Hunts Point, southwest of.............		40 48	73 53	+0 01	-0 10	+0 01	-0 05	0.5	0.3	0.0 --	1.7 108	0.0 --	1.3 280
3101	N. Brother I. & S. Brother I., between.		40 47.9	73 54.0	+0 10	+0 06	+0 20	-0 01	0.7	0.4	0.0 --	2.5 066	0.0 --	1.8 253
3106	Port Morris, channel off of...........		40 47.94	73 54.36	-0 07	-0 32	+0 20	+0 03	0.4	0.4	0.0 --	1.5 045	0.0 --	1.7 220
3111	Off Winthrop Ave., Astoria............		40 47.2	73 55.0	+0 04	+0 02	-0 01	-0 11	1.0	0.5	0.0 --	3.4 040	0.0 --	2.5 220
3116	Mill Rock, northeast of...............		40 46.9	73 56.2	-0 23	+0 05	-0 29	-0 32	0.7	0.1	0.0 --	2.3 103	0.0 --	0.6 288
3121	Mill Rock, west of....................		40 46.8	73 56.5	-0 26	+0 08	-0 02	-0 17	0.4	0.2	0.0 --	1.2 000	0.0 --	1.0 180
3126	HELL GATE (off Mill Rock).............		40 46.7	73 56.3	Daily predictions						0.0 --	3.4 050	0.0 --	4.6 230
	Roosevelt Island													
3131	west of, off 75th Street..............		40 46	73 57	-0 02	-0 04	-0 08	+0 07	1.1	1.0	0.0 --	3.8 037	0.0 --	4.7 215
3136	east of, off 36th Avenue..............		40 46	73 57	-0 08	-0 04	-0 08	-0 11	1.0	0.7	0.0 --	3.5 030	0.0 --	3.4 210
3141	west of, off 67th Street..............		40 45.74	73 57.24	+0 13	-0 08	+0 06	+0 11	1.1	0.9	0.0 --	3.6 011	0.0 --	4.0 230
3146	west of, off 63rd Street..............		40 45.58	73 57.27	-0 08	-0 08	0 00	+0 03	0.8	0.6	0.0 --	2.9 036	0.0 --	2.9 223
3151	east of...............................		40 45.49	73 57.08	0 00	-0 06	+0 02	+0 07	0.8	0.6	0.0 --	2.8 028	0.0 --	2.6 200
3156	Manhattan, off 31st Street............		40 44.38	73 50.17	+0 09	-0 11	-0 02	+0 36	0.4	0.5	0.0 --	1.5 000	0.0 --	2.1 175
3161	Newtown Creek entrance................		40 44	73 57	Current weak and variable									
3166	Pier 67, off 19th Street..............		40 44	73 58	-0 08	+0 08	-0 08	+0 07	0.5	0.4	0.0 --	1.8 355	0.0 --	1.9 179
3171	Williamsburg Bridge, 0.3 mile north of.		40 43.08	73 58.24	-0 05	+0 12	-0 01	+0 10	0.8	0.6	0.0 --	2.7 020	0.0 --	2.9 220
3176	Corlears Hook, south of; midstream <15>.		40 42.5	73 58.6	-0 12	+0 01	-0 09	-0 01	0.9	0.7	0.0 --	3.0 058	0.0 --	3.0 233
3181	Brooklyn Bridge, 0.1 mile southwest of.		40 42.2	74 00.0	-0 18	+0 08	-0 04	+0 07	0.9	0.8	0.0 --	2.9 046	0.0 --	3.5 222
3186	Governors I., N of (SEE CAUTION NOTE)..		40 41.8	74 01.0	-0 16	+0 16	-0 20	+0 17	0.4	0.4	0.0 --	1.2 094	0.0 --	1.7 269
3191	Buttermilk Channel....................		40 41.15	74 00.81	-0 12	-0 18	-0 06	+0 18	0.5	0.5	0.0 --	1.8 050	0.0 --	2.4 220
	HARLEM RIVER													
3196	East 105th Street.................<16>		40 47	73 56	-0 20	+0 08	-0 02	-0 17	0.4	0.2	0.0 --	1.2 035	0.0 --	1.0 215
3201	East 117th Street (midchannel) <16>...		40 47.6	73 55.8	-1 16	+0 10			0.4	-	0.0 --	1.3 197	0.0 --	- -
3206	Willis Ave. Bridge, 0.1 mile NW of....		40 48.3	73 55.8	-0 30	0 00	-0 12	-0 13	0.4	0.3	0.0 --	1.3 140	0.0 --	1.3 330
3211	Madison Ave. Bridge...................		40 48.8	73 56.1	-0 20	+0 18	-0 21	-0 14	0.5	0.4	0.0 --	1.8 180	0.0 --	1.7 000
3216	Macombs Dam Bridge....................		40 49.7	73 56.1	-0 20	+0 14	-0 22	-0 11	0.5	0.3	0.0 --	1.7 180	0.0 --	1.4 000
3221	High Bridge...........................		40 50.5	73 55.9	-0 20	+0 08	-0 23	-0 08	0.6	0.4	0.0 --	2.0 189	0.0 --	2.0 015
3226	West 207th Street Bridge..............		40 51.8	73 54.9	-0 22	+0 05	-0 22	-0 02	0.6	0.4	0.0 --	2.0 215	0.0 --	2.0 035
3231	Broadway Bridge.......................		40 52.4	73 54.7	-0 23	+0 08	-0 20	+0 04	0.6	0.5	0.0 --	2.1 116	0.0 --	2.3 299

Endnotes can be found at the end of Table 2.

TABLE 2. - CURRENT DIFFERENCES AND OTHER CONSTANTS, 1983

NO.	PLACE	METER DEPTH (ft)	POSITION Lat. (° ' N)	POSITION Long. (° ' W)	TIME DIFFERENCES Min. before Flood (h.m.)	Flood (h.m.)	Min. before Ebb (h.m.)	Ebb (h.m.)	SPEED RATIOS Flood	Ebb	Minimum before Flood (knots)	(deg.)	Maximum Flood (knots)	(deg.)	Minimum before Ebb (knots)	(deg.)	Maximum Ebb (knots)	(deg.)
	HARLEM RIVER Time meridian, 75°W																	
3236	Spuyten Duyvil Creek entrance............		40 52.68	73 55.46	on HELL GATE, p.46													
					-0 10	+0 12	-0 10	+0 17	0.4	0.3	0.0	--	1.4	100	0.0	--	1.5	285
	LONG ISLAND, South Coast				on THE NARROWS, p.52													
3241	Fire Island Lighted Whistle Bouy 2Fl....		40 29	73 11	See table 5.				-	0.8	0.0	-	-	-	0.0	-	1.5	180
3246	Fire Island Inlet, 22 miles S of <17>...		40 16	73 16	See table 5.				0.5	0.3	0.0	-	0.8	250	0.0	-	0.6	090
3251	Shinnecock Canal, railroad bridge <18>		40 53.2	72 30.1	+0 54	+0 35	+0 27	-0 38	1.5	1.2	0.0	-	2.5	350	0.0	-	2.3	170
3256	Ponquogue bridge, Shinnecock Bay........		40 50.7	72 30.7	-0 06	-0 21	-0 30	+0 37	1.4	1.2	0.0	-	2.4	082	0.0	-	2.4	244
3261	Shinnecock Inlet.........		40 50.6	72 28.7	-0 03	-0 01	+0 29	-1 03	1.8	1.3	0.0	-	3.1	035	0.0	-	2.6	217
3266	Fire I. Inlet, 0.5 mi. S of Oak Beach...		40 37.78	73 18.40	-1 15	-0 49	-0 48	-0 01	0.3	0.3	0.0	-	0.5	076	0.0	-	0.6	277
3271	Jones Inlet.........		40 35.5	73 34.0	-0 54	+0 23	+0 32	-1 05	1.3	1.2	0.0	-	2.2	042	0.0	-	2.3	227
3276	Long Beach, inside, between bridges.....		40 35.7	73 39.6	-1 46	-1 35	-1 03	0 00										
3281	East Rockaway Inlet.........		40 35.4	73 45.3	See table 5.			-1 38										
3286	Ambrose Light.........		40 27	73 49	See table 5.													
3291	Sandy Hook App. Lighted Horn Bouy 2A...		40 27	73 55	See table 5.													
	JAMAICA BAY																	
3296	Rockaway Inlet.........		40 33.7	73 56.1	-1 55	-2 20	-1 33	-2 11	1.1	1.3	0.0	-	1.8	085	0.0	-	2.7	244
3301	Barren Island, east of.........		40 35	73 53	-1 59	-2 28	-2 03	-2 19	0.7	0.9	0.0	-	1.2	004	0.0	-	1.7	192
3306	Canarsie (midchannel, off pier).........		40 37.6	73 53.0	-1 54	-1 38	-1 18	-2 06	0.3	0.4	0.0	-	0.5	045	0.0	-	0.7	222
3311	Beach Channel (bridge).........		40 35	73 49	-1 48	-1 13	-0 57	-1 25	1.1	1.0	0.0	-	1.9	062	0.0	-	2.0	225
3316	Grass Hassock Channel.........		40 36.6	73 47.1	-1 21	-1 02	-0 57	-0 54	0.6	0.5	0.0	-	1.0	052	0.0	-	1.0	228
	NEW YORK HARBOR ENTRANCE																	
3326	Ambrose Channel Entrance.........		40 30.4	73 58.4	-1 20	-1 30	-1 03	-0 38	1.0	1.2	0.0	-	1.7	310	0.0	-	2.3	110
3336	East of West Bank Light <19>.........		40 31.9	74 01.5	-0 04	-1 01	-0 53	+0 15	0.8	0.9	0.9	270	1.3	310	0.5	045	1.8	170
3346	Coney Island Lt., 1.6 miles SSW of......		40 33.04	74 01.4	+0 01	-0 48	-0 24	+0 56	0.5	0.8	0.0	-	0.8	330	0.0	-	1.5	145
3356	Ambrose Channel, north end.........		40 33.8	74 01.6	+0 15	-0 10	-0 09	+0 42	0.8	0.9	0.0	-	1.3	332	0.0	-	1.9	176
3366	Coney Island, 0.2 mile west of.........		40 34.6	74 01.1	-0 49	-1 43	-0 57	-0 07	0.9	1.0	0.0	-	1.5	329	0.0	-	2.0	170
3376	Ft. Lafayette, channel east of.........		40 36.5	74 02.2	-2 13	-0 06	+0 04	-1 50	0.6	0.5	0.0	-	1.1	343	0.0	-	0.9	194
3386	THE NARROWS, midchannel.........		40 36.6	74 02.8	Daily predictions						0.0	-	1.7	340	0.0	-	2.0	160
	NEW YORK HARBOR, Upper Bay																	
3396	Tompkinsville.........		40 38.1	74 03.6	-0 29	+0 20	+0 08	+0 20	0.9	1.0	0.0	-	1.6	004	0.0	-	2.0	172
3406	Bay Bridge Channel.........		40 39.0	74 02.0	-0 27	-0 50	-0 42	-0 36	0.6	0.6	0.0	-	1.0	039	0.0	-	1.1	218
3416	Red Hook Channel.........		40 40.0	74 01.2	-1 03	-0 44	-0 08	-0 30	0.6	0.4	0.0	-	1.0	353	0.0	-	0.7	170
3426	Robbins Reef Light, east of.........		40 39.45	74 03.48	+0 16	+0 16	+0 02	+0 24	0.8	1.2	0.0	-	1.3	016	0.0	-	1.6	204
3436	Red Hook, 1 mile west of.........		40 40.5	74 02.5	+0 41	+1 06	+0 47	+0 52	0.8	1.2	0.0	-	1.3	024	0.0	-	2.3	206
3446	Statue of Liberty, east of.........		40 41.4	74 01.8	+0 57	+0 58	+0 56	+0 59	0.8	1.0	0.0	-	1.4	031	0.0	-	1.9	205

Endnotes can be found at the end of Table 2.

TABLE 2. - CURRENT DIFFERENCES AND OTHER CONSTANTS, 1983

NO.	PLACE	METER DEPTH (ft)	POSITION Lat. (°′N)	POSITION Long. (°′W)	TIME DIFFERENCES Min. before Flood (h.m.)	Flood (h.m.)	Min. before Ebb (h.m.)	Ebb (h.m.)	SPEED RATIOS Flood	Ebb	Minimum before Flood (knots deg.)	Maximum Flood (knots deg.)	Minimum before Ebb (knots deg.)	Maximum Ebb (knots deg.)
	HUDSON RIVER, Midchannel <20> Time meridian, 75°W				on THE NARROWS, p.52									
3456	The Battery, northwest of..........		40 43	74 02	+1 41	+1 26	+1 21	+1 46	0.9	1.2	0.0 --	1.5 015	0.0 --	2.3 194
3466	Desbrosses Street.................		40 43	74 01	+1 43	+1 30	+1 24	+1 52	0.9	1.2	0.0 --	1.5 010	0.0 --	2.3 --
3476	Chelsea Docks.....................		40 45	74 01	+1 27	+1 42	+1 32	+1 38	1.0	1.0	0.0 --	1.7 018	0.0 --	2.0 187
3486	Forty-second Street...............		40 46	74 00	+1 51	+1 41	+1 34	+2 00	1.0	1.2	0.0 --	1.7 030	0.0 --	2.3 --
3496	Ninety-sixth Street...............		40 48	73 59	+1 57	+1 48	+1 42	+2 07	1.0	1.2	0.0 --	1.7 030	0.0 --	2.3 --
3506	Grants Tomb, 123d Street..........		40 49	73 58	+1 59	+1 53	+1 45	+2 10	0.9	1.2	0.0 --	1.6 025	0.0 --	2.3 --
3516	George Washington Bridge..........		40 51	73 57	+1 41	+1 55	+1 50	+2 04	0.9	1.1	0.0 --	1.6 020	0.0 --	2.2 200
3526	Spuyten Duyvil....................		40 53	73 56	+2 11	+2 08	+1 57	+2 24	0.9	1.1	0.0 --	1.6 020	0.0 --	2.1 --
3536	Riverdale.........................		40 54	73 55	+2 11	+2 07	+2 02	+2 32	0.8	1.0	0.0 --	1.4 015	0.0 --	2.0 200
3546	Dobbs Ferry.......................		41 01	73 53	+2 30	+2 33	+2 24	+2 49	0.6	0.8	0.0 --	1.3 010	0.0 --	1.5 --
3556	Tarrytown.........................		41 05	73 53	+2 37	+2 46	+2 40	+3 02	0.6	0.8	0.0 --	1.1 000	0.0 --	1.3 --
3566	Ossining..........................		41 10	73 54	+2 50	+3 02	+3 05	+3 19	0.5	0.7	0.0 --	0.9 320	0.0 --	1.3 --
3576	Haverstraw........................		41 12	73 57	+2 55	+3 08	+3 13	+3 26	0.5	0.7	0.0 --	0.8 335	0.0 --	1.2 --
3586	Peekskill.........................		41 17	73 57	+3 10	+3 24	+3 33	+3 42	0.5	0.6	0.0 --	0.8 000	0.0 --	1.1 185
3596	Bear Mountain Bridge..............		41 19	73 59	+3 21	+3 31	+3 39	+3 48	0.5	0.6	0.0 --	1.0 005	0.0 --	1.2 --
3606	Highland Falls....................		41 22	73 58	+3 24	+3 37	+3 44	+4 02	0.6	0.6	0.0 --	1.0 010	0.0 --	1.1 --
3616	West Point, off Duck Island.......		41 24	73 57	+3 32	+3 47	+3 51	+4 04	0.5	0.6	0.0 --	0.9 005	0.0 --	1.1 --
3625	Newburgh..........................		41 30	74 00	+3 50	+4 06	+4 03	+4 21	0.6	0.6	0.0 --	1.0 005	0.0 --	1.1 --
3636	New Hamburg.......................		41 35	73 57	+4 05	+4 20	+4 11	+4 33	0.6	0.7	0.0 --	1.1 005	0.0 --	1.2 --
3646	Poughkeepsie......................		41 42	73 57	+4 26	+4 37	+4 21	+4 49	0.6	0.7	0.0 --	1.1 005	0.0 --	1.3 --
3656	Hyde Park.........................		41 47	73 57	+4 42	+4 48	+4 30	+5 00	0.7	0.8	0.0 --	1.2 005	0.0 --	1.3 --
3666	Kingston Point <21>..............		41 56	73 57	+5 09	+5 09	+4 54	+5 19	0.8	0.8	0.0 --	1.3 005	0.0 --	1.6 --
3676	Barrytown.........................		42 00	73 56	+5 26	+5 21	+5 10	+5 26	0.8	0.9	0.0 --	1.4 010	0.0 --	1.7 --
3686	Saugerties........................		42 04	73 56	+5 43	+5 42	+5 29	+5 36	0.9	1.0	0.0 --	1.5 000	0.0 --	1.9 --
3696	Silver Point......................		42 09	73 54	+6 01	+6 14	+5 49	+5 50	0.9	1.0	0.0 --	1.5 030	0.0 --	2.0 --
3706	Catskill..........................		42 13	73 51	+6 16	+6 37	+6 09	+6 15	0.9	1.0	0.0 --	1.6 030	0.0 --	2.0 --
3716	Hudson............................		42 15	73 48	+6 23	+6 45	+6 20	+6 44	0.9	0.9	0.0 --	1.6 350	0.0 --	1.8 --
3726	Coxsackie.........................		42 21	73 47	+6 45	+6 57	+6 55	+7 09	0.8	0.8	0.0 --	1.3 355	0.0 --	1.5 --
3736	New Baltimore.....................		42 27	73 47	+7 12	+7 04	+7 13	+7 29	0.5	0.6	0.0 --	0.9 015	0.0 --	1.2 --
3746	Castleton-on-Hudson...............		42 32	73 46	+7 35	+7 11	+7 12	+7 46	0.4	0.4	0.0 --	0.3 020	0.0 --	0.8 --
3756	Albany............................		42 39	73 45	+8 29	+7 32	+6 46	+7 47	0.2	--	0.0 --	-- --	0.0 --	0.7 190
3766	Troy (below the locks) <22>......		42 44	73 42	- -	- -	- -	- -	--	--	-- --	-- --	-- --	-- --
	NEW YORK HARBOR, Lower Bay													
3776	False Hook Channel................		40 28.4	74 00.0	-2 07	-1 36	-1 22	-1 28	1.1	0.7	0.0 --	1.8 320	0.0 --	1.4 135
3786	Sandy Hook, 1.7 miles ENE of north tip..		40 29.7	73 59.0	-1 48	-1 38	-1 06	-1 48	0.8	0.8	0.0 --	1.5 295	0.0 --	1.7 100
3796	Sandy Hook & South Channels, junction..		40 28.9	73 59.6	-1 28	-1 24	-1 13	-1 16	0.8	0.8	0.0 --	1.3 300	0.0 --	1.7 113
3806	Sandy Hook Chan., 0.4 mi. W of north tip		40 28.79	74 01.30	-1 51	-1 55	-1 30	-1 50	1.2	0.8	0.0 --	2.0 235	0.0 --	1.6 050
3816	Sandy Hook Pt., 2 mi W of (channel).....		40 28.8	74 03.6	-1 45	-2 00	-1 50	-1 42	0.4	0.3	0.0 --	0.6 263	0.0 --	0.6 086
3826	Chapel Hill South Channel.........		40 29.90	74 02.8	-2 12	-2 30	-1 40	-2 08	0.4	0.3	0.0 --	0.7 255	0.0 --	0.6 075
3836	New Dorp Beach, 1.2 miles south of......		40 32.4	74 05.8	-4 19	-3 36	-4 35	-4 16	0.2	0.2	0.0 --	0.4 225	0.0 --	0.5 030
3846	Old Orchard Shoal Lt., 1.2 mi. ENE of...		40 31.1	74 04.36	-2 19	-2 07	-1 23	-2 02	0.4	0.2	0.0 --	0.7 270	0.0 --	0.4 085
3856	New Dorp Beach, 1.8 miles SE of <23>....		40 32.9	74 03.7	- -	- -	- -	- -	0.3	0.3	0.0 --	0.5 045	0.0 --	0.5 225
3866	Midland Beach, 2.6 miles SE of <24>.....		40 32.8	74 02.35	+0 00	+0 07	0 00	+0 01	0.6	0.6	0.2 270	0.8 335	0.0 --	1.3 160
3876	Coney Island Lt., 1.5 miles SSE of......		40 33.1	74 00.3	-1 27	-1 56	-0 58	-0 53	0.6	0.6	0.0 --	1.1 310	0.2 068	1.3 125

Endnotes can be found at the end of Table 2.

TABLE 2. - CURRENT DIFFERENCES AND OTHER CONSTANTS, 1903

NO.	PLACE	METER DEPTH (ft)	Lat. N	Long. W	Min. before Flood h.m.	Flood h.m.	Min. before Ebb h.m.	Ebb h.m.	Speed Ratio Flood	Speed Ratio Ebb	Min. before Flood knots	deg	Max. Flood knots	deg	Min. before Ebb knots	deg	Max. Ebb knots	deg
	DELAWARE BAY and RIVER Time meridian, 75°W				on DELAWARE BAY ENTRANCE, p. 58													
4206	Ben Davis Point, 0.8 mile southwest of..		39 16.9	75 18.2	+0 56	+0 59	+1 21	+1 00	0.7	0.4	0.0	--	1.2	308	0.0	--	0.8	122
4211	Cohansey River, 0.5 mile above entrance.		39 20.9	75 21.6	+1 29	+1 21	+1 39	+1 28	0.7	0.7	0.0	--	1.2	074	0.0	--	1.4	254
4216	Bridgeton (Broad Street Bridge) <1>..		39 25.6	75 14.2	--	+2 28	--	+2 31	0.1	0.2	0.0	--	0.2	000	0.0	--	0.3	180
4221	Arnold Point, channel abreast of......		39 22.5	75 27.8	+2 25	+2 18	+2 03	+2 26	1.1	1.1	0.0	--	2.0	336	0.0	--	2.1	156
4226	Smyrna River entrance............		39 21.9	75 30.8	+1 48	+1 42	+2 05	+2 07	0.7	0.8	0.0	--	1.2	250	0.0	--	1.5	070
4231	Stony Point, channel west of.........		39 27.1	75 33.8	+3 23	+2 50	+2 38	+3 06	0.8	1.0	0.0	--	1.5	324	0.0	--	1.9	151
4236	Appoquinimink River entrance.........		39 26.8	75 34.9	+2 33	+2 55	+2 22	+2 34	0.6	0.6	0.0	--	1.0	231	0.0	--	1.2	040
4241	Reedy Island (off end of pier).......		39 30.7	75 33.4	+3 01	+3 01	+2 54	+3 23	1.3	1.4	0.0	--	2.4	027	0.0	--	2.6	194
4246	Alloway Creek ent., 0.2 mile above.....		39 29.9	75 31.5	+2 21	+2 42	+2 19	+1 56	1.2	1.1	0.0	--	2.1	129	0.0	--	2.1	325
4251	New Bridge, Alloway Creek............		39 31.6	75 27.1	+3 03	+3 57	+3 36	+3 36	0.7	0.7	0.0	--	1.3	090	0.0	--	1.4	270
4256	Reedy Point, 0.4 mile east of.........		39 33.53	75 33.13	+3 18	+3 02	+2 54	+4 00	1.0	1.2	0.0	--	1.8	333	0.0	--	2.3	166
4261	Reedy Point, 1.1 miles east of........		39 33.58	75 32.47	+3 19	+3 11	+3 08	+3 36	1.0	0.9	0.0	--	1.8	354	0.0	--	1.7	179
4266	Salem River entrance.................		39 34.2	75 30.1	+3 46	+3 33	+3 37	+4 09	0.8	0.8	0.0	--	1.5	062	0.0	--	1.6	245
4271	Bulkhead Shoal Channel, off Del. City..		39 35.0	75 35.2	+3 16	+2 58	+3 03	+3 44	1.2	1.1	0.0	--	2.1	308	0.0	--	2.1	138
4276	Pea Patch Island, channel east of.....		39 36.0	75 33.9	+3 30	+3 13	+3 33	+3 19	1.3	1.2	0.0	--	2.3	319	0.0	--	2.3	148
4281	Penns Neck, 0.6 mile west of.........		39 37.05	75 34.92	+3 38	+3 38	+3 14	+3 31	0.9	0.9	0.0	--	1.7	002	0.0	--	1.7	167
4286	Penns Neck, 0.3 mile west of.........		39 37.07	75 34.58	+3 22	+3 07	+3 08	+3 37	1.0	0.9	0.0	--	1.8	339	0.0	--	1.7	152
4291	New Castle, channel abreast of........		39 39.1	75 33.2	+4 04	+3 21	+3 34	+4 01	1.1	1.3	0.0	--	1.9	051	0.0	--	2.4	230
4296	Kelly Point, 0.2 mile northwest of....		39 38.9	75 32.8	+3 43	+3 55	+3 24	+3 31	0.9	0.8	0.0	--	1.6	049	0.0	--	1.5	230
4301	Deepwater Point, channel northwest of.		39 42.1	75 30.6	+3 44	+3 54	+3 45	+3 55	1.7	1.4	0.0	--	3.0	029	0.0	--	2.6	215
4306	Christina River, 1 mile above entrance.		39 43	75 32	+3 16	+3 01	+2 58	+2 44	0.4	0.5	0.0	--	0.7	300	0.0	--	0.9	050
4311	Cherry Island Flats, channel east of..		39 44.3	75 29.1	+4 09	+4 08	+4 02	+3 57	0.9	0.7	0.0	--	1.6	027	0.0	--	1.4	207
4316	Oldsmans Point......................		39 45.9	75 28.4	+4 28	+3 42	+4 03	+4 40	0.9	0.8	0.0	--	1.6	027	0.0	--	1.5	210
4321	Marcus Hook.........................		39 48.2	75 24.6	+4 58	+4 19	+4 02	+4 51	0.9	0.8	0.0	--	1.7	061	0.0	--	1.6	232
4326	Eddystone...........................		39 50.8	75 20.5	+5 25	+4 41	+4 31	+4 55	0.9	1.2	0.0	--	1.7	058	0.0	--	2.2	242
4331	Essington Harbor....................		39 51.5	75 18.3	+4 09	+3 54	+4 04	+4 58	0.8	0.6	0.0	--	1.4	096	0.0	--	1.2	274
4336	Crab Point, 0.5 mile east of.........		39 50.8	75 17.0	+4 48	+4 44	+4 44	+4 58	1.2	1.0	0.0	--	2.1	094	0.0	--	1.9	268
4341	Hog Island, channel southeast of.....		39 52.0	75 12.9	+4 53	+4 53	+4 42	+4 52	1.1	1.2	0.0	--	1.9	054	0.0	--	2.2	231
4346	Schuylkill River entrance <1>.......		39 53.2	75 11.7	--	+3 20	--	+4 08	0.3	0.2	0.0	--	0.5	356	0.0	--	0.4	178
4351	Gloucester..........................		39 53.4	75 08.1	+5 13	+5 02	+4 53	+5 00	1.2	1.1	0.0	--	2.2	020	0.0	--	2.0	210
4356	Greenwich Point, northeast of.......		39 54.5	75 07.6	+5 18	+4 53	+4 54	+5 01	0.9	0.8	0.0	--	1.6	002	0.0	--	1.6	188
4361	Camden Marine Terminals, E of Chan. <29>		39 56.4	75 08.2	+5 52	+5 13	+5 16	+5 07	0.8	0.9	0.0	--	1.3	005	0.0	--	1.1	174
4366	Fisher Point........................		39 58.6	75 04.2	+6 07	+5 46	+5 23	+5 06	0.8	0.8	0.0	--	1.4	041	0.0	--	1.7	223
4371	Torresdale, west of channel.........		40 02.4	74 59.4	+6 54	+5 56	+4 59	+5 46	0.5	0.5	0.0	--	0.9	044	0.0	--	1.6	223
4376	Rancocas Creek, off Delanco.........		40 02.6	74 57.6	+6 36	+6 25	+5 51	+6 08	0.6	0.6	0.0	--	1.0	090	0.0	--	0.9	272
4381	Bristol, south of...................		40 05.3	74 52.6	+6 55	+5 31	+4 57	+6 10	0.7	0.8	0.0	--	1.3	024	0.0	--	1.6	200
4386	Burlington Island, channel east of...	8	40 05.7	74 50.2	+7 32	+5 46	+4 16	+6 46	0.5	0.9	0.0	--	0.9	018	0.0	--	1.8	204
4391	Whitehill <30>......................		40 08.2	74 44.2	--	--	--	+7 07	--	0.7	0.0	--	--	--	0.0	--	1.4	233
	DEL., MD. and VA. COAST																	
4396	Indian River Inlet (bridge).........		38 37	75 04	--	+0 05	--	+0 10	1.0	1.1	0.0	--	1.8	265	0.0	--	2.1	085
4401	Fenwick Shoal Lighted Whistle Buoy 2..		38 25	74 46	See table 5.													
4406	Winter-Quarter Shoal Buoy 6WQS <31>...		37 55	74 56	See table 5.													

Endnotes can be found at the end of Table 2.

TABLE 2. - CURRENT DIFFERENCES AND OTHER CONSTANTS, 1983

NO.	PLACE	METER DEPTH (ft)	POSITION Lat. (° ′ N)	POSITION Long. (° ′ W)	TIME DIFF. Min. before Flood (h.m.)	TIME DIFF. Flood (h.m.)	TIME DIFF. Min. before Ebb (h.m.)	TIME DIFF. Ebb (h.m.)	SPEED RATIOS Flood	SPEED RATIOS Ebb	AVG Min. before Flood (knots deg.)	AVG Maximum Flood (knots deg.)	AVG Min. before Ebb (knots deg.)	AVG Maximum Ebb (knots deg.)
	DEL., MD. and VA. COAST Time meridian, 75°W													
4411	Cape Charles, 70 miles east of........		37 05	74 51	See table 5.									
4416	Smith Island Shoal, southeast of......	7	37 05.3	75 43.5	-2 14	-2 12	-2 04	-2 05	0.3	0.3	0.0 --	0.3 298	0.0 --	0.4 068
4421	Chesapeake Light, 4.4 miles northeast of		36 59	75 42	See table 5.									
4426	Cape Henry Light, 2.2 miles southeast of		36 53.9	75 58.7	-1 54	-1 18	-0 39	-1 41	1.0	0.6	0.0 --	1.0 346	0.0 --	0.9 165
	on CHESAPEAKE BAY ENTRANCE, p.64													
	CHESAPEAKE BAY													
4431	Cape Henry Light, 1 mile north of......		36 56.4	76 00.5	+0 04	-0 25	-0 08	-0 25	1.1	1.3	0.0 --	1.1 280	0.0 --	2.0 090
4436	Cape Henry Light, 1.8 miles north of...		36 57.4	76 00.1	-0 23	-0 11	+0 10	-0 17	1.2	1.0	0.0 --	1.2 292	0.0 --	1.5 099
4441	CHESAPEAKE BAY ENTRANCE................	7	36 58.8	76 00.4	Daily predictions						0.0 --	1.0 306	0.0 --	1.5 126
4446	Cape Henry Light, 4.6 miles north of...		37 00.1	75 59.3	-1 05	-0 46	-0 10	-0 54	1.3	0.9	0.0 --	1.3 294	0.0 --	1.3 104
4451	Cape Charles Light, 9.5 mi. WSW of.....	C	37 03.7	76 05.4	-0 12	+0 08	+0 32	-0 05	1.5	0.7	0.0 --	1.5 319	0.0 --	1.4 126
4456	Cape Henry Light, 8.3 mi. northwest of.		37 02.2	76 06.6	-0 22	-0 12	+0 16	-0 05	1.0	0.7	0.0 --	1.0 329	0.0 --	1.1 133
4461	Lynnhaven Roads.......................		36 55.1	76 04.9	-0 58	-0 37	-0 14	-0 41	0.8	0.6	0.0 --	0.8 280	0.0 --	0.9 070
4466	Lynnhaven Inlet bridge................		36 54.4	76 05.6	-1 56	-2 05	-2 12	-3 01	0.6	0.9	0.0 --	0.6 180	0.0 --	1.4 000
	Chesapeake Bay Bridge Tunnel													
4471	Chesapeake Beach, 1.5 miles north of..		36 56.69	76 07.33	-0 09	-0 07	-0 23	-0 31	0.8	0.6	0.0 --	0.8 305	0.0 --	0.9 100
4476	Thimble Shoal Channel.................		36 58.33	76 06.67	-0 53	-0 46	-0 24	-0 39	1.4	0.9	0.0 --	1.4 310	0.0 --	1.3 095
4481	Tail of the Horseshoe.................		36 59.57	76 06.20	-0 25	-0 25	-0 13	-0 59	0.9	0.7	0.0 --	0.9 300	0.0 --	1.0 110
4486	Middle Ground, channel west of.......		37 03.00	76 05.00	-0 10	-0 20	-0 36	+0 04	1.6	0.9	0.0 --	1.6 335	0.0 --	1.3 150
4491	Chesapeake Channel....................		37 02.50	76 04.33	-0 33	-0 17	+0 03	-0 12	1.8	1.0	0.0 --	1.8 335	0.0 --	1.6 145
4496	Fisherman Island, 3.2 miles WSW of...		37 04.00	76 02.25	-1 05	-1 07	-0 46	-1 07	1.2	1.1	0.0 --	1.2 330	0.0 --	1.6 135
4501	Fisherman Island, 1.4 miles WSW of...		37 04.78	76 00.25	-1 47	-0 57	-0 41	-1 33	1.8	0.7	0.0 --	1.8 330	0.0 --	1.1 140
4506	Fisherman I., 1.8 miles south of......		37 03.58	75 58.77	-1 04	-1 00	-0 27	-1 24	1.6	0.9	0.0 --	1.6 320	0.0 --	1.4 120
4511	Fisherman I., 0.4 mile west of........		37 05.57	75 59.33	-0 59	-1 03	-0 35	-1 13	2.0	1.3	0.0 --	2.0 005	0.0 --	2.0 175
4516	Fisherman I., 1.1 miles northwest of..		37 06.50	76 00.00	-1 17	-0 35	-0 06	-0 50	1.8	1.1	0.0 --	1.8 355	0.0 --	1.6 165
4521	Cape Charles, off Wise Point..........	5	37 06.88	75 58.30	-0 29	-0 18	+0 27	+0 49	0.7	0.1	0.0 --	0.7 305	0.0 --	0.2 075
	Little Creek													
4526	North of east jetty..................	10	36 56.05	76 10.60	-2 00	-2 02	-1 42	-1 59	0.9	0.7	0.0 --	0.9 280	0.0 --	1.0 076
4531	0.5 mile north of west jetty.........	10	36 56.32	76 10.81	-1 37	-1 03	-0 42	-1 31	0.9	0.6	0.0 --	0.9 274	0.0 --	0.9 108
4536	Old Plantation Flats Light, west of..		37 14.0	76 04.1	+0 53	+1 06	+1 26	+0 35	1.2	0.9	0.0 --	1.2 005	0.0 --	1.3 175
4541	York Spit Channel....................	7	37 12.9	76 08.5	+0 55	+0 55	+1 05	+0 55	0.8	0.7	0.0 --	0.8 010	0.0 --	1.1 195
4546	Wolf Trap Light, 0.5 mile west of....		37 23.4	76 11.9	+1 05	+1 05	+1 05	+1 45	1.0	0.8	0.0 --	1.0 015	0.0 --	1.2 190
4551	Wolf Trap Light, 5.8 miles east of...		37 23.1	76 04.3	+1 45	+1 45	+1 45	+2 01	0.9	0.9	0.0 --	0.9 015	0.0 --	1.3 175
4556	Stingray Point, 5.5 miles east of....		37 35.0	76 10.4	+1 50	+2 41	+2 52	+2 05	1.0	0.6	0.0 --	1.0 343	0.0 --	0.9 179
4561	Stingray Point, 12.5 miles east of...		37 33.8	76 02.3	+1 40	+2 05	+1 40	+2 01	1.0	0.5	0.0 --	1.0 030	0.0 --	0.8 175
4566	Smith Point, 4.5 miles east of.......		37 52.9	76 08.6	+3 11	+3 14	+3 14	+3 15	0.7	0.5	0.0 --	0.7 352	0.0 --	0.8 163
4571	Smith Point Light, 6 miles north of..		37 58.9	76 11.4	+3 50	+3 35	+3 50	+3 35	0.4	0.7	0.0 --	0.4 350	0.0 --	1.0 135
4576	Point Lookin.........................		38 06.6	76 13.1	+4 35	+4 35	+4 35	+4 15	0.4	0.3	0.0 --	0.4 010	0.0 --	0.5 160
4581	Point No Point.......................		38 09.1	76 14.0	+5 15	+5 10	+5 15	+5 10	0.4	0.4	0.0 --	0.4 355	0.0 --	0.6 150
	on BALTIMORE HARBOR APPROACH, p.70													
4586	Cedar Point, 3.2 miles east of.......		38 18.3	76 18.35	-- --	-2 49	-- --	-3 32	0.2	0.8	0.0 --	0.2 030	0.0 --	0.6 175
4591	Cedar Point, 1.1 miles ENE of........		38 18.27	76 21.10	-3 23	-2 50	-2 36	-3 42	0.5	0.8	0.0 --	0.4 010	0.0 --	0.6 185
4596	Drum Point, 2.8 miles northeast of...		38 20.18	76 21.95	-- --	-3 12	-- --	-2 42	0.2	0.5	0.0 --	0.2 335	0.0 --	0.4 185

Endnotes can be found at the end of Table 2.

TABLE 2. – CURRENT DIFFERENCES AND OTHER CONSTANTS, 1983

CHESAPEAKE BAY
Time meridian, 75°W — on BALTIMORE HARBOR APPROACH, p.70

NO.	PLACE	METER DEPTH (ft)	POSITION Lat. N (° ')	POSITION Long. W (° ')	TIME DIFF. Min. before Flood (h.m.)	TIME DIFF. Flood (h.m.)	TIME DIFF. Min. before Ebb (h.m.)	TIME DIFF. Ebb (h.m.)	SPEED RATIOS Flood	SPEED RATIOS Ebb	AVG Min. before Flood (knots)	(deg.)	AVG Maximum Flood (knots)	(deg.)	AVG Min. before Ebb (knots)	(deg.)	AVG Maximum Ebb (knots)	(deg.)
4601	Cove Point, 0.6 mile northeast of......		38 23.45	76 22.19	-2 55	-3 04	-3 04	-2 51	0.9	1.0	0.0	-	0.7	330	0.0	-	0.8	155
4606	Cove Point, 2.5 miles east of..........		38 23.2	76 19.8	-2 39	-2 48	-2 44	-2 45	0.6	0.8	0.0	-	0.5	310	0.0	-	0.6	155
4611	Cove Point, 3.3 miles east of..........		38 23.65	76 18.95	-3 18	-3 41	-3 48	-3 20	0.5	0.4	0.0	-	0.4	320	0.0	-	0.5	160
4616	Kenwood Beach, 1.5 miles northeast of..		38 31.1	76 28.9	-1 56	-2 41	-2 46	-2 37	0.2	0.4	0.0	-	0.2	340	0.0	-	0.3	160
4621	James Island, 3.4 miles west of........		38 31.5	76 25.2	-2 16	-2 39	-3 01	-2 02	0.5	0.4	0.0	-	0.4	005	0.0	-	0.3	175
4626	James Island, 2.5 miles WNW of.........		38 32.0	76 23.6	-2 31	-2 42	-2 18	-2 36	0.5	0.6	0.0	-	0.4	000	0.0	-	0.5	175
4631	Plum Point, 1.4 miles ESE of...........		38 36.75	76 28.65	-1 31	-1 37	-2 20	-2 04	0.2	0.7	0.0	-	0.2	000	0.0	-	0.6	155
4636	Sharps Island, 3.3 miles WNW of........		38 38.13	76 26.00	- -	-1 30	- -	-1 57	0.5	0.4	0.0	-	0.4	345	0.0	-	0.3	185
4641	Holland Point, 1.6 miles east of.......		38 43.47	76 29.58	-1 05	-0 52	-1 20	-1 20	0.5	0.8	0.0	-	0.3	010	0.0	-	0.6	180
4646	Holland Point, 6.2 miles east of.......		38 43.9	76 23.8	-2 02	-2 07	-1 31	-1 44	0.4	0.3	0.0	-	0.3	355	0.0	-	0.6	135
4651	Holland Point, 4.7 miles ENE of........		38 44.7	76 26.0	-0 50	-0 38	-1 05	-0 45	0.2	0.8	0.0	-	0.2	340	0.0	-	0.6	180
4656	Kent Point, 4 miles southwest of.......		38 47.50	76 26.00	-1 03	-1 04	-1 11	-1 05	0.6	0.6	0.0	-	0.5	025	0.0	-	0.5	210
4661	Kent Point, 1.3 miles south of.........		38 49.00	76 21.85	-3 27	-3 38	-3 53	-3 47	0.6	0.5	0.0	-	0.4	055	0.0	-	0.4	235
4666	Horseshoe Point, 1.7 miles east of.....		38 50.30	76 27.20	-0 52	-0 39	-0 49	-1 10	0.6	0.6	0.0	-	0.5	005	0.0	-	0.5	200
4671	Bloody Point Bar Light, 0.6 mi. NW of..		38 50.37	76 24.17	-0 08	-0 23	-0 05	-0 05	0.9	0.6	0.0	-	0.7	035	0.0	-	0.5	190
4676	Thomas Pt. Shoal Lt., 1.8 mi. SW of....	19	38 52.50	76 27.70	-2 24	-2 27	-1 43	-2 17	0.5	0.4	0.0	-	0.4	340	0.0	-	0.3	190
4681	Thomas Pt. Shoal Lt., 0.4 mi. SE of....		38 53.85	76 25.77	-0 14	-0 40	-1 06	-0 53	0.9	1.1	0.0	-	0.7	010	0.0	-	0.9	185
4686	Tolly Point, 1.6 miles east of.........		38 56.07	76 25.02	-0 03	-0 19	-0 32	-0 24	0.9	0.9	0.0	-	0.5	355	0.0	-	0.7	190
4691	Chesapeake Bay Bridge, main channel....		38 59.50	76 23.67	+0 16	+0 08	-0 17	+0 13	0.9	1.1	0.0	-	0.7	025	0.0	-	0.9	230
4696	BALTIMORE HBR. APP. (off Sandy Point)..		39 00.78	76 22.10	- -	-0 39	-1 17	-0 57	0.3	0.4	0.0	-	0.8	025	0.0	-	0.8	189
4701	Love Point, 1.3 miles ESE of..........		39 02.12	76 16.45	Daily predictions						0.0	-	0.3	170	0.0	-	0.3	345
4706	Love Point, 2.8 miles NNE of..........		39 04.7	76 16.3	Current weak and variable													
4711	Love Point, 2.5 miles north of........		39 04.78	76 18.73	-0 48	-0 39	+0 27	-0 07	0.8	0.5	0.0	-	0.6	055	0.0	-	0.4	240
4716	Craighill Channel, NE of Mountain Pt...		39 04.88	76 23.67	+0 28	+0 40	+0 25	+0 34	0.8	0.9	0.0	-	0.6	350	0.0	-	0.7	175
4721	Craighill Angle, right outside quarter.		39 07.70	76 23.27	+0 12	+0 27	+0 34	+0 23	0.6	0.6	0.0	-	0.5	345	0.0	-	0.5	170
4726	Sevenfoot Knoll Light, 0.8 mi. NE of..		39 09.83	76 23.67	-0 07	+0 44	+0 44	+0 27	0.5	0.2	0.0	-	0.4	345	0.0	-	0.2	160
4731	Swan Point, 2.1 miles west of.........		39 08.75	76 19.67	+1 16	+1 01	+1 05	+0 55	0.6	0.8	0.0	-	0.5	355	0.0	-	0.6	220
4736	Swan Point, 1.6 miles northwest of....		39 09.75	76 18.28	+0 53	+0 44	+0 38	+0 57	0.4	0.9	0.0	-	0.3	020	0.0	-	0.7	215
4741	North Point, 2.5 miles northeast of...	7	39 12.87	76 23.72	+1 25	+1 00	+0 53	+1 06	0.6	0.5	0.0	-	0.3	035	0.0	-	0.4	225
4746	Pooles Island, 4 miles southwest of...		39 13.60	76 19.88	+0 59	+0 48	+0 56	+1 12	0.9	0.8	0.0	-	0.5	025	0.0	-	0.6	210
4751	Tolchester Beach, 0.4 mile WNW of.....		39 13.13	76 15.08	+1 52	+1 37	+1 28	+1 35	0.9	1.2	0.0	-	0.7	015	0.0	-	0.9	225
4756	Pooles Island, 0.8 mile south of......		39 15.7	76 16.4	+1 29	+1 24	+1 12	+1 20	0.6	0.3	0.0	-	0.7	060	0.0	-	1.0	255
4761	Miller Island, 1.5 miles ENE of.......	7	39 16.5	76 19.9	+1 11	+0 15	+1 26	+0 25	1.0	1.5	0.0	-	0.5	000	0.0	-	1.2	185
4766	Pooles Island, 1.4 miles east of......		39 17.2	76 13.9	+1 48	+1 31	+1 37	+1 26	1.4	1.0	0.0	-	0.8	030	0.0	-	1.2	215
4771	Robins Point, 0.7 mile ESE of.........	5	39 17.75	76 16.10	-0 03	-0 14	+0 37	-0 13	1.4	1.5	0.0	-	1.1	025	0.0	-	0.8	210
4776	Worton Point, 1.1 miles northwest of..		39 19.9	76 12.0	+1 43	+1 43	+1 38	+1 32	1.1	1.1	0.0	-	1.1	040	0.0	-	1.2	245
4781	Howell Point, 0.4 mile NNW of.........		39 22.6	76 06.9	+1 28	+1 24	+1 20	+1 18	1.0	1.1	0.0	-	0.9	080	0.0	-	1.1	245
4786	Grove Point, 0.8 mile northwest of....		39 24.0	76 03.1	+1 54	+1 58	+1 41	+1 39	0.8	1.0	0.0	-	0.8	060	0.0	-	0.8	235
4791	Turkey Point, 1.4 miles WSW of........	7	39 26.25	76 02.08	+1 27	+1 19	+1 24	+1 22	0.6	0.9	0.0	-	0.6	030	0.0	-	0.7	220
4796	Spesutie Island, channel north of.....		39 28.83	76 04.90	+1 42	+1 20	+1 49	+1 40	0.6	0.6	0.0	-	0.6	285	0.0	-	0.5	100
4801	Rocky Point, 0.5 mile west of.........		39 29.2	76 00.2	+2 15	+2 15	+1 49	+2 15	0.9	0.6	0.0	-	0.5	030	0.0	-	0.6	190
4806	Red Point, 0.2 mile W of, Northeast R.	7	39 31.75	75 59.08	+1 42	+1 28	+1 57	+1 47	0.9	0.6	0.0	-	0.7	-	0.0	-	0.5	-
4811	Havre de Grace, Susquehanna River.....		39 33.13	76 05.08	Current weak and variable													

Endnotes can be found at the end of Table 2.

TABLE 2. – CURRENT DIFFERENCES AND OTHER CONSTANTS, 1983

NO.	PLACE	METER DEPTH (ft)	POSITION Lat. N (° ')	POSITION Long. W (° ')	TIME DIFF. Min. before Flood (h. m.)	TIME DIFF. Flood (h. m.)	TIME DIFF. Min. before Ebb (h. m.)	TIME DIFF. Ebb (h. m.)	SPEED RATIOS Flood	SPEED RATIOS Ebb	Minimum before Flood (knots)	Minimum before Flood (deg.)	Maximum Flood (knots)	Maximum Flood (deg.)	Minimum before Ebb (knots)	Minimum before Ebb (deg.)	Maximum Ebb (knots)	Maximum Ebb (deg.)
	MOBJACK BAY and PIANKATANK RIVER Time meridian, 75°W				on CHESAPEAKE BAY ENTRANCE, p.64													
5176	New Point Comfort, 1.5 miles west of....		37 17.7	76 18.4	-2 59	-1 58	-2 03	-2 48	0.6	0.3	0.0	--	0.6	320	0.0	--	0.5	130
5181	Bland Point, Piankatank River...........		37 31.8	76 21.9	-0 30	-0 30	-0 30	-0 30	0.4	0.1	0.0	--	0.4	300	0.0	--	0.2	125
5186	Doctor Point, 0.4 mile west of....		37 31.1	76 27.0	-0 28	-0 58	-1 17	-0 37	0.4	0.3	0.0	--	0.4	311	0.0	--	0.4	142
	RAPPAHANNOCK RIVER																	
5191	Mosquito Point, 0.9 mile SSE of....		37 35.72	76 21.08	+0 56	+1 31	+1 38	+0 41	0.7	0.6	0.0	--	0.7	265	0.0	--	0.8	090
5196	Mosquito Point............		37 35.8	76 21.5	+0 45	+0 45	+0 45	+0 45	0.6	0.4	0.0	--	0.6	290	0.0	--	0.6	115
5201	Orchard Point, 1.0 mile south of.......		37 37.97	76 27.45	+0 49	+1 35	+1 50	+0 52	0.5	0.4	0.0	--	0.5	270	0.0	--	0.6	085
5206	Millenbeck Wharf, Corrotoman River......		37 39.9	76 29.0	-- --	-- --	-- --	-- --	--	0.3	0.0	--	0.3	000	0.0	--	0.3	186
5211	Towles Point....		37 37.8	76 30.4	+1 06	+1 07	+2 10	+1 25	0.6	0.3	0.0	--	0.6	274	0.0	--	0.5	103
5216	Rogue Point, 0.8 mile WNW of....		37 40.28	76 33.20	-- --	+1 44	-- --	+1 27	0.6	0.4	0.0	--	0.6	000	0.0	--	0.6	195
5221	Waterview, 1.3 miles NNE of....		37 44.95	76 35.92	+1 41	+1 59	+2 46	+2 10	0.7	0.4	0.0	--	0.7	340	0.0	--	0.6	155
5226	Tarpley Point, 1.5 miles south of.......		37 46.15	76 39.12	+2 16	+2 37	+3 20	+2 39	0.7	0.5	0.0	--	0.7	300	0.0	--	0.7	105
5231	Jones Point, 1.4 miles NNW of.......		37 48.03	76 41.58	+2 04	+2 23	+3 19	+2 27	1.1	0.6	0.0	--	1.1	315	0.0	--	0.8	105
5236	Sharps, 1.2 miles south of.......		37 48.18	76 41.92	+2 19	+2 46	+3 52	+3 01	0.9	0.5	0.0	--	1.0	290	0.0	--	0.8	095
5241	Bowlers Rock, 0.2 mile north of.......		37 49.58	76 44.00	+2 27	+2 41	+3 37	+2 50	1.0	0.7	0.0	--	1.0	315	0.0	--	1.1	135
5246	Accaceek Point, 0.3 mile southwest of...		37 52.52	76 46.40	+2 40	+2 48	+3 27	+3 13	1.2	0.7	0.0	--	1.2	335	0.0	--	1.0	150
5251	Tappahannock Bridge, 1.8 miles SE of....		37 55.10	76 49.27	+3 08	+3 07	+3 56	+3 28	1.4	0.9	0.0	--	1.4	315	0.0	--	1.3	105
5256	Tappahannock Bridge.......		37 56.0	76 51.2	+3 40	+3 40	+3 40	+3 40	1.3	0.8	0.0	--	1.3	315	0.0	--	1.2	135
5261	Port Royal.....		38 10.5	77 11.4	+6 10	+6 10	+6 10	+6 10	0.7	0.5	0.0	--	0.7	310	0.0	--	0.7	130
	POCOMOKE SOUND																	
5266	Pocomoke Sound Approach............		37 38.00	75 57.90	-- --	+1 12	-- --	+1 31	0.7	0.5	0.0	--	0.7	009	0.0	--	0.7	196
5271	Pungoteague Creek entrance.....		37 40.48	75 51.90	-- --	-- --	-- --	-- --	--	--	0.0	--	0.3	094	0.0	--	0.2	254
5276	Watts Island, 4 miles south of.........	6	37 43.2	75 54.0	+0 17	+0 01	+0 27	-0 04	0.6	0.4	0.0	--	0.6	027	0.0	--	0.6	247
5281	Watts Island, 2.2 miles east of........	7	37 47.9	75 50.6	+0 44	+1 10	+1 40	+1 03	1.3	0.9	0.0	--	1.3	027	0.0	--	1.3	209
5286	Pocomoke R., 0.5 mile below Shelltown...		37 58.3	75 38.7	+3 30	+3 00	+3 30	+3 00	1.1	0.6	0.0	--	1.1	045	0.0	--	0.9	170
	TANGIER SOUND																	
5291	Tangier Sound Light, 1.5 miles NE of....		37 48.5	75 57.4	+1 30	+2 02	+2 15	+1 39	1.2	0.7	0.0	--	1.2	014	0.0	--	1.1	220
5296	Jane's Island............		38 00.0	75 54.5	+3 40	+3 25	+3 40	+3 25	0.9	0.6	0.0	--	0.9	000	0.0	--	0.9	210
5301	Kedges Straits, off Solomons Lump......		38 03.1	76 00.8	+0 20	+0 32	+0 50	+0 09	0.9	0.8	0.0	--	0.9	104	0.0	--	1.2	280
5306	Manokin River entrance........		38 05.5	75 53.6	-- --	+2 04	-- --	+2 32	0.9	0.4	0.0	--	0.9	019	0.0	--	0.6	182
5311	Deal Island, 0.9 mile west of........		38 08.2	75 58.7	+3 08	+3 26	+3 33	+3 15	0.9	0.7	0.0	--	0.9	354	0.0	--	1.0	179
5316	Frog Point, 1.6 miles south of.........		38 12.6	75 57.3	+3 19	+3 00	+3 41	+3 31	1.0	0.7	0.0	--	1.0	048	0.0	--	1.1	240
	Wicomico River																	
5321	Victor Point, 0.8 mile southwest of..		38 14.3	75 51.8	+3 10	+2 54	+3 49	+3 34	0.6	0.6	0.0	--	0.6	034	0.0	--	0.9	242
5326	Whitehaven...........		38 15.9	75 47.5	+2 56	+3 45	+4 02	+3 01	1.1	0.7	0.0	--	1.1	089	0.0	--	1.1	284
5331	Whitehaven, 2.5 miles above...........	4	38 17.8	75 45.5	+3 00	+3 13	+3 45	+2 55	1.0	0.7	0.0	--	1.0	006	0.0	--	1.1	188
5336	Salisbury, 2 miles below............	4	38 20.4	75 38.3	+3 23	+3 31	+4 03	+3 28	0.6	0.5	0.0	--	0.6	085	0.0	--	0.8	258
5341	Sandy Point, Nanticoke River...........		38 14.8	75 55.7	+3 14	+3 36	+4 21	+3 39	1.2	0.7	0.0	--	1.2	000	0.0	--	1.1	182

Endnotes can be found at the end of Table 2.

TABLE 2. – CURRENT DIFFERENCES AND OTHER CONSTANTS, 1983

NO.	PLACE	METER DEPTH (ft)	POSITION Lat. (N)	POSITION Long. (W)	TIME DIFF. Min. before Flood (h.m.)	TIME DIFF. Flood (h.m.)	TIME DIFF. Min. before Ebb (h.m.)	TIME DIFF. Ebb (h.m.)	SPEED RATIO Flood	SPEED RATIO Ebb	Min. before Flood (knots)	Min. before Flood (deg.)	Maximum Flood (knots)	Maximum Flood (deg.)	Min. before Ebb (knots)	Min. before Ebb (deg.)	Maximum Ebb (knots)	Maximum Ebb (deg.)
	PORT ROYAL SOUND Time meridian, 75°W																	
	on CHARLESTON HARBOR, p.82																	
6726	Beaufort River..................	15	32 24.2	80 40.3	+0 31	+0 45	+1 04	+0 21	0.4	0.4	0.1	286	0.9	012	0.0	--	1.0	200
6731	Beaufort, Beaufort River.......	12	32 25.8	80 40.6	+0 22	+0 44	+1 11	+0 05	0.6	0.5	0.0	--	1.1	073	0.0	--	1.1	257
6736	Beaufort Airport, Beaufort River	15	32 27.0	80 39.8	+0 52	+1 05	+1 24	+0 56	0.5	0.4	0.0	--	0.9	333	0.0	--	0.9	152
6741	Brickyard Creek................	10	32 28.4	80 41.5	+1 15	-0 04	+2 53	+2 46	0.4	0.4	0.0	--	0.8	351	0.0	--	0.8	171
6746	Skull Creek, north entrance....		32 15.8	80 44.5	-2 23	-1 54	-1 55	-2 26	0.4	0.5	0.0	--	0.7	222	0.0	--	1.2	035
6751	Daws Island, SE of, Broad River	15	32 18.1	80 43.5	+0 13	-0 29	+0 42	+0 19	0.7	0.7	0.0	--	1.4	330	0.1	048	1.5	150
6756	Parris Island Lookout Tower, Broad River	15	32 18.7	80 42.4	+0 06	-0 41	+0 32	+0 04	0.6	0.6	0.0	--	1.1	339	0.0	--	1.4	152
6761	Daws Island, south of, Chechessee River	15	32 17.2	80 44.6	-0 02	-0 56	+0 37	+0 19	0.5	0.6	0.1	232	1.0	317	0.1	048	1.3	142
6766	Lemon Island South, Chechessee River.	15	32 21.0	80 44.4	+0 09	+0 45	+0 41	-0 14	0.6	0.6	0.0	--	0.9	359	0.0	--	1.3	175
6771	Broad River Bridge, S of, Broad River.	15	32 22.9	80 46.6	+0 19	-0 49	+0 52	-0 05	0.6	0.6	0.0	--	1.1	341	0.0	--	1.5	156
6776	Byrd Creek Entrance, SE of, Broad River.	12	32 27.4	80 49.1	+0 54	+0 17	+1 35	+0 40	0.5	0.4	0.0	--	0.9	354	0.0	--	1.0	174
6781	Little Barnwell I., E of, Whale Branch R	6	32 30.1	80 47.2	+1 08	+2 29	+1 57	+0 28	0.5	0.4	0.0	--	1.0	354	0.0	--	0.8	175
	CALIBOGUE SOUND on SAVANNAH RIVER ENTRANCE, p.88																	
6786	Braddock Point, SW of, Calibogue Sound..	10	32 06.3	80 50.2	-0 55	+0 04	+0 11	-1 17	1.0	0.8	0.0	--	1.6	006	0.1	095	2.0	183
6791	Haig Point Light, NW of, Cooper River...	10	32 08.9	80 50.5	-1 31	-0 17	-0 25	-1 25	0.5	0.5	0.0	--	0.8	278	0.0	--	1.4	094
6796	Ramshorn Creek Light, E of, Cooper River	6	32 07.8	80 52.9	-0 34	-1 05	+0 30	-1 30	0.6	0.5	0.0	--	1.0	280	0.0	--	1.3	098
6801	Spanish Wells, Calibogue Sound..........	30	32 11.2	80 47.1	-0 54	+0 39	+0 27	-1 23	0.8	0.6	0.0	--	1.4	028	0.1	309	1.5	204
6806	Skull Creek, south entrance.............	10	32 13.4	80 47.1	-0 02	+2 45	+1 38	+0 42	0.5	0.4	0.0	--	0.7	053	0.0	--	0.9	231
6811	Mackay Creek, south entrance............	10	32 13.2	80 47.4	-0 34	-0 09	+0 27	-0 39	0.4	0.4	0.0	--	0.7	033	0.0	--	1.2	212
	NEW and WRIGHT RIVERS																	
6816	Bloody Pt., 0.5 mile north of, New R....		32 05.3	80 52.8	-1 43	-0 12	-0 38	-2 26	0.8	0.5	0.0	--	1.2	332	0.0	--	1.3	147
6821	Bloody Pt., 0.5 mile west of, New R.....		32 04.9	80 53.0	-1 27	-0 33	-0 21	-1 39	1.1	0.7	0.0	--	1.7	267	0.0	--	1.8	092
6826	Wright R., 0.2 mile above Walls Cut.....		32 05.1	80 55.3	-1 18	-0 28	-0 21	-1 29	0.7	0.6	0.0	--	1.2	332	0.0	--	1.6	142
6831	Fields Cut <39>.........................		32 05	80 57			-1 45	-2 04		0.7					0.0	--	1.9	042
6836	Walls Cut, Turtle Island................	6	32 04.9	80 55.0	-3 09	-1 09	-0 57	-3 18	0.6	0.4	0.2	087	1.0	294	0.1	060	0.9	100
6841	Daufuskie Landing Light, south of,......	10	32 06.1	80 53.9	-0 33	+0 52	+0 17	-1 58	0.9	0.7	0.0	--	1.5	043	0.0	--	1.7	226
	SAVANNAH RIVER See table 5. — Daily predictions																	
6851	Savannah Light, 1.2 miles southeast of..		31 57	80 40	+0 02	+0 39	+0 30	-0 04	1.1	1.2	0.0	--	1.6	260	0.0	--	2.6	082
6861	SAVANNAH RIVER ENT. (between jetties)...		32 02.2	80 51.5	-0 15	+0 06	+0 14	-0 01	1.4	1.1	0.0	--	1.8	283	0.0	--	3.1	098
6871	Fort Pulaski...........................		32 02.2	80 54.1	-0 04	+0 19	+0 21	-0 29	1.3	1.2	0.0	--	2.2	316	0.0	--	2.8	140
6881	Fort Pulaski, 1.8 miles above...........		32 02.7	80 55.9	-3 19	-2 57	-0 49	-2 57	0.4	0.5	0.0	--	2.1	296	0.0	--	3.0	116
6891	Fort Pulaski, 4.8 miles above...........		32 04.5	80 58.6		-0 25			0.2				0.7	251				
6896	McQueen Island Cut......................	10	32 03.9	80 59.2		-0 55			0.5				0.4	252			1.2	069
6901	Elba Island Cut, NE of, Savannah River..	10	32 04.4	80 57.9	-0 14	+0 03	-0 22	-0 27	0.9	1.0	0.1	202	1.4	288	0.1	183	2.6	104
6906	Elba Island, NE of, Savannah River.....	10	32 05.4	80 59.6	+0 21	+0 28	-0 20	-0 40	0.7	1.0	0.0	--	1.1	329	0.0	--	2.5	149
6911	Elba Island, west of, Savannah River...	10	32 05.7	81 01.2	-0 03	+0 04	-0 15	-1 06	0.6	0.6	0.0	--	0.9	219	0.0	--	1.6	040
6921	Fig Island, north of, Back River.......		32 05.1	81 03.0	-0 26	+0 54	-0 10	-1 13	0.6	0.6	0.0	--	1.0	280	0.0	--	1.5	094
6931	South Channel, western end.............		32 05.3	81 01.0	+0 02	+0 06	+0 18	-0 48	0.6	0.6	0.0	--	1.0	300	0.0	--	1.5	122

Endnotes can be found at the end of Table 2.

TABLE 2. - CURRENT DIFFERENCES AND OTHER CONSTANTS, 1983

NO.	PLACE	METER DEPTH (ft)	POSITION Lat. °N	POSITION Long. °W	TIME DIFFERENCES Min. before Flood h.m.	Flood h.m.	Min. before Ebb h.m.	Ebb h.m.	SPEED RATIOS Flood	Ebb	Minimum before Flood knots	deg.	Maximum Flood knots	deg.	Minimum before Ebb knots	deg.	Maximum Ebb knots	deg.
	BOCA CIEGA BAY and ST. JOSEPH SOUND Time meridian, 90°W				on TAMPA BAY ENTRANCE, p.112													
8731	The Narrows (Indian Rocks Beach Br.)....		27 52.6	82 51.0	-0 55	-0 38	-0 55	-1 16	0.5	0.2	0.0	--	0.6	180	0.0	--	0.2	000
8741	Clearwater Pass, 0.2 mi. NE of Sand Key.		27 57.4	82 49.4	-2 56	-3 02	-1 56	-2 12	1.3	0.8	0.0	--	1.3	179	0.0	--	1.1	348
8751	Clearwater Harbor....		27 57.9	82 48.4	-- --	-- --	-- --	-- --	--	--	0.0	--	0.4	021	0.0	--	0.3	214
8761	St. Joseph Sound, off....		28 05.0	82 55.0	-- --	-- --	-- --	-- --	--	--	0.0	--	0.4	018	0.0	--	0.6	195
					on MIAMI HARBOR ENTRANCE, p.100													
8771	Anclote Anchorage....		28 10.0	82 49.8	+2 42	+2 24	+2 28	+2 18	0.3	0.4	0.0	--	0.6	006	0.0	--	0.8	195
	APALACHEE BAY				on TAMPA BAY ENTRANCE, p.112													
8781	St. Marks River approach....		30 02.8	84 10.8	-1 29	-0 59	+0 12	-0 30	0.6	0.4	0.0	--	0.6	339	0.0	--	0.5	170
8791	Four Mile Point, St. Marks River....		30 06.7	84 12.2	-0 45	-0 27	+0 46	-0 48	0.4	0.3	0.0	--	0.4	358	0.0	--	0.4	187
8801	St. Marks, St. Marks River....		30 09.3	84 12.1	+1 06	+0 51	-0 01	+0 01	0.3	0.3	0.0	--	0.3	067	0.0	--	0.4	247
	PENSACOLA BAY Time meridian, 90°W				on MOBILE BAY ENTRANCE, p.118													
8811	Pensacola Bay entrance, midchannel....		30 20.1	87 18.0	-0 48	-0 31	+0 18	-1 15	1.1	1.2	0.0	--	1.6	074	0.0	--	1.8	256
	MOBILE BAY																	
8821	Main Ship Channel entrance....		30 09.2	88 03.2	-- --	+0 50	-- --	+0 50	0.5	0.7	0.2	235	0.7	344	0.0	175	1.0	182
8831	MOBILE BAY ENTRANCE (off Mobile Point).		30 13.6	88 02.1	Daily predictions						0.0	--	1.4	027	0.0	--	1.5	190
8841	Channel, 6 miles N of Mobile Point....		30 19.8	88 01.7	+0 15	+1 16	+1 26	+0 43	0.4	0.3	0.0	--	0.6	032	0.0	--	0.5	208
8851	Great Point Clear, channel west of....		30 29.4	88 01.1	Current weak and variable													
8861	Mobile River entrance....		30 40.2	88 02.0	+5 36	+4 54	+4 44	+2 45	0.2	0.5	0.0	--	0.3	333	0.0	--	0.7	151
8871	Tensaw River entrance (bridge)....		30 40.9	88 00.7	+2 04	+1 35	-1 00	-0 21	0.3	0.7	0.0	--	0.4	029	0.0	--	1.0	222
	Pass Aux Herons																	
8881	Entrance to Mississippi Sound <48>....		30 17.3	88 07.8	+0 09	+0 15	+0 22	+0 02	0.9	0.9	0.0	--	1.3	068	0.0	--	1.3	245
	MISSISSIPPI SOUND																	
8891	Pascagoula River highway bridge <27>....		30 22.3	88 33.8	-- --	+0 48	-- --	-1 02	0.9	0.8	0.0	--	1.2	016	0.0	--	1.2	201
	LOUISIANA COAST																	
8901	Quatre Bayoux Pass, Barataria Bay....		29 18.6	89 51.1	+1 37	+1 04	+0 43	+0 06	0.9	0.9	0.0	--	1.2	288	0.0	--	1.3	103
8911	Pass Abel, Barataria Bay....		29 17.7	89 54.2	+0 53	+1 00	+0 13	-0 03	0.6	1.1	0.0	--	0.9	317	0.0	--	1.6	143
8921	Barataria Pass, Barataria Bay....		29 16.3	89 56.9	+2 29	+1 23	+1 01	+0 19	1.1	0.9	0.0	--	1.5	315	0.0	--	1.3	120
8931	Barataria Bay, 1.1 mi. NE of Manila....		29 26.2	89 57.6	+4 41	+3 35	+3 10	+4 12	0.3	0.3	0.0	--	0.4	356	0.0	--	0.5	160
8941	Caminada Pass, Barataria Bay....		29 11.9	90 02.8	+1 44	+0 03	+0 56	+0 38	1.1	1.0	0.0	--	1.5	297	0.0	--	1.5	118
8951	Seabrook Bridge, New Orleans <1>....		30 01.9	90 02.1	-- --	+7 37	-- --	+7 57	0.9	0.6	0.0	--	1.2	350	0.0	--	0.9	170

Endnotes can be found at the end of Table 2.

TABLE 2. – CURRENT DIFFERENCES AND OTHER CONSTANTS, 1983

NO.	PLACE	METER DEPTH (ft)	POSITION Lat. ° ′ N	POSITION Long. ° ′ W	TIME DIFF. Min. before Flood h.m.	Flood h.m.	Min. before Ebb h.m.	Ebb h.m.	SPEED RATIOS Flood	Ebb	Min. before Flood (knots deg.)	Maximum Flood (knots deg.)	Min. before Ebb (knots deg.)	Maximum Ebb (knots deg.)
	LOUISIANA COAST Time meridian, 90°W				on GALVESTON BAY ENTRANCE, p.124									
8961	Cat Island Pass, Terrebonne Bay........		29 04.8	90 34.4	-2 45	-1 25	-2 40	-3 40	0.6	0.6	0.0 --	1.1 013	0.0 --	1.5 195
8971	Wine Island Pass........		29 04.2	90 38.0	-4 46	-4 31	-5 13	-4 58	1.0	0.8	0.0 --	1.7 325	0.0 --	1.9 160
8981	Caillou Boca, Caillou Bay........		29 03.5	90 48.5	-0 46	-0 09	+1 24	-0 46	0.8	0.3	0.0 --	1.3 095	0.0 --	0.7 264
8991	Calcasieu Pass........		29 46.4	93 20.7	-0 18	-0 43	+2 12	-0 44	1.0	1.0	0.0 --	1.7 020	0.0 --	2.3 205
9001	Calcasieu Pass, 35 miles south of.......		29 10.15	93 19.23	Current weak and variable				--	--	-- --	-- --	-- --	-- --
9011	Calcasieu Pass, 67 miles south of <49>..		28 39.80	93 19.95					--	--	-- --	-- --	-- --	-- --
	TEXAS													
	Sabine Pass													
9021	Texas Point, 1.7 miles SSE of........		29 39.0	93 49.6	-0 14	-0 34	-0 15	-0 21	0.6	0.7	0.0 --	1.1 335	0.0 --	1.6 145
9031	Sabine, channel east of........		29 43.3	93 51.7	-0 15	-0 02	-0 15	+0 04	0.9	0.7	0.0 --	1.6 335	0.0 --	1.7 140
9041	Port Arthur Canal entrance........		29 45.6	93 54.1	+0 53	+1 34	+0 55	+1 12	0.5	0.6	0.0 --	0.9 310	0.0 --	1.3 110
9051	Mesquite Pt., La. Causeway bridge.....		29 45.95	93 53.70	-0 21	-0 22	-0 20	-0 35	0.9	1.0	0.0 --	1.6 330	0.0 --	2.2 150
	GALVESTON BAY													
9061	GALVESTON BAY ENT. (between jetties)..		29 20.8	94 42.3	Daily predictions				1.0	0.8	0.0 --	1.7 299	0.0 --	2.3 102
9071	Bolivar Roads, 0.5 mi. N of Ft. Point..		29 20.8	94 46.1	+0 25	+0 26	+1 15	+0 14	0.6	0.4	0.0 --	1.7 287	0.0 --	1.8 111
9081	Quarantine Station, 0.3 mile S of <27>..		29 19.8	94 46.7	-- --	-1 21	-- --	-0 59	1.0	0.6	0.0 --	1.1 196	0.0 --	0.8 009
9091	Galveston Channel, west end <27>........		29 18.6	94 49.2	-- --	+0 01	-- --	-0 17	1.0	0.6	0.0 --	1.7 272	0.0 --	1.5 103
9101	Galveston Causeway RR. bridge........		29 17.80	94 53.13	-0 24	-0 32	-- --	+0 05	0.4	0.4	0.0 --	0.7 210	0.0 --	0.8 025
9111	Houston Channel, W of Port Bolivar......		29 21.8	94 47.8	+0 18	+0 35	+1 18	+0 24	0.8	0.6	0.0 --	1.3 330	0.0 --	1.4 166
9121	Houston Ship Channel (Red Fish Bar).....		29 30.2	94 52.5	+3 11	+1 51	+0 12	+1 29	0.8	0.8	0.0 --	1.3 321	0.0 --	1.8 146
	TEXAS COAST													
9131	Matagorda Channel (entrance jetty)......		28 25.3	96 19.4	-0 56	-0 28	-0 18	-1 14	1.2	0.8	0.0 --	2.0 317	0.0 --	1.9 142
9141	Aransas Pass........		27 50.1	97 02.65	+0 34	+1 03	+0 50	-0 08	0.5	0.5	0.0 --	0.9 312	0.0 --	1.2 116
9151	Sabine Bank <54>........		29 18.20	94 00.20	-- --	-- --	-- --	-- --	--	--	-- --	-- --	-- --	-- --
9161	Heald Bank, 28 miles SSE of <54>........		28 40.17	93 59.60	-- --	-- --	-- --	-- --	--	--	-- --	-- --	-- --	-- --
	PUERTO RICO Time meridian, 60°W				on VIEQUES PASSAGE, p.130									
9171	Punta Ostiones, 1.5 miles west of........		18 05.2	67 13.6	-0 26	-0 52	-0 04	-0 35	1.7	1.3	0.0 --	1.0 187	0.0 --	0.9 001
9181	VIEQUES PASSAGE........		18 11.3	65 37.1	Daily predictions				0.7	0.9	0.0 --	0.6 250	0.0 --	0.7 057
9191	Vieques Sound........		18 15.87	65 34.20	-0 44	-1 16	-1 28	-1 05	0.7	1.0	0.0 --	0.4 180	0.0 --	0.6 355
9201	Largo Shoals, west of........		18 19	65 35	-0 52	-1 28	-1 33	-1 08	0.3	0.1	0.0 --	0.4 186	0.0 --	0.7 330
9211	Ramos Cay, 0.3 mile SE of <1>........		18 18.6	65 36.4	-- --	-0 42	-- --	-0 44	0.3	0.7	0.0 --	0.2 120	0.0 --	0.1 284
9221	Palominos Island, 0.9 mile SW of <13>..		18 20.1	65 34.8	-- --	-- --	-- --	-0 48	--	0.6	0.0 --	-- --	-- --	0.5 307
9231	Fajardo Harbor (channel)........		18 20	65 37	-1 13	-1 52	-2 27	-1 45	0.5	1.6	0.0 --	0.3 162	-- --	1.1 339
9241	Isla Marina, 0.2 mile west of <1> <13>..		18 20.50	65 37.38	-- --	-- --	-- --	-2 06	--	1.0	-- --	-- --	-- --	0.7 335
9251	Coronala Laja, 0.4 mile NW of <1> <13>..		18 21.6	65 37.3	-- --	-- --	-- --	-1 33	--	0.4	-- --	-- --	-- --	0.3 000
9261	Pasaje de San Juan <1> <13>........		18 23.9	65 36.9	-- --	-- --	-- --	-1 15	--	1.7	-- --	-- --	-- --	1.2 310
9271	Bahia de San Juan........		18 27.23	66 06.6	Current weak and variable				--	--	-- --	-- --	-- --	-- --
9281	Bahia de San Juan entrance <50>........		18 28.3	66 07.6	-- --	-- --	-- --	-- --	--	--	-- --	-- --	-- --	-- --

Endnotes can be found at the end of Table 2.

< 1> The times of minimum before flood and ebb are indefinite.

< 2> Current speeds up to 9.0 knots have been observed in the vicinity of the Boilers.

< 3> Current turns westward just before the end of the flood.

< 4> Current tends to rotate counterclockwise, flood direction swinging from westward to southward.

< 5> Observations indicate that current floods about 11 hours and ebbs about 1 1/2 hours. Minimum before flood occurs about 4 1/2 hours earlier, maximum flood about 1 hour later, minimum before ebb about 1/2 hour later, and maximum ebb about 1 1/2 hours earlier than corresponding predictions at Portsmouth Harbor Entrance. Average ebb speed is less than 0.5 knot.

< 6> Current is variable; current speeds are usually less than 1 knot. Currents are strong in the entrance to Menemsha Pond.

< 7> In the open waters of Buzzards Bay, except in the entrance and off Penikese Island and West Island (see table-2, no. 1080-1190), the current is too weak and variable to be predicted.

< 8> The currents in Narragansett Bay have a pronounced irregularity which is evidenced at times during the month by a long period of approximate slack water preceding the flood, and at other times by a double flood of two distinct maximums of speed seperated by a period of lesser speed. These peculiarities appear to be somewhat unstable, consequently, flood currents differing from those predicted should be expected. The ebb current is fairly regular and the predictions for maximum ebb will usually agree closely with the current encountered.

< 9> At minimum flood, current sometimes ebbs for a short period.

<10> At minimum flood, current frequently ebbs for a short period.

<11> Flood is too weak to be predicted. Time difference gives mid-point of 4 hour stand of weak and variable current and time of maximum ebb.

<12> Inside breakwaters, in channel, the current is only 0.4 knot.

<13> Current seldom floods.

<14> Near Tongue Point, Bridgeport Harbor, the current is weak and irregular.

<15> The current on the Manhattan side of the channel is about 0.5 knot stronger, and on the Brooklyn side about 0.5 knot weaker, than at this station.

<16> The ebb or northerly current is weak and variable. East of the channel the current flows southward practically all the time, but with changing speed, the maximum speed being about the same as in mid-channel and occuring about the same time. On the Manhattan side, just off the piers, the flood or southerly current is weak and variable but the ebb or northerly current has an average maximum speed of about 2 knots which occurs about the time of maximum ebb at Hell Gate.

<17> Tidal current is weak, averaging about 0.1 knot at maximum.

<18> For maximum southward current only, the gates of the lock being closed to prevent northward flow. Apply difference and ratio to maximum ebb at The Narrows.

<19> Current is rotary, turning clockwise. Minimum current of 0.9 knot sets southwest about time of "Minimum before flood" at The Narrows. Minimum current of 0.5 knot sets northeast about 1 hour before "Minimum before ebb" at The Narrows.

<20> The values for the Hudson River are for the summer months, when the freshwater discharge is a minimum.

<21> In Roundout Creek entrance between lights, eddies on the flood make navigation difficult. Litle difficulty will be experienced on the ebb.

<22> Current does not flood.

<23> Current is rotary, turning clockwise. It flows northwest at times of "Minimum before flood" at The Narrows; northeast 1 hour after maximum flood; southeast 1 1/2 hours after "Minimum before ebb"; and southwest 2 hours after maximum ebb.

<24> Current is rotary, turning clockwise. Minimum current of 0.2 knot sets west about the time of "Minimum before flood" at The Narrows. Minimum current of 0.2 knot sets ENE about the time of "Minimum before ebb" at The Narrows.

<25> In Sandy Hook Bay (except in southern extremity) the current is weak.

<26> Tidal current is weak and rotary, averaging about 0.1 knot at maximum.

<27> The times of minimum before flood and ebb are variable.

<28> Current usually ebbs during period 3 hours before to 3 hours after maximum ebb. Flood is weak and variable.

<29> To obtain speeds in midchannel use speed ratio 0.8.

<30> Flood is usually weak and of short duration. A weak ebb or flood current occurs about 6 hours after maximum flood at Delaware Bay Entrance.

<31> Tidal current is weak and rotary, averaging less than 0.1 knot.

<32> Current tends to rotate clockwise. At times for "Minimum before flood" there may be a weak current flowing southward while at times for "Minimum before ebb" there may be a weak current flowing northward.

<33> Just off southernmost point, current turns about 1 hour earlier than in midchannel.

<34> Current tends to rotate clockwise. At times for "Minimum before flood" there may be a weak current flowing WSW while at times for "Minimum before ebb" there may be a weak current flowing ENE.

<35> Do not use difference or ratio for lesser maximum ebb current as it is weak and variable.

<36> Current tends to rotate clockwise. At times for "Minimum before flood" there may be a weak current flowing southwest, while at times for "Minimum before ebb" there may be a weak current flowing north.

<37> Flood usually flows northward, however, direction is variable.

<38> The combination of currents from Stono River and North Edisto River in the vicinity of the Southern S.A.L. Ry. bridge produces eight changes a day in direction of flow instead of the usual four. Approximate times of the minimums are as follows: current turns south about 2h 50m before flood begins and 3h 00m before ebb begins at Charleston Harbor; current north about 1h 10m after flood begins and 20 minutes before ebb begins at Charleston Harbor. Caution is advised when running north with a fair current as a cross current from the old channel of the Stono River is encountered at the south approach to the bridge.

<39> Flood is variable, current sometimes changing to ebb for a short time during the flood period.

<40> Due to changes in the waterway average speed values given are probably too large.

<41> Flood usually occurs in a southerly direction and the ebb in a northeastwardly direction.

<42> Flood is weak and variable.

<43> Current tends to rotate clockwise. At times for "Minimum before flood" there may be a weak current flowing northward while at times for "Minimum before ebb" there may be a weak current flowing southeastward.

<44> For greater ebb only.

<45> Tidal current is rotary, turning clockwise, with an average speed of about 0.3 knot.

<46> The strength of flood is usually about 2 knots. The speed ratio for strength of ebb is 0.8, except for an ebb speed at Tampa Bay entrance less than 1 knot or marked with an asterisk. In this case take the ebb speed at Johns Pass to be about 1 knot.

<47> For greater ebb. Lesser ebb is almost equal to greater ebb.

<48> Currents are materially affected by winds.

<49> Current is weak and variable. Current is somewhat rotary turning clockwise.

<50> Current is normally weak and variable, but winds may cause heavy swells.

<51> Minimum ebb is extremely weak, possibly flooding for a short period.

<52> Every other ebb phase exhibits a double ebb pattern. For single ebb phases use time differences and speed ratios of the first ebb.

<53> Ebb is weak and variable.

<54> Current is somewhat rotary, speed seldom exceeds 0.3 knot.

<55> Flood is weak and variable with speeds less than or equal to 0.2 knot. Minimums are indefinite.

<56> Turbulence with hazardous current speeds of 6 to 7 knots have been reported near the bridges in the canal. Extreme caution should be exercised.

CAUTION--During the first 2 hours of flood in channel north of Governers Island the current in Hudson River is still ebbing while during the first 1 1/2 hours of ebb in this channel the current in Hudson River is still flooding. (See Tidal Current Charts, New York Harbor.) At such times special care must be taken by large ships in navigating this channel.

ROTARY TIDAL CURRENTS

(Time: Hours after Minimum before Flood at Boston Harbor)

Station No.	Depth (ft.)	0.0	0.5	1.0	1.5	2.0	2.5	3.0	3.5	4.0	4.5	5.0	5.5	6.0	6.5	7.0	7.5	8.0	8.5	9.0	9.5	10.0	10.5	11.0	11.5	12.0	
393	10	0.03	0.22	0.23	0.24	0.23	0.26	0.25	0.27	0.32	0.33	0.33	0.32	0.31	0.28	0.29	0.28	0.27	0.27	0.28	0.27	0.26	0.27	0.23	0.21	0.21	knots
		265	266	265	268	270	268	282	303	319	327	333	340	357	025	067	068	070	074	073	080	076	079	073	073	051	degrees
395	10	0.30	0.40	0.45	0.43	0.46	0.48	0.50	0.53	0.51	0.52	0.50	0.51	0.51	0.52	0.49	0.50	0.48	0.52	0.49	0.46	0.46	0.43	0.40	0.40	0.36	knots
		210	261	258	247	248	247	262	280	280	304	340	345	009	044	049	061	068	070	074	079	082	081	090	081	123	degrees
397	10	0.29	0.30	0.30	0.31	0.32	0.34	0.34	0.35	0.37	0.36	0.35	0.35	0.34	0.34	0.34	0.35	0.34	0.36	0.35	0.34	0.36	0.35	0.34	0.32	0.18	knots
		200	209	212	222	229	243	247	259	265	268	284	331	002	018	042	056	058	064	065	075	080	085	086	095	132	degrees
399	10	0.50	0.49	0.52	0.55	0.56	0.57	0.54	0.53	0.55	0.54	0.55	0.55	0.52	0.50	0.52	0.50	0.49	0.51	0.51	0.51	0.50	0.51	0.49	0.50	0.49	knots
		138	140	220	243	284	260	252	241	250	244	240	228	211	160	078	062	081	093	085	093	091	087	095	116	130	degrees
401	10	0.20	0.20	0.21	0.22	0.24	0.23	0.25	0.25	0.26	0.24	0.26	0.25	0.24	0.24	0.23	0.24	0.23	0.22	0.21	0.21	0.21	0.20	0.20	0.20	0.20	knots
		306	342	340	244	228	232	223	232	200	210	216	271	290	351	357	051	059	048	045	028	037	052	028	035	011	degrees
403	10	0.42	0.44	0.43	0.45	0.46	0.46	0.46	0.47	0.48	0.48	0.49	0.46	0.48	0.30	0.50	0.50	0.49	0.48	0.47	0.47	0.47	0.47	0.45	0.42	0.41	knots
		221	223	214	221	213	211	215	219	219	227	235	230	221	254	019	015	009	357	052	053	055	070	135	193	206	degrees
405	10	0.42	0.44	0.45	0.45	0.47	0.50	0.46	0.47	0.45	0.44	0.44	0.40	0.45	0.47	0.44	0.44	0.47	0.44	0.42	0.42	0.43	0.47	0.40	0.43	0.45	knots
		213	197	193	182	175	135	178	183	222	247	267	306	330	346	328	344	335	327	334	341	337	338	306	274	240	degrees
417	15	0.11	0.26	0.51	0.53	0.55	0.52	0.50	0.54	0.47	0.50	0.46	0.45	0.46	0.45	0.48	0.51	0.57	0.62	0.66	0.67	0.64	0.62	0.51	0.40	0.25	knots
		191	292	295	304	303	312	308	319	313	331	354	358	010	030	046	059	089	108	109	122	121	119	132	129	134	degrees
419	10	0.30	0.30	0.38	0.39	0.38	0.36	0.37	0.37	0.36	0.36	0.35	0.34	0.30	0.20	0.19	0.25	0.30	0.33	0.35	0.36	0.38	0.38	0.36	0.36	0.32	knots
		251	307	331	342	332	336	343	341	343	350	347	006	029	081	114	138	146	160	165	172	173	173	190	203	233	degrees
461	10	0.34	0.39	0.41	0.42	0.35	0.35	0.34	0.37	0.39	0.38	0.35	0.35	0.32	0.32	0.36	0.40	0.41	0.35	0.31	0.32	0.31	0.27	0.07	0.20	0.25	knots
		267	264	261	261	259	251	235	230	220	209	199	197	146	087	069	070	071	046	030	018	024	046	024	269	272	degrees
489	10	0.33	0.35	0.36	0.35	0.36	0.34	0.40	0.39	0.40	0.42	0.45	0.37	0.35	0.32	0.35	0.37	0.34	0.33	0.35	0.35	0.34	0.03	0.29	0.31	0.24	knots
		007	010	024	034	060	343	348	007	063	025	095	064	081	103	102	103	104	117	135	139	158	215	339	353	355	degrees
*513	10	0.17	0.16	0.18	0.16	0.13	0.17	0.19	0.21	0.22	0.18	0.19	0.21	0.18	0.22	0.25	0.24	0.26	0.27	0.28	0.28	0.29	0.28	0.25	0.23	0.18	knots
		086	095	090	088	090	095	090	093	083	083	081	077	082	072	072	070	069	067	070	070	073	077	085	082	085	degrees
565	10	0.22	0.27	0.29	0.09	0.37	0.40	0.44	0.45	0.44	0.44	0.44	0.48	0.50	0.51	0.47	0.42	0.39	0.37	0.37	0.37	0.36	0.32	0.30	0.23	0.10	knots
		217	199	209	199	052	061	074	077	066	047	032	025	029	041	061	077	082	076	071	070	070	064	069	070	085	degrees
565	20	0.15	0.22	0.24	0.05	0.28	0.30	0.31	0.36	0.34	0.33	0.35	0.36	0.40	0.43	0.39	0.30	0.28	0.34	0.35	0.34	0.32	0.29	0.23	0.16	0.09	knots
		271	238	231	251	030	031	076	073	064	040	029	021	021	030	049	067	067	058	056	050	050	047	044	032	005	degrees
617	10	0.20	0.23	0.27	0.45	0.41	0.40	0.35	0.30	0.28	0.32	0.34	0.35	0.33	0.29	0.29	0.32	0.33	0.33	0.33	0.32	0.32	0.30	0.26	0.24	0.24	knots
		246	232	282	351	019	025	024	009	355	343	338	339	345	007	013	008	002	356	345	336	333	331	331	320	305	degrees
617	20	0.15	0.19	0.20	0.33	0.34	0.30	0.24	0.21	0.22	0.28	0.31	0.33	0.32	0.29	0.26	0.27	0.28	0.29	0.31	0.29	0.26	0.21	0.17	0.14	0.10	knots
		220	214	232	001	020	027	024	003	345	340	333	332	331	351	009	008	003	350	339	334	329	322	322	315	254	degrees

* In Reserved Channel, the tidal current is weak, averaging less than 0.1 knot. During a 7-day observation period, the total current set was consistently eastward.

TABLE 3.—VELOCITY OF CURRENT AT ANY TIME

EXPLANATION

Though the predictions in this publication give only the slacks and maximum currents, the velocity of the current at any intermediate time can be obtained approximately by the use of this table. Directions for its use are given below the table.

Before using the table for a place listed in table 2, the predictions for the day in question should first be obtained by means of the differences and ratios given in table 2.

The examples below follow the numbered steps in the directions.

Example 1.—Find the velocity of the current in The Race at 6:00 on a day when the predictions which immediately precede and follow 6:00 are as follows:

(1)	Slack Water		Maximum (Flood)	
	Time		*Time*	*Velocity*
	4:18		7:36	3.2 knots

Directions under the table indicate table A is to be used for this station.

(2) Interval between slack and maximum flood is 7:36−4:18=3ʰ18ᵐ. Column heading nearest to 3ʰ18ᵐ is 3ʰ20ᵐ.

(3) Interval between slack and time desired is 6:00−4:18=1ʰ42ᵐ. Line labeled 1ʰ40ᵐ is nearest to 1ʰ42ᵐ.

(4) Factor in column 3ʰ20ᵐ and on line 1ʰ40ᵐ is 0.7. The above flood velocity of 3.2 knots multiplied by 0.7 gives a flood velocity of 2.24 knots (or 2.2 knots, since one decimal is sufficient) for the time desired.

Example 2.—Find the velocity of the current in the Harlem River at Broadway Bridge at 16:30 on a day when the predictions (obtained using the difference and ratio in table 2) which immediately precede and follow 16:30 are as follows:

(1)	Maximum (Ebb)		Slack Water
	Time	*Velocity*	*Time*
	13:49	2.5 knots	17:25

Directions under the table indicate table B is to be used, since this station in table 2 is referred to Hell Gate.

(2) Interval between slack and maximum ebb is 17:25−13:49=3ʰ36ᵐ. Hence, use column headed 3ʰ40ᵐ.

(3) Interval between slack and time desired is 17:25−16:30=0ʰ55ᵐ. Hence, use line labeled 1ʰ00ᵐ.

(4) Factor in column 3ʰ40ᵐ and on line 1ʰ00ᵐ is 0.5. The above ebb velocity of 2.5 knots multiplied by 0.5 gives an ebb velocity of 1.2 knots for the desired time.

When the interval between slack and maximum current is greater than 5ʰ40ᵐ, enter the table with one-half the interval between slack and maximum current and one-half the interval between slack and the desired time and use the factor thus found.

189

TABLE 3.—VELOCITY OF CURRENT AT ANY TIME

TABLE A

Interval between slack and maximum current

Interval between slack and desired time (h. m.)	1 20	1 40	2 00	2 20	2 40	3 00	3 20	3 40	4 00	4 20	4 40	5 00	5 20	5 40
0 20	0.4	0.3	0.3	0.2	0.2	0.2	0.2	0.1	0.1	0.1	0.1	0.1	0.1	0.1
0 40	0.7	0.6	0.5	0.4	0.4	0.3	0.3	0.3	0.3	0.2	0.2	0.2	0.2	0.2
1 00	0.9	0.8	0.7	0.6	0.6	0.5	0.5	0.4	0.4	0.4	0.3	0.3	0.3	0.3
1 20	1.0	1.0	0.9	0.8	0.7	0.6	0.6	0.5	0.5	0.5	0.4	0.4	0.4	0.4
1 40	......	1.0	1.0	0.9	0.8	0.8	0.7	0.7	0.6	0.6	0.5	0.5	0.5	0.4
2 00	......	......	1.0	1.0	0.9	0.9	0.8	0.8	0.7	0.7	0.6	0.6	0.6	0.5
2 20	......	......	......	1.0	1.0	0.9	0.9	0.8	0.8	0.7	0.7	0.7	0.6	0.6
2 40	......	......	......	......	1.0	1.0	1.0	0.9	0.9	0.8	0.8	0.7	0.7	0.7
3 00	......	......	......	......	......	1.0	1.0	1.0	0.9	0.9	0.8	0.8	0.8	0.7
3 20	......	......	......	......	......	......	1.0	1.0	1.0	0.9	0.9	0.9	0.8	0.8
3 40	......	......	......	......	......	......	......	1.0	1.0	1.0	0.9	0.9	0.9	0.9
4 00	......	......	......	......	......	......	......	......	1.0	1.0	1.0	1.0	0.9	0.9
4 20	......	......	......	......	......	......	......	......	......	1.0	1.0	1.0	1.0	0.9
4 40	......	......	......	......	......	......	......	......	......	......	1.0	1.0	1.0	1.0
5 00	......	......	......	......	......	......	......	......	......	......	......	1.0	1.0	1.0
5 20	......	......	......	......	......	......	......	......	......	......	......	......	1.0	1.0
5 40	......	......	......	......	......	......	......	......	......	......	......	......	......	1.0

TABLE B

Interval between slack and maximum current

Interval between slack and desired time (h. m.)	1 20	1 40	2 00	2 20	2 40	3 00	3 20	3 40	4 00	4 20	4 40	5 00	5 20	5 40
0 20	0.5	0.4	0.4	0.3	0.3	0.3	0.3	0.3	0.2	0.2	0.2	0.2	0.2	0.2
0 40	0.8	0.7	0.6	0.5	0.5	0.5	0.4	0.4	0.4	0.4	0.3	0.3	0.3	0.3
1 00	0.9	0.8	0.8	0.7	0.7	0.6	0.6	0.5	0.5	0.5	0.4	0.4	0.4	0.4
1 20	1.0	1.0	0.9	0.8	0.8	0.7	0.7	0.6	0.6	0.6	0.5	0.5	0.5	0.5
1 40	......	1.0	1.0	0.9	0.9	0.8	0.8	0.7	0.7	0.7	0.6	0.6	0.6	0.6
2 00	......	......	1.0	1.0	0.9	0.9	0.9	0.8	0.8	0.7	0.7	0.7	0.7	0.6
2 20	......	......	......	1.0	1.0	1.0	0.9	0.9	0.8	0.8	0.8	0.7	0.7	0.7
2 40	......	......	......	......	1.0	1.0	1.0	0.9	0.9	0.9	0.8	0.8	0.8	0.7
3 00	......	......	......	......	......	1.0	1.0	1.0	0.9	0.9	0.9	0.9	0.8	0.8
3 20	......	......	......	......	......	......	1.0	1.0	1.0	0.9	0.9	0.9	0.9	0.8
3 40	......	......	......	......	......	......	......	1.0	1.0	1.0	1.0	0.9	0.9	0.9
4 00	......	......	......	......	......	......	......	......	1.0	1.0	1.0	1.0	0.9	0.9
4 20	......	......	......	......	......	......	......	......	......	1.0	1.0	1.0	1.0	0.9
4 40	......	......	......	......	......	......	......	......	......	......	1.0	1.0	1.0	1.0
5 00	......	......	......	......	......	......	......	......	......	......	......	1.0	1.0	1.0
5 20	......	......	......	......	......	......	......	......	......	......	......	......	1.0	1.0
5 40	......	......	......	......	......	......	......	......	......	......	......	......	......	1.0

Use table A for all places except those listed below for table B.
Use table B for Cape Cod Canal, Hell Gate, Chesapeake and Delaware Canal and all stations in table 2 which are referred to them.

1. From predictions find the time of slack water and the time and velocity of maximum current (flood or ebb), one of which is immediately before and the other after the time for which the velocity is desired.
2. Find the interval of time between the above slack and maximum current, and enter the top of table A or B with the interval which most nearly agrees with this value.
3. Find the interval of time between the above slack and the time desired, and enter the side of table A or B with the interval which most nearly agrees with this value.
4. Find, in the table, the factor corresponding to the above two intervals, and multiply the maximum velocity by this factor. The result will be the approximate velocity at the time desired.

TABLE 4.—DURATION OF SLACK

The predicted times of slack water given in this publication indicate the instant of zero velocity, which is only momentary. There is a period each side of slack water, however, during which the current is so weak that for practical purposes it may be considered as negligible.

The following tables give, for various maximum currents, the approximate period of time during which weak currents not exceeding 0.1 to 0.5 knot will be encountered. This duration includes the last of the flood or ebb and the beginning of the following ebb or flood, that is, half of the duration will be before and half after the time of slack water.

Table A should be used for all places *except* those listed below for table B.

Table B should be used for **Cape Cod Canal, Hell Gate, Chesapeake and Delaware Canal,** and all stations in table 2 which are referred to them.

Duration of weak current near time of slack water

TABLE A

Maximum current	Period with a velocity not more than—				
	0.1 knot	0.2 knot	0.3 knot	0.4 knot	0.5 knot
Knots	Minutes	Minutes	Minutes	Minutes	Minutes
1.0	23	46	70	94	120
1.5	15	31	46	62	78
2.0	11	23	35	46	58
3.0	8	15	23	31	38
4.0	6	11	17	23	29
5.0	5	9	14	18	23
6.0	4	8	11	15	19
7.0	3	7	10	13	16
8.0	3	6	9	11	14
9.0	3	5	8	10	13
10.0	2	5	7	9	11

TABLE B

Maximum current	Period with a velocity not more than—				
	0.1 knot	0.2 knot	0.3 knot	0.4 knot	0.5 knot
Knots	Minutes	Minutes	Minutes	Minutes	Minutes
1.0	13	28	46	66	89
1.5	8	18	28	39	52
2.0	6	13	20	28	36
3.0	4	8	13	18	22
4.0	3	6	9	13	17
5.0	3	5	8	10	13

When there is a difference between the velocities of the maximum flood and ebb preceding and following the slack for which the duration is desired, it will be sufficiently accurate for practical purposes to find a separate duration for each maximum velocity and take the average of the two as the duration of the weak current.

TABLE 5.—ROTARY TIDAL CURRENTS

EXPLANATION

Offshore and in some of the wider indentations of the coast, the tidal current is quite different from that found in the more protected bays and rivers. In these inside waters the tidal current is of the reversing type. It sets in one direction for a period of about 6 hours after which it ceases to flow momentarily and then sets in the opposite direction during the following 6 hours. Offshore the current, not being confined to a definite channel, changes its direction continually and never comes to a slack, so that in a tidal cycle of about 12½ hours it will have set in all directions of the compass. This type of current is therefore called a *rotary current*.

A characteristic feature of the rotary current is the absence of slack water. Although the current generally varies from hour to hour, this variation from greatest current to least current and back again to greatest current does not give rise to a period of slack water. When the velocity of the rotary tidal current is least, it is known as the minimum current, and when it is greatest it is known as the maximum current. The minimum and maximum velocities of the rotary current are thus related to each other in the same way as slack and strength of current, a minimum velocity of the current following a maximum velocity by an interval of about 3 hours and being followed in turn by another maximum after a further interval of 3 hours.

In the following table there are given for a number of offshore stations the direction and average velocity of the rotary tidal current for each hour of the tidal cycle referred to predictions for a station in table 1. All times are eastern standard for the 75th meridian.

The velocities given in the table are average. The Moon at new, full, or perigee tends to increase the velocities 15 to 20 percent above average. When perigee occurs at or near the time of new or full Moon the velocities will be 30 to 40 percent above average. Quadrature and apogee tend to decrease the velocities below average by 15 to 20 percent. When apogee occurs at or near quadrature they will be 30 to 40 percent below average. The velocities will be about average when apogee occurs at or near the time of new or full Moon and also when perigee occurs at or near quadrature. (See table of astronomical data.)

The direction of the current is given in degrees, *true*, reading clockwise from 0° at north, and is the direction *toward* which the water is flowing.

The velocities and directions are for the tidal current only and do not include the effect of winds. When a wind is blowing, a wind-driven current will be set up which will be in addition to the tidal current, and the actual current encountered will be a combination of the wind-driven current and tidal current. See the chapters on "Wind-Driven Currents" and "The Combination of Currents."

As an example, in the following table the current at Nantucket Shoals is given for each hour after maximum flood at Pollock Rip Channel. Suppose it is desired to find the direction and velocity of the current at Nantucket Shoals at 3:15 p.m. (15:15) eastern standard time on a day when maximum flood at Pollock Rip Channel is predicted in table 1 to occur at 13:20 eastern standard time. The desired time is therefore about 2 hours after maximum flood at Pollock Rip Channel, and from the following table the tidal current at Nantucket Shoals at this time is setting 15° *true* with an average velocity of 0.8 knot. If this day is near the time of new Moon and about halfway between apogee and perigee, then the distance effect of the Moon will be nil and the phase effect alone will operate to increase the velocity by about 15 percent, to 0.9 knot. If a wind has been blowing, determine the direction and velocity of the wind-driven current from the chapter on "Wind-Driven Currents" and combine it with the above tidal current as explained in the chapter on "The Combination of Currents."

193

Caution.—Velocities from 1½ to 3 knots have been observed at most of the stations in this table. Near Diamond Shoal Light a velocity of 4 knots has been recorded.

At some offshore stations, such as near the entrance to Chesapeake Bay, the tidal current is directed alternately toward and away from the bay entrance with intervening periods of slack water, so that it is essentially a reversing current. For such places, differences for predicting are given in table 2.

TABLE 5.—ROTARY TIDAL CURRENTS

195

Georges Bank — Lat. 41°50' N., long. 66°37' W.

Hours after maximum flood at Pollock Rip Channel, see page 28

Time	Direction (true) Degrees	Velocity Knots
0	285	0.9
1	304	1.1
2	324	1.2
3	341	1.1
4	10	1.0
5	43	0.9
6	89	1.0
7	127	1.3
8	147	1.6
9	172	1.4
10	197	0.9
11	232	0.8

Georges Bank — Lat. 41°54' N., long. 67°08' W.

Hours after maximum flood at Pollock Rip Channel, see page 28

Time	Direction (true) Degrees	Velocity Knots
0	298	1.1
1	325	1.4
2	344	1.5
3	0	1.2
4	33	0.7
5	82	0.8
6	118	1.1
7	138	1.5
8	153	1.2
9	178	1.1
10	208	0.9
11	236	0.8

Georges Bank — Lat. 41°48' N., long. 67°34' W.

Hours after maximum flood at Pollock Rip Channel, see page 28

Time	Direction (true) Degrees	Velocity Knots
0	325	1.5
1	332	2.1
2	342	2.0
3	358	1.3
4	35	0.7
5	99	0.8
6	126	1.3
7	150	2.0
8	159	1.9
9	169	1.7
10	197	1.2
11	275	0.9

Georges Bank — Lat. 41°42' N., long. 67°37' W.

Hours after maximum flood at Pollock Rip Channel, see page 28

Time	Direction (true) Degrees	Velocity Knots
0	316	1.1
1	341	1.3
2	356	1.0
3	16	0.8
4	43	0.6
5	92	0.8
6	122	1.0
7	146	1.1
8	170	1.1
9	195	1.0
10	215	1.0
11	272	0.9

Georges Bank — Lat. 41°41' N., long. 67°49' W.

Hours after maximum flood at Pollock Rip Channel, see page 28

Time	Direction (true) Degrees	Velocity Knots
0	318	1.6
1	320	1.8
2	325	1.4
3	330	0.8
4	67	0.3
5	111	0.9
6	117	1.5
7	126	1.7
8	144	1.7
9	160	1.1
10	242	0.8
11	292	1.2

Georges Bank — Lat. 41°30' N., long. 68°07' W.

Hours after maximum flood at Pollock Rip Channel, see page 28

Time	Direction (true) Degrees	Velocity Knots
0	312	1.5
1	338	1.7
2	346	1.5
3	14	1.1
4	59	0.9
5	99	0.9
6	123	1.3
7	144	1.7
8	160	1.6
9	187	1.3
10	244	1.0
11	274	1.1

Georges Bank — Lat. 41°29' N., long. 67°04' W.

Hours after maximum flood at Pollock Rip Channel, see page 28

Time	Direction (true) Degrees	Velocity Knots
0	277	1.0
1	302	1.2
2	329	1.4
3	348	1.3
4	15	1.2
5	48	1.1
6	85	1.2
7	122	1.4
8	145	1.5
9	166	1.3
10	194	1.2
11	223	1.1

Georges Bank — Lat. 41°14' N., long. 67°38' W.

Hours after maximum flood at Pollock Rip Channel, see page 28

Time	Direction (true) Degrees	Velocity Knots
0	305	1.4
1	332	1.6
2	355	1.6
3	15	1.4
4	38	1.1
5	77	0.9
6	112	1.2
7	141	1.6
8	162	1.6
9	187	1.5
10	214	1.4
11	252	1.2

Georges Bank — Lat. 41°13' N., long. 68°20' W.

Hours after maximum flood at Pollock Rip Channel, see page 28

Time	Direction (true) Degrees	Velocity Knots
0	319	1.5
1	332	2.0
2	345	1.4
3	9	0.8
4	42	0.6
5	80	0.7
6	118	1.0
7	138	1.3
8	154	1.4
9	169	1.5
10	188	1.3
11	236	0.9

Georges Bank — Lat. 40°48' N., long. 67°40' W.

Hours after maximum flood at Pollock Rip Channel, see page 28

Time	Direction (true) Degrees	Velocity Knots
0	304	0.9
1	340	0.9
2	353	0.8
3	29	0.6
4	56	0.6
5	83	0.6
6	107	0.9
7	140	1.0
8	156	1.0
9	175	0.9
10	202	0.8
11	245	0.8

Georges Bank — Lat. 40°49' N., long. 68°34' W.

Hours after maximum flood at Pollock Rip Channel, see page 28

Time	Direction (true) Degrees	Velocity Knots
0	301	1.2
1	326	1.5
2	345	1.4
3	8	1.1
4	36	0.8
5	69	0.8
6	106	1.0
7	139	1.4
8	153	1.5
9	175	1.4
10	201	1.1
11	237	0.9

Great South Channel, Georges Bank — Lat. 40°31' N., long. 68°47' W.

Hours after maximum flood at Pollock Rip Channel, see page 28

Time	Direction (true) Degrees	Velocity Knots
0	320	0.7
1	331	0.9
2	342	1.1
3	3	1.0
4	23	0.8
5	63	0.4
6	129	0.7
7	140	0.9
8	164	1.0
9	179	1.0
10	190	0.8
11	221	0.6

TABLE 5.—ROTARY TIDAL CURRENTS

Nantucket Shoals
Lat. 40°37′ N., long. 69°37′ W.

Time	Direction (true)	Velocity
Hours after maximum flood at Pollock Rip Channel, see page 28	Degrees	Knots
0	323	0.6
1	355	0.7
2	15	0.8
3	38	0.8
4	55	0.8
5	85	0.7
6	125	0.6
7	162	0.7
8	192	0.8
9	212	0.8
10	232	0.8
11	257	0.7

Great South Channel, Georges Bank
Lat. 41°10′ N., long. 68°56′ W.

Time	Direction (true)	Velocity
Hours after maximum flood at Pollock Rip Channel, see page 28	Degrees	Knots
0	318	0.5
1	349	0.7
2	352	1.1
3	356	1.0
4	359	0.7
5	18	0.4
6	106	0.4
7	157	0.7
8	165	1.0
9	173	1.0
10	180	0.8
11	204	0.6

Davis Bank, Nantucket Shoals, 15 miles SE. of Nantucket I.
Lat. 41°07′ N., long. 69°41′ W.

Time	Direction (true)	Velocity
Hours after maximum flood at Pollock Rip Channel, see page 28	Degrees	Knots
0	15	1.5
1	28	2.1
2	32	2.4
3	35	2.1
4	37	1.1
5	128	0.4
6	197	1.2
7	204	1.9
8	205	2.2
9	206	2.2
10	213	1.6
11	307	0.7

Davis Bank, Nantucket Shoals (west), 15 miles SE. of Nantucket I.
Lat. 41°03′ N., long. 69°47′ W.

Time	Direction (true)	Velocity
Hours after maximum flood at Pollock Rip Channel, see page 28	Degrees	Knots
0	346	0.9
1	28	1.2
2	47	1.3
3	73	1.1
4	103	0.8
5	132	0.9
6	182	0.8
7	215	1.2
8	240	1.1
9	251	0.9
10	267	0.7
11	302	0.7

Davis Bank, Nantucket Shoals (middle), 17.5 miles SE. of Nantucket I.
Lat. 41°02′ N., long. 69°43′ W.

Time	Direction (true)	Velocity
Hours after maximum flood at Pollock Rip Channel, see page 28	Degrees	Knots
0	23	0.8
1	27	1.5
2	28	1.9
3	29	1.8
4	46	1.1
5	115	0.4
6	191	1.2
7	202	1.9
8	215	1.7
9	225	1.5
10	233	0.9
11	270	0.2

Davis Bank, Nantucket Shoals (east), 18.5 miles SE. of Nantucket I.
Lat. 41°02′ N., long. 69°41′ W.

Time	Direction (true)	Velocity
Hours after maximum flood at Pollock Rip Channel, see page 28	Degrees	Knots
0	30	0.6
1	36	1.3
2	38	1.5
3	50	1.4
4	80	1.1
5	105	0.8
6	178	0.6
7	230	1.3
8	235	1.7
9	238	1.4
10	241	1.0
11	265	0.3

Nantucket Island, 28 miles east of
Lat. 41°20′ N., long. 69°21′ W.

Time	Direction (true)	Velocity
Hours after maximum flood at Pollock Rip Channel, see page 28	Degrees	Knots
0	19	0.9
1	7	1.3
2	359	1.4
3	351	1.1
4	334	0.5
5	221	0.3
6	198	0.8
7	185	1.1
8	184	1.1
9	184	0.9
10	183	0.7
11	60	0.1

Monomoy Point, 23 miles east of
Lat. 41°35′ N., long. 69°30′ W.

Time	Direction (true)	Velocity
Hours after maximum flood at Pollock Rip Channel, see page 28	Degrees	Knots
0	320	0.7
1	324	1.0
2	326	0.9
3	330	0.7
4	334	0.3
5	144	0.1
6	145	0.5
7	146	0.8
8	147	0.9
9	148	0.8
10	150	0.4
11	230	0.1

Nauset Beach Light, 5 miles NE. of
Lat. 41°56′ N., long. 69°54′ W.

Time	Direction (true)	Velocity
Hours after maximum flood at Pollock Rip Channel, see page 28	Degrees	Knots
0	315	0.5
1	327	0.6
2	340	0.5
3	357	0.2
4	16	0.1
5	124	0.2
6	132	0.4
7	135	0.6
8	139	0.6
9	145	0.4
10	269	0.2
11	297	0.2

Great Round Shoal Channel entrance, Nantucket Sound entrance.
Lat. 41°26′ N., long. 69°44′ W.

Time	Direction (true)	Velocity
Hours after maximum flood at Pollock Rip Channel, see page 28	Degrees	Knots
0	32	1.6
1	45	1.4
2	68	1.3
3	95	1.1
4	140	0.8
5	192	1.2
6	210	1.5
7	220	1.5
8	235	1.2
9	284	0.9
10	303	0.8
11	350	1.2

Great Round Shoal Channel Buoy 9, 0.3 mile NE. of
Lat. 41°24′ N., long. 69°55′ W.

Time	Direction (true)	Velocity
Hours after maximum flood at Pollock Rip Channel, see page 28	Degrees	Knots
0	47	1.0
1	60	1.3
2	70	1.3
3	91	0.8
4	153	0.5
5	211	0.7
6	234	0.9
7	247	1.3
8	252	1.1
9	260	0.9
10	305	0.3
11	35	0.4

Great Round Shoal Channel, 4 miles NE. of Great Pt., Nantucket Sound.
Lat. 41°26′ N., long. 69°59′ W.

Time	Direction (true)	Velocity
Hours after maximum flood at Pollock Rip Channel, see page 28	Degrees	Knots
0	80	0.8
1	88	1.1
2	96	1.3
3	104	1.0
4	129	0.5
5	213	0.5
6	267	1.1
7	275	1.4
8	280	1.2
9	284	0.7
10	328	0.2
11	42	0.4

TABLE 5.—ROTARY TIDAL CURRENTS

197

Cuttyhunk I., 3¼ miles SW. of. Lat. 41°23′ N., long. 71°00′ W.

Hours after maximum flood at Pollock Rip Channel, see page 28

Time	Direction (true) Degrees	Velocity Knots
0	356	0.4
1	15	0.3
2	80	0.2
3	123	0.3
4	146	0.5
5	158	0.5
6	173	0.4
7	208	0.3
8	267	0.2
9	306	0.3
10	322	0.3
11	335	0.4

Gooseberry Neck, 2 miles SSE. of Buzzards Bay entrance. Lat. 41°27′ N., long. 71°01′ W.

Hours after maximum flood at Pollock Rip Channel, see page 28

Time	Direction (true) Degrees	Velocity Knots
0	52	0.6
1	65	0.4
2	108	0.2
3	168	0.3
4	210	0.4
5	223	0.5
6	232	0.5
7	249	0.3
8	274	0.2
9	321	0.2
10	16	0.3
11	38	0.5

Browns Ledge, Massachusetts. Lat. 41°20′ N., long. 71°06′ W.

Hours after maximum flood at Pollock Rip Channel, see page 28

Time	Direction (true) Degrees	Velocity Knots
0	330	0.3
1	12	0.3
2	28	0.3
3	104	0.4
4	118	0.4
5	123	0.4
6	168	0.3
7	205	0.2
8	201	0.3
9	270	0.3
10	282	0.4
11	318	0.5

Point Judith, Harbor of Refuge, Block Island Sound (west entrance). Lat. 41°22′ N., long. 71°31′ W.

Hours after maximum flood at The Race, see page 34

Time	Direction (true) Degrees	Velocity Knots
0	197	0.2
1	160	0.2
2	151	0.4
3	159	0.5
4	146	0.5
5	124	0.5
6	109	0.4
7	104	0.2
8	90	0.1
9	30	0.1
10	336	0.1
11	209	0.1

Point Judith, 4.5 miles SW. of, Block Island Sound. Lat. 41°18′N., long. 71°33′ W.

Hours after maximum flood at The Race, see page 34

Time	Direction (true) Degrees	Velocity Knots
0	264	0.6
1	270	0.6
2	270	0.5
3	280	0.2
4	62	0.2
5	70	0.6
6	78	0.7
7	95	0.5
8	105	0.3
9	120	0.1
10	286	0.1
11	277	0.3

Grace Point, 2 miles NW. of, Block Island Sound. Lat. 41°12′ N., long. 71°38′ W.

Hours after maximum flood at The Race, see page 34

Time	Direction (true) Degrees	Velocity Knots
0	304	0.2
1	2	0.2
2	28	0.4
3	28	0.6
4	37	0.7
5	71	0.6
6	86	0.6
7	126	0.4
8	137	0.2
9	213	0.1
10	256	0.1
11	267	0.1

Little Gull I., 3.7 miles ESE. of, Block Island Sound. Lat. 41°11′ N., long. 72°02′ W.

Hours after maximum flood at The Race, see page 34

Time	Direction (true) Degrees	Velocity Knots
0	271	0.8
1	284	0.5
2	320	0.2
3	68	0.2
4	77	0.7
5	95	1.1
6	118	1.6
7	128	1.2
8	150	0.6
9	171	0.2
10	221	0.4
11	228	0.7

Sandy Hook Approach Lighted Horn Buoy 2A, 0.2 mile W. of Lat. 40°27′ N., long. 73°55′ W.

Hours after maximum flood at The Narrows, N.Y. Hbr., see page 46

Time	Direction (true) Degrees	Velocity Knots
0	313	0.4
1	325	0.3
2	356	0.2
3	55	0.2
4	94	0.3
5	118	0.4
6	136	0.6
7	147	0.5
8	177	0.2
9	256	0.2
10	290	0.3
11	298	0.4

Fenwick Shoal Lighted Whistle Buoy 2 off Delaware coast. Lat. 38°25′ N., long. 74°46′ W.

Hours after maximum flood at Delaware Bay Entrance, see page 52

Time	Direction (true) Degrees	Velocity Knots
0	342	0.2
1	349	0.2
2	357	0.1
3	43	0.1
4	110	0.1
5	135	0.2
6	150	0.3
7	165	0.3
8	185	0.2
9	226	0.1
10	282	0.1
11	318	0.2

*Frying Pan Shoals, off Cape Fear, Lat. 33°34′ N., long. 77°49′ W.

Hours after maximum flood at Charleston Harbor, see page 76

Time	Direction (true) Degrees	Velocity Knots
0	335	0.3
1	10	0.2
2	50	0.2
3	90	0.3
4	110	0.3
5	128	0.3
6	150	0.3
7	188	0.2
8	235	0.2
9	268	0.3
10	290	0.3
11	305	0.3

Cape Romain, 5 miles SE. of Lat. 32°57′ N., long. 79°17′ W.

Hours after maximum flood at Charleston Harbor, see page 76

Time	Direction (true) Degrees	Velocity Knots
0	6	0.2
1	38	0.2
2	55	0.3
3	67	0.3
4	93	0.3
5	114	0.3
6	167	0.2
7	212	0.2
8	242	0.3
9	244	0.4
10	262	0.3
11	292	0.3

Cape Romain, 6.9 miles SW. of Lat. 32°54′ N., long. 79°26′ W.

Hours after maximum flood at Charleston Harbor, see page 76

Time	Direction (true) Degrees	Velocity Knots
0	317	0.3
1	350	0.2
2	19	0.2
3	71	0.3
4	115	0.3
5	111	0.3
6	132	0.2
7	160	0.2
8	216	0.2
9	251	0.2
10	266	0.3
11	303	0.3

*Current during June-August usually sets eastward, average velocity ½ knot.

TABLE 5.—ROTARY TIDAL CURRENTS

Capers Inlet, 1.9 miles east of
Lat. 32°50′ N., long. 79°40′ W.

(Hours after maximum flood at Charleston Harbor, see page 76)

Time	Direction (true) Degrees	Velocity Knots
0	12	0.1
1	58	0.1
2	52	0.2
3	53	0.2
4	67	0.1
5	98	0.1
6	129	0.1
7	214	0.1
8	222	0.2
9	254	0.2
10	246	0.1
11	247	0.1

Capers Inlet, 3.6 miles SE. of
Lat. 32°49′ N., long. 79°38′ W.

(Hours after maximum flood at Charleston Harbor, see page 76)

Time	Direction (true) Degrees	Velocity Knots
0	302	0.2
1	357	0.1
2	34	0.1
3	17	0.2
4	89	0.2
5	94	0.2
6	112	0.2
7	116	0.2
8	189	0.1
9	249	0.2
10	268	0.2
11	282	0.2

Charleston Entrance, 37 miles east of
Lat. 32°42′ N., long. 70°06′ W.

(Hours after maximum flood at Charleston Harbor, see page 76)

Time	Direction (true) Degrees	Velocity Knots
0	328	0.3
1	350	0.3
2	20	0.2
3	65	0.2
4	95	0.3
5	118	0.3
6	140	0.3
7	163	0.3
8	195	0.2
9	235	0.2
10	268	0.2
11	295	0.3

Charleston Lighted Whistle Buoy 2C, off Charleston Harbor entrance.
Lat. 32°41′ N., long. 79°43′ W.

(Hours after maximum flood at Charleston Harbor, see page 76)

Time	Direction (true) Degrees	Velocity Knots
0	300	0.2
1	332	0.2
2	17	0.1
3	55	0.2
4	77	0.3
5	93	0.3
6	117	0.3
7	153	0.2
8	207	0.2
9	242	0.2
10	260	0.3
11	275	0.3

Folly Island, 2 miles east of
Lat. 32°39′ N., long. 79°52′ W.

(Hours after maximum flood at Charleston Harbor, see page 76)

Time	Direction (true) Degrees	Velocity Knots
0	346	0.1
1	24	0.2
2	58	0.3
3	76	0.3
4	102	0.3
5	121	0.2
6	164	0.1
7	222	0.2
8	256	0.2
9	256	0.3
10	271	0.3
11	290	0.2

Folly Island, 3.5 miles east of
Lat. 32°38′ N., long. 79°50′ W.

(Hours after maximum flood at Charleston Harbor, see page 76)

Time	Direction (true) Degrees	Velocity Knots
0	322	0.1
1	47	0.2
2	69	0.2
3	86	0.2
4	96	0.2
5	115	0.2
6	148	0.1
7	215	0.1
8	256	0.2
9	260	0.2
10	265	0.2
11	285	0.1

Martins Industry, 5 miles east of, off Port Royal Sound.
Lat. 32°06′ N., long. 80°28′ W.

(Hours after maximum flood at Charleston Harbor, see page 76)

Time	Direction (true) Degrees	Velocity Knots
0	282	0.4
1	293	0.3
2	330	0.1
3	30	0.1
4	75	0.3
5	92	0.4
6	102	0.5
7	110	0.4
8	140	0.2
9	200	0.2
10	250	0.3
11	271	0.4

Savannah Light, 1.2 miles SE. of
Lat. 31°57′ N., long. 80°40′ W.

(Hours after maximum flood at Savannah River Entrance, see page 82)

Time	Direction (true) Degrees	Velocity Knots
0	296	0.3
1	308	0.2
2	326	0.1
3	45	0.1
4	90	0.2
5	107	0.3
6	114	0.3
7	123	0.3
8	145	0.2
9	213	0.1
10	267	0.2
11	283	0.3

Brunswick Lighted Whistle Buoy 2B, off St. Simons Sound.
Lat. 31°00′ N., long. 81°10′ W.

(Hours after maximum flood at Miami Harbor Entrance, see page 94)

Time	Direction (true) Degrees	Velocity Knots
0	308	0.3
1	340	0.2
2	42	0.1
3	90	0.3
4	111	0.4
5	122	0.4
6	130	0.3
7	141	0.2
8	220	0.1
9	260	0.2
10	289	0.4
11	297	0.4

Miami Outer Bay Cut Entrance
Lat. 25°46′ N., long. 80°06′ W.

(Hours after maximum flood at Miami Harbor Entrance, see page 94)

Time	Direction (true) Degrees	Velocity Knots
0	338	0.1
1	319	0.1
2	352	0.1
3	18	0.1
4	36	0.1
5	30	0.2
6	25	0.1
7	32	0.1
8	25	0.1
9	26	0.1
10	6	0.2
11	355	0.1

TABLE 5.—ROTARY TIDAL CURRENTS   199

Fire Island Inlet, N.Y., 22 miles south of:
    Tidal current is weak, averaging about 0.1 knot at strength.

Fire Island Lighted Whistle Buoy 2 FI:
    Tidal current is weak, averaging about 0.2 knot at strength.

Ambrose Light, New York Harbor entrance:
    Tidal current is weak, averaging about 0.2 knot at strength.

Cape May, N.J., 72 miles east of:
    Tidal current is weak, averaging about 0.1 knot at strength.

Five-Fathom Bank Northeast Lighted Whistle Buoy 2 FB:
    Tidal current is weak, averaging about 0.2 knot at strength.

Winter-Quarter Shoal Lighted Whistle Buoy 6WQS, 9.2 miles SE. of, off Assateague I.:
    Tidal current is weak, averaging less than 0.1 knot.

Cape Charles, 70 miles east of:
    Tidal current is weak, averaging about 0.2 knot at strength.

Chesapeake Light, 4.4 miles NE. of, off Chesapeake Bay entrance, Va.:
    Tidal current is weak and variable.

Cape Lookout Shoals Lighted Whistle Buoy 14:
    Tidal current is weak, averaging about 0.2 knot at strength. Current during June-August usually sets eastward, average velocity ½ knot.

Ocracoke Inlet, 3½ miles SSE. of:
    Tidal current is weak, averaging about 0.1 knot at strength.

Diamond Shoal Light, 3.9 miles SSW. of:
    Tidal current is weak, averaging less than 0.1 knot at strength. Current during June-August usually sets northeastward, average velocity ¼ knot.

Frying Pan Shoals Light, 14.3 miles NW. of:
    Tidal current is weak, averaging about 0.2 knot at strength. Current during June-August usually sets eastward, average velocity ½ knot.

St. Johns Point, 5 miles east of, Fla.:
    Tidal current is weak, averaging about 0.2 knot at strength.

Fowey Rocks Light, 1.5 miles SW. of:
    Tidal current is weak and variable.

THE GULF STREAM

The region where the Gulf of Mexico narrows to form the channel between Florida Keys and Cuba may be regarded as the head of the Gulf Stream. From this region the stream sets eastward and northward through the Straits of Florida, and after passing Little Bahama Bank it continues northward and then northeastward, following the general direction of the 100-fathom curve as far as Cape Hatteras. The flow in the Straits is frequently referred to as the Florida Current.

Shortly after emerging from the Straits of Florida, the stream is joined by the Antilles Current, which flows northwesterly along the open ocean side of the West Indies before uniting with the water which has passed through the straits. Beyond Cape Hatteras the combined current turns more and more eastward under the combined effects of the deflecting force of the Earth's rotation and the eastwardly trending coastline, until the region of the Grand Banks of Newfoundland is reached.

Eastward of the Grand Banks the whole surface is slowly driven eastward and northeastward by the prevailing westerly winds to the coastal waters of northwestern Europe. For distinction, this broad and variable wind-driven surface movement is sometimes referred to as the North Atlantic Drift or Gulf Stream Drift.

In general, the Gulf Stream as it issues into the sea through the Straits of Florida may be characterized as a swift, highly saline current of blue water whose upper stratum is composed of warm water.

On its western or inner side, the Gulf Stream is separated from the coastal waters by a zone of rapidly falling temperature, to which the term "cold wall" has been applied. It is most clearly marked north of Cape Hatteras but extends, more or less well defined, from the Straits to the Grand Banks.

Throughout the whole stretch of 400 miles in the Straits of Florida, the stream flows with considerable velocity. Abreast of Havana, the average surface velocity in the axis of the stream is about 2½ knots. As the cross-sectional area of the stream decreases, the velocity increases gradually, until abreast of Cape Florida it becomes about 3½ knots. From this point within the narrows of the straits, the velocity along the axis gradually decreases to about 2½ knots off Cape Hatteras, N.C. These values are for the axis of the stream where the current is a maximum, the velocity of the stream decreasing gradually from the axis as the edges of the stream are approached. The velocity of the stream, furthermore, is subject to fluctuations brought about by variations in winds and barometric pressure.

The following tables give the mean surface velocity of the Gulf Stream in two cross sections in the Straits of Florida:

Between Rebecca Shoal and Cuba		Between Fowey Rocks and Gun Cay	
Distance south of Rebecca Shoal	Mean surface velocity observed	Distance east of Fowey Rocks	Mean surface velocity observed
Nautical miles	Knots	Nautical miles	Knots
20	0.3	8	2.7
35	0.7	11½	3.5
50	2.2	15	3.2
68	2.2	22	2.7
86	0.8	29	2.1
		36	1.7

Crossing the Gulf Stream at Jupiter or Fowey Rocks, an average allowance of 2½ knots in a northerly direction should be made for the current.

Crossing the stream from Havana, a fair allowance for the average current between 100-fathom curves is 1.1 knots in an east-north-easterly direction.

From within the straits, the axis of the Gulf Stream runs approximately parallel with the 100-fathom curve as far as Cape Hatteras. Since this stretch of coast line sweeps northward in a sharper curve than does the 100-fathom line, the stream lies at varying distances from the shore. The lateral boundaries of the current within the straits are fairly well fixed, but when the stream flows into the sea the eastern boundary becomes somewhat vague. On the western side, the limits can be defined approximately since the waters of the stream differ in color, temperature, salinity, and flow from the inshore coastal waters. On the east, however, the Antilles Current combines with the Gulf Stream, so that its waters here merge gradually with the waters of the open Atlantic. Observations of the National Ocean Survey indicate that, in general, the average position of the inner edge of the Gulf Stream as far as Cape Hatteras lies inside the 50-fathom curve. The Gulf Stream, however, shifts somewhat with the seasons, and is considerably influenced by the winds which cause fluctuations in its position, direction, and velocity; consequently, any limits which are assigned refer to mean or average positions.

The approximate mean positions of the inner edge and axis (point where greatest velocity may be found) are indicated in the following table:

Approximate mean position of the Gulf Stream

Locality	Inner edge	Axis
	Nautical miles	*Nautical miles*
North of Havana, Cuba		25
Southeast of Key West, Fla.		45
East of Fowey Rocks, Fla.		10
East of Miami Beach, Fla.		15
East of Palm Beach, Fla.		15
East of Jupiter Inlet, Fla.		20
East of Cape Canaveral, Fla.	10	45
East of Daytona Beach, Fla.	25	75
East of Ormond Beach, Fla.	25	75
East of St. Augustine, Fla. (coast line)	40	85
East of Jacksonville, Fla. (coast line)	55	90
Southeast of Savannah, Ga. (coast line)	65	95
Southeast of Charleston, S.C. (coast line)	55	90
Southeast of Myrtle Beach, S.C.	60	100
Southeast of Cape Fear, N.C. (light)	35	75
Southeast of Cape Lookout, N.C. (light)	20	50
Southeast of Cape Hatteras, N.C.	10	35
Southeast of Virginia Beach, Va.	85	115
Southeast of Atlantic City, N.J.	120	
Southeast of Sandy Hook, N.J.	150	

At the western end of the Straits of Florida the limits of the Gulf Stream are not well defined, and for this reason the location of the inner edge has been omitted for Havana, Cuba, and Key West, Fla., in the above table. Between Fowey Rocks and Jupiter Inlet the inner edge is deflected westward and lies very close to the shore line.

Along the Florida Reefs between Alligator Reef and Dry Tortugas the distance of the northerly edge of the Gulf Stream from the edge of the reefs gradually increases toward the west. Off Alligator Reef it is quite close inshore, while off Rebecca Shoal and Dry Tortugas it is possibly 15 to 20 miles south of the 100-fathom curve. Between the reefs and the northern edge of the Gulf Stream the currents are ordinarily tidal and are subject at all times to considerable modification by local winds and barometric conditions. This neutral zone varies in both length and breadth; it may extend along the reefs a greater or less distance than stated, and its width varies as the northern edge of the Gulf Stream approaches or recedes from the reefs.

The approximate position of the axis of the Gulf Stream for various regions is shown on the following National Ocean Survey Charts: No. 1002, Straits of Florida; No. 1007, South Carolina to Cuba; No. 1112, Cape Canaveral to Key West; No. 1113, Alligator Reef to Havana. Chart No. 1001 shows the axis and the position of the inner edge of the Gulf Stream from Cape Hatteras to Straits of Florida.

WIND-DRIVEN CURRENTS

A wind continuing for some time will produce a current the velocity of which depends on the velocity of the wind, and unless the current is deflected by some other cause, the deflective force of the earth's rotation will cause it to set to the right of the direction of the wind in the northern hemisphere and to the left in the southern hemisphere.

The current produced at off-shore locations by local winds of various strengths and directions has been investigated from observations made at 20 lightships (some of which have since been moved) from Portland, Maine, to St. Johns River, Fla. The observations were made hourly and varied in length from 1 to 2 years at most of the locations to 5½ years at Nantucket Shoals and 9 years at Diamond Shoal. The averages obtained are given below and may prove helpful in estimating the probable current that may result from various winds at the several locations.

Caution.—There were of course many departures from these averages of velocity and direction, for the wind-driven current often depends not only on the length of time the wind blows but also on factors other than the local wind at the time and place of the current. The mariner must not, therefore, assume that the given wind will always produce the indicated current.

It should be remembered, too, that the current which a vessel experiences at any time is the resultant of the combined actions of the tidal current, the wind-driven current, and any other currents such as the Gulf Stream or currents due to river discharge.

Velocity.—The table below shows the average velocity of the current due to winds of various strengths.

Wind velocity (miles per hour)	10	20	30	40	50
Average current velocity (knots) due to wind at following lightship stations:					
Boston and Barnegat	0.1	0.1	0.2	0.3	0.3
Diamond Shoal and Cape Lookout Shoals	0.5	0.6	0.7	0.8	1.0
All other locations	0.2	0.3	0.4	0.5	0.6

Direction.—The position of the shore line with respect to the station influences considerably the direction of the currents due to certain winds. The following table shows for each station the average number of degrees by which the wind-driven current is deflected to the right or left (—) of the wind. Thus at Cape Lookout Shoals the table indicates that with a north wind the wind-driven current flows on the average 030° west of south, and with an east wind it flows 029° south of west.

203

Average deviation of current to right of wind direction

[A minus sign (−) indicates that the current sets to the left of the wind]

Old Lightship Stations	Lat.	Long.	N.	NNE.	NE.	ENE.	E.	ESE.	SE.	SSE.	S.	SSW.	SW.	WSW.	W.	WNW.	NW.	NNW.
Portland	43 32	70 06	24	14	9	8	−2	−14	0	26	15	18	18	24	15	34	13	18
Boston	42 20	70 45		−1		21		32		21		20		2		19		15
Pollock Rip Slue	41 37	69 54	6	6	48	−38	30	−63	−24	−75	−25	167	70	69	36	63	30	19
Nantucket Shoals	40 37	69 37	44	46	28	24	9	10	12	3	26	0	0	18	30	39	41	48
Hen and Chickens	41 27	71 01	16	14	−7	−1	−14	3	−39	−36	25	56	35	30	20	16	16	8
Brenton Reef	41 26	71 23	34	25	22	19	25	1	−7	8	27	48	23	41	41	31	21	34
Fire Island	40 29	73 11	35	23	15	8	2	−17	31	55	40	41	31	14	−2	0	25	37
Ambrose Channel	40 27	73 41	30	40	21	11	18	72	27	112	82	70	63	46	37	22	23	31
Scotland	40 27	73 55	10	−12	−26	−36	−61	−36	−92	−150	90	33	77	44	16	30	27	13
Barnegat	39 46	73 56	6	6	−13	−9	−16	−7	33	54	55	30	14	8	0	−5	21	29
Northeast End	38 58	74 30	30	14	−3	−11	−20	−31	−42	−29	37	44	25	18	7	16	25	18
Overfalls	38 48	75 01	28	−6	−1	−2	−40	−60	−78	−22	68	38	56	54	32	31	32	45
Winter-Quarter Shoal	37 55	74 56	18	−1	−5	−21	−27	−35	−19	31	33	20	4	14	9	8	28	37
Chesapeake	36 59	75 42	18	−2	−4	6	−6	23	73	71	57	38	27	20	22	18	15	22
Diamond Shoal	35 05	75 20	11	3	−3	30	65	88	74	52	40	22	7	−10	−13	−17	−25	−4
Cape Lookout Shoals	34 18	76 24	30	24	2	2	−29		21	80	54	31	32	21	−2	18	5	−5
Frying Pan Shoals	33 34	77 40	34	34	18	6	2	9	48	55	48	38	26	14	−7	−12	−27	−6
Savannah	31 57	80 40	12	12	−9	−18	−23	−40	17	50	43	17	7	−8	−10	7	15	33
Brunswick	31 00	81 10	17	−2	−10	−28	−18	−21	37	29	23	2	6	−21	−21	−26	16	18
St. Johns	30 23	81 18	3	−12	−27	−47	−84	30	35	26	26	27	1	10	−8	−17	6	x

THE COMBINATION OF CURRENTS

In determining from the current tables the velocity and direction of the current at any time, it is frequently necessary to combine the tidal current with the wind-driven current. The following methods indicate how the resultant of two or more currents may be easily determined.

Currents in the same direction.—When two or more currents set in the same direction it is a simple matter to combine them. The resultant current will have a velocity which is equal to the sum of all the currents and it will set in the same direction.

For example, a vessel is near the Nantucket Shoals station at a time when the tidal current is setting 120° with a velocity of 0.6 knot, and at the same time a wind of 40 miles per hour is blowing from west; what current will the vessel be subject to at that time? Since a wind of 40 miles from west will give rise to a current setting 120° with a velocity of 0.5 knot, the combined tidal and wind-driven currents will set in the same direction (120°) with a velocity of 0.6+0.5=1.1 knots.

Currents in opposite directions.—The combination of currents setting in opposite directions is likewise a simple matter. The velocity of the resultant current is the difference between the opposite setting currents, and the direction of the resultant current is the same as that of the greater current.

As an example, let it be required to determine the velocity of the current at the Nantucket Shoals station when the tidal current is setting 205° with a velocity of 0.8 knot, and when a wind of 40 miles per hour is blowing from south. The current produced by a wind of 40 miles per hour from south would set 025° with a velocity of 0.5 knot. The tidal and wind-driven currents therefore set in opposite directions, the tidal current being the stronger. Hence the resultant current will set in the direction of the tidal current (205°) with a velocity of 0.8—0.5=0.3 knot.

Currents in different directions.—The combination of two or more currents setting neither in the same nor in opposite direction, while not as simple as in the previous cases, is nevertheless not difficult, the best method being a graphic method. Taking the combination of two currents as the simplest case, we draw from a given point as origin, a line the direction of which is the direction of one of the currents to be combined and whose length represents the velocity of that current to some suitable scale; from the end of this line we draw another line the direction and length of which, to the same scale, represents the other of the currents to be combined; then a line joining the origin with the end of our second line gives the direction and velocity of the resultant current.

As an example, let us take Nantucket Shoals station at a time when the tidal current is 0.7 knot setting 355° and a wind of 50 miles per hour is blowing from west-southwest; the wind-driven current according to the preceding chapter would therefore be about 0.6 knot setting 085°.

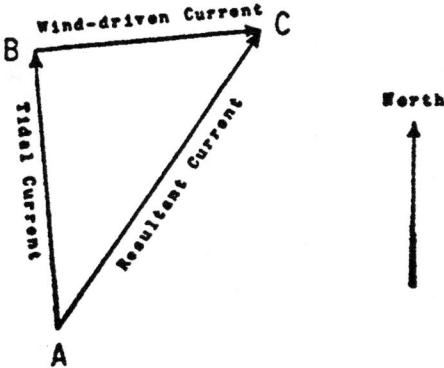

Combination of tidal current and wind-driven current

Using a scale of 2 inches to the knot we draw from the point A in the diagram above, the line AB 1.4 inches in length directed 355° to represent the tidal current. From B we then draw the line BC 1.2 inches in length directed 085° to represent the wind current. The line AC represents the resultant current and on being measured is found to be about 1.8 inches in length directed 035°. Hence the resultant current sets 035° with a velocity of 0.9 knot.

The combination of three or more currents is made in the same way as above, the third current to be combined being drawn from the point C, the resultant current being given by joining the origin A with the end of the last line. For drawing the lines, a parallel rule and compass rose will be found convenient, or a protractor or polar coordinate paper may be used.

CURRENT DIAGRAMS

EXPLANATION

"Current diagram" is a graphic table that shows the velocities of the flood and ebb currents and the times of slack and strength over a considerable stretch of the channel of a tidal waterway. At definite intervals along the channel the velocities of the current are shown with reference to the times of turning of the current at some reference station. This makes it a simple matter to determine the approximate velocity of the current along the channel for any desired time.

In using the diagrams, the desired time should be converted to hours before or after the time of the *nearest* predicted slack water at the reference station.

Besides showing in compact form the velocities of the current and their changes through the flood and ebb cycles, the current diagram serves two other useful purposes. By its use the mariner can determine the most advantageous time to pass through the waterway in order to carry the most favorable current and also the velocity and direction of the current that will be encountered in the channel at any time.

Each diagram represents average durations and average velocities of flood and ebb. The durations and velocities of flood and ebb vary from day to day. Therefore predictions for the reference station at times will differ from average conditions and when precise results are desired the diagrams should be modified to represent conditions at such particular times. This can be done by changing the width of the shaded and unshaded portions of the diagram to agree in hours with the durations of flood and ebb, respectively, as given by the predictions for that time. The velocities in the shaded area should then be multiplied by the ratio of the predicted flood velocity to the average flood velocity (maximum flood velocity given opposite the name of the reference station on the diagram) and the velocities in the unshaded area by the ratio of the predicted ebb velocity to the average ebb velocity.

In a number of cases approximate results can be obtained by using the diagram as drawn and modifying the final result by the ratio of velocities as mentioned above. Thus if the diagram in a particular case gives a favorable flood velocity averaging about 1.0 knot and the ratio of the predicted flood velocity to the average flood velocity is 0.5 the approximate favorable current for the particular time would be $1.0 \times 0.5 = 0.5$ knot.

VINEYARD AND NANTUCKET SOUNDS

EXPLANATION OF CURRENT DIAGRAM

The current diagram on the opposite page represents average conditions of the surface currents along the middle of the channel from Gay Head to the east end of Pollock Rip Channel, the scale being too small to show details.

Easterly streams are designated "Flood" and westerly streams "Ebb." The small figures in the diagram denote the velocity of the current in knots and tenths. The times are referred to slack waters at Pollock Rip Channel (Butler Hole), daily predictions for which are given in Table 1 of these current tables.

The speed lines are directly related to the diagram. By transferring to the diagram the direction of the speed line which corresponds to the ship's speed, the diagram will show the general direction and velocity of the current encountered by the vessel in passing through the sounds or the most favorable time, with respect to currents, for leaving any place shown on the left margin.

To determine velocity and direction of current.—With parallel rulers transfer to the diagram the direction of the speed line corresponding to normal speed of vessel, moving edge of ruler to the point where the horizontal line representing place of departure intersects the vertical line representing the time of day in question. If the ruler's edge lies within the shaded portion of the diagram, a flood current will be encountered; if within the unshaded, an ebb current; and if along the boundary of both, slack water. The figures on the diagram along the edge of the rule will show the velocity of the current encountered at any place indicated on the left margin of the diagram.

Example.—A 12-knot vessel bound westward enters Pollock Rip Channel at 0700 of a given day, and it is desired to ascertain the velocity and direction of the current which will be encountered on its passage through the sounds. Assuming that on the given day ebb begins at Pollock Rip Channel at 0508 and flood begins at 1120, the time 0700 will be about 2 hours after ebb begins. With parallel rulers transfer to the diagram the 12-knot speed line "Westbound", placing edge of rule on the point where the vertical line "2 hours after ebb begins at Pollock Rip Channel" intersects the horizontal 47-mile line which is the starting point. It will be found that the edge of the ruler passes through the unshaded portion of the diagram, the velocities along the edge averaging about 1.4 knots. The vessel will therefore have a favorable ebb current averaging about 1.4 knots all the way to Gay Head. It will also be seen that the edge of the ruler crosses the horizontal 16-mile line (at East Chop) about halfway between the figures 1.6 and 2.2. Therefore, when passing the vicinity of East Chop she will have a favorable current of almost 2 knots.

To determine the time of a favorable current for passing through the sounds.—With parallel rulers transfer to the diagram the direction of the speed line corresponding to normal speed of vessel, moving the rule over the diagram until its edge runs as nearly as possible through the general line of largest velocities of shaded portion if eastbound and unshaded portion if westbound, giving consideration only to that part of the diagram which lies between place of departure and destination. An average of the figures along the edge of the ruler will give the average strength of current. The time (before or after flood begins or ebb begins at Pollock Rip Channel) for leaving any place shown on the left margin will be indicated vertically above the point where the ruler cuts a line drawn horizontally through the name of the place in question.

Example.—A 12-knot vessel will leave Gay Head for Pollock Rip Channel on a day when flood begins at Pollock Rip Channel at 0454 and ebb begins at 1104. At what time should she get under way so as to carry the most favorable current all the way through the sounds?

Place parallel rulers along the 12-knot speed line "Eastbound." Transfer the direction to the shaded portion of the diagram and as near as possible to the axis so as to include the greatest possible number of larger current velocities. It will be found that the edge of the rule cuts the horizontal line at Gay Head at the point representing "3 hours after flood begins at Pollock Rip Channel", and that the average of the currents along the edge of rulers is about 0.8 knot in a favorable direction. For the given day flood begins at Pollock Rip Channel at 0454; hence, if the vessel leaves Gay Head 3 hours later, or about 0754, whe will average a favorable current of almost 1 knot all the way.

ASTRONOMICAL DATA, 1983

January

	d	h	m
E	5	22	..
◗	6	04	00
S	13	06	..
A	14	05	..
●	14	05	08
E	20	17	..
◐	22	05	33
N	27	05	..
P	28	11	..
O	28	22	26

February

	d	h	m
E	2	06	..
◗	4	19	17
S	9	12	..
A	10	08	..
●	13	00	32
E	16	22	..
◐	20	17	32
N	23	14	..
P	25	22	..
O	27	08	58

March

	d	h	m
E	1	16	..
◗	6	13	16
S	8	18	..
A	9	23	..
●	14	17	43
E	16	04	..
☉1	21	04	39
◐	22	02	25
N	22	20	..
P	25	22	..
O	28	19	27
E	29	02	..

April

	d	h	m
S	5	01	..
◗	5	08	38
A	6	18	..
E	12	11	..
●	13	07	58
N	19	02	..
◐	20	08	58
P	21	08	..
E	25	11	..
O	27	06	31

May

	d	h	m
S	2	10	..
A	4	13	..
◗	5	03	43
E	9	20	..
●	12	19	25
N	16	08	..
P	16	16	..
◐	19	14	17
E	22	18	..
O	26	18	48
S	29	18	..

June

	d	h	m
A	1	08	..
◗	3	21	07
E	6	05	..
●	11	04	37
N	12	17	..
P	13	06	..
◐	17	19	46
E	18	23	..
☉2	21	23	09
O	25	08	32
S	26	01	..
A	28	23	..

July

	d	h	m
◗	3	12	12
E	3	14	..
N	10	03	..
●	10	12	18
P	11	10	..
E	16	05	..
◐	17	02	50
S	23	07	..
O	24	23	27
A	26	07	..
E	30	20	..

August

	d	h	m
◗	2	00	52
N	6	13	..
P	8	19	..
●	8	19	18
E	12	13	..
◐	15	12	47
S	19	12	..
A	22	09	..
O	23	14	59
E	27	01	..
◗	31	11	22

September

	d	h	m
N	2	21	..
P	6	05	..
●	7	02	35
E	8	22	..
◐	14	02	24
S	15	18	..
A	18	17	..
O	22	06	36
E	23	06	..
☉3	23	14	42
◗	29	20	05
N	30	04	..

October

	d	h	m
P	4	11	..
E	6	08	..
●	6	11	16
S	13	02	..
◐	13	19	42
A	16	08	..
E	20	13	..
O	21	21	53
N	27	10	..
◗	29	03	37

November

	d	h	m
P	1	03	..
E	2	18	..
●	4	22	21
S	9	10	..
◐	12	15	49
A	13	03	..
E	16	22	..
O	20	12	29
N	23	16	..
P	26	02	..
◗	27	10	50
E	30	01	..

December

	d	h	m
●	4	12	26
S	6	19	..
A	11	01	..
◐	12	13	09
E	14	07	..
O	20	02	00
N	21	00	..
☉4	22	10	30
P	22	18	..
◗	26	18	52
E	27	06	..

LUNAR DATA:
● – new Moon
◐ – first quarter
○ – full Moon
◗ – last quarter
A – Moon in apogee
P – Moon in perigee
N – Moon farthest north of Equator
E – Moon on Equator
S – Moon farthest south of Equator

SOLAR DATA:
☉1 – March equinox
☉2 – June solstice
☉3 – September equinox
☉4 – December solstice

Greenwich mean time (GMT) or universal time (UT) is the mean solar time on the Greenwich meridian reckoned in days of 24 mean solar hours written as 00^h at midnight and 12^h at noon. To convert the above times to those of other standard time meridians, add 1 hour for each 15° of east longitude of the desired meridian and subtract 1 hour for each 15° of west longitude. This table was compiled from data taken from the American Ephemeris and Nautical Almanac.

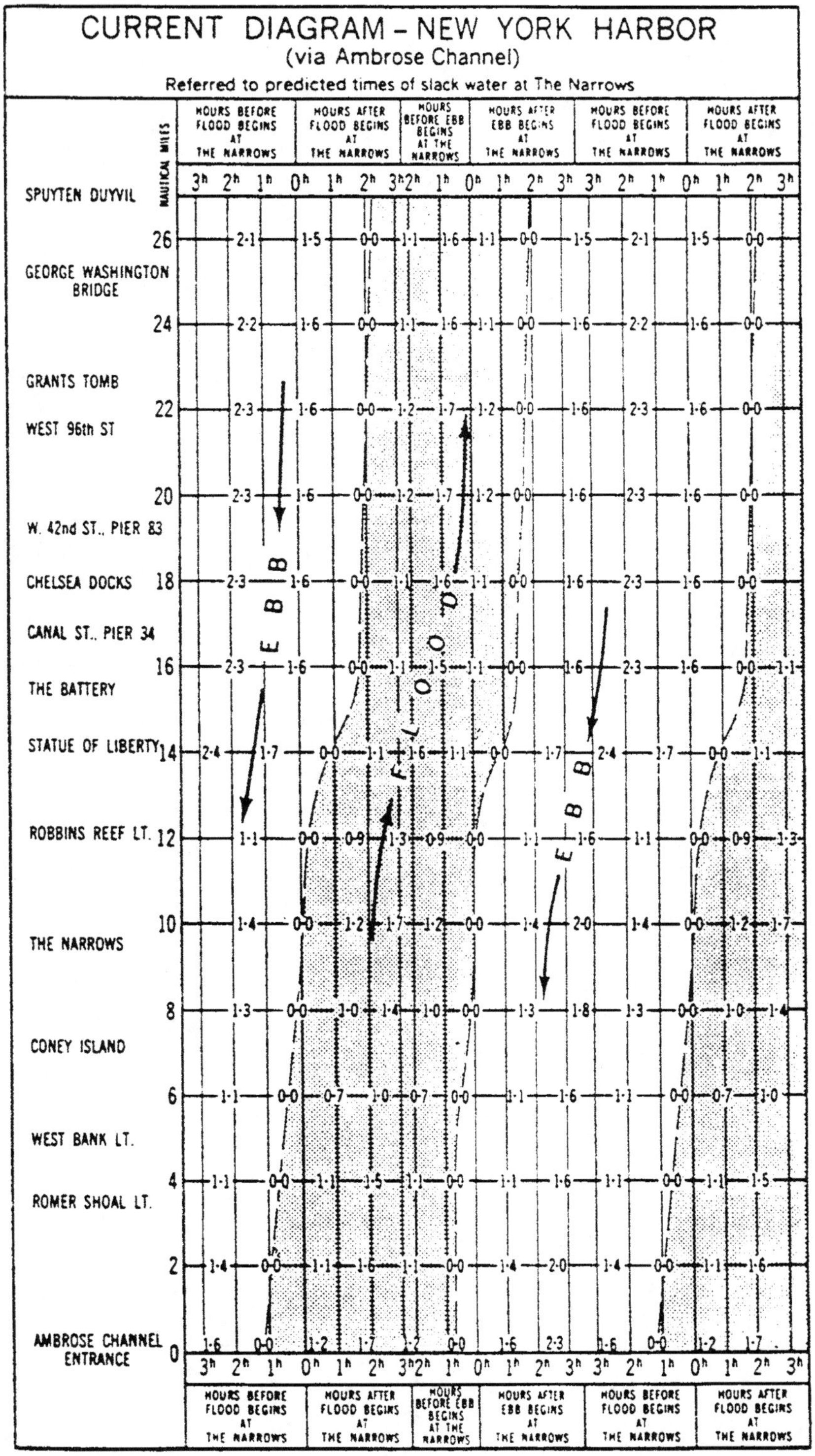

CURRENT DIAGRAM – NEW YORK HARBOR
(via Ambrose Channel)
Referred to predicted times of slack water at The Narrows

		HOURS BEFORE FLOOD BEGINS AT THE NARROWS			HOURS AFTER FLOOD BEGINS AT THE NARROWS			HOURS BEFORE EBB BEGINS AT THE NARROWS		HOURS AFTER EBB BEGINS AT THE NARROWS			HOURS BEFORE FLOOD BEGINS AT THE NARROWS			HOURS AFTER FLOOD BEGINS AT THE NARROWS		
NAUTICAL MILES		3ʰ	2ʰ	1ʰ	0ʰ	1ʰ	2ʰ	3ʰ	2ʰ	1ʰ	0ʰ	1ʰ	2ʰ	3ʰ	3ʰ 2ʰ 1ʰ 0ʰ		1ʰ 2ʰ 3ʰ
SPUYTEN DUYVIL	26		2·1	1·5	0·0	1·1	1·6	1·1		0·0	1·5		2·1	1·5	0·0		
GEORGE WASHINGTON BRIDGE	24		2·2	1·6	0·0	1·1	1·6	1·1		0·0	1·6		2·2	1·6	0·0		
GRANTS TOMB / WEST 96th ST	22		2·3	1·6	0·0	1·2	1·7	1·2		0·0	1·6		2·3	1·6	0·0		
W. 42nd ST., PIER 83	20		2·3	1·6	0·0	1·2	1·7	1·2		0·0	1·6		2·3	1·6	0·0		
CHELSEA DOCKS	18		2·3	1·6	0·0	1·1	1·6	1·1		0·0	1·6		2·3	1·6	0·0		
CANAL ST., PIER 34 / THE BATTERY	16		2·3	1·6	0·0	1·1	0·5	1·1		0·0	1·6		2·3	1·6	0·0 1·1		
STATUE OF LIBERTY	14	2·4	1·7	0·0	1·1	1·6	1·1	0·0		1·7	2·4	1·7	0·0 1·1				
ROBBINS REEF LT.	12		1·1	0·0	0·9	1·3	0·9	0·0	1·1	1·6	1·1	0·0	0·9	1·3		
THE NARROWS	10		1·4	0·0	1·2		1·2	0·0	1·4	2·0	1·4	0·0	1·2	1·7		
CONEY ISLAND	8		1·3	0·0	1·0	1·0	1·0	0·0	1·3	1·8	1·3	0·0	1·0	1·4		
WEST BANK LT.	6		1·1	0·0	0·7	1·0	0·7	0·0	1·1	1·6	1·1	0·0	0·7	1·0		
ROMER SHOAL LT.	4		1·1	0·0	1·1	1·5	1·1	0·0	1·1	1·6	1·1	0·0	1·1	1·5		
	2		1·4	0·0	1·1	1·6	1·1	0·0	1·4	2·0	1·4	0·0	1·1	1·6		
AMBROSE CHANNEL ENTRANCE	0		1·6	0·0	1·2	1·7		0·0	1·6	2·3	1·6	0·0	1·2	1·7		

FLOOD — EBB — FLOOD — EBB

| HOURS BEFORE FLOOD BEGINS AT THE NARROWS | HOURS AFTER FLOOD BEGINS AT THE NARROWS | HOURS BEFORE EBB BEGINS AT THE NARROWS | HOURS AFTER EBB BEGINS AT THE NARROWS | HOURS BEFORE FLOOD BEGINS AT THE NARROWS | HOURS AFTER FLOOD BEGINS AT THE NARROWS |

SPEED LINES

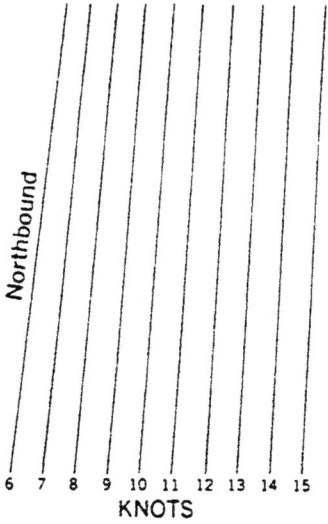

Northbound

6 7 8 9 10 11 12 13 14 15
KNOTS

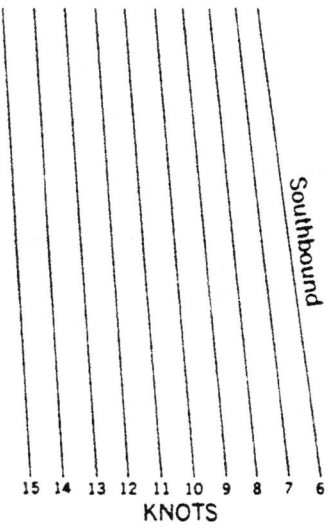

Southbound

15 14 13 12 11 10 9 8 7 6
KNOTS

DELAWARE BAY AND RIVER
EXPLANATION OF CURRENT DIAGRAM

This current diagram represents only average conditions of the surface currents along the middle of the channel between Bristol and Delaware Bay Entrance, the scale being too small to show details.

Northerly streams are designated "Flood" and southerly streams "Ebb." The small figures in the diagram denote the velocity of the current in knots and tenths. The times are referred to slack waters at Delaware Bay Entrance, daily predictions for which are given in Table 1 of these current tables.

The speed lines are directly related to the diagram. By transferring to the diagram the direction of the speed line which corresponds to the ship's speed, the diagram will show the general direction and velocity of the current encountered by the vessel in passing up or down the bay and river or the most favorable time, with respect to currents, for leaving any place shown in the left margin.

To determine velocity and direction of current.—With parallel rulers transfer to the diagram the direction of the speed line corresponding to the normal speed of vessel, moving edge of ruler to the point where the horizontal line representing place of departure intersects the vertical line representing the time in question. If the ruler's edge lies within the shaded portion of the diagram, a flood current will be encountered; if within the unshaded, an ebb current, and if along the boundary of both, slack water. The figures in the diagram along the edge of the ruler will show the velocity of the current encountered at any place indicated in the left margin of the diagram.

Example.—A 15-knot vessel bound southward leaves Philadelphia (Chestnut Street) at 0330 of a given day and it is desired to ascertain the velocity and direction of the current which will be encountered between Philadelphia and Delaware Bay Entrance. Assuming that on the given day flood begins at Delaware Bay Entrance at 0436 and ebb begins at 1038, the time 0330 will be about 1 hour before flood begins. With parallel rulers transfer to the diagram the 15-knot speed line "Southbound" placing the edge of ruler on the intersection of the vertical line "1 hour before flood begins at Delaware Bay Entrance" and a horizontal line through Philadelphia (Chestnut Street) which is the starting point. It will be found that the edge of the ruler passes through an unshaded (ebb) portion with an average velocity of about 1.3 knots from Philadelphia to the vicinity of Arnold Point, and the rest of the way through a shaded (flood) portion with an average velocity of about 0.8 knot. The vessel will therefore have a favorable current averaging about 1.3 knots to the vicinity of Arnold Point and an unfavorable current averaging about 0.8 knot the rest of the way to Delaware Bay Entrance.

To determine the time of a favorable current for passing up or down the bay and river.—With parallel rulers transfer to the diagram the direction of the speed line corresponding to normal speed of vessel, moving the ruler over the diagram until its edge runs as nearly as possible through the general line of largest velocities of shaded portion if northbound or unshaded portion if southbound giving consideration only to that part of diagram which lies between places of departure and destination. An average of the figures along edge of ruler will give the average velocity of current. The time (before or after flood begins or ebb begins at Delaware Bay Entrance) for leaving any place shown in the left margin will be indicated vertically above or below the point where the ruler cuts a line drawn horizontally through the place in question.

Example.—A 12-knot vessel will leave Delaware Bay Entrance on a day when flood begins at 0505 and ebb begins at 1112. At what time should she get under way so as to carry the most favorable current all the way to Philadelphia? With parallel rulers transfer to the diagram the direction of 12-knot speed line "Northbound" to the shaded portion of diagram and as near as possible to the axis so as to include the greatest number of larger velocities. The edge of the ruler will cut the horizontal line at Delaware Bay Entrance near the vertical line "2 hours after flood begins at Delaware Bay Entrance" and the velocities along the ruler's edge will average about 1.7 knots. On the given day flood begins at Delaware Bay Entrance at 0505, hence, if the vessel leaves about 2 hours later, i.e., about 0700, she will have a favorable current averaging about 1.7 knots all the way.

Note.—It is readily seen by transferring southbound speed lines to this diagram that southbound vessels can carry a favorable current for about 50 miles only.

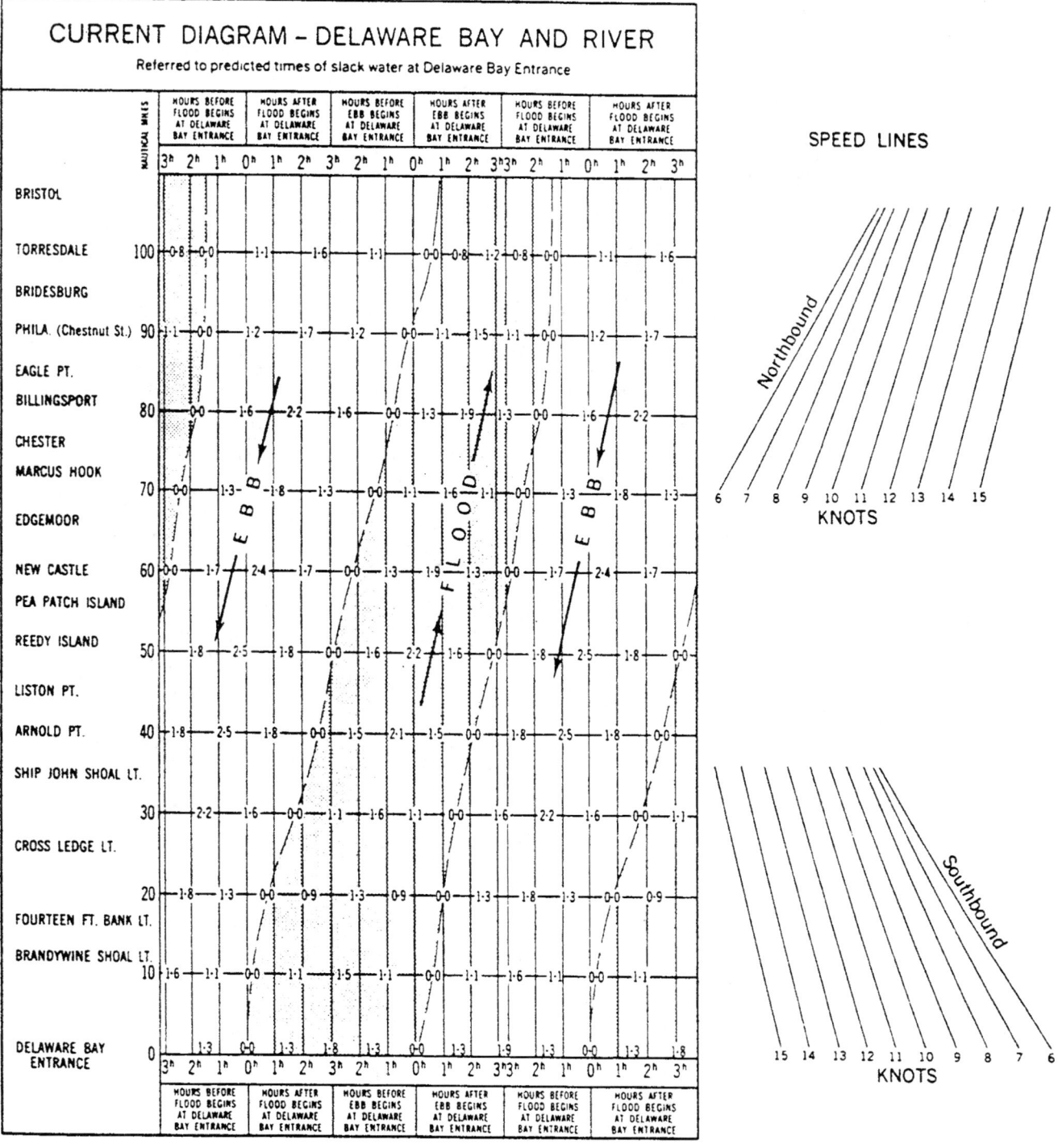

CHESAPEAKE BAY

EXPLANATION OF CURRENT DIAGRAM

This current diagram represents only average conditions of the surface currents along the middle of the channel from Cape Henry Light to Baltimore, the scale being too small to show details.

Northerly streams are designated "Flood" and southerly streams "Ebb." The small figures in the diagram denote the velocity of the current in knots and tenths. The times are referred to slack waters at Chesapeake Bay entrance, daily predictions for which are given in Table 1 of these current tables.

The speed lines are directly related to the diagram. By transferring to the diagram the direction of the speed line which corresponds to the ship's speed, the diagram will show the general direction and velocity of the current encountered by the vessel in passing up or down the bay or the most favorable time, with respect to currents, for leaving any place shown in the left margin.

To determine velocity and direction of current.—With parallel rulers transfer to the diagram the direction of the speed line corresponding to the normal speed of vessel, moving edge of ruler to the point where the horizontal line representing place of departure intersects the vertical line representing the time in question. If the ruler's edge lies within the shaded portion of the diagram, a flood current will be encountered; if within the unshaded, an ebb current, and if along the boundary of both, slack water. The figures in the diagram along the edge of the ruler will show the velocity of the current encountered at any place indicated in the left margin of the diagram.

Example.—A 12-knot vessel bound for Baltimore passes Cape Henry Light at 1430 of a given day, and it is desired to ascertain the velocity and direction of the current which will be encountered. Assuming that on the given day flood begins at Chesapeake Bay entrance at 1256 and ebb begins at 1803, the time 1430 will be about 1½ hours after flood begins. With parallel rulers transfer to diagram the 12-knot speed line "Northbound," placing edge of ruler so that it will cross the horizontal line opposite Cape Henry at a point "1½ hours after flood begins at the entrance." It will be found that the edge of the ruler passes through strength of current in the shaded portion of diagram averaging about 0.7 knot. The vessel will, therefore, have a favorable current averaging about 0.7 knot all the way to Baltimore.

To determine the time of a favorable current for passing through the bay.—With parallel rulers transfer to the diagram the direction of the speed line corresponding to normal speed of vessel, moving the ruler over the diagram until its edge runs approximately through the general line of greatest current of unshaded portion if southbound and shaded portion if northbound. An average of the figures along edge of ruler will give average strength of current. The time (before or after ebb or flood begins at the entrance) for leaving any place in the left margin of diagram will be found vertically above the point where the parallel ruler cuts the horizontal line opposite the place in question.

Example.—A 12-knot vessel in Baltimore Harbor desires to leave for Cape Henry Light on the afternoon of a day when flood begins at Chesapeake Bay entrance at 1148 and ebb begins at 1718. At what time should she get under way so as to carry the most favorable current?

Place parallel rulers along the 12-knot speed line "Southbound." Transfer this direction to the diagram and move it along so as to include the greatest possible number of larger current velocities in the unshaded portion of the diagram. The most favorable time for leaving Baltimore thus found is about 1 hour after flood begins at the entrance, or about 1248. There will be an unfavorable current of about 0.2 knot as far as Seven Foot Knoll Light; after passing this light there will be an average favorable current of about 0.3 knot as far as Cove Point Light; from Cove Point Light to Bluff Point a contrary current averaging about 0.3 knot will be encountered; from Bluff Point to Tail of the Horseshoe there will be an average favorable current of about 0.9 knot; and from Tail of the Horseshoe to Cape Henry an average contrary current of about 0.2 knot will again be encountered.

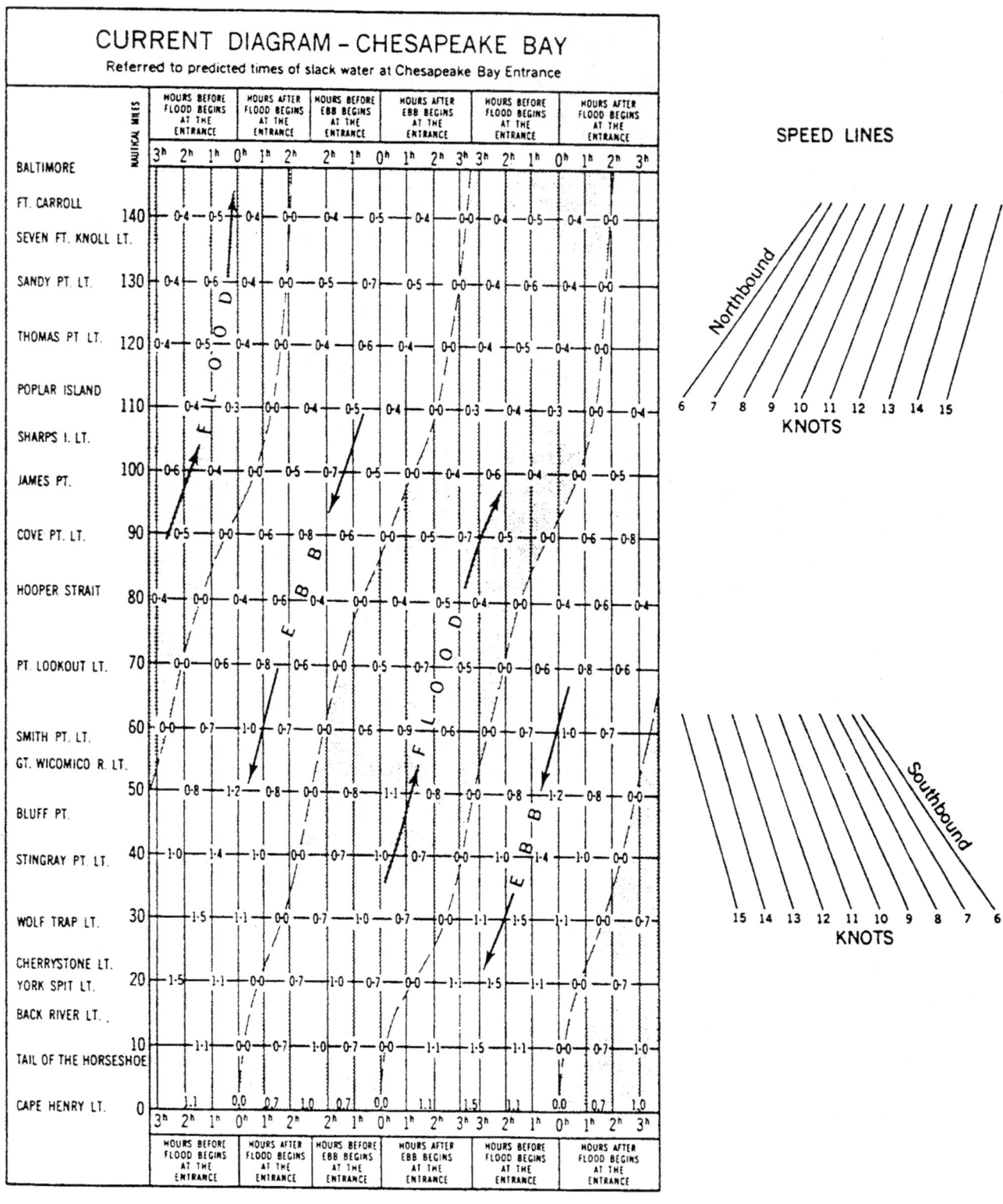

TIDE TABLES

Advance information relative to the rise and fall of the tide is given in annual tide tables. These tables include the predicted times and heights of high and low waters for every day in the year for a number of reference stations and differences for obtaining similar predictions for numerous other places.

Tide Tables, Central and Western Pacific Ocean and Indian Ocean.
Tide Tables, East Coast of North and South America (Including Greenland).
Tide Tables, Europe and West Coast of Africa (Including the Mediterranean Sea).
Tide Tables, West Coast of North and South America (Including the Hawaiian Islands).

TIDAL BENCH MARKS

To provide permanent points for the observed heights of the tide and the tidal datum planes determined therefrom, a system of bench marks is established at each tide station. The descriptions and elevations of these bench marks along our coast are compiled, published, and available for distribution. Requests for such bench mark data should specify the coastal locality for which the information is desired.

TIDAL CURRENT TABLES

Accompanying the rise and fall of the tide is a periodic horizontal flow of the water known as the tidal current. Advance information relative to these currents is made available in annual tidal current tables which include daily predictions of the times of slack water and the times and velocities of strength of flood and ebb currents for a number of waterways together with differences for obtaining predictions for numerous other places.

Tidal Current Tables, Atlantic Coast of North America.
Tidal Current Tables, Pacific Coast of North America and Asia.

TIDAL CURRENT CHARTS

Each publication consists of a set of 12 charts which depict, by means of arrows and figures, the direction and speed of the tidal current for each hour of the tidal cycle. The charts, which may be used for any year, present a comprehensive view of the tidal current movement in the respective waterways as a whole and also supply a means for readily determining for any time the direction and speed of the current at various localities throughout the water areas covered. The Narragansett Bay tidal current chart is to be used with the annual tide tables. The other charts require the annual tidal current tables.

Tidal Current Charts, Boston Harbor.
Tidal Current Charts, Charleston Harbor, S.C.
Tidal Current Charts, Delaware Bay and River.
Tidal Current Charts, Long Island Sound and Block Island Sound.
Tidal Current Charts, Narragansett Bay.
Tidal Current Charts, Narragansett Bay to Nantucket Sound.
Tidal Current Charts, New York Harbor.
Tidal Current Charts, Puget Sound, Northern Part.
Tidal Current Charts, Puget Sound, Southern Part.
Tidal Current Charts, San Francisco Bay.
Tidal Current Charts, Upper Chesapeake Bay.
Tidal Current Charts, Tampa Bay.

TIDAL CURRENT DIAGRAMS

The tidal current diagrams are a series of 12 monthly diagrams to be used with the tidal current charts to give the user a convenient method to determine the current flow on a particular day.

Tidal Current Diagrams for Long Island Sound and Block Island Sound.
Tidal Current Diagrams for Boston Harbor.
Tidal Current Diagrams for New York Harbor.
Tidal Current Diagrams for Upper Chesapeake Bay.

ANNUAL INEQUALITY—Seasonal variation in the water level or current, more or less periodic, due chiefly to meteorological causes.

APOGEAN TIDES OR TIDAL CURRENTS—Tides of decreased range or currents of decreased speed occurring monthly as the result of the Moon being in apogee (farthest from the Earth).

AUTOMATIC TIDE GAGE—An instrument that automatically registers the rise and fall of the tide. In some instruments, the registration is accomplished by recording the heights at regular intervals in digital format, in others by a continuous graph in which the height, versus corresponding time of the tide, is recorded.

BENCH MARK (BM)—A fixed physical object or marks used as reference for a vertical datum. A *tidal bench mark* is one near a tide station to which the tide staff and tidal datums are referred. A *geodetic bench mark* identifies a surveyed point in the National Geodetic Vertical Network.

CHART DATUM—The tidal datum to which soundings on a chart are referred. It is usually taken to correspond to a low water elevation of the tide, and its depression below mean sea level is represented by the symbol Z_o.

CURRENT—Generally, a horizontal movement of water. Currents may be classified as *tidal* and *nontidal*. Tidal currents are caused by gravitational interactions between the Sun, Moon, and Earth and are a part of the same general movement of the sea that is manifested in the vertical rise and fall, called *tide*. Nontidal currents include the permanent currents in the general circulatory systems of the sea as well as temporary currents arising from more pronounced meteorological variability.

CURRENT DIFFERENCE—Difference between the time of slack water (or minimum current) or strength of current in any locality and the time of the corresponding phase of the tidal current at a reference station, for which predictions are given in the *Tidal Current Tables*.

CURRENT ELLIPSE—A graphic representation of a rotary current in which the velocity of the current at different hours of the tidal cycle is represented by radius vectors and vectorial angles. A line joining the extremities of the radius vectors will form a curve roughly approximating an ellipse. The cycle is completed in one-half tidal day or in a whole tidal day according to whether the tidal current is of the semidiurnal or the diurnal type. A current of the mixed type will give a curve of two unequal loops each tidal day.

CURRENT METER—An instrument for measuring the speed and direction or just the speed of a current. The measurements are usually Eulerian since the meter is most often fixed or moored at a specific location.

DATUM (vertical)—For marine applications, a base elevation used as a reference from which to reckon heights or depths. It is called a *tidal datum* when defined by a certain phase of the tide. Tidal datums are local datums and should not be extended into areas which have differing topographic features without substantiating measurements. In order that they may be recovered when needed, such datums are referenced to fixed points known as *bench marks*.

DAYLIGHT SAVING TIME—A time used during the summer in some localities in which clocks are advanced 1 hour from the usual standard time.

DIURNAL—Having a period or cycle of approximately 1 tidal day. Thus, the tide is said to be diurnal when only one high water and one low water occur during a tidal day, and the tidal current is said to be diurnal when there is a single flood and single ebb period in the tidal day. A rotary current is diurnal if it changes its direction through all points of the compass once each tidal day.

DIURNAL INEQUALITY—The difference in height of the two high waters or of the two low waters of each day; also the difference in speed between the two flood tidal currents or the two ebb tidal currents of each day. The difference changes with the declination of the Moon and to a lesser extent with the declination of the Sun. In general, the inequality tends to increase with an increasing declination, either north or south, and to diminish as the Moon approaches the Equator. *Mean diurnal high water inequality* (DHQ) is one-half the average difference between the two high waters of each day observed over a specific 19-year Metonic cycle (the National Tidal Datum Epoch). It is obtained by subtracting the mean of all high waters from the mean of the higher high waters. *Mean diurnal low water inequality* (DLQ) is one-half the average difference between the two low waters of each day observed over a specific 19-year Metonic cycle (the National Tidal Datum Epoch). It is obtained by subtracting the mean of the lower low waters from the mean of all low waters. *Tropic high water inequality* (HWQ) is the average difference between the two high waters of the day at the times of the tropic tides. *Tropic low water inequality* (LWQ) is the average difference between the two low waters of the day at the times of the tropic tides. Mean and tropic inequalities as defined above are applicable only when the type of tide is either semidiurnal or mixed. Diurnal inequality is sometimes called *declinational inequality*.

DOUBLE EBB—An ebb tidal current where, after ebb begins, the speed increases to a maximum called *first ebb*; it then decreases, reaching a *minimum ebb* near the middle of the ebb period (and at some places it may actually run in a flood direction for a short period); it then again ebbs to a maximum speed called *second ebb* after which it decreases to slack water.

DOUBLE FLOOD—A flood tidal current where, after flood begins, the speed increases to a maximum called *first flood*; it then decreases, reaching a *minimum flood* near the middle of the flood period (and at some places it may actually run in an ebb direction for a short period); it then again floods to a maximum speed called *second flood* after which it decreases to slack water.

DOUBLE TIDE—A double-headed tide, that is, a high water consisting of two maxima of nearly the same height separated by a relatively small depression, or a low water consisting of two minima separated by a relatively small elevation. Sometimes, it is called an *agger*.

DURATION OF FLOOD AND DURATION OF EBB—*Duration of flood* is the interval of time in which a tidal current is flooding, and the *duration of ebb* is the interval in which it is ebbing. Together they cover, on an average, a period of 12.42 hours for a semidiurnal tidal current or a period of 24.84 hours for a diurnal current. In a normal semidiurnal tidal current, the duration of flood and duration of ebb will each be approximately equal to 6.21 hours, but the times may be modified greatly by the presence of a nontidal flow. In a river the duration of ebb is usually longer than the duration of flood because of the freshwater discharge, especially during the spring when snow and ice melt are the predominant influences.

DURATION OF RISE AND DURATION OF FALL—*Duration of rise* is the interval from low water to high water, and *duration of fall* is the interval from high water to low water. Together they cover, on an average, a period of 12.42 hours for a semidiurnal tide or a period of 24.84 hours for a diurnal tide. In a normal semidiurnal tide, the duration of rise and duration of fall will each be approximately equal to 6.21 hours, but in shallow waters and in rivers there is a tendency for a decrease in the duration of rise and a corresponding increase in the duration of fall.

EBB CURRENT—The movement of a tidal current away from shore or down a tidal river or estuary. In the mixed type of reversing tidal current, the terms *greater ebb* and *lesser ebb* are applied respectively to the ebb tidal currents of greater and lesser speed of each day. The terms *maximum ebb* and *minimum ebb* are applied to the maximum and minimum speeds of a current running continuously ebb, the speed alternately increasing and decreasing without coming to a slack or reversing. The expression *maximum ebb* is also applicable to any ebb current at the time of greatest speed.

EQUATORIAL TIDAL CURRENTS—Tidal currents occurring semimonthly as a result of the Moon being over the Equator. At these times the tendency of the Moon to produce a diurnal inequality in the tidal current is at a minimum.

EQUATORIAL TIDES—Tides occurring semimonthly as the result of the Moon being over the Equator. At these times the tendency of the Moon to produce a diurnal inequality in the tide is at a minimum.

FLOOD CURRENT—The movement of a tidal current toward the shore or up a tidal river or estuary. In the mixed type of reversing current, the terms *greater flood* and *lesser flood* are applied respectively to the flood currents of greater and lesser speed of each day. The terms *maximum flood* and *minimum flood* are applied to the maximum and minimum speeds of a flood current, the speed of which alternately increases and decreases without coming to a slack or reversing. The expression *maximum flood* is also applicable to any flood current at the time of greatest speed.

GREAT DIURNAL RANGE (*Gt*)—The difference in height between mean higher high water and mean lower low water. The expression may also be used in its contracted form, *diurnal range*.

GULF COAST LOW WATER DATUM—A chart datum. Specifically, the tidal datum designated for the coastal waters of the Gulf Coast of the United States. It is defined as *mean lower low water* when the type of tide is mixed and *mean low water* when the type of tide is diurnal.

HALF-TIDE LEVEL—*See mean tide level*.

HIGH WATER (HW)—The maximum height reached by a rising tide. The height may be due solely to the periodic tidal forces or it may have superimposed upon it the effects of prevailing meteorological conditions. Use of the synonymous term, *high tide*, is discouraged.

HIGHER HIGH WATER (HHW)—The higher of the two high waters of any tidal day.

HIGHER LOW WATER (HLW)—The higher of the two low waters of any tidal day.

HYDRAULIC CURRENT—A current in a channel caused by a difference in the surface level at the two ends. Such a current may be expected in a strait connecting two bodies of water in which the tides differ in time or range. The current in the East River, N.Y., connecting Long Island Sound and New York Harbor, is an example.

KNOT—A speed unit of 1 international nautical mile (1,852.0 meters or 6,076.11549 international feet) per hour.

LOW WATER (LW)—The minimum height reached by a falling tide. The height may be due solely to the periodic tidal forces or it may have superimposed upon it the effects of meteorological conditions. Use of the synonymous term, *low tide*, is discouraged.

LOWER HIGH WATER (LHW)—The lower of the two high waters of any tidal day.

LOWER LOW WATER (LLW)—The lower of the two low waters of any tidal day.

LUNAR DAY—The time of the rotation of the Earth with respect to the Moon, or the interval between two successive upper transits of the Moon over the meridian of a place. The mean lunar day is approximately 24.84 solar hours long, or 1.035 times as long as the mean solar day.

LUNAR INTERVAL—The difference in time between the transit of the Moon over the meridian of Greenwich and over a local meridian. The average value of this interval expressed in hours is 0.069 L, in which L is the local longitude in degrees, positive for west longitude and negative for east longitude. The lunar interval equals the difference between the local and Greenwich interval of a tide or current phase.

LUNICURRENT . INTERVAL—The interval between the Moon's transit (upper or lower) over the local or Greenwich meridian and a specified phase of the tidal current following the transit. Examples: *strength of flood interval* and *strength of ebb interval*, which may be abbreviated to *flood interval* and *ebb interval*, respectively. The interval is described as local or Greenwich according to whether the reference is to the Moon's transit over the local or Greenwich meridian. When not otherwise specified, the reference is assumed to be local.

LUNITIDAL INTERVAL—The interval between the Moon's transit (upper or lower) over the local or Greenwich meridian and the following high or low water. The average of all high water intervals for all phases of the Moon is known as *mean high water lunitidal interval* and is abbreviated to *high water interval* (HWI). Similarly the *mean low water lunitidal interval* is abbreviated to *low water interval* (LWI). The interval is described as local or Greenwich according to whether the reference is to the transit over the local or Greenwich meridian. When not otherwise specified, the reference is assumed to be local.

MEAN HIGH WATER (MHW)—A tidal datum. The average of all the high water heights observed over the National Tidal Datum Epoch. (See High Water.) For stations with shorter series, simultaneous observational comparisons are made with a control tide station in order to derive the equivalent of a 19-year datum.

MEAN HIGHER HIGH WATER (MHHW)—A tidal datum. The average of the highest high water height of each tidal day observed over the National Tidal Datum Epoch. For stations with shorter series, simultaneous observational comparisons are made with a control tide station in order to derive the equivalent of a 19-year datum.

MEAN HIGHER HIGH WATER LINE (MHHWL)—The intersection of the land with the water surface at the elevation of mean higher high water.

MEAN LOW WATER (MLW)—A tidal datum. The average of all the low water heights observed over the National Tidal Datum Epoch. (See Low Water.) For stations with shorter series, simultaneous observational comparisons are made with a control tide station in order to derive the equivalent of a 19-year datum.

MEAN LOW WATER SPRINGS (MLWS)—A tidal datum. Frequently abbreviated *spring low water*. The arithmetic mean of the low water heights occurring at the time of the spring tides observed over a specific 19-year Metronic cycle (the National Tidal Datum Epoch).

MEAN LOWER LOW WATER (MLLW)—A tidal datum. The average of the lowest low water height of each tidal day observed over the National Tidal Datum Epoch. For stations with shorter series, simultaneous observational comparisons are made with a control tide station in order to derive the equivalent of a 19-year datum.

MEAN RANGE OF TIDE (Mn)—The difference in height between mean high water and mean low water.

MEAN RIVER LEVEL—A tidal datum. The average height of the surface of a tidal river at any point for all stages of the tide observed over a 19-year Metonic cycle (the National Tidal Datum Epoch), usually determined from hourly height readings. In rivers subject to occasional freshets the river level may undergo wide variations, and for practical purposes certain months of the year may be excluded in the determination of tidal datums. For charting purposes, tidal datums for rivers are usually based on observations during selected periods when the river is at or near low water stage.

MEAN SEA LEVEL (MSL)—A tidal datum. The arithmetic mean of hourly water elevations observed over a specific 19-year Metonic cycle (the National Tidal Datum Epoch). Shorter series are specified in the name; e.g., monthly mean sea level and yearly mean sea level.

MEAN TIDE LEVEL (MTL)—Also called half-tide level. A tidal datum midway between mean high water and mean low water.

MIXED TIDE—Type of tide with a large inequality in the high and/or low water heights, with two high waters and two low waters usually occurring each tidal day. In strictness, all tides are mixed but the name is usually applied to the tides intermediate to those predominantly semidiurnal and those predominantly diurnal.

NEAP TIDES OR TIDAL CURRENTS—Tides of decreased range or tidal currents of decreased speed occurring semimonthly as the result of the Moon being in quadrature. The *neap range* (Np) of the tide is the average semidiurnal range occurring at the time of neap tides and is most conveniently computed from the harmonic constants. It is smaller than the mean range where the type of tide is either semidiurnal or mixed and is of no practical significance where the type of tide is diurnal. The average height of the high waters of the neap tides is called *neap high water* or *high water neaps* (MHWN) and the average height of the corresponding low waters is called *neap low water* or *low water neaps* (MLWN).

PERIGEAN TIDES OR TIDAL CURRENTS—Tides of increased range or tidal currents of increased speed occurring monthly as the result of the Moon being in perigee or nearest the Earth. The *perigean range* (Pn) of tide is the average semidiurnal range occurring at the time of perigean tides and is most conveniently computed from the harmonic constants. It is larger than the mean range where the type of tide is either semidiurnal or mixed, and is of no practical significance where the type of tide is diurnal.

RANGE OF TIDE—The difference in height between consecutive high and low waters. The *mean range* is the difference in height between mean high water and mean low water. Where the type of tide is diurnal the mean range is the same as the diurnal range. For other ranges, see great diurnal, spring, neap, perigean, apogean, and tropic tides.

REFERENCE STATION—A tide or current station for which independent daily predictions are given in the *Tide Tables* and *Tidal Current Tables*, and from which corresponding predictions are obtained for subordinate stations by means of differences and ratios.

REVERSING CURRENT—A tidal current which flows alternately in approximately opposite directions with a slack water at each reversal of direction. Currents of this type usually occur in rivers and straits where the direction of flow is more or less restricted to certain channels. When the movement is towards the shore or up a stream, the current is said to be flooding, and when in the opposite direction it is said to be ebbing. The combined flood and ebb movement including the slack water covers, on an average, 12.42 hours for the semidiurnal current. If unaffected by a nontidal flow, the flood and ebb movements will each last about 6 hours, but when combined with such a flow, the durations of flood and ebb may be quite unequal. During the flow in each direction the speed of the current will vary from zero at the time of slack water to a maximum about midway between the slacks.

ROTARY CURRENT—A tidal current that flows continually with the direction of flow changing through all points of the compass during the tidal period. Rotary currents are usually found offshore where the direction of flow is not restricted by any barriers. The tendency for the rotation in direction has its origin in the Coriolis force and, unless modified by local conditions, the change is clockwise in the Northern Hemisphere and counterclockwise in the Southern. The speed of the current usually varies throughout the tidal cycle, passing through the two maxima in approximately opposite directions and the two minima with the direction of the current at approximately 90° from the direction at time of maximum speed.

SEMIDIURNAL—Having a period or cycle of approximately one-half of a tidal day. The predominating type of tide throughout the world is semidiurnal, with two high waters and two low waters each tidal day. The tidal current is said to be semidiurnal when there are two flood and two ebb periods each day.

SET (OF CURRENT)—The direction *towards* which the current flows.

SLACK WATER—The state of a tidal current when its speed is near zero, especially the moment when a reversing current changes direction and its speed is zero. The term is also applied to the entire period of low speed near the time of turning of the current when it is too weak to be of any practical importance in navigation. The relation of the time of slack water to the tidal phases varies in different localities. For standing tidal waves, slack water occurs near the times of high and low water, while for progressive tidal waves, slack water occurs midway between high and low water.

SPRING TIDES OR TIDAL CURRENTS—Tides of increased range or tidal currents of increased speed occurring semimonthly as the result of the Moon being new or full. The *spring range* (Sg) of tide is the average semidiurnal range occurring at the time of spring tides and is most conveniently computed from the harmonic constants. It is larger than the mean range where the type of tide is either semidiurnal or mixed, and is of no practical significance where the type of tide is diurnal. The mean of the high waters of the spring tide is called *spring high water* or *mean high water springs* (MHWS), and the average height of the corresponding low waters is called *spring low water* or *mean low water springs* (MLWS).

STAND OF TIDE—Sometimes called a platform tide. An interval at high or low water when there is no sensible change in the height of the tide. The water level is stationary at high and low water for only an instant, but the change in level near these times is so slow that it is not usually perceptible. In general, the duration of the apparent stand will depend upon the range of tide, being longer for a small range than for a large range, but where there is a tendency for a double tide the stand may last for several hours even with a large range of tide.

STANDARD TIME—A kind of time based upon the transit of the Sun over a certain specified meridian, called the *time meridian*, and adopted for use over a considerable area. With a few exceptions, standard time is based upon some meridian which differs by a multiple of 15° from the meridian of Greenwich.

STRENGTH OF CURRENT—Phase of tidal current in which the speed is a maximum; also the speed at this time. Beginning with slack before flood in the period of a reversing tidal current (or minimum before flood in a rotary current), the speed gradually increases to flood strength and then diminishes to slack before ebb (or minimum before ebb in a rotary current), after which the current turns in direction, the speed increases to ebb strength and then diminishes to slack before flood completing the cycle. If it is assumed that the speed throughout the cycle varies as the ordinates of a cosine curve, it can be shown that the average speed for an entire flood or ebb period is equal to $2/\pi$ or 0.6366 of the speed of the corresponding strength of current.

SUBORDINATE CURRENT STATION—(1) A current station from which a relatively short series of observations is reduced by comparison with simultaneous observations from a control current station.

(2) A station listed in the *Tidal Current Tables* for which predictions are to be obtained by means of differences and ratios applied to the full predictions at a reference station.

SUBORDINATE TIDE STATION—(1) A tide station from which a relatively short series of observations is reduced by comparison with simultaneous observations from a tide station with a relatively long series of observations. (2) A station listed in the *Tide Tables* for which predictions are to be obtained by means of differences and ratios applied to the full predictions at a reference station.

TIDAL CURRENT TABLES—Tables which give daily predictions of the times and speeds of the tidal currents. These predictions are usually supplemented by current differences and constants through which additional predictions can be obtained for numerous other places.

TIDAL DIFFERENCE—Difference in time or height of a high or low water at a subordinate station and at a reference station for which predictions are given in the *Tide Tables*. The difference, when applied according to sign to the prediction at the reference station, gives the corresponding time or height for the subordinate station.

TIDE—The periodic rise and fall of the water resulting from gravitational interactions between the Sun, Moon, and Earth. The vertical component of the particulate motion of a tidal wave. Although the accompanying horizontal movement of the water is part of the same phenomenon, it is preferable to designate the motion as tidal current.

TIDE TABLES—Tables which give daily predictions of the times and heights of high and low waters. These predictions are usually supplemented by tidal differences and constants through which additional predictions can be obtained for numerous other places.

TIME MERIDIAN—A meridian used as a reference for time.

TROPIC CURRENTS—Tidal currents occurring semimonthly when the effect of the Moon's maximum declination is greatest. At these times the tendency of the Moon to produce a diurnal inequality in the current is at a maximum.

TROPIC RANGES—The *great tropic range* (Gc), or *tropic range*, is the difference in height between tropic higher high water and tropic lower low water. The *small tropic range* (Sc) is the difference in height between tropic lower high water and tropic higher low water. The *mean tropic range* (Mc) is the mean between the great tropic range and the small tropic range. The small tropic range and the mean tropic range are applicable only when the type of tide is semidiurnal or mixed. Tropic ranges are most conveniently computed from the harmonic constants.

TROPIC TIDES—Tides occurring semimonthly when the effect of the Moon's maximum declination is greatest. At these times there is a tendency for an increase in the diurnal range. The tidal datums pertaining to the tropic tides are designated as *tropic higher high water* (TcHHW), *tropic lower high water* (TcLHW), *tropic higher low water* (TcHLW), and *tropic lower low water* (TcLLW).

TYPE OF TIDE—A classification based on characteristic forms of a tide curve. Qualitatively, when the two high waters and two low waters of each tidal day are approximately equal in height, the tide is said to be *semidiurnal;* when there is a relatively large diurnal inequality in the high or low waters or both, it is said to be *mixed;* and when there is only one high water and one low water in each tidal day, it is said to be *diurnal.*

VANISHING TIDE—In a mixed tide with very large diurnal inequality, the lower high water (or higher low water) frequently becomes indistinct (or vanishes) at time of extreme declinations. During these periods the diurnal tide has such overriding dominance that the semidiurnal tide, although still present, cannot be readily seen on the tide curve.

INDEX TO STATIONS, 1983
(Numbers refer to table 2)

[Stations marked with an asterisk (*) are reference stations for which daily predictions are given in table 1. Page numbers of reference stations are given in parentheses.]

225

	NO.
Manhattan, East River, N.Y..............	3156
Manilla...............................	8931
Manokin River entrance................	5306
Manomet Point.........................	1271
Marblehead Channel....................	611
Marcus Hook..........................	4321
Martha's Vineyard.....................	1336
Martins Industry......................	6676
Marvin Island........................	501
Maryland Point........................	5471
Matagorda Channel.....................	9131
Matinecock Point.............	2946,2951
Matlacha Pass.........................	8121
Mattapoisett Harbor...................	1751
Mattaponi River.................	5151,5156
Mattituck Point.......................	2661
Maurice River......................	4166-4176
Mauricetown..........................	4171
Maximo Pt., bridge 0.8 mile south of...	8671
Mayport..............................	7601
Megansett Harbor......................	1706
Menemsha Bight........................	1586
Merrimack River entrance..............	581
Mesquite Point........................	9051
Miacomet Pond.........................	1326
Miami Harbor...................	7851-7891
Miami Harbor entrance * (100)..........	7881
Miami Outer Bay Cut entrance...........	7871
Middle Branch ent., Patapsco River.....	5751
Middle Ground, Chesapeake Bay.........	4486
Middle Marshes.......................	5986
Midland Beach........................	3866
Midnight Pass entrance................	8201
Mile Point...........................	7611
Miles River......................	5656,5661
Milford Point.........................	2736
Mill Rock, Hell Gate...........	3116,3121
Miller Island.........................	4761
Millville............................	4176
Mispillion River......................	4141
Mississippi Sound.....................	8891
Mobile Bay.....................	8821-8881
Mobile Bay entrance * (118)...........	8831
Mobile Point.....................	8831,8841
Mobile River entrance.................	8861
Mobjack Bay......................	5176-5186
Monomoy Point..........	1306,1356,1376
Montauk Harbor entrance...............	2266
Montauk Point...................	2231-2241
Montgomery...........................	7161
Moon Head.......................	1101,1126
Moosabec Reach.................	106,111
Morehead City....................	5941,5946
Moreland.............................	6386
Morgan Island...................	6616,6646
Moser Channel........................	7931
Mosquito Point...................	5191,5196
Mount Hope Bay..................	1961,1971
Mount Hope Bridge....................	1951
Mount Prospect.......................	2271
Mountain Point........................	5691
Mud River............................	7281
Mulberry Point........................	5611
Mulford Point.........................	2601
Mullet Key Channel entrance...........	8311
Mullet Key Shoal Light................	8351
Muscongus Sound......................	156
Muskeget Channel.....................	1436
Muskeget Island......................	1426
Muskeget Rock........................	1431
Myakka River Bridge..................	8151
Myrtle Sound.........................	6051
Mystic, Mystic River, Conn...........	2421
Mystic River Bridge, Mass..........	941,946

N	NO.
Nahant.............................	651-661
Nansemond River..................	4956-4966
Nanticoke River..................	5341,5346
Nantucket Harbor entrance.............	1416
Nantucket Island.....................	1316
Nantucket Shoals.....................	1311
Nantucket Sound..................	1356-1551
Napatree Point........................	2396
Narragansett Bay.................	1811-2101
Nasketucket Bay......................	1746
Nassau River.........................	7561
Nassau Sound....................	7541-7571
Nauset Beach Light...................	1291
Neponset River.......................	966
Newport.........................	5951,5956
New Baltimore........................	3736
New Bedford Harbor...................	1731
New Brighton.........................	4006
New Castle...........................	4291
New Ground...........................	8041
New Hamburg..........................	3636
New Haven Harbor entrance.............	2701
New Jersey Coast.................	4051-4101
New London Harbor entrance............	2471
New Pass, Sarasota Bay................	8231
New Point Comfort....................	5176
New River.......................	6816,6821
New York Harbor......... 3326-3446,3776-3906
Newark Bay......................	4021-4036
Newburgh............................	3626
Newburyport..........................	586
Newport Harbor.......................	1881
Newport News...........	4891-4906,4971-4981
Newtown Creek........................	3161
Niantic..............................	2516
No Name Key..........................	7951
Noank................................	2416
Nobles Island...................	546,551
Nobska Point....................	1551,1561
Nomini Creek entrance.................	5411
North Brother Island.................	3101
North Charleston.....................	6341
North Edisto River entrance...........	6526
North Haven Peninsula.................	2371
North Hill Point......................	2431
North Newport River..................	7251
North Point, Chesapeake Bay...........	4741
North Santee River entrance...........	6161
Northbury............................	5171
Northport Bay........................	2871
Northport Bay entrance................	2866
Norton Point.........................	1566
Norton Shoal.........................	1446
Norwalk River........................	2841
Nowell Creek entrance.................	6431
Nubble Channel.......................	1036
Nut Island.....................	1111,1116

O	NO.
Oak Neck Point.......................	2926
Oatland Island.......................	7081
Ocracoke Inlet.............	5851-5881,5901
Odingsell River Entrance..............	7166
Ogeechee River...................	7201,7211
Old Fernandina.......................	7511
Old Ferry Point......................	3071
Old Field Point..................	2766,2771
Old Harbor Point.....................	2151
Old Man Shoal, Nantucket Shoals........	1321
Old Orchard Shoal Light...............	3846
Old Plantation Flats Light............	4536

NO.

South Carolina Coast	6161-6186
South Edisto River	6556-6586
South River, Md.	5671
South River, N.J.	3956
South Santee River entrance	6166
Southport	6006,6011
Southwest Ledge	2211,2216
Sow and Pigs Reef	1671
Spanish Wells	6801
Spectacle Island	866-891
Spesutie Island	4796
Spuyten Duyvil	3526
Spuyten Duyvil Creek entrance	3236
Squantum	1131
Squantum Point	956,961
Squash Meadow	1516
Stafford Island	7501
Stage Harbor	1366
Stamford Harbor entrance	2911
Statue of Liberty	3446
Stingray Point	4556,4561
Stoddard Hill	2486
Stodders Neck	1196
Stono Inlet	6476
Stono River	6476-6506
Stony Point	4231
Stratford Point	2776,2781
Stratford Shoal	2721
Strawberry Hill	1141
Sugarloaf Island	5936
Sullivans Island	6221
Sunken Ledge	1091
Sunshine Skyway Bridge	8391
Sunny Point	4552
Susquehanna River	4811
Swan Point, Chesapeake Bay	4731,4736
Swan Point, Potomac River	5441

T

Tail of the Horseshoe	4481
Tampa Bay	8271-8651
Tampa Bay entrance * (112)	8291
Tangier Sound	5291-5356
Tangier Sound Light	5291
Tappahannock Bridge	5251,5256
Tarpaulin Cove	1571
Tarpley Point	5226
Tarrytown	3556
Teaches Hole Channel	5861
Tensaw River entrance	8871
Terrebonne Bay	8961
Texas Point	9021
Thames River	2476-2491
The Battery	3456
The Cove	6261
The Graves	726
The Narrows, Fla	8731
The Narrows, New York Harbor * (52)	3386
The Race	2436-2451
The Race * (34)	2441
The Tee	6391
Thieves Ledge	731
Thimble Shoal Channel	4476
Thimble Shoal Light	4816
Thomas Pt. Shoal Light	4676,4681
Thompson Island	891,896
Throgs Neck * (40)	3056,3061
Thunderbolt	7076
Tilghman Point	5646
Tiverton	1821,1831
Tocoi	7751
Tolchester Beach	4751
Tolly Point	4686

NO.

Tombstone Point	5926
Tompkinsville	3396
Torresdale	4371
Tottenville	3966
Towles Point	5211
Town Creek	6246,6251
Town Point Bridge	4961
Treasure Island	8701,8721
Tred Avon River	5601,5606
Tremley Point	3981
Troy	3766
Tuckernuck Island	1331
Tuckernuck Shoal	1406
Tue Marshes Light	5081-5091
Tufts Point	3971
Turkey Point, Eastern Bay	5631
Turkey Point, Elk River	4791
Turtle River	7381
Turning Basin, Beaufort Inlet	5931
Turning Basin, Northeast River	6096
Twotree Island Channel	2511

U

Upper Hell Gate	206
Upper Machodoc Creek entrance	5451
Upper Midnight Channel	6056

V

Valiant Rock	2441
Venice Inlet	8171
Vernon River	7151,7161
Victor Point	5321
Vieques Passage * (130)	9181
Vieques Sound	9191
Vineyard Haven	1526
Vineyard Sound	1556-1656
Virginia Beach	5816,5821

W

W Howard Frankland Bridge	8601
Waccamaw River	6151,6156
Wadmalaw River	6531-6541
Wakema	5151
Walkerton	5156
Wallace Channel	5881
Walls Cut	6836
Wando River	6411-6436
Wappoo Creek	6446
Waquoit Bay	1541
Wareham River	1761,1766
Warren	2071
Warren River	2061,2071
Washington, D.C.	5516,5521
Washington Canal, N.J.	3951
Wasque Point	1441
Wassaw Island	7046
Wassaw Island, Ossabaw Sound	7171
Wassaw Island, Wassaw Sound	7006
Wassaw Sound	7016-7126
Watch Hill Point	2221,2226
Waterview	5221
Watts Island	5276,5281
Weepecket Island	1691
Weir River	1136
Wellfleet Harbor	1246
West Chop	1531,1556
West Falmouth Harbor	1701
West Head	1086,1091,1106
West Island	1736,1741
West Marsh Island	6466
West New Brighton	4001

	NO.
West Norfolk Bridge	4921
West Penobscot Bay	146
West Point, N.Y.	3616
West Point, Va.	5141
West River	5666
Western Passage, Maine	91,96
Westport River	1661
Weymouth Back River	1186
Whale Branch River	6666
Whitehaven	5326,5331
Whitehill	4391
White Point	6546
Whooping Island	6551
Wickford Harbor	2011
Wicomico River, Tangier Sound	5321-5336
Wicopesset Island	2246
Wilcox Island Park	2581
Willets Point	3061
Williamsburg Bridge	3171
Williman Creek	6651
Willoughby Bay	4871
Willoughby Spit	4861,4866
Wilmington, N.C.	6086
Wilmington Island	7021
Wilmington River	7056,7076,7096
Windmill Point, Mass.	1061,1156

	NO.
Windmill Point, Va.	5036
Wine Island Pass	8971
Winter Point	7721
Winter-Quarter Shoal	4406
Winthrop Head	716
Winthrop Point	2476
Winyah Bay	6111-6156
Wolf Trap Light	4546,4551
Woods Hole	1611-1621
Woods Point	6371
Wooster Island	2751
Worton Point	4776
Wreck Shoal	1491
Wright River	6826
Wye River	5651

Y

Yellow House Creek	6361
Yellow House Landing	6366
Yeocomico River entrance	5386
York Harbor entrance	371
York River	5071-5171
York Spit Channel	4541
York Spit Light	5076
Yorktown	5096

☆U.S. GOVERNMENT PRINTING OFFICE: 1982-360-997/2198

ISBN 0-16-042688-X

90000

9 780160 426889